CORE-PLUS MATHEMATICS PROJECT

Contemporary Mathematics in Context

A Unified Approach

Teacher's Guide

CORE-PLUS MATHEMATICS PROJECT

Contemporary Mathematics in Context

A Unified Approach

Arthur F. Coxford
James T. Fey
Christian R. Hirsch
Harold L. Schoen
Gail Burrill
Eric W. Hart
Ann E. Watkins
with
Mary Jo Messenger
Beth E. Ritsema
Rebecca K. Walker

New York, New York Columbus, Ohio Chicago, Illinois Peoria, Illinois Woodland Hills, California

Glencoe/McGraw-Hill 

A Division of The ***McGraw·Hill*** *Companies*

This project was supported, in part, by the National Science Foundation.
The opinions expressed are those of the authors and not necessarily those of the Foundation.

Send all inquiries to:
Glencoe/McGraw-Hill
8787 Orion Place
Columbus, OH 43240-4027

ISBN 0-07-827547-4 (Part A)
ISBN 0-07-827548-2 (Part B)

Contemporary Mathematics in Context
Course 3 Part A Teacher's Guide

1 2 3 4 5 6 7 8 9 10 004/004 10 09 08 07 06 05 04 03 02

About the Core-Plus Mathematics Project

The **Core-Plus Mathematics Project (CPMP)** is a multi-year project funded by the National Science Foundation to develop student and teacher materials for a complete high school mathematics curriculum. Courses 1–3 comprise a core curriculum appropriate for *all* students. The fourth-year course continues the preparation of students for college mathematics.

Development Team

Project Directors

Christian R. Hirsch
Western Michigan University

Arthur F. Coxford
University of Michigan

James T. Fey
University of Maryland

Harold L. Schoen
University of Iowa

Senior Curriculum Developers

Gail Burrill
University of Wisconsin-Madison

Eric W. Hart
Western Michigan University

Ann E. Watkins
California State University, Northridge

Professional Development Coordinator

Beth E. Ritsema
Western Michigan University

Evaluation Coordinator

Steven W. Ziebarth
Western Michigan University

Advisory Board

Diane Briars
Pittsburgh Public Schools

Jeremy Kilpatrick
University of Georgia

Kenneth Ruthven
University of Cambridge

David A. Smith
Duke University

Edna Vasquez
Detroit Renaissance High School

Curriculum Development Consultants

Alverna Champion
Grand Valley State University

Cherie Cornick
Wayne County Alliance for Mathematics and Science

Edgar Edwards
(Formerly) Virginia State Department of Education

Richard Scheaffer
University of Florida

Martha Siegel
Towson University

Edward Silver
University of Michigan

Lee Stiff
North Carolina State University

Technical Coordinator

Wendy Weaver
Western Michigan University

Collaborating Teachers

Emma Ames
Oakland Mills High School, Maryland

Cheryl Bach Hedden
Sitka High School, Alaska

Mary Jo Messenger
Howard County Public Schools, Maryland

Valerie Mills
Ann Arbor Public Schools, Michigan

Jacqueline Stewart
Okemos High School, Michigan

Michael Verkaik
Holland Christian High School, Michigan

Marcia Weinhold
Kalamazoo Area Mathematics and Science Center, Michigan

Graduate Assistants

Judy Flowers
University of Michigan

Gina Garza-King
Western Michigan University

Robin Marcus
University of Maryland

Chris Rasmussen
University of Maryland

Bettie Truitt
University of Iowa

Roberto Villarubi
University of Maryland

Rebecca Walker
Western Michigan University

Production and Support Staff

James Laser

Kelly MacLean

Michelle Magers

Cheryl Peters

Jennifer Rosenboom

Anna Seif

Kathryn Wright

Teresa Ziebarth
Western Michigan University

Software Developers

Jim Flanders
Colorado Springs, Colorado

Eric Kamischke
Interlochen, Michigan

Core-Plus Mathematics Project Field-Test Sites

Special thanks are extended to these teachers and their students who participated in the testing and evaluation of Course 3.

Ann Arbor Huron High School
Ann Arbor, Michigan
Ginger Gajar
Brenda Garr

Ann Arbor Pioneer High School
Ann Arbor, Michigan
Jim Brink
Tammy Schirmer

Arthur Hill High School
Saginaw, Michigan
Virginia Abbott

Battle Creek Central High School
Battle Creek, Michigan
Teresa Ballard
Steven Ohs

Bedford High School
Temperance, Michigan
Ellen Bacon
David J. DeGrace

Bloomfield Hills Andover High School
Bloomfield Hills, Michigan
Jane Briskey
Homer Hassenzahl
Cathy King
Linda Robinson
Mike Shelly
Roger Siwajek

Brookwood High School
Snellville, Georgia
Ginny Hanley
Marie Knox

Caledonia High School
Caledonia, Michigan
Deborah Bates
Jenny Diekevers
Kim Drefcenski
Larry Timmer
Gerard Wagner

Centaurus High School
Lafayette, Colorado
Gail Reichert

Clio High School
Clio, Michigan
Bruce Hanson
Lee Sheridan

Davison High School
Davison, Michigan
Evelyn Ailing
John Bale
Dan Tomczak

Dexter High School
Dexter, Michigan
Kris Chatas

Ellet High School
Akron, Ohio
Marcia Csipke
Jim Fillmore

Firestone High School
Akron, Ohio
Barbara Crucs

Flint Northern High School
Flint, Michigan
Al Wojtowicz

Goodrich High School
Goodrich, Michigan
John Doerr
Barbara Ravas
Bonnie Stojek

Grand Blanc High School
Grand Blanc, Michigan
Charles Carmody
Maria Uhler-Chargo

Grass Lake Junior/Senior High School
Grass Lake, Michigan
Brad Coffey
Larry Poertner

Gull Lake High School
Richland, Michigan
Dorothy Louden

Kalamazoo Central High School
Kalamazoo, Michigan
Gloria Foster
Amy Schwentor

Kelloggsville Public Schools
Wyoming, Michigan
Nancy Hoorn
Steve Ramsey
John Ritzler

Midland Valley High School
Langley, South Carolina
Ron Bell
Janice Lee

North Lamar High School
Paris, Texas
Tommy Eads
Barbara Eatherly

Okemos High School
Okemos, Michigan
Lisa Magee
Jacqueline Stewart

Portage Northern High School
Portage, Michigan
Pete Jarrad
Scott Moore
Jerry Swoboda

Prairie High School
Cedar Rapids, Iowa
Dave LaGrange
Judy Slezak

San Pasqual High School
Escondido, California
Damon Blackman
Ron Peet

Sitka High School
Sitka, Alaska
Mikolas Bekeris
Cheryl Bach Hedden
Dan Langbauer
Tom Smircich

Sturgis High School
Sturgis, Michigan
Kathy Parkhurst
Jo Ann Roe

Sweetwater High School
National City, California
Bill Bokesch

Tecumseh High School
Tecumseh, Michigan
Jennifer Keffer
Elizabeth Lentz
Carl Novak

Traverse City High School
Traverse City, Michigan
Diana Lyon-Schumacher
Ken May
Diane Moore

Vallivue High School
Caldwell, Idaho
Scott Coulter
Kathy Harris

Ypsilanti High School
Ypsilanti, Michigan
Keith Kellman
Mark McClure
Valerie Mills

Overview of Course 3

Part A

Unit 1 Multiple-Variable Models

Multiple-Variable Models develops student ability to construct and reason with linked quantitative variables and relations involving several variables and several constraints.
Topics include formulas, including the Law of Sines and the Law of Cosines, relating several variables by a single equation; systems of equations with several dependent variables or constraints; patterns of change in one or more variables in response to changes in others; solution of systems of equations and inequalities; and linear programming.

Lesson 1 *Linked Variables*
Lesson 2 *Algebra, Geometry, and Trigonometry*
Lesson 3 *Linked Equations*
Lesson 4 *Linear Programming*
Lesson 5 *Looking Back*

Unit 2 Modeling Public Opinion

Modeling Public Opinion develops student understanding of how public opinion can be measured. The situations analyzed include elections (where there are more than two choices) and sample surveys, including political polling.
Topics include preferential voting, vote-analysis methods, Arrow's theorem, fairness in social decision making; surveys, sampling, sampling distributions, relationship between a sample and a population, confidence intervals, margin of error; and critical analysis of elections and surveys.

Lesson 1 *Voting Models*
Lesson 2 *Surveys and Samples*
Lesson 3 *Sampling Distributions: From Population to Sample*
Lesson 4 *Confidence Intervals: From Sample to Population*
Lesson 5 *Looking Back*

Unit 3 Symbol Sense and Algebraic Reasoning

Symbol Sense and Algebraic Reasoning develops student ability to represent and draw inferences about algebraic relations and functions using symbolic expressions and manipulations.
Topics include formalization of function concept, notation, domain, and range; use of polynominal, exponential, and rational expressions to model relations among quantitative variables; field properties of real numbers and their application to expression of algebraic relations in equivalent forms and to solution of equations and inequalities by methods including factoring and the quadratic formula; and algebraic proof.

Lesson 1 *Algebra and Functions*
Lesson 2 *Algebraic Operations: Part 1*
Lesson 3 *Algebraic Operations: Part 2*
Lesson 4 *Reasoning to Solve Equations and Inequalities*
Lesson 5 *Proof through Algebraic Reasoning*
Lesson 6 *Looking Back*

Unit 4 Shapes and Geometric Reasoning

Shapes and Geometric Reasoning introduces students to formal reasoning and deduction in geometric settings.
Topics include inductive and deductive reasoning, counterexamples, the role of assumptions in proof; conclusions concerning supplementary and vertical angles and the angles formed by parallel lines and transversals; conditions insuring similarity and congruence of triangles and their application to quadrilaterals and other shapes; and necessary and sufficient conditions for parallelograms.

Lesson 1 *Reasoned Arguments*
Lesson 2 *Reasoning about Similar and Congruent Triangles*
Lesson 3 *Parallelograms: Necessary and Sufficient Conditions*
Lesson 4 *Looking Back*

Overview of Course 3

Part B

Unit 5 Patterns in Variaton

Patterns in Variation extends student understanding of the measurement of variation, develops student ability to use the normal distribution as a model of variation, and introduces students to the probability and statistical inference involved in the control charts used in industry for statistical process control.

Topics include standard deviation and its properties, normal distribution and its relation to standard deviation, statistical process control, control charts, control limits, mutually exclusive events, and the Addition Rule of Probability.

Lesson 1 *Measuring Variation with the Standard Deviation*
Lesson 2 *The Normal Distribution*
Lesson 3 *Statistical Process Control*
Lesson 4 *Looking Back*

Unit 6 Families of Functions

Families of Functions reviews and extends student ability to recognize different function patterns in numerical and graphical data and to interpret and construct appropriate symbolic representations modeling those data patterns.

Topics include review of linear, polynominal, exponential, rational, and trigonometric functions (including effects of parameters on numeric and graphic patterns) and construction of function rules for function tables and graphs that are transformations of basic types (translation, reflection, stretch).

Lesson 1 *Function Models Revisited*
Lesson 2 *Customizing Models 1: Reflections and Vertical Transformations*
Lesson 3 *Customizing Models 2: Horizontal Transformations*
Lesson 4 *Looking Back*

Unit 7 Discrete Models of Change

Discrete Models of Change extends student ability to represent, analyze, and solve problems in situations involving sequential and recursive change.

Topics include iteration and recursion as tools to model and analyze sequential change in real-world contexts; arithmetic, geometric, and other sequences; arithmetic and geometric series; finite differences; linear and nonlinear recurrence relations; and function iteration, including graphical iteration and fixed points.

Lesson 1 *Modeling Sequential Change Using Recursion*
Lesson 2 *A Discrete View of Function Models*
Lesson 3 *Iterating Functions*
Lesson 4 *Looking Back*

Capstone Making the Best of It: Optimal Forms and Strategies

Making the Best of It: Optimal Forms and Strategies is a thematic, two-week project-oriented activity that enables students to pull together and apply the important mathematical concepts and methods developed throughout the course.

Contents

Correlation of Course 3 to NCTM Standards **xii**
Curriculum Overview **xiii**
Implementing the Curriculum **xviii**
Managing Classroom Activities **xx**

Unit 1 Multiple-Variable Models

Lesson 1 *Linked Variables* **2**
INVESTIGATIONS
1 Stressed to the Breaking Point **3**
2 Go with the Flow **6**
3 Combining Rates and Times **11**
4 Taking Algebraic X-Rays **14**
MORE **16**

Lesson 2 *Algebra, Geometry, and Trigonometry* **25**
INVESTIGATIONS
1 Triangulation **26**
2 The Law of Sines **28**
3 The Law of Cosines **32**
4 Solving for ... **36**
MORE **40**

Lesson 3 *Linked Equations* **46**
INVESTIGATIONS
1 Comparison Shopping **47**
2 Supply and Demand **49**
3 Peak Profit **52**
MORE **57**

Lesson 4 *Linear Programming* **63**
INVESTIGATIONS
1 Picture Your Options **64**
2 Using an Algebraic Model **68**
3 Finding the Best Feasible Points **74**
4 Linear Equations and Inequalities **78**
MORE **80**

Lesson 5 *Looking Back* **86**

Unit 2 Modeling Public Opinion

Lesson 1 *Voting Models* **92**
INVESTIGATIONS
1 Ranking Choices **93**
2 Different Methods, Different Winners **96**
3 Fair Is Fair, Isn't It? **102**
MORE **106**

Lesson 2 *Surveys and Samples* **115**
INVESTIGATIONS
1 Surveys, Voting, and Censuses **116**
2 Bias in Surveys **121**
3 Selecting a Sample **124**
MORE **128**

Lesson 3 *Sampling Distributions: From Population to Sample* **135**
INVESTIGATIONS
1 Is It Likely or Unlikely? **136**
2 Box Plot Charts for a Fixed Sample Size **140**
3 Standard Charts for Different Sample Sizes **143**
MORE **148**

Lesson 4 *Confidence Intervals: From Sample to Population* **153**
INVESTIGATION
1 Likely Populations **154**
MORE **159**

Lesson 5 *Looking Back* **165**

Unit 3 Symbol Sense and Algebraic Reasoning

Lesson 1 *Algebra and Functions* **170**

INVESTIGATIONS
1 Defining Functions **171**
2 Functions with Symbolic Rules **175**
MORE **179**

Lesson 2 *Algebraic Operations: Part 1* **187**

INVESTIGATIONS
1 How to Succeed in Business **188**
2 Equivalent Expressions **192**
3 What a Difference Subtraction Makes **197**
MORE **201**

Lesson 3 *Algebraic Operations: Part 2* **208**

INVESTIGATIONS
1 Products and Factoring **209**
2 Special Products and Factoring **212**
3 Division and Fractions **215**
MORE **218**

Lesson 4 *Reasoning to Solve Equations and Inequalities* **225**

INVESTIGATIONS
1 Reasoning About Linear Equations and Inequalities **226**
2 Reasoning About Quadratic Equations and Inequalities **229**
MORE **234**

Lesson 5 *Proof through Algebraic Reasoning* **240**

INVESTIGATIONS
1 Proving It Always Works **241**
2 Algebraic Reasoning in Geometry and Statistics **243**
MORE **247**

Lesson 6 *Looking Back* **253**

Unit 4 Shapes and Geometric Reasoning

Lesson 1 *Reasoned Arguments* **260**

INVESTIGATIONS
1 Analyzing Arguments **261**
2 Reasoning *to* and *from* If-Then Statements **266**
MORE **272**
3 Reasoning about Intersecting Lines and Angles **279**
4 Parallel Lines, Transversals, and Angles **282**
MORE **288**

Lesson 2 *Reasoning about Similar and Congruent Triangles* **297**

INVESTIGATIONS
1 When Are Two Triangles Similar? **298**
2 When Are Two Triangles Congruent? **304**
MORE **310**
3 Reasoning with Congruence and Similarity Conditions **316**
MORE **319**

Lesson 3 *Parallelograms: Necessary and Sufficient Conditions* **325**

INVESTIGATIONS
1 Reasoning about Parallelograms **326**
2 Special Kinds of Parallelograms **330**
MORE **333**

Lesson 4 *Looking Back* **340**

Index of Mathematical Topics **345**
Index of Contexts **349**

Correlation of Course 3 to NCTM Standards

The *Contemporary Mathematics in Context* curriculum and the instructional and assessment practices it promotes address the focal points of the National Council of Teachers of Mathematics' *Principles and Standards for School Mathematics.* By design, the **process standards** on Problem Solving, Reasoning and Proof, Communication, Connections, and Representation are an integral part of each lesson of every unit in the curriculum.

The chart below correlates Course 3 units with the **content standards** for grades 9–12 in terms of focus (✓) and connections (+).

Correlation of Course 3 to NCTM Standards					
Course 3 Units / **NCTM Grades 9–12 Content Standards**	Number and Operations	Algebra	Geometry	Measurement	Data Analysis and Probability
Multiple-Variable Models	✓	✓	✓	+	
Modeling Public Opinion	+			+	✓
Symbol Sense and Algebraic Reasoning	✓	✓	+	+	+
Shapes and Geometric Reasoning	✓	+	✓	+	+
Patterns in Variation	+	+		+	✓
Families of Functions	+	✓	✓	+	+
Discrete Models of Change	+	✓	+	+	+
Capstone—Making the Best of It: Optimal Forms and Strategies	+	✓	✓	+	✓

Curriculum Overview

Introduction

Contemporary Mathematics in Context Course 3 continues a four-year integrated mathematics program developed by the **Core-Plus Mathematics Project (CPMP)**. The curriculum builds upon the theme of mathematics as sense-making. Through investigations of real-life contexts, students develop a rich understanding of important mathematics that makes sense to them and, in turn, enables them to make sense out of new situations and problems. The curriculum materials have the following mathematical and instructional features.

Unified Content

Each year the curriculum advances students' understanding of mathematics along interwoven strands of algebra and functions, statistics and probability, geometry and trigonometry, and discrete mathematics. These strands are unified by fundamental themes, by common topics, and by mathematical habits of mind such as visual thinking, recursive thinking, and searching for and explaining patterns.

Mathematical Modeling

The curriculum emphasizes mathematical modeling, including the processes of data collection, representation, interpretation, prediction, and simulation.

Access and Challenge

The curriculum is designed to make more mathematics accessable to more students, while at the same time challenging the most able students. Differences in students' performance and interest can be accommodated by the depth and level of abstraction to which core topics are pursued, by the nature and degree of difficulty of applications, and by providing opportunities for student choice of homework tasks and projects.

Technology

Numerical, graphics, and programming/link capabilities such as those found on many graphing calculators are assumed and appropriately used throughout the curriculum. This use of technology permits the curriculum and instruction to emphasize multiple representations (verbal, numerical, graphical, and symbolic) and to focus on goals in which mathematical thinking and problem solving are central.

Active Learning

Instructional materials promote active learning and teaching centered around collaborative small-group investigations of problem situations, followed by teacher-led whole class summarizing activities that lead to analysis, abstraction, and further application of underlying mathematical ideas. Students are actively engaged in exploring, conjecturing, verifying, generalizing, applying, proving, evaluating, and communicating mathematical ideas.

Multi-dimensional Assessment

Comprehensive assessment of student understanding and progress through both curriculum-embedded assessment opportunities and supplementary assessment tasks supports instruction and enables monitoring and evaluation of each student's performance in terms of mathematical processes, content, and dispositions.

This curriculum promises to make mathematics accessible and more meaningful to more students. Developing mathematics along multiple strands nurtures the differing strengths and talents of students and simultaneously helps them to develop diverse mathematical insights. Developing mathematics from a modeling perspective permits students to experience mathematics as a means of making sense of data and problems that arise in diverse contexts within and across cultures. Engaging students in collaborating on tasks in small groups develops their ability to both deal with, and find commonality in, diversity of ideas. Using calculators as a means for learning and doing mathematics enables students to develop versatile ways of dealing with realistic situations and reduces the manipulative skill filter which has prevented large numbers of students from continuing their study of significant mathematics. In addition, calculator graphics offer powerful new ways of visualizing mathematics across each of the strands.

Unified Mathematics

Contemporary Mathematics in Context is a unified curriculum that replaces the traditional Algebra-Geometry-Advanced Algebra/Trigonometry-Precalculus sequence. Each course features "strands" of algebra and functions, statistics and probability, geometry and trigonometry, and discrete mathematics. Each of these strands is developed within focused units, connected by fundamental ideas such as symmetry, matrices, functions, and data analysis and curve-fitting. The strands also are connected across units by mathematical habits of mind such as visual thinking, recursive thinking, searching for and explaining patterns, making and checking conjectures, reasoning with multiple representations, inventing mathematics, and providing convincing arguments and proofs. The strands are unified further by the fundamental themes of data, representation, shape, and change. Important mathematical ideas are frequently revisited through the attention to connections within and across strands, enabling students to develop a robust connected understanding of mathematics.

Algebra and Functions

The algebra and functions strand develops student ability to recognize, represent, and solve problems involving relations among quantitative variables. Central to the development is the use of functions as mathematical models. The key algebraic models in the curriculum are linear, exponential, power, polynomial, logarithmic, rational, and trigonometric functions. Each algebraic model is investigated in at least four linked representations—verbal, graphic, numeric, and symbolic—with the aid of technology. Attention is also given to modeling systems of equations, both linear and nonlinear, and to symbolic reasoning and manipulation.

Statistics and Probability

The primary role of the statistics and probability strand is to develop student ability to analyze data intelligently, to recognize and measure variation, and to understand the patterns that underlie probabilistic situations. The ultimate goal is for students to understand how inferences can be made about a population by looking at a sample from that population. Graphical methods of data analysis, simulations, sampling, and experience with the collection and interpretation of real data are featured.

Geometry and Trigonometry

The primary goal of the geometry and trigonometry strand is to develop visual thinking and student ability to construct, reason with, interpret, and apply mathematical models of patterns in the visual world and physical contexts. The focus is on describing patterns with regard to shape, size, and location; representing visual patterns with drawings, coordinates, or vectors; predicting changes and invariants in shape; and organizing geometric facts and relationships through deductive reasoning.

Discrete Mathematics

The discrete mathematics strand develops student ability to model and solve problems involving enumeration, sequential change, decision-making in finite settings, and relationships among a finite number of elements. Topics include matrices, vertex-edge graphs, recursion, voting methods, and systematic counting methods (combinatorics). Key themes are discrete mathematical modeling, existence (*Is there a solution?*), optimization (*What is the best solution?*), and algorithmic problem solving (*Can you efficiently construct a solution?*).

Organization of Course 3

The curriculum for Course 3 consists of seven units and a culminating capstone experience. Each of the units is comprised of four to six multi-day lessons in which major ideas are developed through investigations of rich applied problems. Units vary in length from approximately four to six weeks. The final element of Course 3, the capstone, is a thematic two-week project-oriented activity that enables students to pull together and apply the important modeling concepts and methods developed in the entire course.

In developing Course 3, the Core-Plus Mathematics Project chose mathematical content which the developers believed was the most important mathematics all eleventh-grade students should have the opportunity to learn. In particular, the content of the last units in the text is not viewed as optional as is often the case with traditional textbooks. As with Courses 1 and 2, the text for Course 3 is available in a two-volume edition. A school block-scheduling classes will find flexibility for designing course content with two volumes that is not normally available with single volume textbooks.

The organization of the student text differs in several other ways from traditional textbooks. There are no boxed-off definitions, "worked-out" examples, or content summaries. Students learn mathematics by doing mathematics. Concept images are developed as students complete investigations; later concept definitions appear. Mathematical ideas are developed and then shared by groups of students at strategically placed Checkpoints in the lessons. This discussion leads to a class summary of shared understandings.

Instructional Model

The manner in which students encounter mathematical ideas can contribute significantly to the quality of their learning and the depth of their understanding. Lessons in *Contemporary Mathematics in Context* are therefore designed around a specific cycle of instructional activities intended primarily for small-group work in the classroom and for individual work outside of the classroom.

In Class The four-phase cycle of classroom activities—*Launch, Explore, Share and Summarize*, and *Apply*—is designed to actively engage students in investigating and making sense of problem situations, in constructing important mathematical concepts and methods, in generalizing and proving mathematical relationships, and in communicating their thinking and the results of their efforts. The summary below describes these phases of classroom instruction.

In-Class Instruction

LAUNCH full-class discussion

Think About This Situation

The lesson begins with a teacher-led discussion of a problem situation and of related questions to **think about**. This discussion sets the context for the student work to follow and helps to generate student interest; it also provides an opportunity for the teacher to assess student knowledge and to clarify directions for the group activities. *Teacher is director and moderator.*

EXPLORE small-group investigation

INVESTIGATION

Classroom activity then shifts to having students **investigate** focused problems and questions related to the launching situation by gathering data, looking for patterns, constructing models and meanings, and making and verifying conjectures. As students collaborate in small groups, the teacher circulates from group to group providing guidance and support, clarifying or asking questions, giving hints, providing encouragement, and drawing group members into the discussion to help groups work more cooperatively. The unit materials and related questions posed by students drive the learning. *Teacher is facilitator.*

SHARE AND SUMMARIZE full-class discussion

Checkpoint

A teacher-led full-class discussion (referred to as a Checkpoint) of concepts and methods developed by different small groups then provides an opportunity to **share** progress and thinking. This discussion leads to a class **summary** of important ideas or to further exploration of a topic if competing perspectives remain. Varying points of view and differing conclusions that can be justified should be encouraged. *Teacher is moderator.*

APPLY individual task

On Your Own

Finally, students are given a task to complete on their own to **assess** their initial understanding of concepts and methods. The teacher circulates in the room assessing levels of understanding. *Teacher is intellectual coach.*

Out of Class In addition to the classroom investigations, *Contemporary Mathematics in Context* provides sets of MORE tasks, which are designed to engage students in ***M**odeling* with, ***O**rganizing*, ***R**eflecting* on, and ***E**xtending* their mathematical knowledge. MORE tasks are provided for each lesson in the CPMP materials and are central to the learning goals of each lesson. These tasks are intended primarily for individual work outside of class. Selection of MORE tasks should be based on student performance and the availability of time and technology. Also, students should exercise some choice of tasks to pursue, and at times they should be given the opportunity to pose their own problems and questions to investigate. The chart below describes the types of tasks in a typical MORE set.

MORE: Out-of-Class Activities	
Modeling	*Modeling* tasks are related to or provide new contexts to which students can apply the ideas and methods that they have developed in the lesson.
Organizing	*Organizing* tasks offer opportunities for integrating the formal mathematics underlying the mathematical models developed in the lesson and for making connections with other strands.
Reflecting	*Reflecting* tasks encourage thinking about thinking, about mathematical meanings, and about processes, and promote self-monitoring and evaluation of understanding.
Extending	*Extending* tasks permit further, deeper, or more formal study of the topics under investigation.

Summarizing Activities In the *Contemporary Mathematics in Context* curriculum, students learn mathematics by doing mathematics. However, it is important that students prepare and maintain summaries of important concepts and methods that are developed. To assist in this matter, the "On Your Own" task in the final lesson of each unit asks students to prepare, in outline form, a summary of the important ideas developed in the unit. Templates to guide preparation of these unit summaries can be found in the *Teaching Resources*. In addition, students should create a Math Toolkit that organizes important class-generated ideas and selected Checkpoint responses as they complete investigations. "Constructing a Math Toolkit" prompts are provided in this *Teacher's Guide* to assist in identifying key concepts and methods as they are developed by students. (See the *Teaching Resources* for blackline masters to assist students in organizing their Math Toolkits.)

Curriculum-Embedded Assessment

Assessing what students know and are able to do is an integral part of *Contemporary Mathematics in Context* and there are opportunities for assessment in each phase of the instructional cycle. Initially, as students pursue the investigations that make up the curriculum, the teacher is able to informally assess student understanding of mathematical processes, content, and their disposition toward mathematics. Then at the end of each investigation, the Checkpoint and class discussion provide an opportunity for teachers to assess the levels of understanding that various groups of students have reached as they share and summarize their findings. Finally, the "On Your Own" problems and the tasks in the MORE sets provide further opportunities to assess the level of understanding of each individual student.

A more detailed description of the CPMP assessment program is given on pages xxi–xxv of this text and in *Implementing the Core-Plus Mathematics Curriculum.*

Implementing the Curriculum

Planning for Instruction

The *Contemporary Mathematics in Context* curriculum is not only changing what mathematics all students have the opportunity to learn, but also changing how that learning occurs and is assessed. Active learning is most effective when accompanied with active teaching. Just as the student text is designed to actively engage students in doing mathematics, the teacher's resource materials are designed to support teachers in planning for instruction; in observing, listening, questioning, facilitating student work, and orchestrating classroom discussion; and in managing the classroom.

The *Teacher's Guide* provides suggestions, based on the experiences of field-test teachers, for implementing this exciting new curriculum in your classroom. You probably will find new ideas that can at first be overwhelming. The developers highly recommend that teachers who are teaching *Contemporary Mathematics in Context* for the first time do so at least in pairs who share a common planning period.

Each of the items listed below is included in the *Teacher's Guide* for each unit.

- Unit Overview
- Objectives, suggested timeline, and materials needed
- Instructional notes and suggestions
- Suggested assignments for each MORE set
- Solutions for Investigations and MORE tasks
- Unit summary and a look ahead ("Looking Back, Looking Ahead")

The *Teaching Resources* include blackline masters for creating transparencies and handouts. *Assessment Resources* include quizzes for individual lessons, end-of-unit exams, take-home assessment tasks, projects, and semester exam tasks. Special calculator software has been developed to support students' investigations and modeling applications in each of the four strands. The software for the TI-82, TI-83, and TI-92 graphing calculators is available on disk for downloading from Macintosh and DOS- or Windows-based (PC) computers.

Each unit of *Contemporary Mathematics in Context* includes either content which may be new to many teachers or new approaches to familiar content. Thus, a first step toward planning the teaching of a unit is to review the scope and sequence of the unit. This review provides an overall feel for the goals of the unit and how it holds together. The *Scope and Sequence* guide shows how the specific mathematical topics fit in the complete four-year curriculum. Working through the student investigations, if possible with a colleague, provides help in thinking about and understanding mathematical ideas that may be unfamiliar.

In the *Teacher's Guide* you will find teaching notes for each lesson, including instructional suggestions and sample student responses to investigations and MORE sets. Thinking about the range of possible responses and solutions to problems in a lesson proves to be very helpful in facilitating student work.

Although not stated, it is assumed that students have access to graphing calculators at all times for in-class work and ideally for out-of-class work as well. Downloading and becoming familiar with the specially-designed calculator software will require advanced planning, as will acquiring physical materials.

The developers recommend that the homework (MORE) assignment *not* be held off until the end of the lesson or the investigation just preceding the MORE set. Some teachers choose to post the MORE assignment at the beginning of a lesson along with the due date—usually a day or two following planned completion of the lesson. Other teachers prefer to assign particular MORE tasks at appropriate points during the course of the multiday lesson and then assign the remaining tasks toward the end of the lesson. Note that all recommended assignments include provision for student choice of some tasks. This is but one of many ways in which this curriculum is designed to accommodate and support differences in students' interests and performance levels.

It is strongly recommended that student solutions to Organizing tasks be discussed in class. These tasks help students organize and formalize the mathematics developed in context and connect it to other mathematics they have studied. Structuring the underlying mathematics and building connections are best accomplished by comparing and discussing student work and synthesizing key ideas within the classroom.

Orchestrating Lessons

The *Contemporary Mathematics in Context* materials are designed to engage students in a four-phase cycle of classroom activities. The activities often require both students and teachers to assume roles quite different than those in more traditional mathematics classrooms. Sophomores or juniors beginning Course 3 should be quite familiar with their roles in the classroom. Although realistic problem solving and investigative work by students are the heart of the curriculum, how teachers orchestrate the launching of an activity and the sharing and summarizing of results is critical to successful implementation. Teachers who have not taught Courses 1 or 2 should collaborate with colleagues who can assist them in gaining expertise in their new role.

Students enter the classroom with differing backgrounds, experience, and knowledge. These differences can be viewed as assets. Engaging the class in a free-flowing give-and-take discussion of how students think about the launch situations serves to connect lessons with the informal understandings of data, shape, change, and chance that students bring to the classroom. Try to maximize the participation of students in these discussions by emphasizing that their ideas and possible approaches are valued and important and that definitive answers are not necessarily expected at this time.

Once launched, a lesson may involve students working together collaboratively in small groups for a period of days punctuated occasionally by brief, whole-class discussion of questions students have raised. In this setting, the lesson becomes driven primarily by the instructional materials themselves. Rather than orchestrating class discussion, the teacher shifts to circulating among the groups and observing, listening, and interacting with students by asking guiding or probing questions. These small-group investigations lead to (re)invention of important mathematics that makes sense to students. Sharing and agreeing as a class on the mathematical ideas that groups are developing is the purpose of the Checkpoints in the instructional materials.

Class discussions at Checkpoints are orchestrated somewhat differently than during the launch of a lesson. At this stage, mathematical ideas and methods still may be under development and may vary for individual groups. So class discussion should involve groups comparing their methods and results, analyzing their work, and arriving at conclusions agreed upon by the class.

The investigations deepen students' understanding of mathematical ideas and extend their mathematical language in contexts. Technical terminology and symbolism are introduced as needed. This sometimes occurs in student materials immediately following a Checkpoint and before the corresponding "On Your Own" task. These connections should be introduced by the teacher as a natural way of closing the class discussion summarizing the Checkpoint.

Managing Classroom Activities

Active Learning and Collaborative Work

The *Contemporary Mathematics in Context* curriculum materials are designed to promote active, collaborative learning and group work for two important reasons. First, a collaborative environment fosters students' ability to make sense of mathematics and develop deep mathematial understandings. Collaborative learning is an effective method for engaging all the students in the learning process, particularly students who have been underrepresented in mathematics classes. Second, practice in collaborative learning in the classroom is practice for real life: students develop and exercise the same skills in the classroom that they need in their lives at home, in the community, and in the workplace.

Value of Individuals

Perhaps the most fundamental belief underlying the use of collaborative learning is that every student is viewed as a valuable resource and contributor. In other words, every student participates in group work and is given the opportunity and time to voice ideas and opinions. Implementing this concept is not easy. It does not happen automatically. In order to set a tone that will promote respect for individuals and their contributions, classroom rules should be established and agreed upon by the learning community. Students should be included in the process of formulating the rules. The teacher should initiate a discussion of group rules and then post them in the classroom. The teacher should model all of the rules correctly to show that "we" begins with "me." Those who do not adhere to the rules must accept the consequences in accordance with classroom or school disciplinary procedures.

Importance of Social Connections

Even in classrooms in which the rules for showing respect have been clearly established, experience has shown that students still cannot talk with one another about mathematics (or social studies, or literature, or any other subject) if they do not first have positive social connections.

One way to develop this kind of common base is through team-building activities. These short activities may be used at the beginning of the year to help students get acquainted with the whole class and may be used during the year whenever new groups are formed to help groupmates know one another better. Team-building activities help students learn new and positive things about classmates with whom they may have attended classes for years, but have not known in depth. The time taken for these quick team-builders pays off later in helping students feel comfortable enough to work with the members of their group.

Need for Teaching Social Skills

Experience also has shown that social skills are critical to the successful functioning of any small group. Because there is no guarantee that students of any particular age will have the social skills necessary for effective group work, it often is necessary to teach these skills to build a collaborative learning environment.

These social skills are specific skills, not general goals. Examples of specific social skills that the teacher can teach in the classroom include responding to ideas respectfully, keeping track of time, disagreeing in an agreeable way, involving everyone, and following directions. Though goals such as cooperating and listening are important, they are too general to teach.

One method of teaching social skills is to begin by selecting a specific skill and then having the class brainstorm to develop a script for practicing that skill. Next, the students practice that skill during their group work. Finally, in what is called the processing, the students discuss within their groups how well they performed the assigned social skill. Effective teaching of social skills requires practicing and processing; merely describing a specific social skill is not enough. Actual practice and processing are necessary for students to really learn the skill and to increase the use of appropriate behaviors during group work and other times during class.

One of the premises of collaborative learning is that by developing the appropriate skills through practice, anyone in the class can learn to work in a group with anyone else. Learning to work in groups is a continuous process, however, and the process can be helped by decisions that the teacher makes. *Implementing the Core-Plus Mathematics Curriculum* provides information and support to help teachers make decisions about group size, composition, method of selection, student reaction to working in groups, and the duration of groups. (It also provides advice on dealing effectively with student absences.)

The culture created within the classroom is crucial to the success of this curriculum. It is important to inculcate in students a sense of inquiry and responsibility for their own learning. Without this commitment, active, collaborative learning by students cannot be effective. In order for students to work collaboratively, they must be able to understand the value of working together. Some students seem satisfied with the rationale that it is important in the business world. Others may need to understand that the struggle of verbalizing their thinking, listening to others' thinking, questioning themselves and other group members, and coming to an agreement increases their understanding and retention of the mathematics while contributing to the formation of important thinking skills or habits of mind.

Issues of helping students to work collaboratively will become less pressing as both you and your students experience this type of learning. You may find it helpful to refer to *Implementing the Core-Plus Mathematics Curriculum* and discuss effective cooperative groups with colleagues a few weeks into the semester.

Assessment

Throughout the *Contemporary Mathematics in Context* curriculum, the term "assessment" is meant to include all instances of gathering information about students' levels of understanding and their disposition toward mathematics for purposes of making decisions about instruction. You may want to consult the extended section on assessment in *Implementing the Core-Plus Mathematics Curriculum.*

The dimensions of student performance that are assessed in this curriculum (see chart below) are consistent with the assessment recommendations of the National Council of Teachers of Mathematics in the *Assessment Standards for School Mathematics* (NCTM, 1995). They are much broader than those of a typical testing program.

Assessment Dimensions

Process	Content	Attitude
Problem Solving	Concepts	Beliefs
Reasoning	Applications	Perseverance
Communication	Representational Strategies	Confidence
Connections	Procedures	Enthusiasm

Sources of Assessment Information

Several kinds of assessment are available to teachers using *Contemporary Mathematics in Context.* Some of these sources reside within the curriculum itself; some of them are student-generated; and some are supplementary materials designed specifically for assessment. Understanding the nature of these sources is a prerequisite for selecting assessment tools, establishing guidelines on how to score assessments, making judgments about what students know and are able to do, and assigning grades.

Curriculum Sources

Two features of the curriculum, questioning and observation by the teacher, provide fundamental and particularly useful ways of gathering assessment information. The student text uses questions to facilitate student understanding of new concepts, of how these concepts fit with earlier ideas and with one another, and of how they can be applied in problem situations. Whether students are working individually or in groups, the teacher is given a window to watch how the students think about and apply mathematics as they attempt to answer the questions posed by the curriculum materials. In fact, by observing how students respond to the curriculum-embedded questions, the teacher can assess student performance across all process, content, and attitude dimensions described in the chart on page xxi.

Specific features in the student material that focus on different ways students respond to questions are the Checkpoint, "On Your Own," and MORE (***M**odeling,* ***O**rganizing,* ***R**eflecting,* and ***E**xtending*) sets. Checkpoint features are intended to bring students together, usually after they have been working in small groups, so they may share and discuss the progress each group has made during a sequence of related activities. Each Checkpoint is intended to be a whole-class discussion, so it should provide an opportunity for teachers to assess, informally, the levels of understanding that the various groups of students have reached.

Following each Checkpoint, the "On Your Own" tasks are meant to be completed by students working individually. Student responses to these tasks provide an opportunity for teachers to assess the level of understanding of each student.

The tasks in the MORE sets serve many purposes, including post-investigation assessment. Each type of task in a MORE set has a different instructional purpose. Modeling tasks help students demonstrate how well they understand and can apply the concepts and procedures developed in an investigation. Organizing tasks demonstrate how well students understand connections between the content of an investigation and other mathematical and real-world ideas. In-class discussions based on Organizing tasks are a crucial step in assisting students' development of a full understanding of the mathematical content and connections. Reflecting tasks provide insights into students' beliefs, attitudes, and judgments of their own competence. Extending tasks show how well students are able to extend the present content beyond the level addressed in an investigation. The performance of students or groups of students in each of these types of tasks provides the teacher with further information to help assess applicability, connectedness, and depth of the students' evolving understanding of mathematics.

Finally, an opportunity for group self-assessment is provided in the last element of each unit, the "Looking Back" lesson. These tasks help students pull together and demonstrate what they have learned in the unit and at the same time provide helpful review and confidence-building for students.

Student-Generated Sources

Other possible sources of assessment information are writings and materials produced by students in the form of student mathematics toolkits and journals.

Mathematics Toolkits Students should create a Math Toolkit that organizes important class-generated ideas and selected Checkpoint responses as they complete investigations. Constructing a Math Toolkit prompts are provided in the *Teacher's Guide* to assist in identifying key concepts and methods as they are developed by students. (See the *Teaching Resources* for blackline masters to assist students in organizing their Math Toolkits.)

Journals Student journals are notebooks in which students are encouraged to write (briefly, but frequently) their personal reflections concerning the class, the mathematics they are learning, and their progress. These journals are an excellent way for the teacher to gain insights into how individual students are feeling about the class, what they do and do not understand, and what some of their particular learning difficulties are. For many students, the journal is a non-threatening way to communicate with the teacher about matters that may be too difficult or too time-consuming to talk about directly. Journals also encourage students to assess their own understanding of, and feelings about, the mathematics they are studying. The teacher should collect, read, and respond to each journal at least once a month.

The *Contemporary Mathematics in Context* assessment program provides many items that can be placed in students' portfolios, including reports of individual and group projects, Math Toolkit or journal entries, teacher-completed observation checklists, end-of-unit assessments especially the take-home tasks and projects. See *Implementing the Core-Plus Mathematics Curriculum* for additional portfolio information.

Assessment Resources

The *Contemporary Mathematics in Context* teacher resource materials include for each unit a third source of assessment information—*Assessment Resources*. Included in the *Assessment Resources* are end-of-lesson quizzes and end-of-unit assessments in the form of an in-class unit exam, take-home assessment tasks, and projects. Calculators are required in most cases and are intended to be available to students. Teacher discretion should be used regarding student access to their textbook and Math Toolkit for assessments. In general, if the goals to be assessed are problem solving and reasoning, while memory of facts and procedural skill are of less interest, resources should be allowed. However, if automaticity of procedures or unaided recall are being assessed, it is appropriate to prohibit resource materials. Since many rich opportunities for assessing students are embedded in the curriculum itself, you may choose not to use all the lesson quizzes for each unit.

End-of-Lesson Quizzes Two forms of a quiz covering the main ideas of each lesson are provided. These quizzes, which are the most traditional of all the assessment methods and instruments included with the *Contemporary Mathematics in Context* materials, are comprised of fairly straightforward problems meant to determine if students have developed understanding of the important concepts and procedures of each lesson.

In-Class Exams Two forms of in-class exams are provided for each unit and are intended to be completed in a 50-minute class period. The two forms of each exam are not necessarily equivalent, although they assess essentially the same mathematical ideas. Teachers should preview the two versions carefully, and feel free to revise or delete items and add new ones, if necessary, using the *Assessment and Maintenance Worksheet Builder* CD-ROM.

Take-Home Assessments Take-home assessment tasks are included for each unit. The students or the teacher should choose one or, at most, two of these tasks. These assessments, some of which are best done by students working in pairs or small groups, provide students with the opportunity to organize the information from the completed unit, to extend the ideas of the unit into other areas of interest to them, to work with another student or group of students, and to avoid the time pressure often generated by in-class exams.

Projects Assessment traditionally has been based on evaluating work that students have completed in a very short time period and under restricted conditions. Some assessment, however, should involve work done over a longer time period and with the aid of resources. Thus, assessment projects are included in unit assessments. These projects, which are intended to be completed by small groups of students, provide an opportunity for students to conduct an investigation that extends and applies the main ideas from the unit and to write a summary of their findings.

Midterm and Final Assessment A bank of assessment tasks, from which to construct an exam that fits your particular class needs and emphases, is also provided.

Scoring Assessments

High expectations of the quality of students' written work will encourage students to reach their potential. Assigning scores to open-ended assessments and to observations of students' performance requires more subjective judgment by the teacher than does grading short-answer or multiple-choice tests. It is therefore not possible to provide a complete set of explicit guidelines for scoring open-ended assessment items and written or oral reports. However, some general guidelines may be helpful. When scoring student work on open-ended assessment tasks, the goal is to reward in a fair and consistent way the kinds of thinking and understanding that the task is meant to measure. To score open-ended assessment tasks, teachers should have a general rubric, or scoring scheme, with several response levels in mind; a specific rubric; and anchor items. (See *Implementing the Core-Plus Mathematics Curriculum* for more details.) The general rubric is the foundation for scoring across a wide range of types of open-ended tasks. The following general rubric can be used for most assessment tasks provided with *Contemporary Mathematics in Context.*

General Scoring Rubric

4 points	Contains complete response with clear, coherent, and unambiguous explanation; includes clear and simple diagram, if appropriate; communicates effectively to identified audience; shows understanding of question's mathematical ideas and processes; identifies all important elements of question; includes examples and counterexamples; gives strong supporting arguments
3 points	Contains good solid response with some, but not all, of the characteristics above; explains less completely; may include minor error of execution but not of understanding
2 points	Contains complete response, but explanation is muddled; presents incomplete arguments; includes diagrams that are inappropriate or unclear, or fails to provide a diagram when it would be appropriate; indicates some understanding of mathematical ideas, but in an unclear way; shows clear evidence of understanding some important ideas while also making one or more fundamental, specific errors
1 point	Omits parts of question and response; has major errors; uses inappropriate strategies
0 points	No response; frivolous or irrelevant response

Assigning Grades

Because the *Contemporary Mathematics in Context* approach and materials provide a wide variety of assessment information, the teacher will be in a good position to assign a fair grade for student work. With such a wide choice for assessment, a word of caution is appropriate: *it is easy to overassess students, and care must be taken to avoid doing so.* A quiz need not be given after every lesson nor an in-class exam after every unit. The developers believe it is best to vary assessment methods from lesson to lesson, and from unit to unit. If information on what students understand and are able to do is available from their homework and in-class work, it may not be necessary to take the time for a formal quiz after each lesson. Similarly, information from project work may replace an in-class exam.

Deciding exactly how to weigh the various kinds of assessment information is a decision that the teacher will need to make and communicate clearly to the students.

Maintaining Skills

The developers have identified a set of paper-and-pencil technical competencies that all students should acquire. To provide additional practice with these core competencies, a special maintenance feature is included in blackline master form in the *Teaching Resources* or on the *Assessment and Maintenance Worksheet Builder* CD-ROM. Beginning with Unit 4 of Course 1, "Graph Models," and then continuing with each unit thereafter, a supplementary set of maintenance tasks provides periodic review and additional practice of basic skills. These skills will be continually revisited to ensure mastery by each student at some point in the curriculum.

Use of the maintenance material following the start of Lesson 2 of each unit will allow students time to work simultaneously on skills during the latter part of a unit without interrupting the flow of the unit. You may wish to allow a few minutes at the end of selected class periods to revisit these skills with various groups of students who need assistance while other groups choose an Extending task to complete.

The maintenance material prepared for each unit spans technical competencies across each of the strands. In each case, the first presented task is a contextual problem, but the remaining tasks are not contextualized. Students should *not* use a calculator for these tasks unless so directed.

Reference and Practice Books (RAP Books)

A *Reference and Practice* book is available to accompany Course 3 of the program. The Course 3 RAP book provides students with summaries of concepts and skills from Course 2; practice sets to review and maintain concepts and skills; and exercise sets that provide test-taking practice for standardized tests. This handbook also contains tips for taking standardized tests. These supplements are intended for student reference and use outside of regularly scheduled class times. Suggested assignments are listed in the Planning Guide for each unit.

Additional Resources

The Core-Plus Mathematics Project (CPMP) maintains a Web site at www.wmich.edu/cpmp as a resource for schools. You may find the "Frequently Asked Questions" helpful as you think about your uniform district replies to community questions.

In addition, CPMP moderates a listserv that allows teachers to have discussions about mathematical content and implementation of *Contemporary Mathematics in Context*. For additional information and to subscribe to the listserv, email cpmp@wmich.edu.

Unit 1

Multiple-Variable Models

UNIT OVERVIEW In the algebra and functions strand of Courses 1 and 2, students have developed an understanding of linear, exponential, and power models. In this unit, students expand their understanding of algebraic relations to include models in which more than two variables are involved. Linear models, power models, quadratic models, and trigonometric models are explored in new ways and in more complex situations. As in previous courses of *Contemporary Mathematics in Context*, these models are introduced to the students through the analysis of data and real-life situations. By the end of this unit, students should have a good understanding of a variety of means for exploring different multiple-variable situations through the use of tables, graphs, and symbolic representations.

In the first lesson, students operate with contexts involving one relation among more than two variables. Through the investigations, students explore how changes in one variable affect the values of other variables. The varied activities in this lesson include a number of flow-rate situations that students are likely to experience in their science classes.

In Lesson 2, students work with multiple-variable situations that involve algebra, geometry, and trigonometry. The trigonometry provides opportunities for students to explore problems different from those in the previous lesson, yet the algebraic reasoning behind the solutions is similar to problems from Lesson 1. In this second lesson, the students solve problems involving the Law of Sines and the Law of Cosines. In all of the problem situations, the students are confronted with equations involving more than two variables.

In Lesson 3, the investigations involve two or more output variables related to the same input variable. The students explore such systems of equations and determine algebraic models, tables, and graphs for them. They also examine inequalities related to these systems and, again, they explore the inequalities by considering the models, tables, and graphs.

In Lesson 4, linear programming is used to motivate interest in and to show one reason for graphing linear inequalities. Students are guided to discover the feasible region for a linear programming problem, what the boundaries of that region are, and finally, that the best solution is always at a vertex of the feasible region. In the last investigation, students gain more experience graphing and solving systems of equations.

Multiple-Variable Models

Unit 1

2 • **Lesson 1**
Linked Variables

25 • **Lesson 2**
Algebra, Geometry, and Trigonometry

46 • **Lesson 3**
Linked Equations

63 • **Lesson 4**
Linear Programming

86 • **Lesson 5**
Looking Back

1

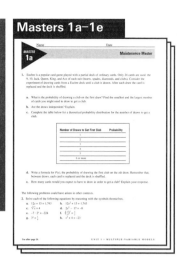

Masters 1a–1e

Unit 1 Objectives

- To develop an understanding of and the ability to solve problems involving multiple-variable relations (including trigonometric relations) where one equation relates more than two variables
- To develop the ability to solve multiple-variable equations for one variable in terms of the other variables
- To model situations with systems of equations and inequalities where two or more output variables are related to the same input variable, and to apply those systems to solve problems

Collaborative Learning

The *Contemporary Mathematics in Context* curriculum is designed around small-group collaborative learning. Effective collaborative learning requires familiarity with the factors in the composition and selection of groups as well as practice in classroom techniques for managing collaborative learning. For detailed information on these areas, see *Implementing the Core-Plus Mathematics Curriculum.*

Most students in this course have worked collaboratively during Courses 1 and 2. However, they are now in a classroom with different students and perhaps a different teacher. You may wish to create collaborative group guidelines with the assistance of your students. During this first unit, it is important for students to focus on the guidelines that help facilitate collaborative learning and to reinforce the skills that they began developing in Courses 1 and 2. A good way to do this is to formally incorporate group-processing questions into your lessons, at least through the first unit. A good time to do this is immediately following discussion of the Checkpoints. The time you spend on this now will be returned through more efficient, smooth, and productive group work throughout the year.

Group-processing questions may be open-ended or fill-in-the-blank. You will find sample questions immediately following the Checkpoint solutions throughout the teacher's notes for this unit. You may choose one or create your own to fit your particular emphasis for the day. Teaching Masters 118 and 119 will assist you in pacing and evaluating group work.

Maintenance Resource

NOTE: You may also wish to use the CMIC *Reference and Practice* book for Course 3. See page xxv and the unit planning guide for more information.

The Teaching Resources for each unit begin with a series of masters entitled Maintenance. Items on the Maintenance masters reflect mathematics skills that students may need to practice periodically over the year. Concepts introduced in a unit may be included on any subsequent Maintenance pieces. The first task presented is a contextual problem, but remaining tasks are not contextualized. Students should *not* use a calculator for these tasks unless so directed.

You may wish to ask students to complete the tasks over a three-day period while they are in the process of completing a multi-day investigation. The developers recommend that Maintenance tasks be assigned at any point after students have completed Lesson 1 of a unit. This allows the students time to get accustomed to the new focus of the unit without interruption. You may wish to allow a few minutes at the end of selected class periods to revisit these skills with various groups of students who need assistance while other groups choose an Extending task.

See Masters 1a–1e for Maintenance tasks that students can work on following Lesson 1.

Unit 1 Planning Guide

Unit 1

Lesson Objectives	MORE Assignments	Suggested Pacing	Materials
Lesson 1 *Linked Variables* • To explore multiple-variable relationships such as $W = \frac{kT}{L}$, $F = RT$, and $I = \frac{V}{R}$ through tables, graphs, and symbolic rules • To identify how changes in one variable affect the values of the other variables in a multiple-variable relation • To compare combinations of rates and times of the basic form $z = ax + by$ • To solve equations involving several variables for one of the variables in terms of the others	**after page 5** Students can begin Reflecting Task 1 or 2 from p. 16. **after page 10** Students can begin Modeling Task 1, 2, 3, or 4 or Reflecting Task 4 from p. 16. **after page 14** Students can begin Organizing Task 2 or 3 from p. 16. **page 16** **Modeling:** Choose one* **Organizing:** 4, 6, 7, and 2 or 3* **Reflecting:** 1, and 2 or 4* **Extending:** 1 and choice of one*	7 days	• Uncooked vermicelli, linguini, or fettuccini pasta • Paper cups (5 oz) • Paper clips • Newspaper • Pennies or fishing weights • Electronic balance (optional) • Teaching Resources 2–8 • Assessment Resources 1–6 • *Optional*: RAP Book Exercise Set 1
Lesson 2 *Algebra, Geometry, and Trigonometry* • To find measures of sides and angles in right triangles from given information • To find measures of sides and angles in triangles using the Law of Sines • To find measures of sides and angles in triangles using the Law of Cosines • To solve equations involving several variables for one of the variables in terms of the others	**after page 27** Students can begin Organizing Task 1 from p. 40 or Maintenance Item 7 from Teaching Master 1b. **after page 31** Students can begin Modeling Task 2 or Extending Task 2 from p. 40. **after page 36** Students can begin Modeling Task 1, 4, or 5 or Extending Task 1 or 4 from p. 40. **page 40** **Modeling:** 1 or 5, or 2 and 4* **Organizing:** 1, and 3 or 4* **Reflecting:** 2 **Extending:** Choose one*	6 days	• Centimeter rulers • Linkage strips that allow 12 cm and 16 cm sides • Teaching Resources 1a–1e, 9–13 • Assessment Resources 7–12 • *Optional*: RAP Book Exercise Set 2
Lesson 3 *Linked Equations* • To model situations with algebraic equations and inequalities • To solve systems of equations where two or more output variables are related to the same input variable	**after page 49** Students can begin Modeling Task 1 or 2 or Organizing Task 2 from p. 57. **after page 52** Students can begin Modeling Task 4, Reflecting Task 1 or 4, or Extending Task 1 or 2 from p. 57. **page 57** **Modeling:** 3 and choice of one* **Organizing:** 2 or 3, and 4* **Reflecting:** 1 and 4 **Extending:** Choose one*	6 days	• Colored pencils • Teaching Resources 14–19 • Assessment Resources 13–18
Lesson 4 *Linear Programming* • To solve systems of linear equations • To solve linear programming problems • To graph inequalities or systems of inequalities in the forms $ax + by \leq c$, $ax + by \geq c$, $y \leq a + bx$, and $y \geq a + bx$	**after page 73** Students can begin Organizing Task 1 from p. 80. **after page 77** Students can begin Modeling Task 1, 2, 3, or 4; Reflecting Task 2; or Extending Task 1 or 2 from p. 80. **page 80** **Modeling:** 3 and choice of one* **Organizing:** 1 and 5 **Reflecting:** 1 and 2 **Extending:** Choose one*	9 days	• Graph paper • Teaching Resources 20–34 • Assessment Resources 19–26 • *Optional*: RAP Book Exercise Set 3
Lesson 5 *Looking Back* • To review the major objectives of the unit		3 days (includes testing)	• Teaching Resources 35a–35c • Unit Summary Master • Assessment Resources 27–42 • *Optional*: RAP Book Practice Set 1

**When choice is indicated, it is best to leave the choice to the student.*

Note: *It is important that Organizing tasks are discussed as a whole class after they have been assigned as homework.*

Lesson 1 Linked Variables

Karate is a very impressive form of the martial arts. You may have seen live or video exhibitions of highly trained men and women breaking bricks and boards with chops from their hands, feet, or even heads. Some of you may have even attempted a karate chop and discovered that, without proper technique and training, it can hurt.

Think About This Situation

Karate chops break bricks and boards by applying carefully aimed bursts of energy. Different targets require different amounts of energy. Think about the four target boards pictured here:

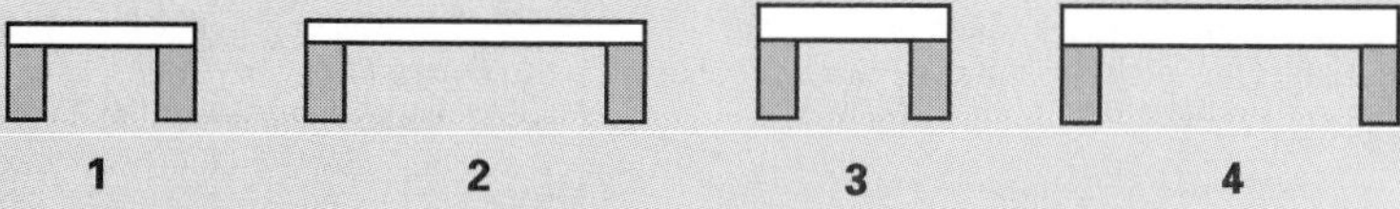

a Which board do you think would require the greatest energy to break?

b The target boards differ in length and thickness. How would you expect those two variables to affect required breaking energy?

c Breaking energy E depends on board length L and thickness T. What sort of equation might be used to express E as a function of L and T?

d What other variables would you consider in judging the energy required to break a board? How would you expect those variables to be related to each other and to E, L, and T?

2 UNIT 1 • MULTIPLE-VARIABLE MODELS

Lesson 1 *Linked Variables*

LESSON OVERVIEW The introduction to this lesson is designed to stimulate students to think about a situation where there are more than two variables related by one equation. Some students probably will have a fairly good intuitive sense about which board will require the greatest energy to break, but they probably have not thought about the fact that the amount of energy required is related directly to the thickness of the board and inversely to the length. In real-world problem situations there often are many variables operating at the same time. In this lesson, students will explore both combined and joint variation situations. The situations are centered around Ohm's Law and other flow rates. Students explore how changes in one of the variables affect the values of other variables.

The simple flow-rate problems are followed by combinations of these models, such as two machines operating at different rates and times, or two trips being made at different rates and times. Students explore these situations through concrete examples, and then they generalize the situations with algebraic models and solve their models for different variables.

Lesson Objectives

- To explore multiple-variable relationships such as $W = \frac{kT}{L}$, $F = RT$, and $I = \frac{V}{R}$ through tables, graphs, and symbolic rules
- To identify how changes in one variable affect the values of the other variables in a multiple-variable relation
- To compare combinations of rates and times of the basic form $z = ax + by$
- To solve equations involving several variables for one of the variables in terms of the others

Master 2

MASTER 2 — Transparency Master

Think About This Situation

Karate chops break bricks and boards by applying carefully aimed bursts of energy. Different targets require different amounts of energy. Think about the four target boards pictured here:

1 2 3 4

ⓐ Which board do you think would require the greatest energy to break?

ⓑ The target boards differ in length and thickness. How would you expect those two variables to affect required breaking energy?

ⓒ Breaking energy *E* depends on board length *L* and thickness *T*. What sort of equation might be used to express *E* as a function of *L* and *T*?

ⓓ What other variables would you consider in judging the energy required to break a board? How would you expect those variables to be related to each other and to *E*, *L*, and *T*?

Use with page 2. UNIT 1 • MULTIPLE-VARIABLE MODELS

LAUNCH full-class discussion

Think About This Situation

See Teaching Master 2.

ⓐ Responses may vary. If students have difficulty verbalizing their reasons, you may wish to refer to the diagrams; ask them if the boards in diagram 2 or 4 would be more difficult to break and why. Final answers are not needed at this time, but students should indicate reasons for their thinking. Most students probably will choose board 3.

ⓑ The thicker the board is, the harder to break. The shorter the board, the harder to break.

ⓒ Based on their experience, students might suggest a power model or a linear model. If students have trouble thinking of an equation, do not be dismayed. These issues will be explored in the first investigation.

See additional Teaching Notes on page T90C.

Unit 1

Master 3

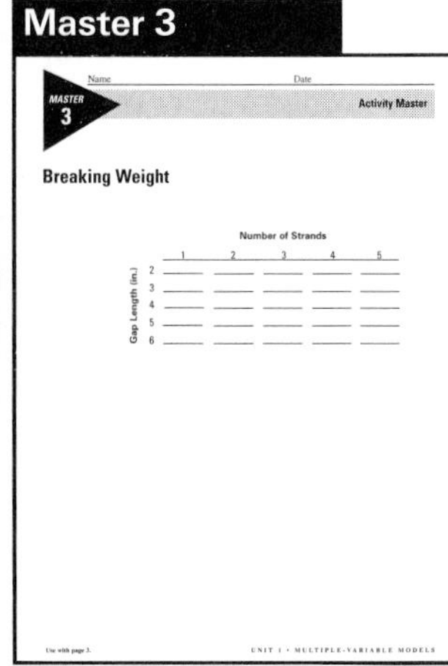
Name Date

MASTER 3 Activity Master

Breaking Weight

Gap Length (in.)	Number of Strands 1	2	3	4	5
2					
3					
4					
5					
6					

EXPLORE small-group investigation

INVESTIGATION 1 Stressed to the Breaking Point

In this first investigation, students will explore the amount of weight that can be supported by strands of pasta, while varying the thickness or the number of strands and the span or distance between the supports. This lab is very engaging for the students! You might begin by telling students they are going to find out more about the relation among the variables *E*, *L*, and *T* from the "Think About This Situation," Part c. If they collect good data, they should be able to model the relation among the variables with some kind of equation. You may wish to demonstrate the equipment and ask students for suggestions or questions about the method of data collection.

The following tips can help the lab go smoothly:

- Have each group collect data for a given span or distance and contribute their data in Activity 1. Each group should find the appropriate model for their own data and contribute that in Activity 2. This will allow each group to keep the positions of the desks fixed and simply vary the number of strands. If you have enough groups, assign an additional span distance of 3.5" or 4.5". Using very wide spans is difficult to manage; the pasta tends to bend and pivot before it breaks.
- Vermicelli works very nicely. One box is enough for 4 or 5 classes.
- Cleaning up is easy if you supply each group with a newspaper to spread on the floor to collect the broken pasta.
- Make the containers for the pennies or weights ahead of time by attaching three paper clips to the top of a disposable cup, equidistant from each other, and then join these with a fourth paper clip which will slip over the pasta. You will need one per group. For narrow spans with many strands of pasta, you may be surprised by the number of pennies that the "bridge" will hold; very small cups will soon be useless. Generally these cup and clip arrangements will hold up well and should last for multiple class use, but you would be wise to have a spare or two. You may wish to construct these containers before class.
- Keeping the pasta perpendicular to the desk edge, without actually holding the pasta down, will give more consistent data.
- Keeping the cup in the middle of the pasta, likewise, gives better results.
- Adding pennies gently, one at a time, gives better results than dropping in several pennies from a height above the cup.
- If it is not possible for you to borrow electronic balances from your science department, have the students record the number of pennies that were supported instead of the weight.

See additional Teaching Notes on page T90C.

INVESTIGATION 1 Stressed to the Breaking Point

The key factor in those amazing karate exhibitions is actually the speed of the attacking fist or foot. In other situations, the important factor is how much weight a structure like a bridge, beam, or suspension cable can hold without breaking. The breaking weight of any structure certainly depends on the material used. But there are some common patterns relating breaking weight, length, and thickness in every case. You can discover the nature of those relations with a simple experiment!

Collect Data Get several long strands of dry pasta (such as spaghetti, vermicelli, linguine, or fettuccine), some paper clips, a paper cup, and a bunch of pennies or fishing weights. With two desktops or tables as supports and pasta as "bridges," use paper clips to hang the paper cup from the pasta. Add weight until the pasta breaks.

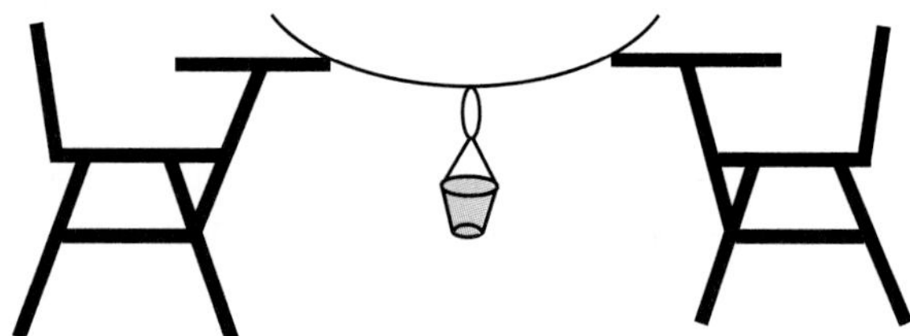

1. Find the breaking weight of one strand of pasta that spans gaps of different lengths. Use lengths from 2 to 6 inches in steps of 1 inch. Then try thicker bridges by using 2, 3, 4, and 5 strands of pasta. Record the (*gap length, number of strands, breaking weight*) data in a table like the one below.

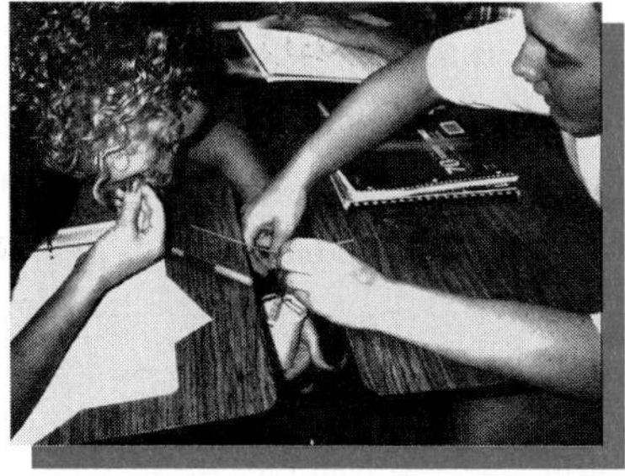

Breaking Weight

		Number of Strands				
		1	2	3	4	5
Gap Length (in.)	2					
	3					
	4					
	5					
	6					

LESSON 1 • LINKED VARIABLES 3

Look for Patterns Study the breaking-weight data from your experiment. Look for patterns that relate the three variables. Then complete the following activities about algebraic models of the relation among thickness, length, and breaking weight.

2. To discover how breaking weight W changes as the thickness T (in number of strands) of the pasta bridge increases, it might help to focus first on the data for bridges 5 inches in length and of several different thicknesses.

a. Use your graphing calculator or computer software to make a scatterplot of the (T, W) data and to find an equation modeling the relation between those variables.

b. How is the equation that seems to model the pattern in your (*thickness, breaking weight*) data for the 5-inch bridge similar to, and different from, other algebraic equations that you have studied?

c. Now make scatterplots and find modeling equations relating T and W for bridges of other lengths. Share the workload among members of your group. Compare the results in each case.

d. Based on your results from Parts a–c, write your conclusions about the way breaking weight seems to change as the thickness of the bridge increases.

3. Examine your experimental data and consider the way breaking weight W changes if only the length L of the pasta bridge increases.

a. It might help to focus first on the data for a pasta bridge of one strand. Use your graphing calculator or computer software to make a scatterplot of the (L, W) data and to find an equation modeling the relation between those variables.

b. Next have members of your group share the workload to make scatterplots and find modeling equations relating L and W for bridges of two, three, four, or five strands. Compare the results in each case.

c. Based on your results from Parts a and b, write your conclusions about the way breaking weight seems to change as the length of the bridge increases.

4. Since breaking weight depends on both bridge length and thickness, it would be helpful to express that joint relation with a single equation. Here are four possibilities that were suggested by students in a class at Arbor High School:

$$W = 10T + L \qquad W = 10T - L \qquad W = 10T \times L \qquad W = \frac{10T}{L}$$

a. Which of these equations gives patterns that are most similar to the data from your own experiments? How is that equation similar to, and different from, other algebraic rules that you have studied?

b. How could you modify the rule in Part a to fit the specific numerical data from your own experiments better?

4 UNIT 1 • MULTIPLE-VARIABLE MODELS

2. **In order to divide the work involved in the data analysis, it is helpful to assign each group a particular row of data for Activity 2. The group should put the mathematical model that they determine on the board to the right of the row. This will allow the class to see all of the models, which will help them recognize the general patterns associated with this situation. Remember that it is not as important for students to find the individual numbers for a particular model as it is that they recognize that the pattern describing the relation between breaking weight and the number of strands is best represented by a linear model.**

After students have found the models and have written some conclusions, you might pull the class together for a discussion of Activities 1 and 2. This discussion allows you to keep students focused on the overall picture, which is that the relationship between *W* and *T* appears to be linear; *W* increases at a constant rate for any particular gap length. This discussion also gives you an opportunity to review linearity, slope, and intercept. You might ask, "What do slope and intercept mean in this context? How do they appear in the tables and graphs? Why are there different slopes for the different gap lengths?"

Responses will vary. Below are sample responses based on the data provided in Activity 1.

a. For a gap of 5 inches:

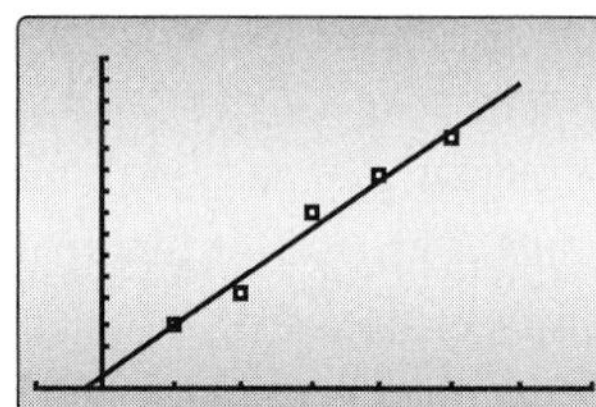

WINDOW
Xmin =-1
Xmax =6
Xscl =1
Ymin =0
Ymax =150
Yscl =10
Xres =1

$y = 21.82x + 6.72$

b. This equation is a linear model. The rate of change is constant. None of the other models studied have a constant rate of change.

c. For a gap of 6 inches:

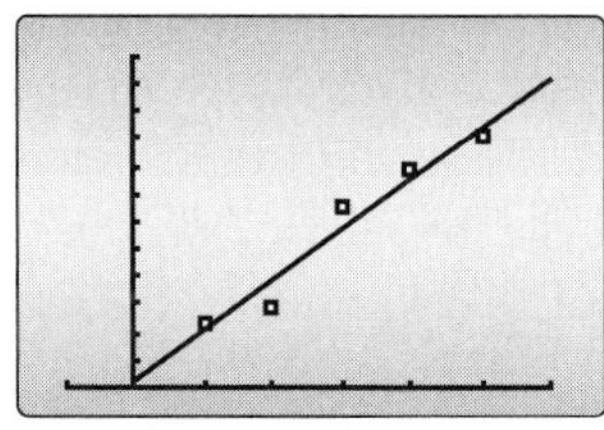

WINDOW
Xmin =-1
Xmax =6
Xscl =1
Ymin =0
Ymax =120
Yscl =10
Xres =1

$y = 18.29x + 2.57$

For a gap of 4.5 inches:

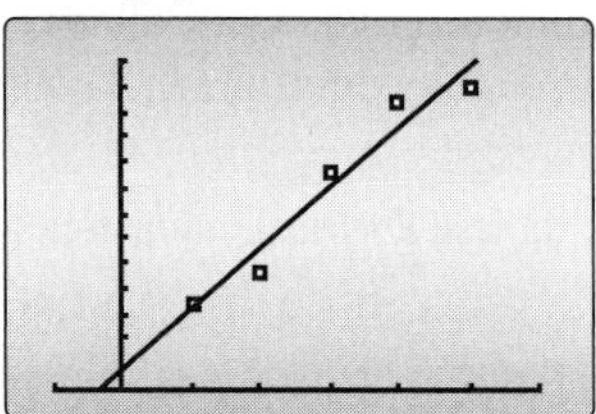

WINDOW
Xmin =-1
Xmax =6
Xscl =1
Ymin =0
Ymax =130
Yscl =10
Xres =1

$y = 23.61x + 8.95$

For a gap of 4 inches:

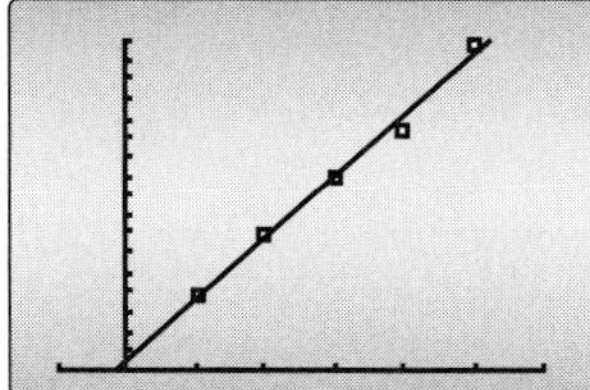

WINDOW
Xmin =-1
Xmax =6
Xscl =1
Ymin =0
Ymax =130
Yscl =10
Xres =1

$y = 31.28x + 6.02$

See additional Teaching Notes on page T90D.

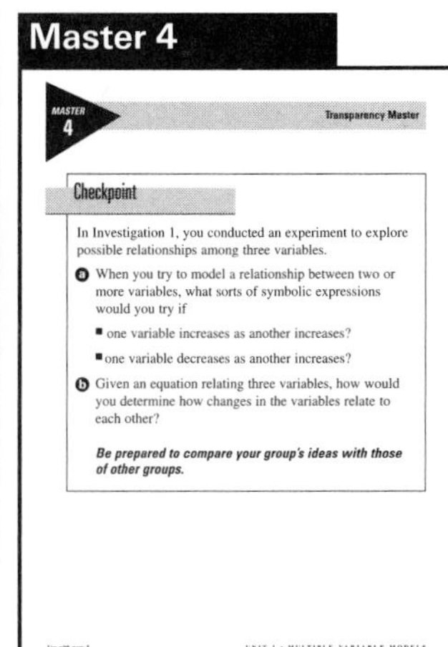
Master 4

MASTER 4 Transparency Master

Checkpoint

In Investigation 1, you conducted an experiment to explore possible relationships among three variables.

a When you try to model a relationship between two or more variables, what sorts of symbolic expressions would you try if

- one variable increases as another increases?
- one variable decreases as another increases?

b Given an equation relating three variables, how would you determine how changes in the variables relate to each other?

Be prepared to compare your group's ideas with those of other groups.

EXPLORE *continued*

SHARE AND SUMMARIZE full-class discussion

Checkpoint

See Teaching Master 4

The initial investigation of this unit is designed to get students thinking about multiple-variable relationships, not to formalize any specific facts or principles. Thus, as students reflect on the pasta-bridge experiment, it seems most appropriate to use this Checkpoint as an opportunity to review prior work with functions. Except where students suggest some incorrect ideas from prior work, most discussion of issues here should be left with the promise that the answers are to be explored in more depth in the investigations that lie ahead. Some possible responses you might expect at this stage are described below.

a Relationships in which one variable increases as another increases could be modeled in any of the following symbolic forms: $y = a + bx$ $(b > 0)$, $y = a(b^x)$ $(a > 0$ and $b > 1)$, $y = x^r$ (for $r > 0$ and $x > 0$).

Relationships in which one variable decreases as another increases could be modeled by the following symbolic forms: $y = a + bx$ $(b < 0)$, $y = a(b^x)$ $(a > 0$ and $b < 1)$, $y = x^r$ (for $r < 0$ and $x > 0$).

One common form of a relationship with more than one independent variable is $z = k\frac{x}{y}$. In these relations, when $k > 0$, increasing x means increasing z (if y is held constant) and increasing y means decreasing z (if x is held constant). This sort of multiple-variable combined variation is developed in the subsequent investigations of this lesson, so don't expect students to formalize it yet. Students should have this idea already and be able to give some plausible explanation of why the expression gives the intended pattern. If the relationship doesn't occur to any group, hold the discussion for later in the unit or refer them back to Activities 3 and 4.

b To study a relationship involving three variables, it makes sense to focus on change in one variable at a time. Commonly, such relationships are given in two standard forms. In one, one of the three variables will be expressed as a function of or in terms of the other two, for example z in terms of x and y. To see the interplay of variables in such a relationship, it makes sense to fix a value of one variable (x or y), let the second variable change, and watch the output z.

In the case of a relationship where some algebraic combination of the three variables is equal to a constant, you may be able to solve the equation for one of the variables in terms of the others and proceed as above. This procedure is developed in the following investigations. Another method is to choose a sequence of values for one of the variables and see what pairs of values for the others will preserve the equality. The basic idea is to hold some things fixed while letting others vary systematically in order to see the effect of that variation. This is a fundamental method of scientific investigation and is not restricted to mathematics. *These are ideas that will unfold throughout this unit, not burst fully articulated from reflection on the initial experimental investigation just completed.*

MORE ASSIGNMENT *pp. 16–24*

Students can now begin Reflecting Task 1 or 2 from the MORE assignment following Investigation 4. Students also may work Maintenance Item 7 at this point to help them prepare for Lesson 2. (See Teaching Masters 1a–1e.)

See additional Teaching Notes on page T90G.

Checkpoint

In Investigation 1, you conducted an experiment to explore possible relationships among three variables.

a When you try to model a relationship between two or more variables, what sorts of symbolic expressions would you try if

- one variable increases as another increases?
- one variable decreases as another increases?

b Given an equation relating three variables, how would you determine how changes in the variables relate to each other?

Be prepared to compare your group's ideas with those of other groups.

On Your Own

The likelihood of a fatal accident in a car, van, or small truck depends on many conditions. Two key variables are speed and mass of the vehicle.

a. What general relationship would you expect among the rate of fatal accidents, speed of the vehicle, and mass of the vehicle?

b. What data on highway accidents would help you find an equation to model the relationship in Part a?

c. If A represents the rate of fatal accidents, s represents vehicle speed, and m represents mass of the vehicle, which of the following equations would you expect to best express the relation among those variables?

i. $A = 200(s + m)$

ii. $A = 200(s - m)$

iii. $A = 200\frac{s}{m}$

iv. $A = 200sm$

LESSON 1 • LINKED VARIABLES 5

INVESTIGATION 2 Go with the Flow

White-water rafting and kayaking are two of the most exciting water sports. But, for most of us, the closest we get to white water is an amusement park ride! Parks all over the country offer a variety of water slides and rides. In almost every case, those slides and rides depend on a flow of water that is pumped through pipes to the top of the slide or ride.

1. Think about some of the water slides you've experienced or seen in pictures.

a. If a park pump will lift water to the top of a slide at a rate of 250 gallons per minute, how much water will it provide in

- 15 minutes?
- 30 minutes?
- 60 minutes?

b. How much water will be pumped in 15 minutes if the pumping rate is increased to

- 500 gallons per minute?
- 750 gallons per minute?
- 1,000 gallons per minute?

c. Write an equation that expresses total water flow F as a function of pumping rate R and time of operation T.

2. Pumps also are used in a variety of other situations, such as city water systems, oil pipelines, tanker trucks, and farm irrigation systems. For example, jet fuel is pumped from a tanker truck into jet tanks between flights. The faster the task can be completed, the faster the airplane can get into the air again. So speed of refueling is important.

a. If a tanker truck can pump 1,500 gallons of jet fuel per minute into a plane, how long will it take to load a total of 7,500 gallons into the plane?

b. Write an equation that gives pumping time T as a function of fuel load F and pumping rate R.

c. How will the pumping time change if the fuel load F increases? If the pumping rate R increases? How are those patterns of change predicted by the equation relating T, F, and R?

d. If a tanker took 20 minutes to load 45,000 gallons of fuel in a plane, at what average rate was the tanker's pump operating?

e. Write an equation that gives pumping rate R as a function of time T and fuel load F.

6 UNIT 1 • MULTIPLE-VARIABLE MODELS

EXPLORE small-group investigation

INVESTIGATION 2 Go with the Flow

Multiple-variable relationships, like those students investigated with pasta and pennies, occur in many situations. This investigation looks at several different contexts. While students work on these activities, you can circulate and ask questions that keep students focused on whether the relationship is increasing or decreasing and whether there is a constant rate or not. Activities 1 through 4 should be quite accessible for all students. Activity 5 involves more reading and a context that most likely is new for students. You may wish to discuss the formula as a class if many groups seem to be confused, but let students try to make sense of the formula first.

1. **a.** ■ 3,750 gallons
■ 7,500 gallons
■ 15,000 gallons

b. ■ 7,500 gallons
■ 11,250 gallons
■ 15,000 gallons

c. $F = R \times T$

2. **a.** 5 minutes

b. $T = \frac{F}{R}$

c. If the fuel load increases, then the pumping time will increase. If the pumping rate increases, then the pumping time will decrease. In the equation $T = \frac{F}{R}$, if the numerator increases, the value of the fraction increases. If the denominator of the fraction increases, the value of the fraction decreases. (If students have difficulty with these ideas, encourage them to try several examples using actual numbers to determine what is happening.)

d. 2,250 gallons per minute

e. $R = \frac{F}{T}$

EXPLORE *continued*

3. Current I (in amperes)

	Resistance R (in ohms)				
Voltage V (in volts)	1	2	3	4	5
1	1	0.5	0.33	0.25	0.2
3	3	1.5	1	0.75	0.6
6	6	3	2	1.5	1.2
9	9	4.5	3	2.25	1.8
12	12	6	4	3	2.4

a. As V increases, I increases.
As R increases, I decreases.

b. Since $I = \frac{V}{R}$, when the numerator increases, I increases, and when the denominator increases, I decreases.

4. a. The resistance of the toaster is $\frac{120}{4}$ or 30 ohms.

In much the same way that water is pumped through pipes of various sizes, electrons are pushed through wires to provide power for electrical appliances of all kinds. In a very simple circuit like the one sketched below, a current of electrons moves along a wire, from a battery to a light bulb. In this example, the light bulb converts some of the electrical energy into heat and light energy.

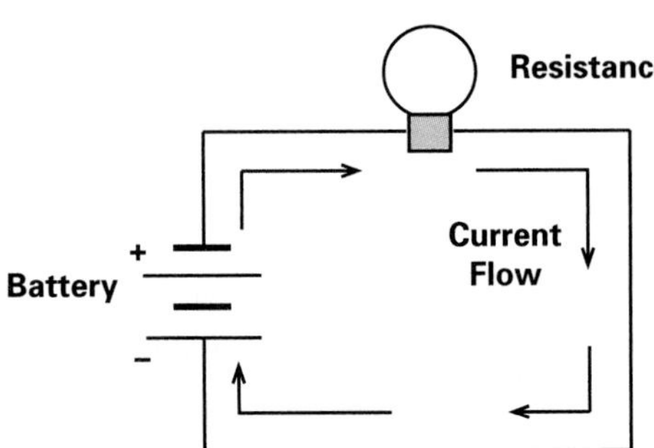

The key variables in such electrical systems are *voltage* (often labeled V and measured in volts), *current* (often labeled I and measured in amperes), and *resistance* (often labeled R and measured in ohms). Those variables are related by a scientific principle called **Ohm's law** that is often expressed as an equation: $I = \frac{V}{R}$.

3. Use Ohm's law to complete a table like the one below, showing the current that can be expected in circuits with several combinations of voltage and resistance.

Current I (in amperes)

		Resistance R (in ohms)				
		1	2	3	4	5
Voltage V (in volts)	1					
	3					
	6					
	9					
	12					

a. How does current in an electrical circuit change as voltage increases? As resistance increases?

b. How could the patterns you noted in Part a be predicted from the form of the algebraic rule relating I to V and R?

4. Electrical instruments can be used to measure the voltage and current in any circuit. With that information, Ohm's law can be used to calculate the resistance of the circuit.

a. If a kitchen toaster draws a current of 4 amperes on a 120-volt circuit, what is the resistance in the toaster?

LESSON 1 • LINKED VARIABLES 7

b. If the starter of a car draws a current of 15 amperes from a 12-volt battery, what is the resistance of that starter?

c. What equation gives resistance R as a function of voltage V and current I?

d. What equation gives voltage V as a function of current I and resistance R?

Water, jet fuel, and electricity are not the only things that flow or are pumped from one place to another. In hot climates the heat seeps into air-conditioned buildings; in cold climates the heat flows out. Scientists and engineers have worked long and hard to find ways to block undesirable heat flow.

Think about what factors or variables will affect the heat flow out through the windows of an apartment or office building during a cold winter day.

5. One equation for estimating heat flow through a solid material such as glass, wood, or aluminum involves five variables:

$$R = kA\frac{\Delta T}{t}$$

The symbols and what they represent are as follows:

R = Rate of heat flow, in Btu's (British thermal units) per hour

k = Thermal conductivity for the specific material

A = Area of the material, in square feet

ΔT = Difference in temperature between outside and inside, in degrees Fahrenheit

t = Thickness of the material, in inches

a. Suppose sheets of glass, wood, and aluminum of the same area and thickness are exposed to the same difference in temperature. How would you expect the rate of heat flow to be different for these sheets of material?

b. The thermal conductivity of glass is 5.8. What is the heat-flow rate for a glass window that is 0.5 inches thick and has an area of 6 square feet, on a day when the outside temperature is 5°F and the inside temperature is 68°F?

c. Suppose that, instead of glass, the same window opening is covered with wood having thermal conductivity of 0.78. What is the heat flow for the same temperature condition, if the wood is 0.5 inches thick?

8 UNIT 1 • MULTIPLE-VARIABLE MODELS

4. **b.** The resistance of the starter is $\frac{12}{15}$ or 0.8 ohms.

c. $R = \frac{V}{I}$

d. $V = R \times I$

5. **a.** Responses will vary. Students will know the correct answer after they have completed Part d, if they do not know that heat loss for aluminum is the greatest and heat loss for wood is the least.

b. $R = 5.8 \times 6 \times \frac{63}{0.5} = 4{,}384.8$ Btu per hour

c. $R = 0.78 \times 6 \times \frac{63}{0.5} = 589.68$ Btu per hour

Unit 1

Master 5

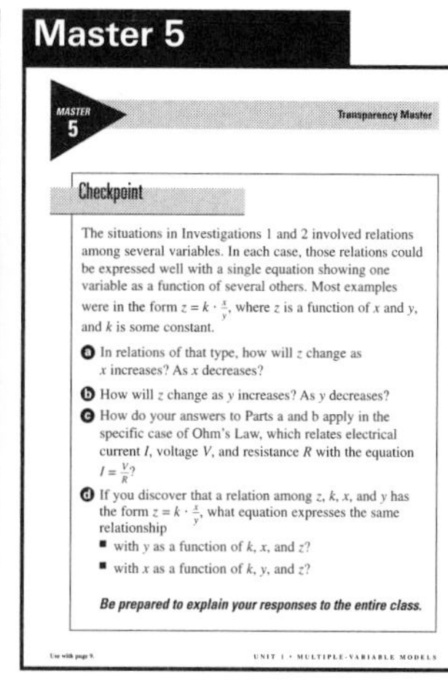

MASTER 5 Transparency Master

Checkpoint

The situations in Investigations 1 and 2 involved relations among several variables. In each case, those relations could be expressed well with a single equation showing one variable as a function of several others. Most examples were in the form $z = k \cdot \frac{x}{y}$, where z is a function of x and y, and k is some constant.

a In relations of that type, how will z change as x increases? As x decreases?

b How will z change as y increases? As y decreases?

c How do your answers to Parts a and b apply in the specific case of Ohm's Law, which relates electrical current I, voltage V, and resistance R with the equation $I = \frac{V}{R}$?

d If you discover that a relation among z, k, x, and y has the form $z = k \cdot \frac{x}{y}$, what equation expresses the same relationship
- with y as a function of k, x, and z?
- with x as a function of k, y, and z?

Be prepared to explain your responses to the entire class.

Use with page 9. UNIT 1 • MULTIPLE-VARIABLE MODELS

EXPLORE *continued*

5. d. $R = 1{,}400 \times 6 \times \frac{63}{0.5} = 1{,}058{,}400$ Btu per hour

e. Students should realize that heat loss is greatest for aluminum and least for wood.

f. Solve $589.68 = 5.8 \times 6 \times \frac{63}{t}$ for t. $t \approx 3.72$ inches

6. a. Materials with low k are good insulators, and those with high k are good conductors of heat. Heat flow is given as $R = kA\frac{\Delta T}{t}$, so you are multiplying by k. A low k value will make the heat flow low, and a high k value will make the heat flow high.

b. If A or ΔT increases, then R increases. If t decreases, then R increases.
If A or ΔT decreases, then R decreases. If t increases, then R decreases.

c. These seem to be logical patterns for heat-flow rate, since the greater the thermal conductivity k the greater the transfer of heat, the bigger the window opening A the greater the heat loss, and the greater the thickness of the material t the harder it is for heat to escape.

SHARE AND SUMMARIZE full-class discussion

Checkpoint

See Teaching Master 5.

Following the Checkpoint in the student text, some old vocabulary is reviewed and new vocabulary introduced. It will help if you have a short discussion about the relationships described and symbolic expressions of those relationships, using the vocabulary provided.

In answering Parts a and b of the Checkpoint, many students are likely to at first ignore the complications caused by the possibility of *k* and *y* being fixed negative numbers. In a class discussion of these parts, you might want to at first overlook implicit assumptions of positive values for fixed values in order to focus on the main effect of direct and inverse variation on the absolute value of *z*.

a If k and y are both positive or both negative, then an increase in x causes an increase in z and a decrease in x causes a decrease in z. If k and y have opposite signs, then changes in x have the opposite effects.

b If k and x are both positive or both negative, then an increase in y causes a decrease in z and a decrease in y causes an increase in z. If k and x have opposite signs, then changes in y have the opposite effects.

c As voltage V increases, current increases; as voltage decreases, current decreases (for constant resistance). As resistance R increases, current decreases; as resistance decreases, current increases (for constant voltage).

d Some students will be able to rewrite these equations easily by referring to a context. For example, $I = \frac{V}{R}$ also could be expressed as $V = R \times I$. Some may be confused by the extra parameter k. You can ask about an arithmetic example. For example: If $3 = \frac{6 \times 2}{4}$, then $3 \times 4 =$ (what)? Or you can demonstrate algebraic operations on equations, multiplying both sides by y, for example. This concept appears more formally in Investigation 4 of this lesson and then again in Lesson 2, so mastery is not expected here.

- $y = \frac{kx}{z}$ ■ $x = \frac{yz}{k}$

NOTE: This is the first Math Toolkit entry for Course 3. Students should have retained their Toolkits from Courses 1 and 2. Those Toolkits should contain the important mathematical ideas from the first two years of this curriculum. You may wish to organize entries by unit or by strands of mathematical content. See Teaching Masters 113–117.

CONSTRUCTING A MATH TOOLKIT: After discussing this Checkpoint, students should describe how they determine the way z changes in the relation $z = k \cdot \frac{x}{y}$ given a certain type of change in x or y. It is important that students understand the way these variables are related.

Group Processing Suggestions

- How did your group decide what to do?
- Name one thing that each person in your group did today that helped you or your group.

d. The thermal conductivity of aluminum is 1,400. What is the heat flow for the window under the same conditions if the opening is covered with aluminum 0.5 inches thick?

e. Review your response to Part a. Were you correct? If not, modify your response.

f. For this window opening, what thickness of glass would be required to achieve the same heat flow rate as the wood in Part c?

6. Consider the equation relating heat flow to several variables and your responses in Activity 5.

a. The symbol k stands for thermal conductivity of the material. Based on your study of the heat-flow relation, would you conclude that materials with low k are good *conductors* of heat (high flow rate) or good *insulators* (low flow rate)? What would you conclude for materials with high k values? What evidence would you use to support your answers?

b. What changes in the variables A, ΔT, and t would cause the rate of heat flow to increase? To decrease?

c. How are the patterns of change you expect reasonable, based on your thinking about the variables involved?

Checkpoint

The situations in Investigations 1 and 2 involved relations among several variables. In each case, those relations could be expressed well with a single equation showing one variable as a function of several others. Most examples were in the form $z = k \cdot \frac{x}{y}$, where z is a function of x and y, and k is some constant.

a In relations of that type, how will z change as x increases? As x decreases?

b How will z change as y increases? As y decreases?

c How do your answers to Parts a and b apply in the specific case of Ohm's law, which relates electrical current I, voltage V, and resistance R with the equation $I = \frac{V}{R}$?

d If you discover that a relation among z, k, x, and y has the form $z = k \cdot \frac{x}{y}$, what equation expresses the same relationship

- with y as a function of k, x, and z?
- with x as a function of k, y, and z?

Be prepared to explain your responses to the entire class.

LESSON 1 • LINKED VARIABLES 9

In the "Power Models" unit of Course 2, you saw that situations in which two quantities vary *directly* with each other could be modeled by equations of the form $y = ax$. Situations in which two quantities vary *inversely* with each other were modeled by rules of the form $y = \frac{a}{x}$. Equations like $z = k \cdot \frac{x}{y}$ are called relations of **combined variation**. It is common to say that *z varies directly with x and inversely with y.*

On Your Own

One important concern of any business is productivity. For example, consider a soft drink factory that has several production lines.

a. If each filling machine in the plant fills 350 bottles per minute, how long will it take such a machine to fill the 70,000 bottles of the factory's soda drunk each day in Detroit, Michigan?

b. At what speed would the machine need to operate in order to fill 70,000 bottles in one 8-hour work shift?

c. How many bottles will be filled if the machine operates at a rate of 450 bottles per minute for an 8-hour shift?

d. Write equations showing the relation among filling rate R in bottles per minute, time T in minutes, and total number of bottles filled B. Express the relation in three different ways:

- B is a function of R and T.
- R is a function of B and T.
- T is a function of B and R.

e. For each equation in Part d, explain the changes in the output variable that will result from increases of each input variable. For example: In the case of the first equation, if R increases, how will B change? If T increases, how will B change?

10 UNIT 1 • MULTIPLE-VARIABLE MODELS

APPLY individual task

On Your Own

a. 200 minutes, or 3 hours and 20 minutes

b. 8,750 bottles per hour, or 146 bottles per minute

c. 216,000 bottles

d.
- $B = R \times T$
- $R = \frac{B}{T}$
- $T = \frac{B}{R}$

e.
- If R increases, B increases.
  If T increases, B increases.
- If B increases, R increases.
  If T increases, R decreases.
- If B increases, T increases.
  If R increases, T decreases.

MORE

ASSIGNMENT *pp. 16–24*

Students can now begin Modeling Task 1, 2, 3, or 4 or Reflecting Task 4 from the MORE assignment following Investigation 4.

Unit 1

Master 6

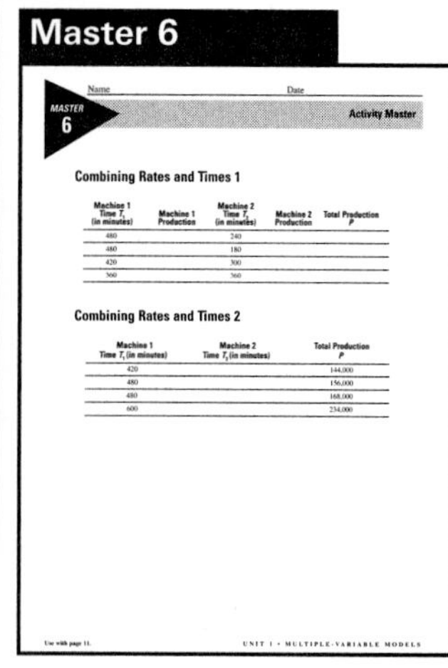

EXPLORE small-group investigation

INVESTIGATION 3 Combining Rates and Times

In Investigation 1, the experiment raised questions about the nature of a particular multiple-variable relationship: Is it direct or inverse, linear or nonlinear? Investigation 2 introduced new contexts, but the relationships were of the same type. In Investigation 3, not only does the context change, but students are introduced to another combined variation.

At the beginning of this investigation, you might briefly remind students of two of the equations they have worked with so far: $W = \frac{10T}{L}$ and $R = \frac{B}{T}$. You can then ask students how these equations are alike. (There are three variables in a combined variation.) Many students will be able to make a general statement of all relationships of this type and explain how the variables are related. Tell them that this investigation is about a bottling company with two different machines filling the bottles. Then ask what variables might the total production depend on. Activities 1–5 approach the creation of a formula for this new context and the possibilities of reformulating the pattern through the use of tables.

See Teaching Master 6.

1. a. In 30 minutes, Machine 1 will fill 300 × 30 or 9,000 cans.
In 400 minutes, Machine 1 will fill 300 × 400 or 120,000 cans.
In T_1 minutes, Machine 1 will fill $300T_1$ cans.

b. Combining Rates and Times 1

Machine 1 Time T_1 (in minutes)	Machine 1 Production	Machine 2 Time T_2 (in minutes)	Machine 2 Production	Total Production P
480	144,000	240	48,000	192,000
480	144,000	180	36,000	180,000
420	126,000	300	60,000	186,000
360	108,000	360	72,000	180,000

c. $P = 300T_1 + 200T_2$

2. a. Combining Rates and Times 2

Machine 1 Time T_1 (in minutes)	Machine 2 Time T_2 (in minutes)	Total Production P
420	90	144,000
480	60	156,000
480	120	168,000
600	270	234,000

INVESTIGATION 3 Combining Rates and Times

Equations relating several variables often can be combined to produce models of even more complex processes. For example, the Kalamazoo Bottling Company might have two production lines for bottling spring water: Machine 1 fills 300 bottles per minute and Machine 2 fills 200 bottles per minute. The total production of the plant is a function of the time that each machine operates.

1. The machines might be run for different amounts of time.

a. How many bottles will Machine 1 fill in 30 minutes? In 400 minutes? In T_1 minutes?

b. Copy and complete the table below to show the total production from different combinations of operating times (in minutes) of the two machines.

Combining Rates and Times 1

Machine 1 Time T_1 (in minutes)	Machine 1 Production	Machine 2 Time T_2 (in minutes)	Machine 2 Production	Total Production P
480		240		
480		180		
420		300		
360		360		

c. Write a single equation relating total production of the plant P to time that the first machine is run T_1 and time that the second machine is run T_2.

2. Suppose that the second bottling machine is older and more expensive to operate, so the plant manager wants to use it as little as necessary to fill production quotas.

a. Calculate the operating time needed for Machine 2 in each of the following cases.

Combining Rates and Times 2

Machine 1 Time T_1 (in minutes)	Machine 2 Time T_2 (in minutes)	Total Production P
420		144,000
480		156,000
480		168,000
600		234,000

LESSON 1 • LINKED VARIABLES 11

b. Describe (in words) the calculations required to find the operating time of Machine 2 for various combinations of the other rate, time, and production figures. Then write an equation showing T_2 as a function of the other variables T_1 and P.

The rate-time-amount relations among variables in the spring water problem occur in many other, quite different situations. For example, most American students and workers spend a great deal of time commuting to and from school or work every day. When we have choices, we are always on the lookout for routes that reduce the distance or time and increase the average speed. The route home is often different in distance, average speed, and time from the route to school or work because of factors like one-way streets, errands, and so on.

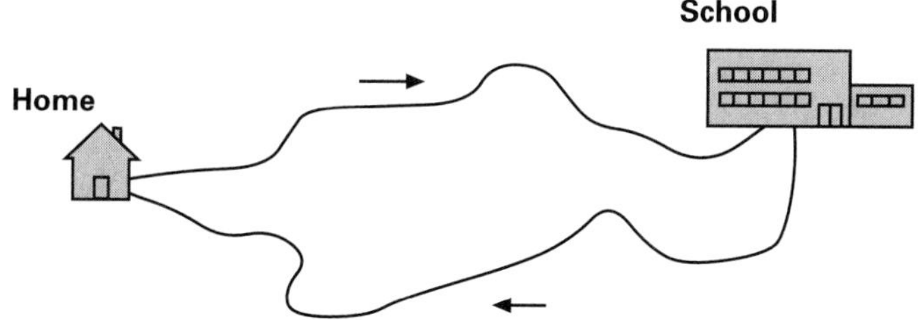

3. Study the data about the following commutes and then find the round-trip distance traveled in each case.

a. Commute to work in 0.6 hour at an average speed of 25 miles per hour and home from work in 1.0 hour at an average speed of 20 miles per hour.

b. Commute to school in $\frac{1}{3}$ hour at an average speed of 30 miles per hour and home from school in $\frac{1}{2}$ hour at an average speed of 24 miles per hour.

c. Commute to work in 1.5 hours at an average speed of 40 miles per hour and home from work in 2.0 hours at an average speed of 30 miles per hour.

4. Write an equation expressing the relationship among the following five variables, using the given letter names.

D = total commuting distance (in miles)

S_1 = average speed to work or school (in miles per hour)

S_2 = average speed home from work or school (in miles per hour)

T_1 = time to work or school (in hours)

T_2 = time home from work or school (in hours)

12 UNIT 1 • MULTIPLE-VARIABLE MODELS

2. **b.** Multiply T_1 by 300 and subtract that number from the total production. This is the number of cans that Machine 2 has to produce. Since the machine can produce 200 cans per minute, this number must be divided by 200.

   $T_2 = \frac{P - 300T_1}{200}$

3. **a.** $(0.6 \times 25) + (1 \times 20) = 35$ miles

   b. $\left(\frac{1}{3} \times 30\right) + \left(\frac{1}{2} \times 24\right) = 22$ miles

   c. $(1.5 \times 40) + (2 \times 30) = 120$ miles

4. $D = S_1T_1 + S_2T_2$

Unit 1

Master 7

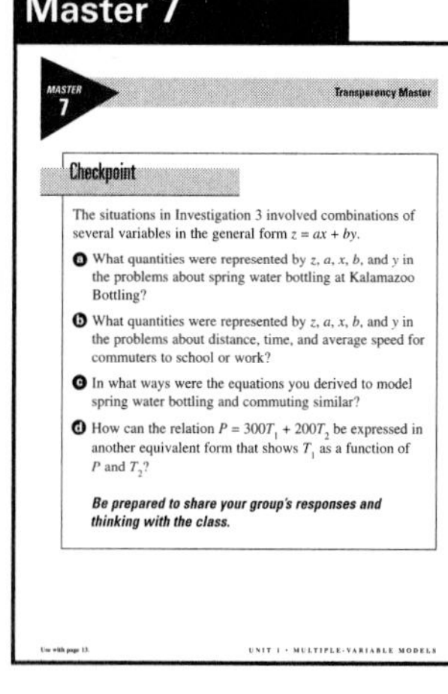
MASTER 7 — Transparency Master

Checkpoint

The situations in Investigation 3 involved combinations of several variables in the general form $z = ax + by$.

(a) What quantities were represented by z, a, x, b, and y in the problems about spring water bottling at Kalamazoo Bottling?

(b) What quantities were represented by z, a, x, b, and y in the problems about distance, time, and average speed for commuters to school or work?

(c) In what ways were the equations you derived to model spring water bottling and commuting similar?

(d) How can the relation $P = 300T_1 + 200T_2$ be expressed in another equivalent form that shows T_1 as a function of P and T_2?

Be prepared to share your group's responses and thinking with the class.

Use with page 13. UNIT 1 • MULTIPLE-VARIABLE MODELS

EXPLORE *continued*

5. **a.** The trip to work was 20 miles, which leaves 25 miles for the trip home.

   25 miles $\div \frac{2}{3}$ hour = 37.5 mph

   b. $(20 \times 0.75) + (25 \times 0.5) = 27.5$ miles

   c. $\frac{5{,}200 - (450 \times 6)}{550} \approx 4.545$ hours or 4 hours and 32.7 minutes

6. If students have trouble with this activity you might suggest that they set up a table like the one below. Encourage them to enter their own quantities for S_1, S_2, T_2, and D and think out how they would get T_1. Some students already will be operating on the symbols using logical steps.

Time to Work T_1	Speed to Work S_1	Time from Work T_2	Speed from Work S_2	Total Distance D

   a. $T_1 = \frac{D - S_2T_2}{S_1}$

   b. $S_2 = \frac{D - S_1T_1}{T_2}$

SHARE AND SUMMARIZE full-class discussion

Checkpoint

See Teaching Master 7.

(a) z = total production

a = rate of Machine 1, in cans per minute (300 cans per min.)

x = time for Machine 1, in minutes

b = rate of Machine 2, in cans per minute (200 cans per min.)

y = time for Machine 2, in minutes

The quantities for a and x may be interchanged as may the quantities for b and y.

(b) z = total distance

a = average rate or speed going oneway, in miles per hour

x = time going, in hours

b = average rate or speed returning the other way, in miles per hour

y = time returning, in hours

The quantities for a and x may be interchanged as may the quantities for b and y.

(c) They both involved the sums of *rate* $\times$ *time*.

(d) $T_1 = \frac{P - 200T_2}{300}$

Students may reason this out from a context, they may substitute some values, or some students already will be working with the symbols in a formal way. Be sure to have students share their ideas so students can see the advantages in another's way of thinking this out. Symbolic reasoning is formalized in Investigation 4.

Group Processing Suggestions

- What actions helped the group to work productively?
- What actions could be added to make the group even more productive?

5. Use the relation in Activity 4 to answer each of the following questions.

a. A commuter's round-trip was 45 miles. The trip to work took $\frac{1}{2}$ hour at an average speed of 40 miles per hour, and the trip home took $\frac{2}{3}$ hour. What was the average speed on the trip home?

b. If a school bus takes 0.75 hour to cover its morning route at an average speed of 20 miles per hour and 0.5 hour in the afternoon at an average speed of 25 miles per hour, what total distance does the bus travel?

c. If an airplane makes a 5,200-mile trip from New York to Los Angeles and back, averaging 450 miles per hour on the 6-hour outbound leg and 550 miles per hour on the return, how long does the return trip take?

6. Rewrite the equation you wrote in Activity 4 to do the following.

a. Express time going to school or work T_1 as a function of the time returning home T_2, the total distance traveled D, and the average speeds of the two parts of the trip S_1 and S_2. (That is, **solve the equation** in Activity 4 **for T_1**.)

b. Express average speed returning home S_2 as a function of the other four variables. (That is, solve the equation in Activity 4 for S_2.)

Checkpoint

The situations in Investigation 3 involved combinations of several variables in the general form $z = ax + by$.

a What quantities were represented by z, a, x, b, and y in the problems about spring water bottling at Kalamazoo Bottling?

b What quantities were represented by z, a, x, b, and y in the problems about distance, time, and average speed for commuters to school or work?

c In what ways were the equations you derived to model spring water bottling and commuting similar?

d How can the relation $P = 300T_1 + 200T_2$ be expressed in another equivalent form that shows T_1 as a function of P and T_2?

Be prepared to share your group's responses and thinking with the class.

LESSON 1 • LINKED VARIABLES 13

On Your Own

In planning entertainment events like concerts, plays, or sports games, one of the first problems is estimating the number of people who will attend and how the attendance will depend on ticket prices. Then you have to use that information to estimate income from ticket sales.

When Friends of Riverview Hospital decided to sponsor a benefit concert in their community's auditorium, they chose two ticket prices: \$5 for students under 18 years of age and \$8 for adults 18 or older. Children under 5 will be admitted free of charge.

a. What total ticket income will the concert generate for the following combinations of ticket sales?

- 200 students and 350 adults
- 150 students and 400 adults

b. Write an equation that gives income as a function of the numbers of tickets sold to students and to adults.

c. Suppose that the concert planners have a goal of \$5,000 in ticket income and they expect to sell 500 tickets to students under 18. How many adult tickets must be sold to reach the income goal?

d. If the income goal is set at \$7,000, what equation shows how the number of adult ticket sales needed to meet that goal depends on the number of tickets that will be sold to students?

e. If the planners want to consider the relation among a variety of ticket prices (k for students and a for adults), ticket sales (x for students and y for adults), and ticket income I, what equation expresses the connection among all five variables?

INVESTIGATION 4 Taking Algebraic X-Rays

Many times in mathematics you encounter two very different situations that turn out to have the same basic structure. If you take an "x-ray" that looks beneath the surface of the situations, you find the same mathematical "skeleton." For example, the relations among variables in Investigations 1, 2, and 3 all led to equations in three basic forms:

$$z = xy \qquad z = \frac{x}{y} \qquad z = ax + by$$

14 UNIT 1 • MULTIPLE-VARIABLE MODELS

APPLY individual task

On Your Own

a. ■ $I = 5(200) + 8(350) = \$3,800$
   ■ $I = 5(150) + 8(400) = \$3,950$

b. Let x represent the number of tickets sold to students and y the number of tickets sold to adults. Then $I = 5x + 8y$.

c. \$5,000 − \$5(500) leaves \$2,500 for the adult tickets. At \$8 per ticket, they must sell 313 tickets to reach the goal of \$5,000.
   That is:
   $5,000 = 5(500) + 8y$
   $y = 312.5$ or 313 tickets

d. $y = \frac{7,000 - 5x}{8}$

e. $I = kx + ay$

MORE
ASSIGNMENT pp. 16–24

Students can now begin Organizing Task 2 or 3 from the MORE assignment following Investigation 4.

EXPLORE small-group investigation

INVESTIGATION 4 Taking Algebraic X-Rays

There are two main ideas being summarized in this investigation: variation and rewriting relationships. Depending on the discussions students have had in previous investigations, you may find that your students have stayed at the arithmetic level of thinking when deciding how to rewrite an equation (plug in some values in a table and think about how you would rewrite the pattern to solve for a missing value), or they may have all but arrived at formal rules for solving equations. While properties of equalities are introduced formally in Lesson 2, the following launch for this investigation should move all students toward symbolic understandings.

Write some tables on the board, such as those shown at the right. Then ask your students the following questions. Students should try to make their explanations as general as possible.

x	y	$z = xy$
4	?	12.8

x	y	$z = \frac{x}{y}$
?	2.1	3

a	x	b	y	$z = ax + by$
3	5	2	?	29

"If $z = xy$, how do you find y if you know x and z? Why does this make sense?"

"If $z = \frac{x}{y}$, how do you find x if you know y and z? Why does this make sense?"

"If $z = ax + by$, how do you find y if you know z, a, x, and b?"

While students work on this investigation, keep an eye on their reasoning. It may be helpful to have some groups share their explanations after everyone has tried all five activities.

EXPLORE *continued*

1. Responses may vary if students wrote other forms of the equations in the previous investigations.

$z = xy$	$z = \frac{x}{y}$	$z = ax + by$
Flow Rate: $F = RT$	Breaking Weight: $W = \frac{T}{L}$	Production: $P = R_1T_1 + R_2T_2$
Production: $B = RT$	Ohm's Law: $I = \frac{V}{R}$	Distance: $D = S_1T_1 + S_2T_2$
	Heat Flow: $R = kA\frac{\Delta T}{t}$	

In answering Activity 2, Parts a–c and f, and Activity 3, Parts a–b and f, many students are likely to at first ignore the complications caused by the possibility of *k* and *y* being fixed negative numbers. In a class discussion of these parts, you might want to at first overlook implicit assumptions of positive values for the fixed values in order to focus on the main effect of direct and inverse variation on the absolute value of *z*.

2. **a.** If y is positive and held constant, then an increase in x causes z to increase; if y is negative and held constant, then an increase in x causes z to decrease.
   b. If y is positive and held constant, then a decrease in x causes z to decrease; if y is negative and held constant, then a decrease in x causes z to increase.
   c. If x is held constant, changes in z as y changes are the same as when x changed in Parts a and b.
   d. $x = \frac{z}{y}$
   e. $y = \frac{z}{x}$
   f. A positive constant multiplier k would not affect the patterns of change in z outlined in Parts a–c. A negative constant multiplier would reverse the patterns of change. Part d would become $x = \frac{z}{ky}$ and Part e would become $y = \frac{z}{kx}$.
3. **a.** If y is positive, then an increase in x causes an increase in z; if y is negative, then an increase in x causes a decrease in z; a decrease in x has the opposite effect in the two cases.
   b. If x is positive, then an increase in y causes a decrease in z; if x is negative, then an increase in y causes an increase in z; a decrease in y has the opposite effect in the two cases.
   c. $x = zy$
   d. $y = \frac{x}{z}$
   e. Several kinds of reasoning could be provided. For example, students might point out that to check a division like $\frac{x}{y} = z$, you can always multiply zy to see if you get x. For the other case, students might suggest that you can multiply both sides of the equation by y and divide both sides by z. The justification for such operations on equations might come from students' prior work in algebra or their sense about number operations. (Principles underlying these operations are made explicit later in this lesson.)
   f. Introduction of the constant k has no effect on answers for Parts a and b if k is positive. If k is negative, all patterns of change will be reversed. For Part c, the answer would become $x = \frac{zy}{k}$; for Part d the answer would become $y = \frac{kx}{z}$.

See additional Teaching Notes on page T90G.

Because those forms occur so often, it helps to be good at predicting the patterns of change that each form implies. It also helps to be good at writing the given equations in other equivalent forms that might be useful for answering particular questions.

1. List the various relations among variables encountered in the previous three investigations and sort them in groups according to the three types at the bottom of page 14.

2. Consider the equation $z = xy$.

a. How will z change as x increases and y is held constant?

b. How will z change as x decreases and y is held constant?

c. How will z change if x is held constant and y varies?

d. Express or solve for x in terms of z and y.

e. Express or solve for y in terms of z and x.

f. Suppose $z = k(xy)$ for some constant k. How would your answers to Parts a–e change?

3. Consider the equation $z = \frac{x}{y}$.

a. How will z change as x increases (or decreases) and y is held constant?

b. How will z change as y changes and x is held constant?

c. Express x in terms of z and y.

d. Solve for y in terms of z and x.

e. What reasoning supports your answers to Parts c and d?

f. Suppose $z = k \cdot \frac{x}{y}$ for some constant k. How would your answers to Parts a–e change?

4. Consider the equation $z = ax + by$.

a. Express or solve for x in terms of a, b, y, and z.

b. Express a in terms of b, x, y, and z.

c. Solve for y in terms of a, b, x, and z.

d. Express b in terms of a, x, y, and z.

e. What common reasoning pattern supports your answers to Parts a–d?

f. If a and b are both positive numbers, how will z change as x or y increases?

5. When solving an equation for one variable in terms of the others, you used strategies involving basic *properties of equality* such as subtracting the same number from both sides of the equation or multiplying (or dividing) both sides of the equation by the same nonzero number. Properties of equality and the strategies for rewriting algebraic equations in equivalent forms often are used in solving problems involving proportions.

a. Explain why the equation $\frac{a}{b} = \frac{c}{d}$ is equivalent to $ad = bc$.

b. Explain why $\frac{a}{b} = \frac{c}{d}$ is equivalent to $\frac{b}{a} = \frac{d}{c}$.

Checkpoint

Suppose you have modeled a situation involving three linked variables x, y, and z.

a How will the value of z change as values of x and y change when $z = xy$? When $z = \frac{x}{y}$? When $z = ax + by$, for various values of a and b?

b In what alternate forms can you express each of the equations in Part a? How do you know that the alternate forms are equivalent to the originals? In each case, how could you use properties of equality to convince someone else that your conclusions are correct?

Be prepared to share your thinking and methods with the class.

On Your Own

Solve each equation below and explain how you used properties of equality in the solution process.

a. Solve $z = 5xy$ for y in terms of x and z.

b. Solve $a = \frac{b}{c}$ for c in terms of a and b.

c. Solve $r = \frac{5s}{t}$ for s in terms of r and t.

d. Solve $p = 8m - 5n$ for m in terms of p and n.

e. Solve $\frac{a}{x} = \frac{b}{c}$ for x in terms of a, b, and c.

MORE Modeling • Organizing • Reflecting • Extending

Modeling

These tasks provide opportunities for you to use the ideas you have learned in the investigations. Each task asks you to model and solve problems in other situations.

1. You may recall from past courses how compound interest causes a savings account to grow at an exponential rate. There is another type of interest called *simple interest*. That interest i depends on the principal invested p, the annual interest rate paid by the bank r, and the time in years for which the money is invested t.

16 UNIT 1 • MULTIPLE-VARIABLE MODELS

SHARE AND SUMMARIZE full-class discussion

Checkpoint

See Teaching Master 8.

ⓐ Students should be able to analyze these relationships without referring to their notes. If students do not mention it, you may need to ask what happens when either a or b, or both, is negative.

ⓑ There are many alternate forms in which the equations in Part a can be expressed. Students should be able to explain how to get from one form to another by using the basic properties of equality.

Group Processing Suggestions

- To what group skills does your group need to pay more attention?
- I helped our group by … .

Master 8

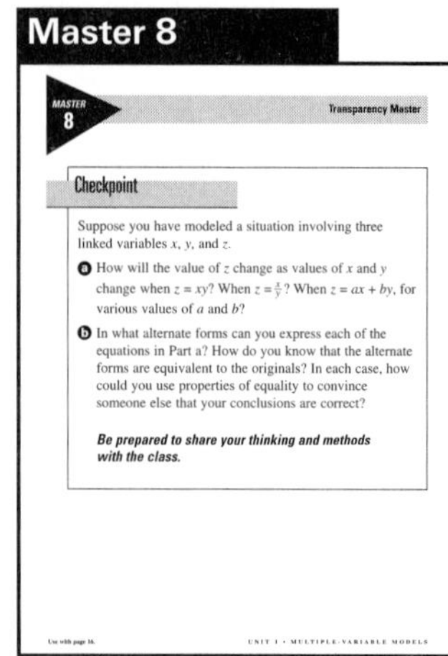
MASTER 8

Transparency Master

Checkpoint

Suppose you have modeled a situation involving three linked variables x, y, and z.

ⓐ How will the value of z change as values of x and y change when $z = xy$? When $z = \frac{x}{y}$? When $z = ax + by$, for various values of a and b?

ⓑ In what alternate forms can you express each of the equations in Part a? How do you know that the alternate forms are equivalent to the originals? In each case, how could you use properties of equality to convince someone else that your conclusions are correct?

Be prepared to share your thinking and methods with the class.

Use with page 16.

UNIT 1 • MULTIPLE-VARIABLE MODELS

CONSTRUCTING A MATH TOOLKIT: Students should describe operations on equations that can help transform equations to equivalent forms (Teaching Master 113).

JOURNAL ENTRY: You may wish to assign Reflecting Task 2 or 4 as a journal entry.

APPLY individual task

On Your Own

a. Divide each side of the equation by $5x$.
$y = \frac{z}{5x}$

b. Multiply each side of the equation by c and then divide each side of the resulting equation by a.
$c = \frac{b}{a}$

c. Multiply each side of the equation by $\frac{t}{5}$, or first multiply each side of the equation by t and then divide each side of the resulting equation by 5.
$s = \frac{rt}{5}$

d. Add $5n$ to both sides of the equation and then divide both sides of the resulting equation by 8.
$m = \frac{p + 5n}{8}$

e. Multiply both sides by cx and then divide both sides of the resulting equation by b.
$x = \frac{ac}{b}$

MORE ASSIGNMENT *pp. 16–24*

Modeling: Choose one*
Organizing: 4, 6, 7, and 2 or 3*
Reflecting: 1, and 2 or 4*
Extending: 1 and choice of one*

**When choice is indicated, it is important to leave the choice to the student.*
NOTE: *It is best if Organizing tasks are discussed as a whole class after they have been assigned as homework.*

MORE independent assignment

Modeling

1. **a.** The interest earned in 1 year will be $0.04 \cdot 500$ or \$20.
   b. The interest earned in 1 year will be $0.08 \cdot 500$ or \$40.
   c. The interest earned in 2 years will be $2(0.08 \cdot 1{,}000)$ or \$160.
   d. $i = prt$, where i is the interest earned, p is the principal, r is the annual interest rate, and t is the time in years.
   e. The required interest rate is $\frac{150}{1{,}000 \cdot 2}$, which is 0.075 or 7.5%.
   f. $r = \frac{i}{pt}$
   g. The required deposit is $\frac{75}{(0.06)(2)}$ or \$625.
2. **a.** The perimeter is $2(5) + 2(3)$ or 16 meters.
   b. The length would be $\frac{45 - 2(5)}{2}$ or 17.5 meters.
   c. Two possible equations showing length as a function of perimeter and width are $L = \frac{P}{2} - W$ and $L = \frac{(P - 2W)}{2}$.
   One possible check uses the values from Part a:
   If $P = 16$ and $W = 3$, then $L = \frac{16}{2} - 3 = 5$ and $L = \frac{(16 - 2 \cdot 3)}{2} = 5$.
   Students also may use values from Part b as a check.
   d. Two possible equations showing width as a function of perimeter and length are $W = \frac{P}{2} - L$ and $W = \frac{(P - 2L)}{2}$.
   One possible check uses the values from Part a:
   If $P = 16$ and $L = 5$, then $W = \frac{16}{2} - 5 = 3$ and $W = \frac{(16 - 2 \cdot 5)}{2} = 3$.
   Students may also use values from Part b as a check.
   e.
   - Since $A = L \cdot W$, you can use the equations in Parts c or d to write the area in terms of either length or width. $A = L \cdot \frac{50 - 2L}{2}$.
   - Now use $y = x \cdot \frac{50 - 2x}{2}$ to produce a table or graph and find the maximum area or solve symbolically.
   - The maximum area is 156.25 square meters and is obtained when the enclosing rectangle is a square that has sides of length 12.5 meters.

a. How much simple interest will be earned by an account if \$500 is invested at 4% annual interest for 1 year?

b. How much simple interest will be earned by an account of \$500 at 8% annual interest for 1 year?

c. How much simple interest will be earned by an account if \$1,000 is invested at 8% annual interest over 2 years? (With simple interest, any interest earned in the first year is *not* added to the principal when calculating interest for the second year.)

d. Write an equation that expresses simple interest earned as a function of principal invested, annual interest rate, and time in years.

e. What interest rate is required to earn \$150 simple interest on \$1,000 invested over 2 years?

f. Write an equation that expresses interest rate as a function of principal, time, and simple interest to be earned.

g. What savings deposit (principal) is required to earn simple interest of \$75 in two years if the account pays 6% annual interest?

2. Recall that the perimeter P of any rectangle can be expressed as a function of the length L and width W of that rectangle in two equivalent ways: $P = 2L + 2W$ or $P = 2(L + W)$.

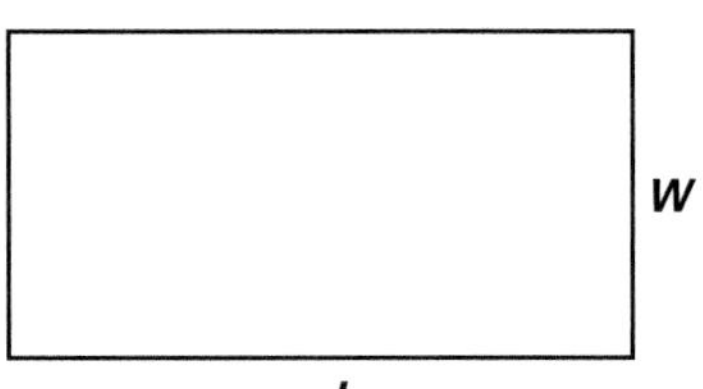

a. Find the perimeter of a rectangle that is 5 meters long and 3 meters wide.

b. Find the length of a rectangle that is to have perimeter 45 meters and width 5 meters.

c. Write an equation expressing length L as a function of perimeter and width of any rectangle. (Do this in two different ways, and check that the two ways produce the same results when specific values for P and W are given.)

d. Write an equation expressing width W as a function of perimeter and length of any rectangle. (Do this in two different ways, and check that the two ways produce the same results when specific values for P and L are given.)

e. Suppose you wished to determine the maximum area of a rectangular garden that could be enclosed with 50 meters of flexible fencing.

- Which of the equations in this task would be most useful in this regard?
- How would you use the equation to find the maximum area?
- What is your best estimate of the maximum area and of the dimensions of the enclosing rectangle?

LESSON 1 • LINKED VARIABLES 17

3. Have you ever noticed that when you use a tire pump on a bicycle tire, the tire warms up as the air pressure inside increases? This illustrates a basic principle of science relating pressure P, volume V, and temperature T in a container: for any specific system, the value of the expression $\frac{PV}{T}$ remains the same even when the individual variables change.

   a. For the expression $\frac{PV}{T}$ to remain constant, what changes in pressure or volume (or both) must result when the temperature increases?

   b. What changes in volume or temperature must result when the pressure increases?

   c. What changes in pressure or volume must result when the temperature decreases?

4. In many consumer businesses, packaging is an important factor in sales. Whether it's cosmetics, food, calculators, or toys, the manufacturer tries to design a package that is attractive but not too expensive to make. That often involves making choices among shapes and sizes of the package options.

   Many foods are packaged in cylindrical cans, and the volume each can holds is determined by its radius and height.

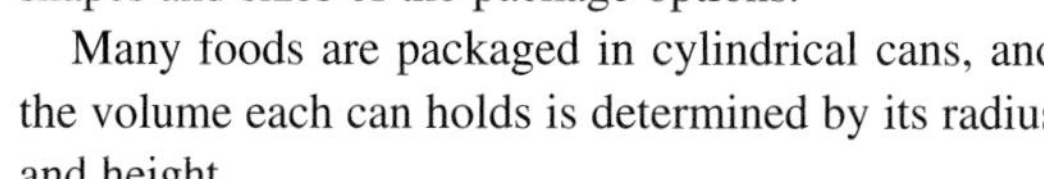

   a. Express volume as a function of radius and height.

   b. If the volume is fixed at 144 cubic inches, what equation would be helpful in showing how to calculate the height for various possible radii?

   c. What is the height of a can that holds 144 cubic inches, if its radius is 2.5 in? If its radius is 3 in? Make sketches of the two cans.

   d. Using the expression for height in Part b, write an equation for the surface area of the can in terms of the radius r.

   e. Which of the two cans in Part c would take less material to make?

   f. Which would be more appropriate as a beverage can? Why?

18 UNIT 1 • MULTIPLE-VARIABLE MODELS

3. **a.** If the temperature increases, then either P or V, or both, must increase.

b. If the pressure increases, then either V must decrease or T must increase, or both.

c. If the temperature decreases, then either P or V, or both, must decrease.

4. **a.** $V = \pi r^2 h$

b. $h = \frac{144}{\pi r^2}$

c. If the radius is 2.5 inches, then the can would be about 7.3 inches tall. If the radius is 3 inches, then the can would be about 5.1 inches tall.

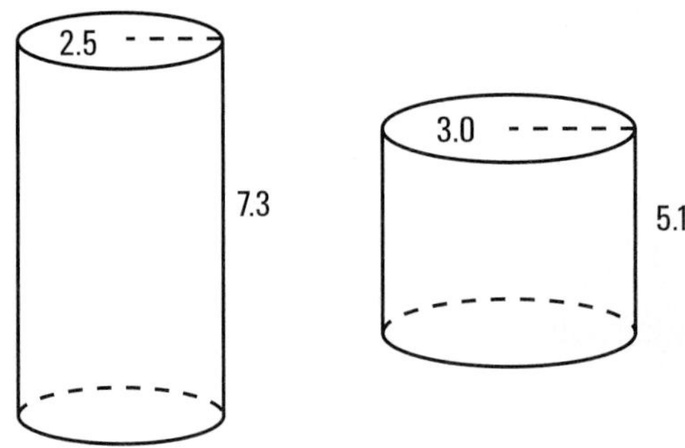

d. $S = 2\pi r^2 + 2\pi rh = 2\pi r^2 + \frac{144}{\pi r^2}(2\pi r) = 2\pi r^2 + \frac{288}{r}$

(The form of students' responses may vary. Any expression equivalent to these is acceptable.)

e. The can with radius of 3 inches would require less material to make. It requires approximately 152.5 square inches of material and the can with radius of 2.5 inches requires approximately 154.5 square inches of material.

f. Student responses may vary. The dimensions of the can with radius of 2.5 inches are close to those of the golden rectangle, so it may be more pleasing to look at. The can with radius of 3 inches would look short and squat and probably would be harder to pour from, since it is so wide.

Organizing

1. **a.** For a triangular pyramid, $V = 4$, $E = 6$, and $F = 4$.
   Check: $V + F = E + 2 \Rightarrow 4 + 4 = 6 + 2 \Rightarrow 8 = 8$

   b. For a square pyramid, $V = 5$, $E = 8$, and $F = 5$.
   Check: $V + F = E + 2 \Rightarrow 5 + 5 = 8 + 2 \Rightarrow 10 = 10$

   c. For a rectangular box, $V = 8$, $E = 12$, and $F = 6$.
   Check: $V + F = E + 2 \Rightarrow 8 + 6 = 12 + 2 \Rightarrow 14 = 14$

   d. $E = V + F - 2$
   For a triangular pyramid, $V + F - 2 = 4 + 4 - 2 = 6 = E$.
   For a square pyramid, $V + F - 2 = 5 + 5 - 2 = 8 = E$.
   For a rectangular box, $V + F - 2 = 8 + 6 - 2 = 12 = E$.

   e. $F = E - V + 2$
   Students may check by substituting values for F, E, and V in an equation or reason symbolically.

2. **a.** $b = \dfrac{y_2 - y_1}{x_2 - x_1}$

   b. $y_1 = y_2 - b(x_2 - x_1)$

   c. $y = y_2 - b(x_2 - x)$
   When you collect like terms in the equation, you get $y = (y_2 - bx_2) + bx$. This is an equation of a line. The coefficient on the x is b, so the slope of the line is b. If (x_2, y_2) is substituted into the equation, the equation is true. So, the line contains the point (x_2, y_2).

   d. $y = 12 + 2(8 - x)$
   $y = 12 + 16 - 2x$
   $y = 28 - 2x$
   The y-intercept of this line is 28.

3. **a.** $(x_m, y_m) = \left(\dfrac{x_1 + x_2}{2}, \dfrac{y_1 + y_2}{2}\right)$

   b. $(x_m, y_m) = \left(\dfrac{2 + 7}{2}, \dfrac{3 + 5}{2}\right) = (4.5, 4)$

   c. $(12, 10) = \left(\dfrac{3 + x_2}{2}, \dfrac{5 + y_2}{2}\right)$ so $\dfrac{3 + x_2}{2} = 12$ and $\dfrac{5 + y_2}{2} = 10$.
   Therefore, $x_2 = 12(2) - 3$ and $y_2 = 10(2) - 5$, so $(x_2, y_2) = (21, 15)$.

   d. $(x_2, y_2) = (2x_m - x_1, 2y_m - y_1)$

Organizing

These tasks will help you organize the mathematics you have learned in the investigations and connect it with other mathematics.

1. In Course 1, you may have discovered the formula $V + F = E + 2$, which relates the number of vertices V, the number of faces F, and the number of edges E of simple polyhedra. A proof of this formula was first provided by the Swiss mathematician, Leonhard Euler in 1752. The relation is often called **Euler's formula**.

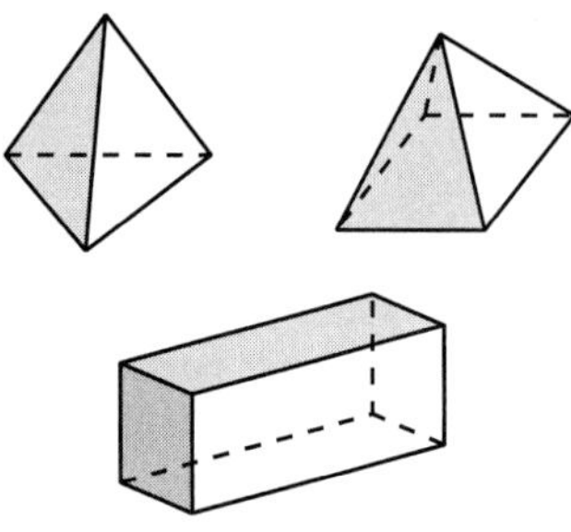

a. What are V, E, and F for a triangular pyramid? Check Euler's formula.

b. What are V, E, and F for a square pyramid? Check Euler's formula.

c. What are V, E, and F for a rectangular box? Check Euler's formula.

d. Write an equivalent form of Euler's formula that expresses E as a function of V and F. Check your answer for the polyhedra given in Parts a–c.

e. Write an equivalent form of the Euler equation that expresses F as a function of V and E. Check your answer.

2. Recall that you can use two points on a line to determine an equation for the line. Suppose two points in a coordinate plane have coordinates (x_1, y_1) and (x_2, y_2).

a. Write a formula that gives the slope b of the line containing the two points.

b. Solve the equation in Part a for y_1 in terms of the other variables.

c. In your equation from Part b, replace the point with coordinates (x_1, y_1) with a general point (x, y) on the line. Explain how this equation is now that of a line with slope b through the point (x_2, y_2).

d. Use your equation from Part c to write the equation of the line that contains the points (8, 12) and has slope –2. What is the y-intercept of this line?

3. Suppose two points in a coordinate plane have coordinates (x_1, y_1) and (x_2, y_2).

a. Write a formula that gives the coordinates (x_m, y_m) of the midpoint of the segment joining those two points.

b. Use the formula in Part a to find the midpoint of the segment joining (2, 3) and (7, 5).

c. If (12, 10) is the midpoint of the segment joining (x_2, y_2) and (3, 5), what are the coordinates (x_2, y_2)?

d. Write a formula that could be used to find one endpoint of a line segment when the other endpoint and the midpoint are given.

4. Formulas linking several variables are common in other school subjects and technical careers. Using mathematical ideas and methods of this lesson, you can make sense of many new situations. Test your skills in the following settings.

a. When providing intravenous fluids for patients needing additional body fluids, health care professionals use the relation $D = \frac{V}{4T}$, where D is the drip rate in drops per minute, V is the prescribed volume of fluid in ccs (cubic centimeters), and T is the prescribed amount of time in hours for the fluid to be given.

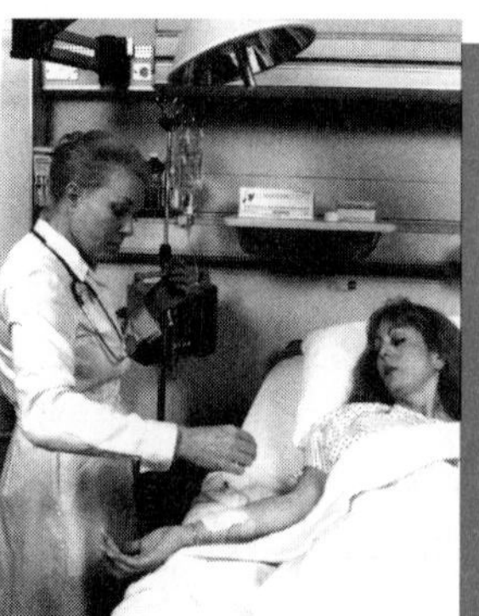

- Rewrite this equation, expressing T as a function of D and V.
- In what kinds of situations would this equivalent equation be useful?

b. During the winter, many people are interested not only in the temperature outside, but also in the *windchill*. The windchill tells how cold it seems when the wind is taken into account. One formula for quickly estimating windchill combines the actual temperature t in degrees Fahrenheit and the wind speed w in miles per hour to give windchill C: $C = t - 1.5w$.

- Solve this equation for w in terms of C and t.
- What information can you get readily from the equivalent equation?

c. Various formulas exist for determining medicinal dosages for children when adult dosages have been specified. One such formula, Clark's rule, is based on the weight w of the child. The formula is $C = \frac{wd}{150}$, where C is the child's dosage and d is the adult dosage.

- At what weight are the two dosages equal?
- Write a rule that expresses adult dosage as a function of weight and child dosage. Under what circumstances might such a rule be useful?

d. In building highways it is necessary to provide for expansion joints, or the highway will expand, buckle, and break on very hot days. Engineers are able to figure how much expansion must be allowed by using the formula $I = 0.000012L(T - t)$, where I is the amount of expansion at temperature T in degrees Fahrenheit; t is the temperature in degrees Fahrenheit at which the highway was built; and L is the length of the highway under construction. (Units for I are the same as for L.)

- Which form would be easier to use in calculating the amount of expansion $I = 0.000012L(T - t)$ or $I = 0.000012LT - 0.000012Lt$? Why?
- Under what conditions can no expansion be expected?

20 UNIT 1 • MULTIPLE-VARIABLE MODELS

4. **a.** ■ $T = \frac{V}{4D}$

■ Responses will vary. This equation could be helpful to the person who is responsible for changing IV bags. That person might know the volume of the fluid and the drip rate, and this equation allows for quick calculation of the amount of time the fluid will last. This will help in scheduling when each patient should be visited.

b. ■ $w = \frac{t - C}{1.5}$ or $w = \frac{C - t}{-1.5}$

■ If you are given the temperature and the windchill, then this equation allows you to find the wind speed.

NOTE: The current windchill formula used by the National Weather Service for Fahrenheit temperature is

$$T_{wc} = 35.74 + 0.6215T - 35.75V^{0.16} + 0.4275TV^{0.16}$$

where T_{wc} is the windchill, V is the wind speed in statute miles per hour, and T is the temperature in degrees Fahrenheit.

---

c. ■ At 150 lb, the child dosage and the adult dosage are equal.

■ $d = \frac{150C}{w}$

Student responses may vary. This might be useful if you know the child dosage and need the appropriate adult dosage of the medication. Perhaps you have run out of adult medication but have the equivalent child medication available.

d. ■ $I = 0.000012LT - 0.000012Lt$

Student responses may vary regarding which form would be easier to use. Most will probably choose the original form since it involves multiplying only once. If students have good reasons for choosing the other, that is fine.

■ The highway will not expand whenever the temperature is the same as (or lower than) the temperature at which the highway was built.

Unit 1

MORE ***continued***

5. **a.** $r = \frac{d}{t}$

   b. $q = \frac{p - 12r}{4}$; $r = \frac{p - 4q}{12}$

   c. $w = \frac{5v}{u}$ and $v = \frac{uw}{5}$

   d. $y = \frac{24 - 6x}{4}$ or $y = 6 - \frac{3}{2}x$

   e. $T = \frac{PR}{V}$

   f. $b = a \tan B$ and $a = \frac{b}{\tan B}$

6. **a.** $3x = 24$
   $x = 8$

   b. $5t = 24$
   $t = \frac{24}{5} = 4.8$

   c. $3x = 45$
   $x = 15$

   d. $23x = 420$
   $x = \frac{420}{23} \approx 18.26$

7. **a.** $y = 3 - \frac{2}{3}x$

   slope $= -\frac{2}{3}$ $\quad$ y-intercept $= 3$

   b. $y = -\frac{7}{5} + \frac{8}{5}x$

   slope $= \frac{8}{5}$ $\quad$ y-intercept $= -\frac{7}{5}$

   c. $y = \frac{3}{2} + \frac{5}{8}x$

   slope $= \frac{5}{8}$ $\quad$ y-intercept $= \frac{3}{2}$

   d. $y = 5 + \frac{4}{3}x$

   slope $= \frac{4}{3}$ $\quad$ y-intercept $= 5$

Reflecting

1. The independent variables are the number of strands and the gap length in inches. The dependent variable is the breaking weight.
2. **a.** Student responses may vary. The Pythagorean Theorem, area, perimeter, surface area, and volume formulas are all geometric examples of equations that involve relations among several variables. Other examples are the correlation coefficient, the sum squared error, interest and distance formulas, and the trigonometric ratios.

   b. Student responses may vary. The physical sciences are full of examples of formulas that involve relations among several variables. From the social sciences, students might find formulas about how insurance rates are set, population growth, or amount of certain nutrients in a person's diet.

5. Based on the patterns you've discovered in working with multiple-variable models of many different situations, do the following:

a. Solve $d = rt$ for r in terms of d and t.

b. Solve $p = 4q + 12r$ for q in terms of p and r. Then solve for r in terms of p and q.

c. Solve $u = \frac{5v}{w}$ for w in terms of u and v. Then solve for v in terms of u and w.

d. Express the relation $6x + 4y = 24$ in an equivalent form where y is a function of x.

e. Express the relation $P = \frac{VT}{R}$ in an equivalent form where T is a function of P, V, and R.

f. For right ΔABC, $\tan B = \frac{b}{a}$. Solve this equation for b and then for a.

6. Solve the following proportions.

a. $\frac{2}{3} = \frac{x}{12}$

b. $\frac{t}{8} = \frac{3}{5}$

c. $\frac{9}{x} = \frac{3}{5}$

d. $\frac{23}{42} = \frac{10}{x}$

7. Rewrite each of the following equations for lines in the equivalent form $y = a + bx$ and determine the slope and y-intercept of each line.

a. $2x + 3y = 9$

b. $7 = 8x - 5y$

c. $12 = 8y - 5x$

d. $-4x + 3y = 15$

Reflecting

These tasks will help you think about what the mathematics you have learned means to you. These tasks also will help you think about what you do and do not understand.

1. Look back at the pasta-breaking experiment in Investigation 1. What are the independent and dependent variables in that experiment?

2. Think about your previous studies in mathematics and in other school subjects.

a. Give an example of an equation from a previous mathematics course (different from those in this lesson) that involves a relation among several variables. Identify the variables and explain the equation used.

b. Give an example of a formula from another school subject that involves a relation among several variables. Identify the variables and explain how the formula is used.

LESSON 1 • LINKED VARIABLES 21

3. The principles that govern flow of electricity often are described in language that talks about flow, like water through a system of pipes, valves, and pumps.

   a. If you think about a water hose connected to an outdoor faucet, what elements of the situation correspond to the following:

      - Current
      - Resistance
      - Voltage

   b. What would it mean to increase or decrease "voltage" in the water faucet model, and how does change in "voltage" affect flow of "current"?

   c. What would it mean to increase or decrease "resistance" in the water faucet model, and how does change in "resistance" affect flow of "current"?

4. The basic principle underlying the operation of air conditioners and heat pumps involves a relation between pressure, volume, and temperature in a container. Check with someone who knows about heating and cooling, and report how those variables change when the machinery is in operation.

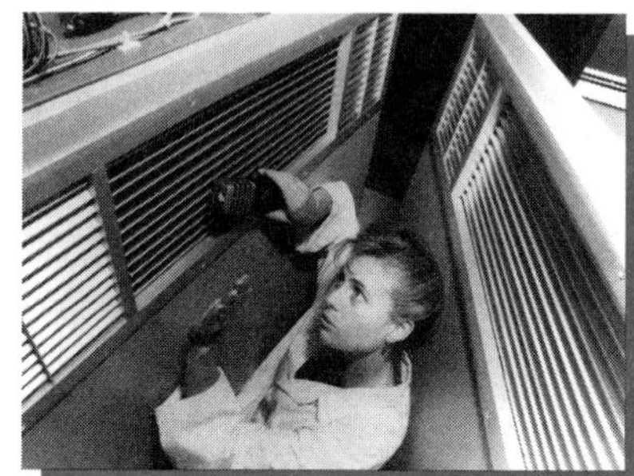

Extending

Tasks in this section provide opportunities for you to explore further or more deeply the mathematics you are learning.

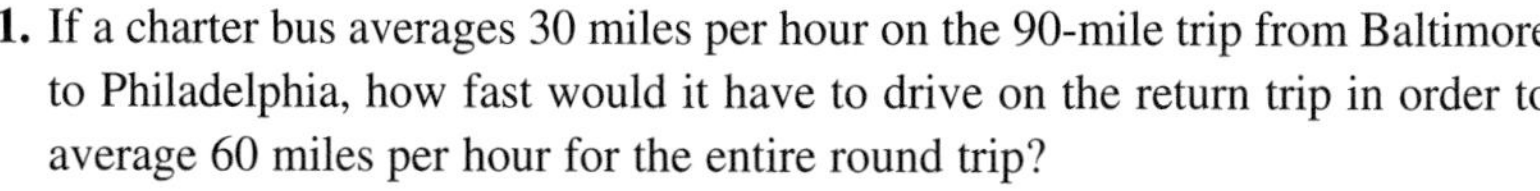

1. If a charter bus averages 30 miles per hour on the 90-mile trip from Baltimore to Philadelphia, how fast would it have to drive on the return trip in order to average 60 miles per hour for the entire round trip?

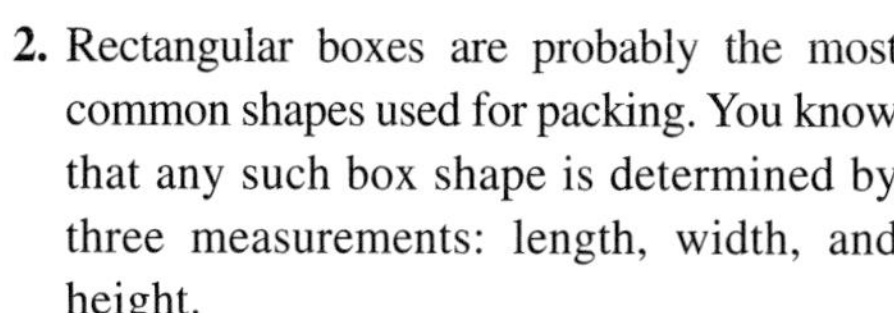

2. Rectangular boxes are probably the most common shapes used for packing. You know that any such box shape is determined by three measurements: length, width, and height.

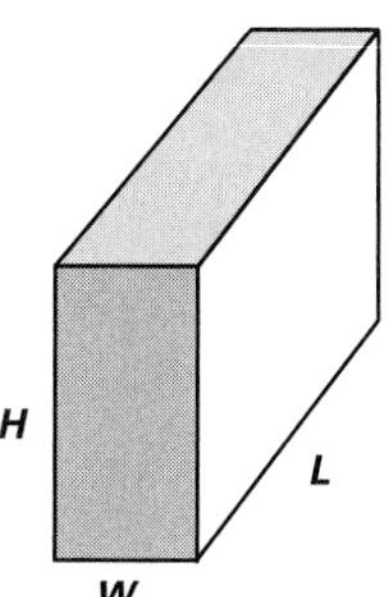

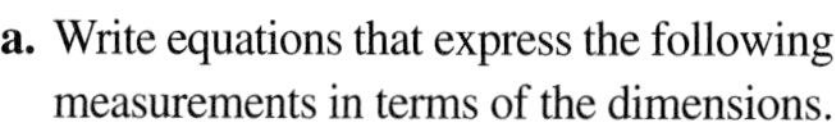

   a. Write equations that express the following measurements in terms of the dimensions.

      - Total surface area A of the box
      - Volume V of the box

22 UNIT 1 • MULTIPLE-VARIABLE MODELS

3. **a.** ■ Current corresponds to flow rate of the water.

■ Resistance depends on diameter of the hose, with narrower diameter providing greater resistance to flow.

■ Voltage corresponds to the amount of opening of the faucet (how far it is turned on), with greater opening providing greater water pressure in the hose.

b. Increasing the "voltage" corresponds to opening the faucet farther; it produces increase in water flow.

c. Increasing the "resistance" to the flow corresponds to constricting the hose; it produces a decrease in water flow.

4. Responses will vary.

Extending

1. In order to average 60 mph for the 180-mile round trip, the round trip must be completed in 3 hours. However, it took the bus 3 hours on the first part of the trip (90 miles at 30 mph), so it is impossible to average 60 miles per hour for the round trip.

2. **a.** ■ $A = 2HW + 2LH + 2LW$

■ $V = L \times W \times H$

MORE *continued*

2. b. ■ $720 = 12 \times 4 \times H \Rightarrow H = \frac{720}{12 \cdot 4} = 15$ inches

■ $720 = L \times 5 \times 12 \Rightarrow L = \frac{720}{5 \cdot 12} = 12$ inches

■ $L = W$ and $H = 20 \Rightarrow 720 = L^2 \times 20 \Rightarrow L = \sqrt{\frac{720}{20}} = 6.$

The dimensions of the bottom would be 6 inches $\times$ 6 inches.

c. ■ $H = \frac{600}{LW}$

■ $L = \frac{600}{HW}$

■ $W = \frac{600}{HL}$

d. The box that is 12 inches long, 4 inches wide, and 15 inches high would require 2(12)(4) + 2(4)(15) + 2(12)(15), or 576 square inches of cardboard (plus a little for overlaps). The box that has dimensions 12 inches by 5 inches by 12 inches would require 2(12)(5) + 2(12)(12) + 2(5)(12), or 528 square inches of cardboard. The third box would require 2(6)(6) + 2(6)(20) + 2(6)(20), or 552 square inches of cardboard. So the box that is 12 $\times$ 5 $\times$ 12 inches requires the least cardboard to produce.

3. a. A current of $\frac{120}{25} + \frac{120}{15}$ or 12.8 amps is used.

b. $\frac{120}{\left(6.5 - \frac{120}{20}\right)}$ or 240 ohms is the resistance of the television set.

b. In designing packages, producers often decide first on the volume the box should hold. Then they have to see what combinations of dimensions would give that volume. Suppose a distributor of breakfast cereal wants the large economy-size container to hold 720 cubic inches of cereal.

- If the length and width of the box are to be 12 inches and 4 inches, respectively, what should the height of the box be?
- If the height of the box is to be 12 inches and the width 5 inches, what should the length of the box be?
- If the bottom of the box is to be a square and the height is to be 20 inches, what will the dimensions of the bottom be?

c. If a shipping box is to have fixed volume of 600 cubic inches, what equations would be convenient for calculating the following?

- Required height for many different combinations of length and width
- Required length for many different combinations of height and width
- Required width for many different combinations of height and length

d. Which box from Part b would take the least cardboard to produce?

3. When several electrical appliances are drawing power from the same supply circuit in your home, the current drawn by the total circuit is the sum of the currents drawn by the separate appliances. The voltage remains constant at the standard 120 volts for household use in the United States. So if two appliances with resistances R_1 and R_2 are operating at the same time, the current flow will be given by the following:

$$I = \frac{120}{R_1} + \frac{120}{R_2}$$

a. If a microwave with resistance 25 ohms and a refrigerator with resistance 15 ohms are operating at the same time on a kitchen circuit, what current is used?

b. Suppose a television and a hairdryer are both operating from the same bedroom circuit, drawing a total current of 6.5 amps. If the resistance of the hairdryer is 20 ohms, what is the resistance of the television set?

LESSON 1 • LINKED VARIABLES 23

4. Refer to Modeling Task 4 on page 18. Suppose a container-manufacturing company is to design and manufacture cylindrical cans for 2-cycle lawn mower engine oil. The volume of each can is to be 0.236 liter. (Note that 1 cm^3 = 1 mL.)

a. In order to minimize the cost of materials, the company wishes to design a can that requires the smallest amount of metal possible. What should the dimensions of the can be?

b. Compare your dimensions in Part a with those of a 0.236-liter can in a local hardware store. Write a brief report of your findings.

5. On many rivers the flow of water is determined by the rate at which water is released from behind power station dams. This is the case on the Savage River in western Maryland, a popular white-water river for kayaking. The speed of a river's current is also affected by the depth of water and the width of the river.

Imagine yourself floating down the Savage River in a kayak or on a raft.

a. How will your speed be related to the rate of water release, the width of the river at various spots, and the depth of the river at various spots?

b. What sort of algebraic equation would show the way that speed is a function of water release rate, stream depth, and stream width?

24 UNIT 1 • MULTIPLE-VARIABLE MODELS

4. **a.** Because 1 cubic centimeter equals 1 milliliter, students need to change 0.236 L to 236 mL before finding the equation for surface area:

$$SA = 2\pi r^2 + \frac{472}{r}$$

Graphing this function and tracing to find the minimum point gives (3.3, 211.4). So the can should have a radius of 3.3 cm and a height of $\frac{236}{(\pi)(3.3)^2}$, or 6.9 cm. The surface area of this can is approximately 211.4 cm^3.

b. Responses may vary; students may need to look around to find such a can. Some companies use non-cylindrical containers instead. The radius of a typical 0.236 liter can of oil is approximately 6.5 cm, and the height is approximately 8 cm. This radius is about the same as that which gives the minimum surface area, but the height is about 1 cm greater. This probably allows extra room at the top, so that when the can is opened, it doesn't spill.

5. **a.** Speed will increase as rate of water release increases.
Speed will decrease as the width of the river increases.
Speed will decrease as the depth of the river increases.

b. For speed S, rate of water release R, width of river W, and depth of river D, the equation will be of the form $S = \frac{kR}{DW}$ where k is some constant.

See Assessment Resources pages 1–6.

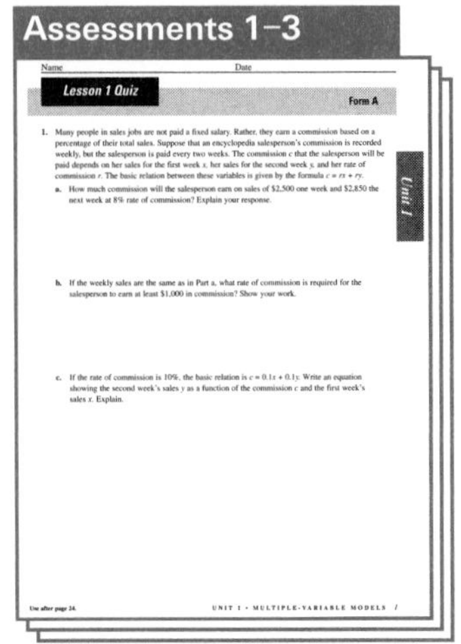

Assessments 1–3

Name Date

Lesson 1 Quiz — Form A

Unit 1

1. Many people in sales jobs are not paid a fixed salary. Rather, they earn a commission based on a percentage of their total sales. Suppose that an encyclopedia salesperson's commission is recorded weekly, but the salesperson is paid every two weeks. The commission c that the salesperson will be paid depends on her sales for the first week x, her sales for the second week y, and her rate of commission r. The basic relation between these variables is given by the formula $c = rx + ry$.
   a. How much commission will the salesperson earn on sales of $2,500 one week and $2,850 the next week at 8% rate of commission? Explain your response.
   b. If the weekly sales are the same as in Part a, what rate of commission is required for the salesperson to earn at least $1,000 in commission? Show your work.
   c. If the rate of commission is 10%, the basic relation is $c = 0.1x + 0.1y$. Write an equation showing the second week's sales y as a function of the commission c and the first week's sales x. Explain.

Use after page 24. UNIT 1 • MULTIPLE-VARIABLE MODELS 1

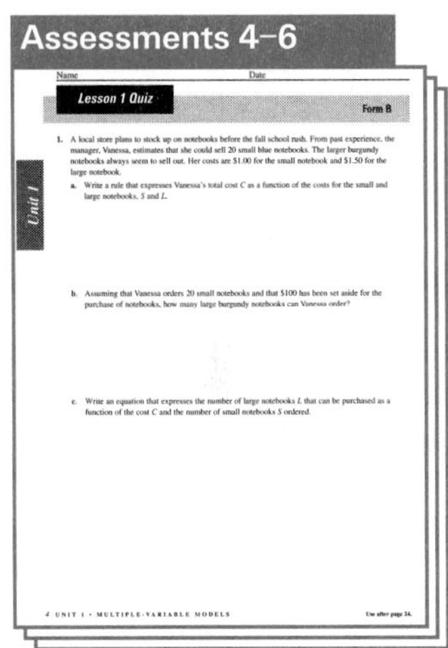

Assessments 4–6

Name Date

Lesson 1 Quiz — Form B

Unit 1

1. A local store plans to stock up on notebooks before the fall school rush. From past experience, the manager, Vanessa, estimates that she could sell 20 small blue notebooks. The larger burgundy notebooks always seem to sell out. Her costs are $1.00 for the small notebook and $1.50 for the large notebook.
   a. Write a rule that expresses Vanessa's total cost C as a function of the costs for the small and large notebooks, S and L.
   b. Assuming that Vanessa orders 20 small notebooks and that $100 has been set aside for the purchase of notebooks, how many large burgundy notebooks can Vanessa order?
   c. Write an equation that expresses the number of large notebooks L that can be purchased as a function of the cost C and the number of small notebooks S ordered.

4 UNIT 1 • MULTIPLE-VARIABLE MODELS Use after page 24.

Unit 1

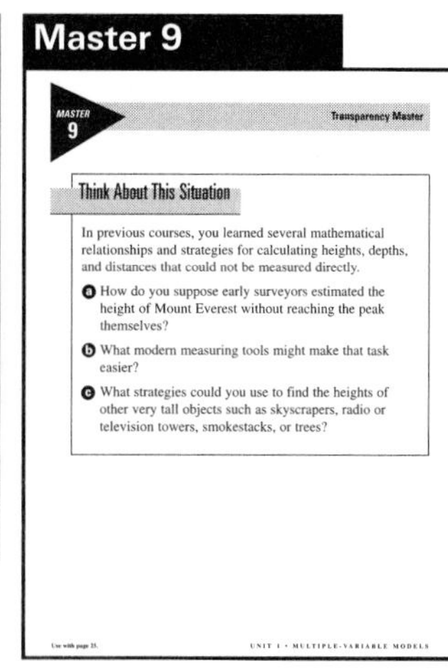
Master 9

MASTER 9 Transparency Master

Think About This Situation

In previous courses, you learned several mathematical relationships and strategies for calculating heights, depths, and distances that could not be measured directly.

a. How do you suppose early surveyors estimated the height of Mount Everest without reaching the peak themselves?

b. What modern measuring tools might make that task easier?

c. What strategies could you use to find the heights of other very tall objects such as skyscrapers, radio or television towers, smokestacks, or trees?

Use with page 25. UNIT 1 • MULTIPLE-VARIABLE MODELS

Lesson 2 *Algebra, Geometry, and Trigonometry*

LESSON OVERVIEW In Lesson 1, students began to develop skills in rewriting multiple-variable equations in order to isolate a particular variable. In this lesson, students will extend their symbolic reasoning skills to more complex equations from geometry and trigonometry. In the first investigation, students encounter problem-solving situations involving right triangle trigonometry. From there, the need arises for additional means of finding measures in triangles that are not right triangles. In the following two investigations, students apply the Law of Sines and then the Law of Cosines as they find measures in triangles and use algebraic equations involving three of four different variables. Finally, in the fourth investigation, the students are introduced to basic properties of numbers and equations. They use these properties to justify strategies for solving an equation for one variable in terms of other variables.

NOTE: The domain and range of trigonometric functions are studied in Unit 3, and the ambiguous case of the Law of Sines is explored in Unit 4.

Lesson Objectives

- To find measures of sides and angles in right triangles from given information
- To find measures of sides and angles in triangles using the Law of Sines
- To find measures of sides and angles in triangles using the Law of Cosines
- To solve equations involving several variables for one of the variables in terms of the others

LAUNCH full-class discussion

Before students read the lesson introduction, you may wish to guide a full-class discussion about the dangers of mountain climbing. Some students may be aware of the dangers of climbing in the Himalayas, where a combination of technical difficulty, lack of oxygen, weather conditions, logistical problems of supplies, physical condition of the climbers, and lack of expertise of guides can and often do create risky situations. Ask them what variables they can identify as part of the total climbing experience. From that discussion, you can lead into how height and oxygen level are related. Because of this relationship, it is important to know accurately the height of a difficult climb. Help students connect this discussion to multiple-variable relationships, and let them know that Lesson 2 introduces some ways to measure heights and distances indirectly.

Think About This Situation

See Teaching Master 9.

a. Students might recall having used similar triangles in Course 2, or they might refer to ratios and proportions.

See additional Teaching Notes on page T90H.

Lesson 2 Algebra, Geometry, and Trigonometry

The highest point on the Earth's surface is the peak of Mount Everest in the Himalaya mountain range along the Tibet-Nepal border in Asia. The mountain is named after a geographer, Sir George Everest, who was the first English surveyor-general of colonial India. But the Tibetan name of *Chomo-Lungma* or Mother Goddess of the World seems a more appropriate title.

The most recent calculations indicate that *Chomo-Lungma* rises 8,872 meters (29,108 feet) above sea level. As early as 1850, surveyors had estimated the height of that peak with error of only 0.4%. The first climbers to actually reach the summit were Tenzing Norgay and Edmund Hillary in 1953.

Think About This Situation

In previous courses, you learned several mathematical relationships and strategies for calculating heights, depths, and distances that could not be measured directly.

a How do you suppose early surveyors estimated the height of Mount Everest without reaching the peak themselves?

b What modern measuring tools might make that task easier?

c What strategies could you use to find the heights of other very tall objects such as skyscrapers, radio or television towers, smokestacks, or trees?

LESSON 2 • ALGEBRA, GEOMETRY, AND TRIGONOMETRY 25

INVESTIGATION 1 Triangulation

One of the most effective strategies for calculating distances to points that cannot be reached is to model the situation with a triangle in which the segment of unknown length is one side and other parts can be measured. If you can make the model a right triangle, there are several ways to calculate the unknown length.

Study the diagram below of a radio transmission tower with two support wires attached to it and to the ground.

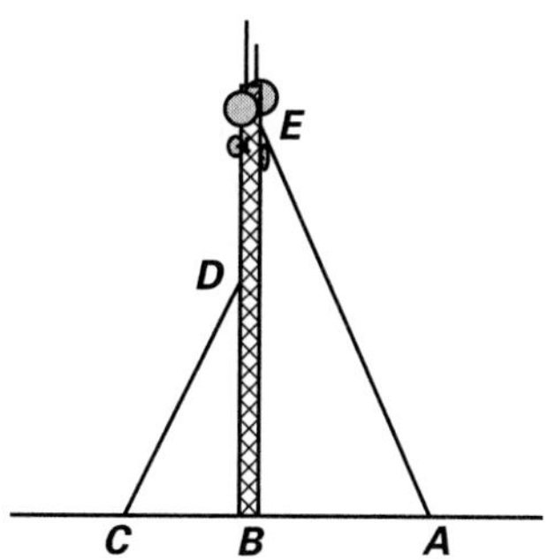

1. First focus on the triangle formed by the tower, the ground, and the shorter support wire.
   a. If $CB = 50$ feet and $BD = 100$ feet, how long is the support wire $\overline{CD}$?
   b. If you were asked to attach a support wire, 125 feet long, from point C to the tower, how high up the tower would you have to climb?
   c. What general relationship among sides of a right triangle have you used in answering Parts a and b?
   d. Refer to the diagram at the right. What calculations are required to find a missing length in a right triangle when the lengths of both legs (r and p) are known? What if the length of one leg and the hypotenuse (r and q, or p and q) are known?

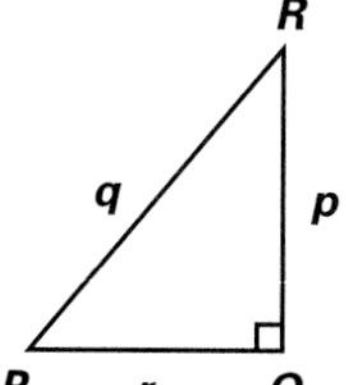

2. Next, focus on the triangle formed by the tower, the ground, and the longer support wire $\overline{AE}$. Length $AB = 75$ feet and $m\angle BAE = 66°$. (The notation $m\angle$ is read *the measure of angle...* .)
   a. How long is the support wire from A to E?
   b. How high up the tower is point E, where the support wire from A is attached?
   c. What is the degree measure of $\angle AEB$?
   d. How could you use the measure of $\angle AEB$ and the length of $\overline{AB}$ to calculate the lengths of $\overline{EB}$ and $\overline{EA}$?
3. Refer to your work in Part a of Activity 1. Use the information to estimate the measures of $\angle BCD$ and $\angle BDC$.

26 UNIT 1 • MULTIPLE-VARIABLE MODELS

EXPLORE small-group investigation

INVESTIGATION 1 Triangulation

This investigation reviews two familiar ways to find a missing side of a right triangle: using the Pythagorean Theorem and using trigonometric ratios. These are treated as further examples of multiple-variable relationships.

Since most of this is review, it should be quickly accessible to students. Encourage students to write down their work so that they can show others their original statements and any rearrangements of those statements. You might post their responses in an easy-to-see place for reference.

Throughout this unit, the calculations and solutions provided may be rounded to less than the number of digits displayed by the calculator but most often will include more significant digits than the application would warrant. You may wish to establish your own classroom procedure for reporting results.

1. **a.** $CD = \sqrt{50^2 + 100^2} \approx 111.8$ feet

   b. $\sqrt{x^2 + 50^2} = 125$

   $x^2 + 50^2 = 125^2$

   $x \approx 114.6$ feet

   You would have to climb approximately 114.6 feet up the tower.

   c. The Pythagorean Theorem was used in answering Parts a and b.

   d. If the lengths of both legs (r and p) are given, $q^2 = r^2 + p^2$ or $q = \sqrt{r^2 + p^2}$. In words, you would square the length of each leg, find the sum of those values, and then determine the square root of that sum.

   If the length of one leg and the hypotenuse (r and q, or p and q) are given, then $r^2 = q^2 - p^2$ or $r = \sqrt{q^2 - p^2}$. In words, you would square the length of the given leg and the hypotenuse, find the difference of those values, and then determine the square root of that difference.

2. **Some groups may need help remembering the trigonometric ratios. They should be recorded in students' Math Toolkits.**

   a. $\frac{75}{AE} = \cos 66°$, so $AE = \frac{75}{\cos 66°} \approx 184.39$ feet.

   b. $\frac{BE}{75} = \tan 66°$, so $BE = 75 \tan 66° \approx 168.45$ feet.

   c. $m\angle AEB = 90° - 66° = 24°$

   d. $\tan \angle AEB = \frac{AB}{BE}$, therefore $BE = \frac{AB}{\tan \angle AEB}$ or $BE = \frac{75}{\tan 24°}$.

   $\sin \angle AEB = \frac{AB}{AE}$, therefore $AE = \frac{AB}{\sin \angle AEB}$ or $AE = \frac{75}{\sin 24°}$.

3. $\cos \angle BCD = \frac{50}{111.8}$ so $m\angle BCD \approx 63.4°$. Since $m\angle BCD + m\angle BDC = 90°$, $m\angle BDC = 26.6°$. Another method is $\tan \angle BCD = \frac{100}{50}$, so $m\angle BCD \approx 63.4°$.

4. Heights of tall structures can be measured indirectly by representing the situation using a right triangle, where one leg represents the height of the object and the other leg represents your distance from the object. Measure the angle of elevation and the distance from the object. Then use the tangent ratio to determine the height of the object.

Unit 1

Master 10

MASTER 10 Transparency Master

Checkpoint

The activities in Investigation 1 required combinations of facts about several parts of right triangles to find information about other parts.

a What general principle relates the lengths of the sides of a right triangle? How can that relationship be used to calculate the length of one side when the other two are known?

b What general relationships connect side and angle measurements in any right triangle? How can those relationships be used to calculate the unknown length of one side when another side length and angle measurement are given?

Be prepared to explain these right triangle relationships and their use to your classmates.

SHARE AND SUMMARIZE full-class discussion

Checkpoint

See Teaching Master 10.

The focus here is on the idea of multiple-variable relationships and how they can be rewritten in several different formats. In order to raise the discussion up to this level, be sure that several rearrangements are demonstrated and explained. In addition, you may want to ask how these relationships are like or unlike the relationships in Lesson 1. ($D = \frac{R}{T}$ has the same format as $\sin P = \frac{p}{q}$.) To help emphasize the similarities, you might ask, "If p increases and q is fixed, will $\sin P$ increase or decrease? If q increases and p is fixed, will $\sin P$ increase or decrease?"

a The Pythagorean Theorem states that $r^2 + p^2 = q^2$. You can solve that equation for any one of the three sides.

$$q = \sqrt{r^2 + p^2}$$
$$p = \sqrt{q^2 - r^2}$$
$$r = \sqrt{q^2 - p^2}$$

b In any right triangle, the sine of an angle equals the opposite side divided by the hypotenuse, the cosine of an angle equals the adjacent side divided by the hypotenuse, and the tangent of an angle equals the opposite side divided by the adjacent side. From these basic relationships you can derive the following:

$\sin P = \frac{p}{q}$	$\cos P = \frac{r}{q}$	$\tan P = \frac{p}{r}$
$q = \frac{p}{\sin P}$	$q = \frac{r}{\cos P}$	$r = \frac{p}{\tan P}$
$p = q \sin P$	$r = q \cos P$	$p = r \tan P$
$\sin R = \frac{r}{q}$	$\cos R = \frac{p}{q}$	$\tan R = \frac{r}{p}$
$q = \frac{r}{\sin R}$	$q = \frac{p}{\cos R}$	$p = \frac{r}{\tan R}$
$r = q \sin R$	$p = q \cos R$	$r = p \tan R$

Make sure that students discuss what to do when sides are known and they are solving for an angle measure. They need to remember to use the inverse functions to determine angle measures when they know the side lengths.

CONSTRUCTING A MATH TOOLKIT: Students should describe how to use the trigonometric ratios to find lengths of sides and angle measures of right triangles. Some students may include numerical examples to clarify the process for themselves (Teaching Master 113).

Group Processing Suggestions

- How did your group make sure everyone understood?
- What questions did you ask to help focus your group discussion toward understanding the mathematics in this investigation?

MORE ASSIGNMENT *pp. 40–45*

Students can now begin Organizing Task 1 from the MORE assignment following Investigation 4. You also may wish to have students begin work on the Maintenance items at this time, if not already assigned. Item 7 would help them review geometry concepts needed in this lesson.

APPLY individual task

On Your Own

a. $\cos 51^\circ = \frac{2{,}700}{AB}$ so $AB = \frac{2{,}700}{\cos 51^\circ} \approx 4{,}290$ feet.

$\tan 51^\circ = \frac{BC}{2{,}700}$ so $BC = 2{,}700 \tan 51^\circ \approx 3{,}334$ feet.

b. $AC = AB \cos \angle BAC$

$BC = AB \sin \angle BAC$

4. Think again about the problem of finding the height (above sea level) of Mount Everest or of other very tall structures. What measurements would allow you to calculate heights that cannot be measured directly? What mathematical principles and relationships would you need to make the calculations?

Checkpoint

The activities in Investigation 1 required combinations of facts about several parts of right triangles to find information about other parts.

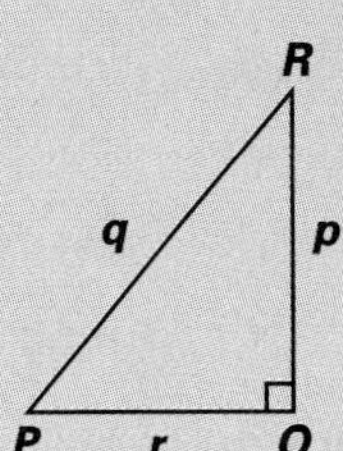

a What general principle relates the lengths of the sides of a right triangle? How can that relationship be used to calculate the length of one side when the other two are known?

b What general relationships connect side and angle measurements in any right triangle? How can those relationships be used to calculate the unknown length of one side when another side length and angle measurement are given?

Be prepared to explain these right triangle relationships and their use to your classmates.

On Your Own

The following sketch shows the start of one surveyor's attempt to determine the height of a tall mountain without climbing to the top herself.

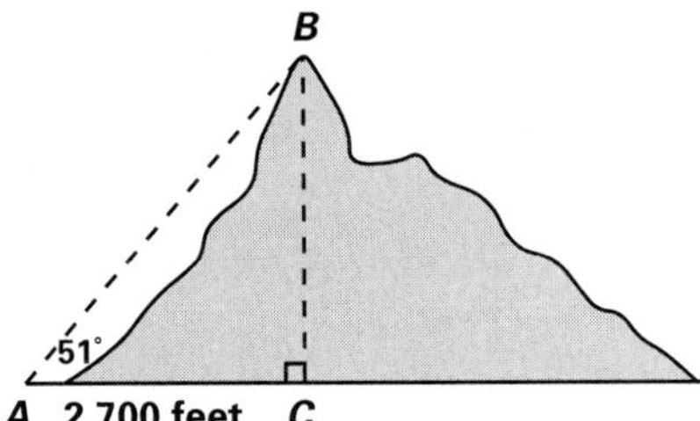

a. Use the given information to calculate the lengths of $\overline{AB}$ and $\overline{BC}$.

b. Suppose that a laser ranging device allowed you to find the length of $\overline{AB}$ and the angle of elevation $\angle BAC$, but you could not measure the length of $\overline{AC}$. How could you use this information (instead of the information from the diagram) to calculate the lengths of $\overline{AC}$ and $\overline{BC}$?

INVESTIGATION 2 The Law of Sines

As you worked on the activities in Investigation 1, you found several ways that the Pythagorean Theorem and the trigonometric ratios (sine, cosine, and tangent) could be used to calculate unknown side lengths of right triangles. If the triangle isn't (or might not be) a right triangle, it's not so easy to model the situation involving the unknown distance, but it can be done.

For example, suppose that two park rangers who are in towers 10 miles apart in a national forest spot a fire that is uphill and far away from both. Suppose that one ranger recognizes the fire location and knows that it is about 4.9 miles from that tower. With this information and the angles given in the diagram below, the rangers can calculate the distance of the fire from the other tower.

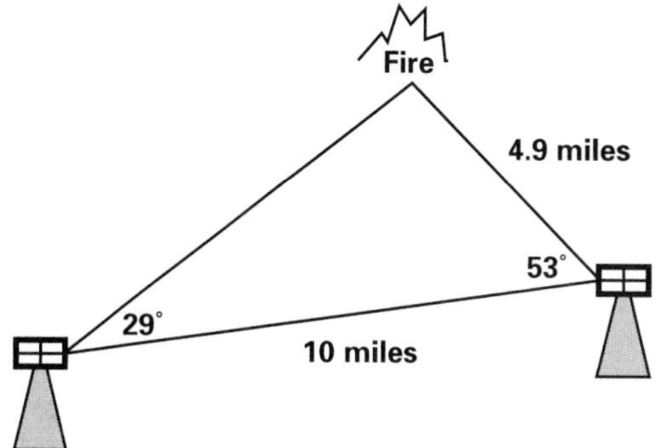

One way to start working on this problem is to divide the obtuse triangle into two right triangles as shown below:

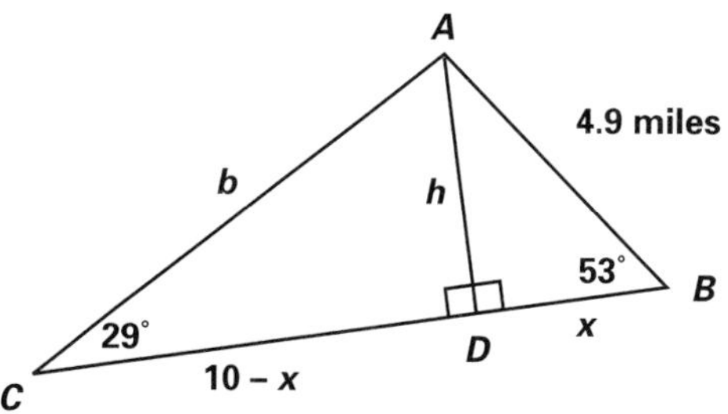

At first that does not seem to help much. Instead of two segments of unknown length, there are now four! On the other hand, there are now three triangles in which you can seek useful relationships among the known sides and angles.

28 UNIT 1 • MULTIPLE-VARIABLE MODELS

EXPLORE small-group investigation

INVESTIGATION 2 The Law of Sines

This investigation uses students' knowledge of trigonometric ratios to develop the Law of Sines. You may wish to discuss the first diagram as a class before students read the introductory prose on page 28. Ask students if they could determine the missing distance. Students often will say, "Use the Pythagorean Theorem," perhaps because the triangle looks roughly right angled, or perhaps because they have not internalized that the Pythagorean Theorem can be used only with right triangles. If no one corrects that misunderstanding, then you can draw another triangle on the board for which squaring the two short sides would clearly not give an answer that is reasonable for the square of the third side.

Once students appreciate that we need a new theory for non-right triangles, draw their attention to the second diagram: "This diagram has two right triangles; why can't we now use the Pythagorean Theorem to our advantage?" (There are too many unknowns.) After this discussion, students will be ready to begin work on Activity 1.

EXPLORE *continued*

1. **While students work on this activity, encourage them to write down any relationships they can. They may not see a way to reason all the way to the length *AC*, but they may well see some relationships that involve *AC*. If any group arrives at a solution, you might have them write it on the board and have the rest of the class discuss it. If no group arrives at a solution, then have each group write whatever relationships they could see in the figure. As a large group you can build a chain of reasoning that uses these relationships. Some possibilities for finding *AC* or *b* follow.**

   i. $h = 4.9 \sin 53^\circ \approx 3.91$

   $b = \frac{h}{\sin 29^\circ} \approx \frac{3.91}{0.4848} \approx 8.07$ miles

   ii. $h = 4.9 \sin 53^\circ \approx 3.91$

   $x = \sqrt{4.9^2 - h^2} = \sqrt{24.01 - 15.29} \approx 2.95$

   $b = \sqrt{h^2 + (10 - x)^2} = \sqrt{3.91^2 + (10 - 2.95)^2} \approx 8.06$ miles

   (or $b = \frac{10 - x}{\cos 29^\circ} \approx \frac{10 - 2.95}{\cos 29^\circ} \approx 8.06$ miles)

2. **You may choose to do Activity 2 as a large group, as it foreshadows the Law of Sines.**

(1)	$\frac{h}{b} = \sin 29^\circ$	Definition of Sine Ratio
(2)	$h = b \sin 29^\circ$	Multiplication Property of Equality
(3)	$\frac{h}{4.9} = \sin 53^\circ$	Definition of Sine Ratio
(4)	$h = 4.9 \sin 53^\circ$	Multiplication Property of Equality
(5)	$b \sin 29^\circ = 4.9 \sin 53^\circ$	Substitution (using 2 and 4)
(6)	$b = \frac{4.9 \sin 53^\circ}{\sin 29}$	Division Property of Equality
(7)	$b = 8.07$ miles	Evaluation or Simplification

3.

(1)	$\frac{h}{b} = \sin A$	Definition of Sine Ratio
(2)	$h = b \sin A$	Multiplication Property of Equality
(3)	$\frac{h}{a} = \sin B$	Definition of Sine Ratio
(4)	$h = a \sin B$	Multiplication Property of Equality
(5)	$b \sin A = a \sin B$	Substitution
(6)	$\frac{\sin A}{a} = \frac{\sin B}{b}$	Division Property of Equality

1. Use trigonometry or the Pythagorean relationship for right triangles to find the length of $\overline{AC}$. When you have one sequence of calculations that gives the desired result, see if you can find a different approach.

2. In one Maryland class, a group presented their solution to Activity 1 and claimed that it was the slickest, quickest method possible. Check each step in their reasoning and explain why each step is or is not correct.

(1) $\frac{h}{b} = \sin 29^\circ$ (3) $\frac{h}{4.9} = \sin 53^\circ$

(2) $h = b \sin 29^\circ$ (4) $h = 4.9 \sin 53^\circ$

(5) $b \sin 29^\circ = 4.9 \sin 53^\circ$

(6) $b = \frac{4.9 \sin 53^\circ}{\sin 29^\circ}$

(7) $b = 8.07$ miles

Compare your solution with this reported solution.

3. The approach in Activity 2 to calculating the unknown side length of a triangle that is not itself a right triangle illustrates a very useful general relationship among sides and angles of *any* triangle. Explain why each step in the following derivation is correct.

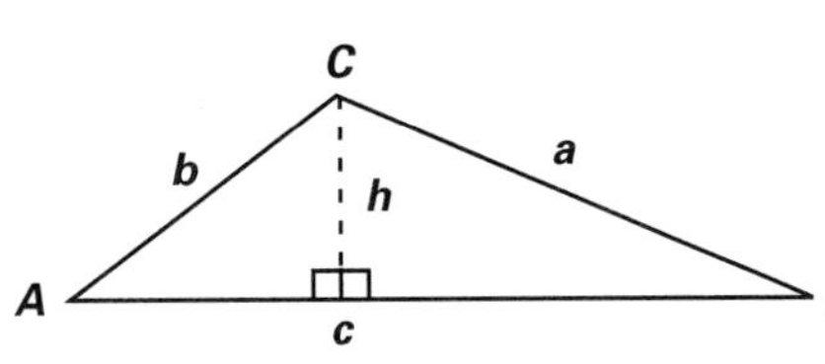

(1) $\frac{h}{b} = \sin A$

(2) $h = b \sin A$

(3) $\frac{h}{a} = \sin B$

(4) $h = a \sin B$

(5) $b \sin A = a \sin B$

(6) $\frac{\sin A}{a} = \frac{\sin B}{b}$

The relationship derived in Activity 3 holds in any triangle and for all three sides and angles as well. It is called the **Law of Sines** and can be written in two equivalent forms:

In any triangle ABC with sides of lengths a, b, and c opposite ∠A, ∠B, and ∠C, respectively:

$$\frac{\sin A}{a} = \frac{\sin B}{b} = \frac{\sin C}{c}$$

or equivalently,

$$\frac{a}{\sin A} = \frac{b}{\sin B} = \frac{c}{\sin C}.$$

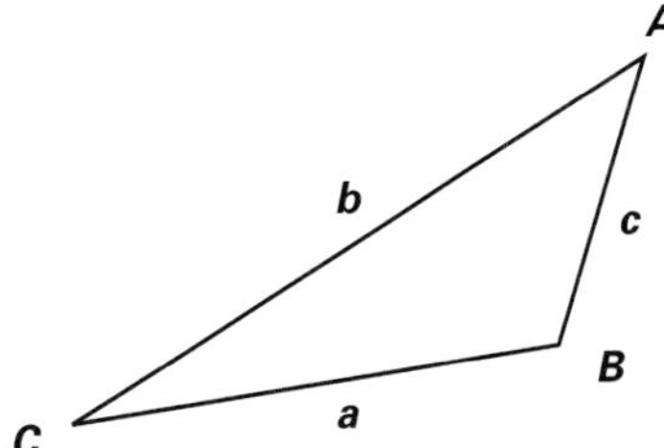

LESSON 2 • ALGEBRA, GEOMETRY, AND TRIGONOMETRY 29

You can use this important relationship to calculate measures of angles and lengths of sides in triangles with even less given information than the fire-spotting problem at the beginning of this investigation. In practice, you only need to use the equality of two of the ratios at any one time.

4. Suppose that the two rangers spot another fire in a different spot, indicated on the next diagram. Use what you know about angles in a triangle and the Law of Sines to find the distances from each tower to the fire.

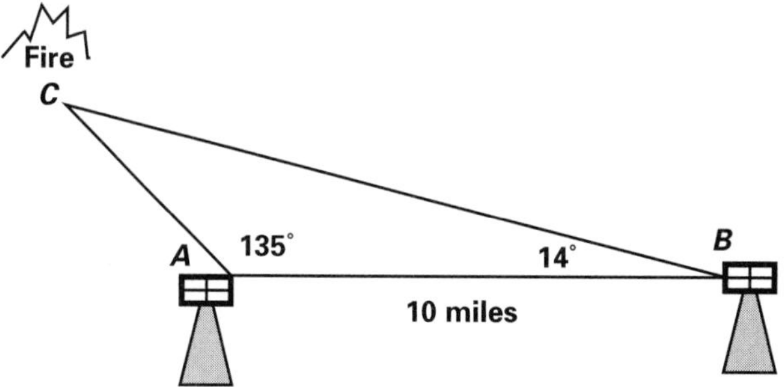

5. In parallelogram *ABCD* below, information is given about one side and two angles formed by the diagonals $\overline{AC}$ and $\overline{BD}$.

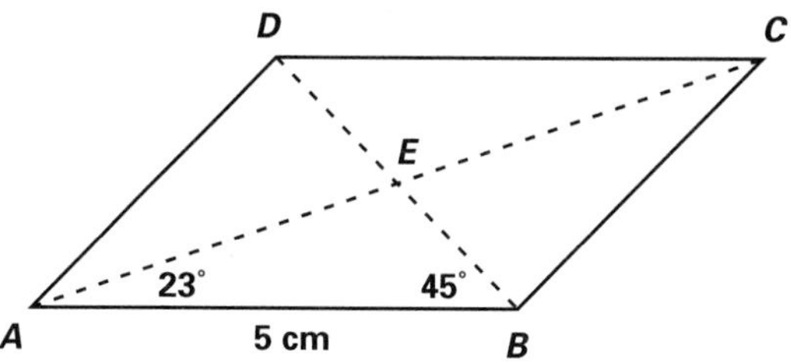

a. Recall from your previous study of mathematics that a parallelogram has 180° rotational symmetry about the point of intersection of its diagonals. Verify this fact by tracing parallelogram *ABCD* on a sheet of paper and rotating the paper about point *E*.

b. Use facts about triangles and the rotational symmetry property of parallelograms to find as much additional information as you can about the other 7 segments and 10 angles in the given figure. Do *not* use trigonometry.

c. Use the Law of Sines to find further information about the segments and angles in the figure.

30 UNIT 1 • MULTIPLE-VARIABLE MODELS

4. $\frac{\sin 31^\circ}{10} = \frac{\sin 135^\circ}{BC}$

$$BC = \frac{10 \sin 135^\circ}{\sin 31^\circ}$$

$$BC \approx 13.73 \text{ miles}$$

$\frac{\sin 31^\circ}{10} = \frac{\sin 14^\circ}{AC}$

$$AC = \frac{10 \sin 14^\circ}{\sin 31^\circ}$$

$$AC \approx 4.70 \text{ miles}$$

5. **a.** Students should verify that parallelograms have 180° rotational symmetry. The inclusion of the diagonals in their analysis of the symmetry will assist them in finding some of the information for Part b.

b. Students should be able to determine the angle measures and lengths in the diagram shown here.

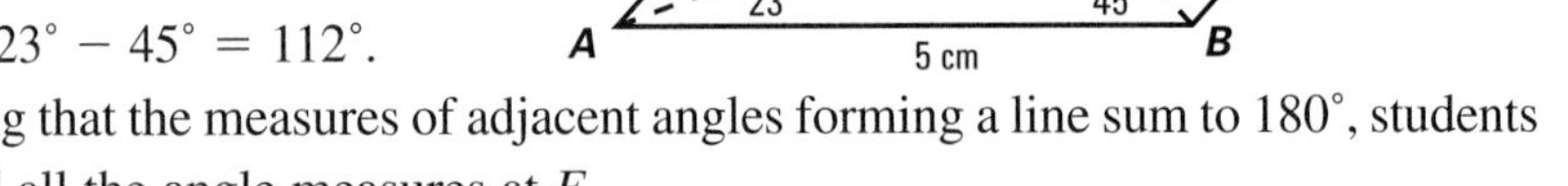

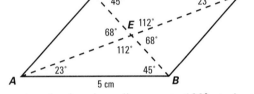

- $DC = 5$ cm because opposite sides of a parallelogram are of equal length.
- $m\angle AEB = 112°$ because $180° - 23° - 45° = 112°$.
- Knowing that the measures of adjacent angles forming a line sum to 180°, students can find all the angle measures at E.
- The 180° rotational symmetry including the diagonals will allow students to reason about $m\angle CDE$ and $m\angle DCE$.

c. $\frac{\sin 112^\circ}{5} = \frac{\sin 23^\circ}{BE} = \frac{\sin 45^\circ}{AE}$

$BE \approx 2.11$ cm; $AE \approx 3.81$ cm. By symmetry, students can also conclude that $EC \approx 3.81$ cm and $ED \approx 2.11$ cm.

Many students probably will not be able to determine the measures of the remaining sides and angles. This is a nice lead-in to the fact that another relationship between the sides and the angles would be helpful. However, it is possible to solve for all of the remaining sides and angles without the Law of Cosines.

You may want to challenge your more able students to try to find the other angle measures and lengths. They can be found in the following manner, using the Law of Sines again.

Let $x = m\angle ADE = m\angle DBC$, then $m\angle DAE = m\angle BCE = 180° - (68° + x) = 112° - x$.

$$\frac{\sin x}{3.81} = \frac{\sin (112^\circ - x)}{2.11}$$

$$\frac{\sin x}{\sin (112^\circ - x)} = \frac{3.81}{2.11} \approx 1.81 \text{ cm}$$

By letting $Y_1 = \frac{\sin x}{\sin (112^\circ - x)}$ and using the table function of the graphing calculator, students can see that x is about 79°.

$$m\angle ADE = m\angle DBC \approx 79^\circ$$

$$m\angle DAE = m\angle BCE = (112^\circ - x) \approx 33^\circ$$

By applying the Law of Sines yet again, we see $\frac{\sin 79^\circ}{3.81} = \frac{\sin 68^\circ}{AD}$ and $AD = BC \approx 3.60$ cm.

Unit 1

Master 11

MASTER 11 — Transparency Master

Checkpoint

The Law of Sines states a relation among sides and angles of any triangle. It can be used to find unknown side lengths or angle measures from given information. Suppose you have modeled a problem situation with $\triangle PQR$ as shown below.

R, p, Q, q, r, P

a What combinations of information about the sides and angles of $\triangle PQR$ will allow you to find the length of $\overline{QR}$? How would you use that information to calculate $\overline{QR}$?

b What combinations of information about the sides and angles of $\triangle PQR$ will allow you to find the measure of $\angle Q$? How would you use that information to calculate $m\angle Q$?

Be prepared to explain your thinking to the entire class.

Use with page 31. UNIT 1 • MULTIPLE-VARIABLE MODELS

SHARE AND SUMMARIZE full-class discussion

Checkpoint

See Teaching Master 11.

If students seem unable to grasp the importance of the questions in this Checkpoint, it might help them to focus on the possible arrangements that will provide an answer for the length *p*. Write on the board the Law of Sines, $\frac{p}{\sin P} = \frac{q}{\sin Q} = \frac{r}{\sin R}$ and then the useful forms $\frac{p}{\sin P} = \frac{q}{\sin Q}$ and $\frac{p}{\sin P} = \frac{r}{\sin R}$, and ask students to think about how these last two equations could be solved for *p*.

a In general, you need to know the measures of $\angle P$ and one other angle, along with the length of the side opposite this other angle. In other words, you can solve for p if you know $\angle P$, $\angle Q$, and side q, or if you know $\angle P$, $\angle R$, and side r:

$$p = q\frac{\sin P}{\sin Q}$$

$$p = r\frac{\sin P}{\sin R}$$

b You need to know the measures of side q, another angle, and the side opposite that angle:

$$m\angle Q = \sin^{-1}\left(q\frac{\sin R}{r}\right)$$

$$m\angle Q = \sin^{-1}\left(q\frac{\sin P}{p}\right)$$

Unless the sine of an angle is 1, there are always two angles less than 180° that have the same sine value. (If one is *x*, the other is 180° − *x*.) So there may be two possibilities for m∠*Q*. This is the *ambiguous case* for the Law of Sines. It is best not to discuss this at this time, unless one of your students mentions it. The Law of Sines, including the ambiguous case, will be explored further in Unit 4, "Shapes and Geometric Reasoning."

CONSTRUCTING A MATH TOOLKIT: Students should include the Law of Sines in their Math Toolkits. They should also indicate the circumstances under which the Law of Sines will help determine the lengths of sides and measures of angles in a triangle.

Group Processing Suggestions

- How did your group make sure your responses to activities made sense?
- Discuss with your group ways to encourage each other to ask questions when something is confusing.

APPLY individual task

On Your Own

The distances can be determined using the Law of Sines.

Beverly: $\frac{\sin 26°}{25} = \frac{\sin 73°}{x}$

$x = \frac{25 \sin 73°}{\sin 26°}$

$x \approx 54.54$ km

Boston: $\frac{\sin 26°}{25} = \frac{\sin 81°}{x}$

$x = \frac{25 \sin 81°}{\sin 26°}$

$x \approx 56.33$ km

The plane is about 54.54 km from the Beverly airport.

MORE ASSIGNMENT *pp. 40–45*

Students can now begin Modeling Task 2 or Extending Task 2 from the MORE assignment following Investigation 4.

Checkpoint

The Law of Sines states a relation among sides and angles of any triangle. It can be used to find unknown side lengths or angle measures from given information. Suppose you have modeled a situation with ΔPQR as shown below.

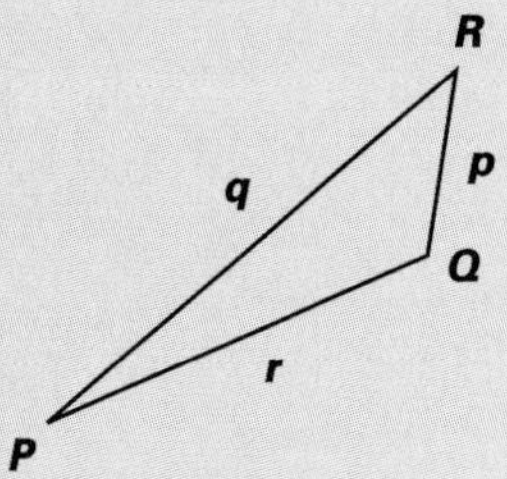

a What combinations of information about the sides and angles of ΔPQR will allow you to find the length of $\overline{QR}$? How would you use that information to calculate QR?

b What combinations of information about the sides and angles of ΔPQR will allow you to find the measure of $\angle Q$? How would you use that information to calculate $m\angle Q$?

Be prepared to explain your thinking to the entire class.

On Your Own

A commuter airplane, off course over the Atlantic Ocean, reported experiencing mechanical problems around 9:15 P.M. The pilot sent two calls, one to Boston Logan International Airport and one to the regional airport in nearby Beverly. Air traffic controllers at the two airports reported the angles shown in the diagram below. How far was the plane from the closer airport?

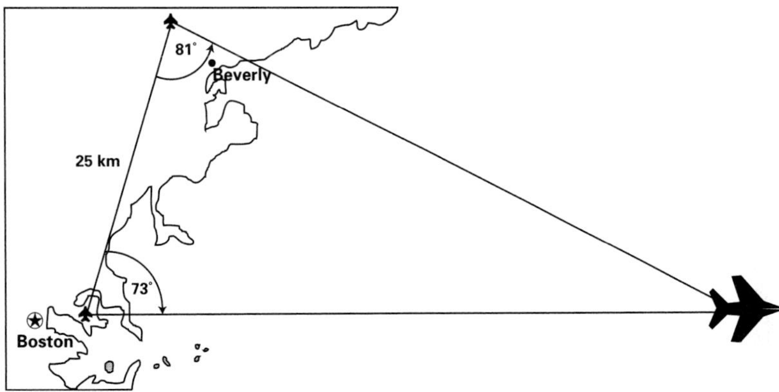

LESSON 2 • ALGEBRA, GEOMETRY, AND TRIGONOMETRY 31

INVESTIGATION 3 The Law of Cosines

For all right triangles, the Pythagorean Theorem shows how the lengths of the two legs and the hypotenuse are related to each other. When that relationship is expressed as an equation, it is possible to solve for any one of the variables in terms of the others. It's natural to wonder what is so special about right triangles and how the relationship among the sides changes as the right angle changes to an acute or obtuse angle.

1. Consider a linkage with two sides of fixed length: 12 cm and 16 cm. Here $AC = 12$ cm and $BC = 16$ cm.

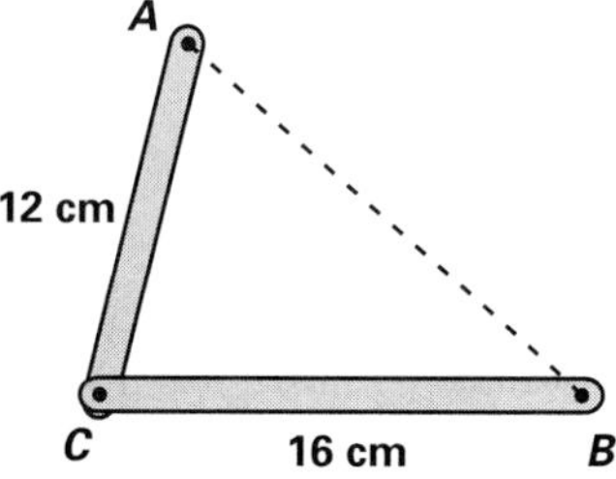

a. What is the distance from A to B when the angle at C is a right angle?

b. How does the distance from A to B change as $\overline{AC}$ is rotated to make smaller and smaller angles at C? How does that distance change if $\overline{AC}$ is rotated to make larger angles at C?

2. Using an actual physical linkage or careful drawings, test your answers to Activity 1 by carefully measuring the distance from point A to point B in these cases:

a. $m\angle C = 30°$

b. $m\angle C = 70°$

c. $m\angle C = 130°$

d. $m\angle C = 150°$

3. Why is it impossible to check the measured distances in Activity 2 by calculations using the Law of Sines, without getting more information?

There is a second trigonometric principle for finding relationships among side lengths and angle measures of any triangle. It is called the **Law of Cosines**.

In any triangle ABC with sides of lengths a, b, and c opposite ∠A, ∠B, and ∠C, respectively:

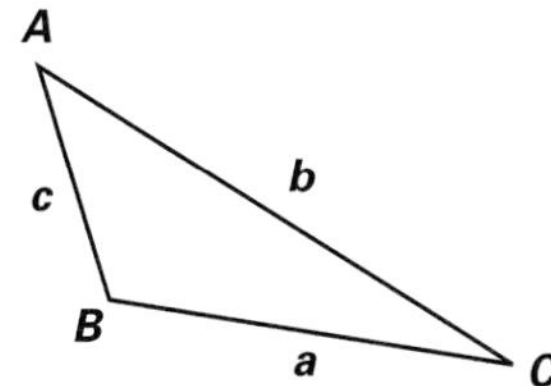

$$c^2 = a^2 + b^2 - 2ab \cos C$$

This is another of those very useful equations that link several geometric variables.

32 UNIT 1 • MULTIPLE-VARIABLE MODELS

EXPLORE small-group investigation

INVESTIGATION 3 The Law of Cosines

Unit 1

This investigation introduces the Law of Cosines, without derivation. In Activities 1, 2, and 7, students use experimentation to see that the Pythagorean relationship can be adjusted for non-right triangles. The Law of Cosines is explored as a multiple-variable relationship in which you need to know specific combinations of variables to solve for the required variable. The Law of Cosines will be derived in Unit 3, "Symbol Sense and Algebraic Reasoning." In Unit 4, "Shapes and Geometric Reasoning" the ambiguous case of the Law of Sines will be addressed.

Before students begin this investigation, you may wish to help students recall that the sum of measures of the angles of a parallelogram is 360° and that the area of a triangle is one-half the length of the base times the height.

NOTE: Students will need a 12 cm and a 16 cm linkage strip for this investigation.

1. **a.** $c = \sqrt{16^2 + 12^2} = 20$ cm

b. As $\overline{AC}$ is rotated to make smaller angles, the distance from A to B gets smaller until it is finally 4 cm when point A is located on $\overline{BC}$. If $\overline{AC}$ is rotated to make larger angles at C, then the distance from A to B gets larger until it is finally equal to 28 cm when point A is located on line BC.

2. Since the students are measuring these sides from their drawings or physical model, their answers will be approximations.

a. $AB \approx 8.2$ cm

b. $AB \approx 16.4$ cm

c. $AB \approx 25.4$ cm

d. $AB \approx 27.1$ cm

3. It is not possible to check these measurements directly using the Law of Sines because only one angle measure is known. In order to solve for a side length using the Law of Sines, it is necessary to know two angle measures and one side length.

NOTE: It is important that students realize that the Law of Sines is useful only with certain arrangements of sides and angles. If a group seems to be having difficulty here, they probably did not develop a deep understanding at the Checkpoint on page 31 about combinations of information needed. Prompt groups by asking them to make and label a diagram corresponding to at least one of the parts of Activity 2. Then suggest they try to use the Law of Sines.

Unit 1

EXPLORE *continued*

4. **a.** Find the sum of the square of a and the square of b. From that sum, subtract the product $2ab \cos C$. Then you must take the square root of the resulting value.

   b. $a^2 = b^2 + c^2 - 2bc \cos A$

   c. $b^2 = a^2 + c^2 - 2ac \cos B$

   d. You need to know the measure of the angle opposite $\overline{QR}$ (which is $\angle P$) and the lengths q and r. The equation would be $p^2 = q^2 + r^2 - 2qr \cos P$.

   e. Yes, you can find the length of $\overline{PR}$. First find $m\angle Q$ by subtracting the sum $m\angle P + m\angle R$ from 180°. Then use the Law of Cosines written in the form $q^2 = r^2 + p^2 - 2rp \cos Q$.

   f. Again find $m\angle Q$ by subtraction: $180° - m\angle P - m\angle R$. Then $q = \frac{p \sin Q}{\sin P}$ or $q = \frac{r \sin Q}{\sin R}$. Student responses may vary regarding their preferred method, but they should support their decisions.

4. The Law of Cosines states a relation among the lengths of three sides of a triangle and the cosine of an angle of the triangle. If you know the lengths of two sides and the measure of the angle between the two sides, you can calculate the length of the third side.

   a. State in words how you would calculate the length c in $\triangle ABC$ if you know a, b, and the measure of $\angle C$.

   b. Write the Law of Cosines to calculate the length a in $\triangle ABC$ if you know b, c, and the measure of $\angle A$.

   c. Write a third form of the Law of Cosines for $\triangle ABC$, for when you know the measure of $\angle B$.

   d. Suppose in $\triangle PQR$ you needed to calculate the length of $\overline{QR}$. What information would you need in order to use the Law of Cosines? Write the equation you would use.

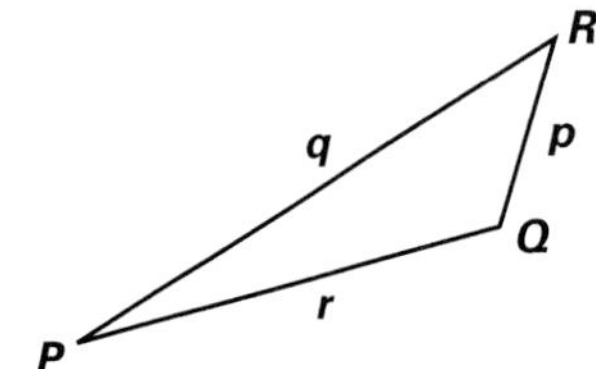

   e. Suppose in $\triangle PQR$ you knew $m\angle P$, $m\angle R$, and the lengths p and r. Could you find the length q using the Law of Cosines? Explain your reasoning.

   f. Using the information given in Part e, how could you find the length q using the Law of Sines? Which method would you prefer to use? Why?

5. Surveyors often are faced with irregular polygonal regions for which they are asked to locate and stake out boundaries, determine elevations, and estimate areas. Some of these tasks can be accomplished by using a site map and a transit as shown in the photo below. In one subdivision of property near a midsize city, a plot of land had the shape and dimensions shown.

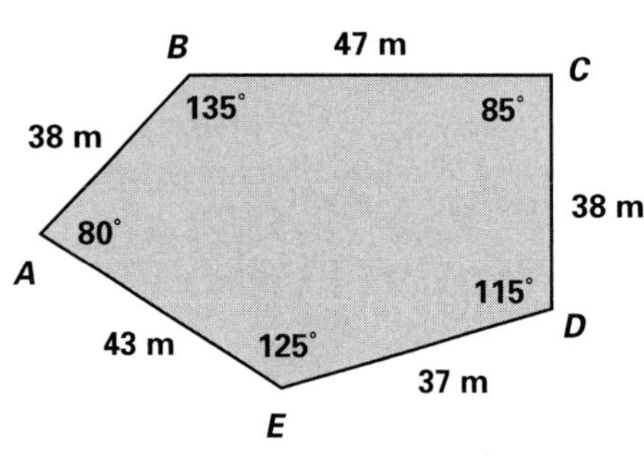

LESSON 2 • ALGEBRA, GEOMETRY, AND TRIGONOMETRY 33

Examine the triangulation of the plot shown below.

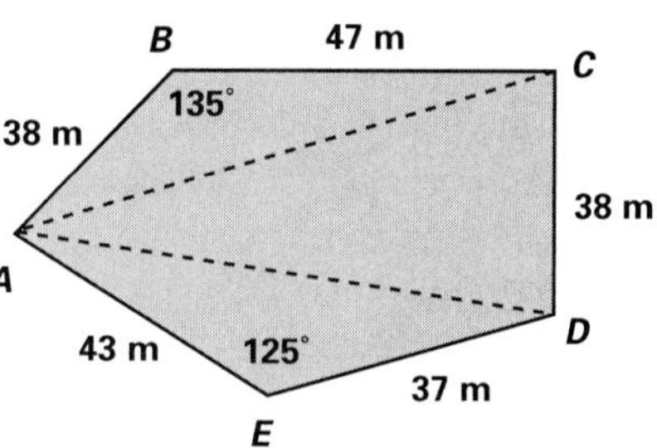

a. How can the Law of Cosines be used to find AC?

b. Find AC to the nearest tenth of a meter.

c. How can the Law of Cosines be used to find AD?

d. Find AD to the nearest tenth of a meter.

6. The Law of Cosines, $c^2 = a^2 + b^2 - 2ab\cos C$, states a relation among the lengths of three sides of a triangle ABC and the cosine of an angle of the triangle. If you know the lengths of all three sides of a triangle, you can calculate the cosine of an angle and then determine the measure of the angle itself.

   a. Solve the equation $c^2 = a^2 + b^2 - 2ab\cos C$ for $\cos C$.

   b. Using your results from Activity 5, find the measure of $\angle BAC$ to the nearest tenth of a degree. What is the measure of the third angle in $\triangle ABC$?

   c. Now find the area of $\triangle ABC$.

   d. Explain how you could determine the area of the entire pentagonal plot.

7. Now that you understand how to use the Law of Cosines, examine more closely its symbolic form and the information it conveys. Consider again the linkage with arms of lengths 12 cm and 16 cm positioned at various possible angles.

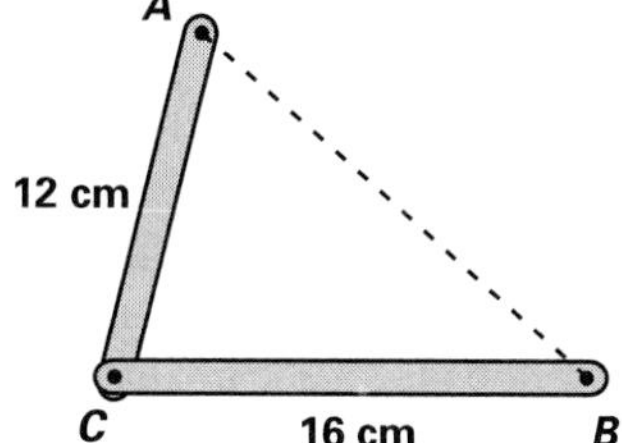

   a. Record your data from Activity 2 in a copy of the table below. Then, using a physical linkage or careful drawings, complete the remainder of your table, showing how the distance from the end of one arm to the other changes as the angle at link point C changes.

m∠*C*	30°	50°	70°	90°	110°	130°	150°
Length *AB*							

34 UNIT 1 • MULTIPLE-VARIABLE MODELS

5. a. To find AC, first select the appropriate version of the Law of Cosines. It helps to label the illustration so it is clear which segments are to be used. In this case, $BC = a$, $AC = b$, and $AB = c$. Use $\angle B$.

$AC^2 = a^2 + c^2 - 2ac \cos B$

$AC^2 = 47^2 + 38^2 - 2(47)(38) \cos 135°$

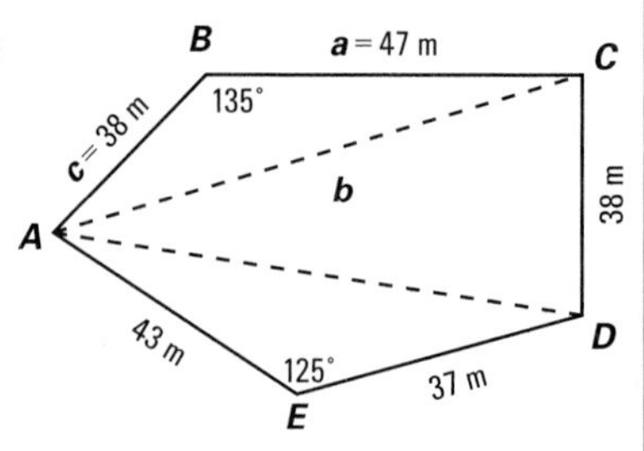

b. $AC^2 = 47^2 + 38^2 - 2(47)(38) \cos 135°$

$AC^2 \approx 6{,}178.79 \text{ m}^2$

$AC \approx 78.6 \text{ m}$

c. Using the two sides $\overline{AE}$ and $\overline{ED}$ and the angle E in the Law of Cosines, we get the equation $AD^2 = 43^2 + 37^2 - 2(43)(37) \cos 125°$.

d. $AD^2 = 43^2 + 37^2 - 2(43)(37) \cos 125°$

$AD^2 \approx 5{,}043.12 \text{ m}^2$

$AD \approx 71.0 \text{ m}$

6. a. $\cos C = \dfrac{c^2 - a^2 - b^2}{-2ab}$ or

$\cos C = \dfrac{a^2 + b^2 - c^2}{2ab}$

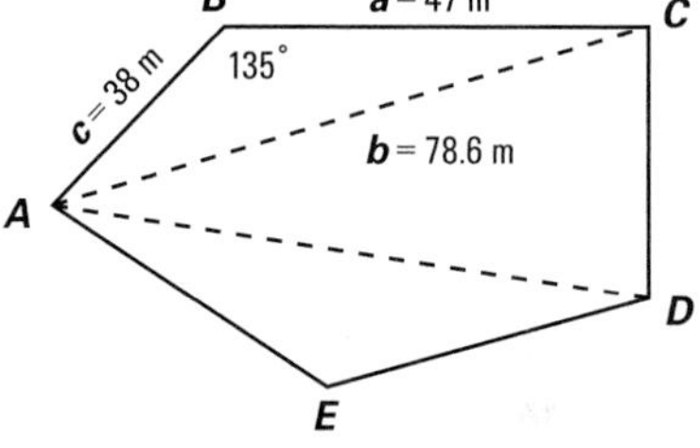

b. $a^2 = b^2 + c^2 - 2bc \cos (\angle BAC)$

$\cos (\angle BAC) = \dfrac{a^2 - b^2 - c^2}{-2bc}$

$\cos (\angle BAC) = \dfrac{47^2 - 78.6^2 - 38^2}{-2(78.6)(38)}$

$\cos (\angle BAC) \approx 0.906$

$m\angle BAC \approx 25.0°$

$m\angle BCA \approx 180° - 135° - 25° \approx 20.0°$

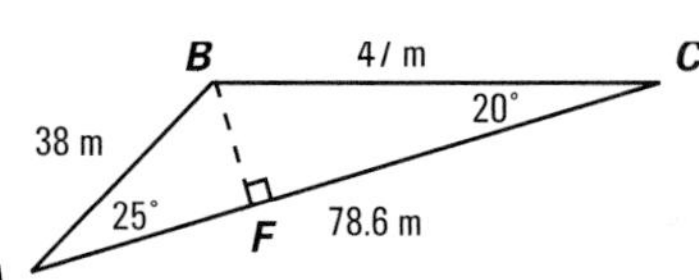

c. To find the area of $\triangle ABC$, you must find the length of an altitude. For example, add a point F to form the altitude, $\overline{BF}$, from vertex B to side AC. The length BF can be found using the equation $\sin 25° = \frac{BF}{38}$. So $BF = 38 \sin 25° \approx 16.06$ m. Thus, the area of $\triangle ABC$ is $\frac{1}{2}(78.6)(16.06)$, or approximately 631.16 square meters.

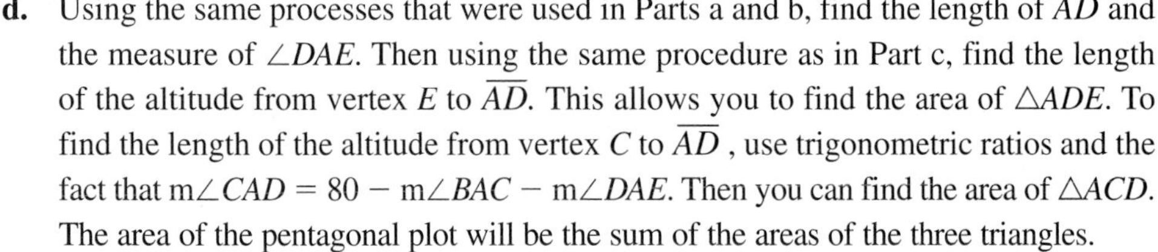

d. Using the same processes that were used in Parts a and b, find the length of $\overline{AD}$ and the measure of $\angle DAE$. Then using the same procedure as in Part c, find the length of the altitude from vertex E to $\overline{AD}$. This allows you to find the area of $\triangle ADE$. To find the length of the altitude from vertex C to $\overline{AD}$, use trigonometric ratios and the fact that $m\angle CAD = 80 - m\angle BAC - m\angle DAE$. Then you can find the area of $\triangle ACD$. The area of the pentagonal plot will be the sum of the areas of the three triangles.

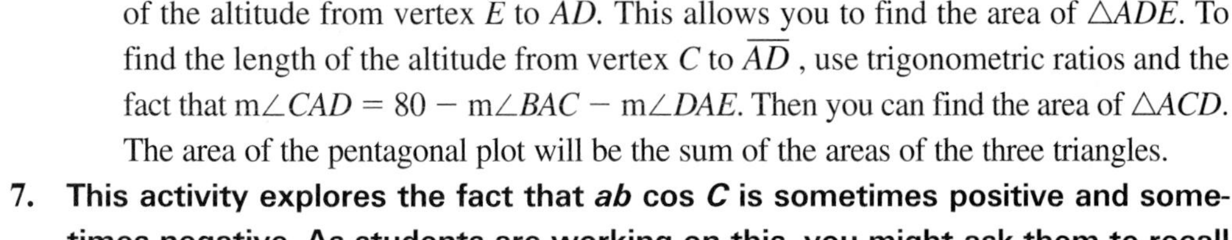

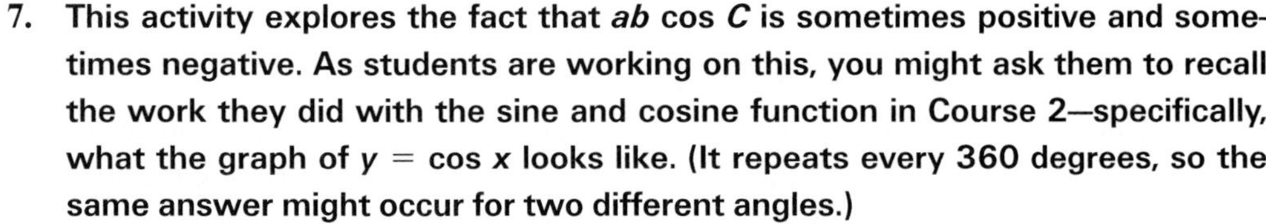

7. This activity explores the fact that *ab* cos *C* is sometimes positive and sometimes negative. As students are working on this, you might ask them to recall the work they did with the sine and cosine function in Course 2—specifically, what the graph of *y* = cos *x* looks like. (It repeats every 360 degrees, so the same answer might occur for two different angles.)

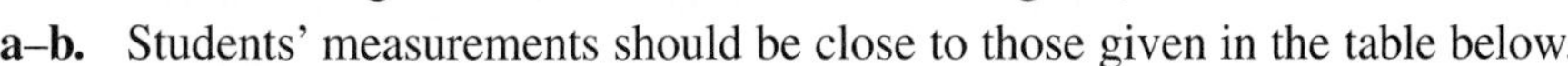

a–b. Students' measurements should be close to those given in the table below.

Distance from *A* to *B*

$m\angle C$	30°	50°	70°	90°	110°	130°	150°
Length *AB* (cm)	8.2	12.4	16.4	20	23.1	25.4	27.1
2*ab* cos *C*	332.6	246.8	131.3	0	−131.3	−246.8	−332.6

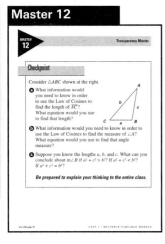

Master 12

MASTER 12 Transparency Master

Checkpoint

Consider $\triangle ABC$ shown at the right.

a. What information would you need to know in order to use the Law of Cosines to find the length of $\overline{AC}$? What equation would you use to find that length?

b. What information would you need to know in order to use the Law of Cosines to find the measure of $\angle A$? What equation would you use to find that angle measure?

c. Suppose you know the lengths a, b, and c. What can you conclude about $m\angle B$ if $a^2 + c^2 > b^2$? If $a^2 + c^2 < b^2$? If $a^2 + c^2 = b^2$?

Be prepared to explain your thinking to the entire class.

EXPLORE *continued*

7. c. When $m\angle C = 90°$, $\cos C = 0$. Therefore the term $2ab \cos C$ would be equal to 0 so $c^2 = a^2 + b^2$. Notice that this is the Pythagorean Theorem.

d. For angles less than 90°, the side opposite will be shorter than the hypotenuse of the right triangle and therefore $|2ab \cos C|$ is subtracted. For angles greater than 90°, the side opposite will be longer than the hypotenuse of the right triangle and therefore $|2ab \cos C|$ is added. Note in the table that when $m\angle C$ is greater than 90°, the values for $2ab \cos C$ are negative. Remember that in the Law of Cosines, $2ab \cos C$ is *subtracted* from $a^2 + b^2$, and consequently, for angles greater than 90°, in order to add a value, it is necessary to subtract the negative value.

8. a.

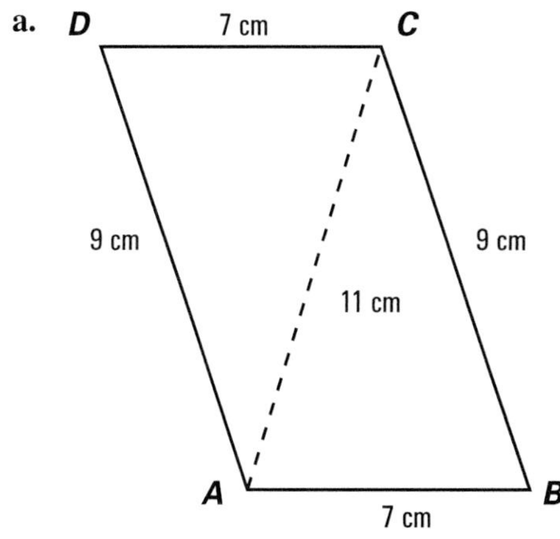

b. In this figure, you only know the lengths of the three sides, and therefore you would have to use the Law of Cosines to determine an angle measure.

c. Students may choose any angle in the triangle. For example, $m\angle B$ can be found using the equation $11^2 = 7^2 + 9^2 - 2(7)(9) \cos B$.

$$11^2 = 7^2 + 9^2 - 2(7)(9) \cos B$$

$$\cos B = \frac{11^2 - 7^2 - 9^2}{-2(7)(9)} \approx 0.0714285714$$

$$m\angle B \approx 85.9°$$

d. Students can use the Law of Sines to find another angle in the triangle in Part c. An example is given.

$$\frac{\sin 85.9°}{11} = \frac{\sin \angle ACB}{7}$$

$$\sin \angle ACB \approx 0.6347$$

$$m\angle ACB \approx 39.4°$$

After the second angle measure has been found, the remainder of the angles can be determined by applying simple relationships. For example, the sum of the angles of a triangle is 180°, so $m\angle BAC \approx 54.7°$. Then, since a parallelogram has 180° rotational symmetry, $m\angle ACD = m\angle BAC \approx 54.7°$, $m\angle CAD = m\angle ACB \approx 39.4°$, and $m\angle ADC = m\angle ABC \approx 85.9°$.

e. The following uses the Law of Cosines to find the length of diagonal BD.

$BD^2 = AD^2 + AB^2 - 2(AD)(AB) \cos (\angle DAB)$

$BD^2 = 9^2 + 7^2 - 2(9)(7) \cos (94.1°)$

$BD^2 \approx 139$

$BD \approx 11.8$ cm

CONSTRUCTING A MATH TOOLKIT: Students should record the Law of Cosines in their Math Toolkits along with an illustration. Ask students to summarize how it can be used to find missing parts of a triangle, given various sets of three parts of the triangle. You also might ask students to identify a set of three parts of a triangle for which they cannot use the Law of Cosines to determine the missing parts (one side, two angles), and note that the Law of Sines could be used in this case.

See additional Teaching Notes on page T90H.

b. Now add a row to your table from Part a showing corresponding values of $2ab \cos C$.

$m\angle C$	30°	50°	70°	90°	110°	130°	150°
Length *AB*							
2*ab* cos *C*							

c. What is $\cos C$ when $m\angle C = 90°$, and how does that simplify the equation for the Law of Cosines?

d. In what sense does the term "$2ab\cos C$" act as a *correction term*, adjusting the Pythagorean relationship for triangles in which $\angle C$ is not a right angle?

8. As you have seen, the Law of Sines and the Law of Cosines can be used to find the measures of unknown angles as well as sides. You have to study given information about side and angle measurements to decide which law to apply. Then you have to work with the resulting equations to solve for the unknown angle or side measurements.

For example, suppose that two sides, $\overline{AB}$ and $\overline{BC}$, and a diagonal, $\overline{AC}$, of a parallelogram *ABCD* measure 7 cm, 9 cm, and 11 cm, respectively.

a. Draw and label a sketch of such a figure.

b. Which of the two trigonometric laws can be used to find the measure of an angle in that parallelogram?

c. Find the measure of an angle to the nearest tenth of a degree.

d. The diagonal *AC* splits the parallelogram *ABCD* into two triangles. Find the remaining measures of the angles in those triangles.

e. Find the length of diagonal *BD*.

Checkpoint

Consider $\triangle ABC$ shown at the right.

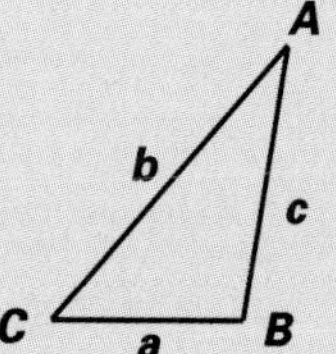

a What information would you need to know in order to use the Law of Cosines to find the length of $\overline{AC}$? What equation would you use to find that length?

b What information would you need to know in order to use the Law of Cosines to find the measure of $\angle A$? What equation would you use to find that angle measure?

c Suppose you know the lengths a, b, and c. What can you conclude about $m\angle B$ if $a^2 + c^2 > b^2$? If $a^2 + c^2 < b^2$? If $a^2 + c^2 = b^2$?

Be prepared to explain your thinking to the entire class.

LESSON 2 • ALGEBRA, GEOMETRY, AND TRIGONOMETRY 35

On Your Own

A surveyor with transit at point *A* sights points *B* and *C* on either side of Asylum Pond. She finds the measure of the angle between the sightings to be 72°.

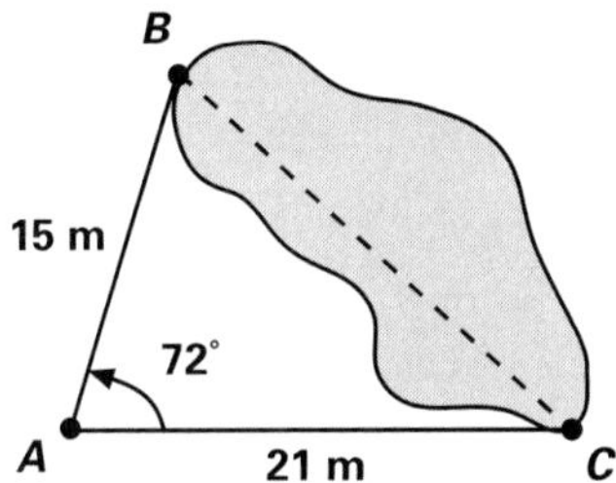

a. Find, to nearest tenth of a meter, the distance *BC* across the pond.

b. Find m∠*B* and m∠*C*.

INVESTIGATION 4 Solving for ...

The Pythagorean relationship, the trigonometric relationships in right triangles, the Law of Sines, and the Law of Cosines all express important connections between side and angle measurements in triangles. Those connections are given by equations involving several variables. The solutions of problems involving those connections often require rewriting the equations so that one of the variables is expressed in terms of the others.

"THIS IS THE PART I ALWAYS HATE."

As you have worked on other problems involving several variables, you have discovered and applied strategies that use several basic properties of numbers and equations. These properties can help you avoid the dilemma suggested in the above cartoon.

36 UNIT 1 • MULTIPLE-VARIABLE MODELS

APPLY individual task

On Your Own

a. $BC = \sqrt{21^2 + 15^2 - 2(21)(15)\cos 72^\circ}$

$BC \approx 21.7$ m

b. $\frac{\sin B}{21} = \frac{\sin 72^\circ}{21.7}$

$\sin B \approx 0.92038$

$m\angle B \approx 67^\circ$

$m\angle C \approx 180^\circ - (67^\circ + 72^\circ)$

$m\angle C \approx 41^\circ$

MORE

ASSIGNMENT pp. 40–45

Students can now begin work on Modeling Task 1, 4, or 5 or Extending Task 1 or 4 from the MORE assignment following Investigation 4.

EXPLORE small-group investigation

INVESTIGATION 4 Solving for ...

This investigation summarizes the work students have done with rewriting relationships. Informal explanations of why it makes sense that two arrangements are really the same relationship are replaced by formal ideas about inverse relationships and properties of equality. Some students may consider this irrelevant. If they already understand from their work with examples that $a = \frac{bc}{d}$ is equivalent to $b = \frac{ad}{c}$, they are unlikely to be impressed by the rules. For some students, there is satisfaction in seeing the logic of what can and cannot be done, and the consistency with which the application of the properties will unravel any equation.

Note that commutativity, associativity, and the multiplicative and additive identities are sometimes used without drawing much attention to them. You may want to review these ideas with your students. However, most students will be comfortable with these ideas, and the emphasis here should be on the operations and properties listed on page 37.

EXPLORE *continued*

1. **Students should find it fairly easy to give numerical examples, but they might have difficulty putting the patterns into words. Encourage them to help each other. Also help them to realize that there are many right answers or ways to say the same thing. In order to have consistency within this *Teacher's Guide*, we have given titles (in bold) to the operations and properties, but your students may wish to use their own words. In either case, be sure they are communicating the proper ideas.**

- **Inverse Operations**

  Inverse of Addition or Subtraction: $p + q = r$ is equivalent to $p = r - q$.

  a. $3 + 2 = 5$ is equivalent to $3 = 5 - 2$
  $10 + 2 = 12$ is equivalent to $10 = 12 - 2$
  $7 + 9 = 16$ is equivalent to $7 = 16 - 9$

  b. If two numbers are added together to equal a third number, then the first (or second) number is equal to the difference of the second (or first) number subtracted from the third.

  Inverse of Division or Multiplication: $p \div q = r$ is equivalent to $p = r \cdot q$ (if $q \neq 0$).

  a. $15 \div 5 = 3$ is equivalent to $15 = 3 \cdot 5$
  $36 \div 4 = 9$ is equivalent to $36 = 9 \cdot 4$
  $20 \div 10 = 2$ is equivalent to $20 = 2 \cdot 10$

  b. If a first number divided by a second number equals a third number, then the first number equals the product of the second and third numbers.

  Inverse of Squaring: $\sqrt{p^2} = p$ (if $p \geq 0$).

  a. $\sqrt{6^2} = 6$
  $\sqrt{10^2} = 10$
  $\sqrt{7^2} = 7$

  b. The square root of a squared number is equivalent to that number when the original number is not negative.

- **Properties of Equality**

  Addition Property of Equality: If $p = q$, then $p + r = q + r$.

  a. $5 + 2 = \frac{10}{2} + 2$
  $24 + 6 = (12)(2) + 6$
  $\frac{12}{3} + 10 = 4 + 10$

  b. Adding the same number to both sides of an equation maintains equality.

  Subtraction Property of Equality: If $p = q$, then $p - r = q - r$.

  a. $10 - 3 = (5 \cdot 2) - 3$
  $16 - 6 = \frac{32}{2} - 6$
  $19 - 2 = (10 + 9) - 2$

  b. Subtracting the same number from both sides of an equation maintains equality.

  Multiplication Property of Equality: If $p = q$, then $p \cdot r = q \cdot r$.

  a. $6 \cdot 2 = (3 \cdot 2) \cdot 2$
  $50 \cdot 10 = (5 \cdot 10) \cdot 10$
  $8 \cdot 5 = \frac{16}{2} \cdot 5$

  b. Multiplying both sides of an equation by the same number maintains equality.

See additional Teaching Notes on page T90I.

- **Inverse Operations** make use of three arithmetic principles.

  For any numbers p, q, and r:

  $p + q = r$ *is equivalent to* $p = r - q$

  $p \div q = r$ *is equivalent to* $p = r \cdot q$ *(if $q \neq 0$)*

  If $p \geq 0$, then $\sqrt{p^2} = p$.

- **Properties of Equality** justify the following operations on equations.

  For any numbers p, q, and r, if $p = q$, then:

  $p + r = q + r$

  $p - r = q - r$

  $p \cdot r = q \cdot r$

  $p \div r = q \div r$ *(if $r \neq 0$)*

  Also, if $p = q$ and $p, q \geq 0$, then $\sqrt{p} = \sqrt{q}$.

1. For each of the given principles of inverse operations and properties of equality shown above, do the following:

a. Give several specific numerical examples illustrating the pattern.

b. Describe the pattern in words, without the use of letter symbols or equations.

In the following activities, you are asked to show how these principles can be applied to answer the questions that arise in working with side and angle relationships of geometric figures.

2. Study the following strategies for solving $c^2 = a^2 + b^2$ for a in terms of b and c, assuming each variable is greater than or equal to zero. Explain how inverse operations and properties of equality justify each step in the solution procedures.

a. Strategy 1

Start with $c^2 = a^2 + b^2$.

Step 1 $c^2 - b^2 = a^2$

Step 2 $\sqrt{c^2 - b^2} = \sqrt{a^2}$

Step 3 $\sqrt{c^2 - b^2} = a$

b. Strategy 2

Start with $c^2 = a^2 + b^2$.

Step 1 $c^2 - b^2 = a^2 + b^2 - b^2$

Step 2 $c^2 - b^2 = a^2$

Step 3 $\sqrt{c^2 - b^2} = \sqrt{a^2}$

Step 4 $\sqrt{c^2 - b^2} = a$

LESSON 2 • ALGEBRA, GEOMETRY, AND TRIGONOMETRY 37

3. Study the following strategies for solving $\sin A = \frac{a}{c}$ for c in terms of a and $\sin A$. Explain how inverse operations and properties of equality justify each step in the solution procedures.

   a. **Strategy 1**

   Start with $\sin A = \frac{a}{c}$.

   Step 1 $c \sin A = a$

   Step 2 $c = \frac{a}{\sin A}$

   b. **Strategy 2**

   Start with $\sin A = \frac{a}{c}$.

   Step 1 $c \cdot \sin A = c \cdot \frac{a}{c}$

   Step 2 $c \cdot \sin A = a$

   Step 3 $c \cdot \sin A \div \sin A = a \div \sin A$

   Step 4 $c = a \div \sin A$

4. Show how to solve the equation $\frac{\sin A}{a} = \frac{\sin B}{b}$ for b in terms of a, $\sin A$, and $\sin B$. Justify each step of your reasoning.

5. Show how to solve the equation $c^2 = a^2 + b^2 - 2ab \cos C$ for $\cos C$ in terms of a, b, and c. Justify each step of your reasoning.

6. It is reported that when solving equations like $a^2 + b^2 = c^2$ for b in terms of a and c, beginning college students often reason as follows:

   $b^2 = c^2 - a^2$

   $b = \sqrt{c^2 - a^2}$

   $b = \sqrt{c^2} - \sqrt{a^2}$

   $b = c - a$

   a. Assuming a, b, and c are positive numbers, what is the error in this reasoning?

   b. What tips would you give to students to help them avoid this type of reasoning error?

The inverse operations and properties of equality strategies for manipulating trigonometric equations into equivalent and more useful forms also apply to equations modeling other relationships.

7. The perimeter P of any rectangle is related to its length L and width W by the formula $P = 2L + 2W$.

   a. Solve the given equation for W in terms of P and L, and be prepared to justify each step in your solution process.

   b. Explain how the new form of the equation could be helpful in exploring this problem: Find the dimensions of 20 rectangles that each have a perimeter of 500 meters.

38 UNIT 1 • MULTIPLE-VARIABLE MODELS

3. **a.** Start with $\sin A = \frac{a}{c}$.

Step 1: $c \sin A = a$ — Inverse of Division

Step 2: $c = \frac{a}{\sin A}$ — Inverse of Multiplication

b. Start with $\sin A = \frac{a}{c}$.

Step 1: $c \cdot \sin A = c \cdot \frac{a}{c}$ — Multiplication Property of Equality

Step 2: $c \cdot \sin A = a$ — Any number divided by itself is 1.

Step 3: $c \cdot \sin A \div \sin A = a \div \sin A$ — Division Property of Equality

Step 4: $c = a \div \sin A$ — Any number divided by itself is 1.

4. Student strategies may differ.

Start: $\frac{\sin A}{a} = \frac{\sin B}{b}$

Step 1: $b \cdot \frac{\sin A}{a} = \frac{\sin B}{b} \cdot b$ — Multiplication Property of Equality (and commutativity)

Step 2: $b \cdot \frac{\sin A}{a} = \sin B$ — Any number divided by itself is 1.

Step 3: $b \cdot \frac{\sin A}{a} \cdot \frac{a}{\sin A} = \sin B \cdot \frac{a}{\sin A}$ — Multiplication Property of Equality

Step 4: $b = \sin B \cdot \frac{a}{\sin A}$ — Any number multiplied by its reciprocal is 1.

5. Student strategies may differ.

Start: $c^2 = a^2 + b^2 - 2ab \cos C$

Step 1: $c^2 - a^2 - b^2 = -2ab \cos C$ — Inverse of Addition

Step 2: $\frac{c^2 - a^2 - b^2}{-2ab} = \frac{-2ab \cos C}{-2ab}$ — Division Property of Equality

Step 3: $\frac{c^2 - a^2 - b^2}{-2ab} = \cos C$ — Any number divided by itself is 1.

6. **a.** The error occurred when $\sqrt{c^2 - a^2}$ was simplified to $\sqrt{c^2} - \sqrt{a^2}$.

b. Responses may vary. One helpful thing that students can do is substitute numbers for the variables and check to see if the two expressions are equal. Students might also take a visual approach by drawing squares on a 3-4-5 right triangle and recognizing that since the order of squaring and adding or subtracting is not interchangeable, it makes sense that the order of addition or subtraction with taking a square root is not interchangeable.

7. **a.** Student strategies may differ.

Start: $P = 2L + 2W$

Step 1: $P - 2L = 2L - 2L + 2W$ — Subtraction Property of Equality

Step 2: $P - 2L = 2W$ — Adding opposites gives 0.

Step 3: $\frac{P - 2L}{2} = \frac{2W}{2}$ — Division Property of Equality

Step 4: $\frac{P - 2L}{2} = W$ — Any number divided by itself is 1.

b. If you substitute 500 for P, the new equation would give you the value of W for any value of L that you substitute into the equation. So you could enter the equation into a graphing calculator or computer software and set up a table to generate the length and width of 20 rectangles that have a perimeter of 500 meters.

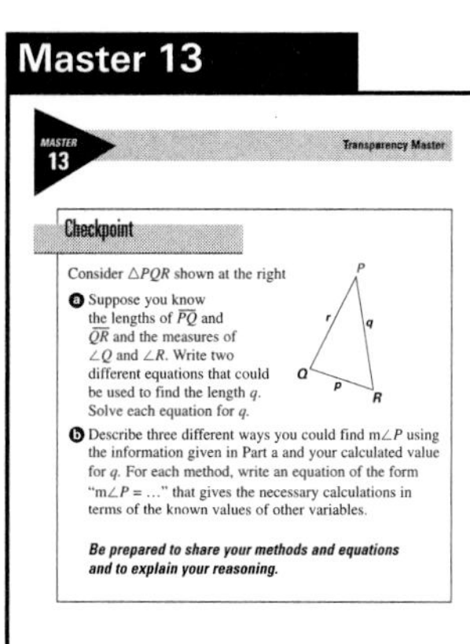
Master 13

MASTER 13 Transparency Master

Checkpoint

Consider $\triangle PQR$ shown at the right

ⓐ Suppose you know the lengths of $\overline{PQ}$ and $\overline{QR}$ and the measures of $\angle Q$ and $\angle R$. Write two different equations that could be used to find the length q. Solve each equation for q.

ⓑ Describe three different ways you could find m$\angle P$ using the information given in Part a and your calculated value for q. For each method, write an equation of the form "m$\angle P = \ldots$" that gives the necessary calculations in terms of the known values of other variables.

Be prepared to share your methods and equations and to explain your reasoning.

UNIT 1 • MULTIPLE-VARIABLE MODELS

EXPLORE *continued*

8. a. $c = \dfrac{5(0.89)}{3} \approx \$1.48$

This answer means that it will cost \$1.48 to buy 5 cans of the item.

$x = \dfrac{60(350)}{4} = 5{,}250$ ft

This means that an object that moves at 350 feet in 4 seconds will move 5,250 feet in 60 seconds or 5,250 feet per minute.

b.

$\dfrac{a}{x} = \dfrac{b}{c}$	Start
$a = x \cdot \dfrac{b}{c}$	Inverse of Division
$ac = xb$	Inverse of Division
$\dfrac{ac}{b} = x$	Inverse of Multiplication

c.

$\dfrac{a}{x} = \dfrac{b}{c}$	Start
$\dfrac{a}{x} \cdot x = \dfrac{b}{c} \cdot x$	Multiplication Property of Equality
$a = \dfrac{b}{c} \cdot x$	Any number divided by itself is 1.
$a \cdot \dfrac{c}{b} = \dfrac{b}{c} \cdot \dfrac{c}{b} \cdot x$	Multiplication Property of Equality (and commutativity)
$\dfrac{ac}{b} = x$	Any number multiplied by its reciprocal is 1.

SHARE AND SUMMARIZE full-class discussion

Checkpoint

See Teaching Master 13.

ⓐ Using the Law of Sines:

$$\frac{q}{\sin Q} = \frac{r}{\sin R}$$

$$q = \frac{r \sin Q}{\sin R}$$

Using the Law of Cosines:

$$q^2 = r^2 + p^2 - 2rp \cos Q$$

$$q = \sqrt{r^2 + p^2 - 2rp \cos Q}$$

ⓑ **i.** Use the sum of angles in a triangle: m$\angle P = 180^\circ -$ m$\angle R -$ m$\angle Q$

ii. Use the Law of Sines: m$\angle P = \sin^{-1}\left(\dfrac{p \sin R}{r}\right)$

iii. Use the Law of Cosines: m$\angle P = \cos^{-1}\left(\dfrac{p^2 - r^2 - q^2}{-2rq}\right)$

Group Processing Suggestions

- What questions were asked in your group today that helped you think more carefully or more deeply about an idea?
- Give an example of how your group tested your thinking during this investigation.

APPLY individual task

On Your Own

a. i. $\cos 25^\circ = \dfrac{WZ}{18}$

$WZ = 18 \cos 25^\circ$

$WZ \approx 16.3$ in.

ii. $\sin 65^\circ = \dfrac{WZ}{18}$

$WZ = 18 \sin 65^\circ$

$WZ \approx 16.3$ in.

See additional Teaching Notes on page T90I.

8. Many practical problems come in the form of simple proportions. For example:

$$\frac{3 \text{ cans}}{\$0.89} = \frac{5 \text{ cans}}{c \text{ dollars}} \quad \text{or} \quad \frac{350 \text{ ft}}{4 \text{ sec}} = \frac{x \text{ ft}}{60 \text{ sec}}$$

a. Solve each of these proportions and interpret your answers.

b. Show how inverse operations can be used to solve the proportion $\frac{a}{x} = \frac{b}{c}$ for x. Assume $a, b, c \neq 0$.

c. Show how properties of equality also can be used to solve the proportion in Part b.

Checkpoint

Consider $\triangle PQR$ shown at the right.

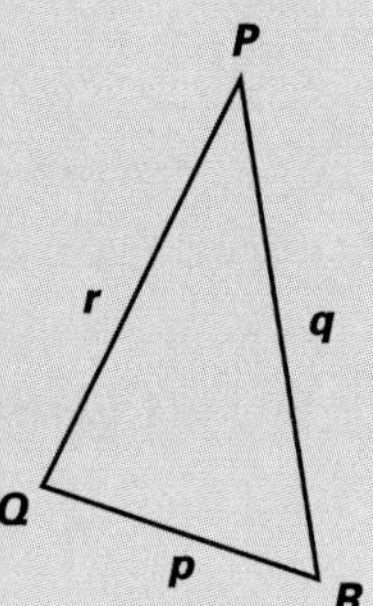

a Suppose you know the lengths of $\overline{PQ}$ and $\overline{QR}$ and the measures of $\angle Q$ and $\angle R$. Write two different equations that could be used to find the length q. Solve each equation for q.

b Describe three different ways you could find m$\angle P$ using the information given in Part a and your calculated value for q. For each method, write an equation of the form "m$\angle P$ = ..." that gives the necessary calculations in terms of the known values of other variables.

Be prepared to share your methods and equations and to explain your reasoning.

On Your Own

In rectangle $WXYZ$ shown here, information is given about a diagonal and an angle it forms with a side.

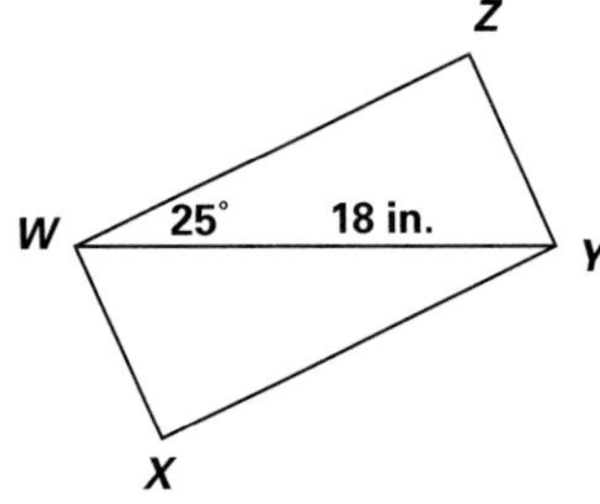

a. Write two different equations that could be used to find the length WZ. Solve each equation for WZ.

b. Using the given information and your answer to Part a, write three different equations that could be used to find the length ZY. Solve each equation for ZY.

LESSON 2 • ALGEBRA, GEOMETRY, AND TRIGONOMETRY 39

MORE Modeling • Organizing • Reflecting • Extending

Modeling

1. Two lighthouses A and B are 50 km apart. At 2 A.M., a freighter moving parallel to line AB is sighted at point C as shown in the diagram below.

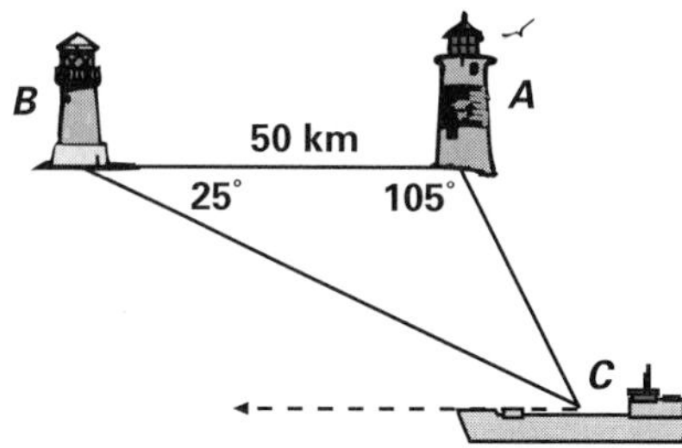

   a. How far is the freighter from lighthouse B? From lighthouse A?

   b. At 3 A.M., the angle at A is 86°. The angle at B is 29°. How far is the freighter from lighthouse B? From lighthouse A?

   c. How far has the freighter moved in the hour?

2. A pilot flying out of Chicago gets word that a major thunderstorm is directly in his plane's path. The pilot turns 35° to the right of his intended course and continues on this new flight path. After avoiding the worst of the storm, he turns 45° to the left of the new course and flies until returning to his original intended line of flight. The plane reaches its original intended course at a point 80 kilometers from the start of the detour.

   a. Draw a sketch of this situation.

   b. How much farther did the aircraft travel due to the detour?

40 UNIT 1 • MULTIPLE-VARIABLE MODELS

MORE independent assignment

Modeling

1. a. $\frac{BC}{\sin 105^\circ} = \frac{50}{\sin 50^\circ}$

$BC = \frac{50 \sin 105^\circ}{\sin 50^\circ} \approx 63.05$ km

The freighter is approximately 63.05 km from lighthouse B.

$\frac{AC}{\sin 25^\circ} = \frac{50}{\sin 50^\circ}$

$AC = \frac{50 \sin 25^\circ}{\sin 50^\circ} \approx 27.58$ km

The freighter is approximately 27.58 km from lighthouse A.

b. $\frac{BC}{\sin 86^\circ} = \frac{50}{\sin 65^\circ}$

$BC = \frac{50 \sin 86^\circ}{\sin 65^\circ} \approx 55.03$ km

The freighter is approximately 55.03 km from lighthouse B.

$\frac{AC}{\sin 29^\circ} = \frac{50}{\sin 65^\circ}$

$AC = \frac{50 \sin 29^\circ}{\sin 65^\circ} \approx 26.75$ km

The freighter is approximately 26.75 km from lighthouse A.

c. From Parts a and b, the lengths of the segments that form the 4° angle (see the diagram on the right) are 63.05 km and 55.03 km. Therefore,

$b = \sqrt{55.03^2 + 63.05^2 - 2(55.03)(63.05) \cos 4^\circ} \approx 9.01$ km.

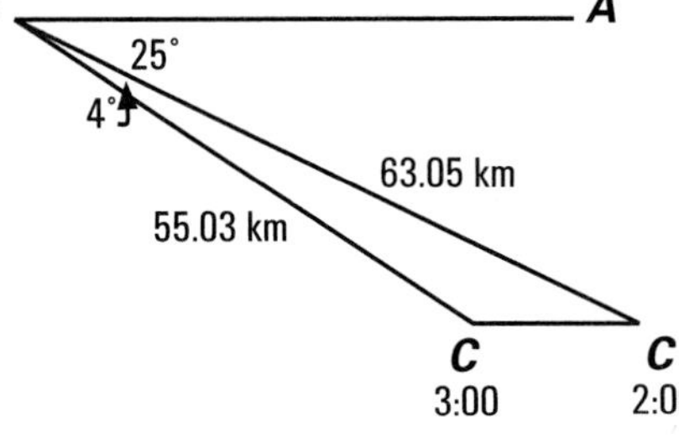

2. a. The pilot is flying from point A to the destination at point C.

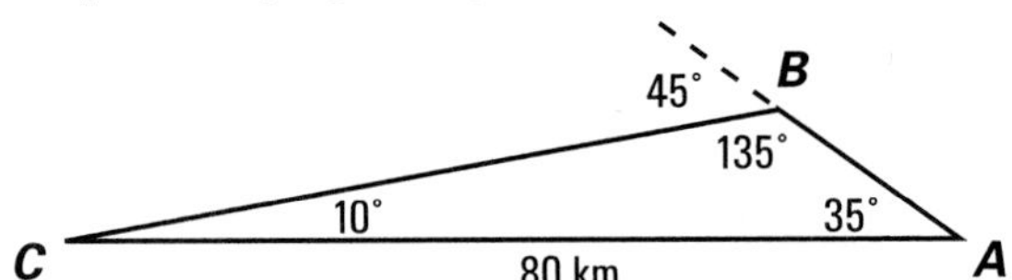

b. 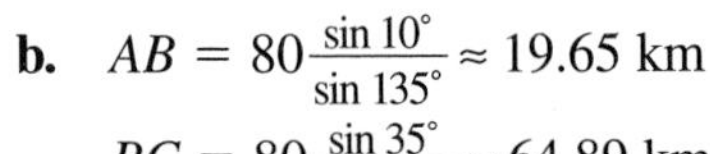

$AB = 80\frac{\sin 10^\circ}{\sin 135^\circ} \approx 19.65$ km

$BC = 80\frac{\sin 35^\circ}{\sin 135^\circ} \approx 64.89$ km

Extra travel distance ≈ 19.65 km + 64.89 km − 80 km ≈ 4.54 km

---

MORE ASSIGNMENT pp. 40–45

Modeling: 1 or 5, or 2 and 4*

Organizing: 1, and 3 or 4*

Reflecting: 2

Extending: Choose one*

**When choice is indicated, it is important to leave the choice to the student.*

NOTE: *It is best if Organizing tasks are discussed as a whole class after they have been assigned as homework.*

MORE *continued*

3. **a.** Students should be able to find all the angles utilizing the line symmetry across the perpendicular bisector of $\overline{AB}$ and only the following information:

(1) $m\angle BDC = m\angle ACD$
$m\angle ADB = m\angle BCA$
$m\angle CAB = m\angle DBA$

(2) The sum of the measure of the angles in a triangle is 180°.

(3) The sum of the measures of two adjacent angles along a line is 180°.

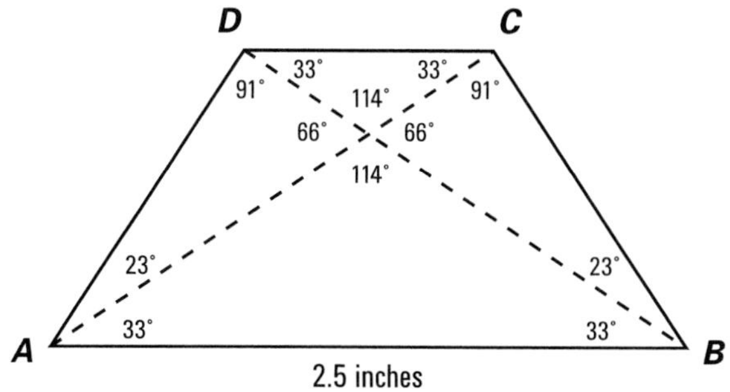

b. Use the Law of Sines to find *AD*, *BD*, and *DC* as shown below.

$\frac{AD}{\sin 33°} = \frac{2.5}{\sin 91°}$

$AD \approx 1.36$ inches

$\frac{BD}{\sin 56°} = \frac{2.5}{\sin 91°}$

$BD \approx 2.07$ inches

$\frac{DC}{\sin 23°} = \frac{1.36}{\sin 33°}$

$DC \approx 0.98$ inches

Then by symmetry we can find the rest of the lengths: $BC = AD \approx 1.36$ inches and $AC = BD \approx 2.07$ inches.

4. The largest angle is opposite the longest side.

Measure of the largest angle $= \cos^{-1}\left(\frac{121^2 + 173^2 - 194^2}{(2)(121)(173)}\right) \approx 80.5°$

5. **a.** There are many ways to approach this multi-step task. Students may choose a different strategy from this one.

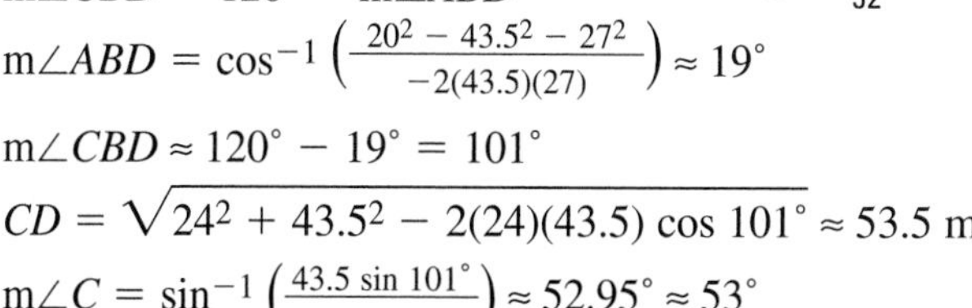

$BD = \sqrt{20^2 + 27^2 - 2(20)(27)\cos 135°}$

≈ 43.5 m

$m\angle CBD = 120° - m\angle ABD$

$m\angle ABD = \cos^{-1}\left(\frac{20^2 - 43.5^2 - 27^2}{-2(43.5)(27)}\right) \approx 19°$

$m\angle CBD \approx 120° - 19° = 101°$

$CD = \sqrt{24^2 + 43.5^2 - 2(24)(43.5)\cos 101°} \approx 53.5$ m

b. $m\angle C = \sin^{-1}\left(\frac{43.5 \sin 101°}{53.5}\right) \approx 52.95° \approx 53°$

$m\angle D = 360° - 135° - 120° - 53° = 52°$

c. Total area = area of $\triangle ABD$ + area of $\triangle CBD$

In $\triangle ABD$, the length of the altitude from point *A* can be found by solving $\sin 19° = \frac{h}{27}$. So $h = 27 \sin 19°$, and the area of $\triangle ABD = \frac{1}{2} \cdot 43.5 \cdot 27 \sin 19° \approx 191$ m^2.

In $\triangle CBD$, the length of the altitude from point *B* can be found by solving $\sin 53° = \frac{h}{24}$. So $h = 24 \sin 53°$, and the area of $\triangle CBD = \frac{1}{2} \cdot 53.5 \cdot 24 \sin 53° \approx$ 513 m^2.

Total area ≈ 191 m^2 + 513 m^2 = 704 m^2

See additional Teaching Notes on page T90J.

3. In isosceles trapezoid $ABCD$ shown below, $\overline{AB} \parallel \overline{CD}$ and $AD = BC$. Use the given information and what you know about line symmetry and angles of triangles to find the additional information requested below.

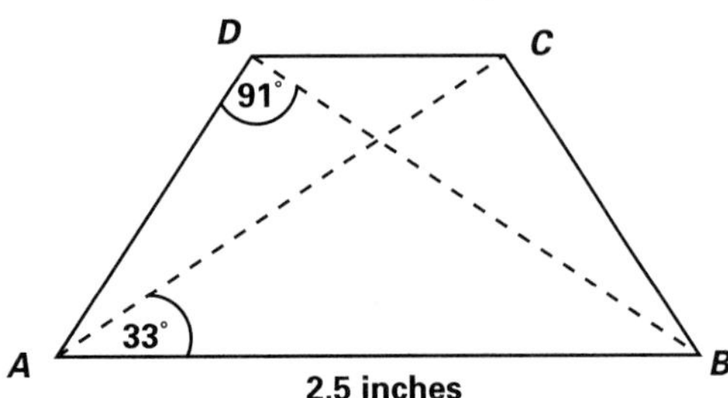

a. Find the measures of all angles shown in the figure.

b. Find the lengths of all segments shown in the figure.

4. A triangular region has sides measuring 121, 173, and 194 meters. Find the measure of the largest angle in the region.

5. A field is in the shape of a quadrilateral as shown.

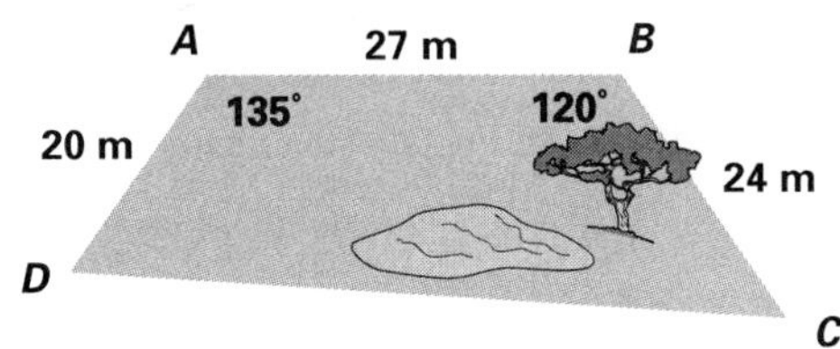

a. Find the measure of its fourth side.

b. Find the measures of the remaining angles of the quadrilateral.

c. Find its area.

Organizing

1. The label on a jar of creamy peanut butter claims that each serving (2 tablespoons) contains 16 grams of fat, 7 grams of carbohydrate, and 8 grams of protein. A recipe for peanut butter cookies calls for 5 tablespoons of peanut butter.

   a. Write proportions whose solutions would tell the number of grams of fat f, carbohydrate c, and protein p from peanut butter in the cookie recipe.

   b. Solve each of the equations in Part a.

   c. Explain how the equations solved in Part b are similar to those involved in using trigonometric relations to find side lengths in right triangles.

LESSON 2 • ALGEBRA, GEOMETRY, AND TRIGONOMETRY 41

2. The triangles sketched below are *similar* with vertex A corresponding to vertex P, B to Q, and C to R.

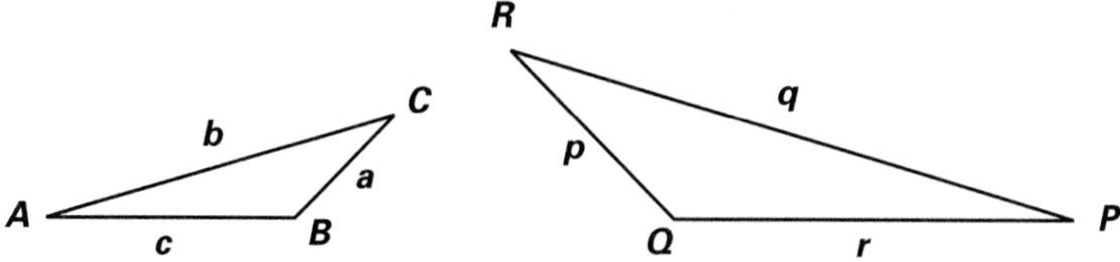

a. Complete the following equation in two different ways: $\frac{a}{p}$ = ________.

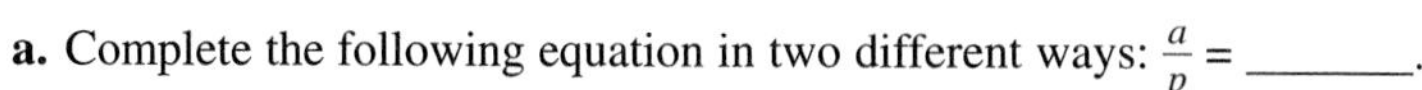

b. In each equation of Part a, solve for p in terms of the other side lengths.

c. Explain how your work in Part b is like that used in applications of the Law of Sines.

3. In Investigation 2 of Lesson 1 (page 6), you modeled situations involving pumping fuel into jet planes or water into amusement park rides. You found several ways to express the relationship between time t, rate of pumping r, and amount pumped a.

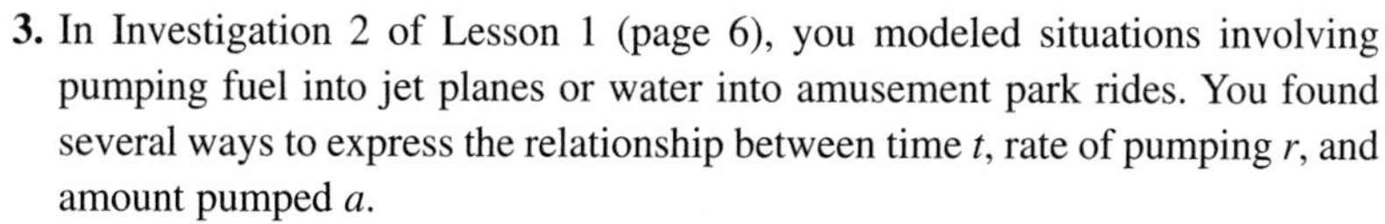

a. Write the relationship among these variables in three different equivalent forms: one showing a as a function of r and t; another showing r as a function of a and t; and a third showing t as a function of a and r.

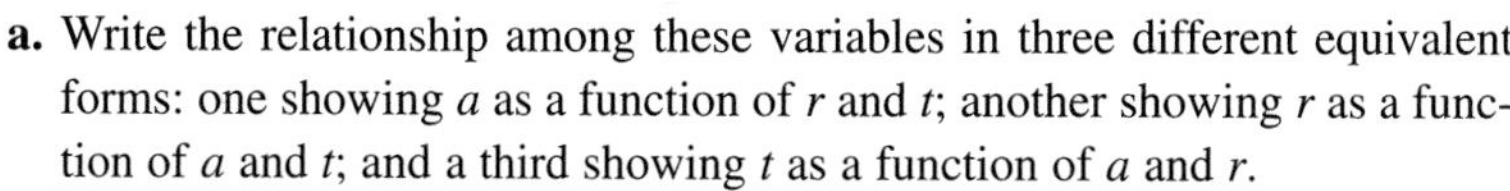

b. Explain the principles that guarantee equivalence of the equations in Part a.

4. Many simple situations can be modeled by writing and solving linear equations of the form $a + bx = c$.

a. Show the general form of solutions for all such equations by solving for x in terms of a, b, and c.

b. Explain the principles that guarantee your answer in Part a is correct.

c. Produce a similar solution formula for equations of the following form:

$$a + bx = c + dx$$

That is, solve for x in terms of a, b, c, and d, and explain the principles that guarantee your formula is correct.

Reflecting

1. In using the Law of Cosines to evaluate the length of one side in a triangle, you need to combine values of a, b, and $\cos C$ with the rule

$$c^2 = a^2 + b^2 - 2ab \cos C.$$

Write two different sequences of operations that will give the correct value for c.

42 UNIT 1 • MULTIPLE-VARIABLE MODELS

2. **a.** $\frac{a}{p} = \frac{b}{q}$ and $\frac{a}{p} = \frac{c}{r}$

   b. $p = \frac{aq}{b}$ and $p = \frac{ar}{c}$

   c. The Law of Sines sets ratios equal. To apply the Law of Sines, you have to solve for one of the unknowns, just as in Part b.

3. **a.** $a = rt$, $r = \frac{a}{t}$, and $t = \frac{a}{r}$

   b. The Inverse of Division or the Multiplication Property of Equality can be used to equate the second two equations to the first.

4. **a–b.** $a + bx = c$

$bx = c - a$	Step 1: Inverse of Addition
$x = \frac{c - a}{b}$	Step 2: Inverse of Multiplication

   c. This part requires the Distributive Property. Review this property with your students if you think such a review might be necessary.

$a + bx = c + dx$

$bx = c + dx - a$	Step 1: Inverse of Addition (and commutativity)
$bx - dx = c - a$	Step 2: Inverse of Addition (and commutativity)
$x(b - d) = c - a$	Step 3: Distributive Property
$x = \frac{c - a}{b - d}$	Step 4: Inverse of Multiplication

Reflecting

1. Two possible sequences follow.

Sequence 1

Step 1: Square *a*.	a^2
Step 2: Square *b*.	b^2
Step 3: Add results of Steps 1 and 2.	$a^2 + b^2$
Step 4: Multiply *a* times *b*.	ab
Step 5: Multiply result of Step 4 by 2.	$2ab$
Step 6: Multiply result of Step 5 by cos *C*.	$2ab \cos C$
Step 7: Subtract result of Step 6 from result of Step 3.	$a^2 + b^2 - 2ab \cos C$
Step 8: Take the square root of result of Step 7.	$\sqrt{a^2 + b^2 - 2ab \cos C}$

Sequence 2

Step 1: Multiply *a* times *b*.	ab
Step 2: Multiply result of Step 1 by −2.	$-2ab$
Step 3: Multiply result of Step 2 by cos *C*.	$-2ab \cos C$
Step 4: Square *b* and add to result of Step 3.	$b^2 - 2ab \cos C$
Step 5: Square *a* and add to result of Step 4.	$a^2 + b^2 - 2ab \cos C$
Step 6: Take the square root of result of Step 5.	$\sqrt{a^2 + b^2 - 2ab \cos C}$

MORE *continued*

2. **a.** If you know three of the variables, you can solve for the fourth.
   b. Again, if you know three of the variables, you can solve for the fourth.
3. **a.** Using the Properties of Equality, the first proportion can be changed into the second. (Students showed this in the general case, in Activity 5 of Investigation 4 from Lesson 1.)
   b. If you are solving for an angle, it's easier to use $\frac{\sin A}{a} = \frac{\sin B}{b}$. If you are solving for a side, it's easier to use $\frac{a}{\sin A} = \frac{b}{\sin B}$. In either case, you are putting the variable that you are solving for in the numerator. Students should understand that it can be solved in either form, but that fewer steps are required for the solution if the variable for which you are solving is in the numerator.
4. **a.** $\sin A = \frac{a \sin C}{c} = \frac{a}{c} \sin C$
   b. If $m\angle C$ is 90°, then $\sin C = 1$ and $\sin A = \frac{a}{c}$, which is the definition of the sine ratio. Otherwise, $\sin C$ is the adjustment factor. So to get the correct value for $\sin A$ when $\angle C$ is not a right angle, you must multiply the ratio of side lengths by the sine of angle C.

Extending

1. **a.** Students should position the linkage carefully and measure the distance from A to B. Their measurements should be close to those provided in the tables below.

m∠C	0°	10°	20°	30°	40°	50°	60°	70°	80°	90°
AB (cm)	4.0	4.7	6.3	8.2	10.3	12.4	14.4	16.4	18.3	20.0

m∠C	100°	110°	120°	130°	140°	150°	160°	170°	180°	190°
AB (cm)	21.6	23.1	24.3	25.4	26.3	27.1	27.6	27.9	28.0	27.9

m∠C	200°	210°	220°	230°	240°	250°	260°	270°	280°	290°
AB (cm)	27.6	27.1	26.3	25.4	24.3	23.1	21.6	20.0	18.3	16.4

m∠C	300°	310°	320°	330°	340°	350°	360°
AB (cm)	14.4	12.4	10.3	8.2	6.3	4.7	4.0

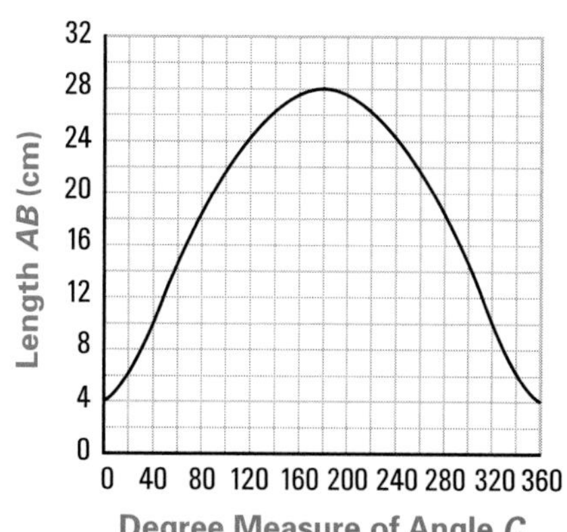

   b. The sine and cosine functions are somewhat similar to this pattern, because they are also periodic functions.
   c. Students should predict that the pattern will continue, and the new portion of the graph will be identical to the portion of the graph from 0° to 360°.

2. Both the Law of Sines and the Law of Cosines give equations relating four geometric variables.

   a. In each case, how many of those variables must be known in order to find the values of the other variables?

   b. The linear equation $a + bx = c$ also has four variables. How many of those variables must be known in order to find the values of the other variables?

3. The Law of Sines comes in two similar forms:

$$\frac{\sin A}{a} = \frac{\sin B}{b} \text{ and } \frac{a}{\sin A} = \frac{b}{\sin B}.$$

   a. Why are these two forms equivalent?

   b. When is each form better to use than the other? Why?

4. For a right triangle labeled as shown below, $\sin A = \frac{a}{c}$. In any triangle with vertices and sides labeled in the same pattern as shown here, the Law of Sines gives $\frac{\sin A}{a} = \frac{\sin C}{c}$.

   a. Rewrite the given Law of Sines to express $\sin A$ as a function of a, c, and $\sin C$.

   b. In what sense does the equation you wrote in Part a show how to adjust the right triangle definition for $\sin A$ to give correct values of $\sin A$ when the angle at C is not a right angle?

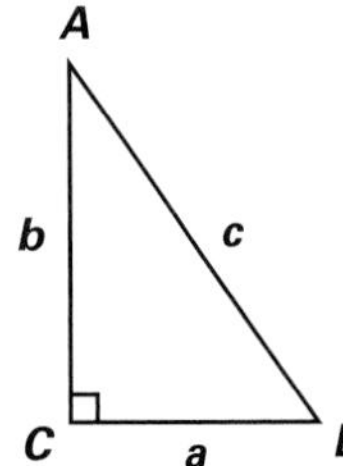

Extending

1. Conduct the following experiment using a linkage with arms of lengths 16 cm and 12 cm joined at point C.

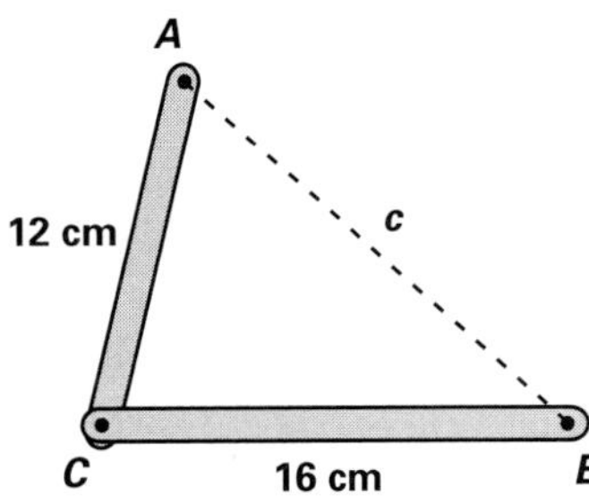

   a. Make a table of values for the length $c = AB$ as the angle at C varies from 0° to 360° in steps of 10°. Then sketch a graph of c as a function of the measure of $\angle C$.

   b. What relations have you studied that have graphs similar to the graph of this relation between the measure of $\angle C$ and the opposite side length c?

   c. How would you expect the table and graph to continue for measures of $\angle C$ from 360° to 720°?

LESSON 2 • ALGEBRA, GEOMETRY, AND TRIGONOMETRY 43

2. A lighthouse 30 meters high stands at the top of a high cliff. The line of sight from a point X on the bow of a ship to point A at the top of the lighthouse is at an angle of 18° to the horizontal. The line of sight from point X to point B at the bottom of the lighthouse makes an angle of 14° with a horizontal line. Draw a sketch of the situation and then determine the approximate height of the cliff.

3. In this lesson, you have investigated and used connections among algebra, geometry, and trigonometry. Examine the algebraic reasoning below, which connects the Pythagorean Theorem to a striking result in trigonometry.

Step 1 $a^2 + b^2 = c^2$

Step 2 $\frac{a^2 + b^2}{c^2} = \frac{c^2}{c^2}$

Step 3 $\frac{a^2}{c^2} + \frac{b^2}{c^2} = 1$

Step 4 $\left(\frac{a}{c}\right)^2 + \left(\frac{b}{c}\right)^2 = 1$

Step 5 $(\sin A)^2 + (\cos A)^2 = 1$

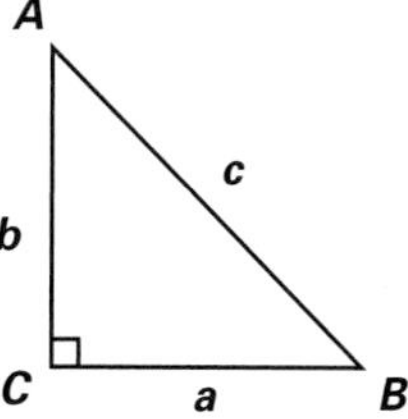

a. Provide an explanation for each step in the above reasoning.

b. Predict the value of $(\sin 43.2°)^2 + (\cos 43.2°)^2$. Check your prediction.

c. For what range of degree measures of $\angle A$ do you think $(\sin A)^2 + (\cos A)^2 = 1$? Explain your reasoning.

4. In general, to find the area of a triangle you need to know the length of one side and the altitude to that base.

a. How could you find the area of any triangle ABC if you were given b and c and the measure of $\angle A$? If given a and c and the measure of $\angle B$?

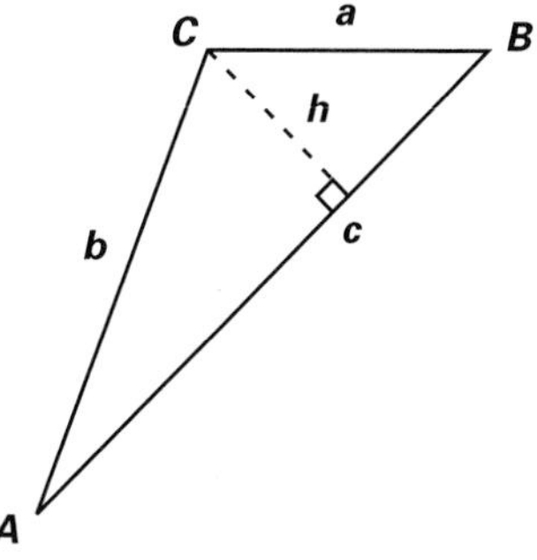

b. If you knew only the lengths of the three sides of a triangle, how could you find the length of an altitude to one of those sides?

c. Use your strategy to find the area of a triangle ABC in which a = 12.5 cm, b = 20 cm, and c = 25 cm.

44 UNIT 1 • MULTIPLE-VARIABLE MODELS

2. **Students may use a variety of methods to solve this problem. It might be instructive if pairs of students who have completed this task compare methods and discuss efficiency.**

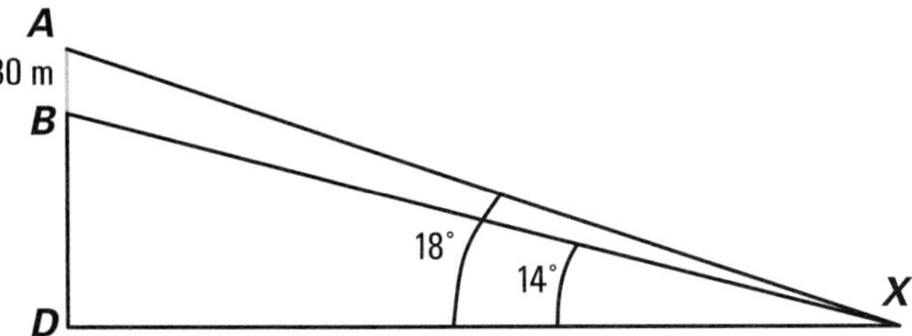

First Solution

The cliff makes one side of a right triangle so $\tan 14^\circ = \frac{BD}{XD}$ and $\tan 18^\circ = \frac{BD + 30}{XD}$. From the first equation, we know that $XD = \frac{BD}{\tan 14^\circ}$. Substituting this value into the second equation gives

$$\begin{aligned} \tan 18^\circ &= \frac{BD + 30}{\frac{BD}{\tan 14^\circ}} \\ &= \frac{\tan 14^\circ}{BD} \cdot BD + \frac{\tan 14^\circ}{BD} \cdot 30 \\ &= \tan 14^\circ + \frac{30 \tan 14^\circ}{BD} \\ \tan 18^\circ - \tan 14^\circ &= \frac{30 \tan 14^\circ}{BD} \\ BD &= \frac{30 \tan 14^\circ}{\tan 18^\circ - \tan 14^\circ} = 98.95 \text{ m} \end{aligned}$$

Second Solution

From $\triangle ADX$ we see that $m\angle A = 90^\circ - 18^\circ = 72^\circ$.
Consider $\triangle ABX$, where $\angle AXB = 4^\circ$.

$$\frac{\sin 4^\circ}{30} = \frac{\sin 72^\circ}{BX}$$
$$BX \approx 409 \text{ m}$$

Using $\triangle XBD$, $\sin 14^\circ = \frac{BD}{409}$, so $BD = 409 \sin 14^\circ = 98.95$ meters.

3. **You may wish to tell students that this is sometimes referred to as the Pythagorean Identity.**

   a. | | |
   |---|---|
   | Step 1: $a^2 + b^2 = c^2$ | Pythagorean Theorem |
   | Step 2: $\frac{a^2}{c^2} + \frac{b^2}{c^2} = \frac{c^2}{c^2}$ | Division Property of Equality (and the Distributive Property) |
   | Step 3: $\frac{a^2}{c^2} + \frac{b^2}{c^2} = 1$ | Any number divided by itself is 1. |
   | Step 4: $\left(\frac{a}{c}\right)^2 + \left(\frac{b}{c}\right)^2 = 1$ | Property of Exponents |
   | Step 5: $(\sin A)^2 + (\cos A)^2 = 1$ | Definition of sine and cosine |

   b. Using the identity in Step 5 of Part a, students should predict that $(\sin 43.2^\circ)^2 + (\cos 43.2^\circ)^2$ will have value 1. They can check their prediction using a calculator or computer software.

   c. Since the derivation that was provided began with the Pythagorean Theorem and a right triangle, it is reasonable to expect that the measure of $\angle A$ will be between 0° and 90°. Some students may experiment and make a conjecture that this is true for all angle measures.

See additional Teaching Notes on page T90J.

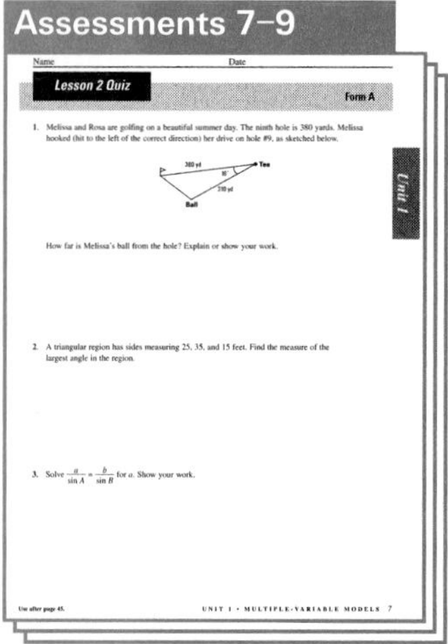
Assessments 7–9

Lesson 2 Quiz Form A

1. Melissa and Rosa are golfing on a beautiful summer day. The ninth hole is 380 yards. Melissa hooked (hit to the left of the correct direction) her drive on hole #9, as sketched below.

How far is Melissa's ball from the hole? Explain or show your work.

2. A triangular region has sides measuring 25, 35, and 15 feet. Find the measure of the largest angle in the region.

3. Solve $\frac{a}{\sin A} = \frac{b}{\sin B}$ for a. Show your work.

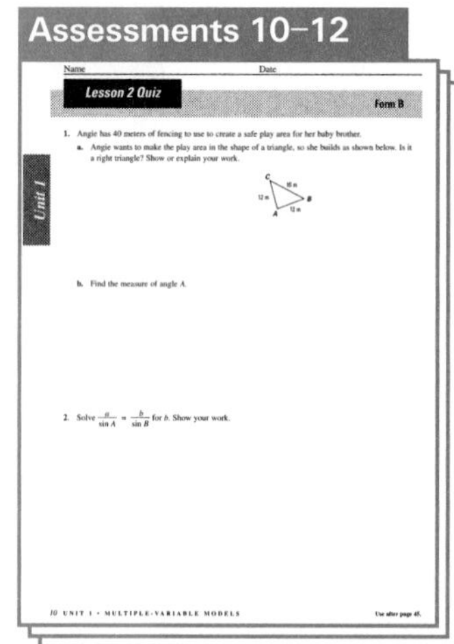
Assessments 10–12

Lesson 2 Quiz Form B

1. Angie has 40 meters of fencing to use to create a safe play area for her baby brother.
   a. Angie wants to make the play area in the shape of a triangle, so she builds as shown below. Is it a right triangle? Show or explain your work.
   b. Find the measure of angle A.

2. Solve $\frac{a}{\sin A} = \frac{b}{\sin B}$ for b. Show your work.

MORE *continued*

5. Student answers will vary depending on what assumptions they make. This example is one possibility.
   Assume that there is one tower, whose height is known, located at position (0, 0). Also assume that the sensing device gives the bearing, the angle of depression, and the distance from the transmitter. In order to determine the location of the transmitter, you would use triangulation to determine the (x, y)-coordinates on the grid. Let the positive y direction point north. For example, if the tower is 500 feet tall, the reported bearing is 140° east of north, and the distance from the transmitter is reported to be 2,000 feet, then the situation would look like this:

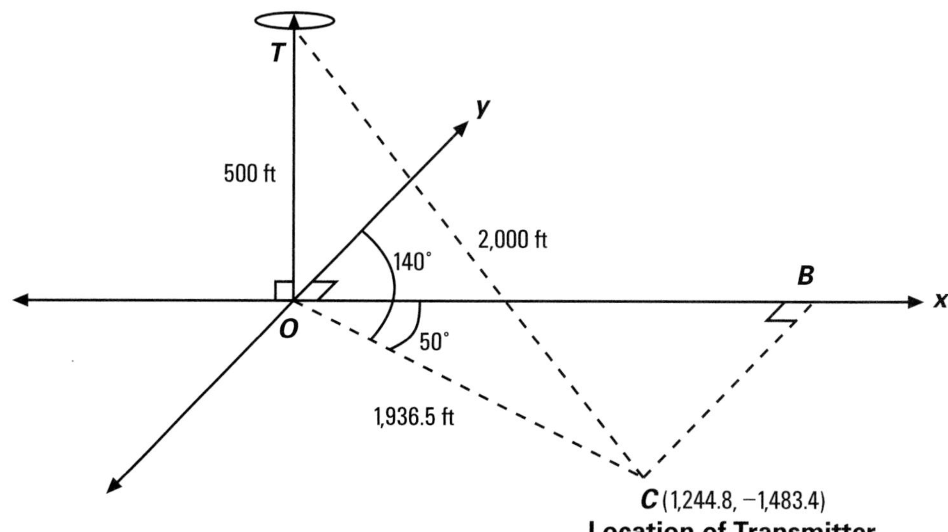

$$OC = \sqrt{2{,}000^2 - 500^2} \approx 1{,}936.5 \text{ ft}$$

$$\sin 50^\circ = \frac{BC}{1{,}936.5}, \text{ or } BC \approx 1{,}483.4 \text{ ft}$$

$$\sin 40^\circ = \frac{OB}{1{,}936.5}, \text{ or } OB \approx 1{,}244.8 \text{ ft}$$

See Assessment Resources pages 7–12.

5. Modern satellite communication systems make it possible for us to determine our exact (within a meter or so accuracy) location on the Earth's surface by sending a signal from a handheld Global Positioning System (GPS) device. The GPS sends signals to satellites, which relate the signal angle and distance to known reference sites. This technology makes it possible to have a system built into an automobile that shows a dashboard map giving both car and selected destination locations and how to reach the destination.

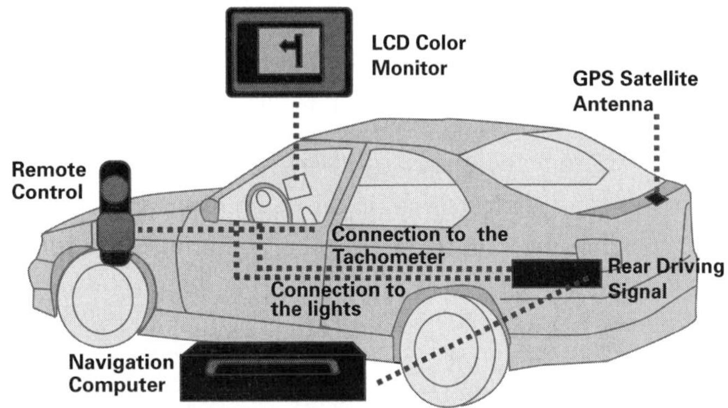

An actual GPS uses *spherical trigonometry* because of the spherical shape of the Earth. But consider a simpler problem of locating objects on a large flat surface, using sensors atop very tall towers. Devise a system that you think would allow the sorts of calculations required to locate a GPS transmitter on a map grid.

LESSON 2 • ALGEBRA, GEOMETRY, AND TRIGONOMETRY 45

Lesson 3 Linked Equations

Modern American businesses use millions of cars and trucks of various sizes to make pickups, deliveries, and service calls. Whether they are hauling dirt, delivering packages or pizzas, or making house calls for mowing lawns or repairing appliances, many businesses need transportation. Unfortunately, start-up businesses often don't have enough cash on hand to buy new cars or trucks or to pay the full price all at once. Other businesses may want to use their cash resources for other things. In any case, renting or leasing a vehicle is an option to consider.

Think About This Situation

The owners of A-1 Auto Parts need a second delivery truck to fill orders from repair shops in their service area. They have to lease the truck, because they don't have enough cash to buy one.

a What do you know about how typical automotive-lease plans work?

b What business conditions will the store owners need to consider as they choose a lease plan?

c How are those conditions related to each other?

d How could you model the relations among variables to help find the best choice among available options?

46 UNIT 1 • MULTIPLE-VARIABLE MODELS

Lesson 3 *Linked Equations*

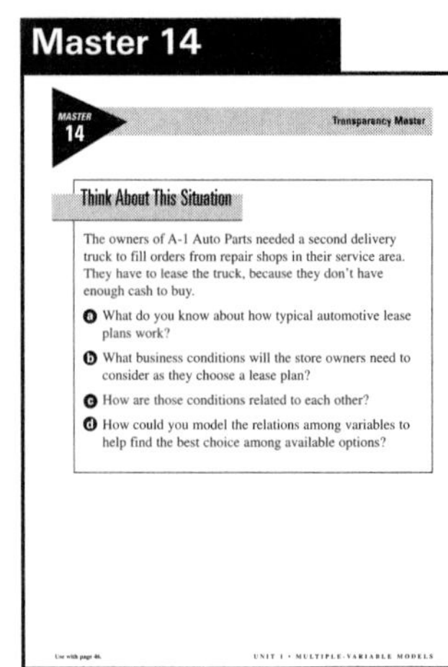
Master 14

The owners of A-1 Auto Parts needed a second delivery truck to fill orders from repair shops in their service area. They have to lease the truck, because they don't have enough cash to buy.

a What do you know about how typical automotive lease plans work?

b What business conditions will the store owners need to consider as they choose a lease plan?

c How are those conditions related to each other?

d How could you model the relations among variables to help find the best choice among available options?

Unit 1

LESSON OVERVIEW The development of the lessons in this unit has been as follows: observing patterns in tables of data, connecting the patterns to symbolic forms (equations) and reformulating the equations, and taking previously known symbolic formulas and rewriting them as appropriate. This lesson extends the study of equations by having students solve systems of linked equations. Additionally, students often rewrite expressions to reduce the number of variables, making graphing a viable option.

The situations in these investigations involve two or more output variables related to the same input variable. In the first investigation, both the number of students who would seek summer jobs and the number of students who could be paid by the Kent County summer jobs budget depend on the pay rate offered. One relationship is an inverse power model, and the other relationship is linear. The students will explore such systems of equations and determine algebraic models, tables, and graphs. They will also examine inequalities related to these systems and explore these relationships by considering the algebraic models, tables, and graphs.

The second investigation explores total payment related to different payment plans. This situation produces a system of equations in which all the equations are linear. The third investigation explores profits related to ticket price, ticket sales, and ticket income. Essentially, students are examining a system of equations with a linear model and a quadratic model. As in the first investigation, students will explore the inequalities related to the situations; they will study the situations through models, tables, and graphs. In all of these investigations, there are two or more different output variables related to the same input variable, thus the lesson title "Linked Equations."

Lesson Objectives

- To model situations with algebraic equations and inequalities
- To solve systems of equations where two or more output variables are related to the same input variable

LAUNCH full-class discussion

Think About This Situation

See Teaching Master 14.

It might help your students connect to the "Think About This Situation" questions if you have an advertisement for a lease arrangement available. Many of your students will be drivers. You might ask them, "What are some of the pros and cons of leasing and buying? What do you get for your $xxx a month? Are there any hidden costs?" This brief discussion should help all students get on the same level of understanding, that in a lease agreement there is a down payment and a monthly payment; maybe the down payment is manageable, but the monthly payments are not, or vice versa.

See additional Teaching Notes on page T90K.

EXPLORE small-group investigation

INVESTIGATION 1 Comparison Shopping

The payments for a leased car are based upon the expected value of the car at the end of the lease period. The leasing company owns the car, but the individual is responsible for maintaining, insuring, and registering it. Often the lease provides for a maximum number of miles that can be driven each year, and there is a charge for every mile over the limit.

The relationship among monthly payment, number of months, down payment, and total cost is the subject of this investigation. If students did not mention these variables in the "Think About This Situation" discussion, you may want to ask them briefly about how these variables contribute to the cost of a lease plan.

Students have used graphs to solve linear equations on many previous occasions, by entering the left side of the equation as one function, for example, $y_1 = ax + b$, and the right side as another, $y_2 = cx + d$. This investigation furthers the idea and has students graph and solve a system of linked equations. In so doing, they are implicitly solving $ax + b = cx + d$.

NOTE: Students should not need to spend much time doing this investigation since they have previously met these ideas in both Course 1 and Course 2 and also likely solved systems of equations graphically in middle school mathematics.

As you facilitate groups writing their functions and making their graphs, you might ask them the following questions:

- **What variable is on the horizontal axis?**
- **What is the meaning of the intersection point?**
- **In general, if (*x*, *y*) is on the line, then (*x*, *y*) satisfies the relationship. What does it mean in this context if a particular (*x*, *y*) is on both lines?**
- **The *y* in these functions is the cost of a lease plan. There are two plans and therefore two different *y* variables. Is it important that the *x* mean the same thing on both graphs?**

1. **a.** The two offers might appeal to people in different circumstances. If the length of the two leases is the same, the balance on one lease would be lower, allowing for a lower monthly payment. Perhaps with a larger down payment the interest rate is lower, and thus, the total amount paid is less.

b. You would expect to pay for insurance, registration, gas and oil, and the maintenance of the truck.

c. Responses will vary. How much money you have to put down on a truck and how much you will be able to afford to pay each month are both factors to consider.

2. $P_A = 2{,}500 + 150M$

$P_B = 500 + 230M$

3. **a.** After 60 months $P_A = \$11{,}500$ and $P_B = \$14{,}300$. So Plan B has the greater total payment after 60 months.

b. From 0 to 24 months, the total payment under Plan A will be greater than that under Plan B.

c. From 26 months to the end of the lease, the total payment under Plan B will be greater than that under Plan A.

d. At the end of 25 months the payments under the two plans will be equal.

INVESTIGATION 1 Comparison Shopping

When the owners of A-1 Auto Parts looked for a delivery truck, they found a small pickup they liked and got the following offers of lease payment plans from the dealer:

Plan A They could make a down payment of \$2,500 and then monthly payments of \$150.

Plan B They could make a down payment of only \$500 and then monthly payments of \$230.

They had to make a choice between higher down payment with lower monthly payments, or lower down payment with higher monthly payments.

1. In your group, think about the situation and the factors that are involved in each offer.

a. What might explain the differences in down payment and monthly payment rates for the two offers?

b. What other costs might there be for a person or business leasing a truck?

c. What factors would you consider in making the choice between the two lease payment plans?

2. In each payment plan, the money you pay to the car dealer adds up as time passes. Write an equation giving total payment as a function of the number of months in the lease for each lease plan. Use M for number of months, P_A for total amount paid under lease Plan A, and P_B for total amount paid under lease Plan B.

3. Study the relations between months and total dollars paid under the two lease plans.

a. Which plan involves the greater total payment after 60 months?

b. For what periods of time will the total payment be greater under Plan A than under Plan B?

c. For what periods of time will the total payment be greater under Plan B than under Plan A?

d. For what periods of time will the total payment under the two plans be equal?

LESSON 3 • LINKED EQUATIONS 47

4. On a single coordinate system like the one to the right, sketch graphs showing the two payment plans, with total payments under each plan as a function of the number of months for which payments have been made. Explain how the graphs illustrate your answers to Activity 3.

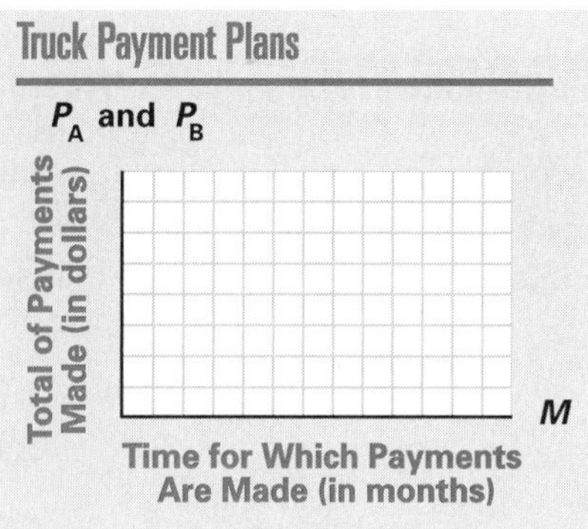

5. Suppose that as a third option you consider buying the truck at the start, with a cash payment of $12,500.
   - **a.** Add another graph to the coordinate system of Activity 4 so it shows the third option too.
   - **b.** For what periods of time will the total payment under Plan A be less than the full purchase price? Explain how this is shown on the graph.
   - **c.** For what periods of time will the total payment under Plan B be less than the full purchase price? Explain how this is shown on the graph.
   - **d.** What advantages and disadvantages are there for buying the truck rather than leasing?

Checkpoint

Comparing various lease or payment plans often involves examining systems of equations. Think about the costs to the consumer for the general situation shown here.

Plan A: $y = a + bx$

Plan B: $y = c + dx$

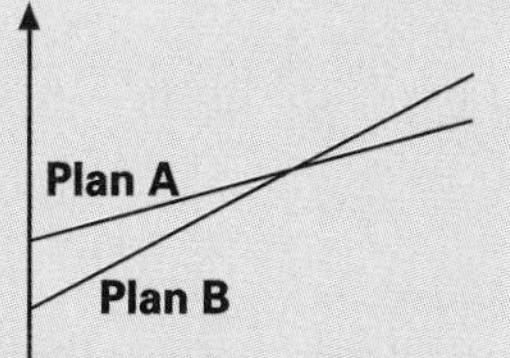

a Typically, on what factors would both equations depend? How are these factors shown in the graph?

b Write an equation or inequality that expresses the conditions under which the following are true:

- Plan A costs less than Plan B.
- Plan B costs less than Plan A.
- Plan A and Plan B cost the same.

c How would you go about solving each equation or inequality?

Be prepared to explain your algebraic relations and solution methods.

48 UNIT 1 • MULTIPLE-VARIABLE MODELS

4. Truck Payment Plans

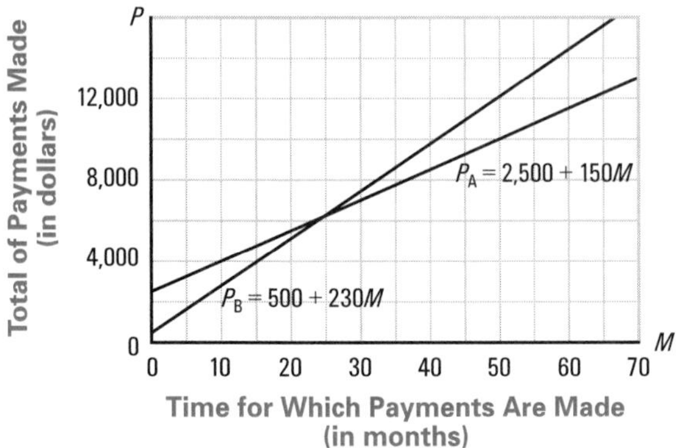

From 0 to 25 months, the line representing Plan A is above the line representing Plan B. At 25 months, the two lines intersect. After that point, the line representing Plan B is above the Plan A line. (Students should realize that if Plan A is above Plan B, Plan A costs more; the y values representing total payments are higher; the corresponding x values indicate the time period.)

5. a. Truck Payment Plans

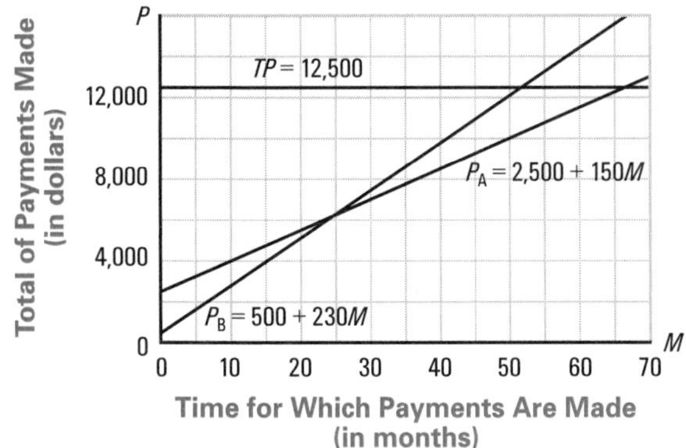

b. For 0 to 66 months, the total payment under Plan A is less than the $12,500 cash payment. At 67 months, Plan A is more than the cash payment. This is determined by finding the intersection point (66.667, 12,500) of the Plan A line and the horizontal line. The time period is shown on the graph by the x values corresponding to the part of the line for Plan A that is below the graph of $y = 12{,}500$.

c. For 0 to 52 months, the total payment under Plan B is less than the $12,500 cash payment. At 53 months, Plan B is more than the cash payment. This is determined by finding the intersection point (52.174, 12,500) of the Plan B line and the horizontal line. The time period is shown on the graph by the x values corresponding to the part of the line for Plan B that is below the graph of $y = 12{,}500$.

d. If you lease the truck, you will be making payments for many months after you've paid the initial value of the truck. If you buy the truck, then you can sell it and regain part of your initial investment. This is an advantage over leasing. Another disadvantage to leasing is the mileage restriction. However, if you lease the truck, you have a smaller initial cash output and your monthly payments may be less than if you buy it and pay for it in installments. Another advantage to leasing for a business is related to tax deductions.

Master 15

MASTER 15 — Transparency Master

Checkpoint

Comparing various lease or payment plans often involves examining systems of equations. Think about the costs to the consumer for the general situation shown here.

Plan A: $y = a + bx$

Plan B: $y = c + dx$

(a) Typically, on what factors would both equations depend? How are these factors shown in the graph?

(b) Write an equation or inequality that expresses the conditions under which the following are true:

- Plan A costs less than Plan B.
- Plan B costs less than Plan A.
- Plan A and Plan B cost the same.

(c) How would you go about solving each equation or inequality?

Be prepared to explain your algebraic relations and solution methods.

Use with page 48. — UNIT 1 • MULTIPLE-VARIABLE MODELS

Unit 1

See additional Teaching Notes on page T90K.

APPLY individual task

On Your Own

a. $C_A = 70$
$C_B = 35 + 0.3M$
$C_C = 25 + 0.5M$

b. For $0 < M < 50$, $C_C < C_B < C_A$.
For $50 < M < 90$, $C_B < C_C < C_A$.
For $90 < M < 116.7$, $C_B < C_A < C_C$.
For $M > 116.7$, $C_A < C_B < C_C$.

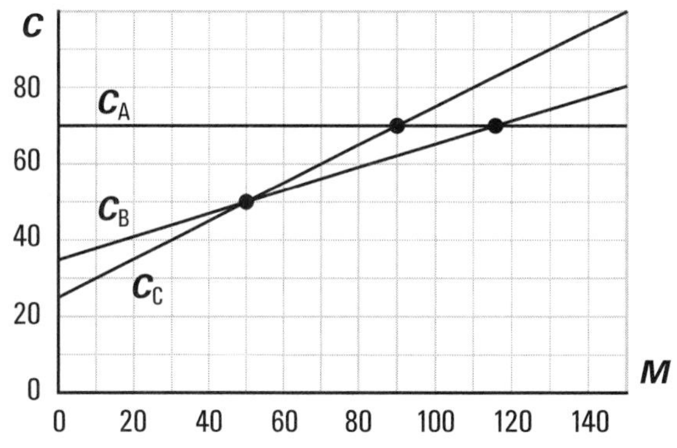

MORE ASSIGNMENT *pp. 57–62*

Students can now begin Modeling Task 1 or 2 or Organizing Task 2 from the MORE assignment following Investigation 3.

EXPLORE small-group investigation

INVESTIGATION 2 Supply and Demand

In this investigation, students extend their understanding of solving linked equations to nonlinear systems. The context also involves two very different output variables, number of hires and number of applicants, for a single input variable, salary.

You may want to create a brief launch to use prior to the Activity 1 class discussion by asking if anyone has ever been frustrated when looking for a summer or weekend job. You might give students the following scenario: "Suppose that a fast-food restaurant is hiring. They can hire a few people and give them lots of hours to work, or they can hire many people and give each of them very few hours to work. Why does this make sense?" (They only need a fixed number of employees at any one time.) "Who would like the first arrangement?" (People who need a living wage.) "Who would like the second arrangement?" (Students who need only spending money.) Then you can continue this discussion using Activity 1.

As students work on Activities 2–4, you might want to ask them about the equations they are creating, using the language of earlier lessons: "What type of models are your equations?" (They should be linear and inverse power models.)

See additional Teaching Notes on page T90L.

On Your Own

Cellular Plus telephone company offers three monthly service plans.

- Plan A costs \$70 per month with unlimited air time.
- Plan B costs \$35 per month plus \$0.30 per minute of air time.
- Plan C costs \$25 per month plus \$0.50 per minute of air time.

a. Write equations showing how the monthly cost for each type of telephone service depends on the number of minutes M of air time. Use C_A, C_B, and C_C to stand for the costs of the three types of service.

b. Compare the three service plans to find the number of minutes of air time for which each is cheapest.

c. Sketch a graph that illustrates your answer to Part b.

INVESTIGATION 2 Supply and Demand

Buying and selling, earning and spending—money and the things it buys play an important part in the lives of most Americans. Well over 100 million of us go to work on a regular basis and use the money we earn to buy things we want and need: food, shelter, clothes, cars, entertainment, and education. When summer approaches, most high school and college students start thinking about finding summer jobs.

Want Ads – Help Wanted

Fast Food– Restaurant seeks summer help; cashiers, cooks, cleanup; 20 hours per week all shifts available. Call 555-5678.

Camp Staff– Summer playground and camp counselors age 15 or older. Good pay and lots of fresh air. Call 555-6543.

Natural Lawns– Summer help needed. \$6.40 per hour. No prior experience required. Call 24 hours 1-800-555-1589.

Child Care– Tiny Tots Day Care Center seeks summer help for child care positions. Hours 7–5 four days per week. Send references to Box Q.

In some cities and towns there is work in shops, restaurants, and seasonal service jobs like lawn mowing, farmwork, or life-guarding. But there often aren't enough jobs to ensure that everyone who wants one will be employed.

To help students find summer work, both to earn money and to get work experience, many city and county governments have special summer jobs programs. Students are hired to do cleanup and construction jobs in parks or other community facilities. As with all other government projects, these programs have a set budget.

LESSON 3 • LINKED EQUATIONS 49

1. In Kent County, the government budget sets aside $100,000 each summer for student salaries in a youth-jobs program. Together as a class, consider some of the decisions the officials who run the program may have to make before announcing their plans and inviting applicants for the jobs.

   a. What decisions can you imagine the jobs-program planners have to make in setting up the program each year?

   b. What limitations would they have to consider in making those decisions?

   c. How are the decisions related to each other; that is, how does one decision affect the other options?

One plan for the Kent County summer jobs program focused on connections among pay for each student worker, hours worked, and number of students who would be interested in jobs at various levels of pay. The jobs-program staff were unsure how much they should offer as pay.

2. Recall that the county has $100,000 to spend on student salaries.

   a. How many student workers can be hired if the county pays $2,000 per worker for a summer contract covering eight weeks? How many can be hired if the county pays only $1,500 per worker?

   b. If the number of students who could be hired is represented by H and the offered summer pay rate is represented by P, what equation gives H as a function of P?

   c. Recall your previous work with algebraic models in Courses 1 and 2. What type of model is your equation in Part b?

   d. Describe the shape of the graph expected for this equation. Describe the pattern in a table of values for this equation.

3. The jobs-program staff figured that if they offered pay that was too low, then few students would be willing to take the jobs. After doing a survey in one high school, they arrived at the following estimates of the relation between summer pay P and number of students A they can expect to apply for the jobs.

Summer Jobs Program

Pay Offered P (dollars)	0	800	1,200	1,600	2,000	2,400
Expected Number of Job Applicants A	0	80	120	160	200	240

   a. Does the pattern in the table seem reasonable? Why or why not?

   b. If the staff wanted to display their options relating offered pay P to expected number of student applicants A in a graph, what type of graph should they use?

   c. What equation is a good model for the relation showing A as a function of P?

   d. What type of model is your equation in Part c?

50 UNIT 1 • MULTIPLE-VARIABLE MODELS

1. **a.** Student responses may include identifying the work that will be available for the youth-jobs program, determining how many youths to hire, deciding how many hours and how many weeks each person should work, and determining how much to pay each person.
   b. The number of youths who might want jobs, the availability of the workers, and the age of the workers are some of the limitations to be considered.
   c. Responses may vary. If the planners set the hourly rate, then the maximum number of worker hours is determined. They could allocate a certain number of hours for each worker and the number of workers, which would determine the rate per hour. (If the rate were unrealistically high, more youths could be included in the program at a lower rate.)
2. **a.** 50 workers; 66 workers
   b. $H = \frac{100{,}000}{P}$
   c. The equation in Part b is an inverse power model.
   d. The graph is a curve in the first quadrant that approaches (is asymptotic to) the positive x-axis as x gets arbitrarily large, and approaches (is asymptotic to) the positive y-axis as x approaches arbitrarily close to zero. In the table of values, as the pay increases, the number of students hired is decreasing at a decreasing rate.
3. **a.** The pattern is reasonable within limits. Since the data are based on a survey, it will not be exact. As the pay increases, so does the expected number of applicants, and each time the number of applicants is $P \div 10$. Also, there would probably be a maximum number of applicants. So, once that has been reached, increasing the pay rate will not bring any more applicants.
   b. They should use a scatterplot where all the points lie on a line.
   c. $A = \frac{P}{10}$ or $A = 0.1P$
   d. The equation in Part c is a linear model with a slope of $\frac{1}{10}$ and y-intercept 0.

Master 16

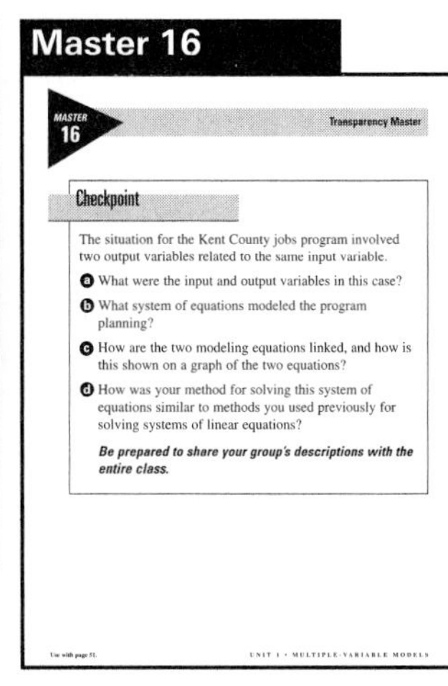

MASTER 16 Transparency Master

Checkpoint

The situation for the Kent County jobs program involved two output variables related to the same input variable.

ⓐ What were the input and output variables in this case?

ⓑ What system of equations modeled the program planning?

ⓒ How are the two modeling equations linked, and how is this shown on a graph of the two equations?

ⓓ How was your method for solving this system of equations similar to methods you used previously for solving systems of linear equations?

Be prepared to share your group's descriptions with the entire class.

EXPLORE *continued*

4. **See the comments regarding this activity in the investigation introduction.**
   a. ■ The expected number of applicants equals the number of jobs, when $P = \$1{,}000$.
      ■ The expected number of applicants exceeds the number of jobs, when $P > \$1{,}000$.
      ■ The expected number of applicants is less than the number of jobs, when $P < \$1{,}000$.
   b. Reports will vary. The report might include tables and graphs like these:

$y = \frac{100{,}000}{x}$ $y = \frac{x}{10}$

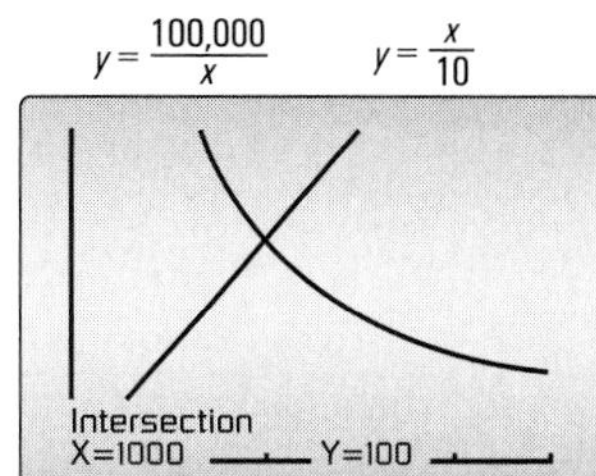

X	Y1	Y2
0	0	ERROR
500	50	200
1000	100	100
1500	150	66.667
2000	200	50
2500	250	40
3000	300	33.333

Y2 = 100000/X

   Some students may recognize that the eight-week contracts are not for 40-hour weeks. They may recommend checking the number of hours of work before deciding on the job offer.

5. a. In this case, the solution indicates the pay for which the expected number of applicants equals the number of students you are able to hire. This is represented by the intersection point on the graph and by equal values in the tables. When students solve symbolically, you may wish to have them justify their steps.

$$\frac{100{,}000}{P} = 0.1P$$

$$100{,}000 = 0.1P^2 \quad \text{Multiplication Property of Equality}$$

$$1{,}000{,}000 = P^2 \quad \text{Division Property of Equality}$$

$$\sqrt{1{,}000{,}000} = P \quad \text{Inverse of Squaring}$$

$$1{,}000 = P \quad \text{Evaluation (taking square root)}$$

   b. The solution to this inequality gives the pay rates for which the number of applicants you can hire is greater than the number of students you expect to apply. This is represented by the graph in the region where the curve is above the line. In the table, you can see that this occurs when the pay offered is less than \$1,000. Using the solution from Part a, students should be able to reason that $\frac{100{,}000}{P}$ will be larger than $0.1P$ when P is less than 1,000.
   c. The solution for this inequality gives the pay rate for which the number of applicants you can hire is less than the number of students you expect to apply. This is represented by the graph in the region where the curve is below the line. In the table, you can see that this occurs when the pay offered is greater than \$1,000. Using the solution from Part a, students can reason that, as P increases from 1,000, the value of $\frac{100{,}000}{P}$ decreases and the value of $0.1P$ increases, so $\frac{100{,}000}{P} < 0.1P$.

SHARE AND SUMMARIZE full-class discussion

Checkpoint

See Teaching Master 16.

ⓐ The input variable is pay offered, and the output variables are number of students who could be hired and expected number of job applicants.

See additional Teaching Notes on page T90L.

4. The decision to be made by officials in the Kent County jobs program is how much pay to offer for the eight-week summer contracts. Use the supply and demand equations from Activities 2 and 3 to do the following.

   a. Begin by finding all possible summer-pay offers for which the expected number of job applicants would

      - equal the number of jobs that could be provided.
      - exceed the number of jobs that could be provided.
      - fall short of the number of jobs that could be provided.

   b. Use the information from Part a and other considerations to write a brief report stating your recommendation on summer-pay rate and explaining your reasoning with supporting tables, graphs, and equations.

5. To make their recommendation more convincing, the program officers told the County Board that they found the optimal pay rate *P* by writing an equation or inequality for each condition given in Activity 4 Part a and then finding solutions for those conditions. Explain how the equation and inequalities given below correspond to problem conditions. Then, explain how the solutions could be found in tables and graphs of the relations among pay, job applications, and students hired. Finally, explain how the solutions could be found by reasoning with the symbols themselves.

   a. $\frac{100{,}000}{P} = 0.1P$

   b. $\frac{100{,}000}{P} > 0.1P$

   c. $\frac{100{,}000}{P} < 0.1P$

Checkpoint

The situation for the Kent County jobs program involved two output variables related to the same input variable.

a. What were the input and output variables in this case?

b. What system of equations modeled the program planning?

c. How are the two modeling equations linked, and how is this shown on a graph of the two equations?

d. How was your method for solving this system of equations similar to methods you used previously for solving systems of linear equations?

Be prepared to share your group's descriptions with the entire class.

LESSON 3 • LINKED EQUATIONS 51

On Your Own

Revise your supply and demand models, your graphs, and your recommendations about pay offers for the following changes in the Kent County budget for student workers' salaries.

a. The budget decreased to a total of $80,000.

b. The budget increased to a total of $120,000.

INVESTIGATION 3 Peak Profit

People running businesses that sell products must make many decisions that affect their profits. Those decisions include deciding what prices to charge for their products.

Consider the case of stage producers who have a contract to bring a musical production to a summer theater. They have to estimate *costs* of putting on the show, *income* from ticket sales and concessions, and the *profit* that can be made. When all these factors are considered, they have to decide what prices to charge for tickets.

The following activities ask you to analyze one possible method of making business plans for such a production. Study each step in the process and see if the proposal seems to use sensible and accurate reasoning.

1. The first step in deciding how to set ticket prices for the musical production was to do market research on what prices people would probably pay. A market research survey produced predictions of ticket sales S that could be expected for various possible ticket prices P. After plotting the data and estimating the best-fitting linear model for the relation between P and S, the equation $S = 2{,}500 - 50P$ was proposed as the probable relation between price and number of tickets that would be sold.

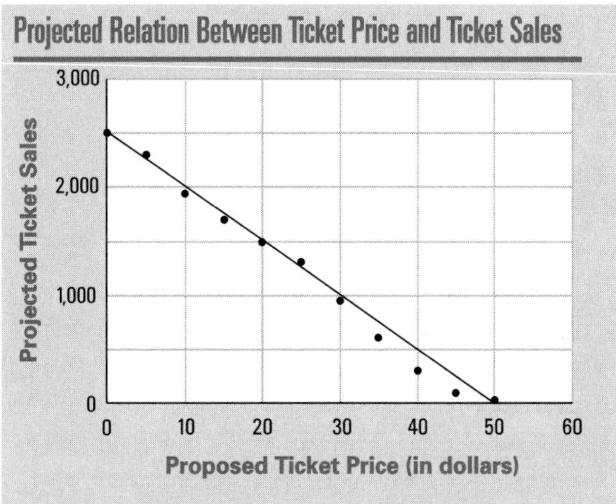

52 UNIT 1 • MULTIPLE-VARIABLE MODELS

APPLY individual task

On Your Own

a. The system of equations becomes $A = \frac{P}{10}$ and $H = \frac{80{,}000}{P}$. If the budget was decreased to \$80,000, then \$894 would be the pay rate for which the expected number of applicants would equal the number of students who could be hired.

b. The system of equations becomes $A = \frac{P}{10}$ and $H = \frac{120{,}000}{P}$. If the budget was increased to \$120,000, then \$1,095 would be the pay rate for which the expected number of applicants would equal the number of students who could be hired.

MORE ASSIGNMENT *pp. 57–62*

Students can now begin Modeling Task 4, Reflecting Task 1 or 4, or Extending Task 1 or 2 from the MORE assignment following Investigation 3.

Unit 1

EXPLORE small-group investigation

INVESTIGATION 3 Peak Profit

In this investigation, students will again solve a nonlinear system. However, this time one of the equations has to be derived in order for the input variable to be the same in both cases. In addition, the meaning of *solution* is emphasized by having students use color (if possible) on the *x*-axis to show solutions more clearly.

A brief launch can be created from the scenario outlined in the text. You might ask questions such as, "How would you begin making plans for a show? How are costs, income and profit related? ($P = I - C$) Do any of these depend on ticket price? On ticket sales?" It typically seems clear to students that income relates to price, though the relation actually is not as linear as students might first suggest. If students suggest that income is directly related to price, ask if the income will continue to go up no matter how high the prices are raised. This brings in the relationship between sales and price. Once it seems clear that all students understand these concepts, you can say that during this investigation, they will learn how to find the best price to charge.

EXPLORE *continued*

1. **a.** The researchers may have used a random method such as a phone survey. Another method would be surveying the target age group or last year's ticket holders and asking each person if he or she would buy a ticket at a particular cost.
   b. As the price increases, the number of tickets sold will decrease at a fairly constant rate.
   c. Responses may vary. It is reasonable that, as the tickets get more expensive, fewer people will want to spend the money to go to the show. Students may not agree with the linearity of the pattern. However, we will continue to use this model, as it is the best available at this point.
   d. If the tickets are free, 2,500 people will want tickets. For every dollar increase in ticket price, 50 fewer people will purchase tickets for the concert.
   e. For each particular price, plot the number of people who said they would pay that price. Then determine the mathematical model using linear regression.
2. **When students are working on this activity, you may want to ask if income seems to be a linear function. (No, it is not increasing at a constant rate.) If they agree it is not linear, you can ask what kind of function would follow such a pattern of increase and then decrease. (The pattern is quadratic.) Students may find the formulas in Part c mysterious. It may help them if you write the following table on the board, with the variable *P* and formula for *S* included:**

Ticket Price, P	0	5	10
Number of Tickets Sold, $S = 2{,}500 - 50P$	2,500	2,250	2,000
Ticket Income, $I = \ldots$?	0	11,250	20,000

Students who realize that $I = P \cdot S$ may see the connection with the offered formulas. Emphasize the vocabulary "as a function of *P*" when you are talking with students.

   a. As the ticket price increases, so does the income—but only up to a point. Then for a ticket price somewhere between \$20 and \$30, the ticket income starts decreasing. The pattern seems reasonable because you would expect the income to increase as you change more. Then, as the ticket price gets very high and people buy fewer tickets, the income would decrease.
   b. Ticket income will be equal to the price of the ticket times the number of tickets sold. Multiply the first two numbers in a column to get the last number in the column.
   c. Both are correct; they are equal to each other. The form $I = P(2{,}500 - 50P)$ more clearly shows that *Income* = *Price* × *Sales*.
   d. A ticket price of \$25 will produce the maximum income of \$31,250.
3. **a.** \$17,500 is the fixed cost and $2S$, which is \$2 per person, represents the variable operating cost.

a. How do you think the producers or their market-research staff gathered the (*ticket price*, *ticket sales*) data that are plotted on the graph?

b. What does the pattern in the graph say about the probable relation between ticket price and number of tickets that would be sold for the musical?

c. Is the pattern in the graph reasonable? Does it match the relation you would expect? Why or why not?

d. In the equation $S = 2{,}500 - 50P$, what do the values 2,500 and –50 tell about the way ticket price and ticket sales are related?

e. How would you find the equation to model the market-research data points?

2. After estimating the connection between ticket prices and probable ticket sales, the producers wanted to see the probable connection between ticket prices P and dollar income I from ticket sales. They created the following table of projections.

Projected Income from Ticket Sales

Ticket Price (dollars)	0	5	10	20	30	40	50
Number of Tickets	2,500	2,250	2,000	1,500	1,000	500	0
Ticket Income (dollars)	0	11,250	20,000	30,000	30,000	20,000	0

a. According to this table, how will ticket income be affected by choice of ticket price? Does the pattern in the table seem reasonable? Why or why not?

b. How could the entries in the "Ticket Income" row be calculated from the other information in the table?

c. Anna proposed the equation $I = P(2{,}500 - 50P)$ for the relation between ticket price and ticket income; James proposed $I = 2{,}500P - 50P^2$. Which of these two rules is correct? Why?

d. What price is likely to give the maximum ticket income? What would that income be?

3. The next step in making the business plan was to estimate operating costs for the production. The planners knew that some costs were fixed (for example, pay for the cast and rent of the theater), but others would vary depending on the number of tickets sold (for example, number of ushers and ticket takers). After estimating all the possible operating costs, they decided on the equation $C = 17{,}500 + 2S$ for operating costs as a function of number of tickets sold.

a. According to that rule, what are the projected fixed operating costs, and what is the projected operating cost for each person who buys a ticket for the musical?

LESSON 3 • LINKED EQUATIONS 53

b. How will operating costs change as the number of tickets sold increases?

c. Since ticket sales seem to depend on price charged $S = 2{,}500 - 50P$, it is possible to express operating cost C as a function of price. What equation would express that relation?

d. How will operating costs change as the ticket price increases?

4. With equations relating projected ticket income to ticket price and operating cost to ticket price, the entertainment promoters tried to put everything together in a picture of the relations among price, costs, and income.

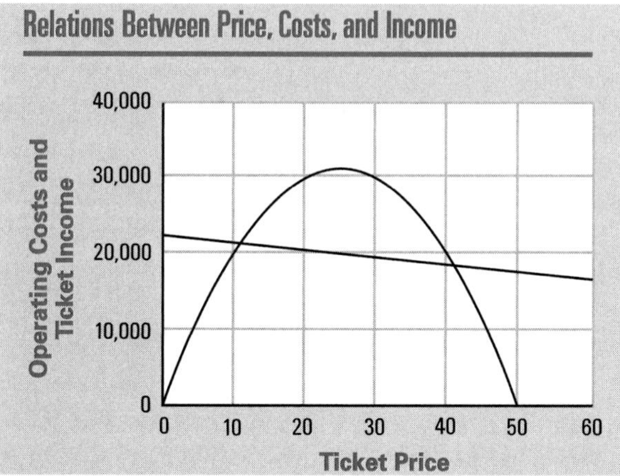

a. These graphs show the relations between ticket price, operating cost, and ticket income. How do they show each of the following?

- Ticket prices for which operating costs exceed income
- Ticket prices for which income exceeds operating costs
- Ticket prices for which costs equal income

b. If you use the rules for income and operating costs as functions of ticket price, what specific numerical answers do you get for the questions in Part a?

c. What questions are answered by solving the following equation and inequalities?

- $2{,}500P - 50P^2 = 22{,}500 - 100P$
- $2{,}500P - 50P^2 < 22{,}500 - 100P$
- $2{,}500P - 50P^2 > 22{,}500 - 100P$

d. Obtain or make a copy of the graphs above relating income, operating costs, and ticket price. On the x-axis, mark those points corresponding to solutions of the equation and inequalities in Part c. If possible, use different colors as suggested below.

- In blue: $2{,}500P - 50P^2 = 22{,}500 - 100P$
- In red: $2{,}500P - 50P^2 < 22{,}500 - 100P$
- In green: $2{,}500P - 50P^2 > 22{,}500 - 100P$

54 UNIT 1 • MULTIPLE-VARIABLE MODELS

Master 17

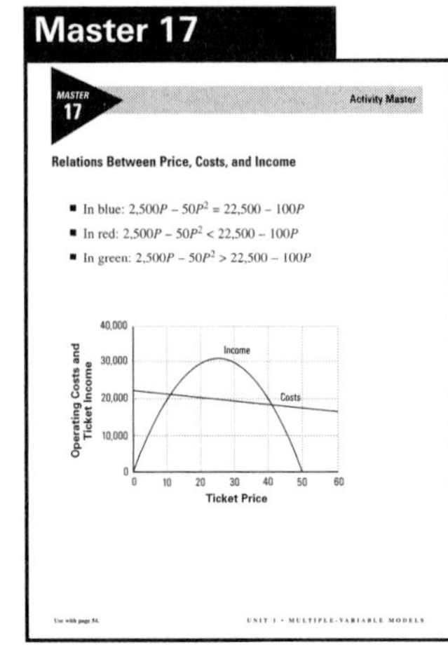

3. **b.** The operating costs will increase by \$2 for each ticket sold.

c. If $C = 17{,}500 + 2S$ and $S = 2{,}500 - 50P$,
then $C = 17{,}500 + 2(2{,}500 - 50P)$ or $C = 22{,}500 - 100P$.

d. As the ticket price increases, overall operating costs decrease. For each dollar increase in ticket price, the operating costs decrease by \$100. This happens because, as the ticket price increases, the number of tickets sold decreases, and the overall cost is dependent upon the number of tickets sold.

4. **a.**

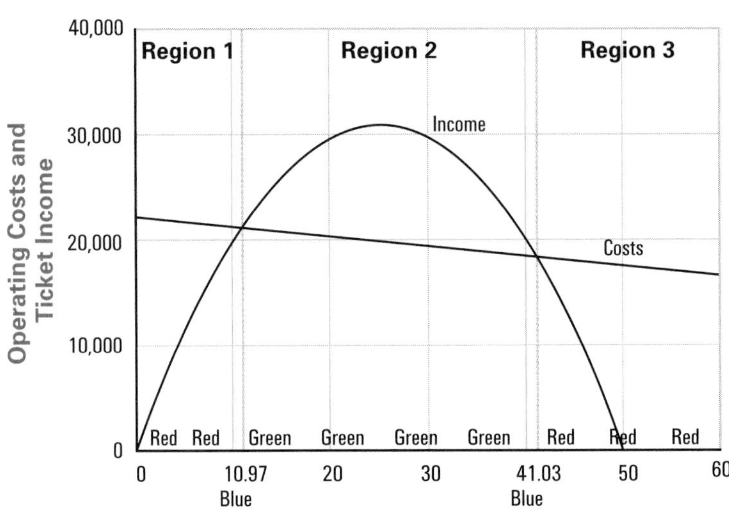

- The prices along the horizontal axis in Regions 1 and 3 indicate costs higher than income, because the cost graph is above the income graph in those regions.
- The prices along the horizontal axis in Region 2 indicate income higher than costs. In that region, the parabola is above the line.
- Costs equal income when the ticket price is \$10.97 and \$41.03. These are the two points where the line and parabola intersect.

b. Numbers are approximate.

- $P < 10.97$ or $P > 41.03$
- $10.97 < P < 41.03$
- $P = 10.97$ and $P = 41.03$

c.
- What are the break-even points at which costs equal income? At what ticket prices will you break even?
- What are the prices for which costs exceed income? At what ticket prices do you lose money?
- What are the prices for which income exceeds costs? At what ticket prices do you make money?

d. **See Teaching Master 17 and the color labels on the graph in Part a. This activity is crucial to reinforcing the understanding of what we mean when we ask for a solution, that is, the input values necessary to make the desired inequality or equation true.**

Masters 18a–18b

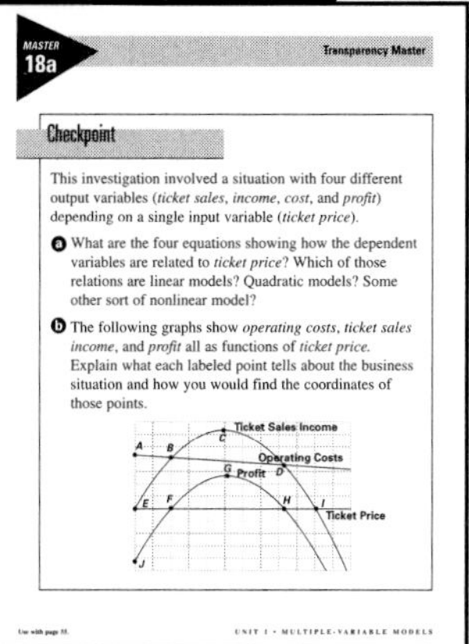
MASTER 18a Transparency Master

Checkpoint

This investigation involved a situation with four different output variables (*ticket sales, income, cost,* and *profit*) depending on a single input variable (*ticket price*).

a What are the four equations showing how the dependent variables are related to *ticket price*? Which of those relations are linear models? Quadratic models? Some other sort of nonlinear model?

b The following graphs show *operating costs, ticket sales income,* and *profit* all as functions of *ticket price.* Explain what each labeled point tells about the business situation and how you would find the coordinates of those points.

EXPLORE *continued*

5. For this activity, students do not have to write the equation for profit in its simplest form in order to be able to graph it and find the maximum profit. However, you may want to ask students to try to write it in simpler equivalent forms.

a. *Profit* $= I - C = (2{,}500 - 50x)x - [17{,}500 + 2(2{,}500 - 50x)]$, where x is the ticket price.

X	Y1
5	-10750
10	-1500
15	5250
20	9500
25	11250
30	10500
35	7250

X=5

b. A ticket price of \$26 gives the maximum profit of \$11,300.

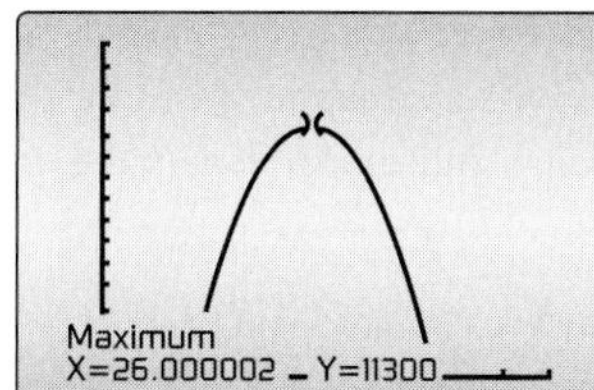

X	Y1
24	11100
25	11250
26	11300
27	11250
28	11100
29	10850
30	10500

X= 24

c. Number of tickets that will be sold: $2{,}500 - 50(26) = 1{,}200$ tickets
Operating costs: $22{,}500 - 100(26) = \$19{,}900$
Ticket sales income: $(2{,}500 - 50 \cdot 26)(26) = \$31{,}200$

SHARE AND SUMMARIZE full-class discussion

Checkpoint

See Teaching Masters 18a–18b.

a *ticket sales* $= 2{,}500 - 50P$
ticket income $= (2{,}500 - 50P)P$
operating costs $= 17{,}500 + 2(2{,}500 - 50P)$
profit $= (2{,}500 - 50P)P - [17{,}500 + 2(2{,}500 - 50P)]$
Students may have equivalent equations to any of these.
Sales and *costs* are linear models. *Income* and *profit* are quadratic models.

b Solution methods may vary.

A: Operation costs that are not dependent on ticket sales. Solve for C when $P = 0$, or use a trace capability of a calculator to determine where the *costs* equation crosses the y-axis.

B: First break-even point where *costs* = *income*. Use a table or graph to determine what ticket price will make $C = I$.

C: Maximum income. Use the trace capability of a calculator to find the maximum point of the income graph.

D: Second break-even point. Use a table or graph to determine what ticket price will make $C = I$.

E: The amount of income you will have if the tickets are free. Determine where the *income* graph crosses the horizontal axis.

CONSTRUCTING A MATH TOOLKIT: You may wish to have your students explain how to use graphs and tables to solve equations and inequalities in their Math Toolkits.

JOURNAL ENTRY: Students may do Reflecting Task 3, 4, or 5 as a journal entry.

See additional Teaching Notes on page T90M.

5. Of course, the producers would probably like to make as large a profit as possible.

   a. Use the equations relating income and expenses to ticket price to produce a table of projected profits for various possible ticket prices.

   b. Use the table and a graph to find the ticket price giving maximum profit for the musical production. What is the maximum profit to be expected?

   c. Use your answer from Part b to estimate the number of tickets that will be sold, the operating cost, and the ticket sales income at the ticket price which gives maximum profit.

Checkpoint

This investigation involved a situation with four different output variables (*ticket sales*, *income*, *cost*, and *profit*) depending on a single input variable (*ticket price*).

a What are the four equations showing how the dependent variables are related to *ticket price*? Which of those relations are linear models? Quadratic models? Some other sort of nonlinear model?

b The following graphs show *operating costs*, *ticket sales income*, and *profit* all as functions of *ticket price*. Explain what each labeled point tells about the business situation and how you would find the coordinates of those points.

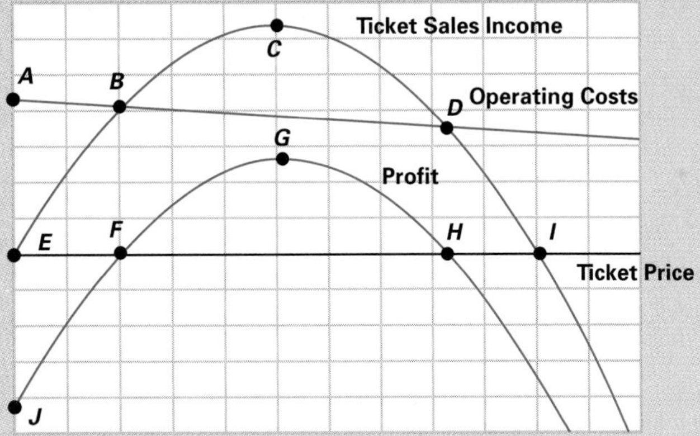

c In what ways is this system similar to, and different from, those modeling the planning of the A-1 Auto Parts truck leasing and the Kent County summer-jobs program in previous investigations?

Be prepared to share and explain your responses.

LESSON 3 • LINKED EQUATIONS 55

On Your Own

When Alicia and Jamal went to apply for restaurant jobs, they each found several different opportunities.

Offer 1, Server:

Pay is \$7.50 per hour, with work uniforms provided free of charge.

Offer 2, Server:

Pay is \$5.25 per hour and includes a \$100 hiring bonus with the first week's check. Again, work uniforms are provided.

Offer 3, Host/Hostess:

Pay is \$8.75 per hour, but new clothes for this job cost about \$250.

The question for both of them was which offer to take. Money that would be earned seemed the only factor, since all three places were close to their homes and all of the jobs were jobs they would enjoy. The parents of both had agreed to loan them the money for new clothes, but the loans had to be repaid as soon as possible.

a. Write equations that will give the possible earnings under each plan as functions of the number of hours worked.

b. Sketch or use a graphing calculator or computer software to display graphs of all three relations in Part a for time worked from 0 to 250 hours. Explain how the graphs can be used to find the best offer for various amounts of time worked.

c. Produce a table showing sample (*hours worked*, *earnings*) data for the three job offers from 0 to 250 hours, in steps of 10 hours. Then explain how the entries help determine the best offer.

d. Using methods of your choice, solve the following equation and inequalities. Then explain what questions about the three offers can be answered by the various solutions.

- $7.50x = 8.75x - 250$
- $5.25x + 100 > 8.75x - 250$
- $7.50x < 5.25x + 100$

56 UNIT 1 • MULTIPLE-VARIABLE MODELS

On Your Own

a. Let E_i be the earnings for the ith option, and let x be the time worked in hours.
$E_1 = 7.50x$
$E_2 = 5.25x + 100$
$E_3 = 8.75x - 250$

b.

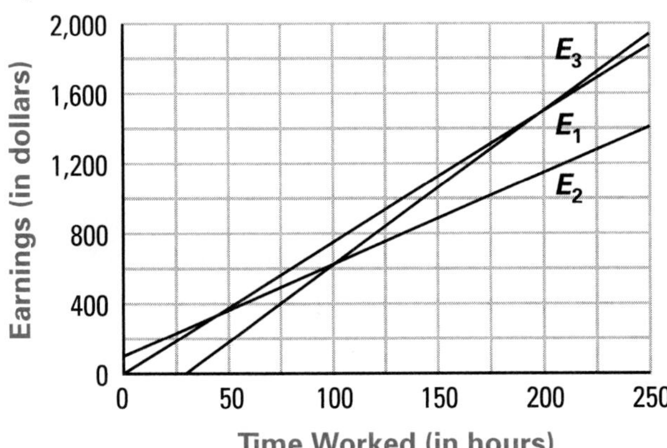

The best offer will always be the line that is on top. The vertical lines designate changes in which offer is best for the particular time periods.

c. **It is not necessary that students record the calculator tables in their work. Rather they should refer to the tables to explain how the entries help determine the best offer.**
For $0 < x < 44.44$, E_2 is the best offer.
For $44.44 < x < 200$, E_1 is the best offer.
For $x > 200$, E_3 is the best offer.

d.
- When are earnings from offer 1 equal to earnings from offer 3? $x = 200$ hours
- When is offer 2 better than offer 3? $x > 100$ hours
- When is offer 1 worse than offer 2? $x < 44.44$ hours

Unit 1

MORE

ASSIGNMENT pp. 57–62

Modeling: 3 and choice of one*
Organizing: 2 or 3, and 4*
Reflecting: 1 and 4
Extending: Choose one*

**When choice is indicated, it is important to leave the choice to the student.*
NOTE: *It is best if Organizing tasks are discussed as a whole class after they have been assigned as homework.*

MORE independent assignment

Modeling

1. Cost Y_1 for East Coast Tour Bus: $Y_1 = 1{,}350$
   Cost Y_2 for Delmarva Charters: $Y_2 = 525 + 2.25x$

   a. 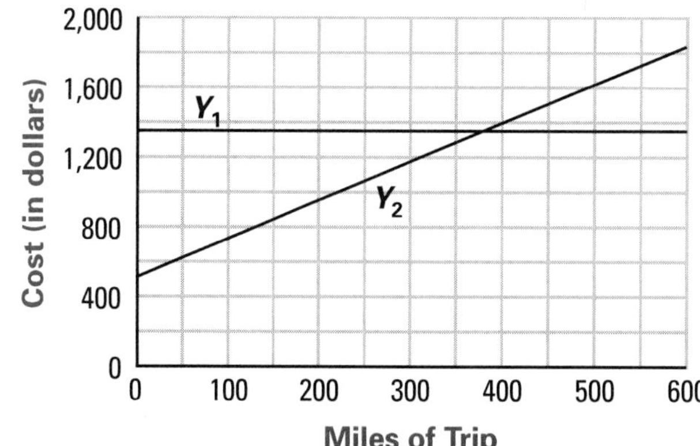

   In order to choose a bus company, find on the x-axis the number of miles the trip will be, and then move vertically up to the lower graph. The lower graph represents the better price for that length trip.

   b. If the round-trip distance was less than 366 miles, then Delmarva Charters offered the better price. If the round-trip distance was more than 366 miles, then East Coast Tours offered the better price.

   c. Any of the following would help:
   $525 + 2.25x < 1{,}350$
   $1{,}350 < 525 + 2.25x$
   $525 + 2.25x = 1{,}350$

2. a. The plan could be the same as for Modeling Task 1 Part b.

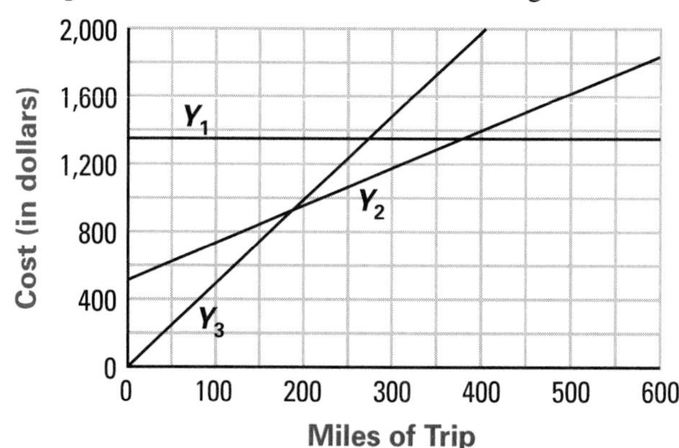

   b. Cost Y_3 for Undercut Transit: $Y_3 = 4.95x$
   Undercut Transit offers the best price, if the round-trip distance is less than 194 miles.

   c. $4.95x < 1{,}350$
   $4.95x < 525 + 2.25x$

MORE

Modeling • Organizing • Reflecting • Extending

Modeling

1. St. Michael School received two bids for charter buses to transport their senior class on a one-week field trip to Washington, DC in April.
   - East Coast Tour Bus company proposed a flat rate of $1,350 per bus.
   - Delmarva Charters offered a price per bus of $525 for a driver and $2.25 per mile for use of the bus.

   a. Sketch graphs that could be used to illustrate the situation, and describe your plan for making a choice between the two companies.

   b. Under what conditions would East Coast Tour Bus offer the better price per bus? When would Delmarva Charters offer the better price per bus?

   c. Write equations or inequalities whose solutions would help make a choice.

2. When Undercut Transit heard about St. Michael School's field trip plan (see Modeling Task 1), they submitted a different bid: $4.95 per mile for each bus, with driver included.

   a. Sketch graphs that illustrate the options, and describe your plan for making a choice among the three competing companies.

   b. Under what conditions will Undercut Transit offer the best price?

   c. Write equations or inequalities whose solutions would help make a choice.

3. At Martin Luther King High School, the athletic booster club sponsors an annual basketball game between teachers and the school's intramural league all-stars. As a research project, the economics class investigated possible ticket prices, attendance, and expenses. They found the following information:

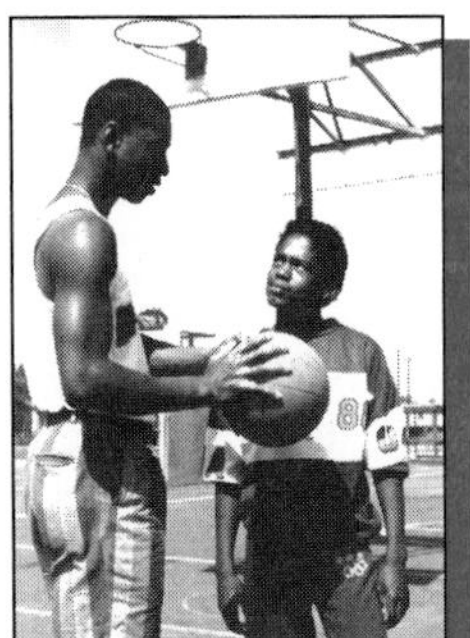

   - The operating costs C (in dollars) would depend on the number of tickets sold T with rule $C = 250 + 0.50T$.
   - The number of tickets sold T would probably depend on price charged P (in dollars) with rule $T = 800 - 100P$.

LESSON 3 • LINKED EQUATIONS 57

a. Examine the equations relating cost, ticket sales, and ticket price. What do the numbers 250, 0.50, 800, and –100 tell about the situation?

b. What single equation would show how operating costs depend on ticket price charged?

Based on their work with ticket prices, ticket sales, and operating costs, the economics class members reached these further conclusions:

- Income from ticket sales I would be related to ticket price P by the equation $I = 800P - 100P^2$.
- Cost of operating the game would be related to ticket price by the equation $C = 650 - 50P$.

c. Sketch graphs that show both income and operating costs as functions of ticket price. Label the points whose coordinates would help answer the following questions:

- For what ticket prices would the game break even; that is, when would operating costs equal income from ticket sales?
- For what ticket prices would ticket revenue be as large as possible?

d. How could the price giving maximum profit be found from the graphs in Part c?

e. Write an equation expressing profit PR as a function of ticket price.

f. Find the maximum profit possible and the ticket price that will give that maximum profit. Explain how to find your answer using an appropriate graph, a table of (*ticket price*, *profit*) values, or some other reasoning method.

4. When John and Carla were 14 years old, they had summer jobs. John saved \$600 from his earnings, and Carla saved \$550 from her earnings. They both decided to put their money into savings accounts.

- John found an account that would pay interest at an annual rate of 8%, but at the end of each year he took out the interest. Each year his original deposit stayed in the account.
- Carla's account only paid 7% interest, but she decided not to withdraw any money. The interest was added to her account at the end of each year, and she began earning interest on the interest added.

a. How much total money would each person receive from the banks if they closed their accounts at the end of only 1 year? How much would they receive if they closed their accounts after 2 years?

58 UNIT 1 • MULTIPLE-VARIABLE MODELS

3. a. The number 250 refers to the fixed operating costs.

The number 0.50 indicates that the operating costs increase \$0.50 with each ticket sold.

The number 800 is the number of people who will come if there is no charge.

The number –100 indicates that, with each \$1 increase in ticket price, the number of tickets sold would decrease by 100.

b. $C = 250 + 0.50(800 - 100P) = 650 - 50P$

c.

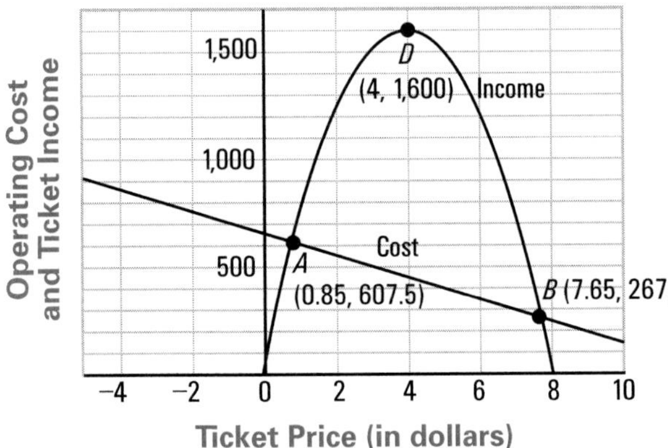

- Points *A* and *B* are the points whose coordinates would help determine the ticket prices for which the game would just break even. (\$0.85 or \$7.65 respectively)
- The *x*-coordinate of point *D* (\$4) would be the ticket price that would give maximum revenue.

d. The price giving maximum profit could be estimated from the graph of Part c, by looking for the place where the income curve is furthest above the operating costs curve.

e. $Profit = I - C = 800P - 100P^2 - (650 - 50P) = 850P - 100P^2 - 650$

f. The maximum profit is \$1,156.25 and occurs when the ticket price is \$4.25. Responses on how to use a graph or table of values to obtain this information will vary.

4. a. Total Received

	After 1 Year	After 2 Years
John	\$648	\$696
Carla	\$588.50	\$629.70

Master 19

Identifying Solutions

MORE *continued*

4. **b.** John: $T_J = 600 + 48n$

Carla: $T_C = 550(1.07)^n$

c.

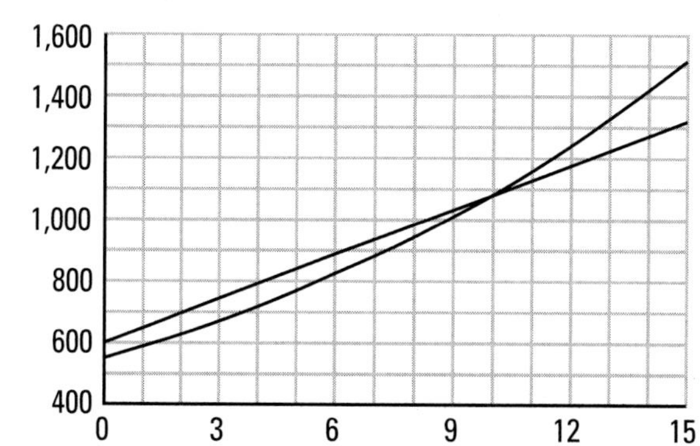

d. After 10 years, Carla's total will be more than John's.

$T_J = 600 + 48(10) = 600 + 480 = \$1{,}080$

$T_C = 550(1.07)^{10} = \$1{,}081.93$

Organizing

1. The income earned is equal to the product of the number of tickets sold and the price per ticket.

$I = (800 - 100P)P = 800P + 100P^2$

To get the modeling equation for total costs in terms of the price of the tickets, take the equation for cost based on number of tickets $C = 250 + 0.50T$ and substitute $800 - 100P$ for T. This gives the following:

$C = 250 + 0.50(800 - 100P)$

$= 250 + 400 - 50P$

$= 650 - 50P$

2. **See Teaching Master 19.**

a.
- Blue: $x = 17$
- Red: $x < 17$
- Green: $x > 17$

b. The equation can be solved by reasoning with the symbolic form as follows:

$20 + 0.5x = 3 + 1.5x$

$17 + 0.5x = 1.5x$

$17 = x$

From here, the inequalities can be solved by reasoning that, when $x > 17$, the value of $3 + 1.5x$ will be greater than the value of $20 + 0.5x$, since it increases at a faster rate. Similarly $20 + 0.5x > 3 + 1.5x$ when $x < 17$. A graphing calculator or computer software can be used to draw graphs or make tables of values. On the graph, the x-coordinate of the point of intersection is the solution to the equation. To solve the inequalities, consider the relative positions of the lines.

b. Write equations showing the total amounts of money that John and Carla would have withdrawn if they closed their accounts after n years.

c. Sketch graphs of the money total models, showing patterns under each plan for 15 years.

d. In how many years, if ever, will Carla's total be more than John's?

Organizing

1. Refer to Modeling Task 3, pages 57 and 58. Explain how the modeling equations $I = 800P - 100P^2$ and $C = 650 - 50P$ can be derived from the planning information about the basketball game.

2. The graphs below show the way two different variables depend on the same input variable x. One equation is $y_1 = 20 + 0.5x$. The other is $y_2 = 3 + 1.5x$.

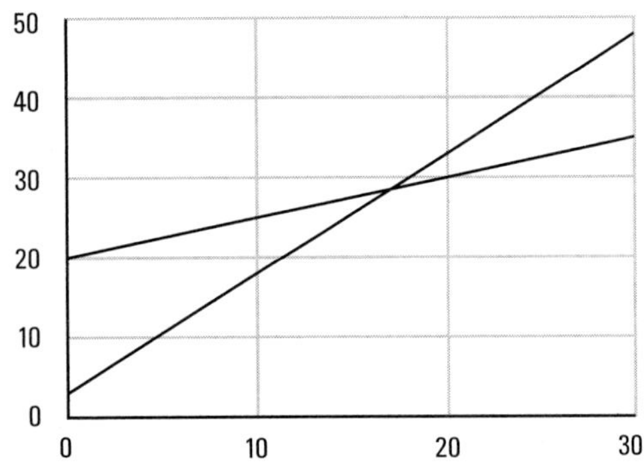

a. Make a copy of these graphs. On the x-axis, mark the points corresponding to solutions of the following equation and inequalities. If possible, use the colors suggested when you mark the points.

- In blue: $20 + 0.5x = 3 + 1.5x$
- In red: $20 + 0.5x > 3 + 1.5x$
- In green: $20 + 0.5x < 3 + 1.5x$

b. Explain how you could solve the equation and inequalities in Part a by reasoning with the symbolic forms and by using a graphing calculator or computer software.

3. The graphs below show the way two different variables depend on the same input variable x. One equation is $y_1 = \frac{50}{x^2}$. The other is $y_2 = x^2 - 5x$.

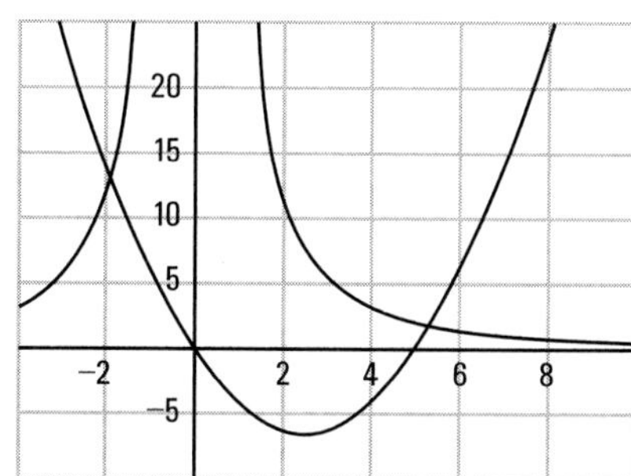

a. Make a copy of these graphs. If possible, color the graph of $y_1 = \frac{50}{x^2}$ in yellow.

b. What connections between equations and graphs for different model types allow you to match $y_1 = \frac{50}{x^2}$ and $y_2 = x^2 - 5x$ to their graphs in this case?

c. On the x-axis, mark the points corresponding to solutions of the following equation and inequalities. If possible, use the colors suggested.

- In blue: $\frac{50}{x^2} = x^2 - 5x$
- In red: $\frac{50}{x^2} > x^2 - 5x$
- In green: $\frac{50}{x^2} < x^2 - 5x$

d. Use the graph and trace or use the table commands of a graphing calculator or computer software to locate accurate estimates of the solutions to the equation and inequalities in Part c.

4. Even if you use technology-produced graphs or tables to solve equations and inequalities, it helps to know the number of solutions expected. That helps you catch mistakes that might be made in entering algebraic expressions or commands into the calculator or computer and provides a check on your selected viewing window. Suppose you are given a system of two equations relating two different variables to the same input variable.

a. Describe the possible number of solutions to the system if both equations are linear. Draw sketches to illustrate each possibility.

b. Describe the possible number of solutions to the system if one equation is linear and one equation is quadratic. Draw sketches to illustrate each possibility.

c. Describe the possible number of solutions to the system if one equation is linear and one equation is exponential. Draw sketches to illustrate each possibility.

d. Describe the possible number of solutions to the system if one equation is linear and one equation is inverse variation. Draw sketches to illustrate each possibility.

60 UNIT 1 • MULTIPLE-VARIABLE MODELS

3. See Teaching Master 19.

a. The curve marked by arrows is $y_1 = \frac{50}{x^2}$ and should be colored yellow.

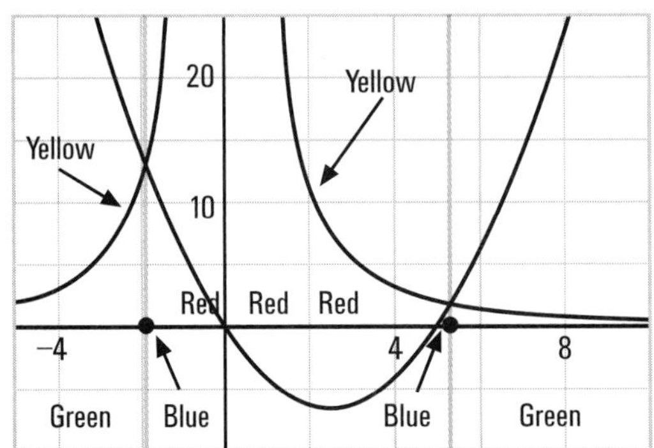

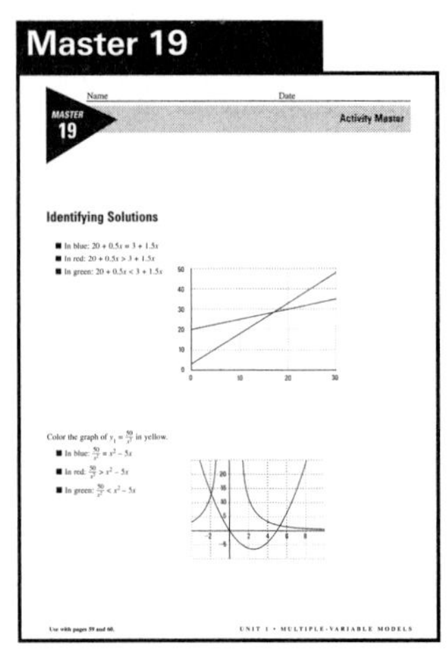

b. The graph of $y_1 = \frac{50}{x^2}$ will have the x- and y-axes as asymptotes. The graph of $y_2 = x^2 - 5x$ is a parabola that opens upward and whose vertex is not at the origin.

c. See graph in Part a.

- Blue: $x = -1.9$ and $x = 5.3$
- Red: $-1.9 < x < 5.3$
- Green: $x < -1.9$ and $x > 5.3$

d.
- $x \approx -1.93$ and $x \approx 5.33$
- $-1.93 < x < 5.33$ (except $x = 0$ where y_1 is not defined)
- $x < -1.93$ and $x > 5.33$

4. a. If both equations are linear, there can be either 0, 1, or an infinite number of solutions. If the two variables are related in the same way to an input variable, then the graphs would be identical and all points that satisfy one line would satisfy the other line.

0 solutions	1 solution	Infinite solutions
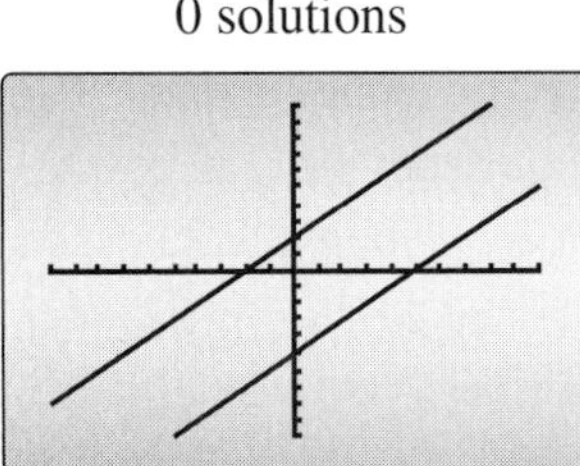	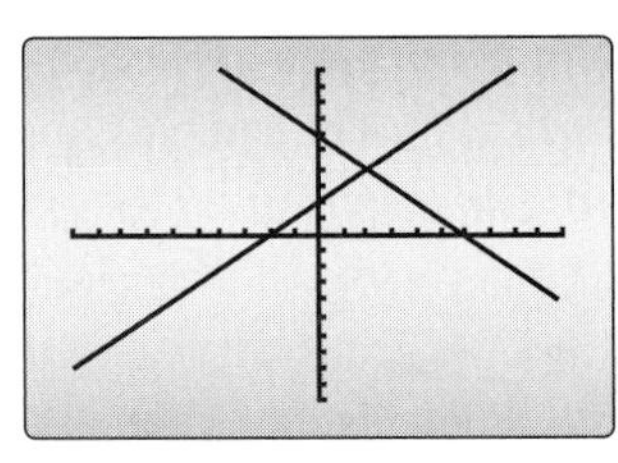	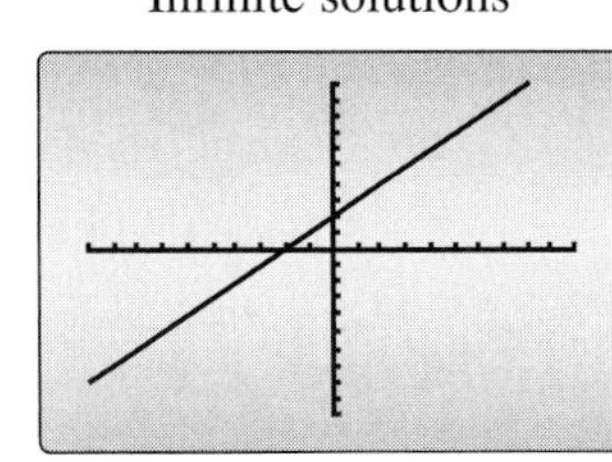

b. There can be either 0, 1, or 2 solutions.

0 solutions	1 solution	2 solutions
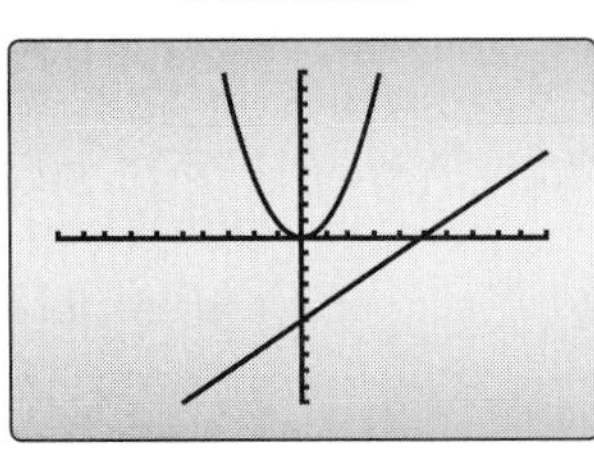	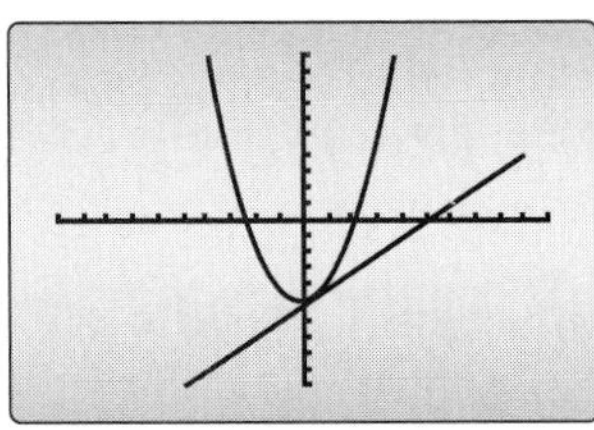	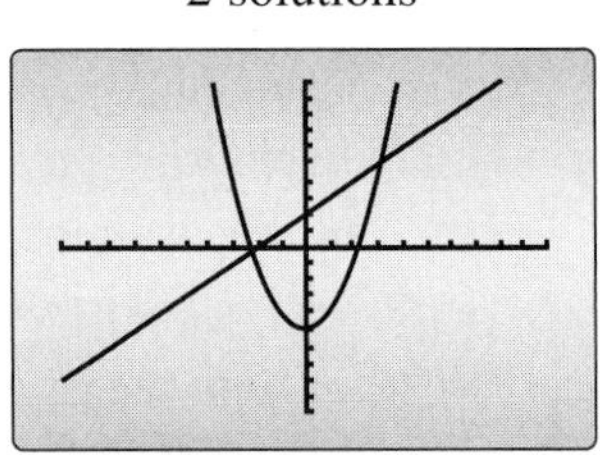

See additional Teaching Notes on page T90N.

MORE *continued*

Reflecting

1. Some of the relationships present are as follows:
   Number of units U is a function of price P per unit.
   Income I is a function of price P per unit.
   Income I is a function of number of units U.
   Operating costs C are a function of price P per unit.
   Operating costs C are a function of number of units U.
   Profit PR is a function of price per unit P.
   Profit PR is a function of number of units U.
2. They could have done a survey to obtain the equation for the number of tickets sold to obtain $T = 800 - 100P$. The cost equation could come from estimating the \$0.50 cost per ticket and a \$250 charge for the use of the gym or referee costs.
3. **a.** Responses will vary, but some possible responses include the level of skill needed, the maturity of the teenagers, the location of the jobs, and the types of jobs.

   b. Responses will vary, but some possible responses include the quality of the bus, the safety features of the bus, and the helpfulness of the rental agents.

   c. Responses will vary, but some possible responses include the number of people who attend the production, the cost of the theater, the cost of hiring the cast, the cost of cleanup, and money made from concessions. Interest level and quality of the performance would affect profit as well.
4. Responses will vary, but students should justify their choices.
5. **a.** Student responses may vary. Often, leasing a vehicle requires a smaller down payment or smaller monthly payments. However, you must keep the car for the agreed upon length of time, and usually there is a limit to the number of miles you may drive each year. If you go over the limit, you must pay a charge per mile for every mile over the limit. Another disadvantage is that at the end of the lease period you do not own the car and have nothing tangible to show for the money spent.

   b. Student responses will vary. The students might figure out the total cost to them over the period of time or use graphs or tables to compare different lease or loan options.

Extending

1. Specific examples for each general case are given below.
   - $ax + b = cx + d$
     0 solutions: $3x + 7 = 3x + 10$
     1 solution: $3x + 7 = -2x + 10$
     Infinite solutions: $3x + 7 = 3x + 7$
   - $ax + b = cx^2 + dx + c$
     0 solutions: $2x - 10 = x^2$
     1 solution: $7 = x^2 + 7$
     2 solutions: $2x + 10 = x^2$

See additional Teaching Notes on page T90N.

Reflecting

1. In this lesson and in the "Power Models" unit of Course 2, you saw that modeling business profit prospects often required consideration of several variables along with the relations among those variables. Key variables include number of units U produced and sold, operating costs C, price P per unit, income I, and profit PR. Using the language "is a function of," describe at least four different relations among U, C, P, I, and PR. (For example, "Income I is a function of units sold U and price P per unit.")

2. Refer to Modeling Task 3, pages 57 and 58. Explain how the economics class at Martin Luther King High School might have determined the modeling rules:

$$C = 250 + 0.50T$$

$$T = 800 - 100P$$

3. The situations of this lesson involved making choices. In each case, there were some mathematical variables to think about when making the choices. However, choices among options usually are not based solely on mathematics.
   a. What nonnumerical factors would you consider in planning a summer job program for teenagers?
   b. What nonnumerical factors would you consider in choosing a charter bus line for a school field trip?
   c. What factors other than ticket price would affect the profits of a musical production?

4. If you were going to use mathematical evidence to convince someone to follow your advice in one of the decision problems of this lesson, which presentation do you think would be most effective: a graph of the relations involved, a table of sample data on the relations involved, or some equations and their solutions concerning the relations involved? Give reasons for your choice.

5. Suppose after graduation you planned to buy a new car or truck.
   a. Research the advantages of leasing a vehicle. What are the disadvantages?
   b. How might you use the mathematics you have studied to help choose a lease or loan plan?

Extending

1. Look again at your answers to Organizing Task 4, page 60, and construct specific equations illustrating each possible pattern.

LESSON 3 • LINKED EQUATIONS 61

2. Think about various ways that you could solve each of the following types of equations.
   - $ax + b = cx + d$
   - $ax + b = cx^2 + dx + e$
   - $ax + b = c(d^x)$
   - $ax + b = \frac{c}{x^2}$

   a. Describe two different graphical ways in which you could solve each of these equations using a graphing calculator or computer software.

   b. In Investigation 4 of Lesson 2, several *properties of equality* were identified. (See page 37.) Two of those properties also relate to inverse operations. They are restated in a slightly different form below.

   (1) If $a + b = c$, then $a = c - b$.

   (2) If $ab = c$, then $a = c \div b$ $\left(\text{or } a = \frac{c}{b}\right)$, provided $b \neq 0$.

   To what properties of equality do these two properties correspond?

   c. Use these properties of equality to explain why both graphical methods you proposed in Part a give the same solutions.

   d. Are there also two different methods for solving these equations using calculator- or computer-produced tables of values? Explain your thinking.

3. The properties of equality restated in Part b of Extending Task 2 are useful for rewriting equations in equivalent forms in which solutions are seen readily. There are two useful, corresponding *properties of inequality*:

   (1) If $a + b > c$, then $a > c - b$.

   (2) If $ab > c$ and $b > 0$, then $a > \frac{c}{b}$.

   If $ab > c$ and $b < 0$, then $a < \frac{c}{b}$.

   a. Test these properties of inequality using different choices of values for a, b, and c.

   b. Write and test corresponding properties for the relation <.

   c. Explain how the properties of equality in Extending Task 2 and these properties of inequality support the reasoning with symbolic forms you used to solve the equation and inequalities in Organizing Task 2, Part b (page 59).

   d. What do you see as the advantages and disadvantages of solving equations and inequalities using symbolic reasoning rather than graphical and tabular methods?

62 UNIT 1 • MULTIPLE-VARIABLE MODELS

Unit 1

2. **a.** One method is to make each side of the equation a different function in the functions list, and then graph them to look for the points of intersection. Another method is to set the equation equal to zero, enter the nonzero expression into the calculator, and then graph the function; the solutions will be the x-intercepts.

b. Statement (1) corresponds to the property "If $p = q$, then $p - r = q - r$." In this case, $p = a + b$, $q = c$, and $r = b$.

Statement (2) corresponds to the property "If $p = q$ and $r \neq 0$, $p \div r = q \div r$." In this case, $p = ab$, $q = c$, and $r = b$.

c. Using the properties of equality only changes the form of the equation, not the solutions of the equation.

d. The same processes can be used to generate the tables of values as were used to generate the graphs. In the first process, look for values of x that produce the same values in each column of the table. In the second process, look for x values that produce the value of zero in the table.

3. **a.** Student responses may vary.

(1) $4 + 2 > 5 \Rightarrow 4 > 5 - 2 \Rightarrow 4 > 3$

(2) $4(2) > 6 \Rightarrow 4 > \frac{6}{2} \Rightarrow 4 > 3$

$4(-2) > -10 \Rightarrow 4 < \frac{-10}{-2} \Rightarrow 4 < 5$

b. If $a + b < c$, then $a < c - b$.

$4 + 5 < 10 \Rightarrow 4 < 10 - 5 \Rightarrow 4 < 5$

If $ab < c$ and $b > 0$, then $a < \frac{c}{b}$.

$4(5) < 30 \Rightarrow 4 < \frac{30}{5} \Rightarrow 4 < 6$

If $ab < c$ and $b < 0$, then $a > \frac{c}{b}$.

$5(-2) < 8 \Rightarrow 5 > \frac{8}{-2} \Rightarrow 5 > -4$

c. Any valid sequence of steps is acceptable.

■ $20 + 0.5x = 3 + 1.5x$

$17 + 0.5x = 1.5x$ Subtraction Property of Equality

$17 = 1.0x$ Subtraction Property of Equality

$17 = x$

■ $20 + 0.5x > 3 + 1.5x$

$17 + 0.5x > 1.5x$ Subtraction Property of Inequality

$17 > 1.0x$ Subtraction Property of Inequality

$17 > x$

■ $20 + 0.5x < 3 + 1.5x$

$17 + 0.5x < 1.5x$ Subtraction Property of Inequality

$17 < 1.0x$ Subtraction Property of Inequality

$17 < x$

d. One advantage is that it is easier to get an exact solution using the properties of equality and inequality. A major disadvantage is that the properties may not allow you to determine the solution, or even if one exists, when both sides of the equation are not linear.

See Assessment Resources pages 13–18.

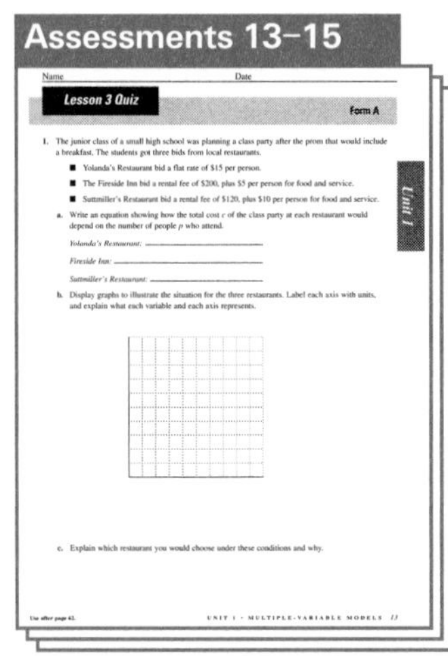

Assessments 16–18

Master 20

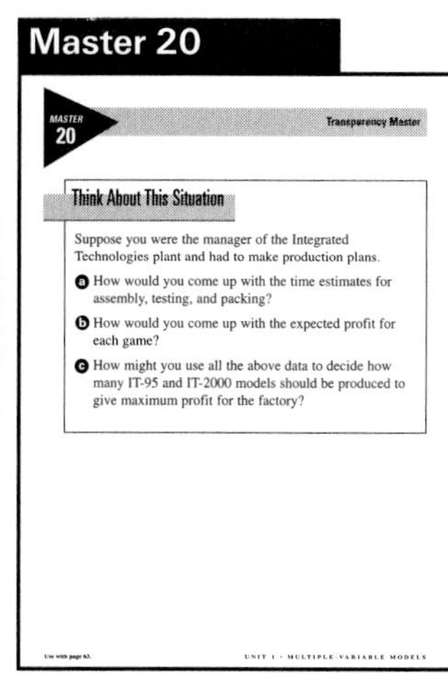
MASTER 20 Transparency Master

Think About This Situation

Suppose you were the manager of the Integrated Technologies plant and had to make production plans.

a How would you come up with the time estimates for assembly, testing, and packing?

b How would you come up with the expected profit for each game?

c How might you use all the above data to decide how many IT-95 and IT-2000 models should be produced to give maximum profit for the factory?

Lesson 4 *Linear Programming*

LESSON OVERVIEW **In this lesson, linear programming is used to generate the need for graphing linear inequalities. Students are guided by Investigations 1–3 to discover the feasible region for a linear programming problem, what the boundaries of that region are, and that the best solution is always at a vertex of the feasible region. In Investigation 4, students solve systems of linear inequalities in a purely mathematical context.**

NOTE: In most problems in this lesson, students will be *crossing out* regions that they do not want, so that the solution set is the *nonshaded portion that remains.* This is not the conventional pattern, but it is helpful for students to be able to see the feasible region of a linear programming problem or the solution set of a system of linear inequalities rather than to have them shaded over.

Lesson Objectives

- To solve systems of linear equations
- To solve linear programming problems
- To graph inequalities or systems of inequalities in the forms $ax + by \leq c$, $ax + by \geq c$, $y \leq a + bx$, and $y \geq a + bx$

LAUNCH **full-class discussion**

Think About This Situation

See Teaching Master 20.

In this introductory situation, students are not expected to know the answers. The goal here is to stimulate their thinking and to get them to understand that these are important questions to ask if you are in business and you want to make money.

In order to help your students connect with this situation, you might want to have a preliminary discussion about the conditions listed. You could ask, "Why might there be only 240 hours of technician time available for assembly work?" (Only 30 trained technicians, each working an 8-hour day.) "Why might the packaging department be able to handle only 500 games per day?" (This might be a function of the number of employees in the department or a function of the equipment available.) "If they make more profit on the IT–2000, why do they make the other model?"

The point of these questions is to make the situation easier to imagine: a busy factory with a specific number of employees, each engaged in his or her own task. Students should begin to realize that the variables (number of models; testing, assembling, and packaging times) are interrelated.

See additional Teaching Notes on page T90N.

Lesson 4 Linear Programming

In previous lessons, you've seen that important decisions in business often involve many variables and relations among those variables. The key to making good decisions is finding a way to organize and compare options.

For example, the plant manager of the Integrated Technologies factory must plan for and supervise production of two video game models, the basic IT-95 and the more advanced IT-2000. Demand for both games is high, so IT can sell whatever is produced.

To plan the work schedule, the manager has to think about these conditions:

- Assembly of each IT-95 takes 0.6 hour, and each IT-2000 takes 0.3 hour of technician time. The plant can apply at most 240 hours of technician time to assembly work each day.
- Testing of each IT-95 takes 0.2 hour, and each IT-2000 takes 0.4 hour. The plant can apply at most 160 hours of technician time each day for testing.
- Packaging time is the same for each model. The packaging department of the plant can handle at most 500 games per day.
- The company makes a profit of $50 on each IT-95 and $75 on each IT-2000.

Think About This Situation

Suppose you were the manager of the Integrated Technologies plant and had to make production plans.

a How would you come up with the time estimates for assembly, testing, and packaging?

b How would you come up with the expected profit for each game?

c How might you use all the above data to decide how many IT-95 and IT-2000 models should be produced to give maximum profit for the factory?

LESSON 4 • LINEAR PROGRAMMING 63

INVESTIGATION 1 Picture Your Options

Many problems like those in the Integrated Technologies factory are solved by a mathematical strategy called **linear programming**. The following investigations will help you understand and learn how to use this important problem-solving strategy, as well as some of the mathematical ideas and skills on which it depends.

The production scheduling problem at Integrated Technologies requires choice among many options. The manager must decide what combination of IT-95 and IT-2000 models will give greatest profit. But there are **constraints** or limits on the choice: there can be *at most* 240 hours of assembly labor required, *at most* 160 hours of testing labor required, and a total of *at most* 500 video games to be packaged for shipping.

1. One way to search for the production plan that will maximize profit is to make some guesses and test the profit prospects for those guesses. For each of the following possible combinations of IT-95 and IT-2000 models, check to see if the three constraints are satisfied. If the constraints are satisfied, find the profit that could be earned.

a. Suppose the manager schedules production of 100 IT-95 and 200 IT-2000 models.

- Will the assembly time for these games be within the limit of 240 hours per day?
- Will the testing time for these games be within the limit of 160 hours per day?
- Will the total number of units produced fall within the packaging limit of 500 per day?
- If the constraints are satisfied, what profit would be earned?

b. Suppose the manager schedules production of 200 IT-95 and 100 IT-2000 models. Investigate the four questions in Part a for this case.

c. Answer the questions in Part a, assuming the manager schedules production of 400 IT-95 and 100 IT-2000 models.

d. Which of these production combinations is the best choice?

As you checked the possible production plans in Activity 1, you tested many options for each phase of production. It would be nice to have a systematic way of organizing the search for a maximum profit decision. One part of the linear programming strategy for solving such problems is to look at a graph of the options.

64 UNIT 1 • MULTIPLE-VARIABLE MODELS

EXPLORE small-group investigation

INVESTIGATION 1 Picture Your Options

This investigation leads students to an optimal solution using only the graph. Because students are not asked to define the constraints symbolically, their answers for the maximum profit or minimum weight may not agree at first attempt. This difficulty is resolved in the next investigation.

The exploration will move along efficiently if different groups are assigned different columns to check in Activity 2. An overhead transparency of the grid makes it possible for each group to show their conclusions about feasibility and to contribute to understanding the whole picture.

After Activity 3, it is best if you draw all students together and discuss the shape of the feasible region. Without boundary lines drawn, it is not clear exactly what shape the region is. Repeat the same kind of summary after Activity 5. At this time, the exact shape of the regions still may not be clear, but students should have realized that the optimal points seem to fall on or near the edge of the region they are describing. Ask them, "Why does it make sense that all the nonfeasible points extend upward and outward in the example about profit?" (We were trying to find combinations that would stay *under* certain limits.) "Why does it make sense that the *feasible* points extend upward and outward in the example about dietary needs?" (We were trying to find combinations that would stay *above* certain limits.)

1. **a.**
- Yes, 120 hours < 240 hours
- Yes, 100 hours < 160 hours
- Yes, 300 < 500
- $20,000

b.
- Yes, 150 hours < 240 hours
- Yes, 80 hours < 160 hours
- Yes, 300 < 500
- $17,500

c.
- No, 270 hours > 240 hours
- Yes, 120 hours < 160 hours
- Yes, 500 = 500
- Constraints are not met, so there is no need to calculate profit.

d. Among these, 100 IT-95s and 200 IT-2000s is the best choice.

Master 21

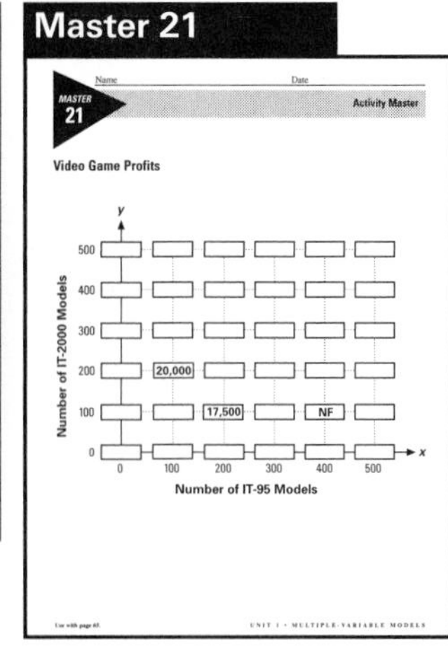

EXPLORE *continued*

2. **See Teaching Master 21.**
   a. The $17,500 at the point (200, 100) is the profit that would be made if 200 IT-95 and 100 IT-2000 models were produced. The "not feasible" at the point (400, 100) indicates that it is not possible to produce that combination of models and stay within the constraints.
   b. Student responses may vary. If the combination (400, 100) can't be produced because it exceeds the available assembly time, it should be obvious that the combinations (400, 200), (400, 300), (400, 400), and (400, 500) can't be produced either, because they will require even more assembly time.
   c–d. **You may wish to ask students how they would like to share the workload for these items. You can place a transparency of Teaching Master 21 on the overhead or project it onto the blackboard and have the students record their results for the entire class to see. Encourage the students to look for patterns so that they don't have to check every lattice point. For example, if the point (100, 400) satisfies all constraints, then the points (100, 300), (100, 200), and (100, 100) will also. Then all that will need to be done for these points is to find the profit.**

Video Game Profits

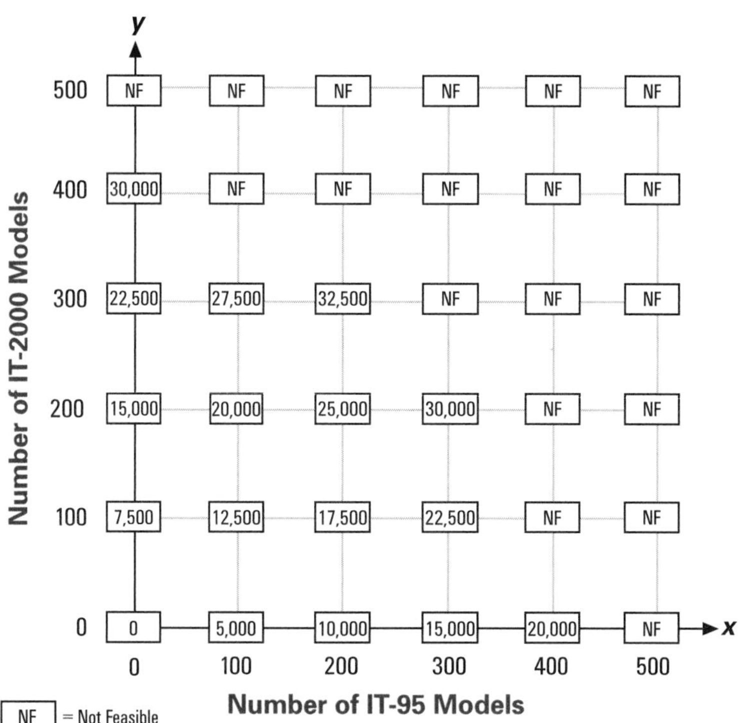

If x represents the number of IT-95 models and y represents the number of IT-2000 models, then the scheduling goal is to find a pair (x, y) that meets the constraints and gives maximum profit. Using a grid like the one below, you can search for the combination of video game models that will give maximum profit. The point (100, 200) represents 100 IT-95 and 200 IT-2000 video games. These numbers satisfy the constraints and give a profit of \$50(100) + \$75(200) or \$20,000.

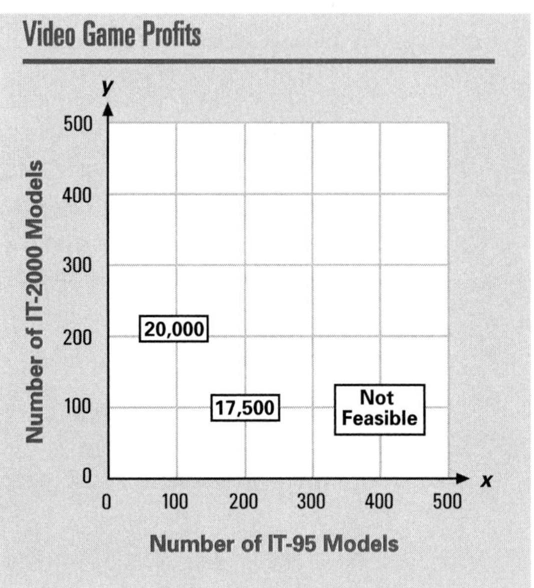

2. Each **lattice point** on the grid (where horizontal and vertical grid lines intersect) represents a possible combination of video game models. Points whose coordinates satisfy all the constraints are called **feasible points**.

   a. Based on your work in Activity 1, explain the labels on the points with coordinates (200, 100) and (400, 100).

   b. Think about how you checked if the three constraints were satisfied. Name another point that you suspect will not be a feasible (possible) point. Check your conjecture.

   c. For the remaining lattice points on this graph, check to see if the constraints are satisfied by the coordinates. Look for patterns that may simplify your work.

   d. If the coordinates of a point satisfy all constraints, calculate and record on a copy of the grid the profit that would be earned by that combination of IT-95 and IT-2000 models. If the point is not feasible, write "NF" on the lattice point to indicate that it is not feasible.

LESSON 4 • LINEAR PROGRAMMING 65

3. Based on the completed grid:

a. Describe the region where all three constraints are satisfied.

b. Pick the number of model IT-95 and IT-2000 video games that you think the factory should produce in order to make maximum profit. Be prepared to explain why you believe that your answer is correct.

Problems like this production scheduling problem—with several *variables*, several *constraints*, and an *objective* like maximizing profit—occur in many different situations. For example, think about the variables and constraints in choosing the foods you eat. Usually you choose things that taste good, but it is important to consider also the cost of that food and the way it satisfies your body's dietary needs.

4. For some people, like athletes or astronauts, selection of a good diet is a carefully planned scientific process. Each person wants a high performance diet at minimal cost or (in the case of astronauts) minimal total weight. Consider the following, simplified version of the problem facing NASA space flight planners who must provide food for astronauts.

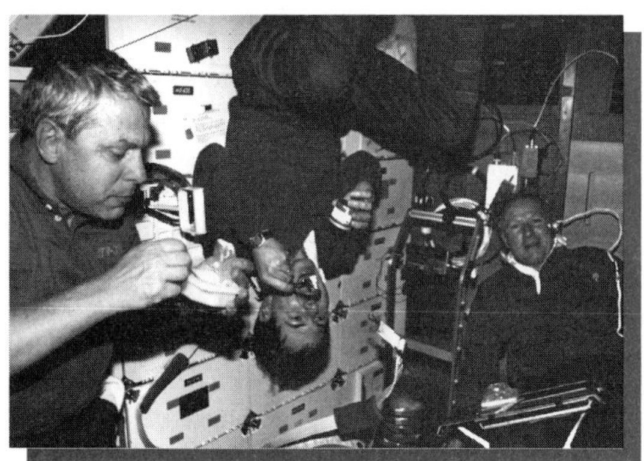

- Suppose there are two kinds of food to be carried on a space shuttle trip: special food bars and cartons of a special drink.
- Each food bar provides 5 grams of fat, 40 grams of carbohydrate, and 8 grams of protein.
- Each carton of drink provides 6 grams of fat, 25 grams of carbohydrate, and 15 grams of protein.
- Minimum daily requirements for each astronaut are *at least* 61 grams of fat, *at least* 350 grams of carbohydrate, and *at least* 103 grams of protein.
- Each food bar weighs 65 grams and each drink weighs 118 grams.

Determining what combination of food bars and drinks will give minimum daily requirements of fat, carbohydrate, and protein with least total weight seems complicated. But you can get a good start toward a solution by doing some systematic testing.

66 UNIT 1 • MULTIPLE-VARIABLE MODELS

3. **a.** Students may describe this region as the lower left corner of the graph. Some will think that all of the points lie below a line, and they may try to describe this line. Some will think that the shape is a quarter circle. The shape is actually bound by a pentagon, but that will be difficult for students to see at this time; it is not necessary that they draw this conclusion yet.

   b. Producing 200 IT-95 models and 300 IT-2000 models maximizes the profit, because the $32,500 profit is the largest in the region. Some students may think that (200, 350) or (225, 300) may still be feasible while giving larger profits. They should check their thinking against the constraints and profit equation.

Unit 1

Master 22

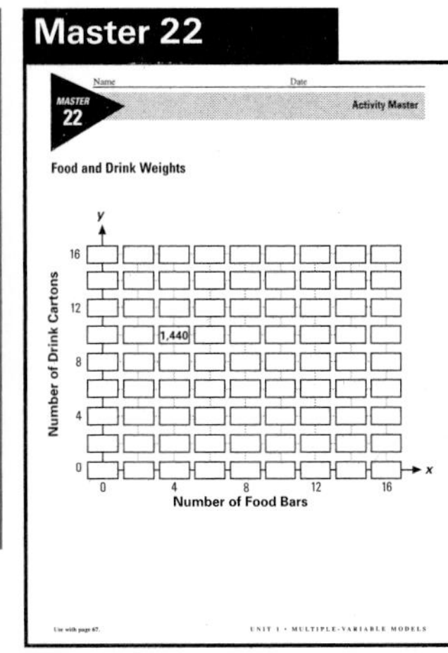

EXPLORE *continued*

4. See Teaching Master 22.

a. ■ Fat $4(5) + 10(6) = 20 + 60 = 80 > 61$
Carbohydrate $4(40) + 10(25) = 160 + 250 = 410 > 350$
Protein $4(8) + 10(15) = 32 + 150 = 182 > 103$
Weight $4(65) + 10(118) = 260 + 1{,}180 = 1{,}440$

■ Fat $10(5) + 4(6) = 74 > 61$
Carbohydrate $10(40) + 4(25) = 500 > 350$
Protein $10(8) + 4(15) = 140 > 103$
Weight $10(65) + 4(118) = 1{,}122$

■ Fat $10(5) + 10(6) = 110 > 61$
Carbohydrate $10(40) + 10(25) = 650 > 350$
Protein $10(8) + 10(15) = 230 > 103$
Weight $10(65) + 10(118) = 1{,}830$

■ This option doesn't meet the constraints for fat, carbohydrate, and protein.
Fat $4(5) + 4(6) = 44 < 61$
Carbohydrate $4(40) + 4(25) = 260 < 350$
Protein $4(8) + 4(15) = 92 < 103$

b–c. You can project Teaching Master 22 onto the blackboard so that the students can post their calculations in order to share them with the entire class. Once again, encourage students to look for patterns that will help them do this efficiently.

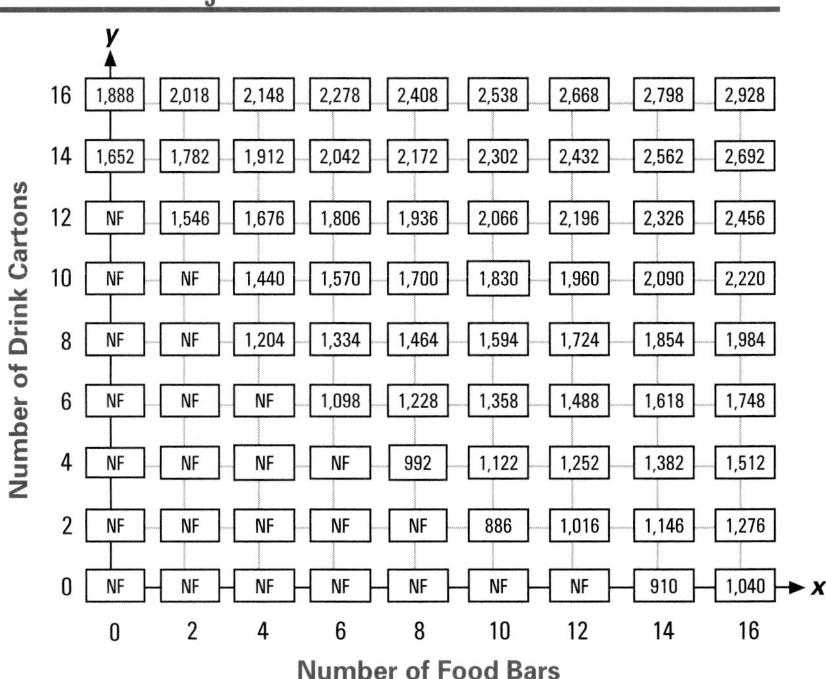

5. a. Some students may describe the region as the upper right-hand portion of the graph. Some students will believe that the feasible points all lie above some line.

b. The minimum weight seems to be 886 grams with 10 bars and 2 drinks. That weight is the lowest of the lattice points shown in the region.

a. For each of the following numbers of food bars and drink cartons, check to see if they will provide at least the daily minimums of fat, carbohydrate, and protein. Then find the total weights of the feasible combinations.

- 4 food bars and 10 cartons of drink
- 10 food bars and 4 cartons of drink
- 10 food bars and 10 cartons of drink
- 4 food bars and 4 cartons of drink

b. Record your findings on a copy of the grid below. The case of 4 food bars and 10 drink cartons already has been plotted. Fill in data for the other combinations you tested in Part a.

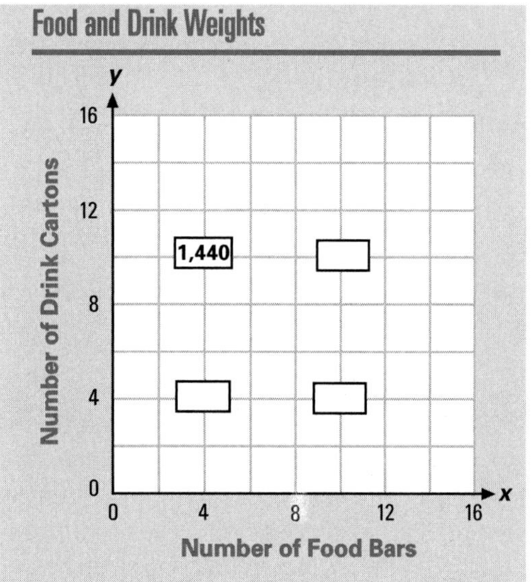

c. Now test the remaining lattice points on this grid to get a picture of the *feasible* combinations of food bars and drink cartons that meet the *constraints*. For each feasible combination, find the total weight and plot it on your copy of the grid.

5. Now analyze the completed grid showing the predicted weight for each feasible lattice point.

a. Describe the region where constraints are met.

b. Use your work to decide how many food bars and drink cartons should be used per astronaut in order to provide minimum daily food requirements while making total weight as small as possible. Be prepared to explain how you can be sure that your answer is correct.

LESSON 4 • LINEAR PROGRAMMING 67

Checkpoint

Problems that can be analyzed by linear programming have several common features: variables, constraints, and an objective.

a What are the variables, constraints, and objective in the video-game-production problem?

b What are the variables, constraints, and objective in the astronaut-diet problem?

c What is a feasible point in a linear programming problem? What would feasible points and "not feasible" points tell you in the video-game-production and astronaut-diet problems?

Be prepared to compare your reponses to those of other groups.

On Your Own

A new store has an option to lease selling space of up to 10,000 square feet. The leased space would be divided into two sections, one for books and the other for music and videos. Furnishings for the two kinds of selling space cost $5 per square foot for books and $7 per square foot for music and videos. The store has a budget of at most $60,000 for furnishings. Each square foot of book-selling space generates an average of $75 per month in sales; each square foot of music-and-video-selling space generates an average of $95 per month in sales.

a. Identify the variables, constraints, and objective.

b. Find two feasible points and one not feasible point, and evaluate the objective at the two feasible points.

c. What mix of book-and-music/video-selling space will maximize sales?

INVESTIGATION 2 Using an Algebraic Model

As you worked on the production-planning problem for Integrated Technologies and on the astronaut-diet problem, you probably thought, "There's *got* to be an easier way than testing all these possible combinations!" It often helps to use a computer or calculator in exploring the many possible options. To use these technology tools, it is essential to express the problem in algebraic form.

Think again about the situation at Integrated Technologies. Recall that assembly time required for each IT-95 was 0.6 hour and for each IT-2000 was 0.3 hour. Using x to represent the number of IT-95 models and y to represent the number of IT-2000 models, the constraint "at most 240 hours of assembly time per day" can be written $0.6x + 0.3y \leq 240$.

68 UNIT 1 • MULTIPLE-VARIABLE MODELS

SHARE AND SUMMARIZE full-class discussion

Checkpoint

See Teaching Master 23.

If your students seem to be grasping the concepts in this investigation, you may wish to use only the Checkpoint on page 72 (following Investigation 2).

ⓐ The variables are x, the number of IT-95 models, and y, the number of IT-2000 models. The constraints are the limitations on production. Assembly of each IT-95 takes 0.6 hour and each IT-2000 takes 0.3 hour of technician time. The total technician time for assembly work can be, at most, 240 hours each day. Testing time can be, at most, 160 hours per day; the IT-95 models take 0.2 hour while the IT-2000 models require 0.4 hour. The company can pack, at most, 500 video games per day. The objective function is the profit that is made.

ⓑ The variables for the astronaut diet problem are the number of food bars, x, and the number of drink cartons, y. The constraints of the problem are the amounts of fat, carbohydrate, and protein that are required. The objective function is the weight.

ⓒ A feasible point is a point that satisfies all of the constraints (or conditions) of the prolem. A nonfeasible point does not satisfy at least one of the constraints; it tells you, for example, that the particular combination of video game models (or food bars and drinks) should not be considered as a solution to the problem.

Master 23

MASTER 23 — Transparency Master

Checkpoint

Problems that can be analyzed by linear programming have several common features: variables, constraints, and an objective.

ⓐ What are the variables, the constraints, and the objective in the video-game-production problem?

ⓑ What are the variables, constraints, and objective in the astronaut-diet problem?

ⓒ What is a feasible point in a linear programming problem? What would feasible points and "not feasible" points tell you in the video-game-production and astronaut-diet problems?

Be prepared to compare your responses to those of other groups.

Use with page 68. UNIT 1 • MULTIPLE-VARIABLE MODELS

Unit 1

APPLY individual task

On Your Own

a. The variables are the areas of two sections of space x for books and y for music and videos. The constraints are $x + y \leq 10{,}000$ square feet of space and $5x + 7y \leq 60{,}000$ dollars for furnishings. The objective function is dollars in sales S represented by $S = 75x + 95y$.

b. Students will find a variety of feasible and nonfeasible points, which should agree with the regions shown below. It is not expected that students will make this graph.

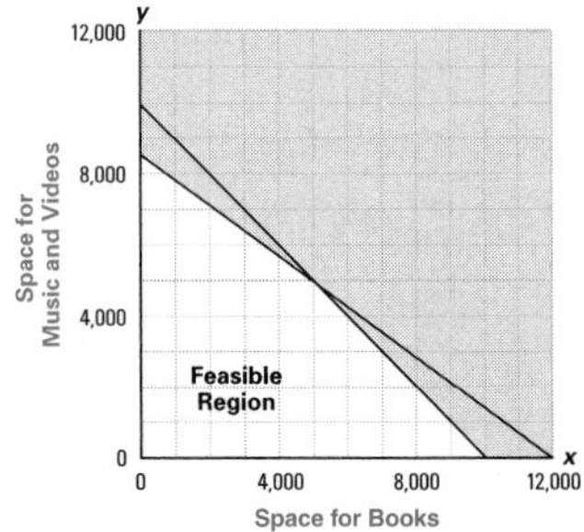

c. The maximum sales of \$850,000 per month will occur if there is 5,000 square feet leased for books and 5,000 square feet leased for music and videos.

See additional Teaching Notes on page T90O.

Unit 1

EXPLORE ***continued***

1. **a.** $0.6x$ represents the amount of time needed to assemble x IT-95s.
   $0.3y$ represents the amount of time needed to assemble y IT-2000s.
   $0.6x + 0.3y$ represents the total amount of time needed to assemble x IT-95s and y IT-2000s.
   b. ■ $0.2x + 0.4y \leq 160$
   ■ $x + y \leq 500$
   ■ *Profit* $= 50x + 75y$
2. **a–b.** Students should substitute the coordinates of their point into the assembly time constraint equation $0.6x + 0.3y \leq 240$.

Unit 1

1. Build an algebraic model for the video-game-production problem.

   a. First analyze the inequality $0.6x + 0.3y \leq 240$. What is represented by $0.6x$? By $0.3y$? By $0.6x + 0.3y$?

   b. Now write inequalities and expressions to represent the following in symbolic form.

      - Testing of each IT-95 takes 0.2 hours and each IT-2000 takes 0.4 hours. The plant can apply at most 160 hours of technician time each day for testing.
      - Packaging time is the same for each video game model. The packaging department of the plant can handle at most 500 games per day.
      - The company makes a profit of \$50 on each IT-95 and \$75 on each IT-2000.

In the language of linear programming, the last expression you wrote is called an **objective function** because it shows how the goal of the problem is a function of, or depends on, the input variables.

Translating a problem into algebraic form is one step toward a solution. But you still have to figure out how to use the *constraint inequalities* and the objective function to solve the given problem. By writing constraints in symbolic form, you can use a graphing calculator or computer software to help produce a graph of the *feasible points*.

2. Look again at the Integrated Technologies scheduling problem and the assembly time constraint. The graph below shows points meeting the assembly time constraint $0.6x + 0.3y \leq 240$. *Points that are* ***not*** *feasible have been shaded out of the picture.*

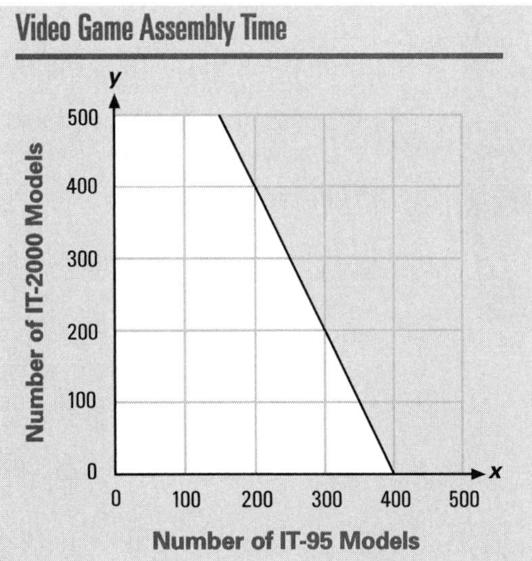

   a. Have each member of your group select a different point from the shaded region and verify that it is not a feasible point.

LESSON 4 • LINEAR PROGRAMMING 69

b. Now, have each group member select a different feasible point and verify that its coordinates satisfy the assembly time constraint inequality.

c. Next, focus on points that lie along the boundary line of the feasible set.

- What do you notice about assembly time required for those combinations of IT-95 and IT-2000 models?
- What is the equation of this boundary line?

d. Share ideas with other students for graphing the boundary of this constraint on feasible points quickly, by hand or using your graphing calculator.

e. Does it seem reasonable that all the feasible points are on one side of the line and all points that are not feasible are on the opposite side of the line? Explain your thinking.

3. Now, consider the packaging time and testing time constraints at Integrated Technologies.

a. On two separate grids, locate points that meet the constraints $x + y \leq 500$ and $0.2x + 0.4y \leq 160$ by shading out the points that are not feasible.

b. Using your results from Part a and a copy of the graph in Activity 2, shade all the points that are not feasible. Describe the region where points have coordinates that meet all three constraints. Describe the boundary of the feasible set you've found.

c. Describe at least three different ways you could find the point of intersection of a pair of boundary conditions. Choose one of those methods and find the coordinates of the point of intersection of a pair of lines on your graph.

d. If you have entered the equation of the boundary line for each constraint in the functions list, another quick way to find the point of intersection of a pair of boundary equations is to use the "intersect" option, if available, on your graphing calculator or computer software. Using the calculator option typically involves selecting the two "curves" whose intersection you wish to find. Consult your manual to learn how to use this option. Find the coordinates of the point of intersection for each remaining pair of boundary lines.

e. Finally, evaluate the objective function, $P = 50x + 75y$, at various points in the feasible region. Try to find the point that gives the largest possible profit. Think about ways to do this without checking every possible (x, y) pair: are there reasonable places to look for the values of x and y that will maximize profit?

f. What would be your recommendation on the numbers of IT–95 and IT–2000 video games that Integrated Technologies should plan to produce each day?

70 UNIT 1 • MULTIPLE-VARIABLE MODELS

2. c. ■ The assembly time for all of the combinations on the boundary line is 240 hours.
   ■ The boundary is the line with equation $0.6x + 0.3y = 240$.

   d. To graph this using a calculator, change the inequality in the constraint equation to an equality, then solve the equation for y. Next, enter the equation in the graphing calculator. It is not necessary to simplify: $y = (240 - 0.6x) \div 0.3$. One way to graph it by hand is to find the two intercepts, and then draw the line containing them.

   e. This probably will seem reasonable to most students. The inequality is essentially a "$y \leq \ldots$" statement. Once a nonfeasible point is found, then all points with the same x-coordinate and a larger y-coordinate also will be nonfeasible. These are all on the same side of the line. Once a feasible point is found, then all points with the same x-coordinate and a smaller y-coordinate also will be feasible. Students should observe that a larger y value would increase $0.6x + 0.3y$, and the total value may exceed 240.

3. **See Teaching Masters 24 and 25.**

   a. See the graphs of $x + y \leq 500$ and $0.2x + 0.4y \leq 160$ below. (You may wish to have students use two pieces of paper with the same size scales and grid for all the constraint equations, so that they can superimpose them and hold them up to the light for Part b.)

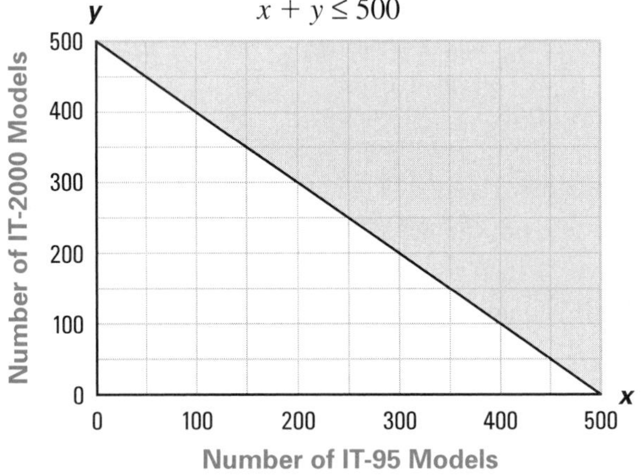

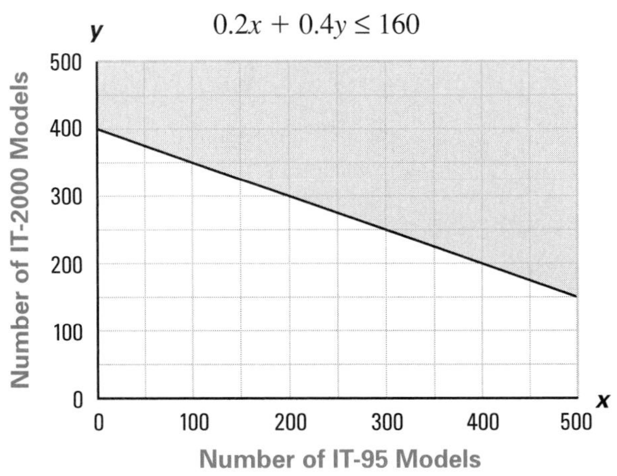

See additional Teaching Notes on page T90P.

Masters 24–25

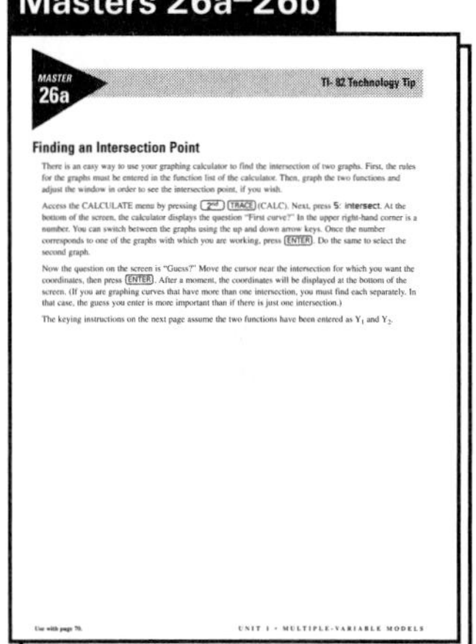

Masters 26a–26b

Masters 27a–27b

MASTER 27a — TI-83 Technology Tip

Finding an Intersection Point

Unit 1

Master 28

MASTER 28 Activity Master

Astronaut Food and Drink

Master 29

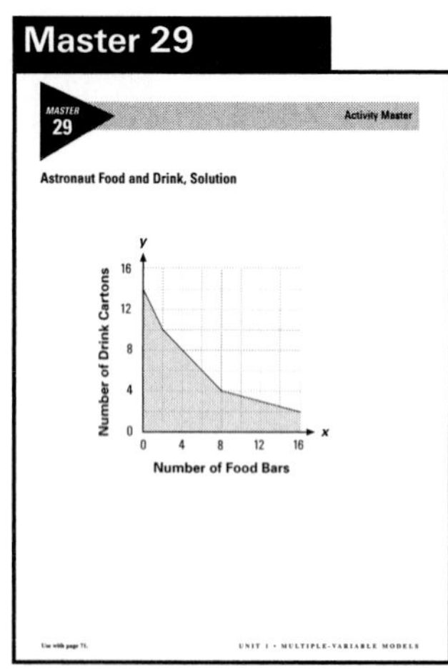

EXPLORE *continued*

4. **See Teaching Masters 28 and 29.**

   a. Letting x represent the number of food bars and y represent the number of drink cartons, the constraints and objective function are as follows:

   - $5x + 6y \geq 61$
   - $40x + 25y \geq 350$
   - $8x + 15y \geq 103$
   - Minimize weight; weight $= 65x + 118y$

   b. Astronaut Food and Drink

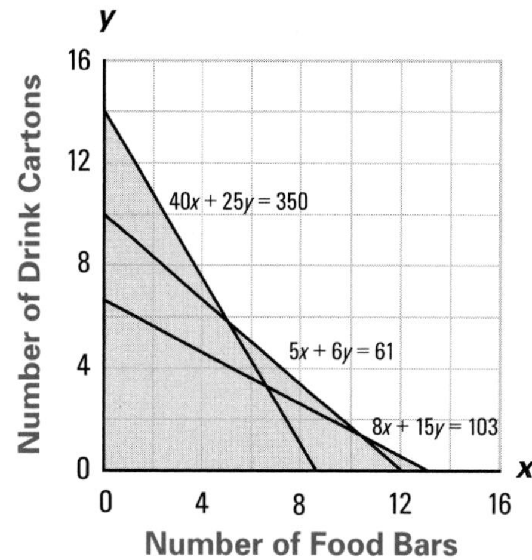

   c. The point that gives the minimum weight is (11, 1). Students may make the connection that this point is at a vertex of the feasible region.

   d. Each astronaut should have 11 food bars and 1 drink carton per day. This combination satisfies all of the daily requirements and only weighs 833 grams.

As you located the feasible set and the maximum profit point for the video-game-production problem, you probably discovered ways to use what you know about linear equations and inequalities to speed the location process. Test your ideas on the astronaut-diet problem described in Activity 4 of Investigation 1 (page 66).

4. Recall that there are two kinds of food to be carried on a space shuttle trip: special food bars and cartons of a special drink.

- Each food bar provides 5 grams of fat, 40 grams of carbohydrate, and 8 grams of protein.
- Each carton of drink provides 6 grams of fat, 25 grams of carbohydrate, and 15 grams of protein.
- Each food bar weighs 65 grams and each drink weighs 118 grams.

a. Translate the *constraints* and *objective* into algebraic form:

- Include *at least* 61 grams of fat.
- Include *at least* 350 grams of carbohydrate.
- Include *at least* 103 grams of protein.
- Keep total weight of food bars and drink cartons as low as possible.

b. On a copy of a grid like the one below, graph each constraint to show the feasible set of (*food bars*, *drink cartons*) combinations.

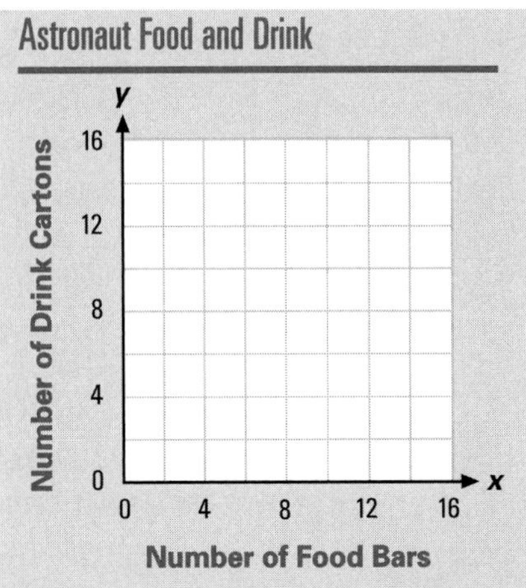

c. Evaluate the objective function at various points in the feasible region to find the point that gives the smallest possible weight. Think about ways to do this without checking every possible (x, y) pair: are there reasonable places to look for the values of x and y that will minimize weight?

d. What would be your recommendation for the combination of food bars and drink cartons that will provide the daily minimums of fat, carbohydrate, and protein with least total weight?

LESSON 4 • LINEAR PROGRAMMING 71

Checkpoint

The video-game-production and astronaut-diet problems are examples of *linear programming* problems. Each involved several *variables*, several *constraints* or limits on those variables, a *feasible set* of values for the variables that meet the constraints, and an *objective function*.

a Review your work on the video-game-production problem.

- What are the variables, constraints, and objective function?
- How can the conditions be expressed in symbolic form?
- What is the feasible set in the problem, and how can the boundaries of that region be located with the help of a graphing calculator or computer software?
- Where in the feasible set does the objective function seem to take its maximum value?

b Review your work on the astronaut-diet problem.

- What are the variables, constraints, and objective function?
- How can the conditions be expressed in symbolic form?
- What is the feasible set in the problem, and how can the boundaries of that region be located with the help of a graphing calculator or computer software?
- Where in the feasible set does the objective function seem to take its minimum value?

c Now consider both linear programming problems.

- What patterns do you see that make it reasonable to use the word *linear* to describe them all? How about the word *programming*?
- If you were faced with another linear programming problem, how would you go about locating the feasible set and finding the points in the set that maximize or minimize the objective function?

Be prepared to share your thinking, methods, and findings with the entire class.

72 UNIT 1 • MULTIPLE-VARIABLE MODELS

SHARE AND SUMMARIZE full-class discussion

Checkpoint

See Teaching Masters 30a–30b.

Students do not need to discuss this Checkpoint in small groups, nor do they need to record this whole Checkpoint. A full-class discussion with students referring to the investigation is sufficient.

a
- The variables are x, the number of IT-95 models, and y, the number of IT-2000 models. The constraints are the limitations on production (assembly time, testing time, and packing time). The objective function is the profit that is made: $P = 50x + 75y$.
- In algebraic form, the constraints are $0.6x + 0.3y \leq 240$, $0.2x + 0.4y \leq 160$, and $x + y \leq 500$. The objective function is $P = 50x + 75y$.
- The feasible set is the region of the graph that satisfies all of the constraints. The boundaries can be found by graphing the related line for each one of the inequalities or constraints.
- The maximum value seems to be \$32,500. For now, students may suggest that it is near the boundary or at a vertex. The next investigation involves a more thorough search and reasoning.

b
- The variables for the astronaut-diet problem are the number of food bars, x, and the number of drink cartons, y. The constraints of the problem are the amounts of fat, carbohydrate, and protein that are required. The objective is to minimize the weight where $W = 65x + 118y$.
- The constraints in symbolic form are $5x + 6y \geq 61$, $40x + 25y \geq 350$, and $8x + 15y \geq 103$. The objective function is $W = 65x + 118y$.
- The feasible set is the region of the graph that satisfies all of the constraints. The boundaries of this region can be found by graphing the related line for each of the constraints.
- The minimum weight value seems to be at the point (11, 1). This is a vertex of the feasible region. (See the fourth bullet of Part a.)

c
- The boundaries for the feasible sets are all defined by lines. Perhaps the word *programming* comes from the notion of organizing the constraints in terms of the variables and examining the situation in a very systematic or programmed way. This word may have come from the fact that these types of problems in real-world situations are solved using computer programs.
- Students should recognize the value of expressing the constraints of the problem in algebraic form. They then should graph those constraints using their calculators or on graph paper. Finally, they need to use points on the boundary to help find the point that minimizes or maximizes the objective function.

JOURNAL ENTRY: Marie suggested that Lesson 3 be titled "Linked Inequalities." What do you think she meant? Do you think it would be a reasonable lesson title? Why or why not?

Masters 30a–30b

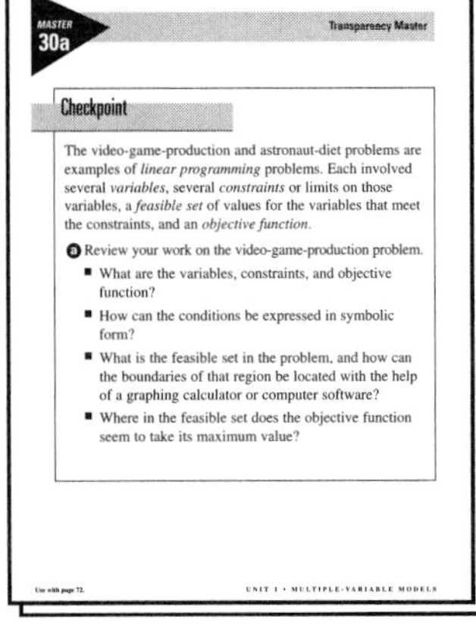

MASTER 30a — Transparency Master

Checkpoint

The video-game-production and astronaut-diet problems are examples of *linear programming* problems. Each involved several *variables*, several *constraints* or limits on those variables, a *feasible set* of values for the variables that meet the constraints, and an *objective function*.

a Review your work on the video-game-production problem.
- What are the variables, constraints, and objective function?
- How can the conditions be expressed in symbolic form?
- What is the feasible set in the problem, and how can the boundaries of that region be located with the help of a graphing calculator or computer software?
- Where in the feasible set does the objective function seem to take its maximum value?

Use with page 72. — UNIT 1 • MULTIPLE-VARIABLE MODELS

Unit 1

CONSTRUCTING A MATH TOOLKIT: Students should explain in their Math Toolkits their methods for graphing equations of the form $ax + by = c$ and for finding the point of intersection of two lines.

Master 31

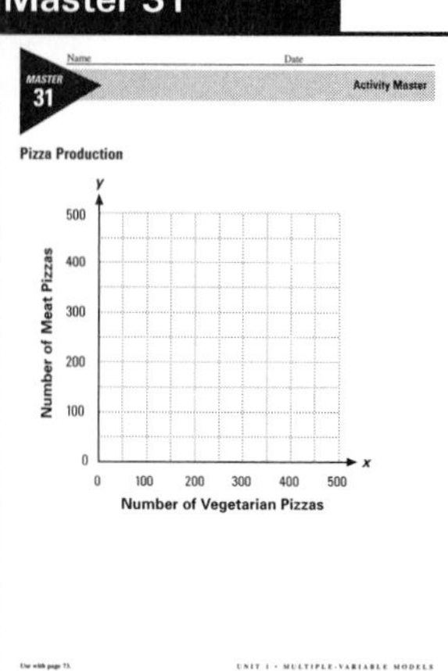

APPLY individual task

On Your Own

See Teaching Master 31.

a. Letting x represent the number of vegetarian pizzas and y represent the number of meat pizzas, the constraints and objective function are as follows:

$$12x + 6y \leq 3{,}600$$
$$x + y \leq 500$$
$$x \leq 200$$
$$\text{Profit} = 3x + 2y \text{ (Maximize)}$$

b. Pizza Production

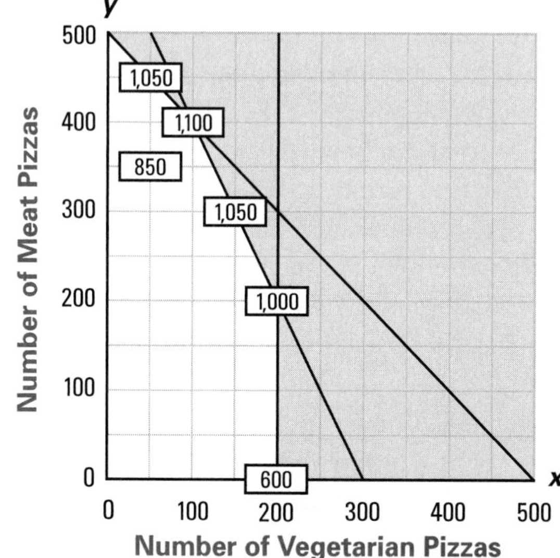

c. The vertices of the feasible region are good places to check. The values of the objective function at the vertices are shown on the graph in Part b. The maximum profit is earned by making 100 vegetarian pizzas and 400 meat pizzas.

MORE ASSIGNMENT pp. 80–85

Students can now begin Organizing Task 1 from the MORE assignment following Investigation 4.

Unit 1

On Your Own

Paisan's Pizza makes gourmet frozen pizzas for sale to supermarket chains. They make only deluxe pizzas, one vegetarian and the other with meat. Their business planning has these constraints and objective:

- Each vegetarian pizza takes 12 minutes of labor and each meat pizza takes 6 minutes of labor. The plant has *at most* 3,600 minutes of labor available each day.
- The plant freezer can handle a total of *at most* 500 pizzas per day.
- Vegetarian pizza is not quite as popular as meat pizza, so the plant makes *at most* 200 of this type each day.
- The sale of each vegetarian pizza earns Paisan's \$3 profit and each meat pizza earns \$2 profit. The company would like to maximize its profit.

a. Translate the constraints and objective in this situation into algebraic form.

b. On a copy of a grid like the one below, graph each constraint to determine the feasible set for this situation.

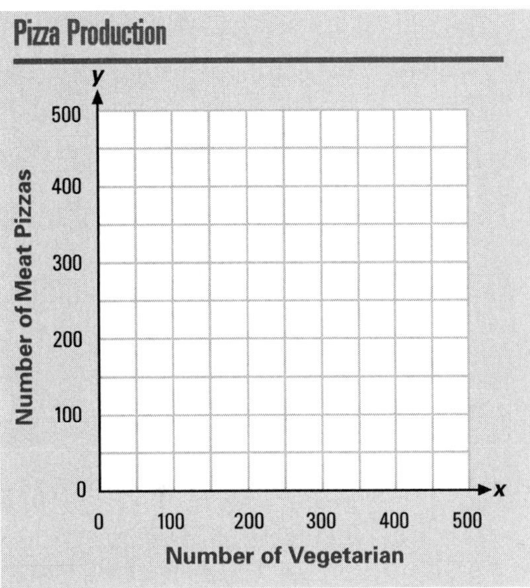

c. Evaluate the objective function at various points in the feasible region to find the point that gives maximum profit.

INVESTIGATION 3 Finding the Best Feasible Points

This lesson began with two situations with several *variables*, several *constraint inequalities*, and an *objective function* to be maximized or minimized. You found that to work effectively in such settings it helped to be skillful in writing, graphing, and interpreting linear equations and linear inequalities. In this investigation, you can put that knowledge of linearity to work and discover the key to finding the best among all *feasible* points.

1. To find the feasible region for the Integrated Technologies production planning problem, you graphed the constraint inequalities below.

$0.6x + 0.3y \leq 240$ $\qquad$ $0.2x + 0.4y \leq 160$ $\qquad$ $x + y \leq 500$

Given these constraints, the objective was to find the combination (*number of IT-95 models, number of IT-2000 models*) that gave maximum profit. The objective function was $P = 50x + 75y$ because the company makes \$50 profit on each IT-95 and \$75 profit on each IT-2000.

a. The feasible set for this situation is shown as the unshaded region in the diagram below. On a copy of this graph, write the linear equations that correspond to each segment of the boundary.

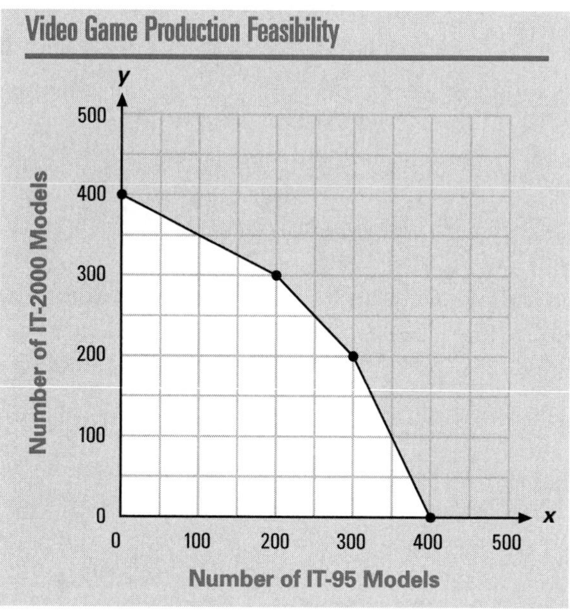

b. Looking at the graph, what do the coordinates of the points at the corners of the feasible region appear to be? Do these coordinates agree with those you found in Activity 3 of Investigation 2 (page 70)? Resolve any differences and then record the correct coordinates on your copy of the graph.

74 UNIT 1 • MULTIPLE-VARIABLE MODELS

EXPLORE small-group investigation

INVESTIGATION 3 Finding the Best Feasible Points

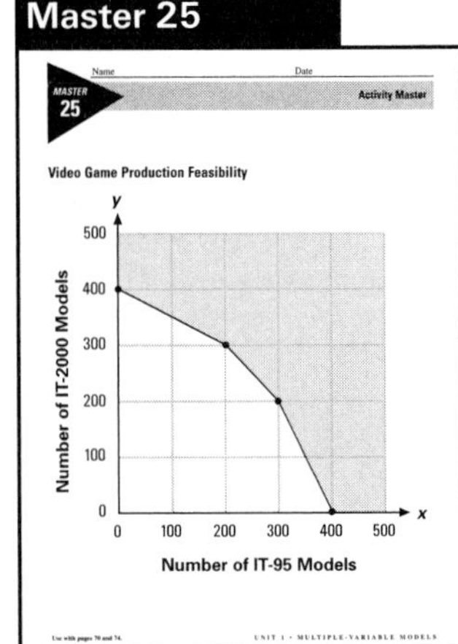

This investigation is the capstone of the previous sequence of investigations. At this point, students know how to use the constraints to divide the feasible from the nonfeasible region. They have been substituting likely pairs of values into the objective function to find the optimal solution, and many students will have realized that the best solutions are on the boundary; they are the pairs of values that "push the envelope." Some students may have already conjectured that the intersection points are the likeliest values for the optimal solution. This conjecture is confirmed informally in this investigation.

As groups of students check that the pairs of values they have conjectured are the "likely candidates," listen to their reasons. You may hear language such as, "If we push any further outward, we will be in the unfeasible region. So points on the edge of the feasible region push the limits as far as they can without breaking the rules." Or, "If a certain (x, y) is feasible, then moving upward as far as you can by increasing y while keeping x the same will give you more and more profit, until you hit the boundary. Moving right, by increasing x, will also increase the profit up to the boundary. An intersection point marks the furthest you can go up and right without violating a constraint." Or, "Points on a boundary are the best for any one constraint. If you push your luck further, you will be in the unfeasible region. So intersection points are the best for two constraints."

1. a. See Teaching Master 25 from Investigation 2.

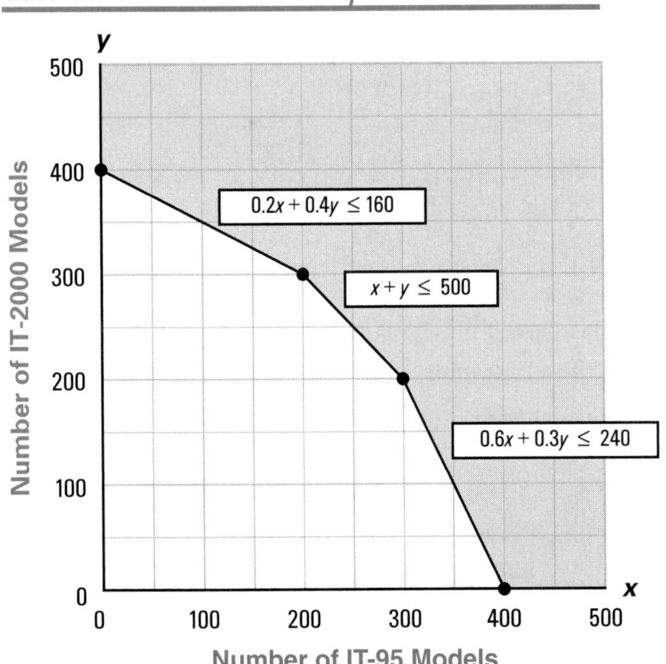

b. The coordinates of the points at the corners of the feasible region are (0, 0), (400, 0), (300, 200), (200, 300), and (0, 400).

EXPLORE *continued*

1. c. Student responses at this point will vary. They should gain insights about the location of the maximum or minimum value of the objective function as they work Activities 1 and 2. These ideas can be shared at the time of the Checkpoint.

- As x and y increase, the value of P increases also.
- Likely candidates are (400, 0), (300, 200), (200, 300), and (0, 400), because the x or y values are large. The actual point at which the maximum is achieved is dependent upon the coefficients of x and y of the objective function. Looking at the equation $P = 50x + 75y$ allows you to eliminate (400, 0) and (300, 200) quickly, because (0, 400) and (200, 300) respectively would give a larger profit.

d. Video Game Profit

IT-95 Models	IT-2000 Models	Profit (in dollars)
400	0	20,000
300	200	30,000
200	300	32,500
0	400	30,000

- The maximum profit is obtained by the point (200, 300).
- Students will compare with other groups to notice that the maximum profit occurs at (200, 300).

NOTE: The table does not contain (0, 0), because it is not a “likely candidate” for a maximum profit.

c. Now think about the objective function $P = 50x + 75y$.

- How does the value of P change as the numbers x and y of video-game models increase within the feasible region?
- Imagine a "production" point (x, y) moving outward across the feasible region in search of maximum profit. Where would you expect the combination (x, y) giving maximum profit to occur? List likely candidates and reasons for your choices.

d. By dividing the work among your group, calculate the profit for each of the points you listed in Part c. Record your tests in a table like the one below.

Video Game Profit

IT-95 Models	IT-2000 Models	Profit (in dollars)

- Of these points, which gives the maximum profit?
- Compare your combination of models to be produced for maximum profit with that found by other groups.

2. The next graph shows the feasible region for the astronaut-diet problem that you also worked on earlier. Remember, the objective was to find a combination of food bars and drink cartons that would give needed fat, carbohydrate, and protein with minimum total weight of the food. The objective function was $W = 65x + 118y$, because each food bar weighed 65 grams and each drink carton weighed 118 grams.

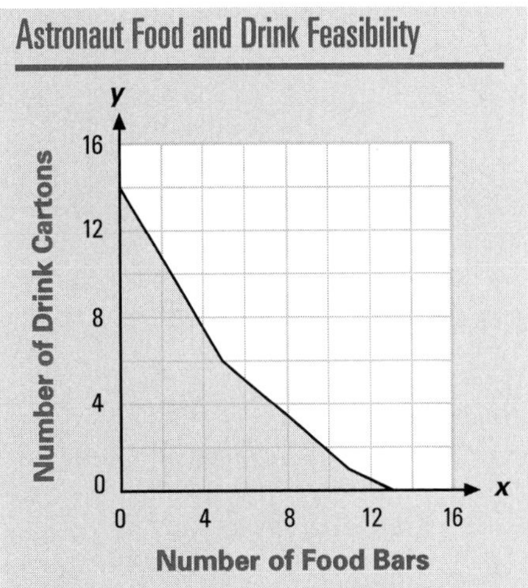

LESSON 4 • LINEAR PROGRAMMING 75

a. Where would you expect the minimum weight combination to occur? List several likely candidates.

b. Calculate the total weight for each combination using a table like the one below. Decide which combination gives minimum weight.

Astronaut Food and Drink

Food Bars	Drink Cartons	Weight (in grams)

c. Explain why it is reasonable that the minimum weight combination occurred where it did in the feasible region.

3. Based on your work in Activities 1 and 2, where do you think the maximum or minimum value of the objective function for a linear programming problem will occur? Why does this make sense?

Checkpoint

You've now worked out solutions to several typical linear programming problems and learned some of the basic mathematical ideas and skills needed. Suppose you were going to describe linear programming to someone who knew some algebra.

a How would you describe the kinds of problems to which linear programming can be applied?

b What steps would you list in the procedure for solving linear programming problems?

c What key idea simplifies the search for "best" feasible points in linear programming problems?

Be prepared to share your group's descriptions with the entire class.

76 UNIT 1 • MULTIPLE-VARIABLE MODELS

2. **a.** The minimum weight will occur at one of the vertex points: (0, 14), (5, 6), or (11, 1). The final boundary point is (12.875, 0), which corresponds to an impossible combination. Students may include (13, 0) instead.

   b. **Astronaut Food and Drink**

Food Bars	Drink Cartons	Weight (in grams)
0	14	1,672
5	6	1,033
11	1	833
13	0	845

   The combination that gives the minimum weight is 11 food bars and 1 drink carton.

   c. The points on the boundary are the minimum combinations that satisfy all the constraints. Since drink cartons weigh close to twice as much as food bars, you probably want to try to use fewer drink cartons than food bars. This makes it reasonable that the point (11, 1) gives the minimum weight.

3. **After students have had a chance to discuss this in their groups, you may wish to ask them to share their reasoning. A formal reason is given here, but students will make their own sense of this and will appreciate hearing the ideas of others.**

To see that the maximum (minimum) of the objective function will be obtained at a vertex of the boundary of the feasible region, consider the following argument:

Assuming there is such a point, if it is not on the boundary, then it is inside the region. But if this is the case, one could move either horizontally or vertically to the boundary. This increases (decreases) either the x- or y-coordinate and, in turn, will increase (decrease) the value of the objective function. Thus, we know that the maximum (minimum) will occur at some point on the boundary of the feasible region.

Now, think of picking any vertex on the boundary and finding the corresponding value of the objective function. Consider a point between that vertex and an adjacent vertex. To "move" from the chosen vertex to this new point, we must "swap" some x's for some y's, or vice versa. Depending on how the objective function weights the x's or y's (its constant rate of change), we have either increased or decreased the value of the objective function. Continue along this constraint line to the adjacent vertex. Because the slope (or rate of change) of the line is constant, if the objective function increased from the vertex to the point, it will continue to increase as you move toward the other vertex. The same would be true for decreasing objective function values. Since the change in the value of the objective function along any one segment of the boundary will be constantly increasing or decreasing, we know that the maximum or minimum will occur at one of the endpoints of the segment. Continuing this thinking for each segment of the boundary region, the overall maximum or minimum will occur at one of the vertices of the feasible region.

Group Processing Suggestions

- How did your group make sure your responses to activities make sense?
- Discuss in your group ways to encourage each other to ask questions when something is confusing.

See additional Teaching Notes on page T90Q.

Master 32

MASTER 32 — Transparency Master

Checkpoint

You've now worked out solutions to several typical linear programming problems and learned some of the basic mathematical ideas and skills needed. Suppose you were going to describe linear programming to someone who knew some algebra.

ⓐ How would you describe the kinds of problems to which linear programming can be applied?

ⓑ What steps would you list in the procedure for solving linear programming problems?

ⓒ What key idea simplifies the search for "best" feasible points in linear programming problems?

Be prepared to share your group's descriptions with the entire class.

Use with page 76. — UNIT 1 • MULTIPLE-VARIABLE MODELS

CONSTRUCTING A MATH TOOLKIT: You might wish to have students record in their Toolkits their responses to Part b of the Checkpoint.

Unit 1

APPLY **individual task**

On Your Own

MORE

ASSIGNMENT *pp. 80–85*

Students can now begin Modeling Task 1, 2, 3, or 4; Reflecting Task 2; or Extending Task 1 or 2 from the MORE assignment following Investigation 4.

a. The intent of this item is to refresh students' memories on how they obtained this graph for the previous "On Your Own" tasks, as well as help them detect any errors in their previous work.

b. The coordinates of the vertices of the feasible region are (0, 500), (100, 400), (200, 200), and (200, 0). The profit should be checked at these points, although students might discount (200, 0) immediately, since (200, 200) clearly would have greater profit.

c. Students' responses may vary. They can trace and zoom on the calculator graph, they can use the intersect feature under the CALC menu, they can use tables of values, or they can use one of several algebraic options.

d. The point (100, 400) gives the maximum profit of $1,100 for Paisan's Pizza.

On Your Own

Recall that Paisan's Pizza had to decide how many of its gourmet pizzas to make for sale to supermarket chains. (See the "On Your Own" on page 73.) They had labor constraints, freezer capacity constraints, and a limited market for the vegetarian style pizza.

In symbolic form, the constraints and objective function could be written:

- $12x + 6y \leq 3{,}600$ (Labor to make pizzas)
- $x + y \leq 500$ (Freezer capacity)
- $x \leq 200$ (Market for vegetarian pizza)
- $P = 3x + 2y$ (Profit function)

The graph below shows the feasible set for this problem.

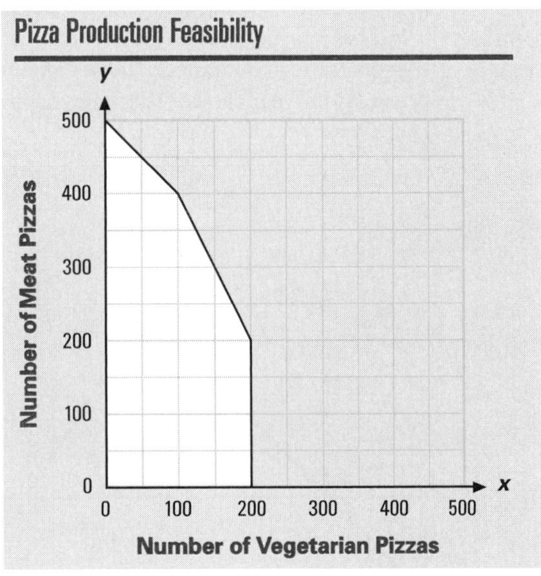

a. Refer to your work for the "On Your Own" on page 73.
- Compare the symbolic forms you developed for the constraints and objective function with those given above. Resolve any differences.
- Compare the feasible set you found for this situation with the graph shown above. Resolve any differences.

b. At what points should you check the profit to see if it is the maximum?

c. Describe at least three ways in which you can determine the coordinates of these points.

d. What combination of vegetarian and meat pizzas will yield the maximum profit for Paisan's Pizza?

LESSON 4 • LINEAR PROGRAMMING 77

INVESTIGATION 4 Linear Equations and Inequalities

In each of the linear programming problems you've worked so far, the constraints have been in two forms: $ax + by \leq c$ or $ax + by \geq c$. To find the feasible sets you had to locate all points with coordinates (x, y) that satisfied those inequalities. So it seems wise to develop some skill in working with inequalities of that type and in anticipating the kinds of graphs to expect.

In the video-game-production and astronaut-diet problems, only positive values of x and y made sense, so graphs were in the first quadrant. Other problems involve negative numbers, so the following activities ask you to investigate inequalities and their graphs considering both positive and negative values of the variables involved. Look for patterns in the results that will help you with other similar problems in the future.

1. Given below are inequalities and graphs that show the coordinate plane split by lines into *half-plane regions*. Match each inequality listed in Parts a through j with the region I through X that represents it, and be prepared to explain the reasons for your choice. The scales on the coordinate axes are 1.

   a. $x \geq 2$ **b.** $x \leq 2$

   c. $2x + 3y \leq 3$ **d.** $2x + 3y \geq 3$

   e. $y \geq x$ **f.** $y \leq x$

   g. $y \leq 0.5x - 2$ **h.** $y \geq 0.5x - 2$

   i. $3x + 2y \geq 4$ **j.** $3x + 2y \leq 4$

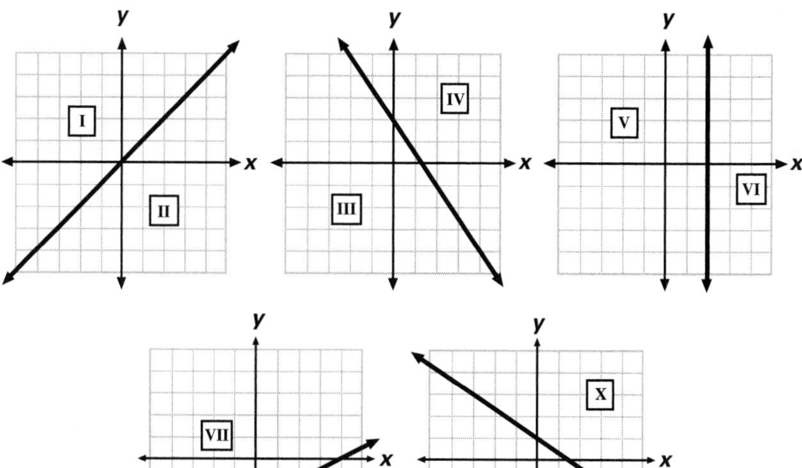

78 UNIT 1 • MULTIPLE-VARIABLE MODELS

EXPLORE small-group investigation

INVESTIGATION 4 Linear Equations and Inequalities

Master 33

Unit 1

This investigation gives students the opportunity to practice with abstract inequalities and to extend the graphs into all four quadrants. Since previous investigations had contexts that limited the graph to the first quadrant, it always was implied that $x \geq 0$ and $y \geq 0$. In the following practice, students will have to graph horizontal and vertical boundaries. You might wish to begin by asking students to graph some lines:

- $y = 2x + 3$
- $y = 2x$
- $y = 3$
- $y = -x$
- $y = -3$
- $x + 2y = 0$
- $x - 2y = 3$
- $x = 3$
- $x = -3$
- $3x = 2y - 3$

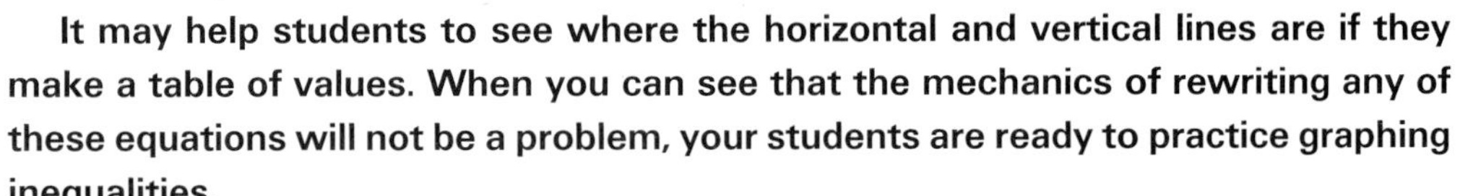

It may help students to see where the horizontal and vertical lines are if they make a table of values. When you can see that the mechanics of rewriting any of these equations will not be a problem, your students are ready to practice graphing inequalities.

Even though the examples are in a theoretical context, students still have to describe the region as "feasible" or "nonfeasible." This implies that the points in these regions represent potential solutions for the system. As you observe your students working, you can assess whether they need any additional practice.

1. **See Teaching Master 33.**

   Explanations may vary, but students should discuss the line as representing the part of the equation where the two sides are equal. They also should indicate that points on one side of the line fit the inequality.

   a. VI **b.** V
   c. IX **d.** X
   e. I **f.** II
   g. VIII **h.** VII
   i. IV **j.** III

Unit 1

Master 34

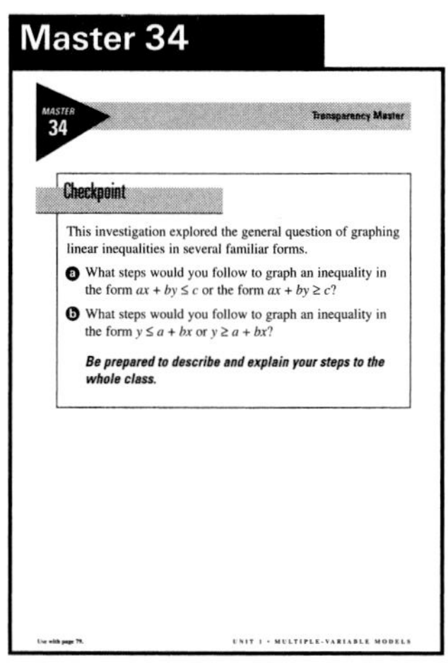
MASTER 34 Transparency Master

Checkpoint

This investigation explored the general question of graphing linear inequalities in several familiar forms.

ⓐ What steps would you follow to graph an inequality in the form $ax + by \leq c$ or the form $ax + by \geq c$?

ⓑ What steps would you follow to graph an inequality in the form $y \leq a + bx$ or $y \geq a + bx$?

Be prepared to describe and explain your steps to the whole class.

Use with page 79. UNIT 1 • MULTIPLE-VARIABLE MODELS

EXPLORE *continued*

2. **Note that the portion of the graph not represented by the inequality has been shaded. Some students may do the opposite, but the feasible region should be marked in either case. Of course, it is more important that students show they understand which region is feasible than that they shade correctly.**

The first step in graphing the inequalities is to graph the related line. Students may suggest the strategy of testing a particular point to determine where the feasible region is located. Another strategy to determine the feasible region would be to solve the inequality for y (on the left), and then the feasible region would be above the line if the > symbol is involved or below the line if the < symbol is used.

a. $y \geq -x$

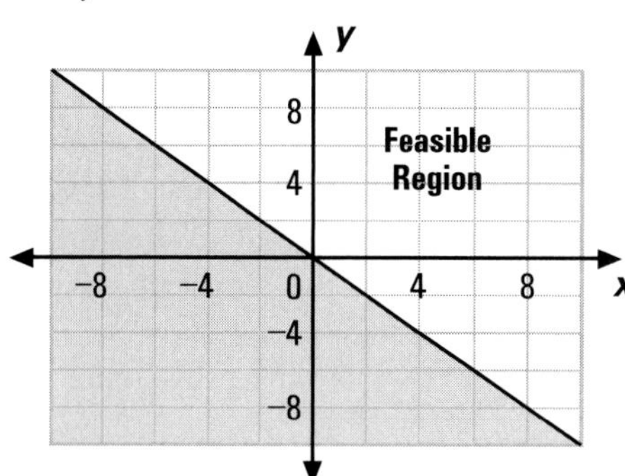

b. $y \leq 2x + 3$

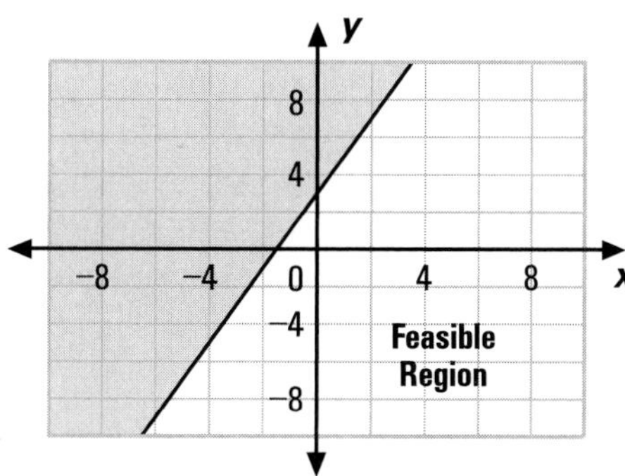

c. $y \geq -4$

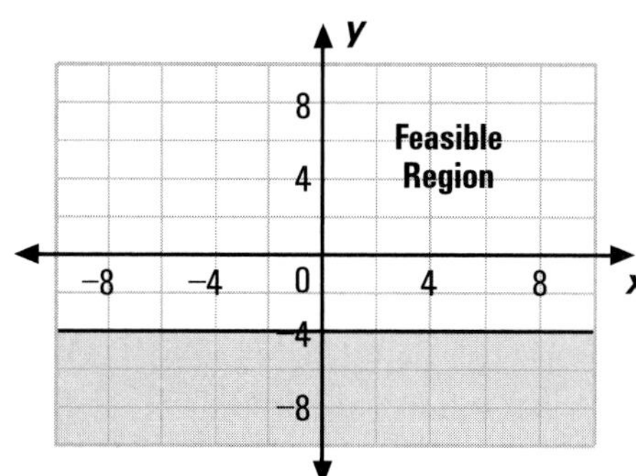

d. $2x + 6y \leq 12$

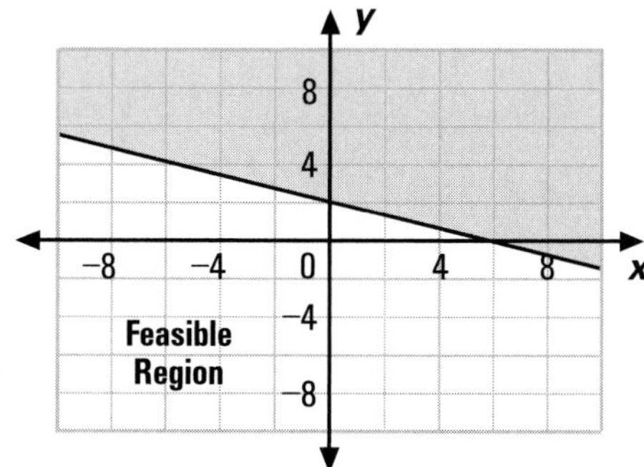

3. $y \leq 2x + 3$ and $y \geq -x$

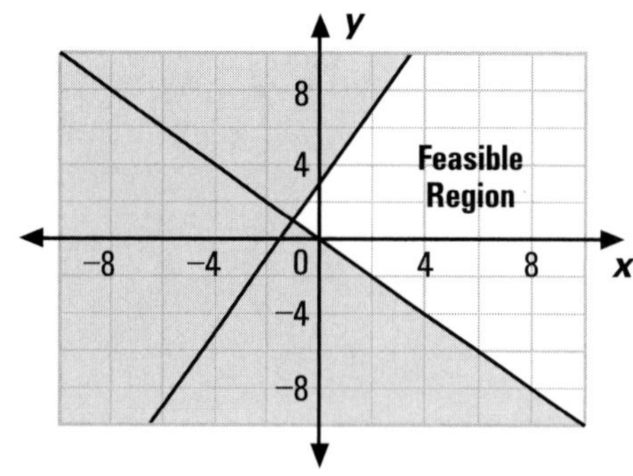

4. $-3x + y \geq -2$ and $x + y \leq 6$

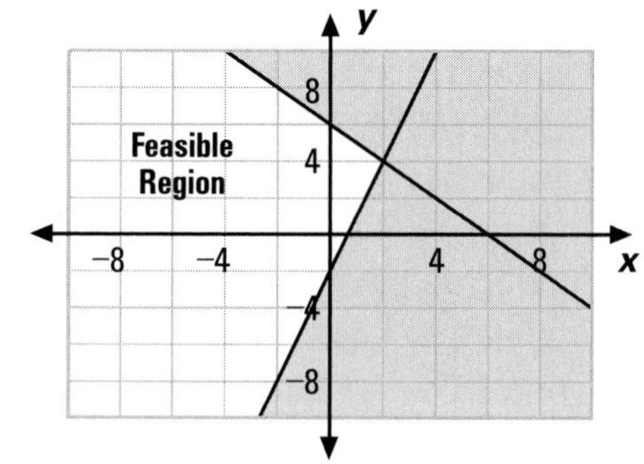

CONSTRUCTING A MATH TOOLKIT: After this Checkpoint, students should record a method for graphing an inequality of the form $ax + by \leq c$ or $ax + by \geq c$.

See additional Teaching Notes on page T90R.

2. On separate coordinate axes, sketch graphs for each of the following inequalities. In each case, outline and label as *feasible* the region that meets the given condition. Be prepared to explain your strategy in each case.

   a. $y \geq -x$ **b.** $y \leq 2x + 3$

   c. $y \geq -4$ **d.** $2x + 6y \leq 12$

3. On a single coordinate system, outline and label as *feasible* the region whose points satisfy the constraints $y \leq 2x + 3$ and $y \geq -x$.

4. On a single coordinate system, outline and label as *feasible* the region whose points satisfy the constraints $-3x + y \geq -2$ and $x + y \leq 6$.

5. On a single coordinate system, outline and label as *feasible* the region whose points satisfy the constraints $x + y \leq 4$ and $x - 2y \geq 6$.

Checkpoint

This investigation explored the general question of graphing linear inequalities in several familiar forms.

a What steps would you follow to graph an inequality in the form $ax + by \leq c$ or the form $ax + by \geq c$?

b What steps would you follow to graph an inequality in the form $y \leq a + bx$ or $y \geq a + bx$?

Be prepared to describe and explain your steps to the whole class.

On Your Own

The sketch at the right shows a graph of the equation $5x + 2y = 6$.

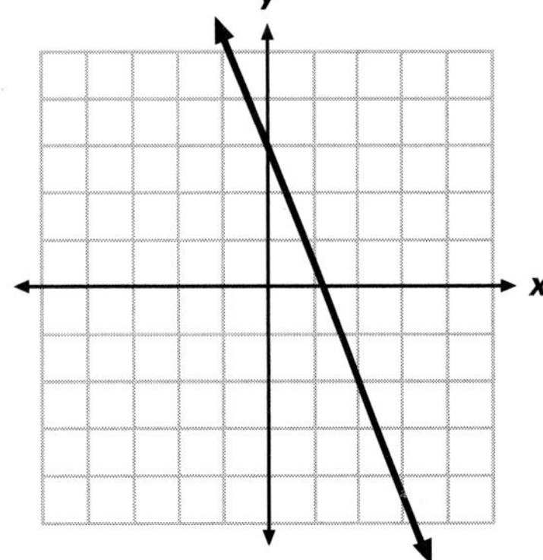

a. Sketch a copy of this graph. Shade and label as feasible the regions where points have coordinates satisfying the inequalities:

- $5x + 2y \geq 6$
- $5x + 2y \leq 6$

b. Describe two methods for graphing the linear equation $5x + 2y = 6$.

LESSON 4 • LINEAR PROGRAMMING 79

MORE

Modeling • Organizing • Reflecting • Extending

Modeling

1. The Backstage Dance Studio director must plan for and operate many different classes, 7 days a week, at all hours of the day. Saturday is a very important day for younger students, and each Saturday class fills up quickly.

To plan the Saturday schedule, the director has to consider these facts:

- It's not easy to find enough good teachers, so the studio can offer at most 8 tap classes and at most 5 jazz classes.
- The studio has limited classroom space, so it can offer a total of at most 10 classes for the day.
- The studio makes profit of \$150 from each tap class and \$250 from each jazz class.

a. What are the variables in this situation?

b. Write algebraic inequalities giving the constraints on the variables.

c. The director wants to make as much profit as possible. Write the objective function for this situation.

d. Graph the constraints and outline the feasible set for the situation.

e. Find the schedule of classes that gives maximum profit.

f. The director of Backstage Dance Studio really wants to promote interest in dance, so she also wants to maximize the number of children who can take classes. Each tap class can accommodate 10 students, and each jazz class can accommodate 15 students.

Write an objective function that reflects the maximum number of students, rather than maximum profit. Find the schedule that gives maximum student participation.

80 UNIT 1 • MULTIPLE-VARIABLE MODELS

Modeling

1. **a.** The variables are the number of tap classes and the number of jazz classes offered.

 b. If x represents the number of tap classes and y represents the number of jazz classes, then the constraints are $x \leq 8$, $y \leq 5$, and $x + y \leq 10$.

 c. The objective function is $Profit = 150x + 250y$.

 d.

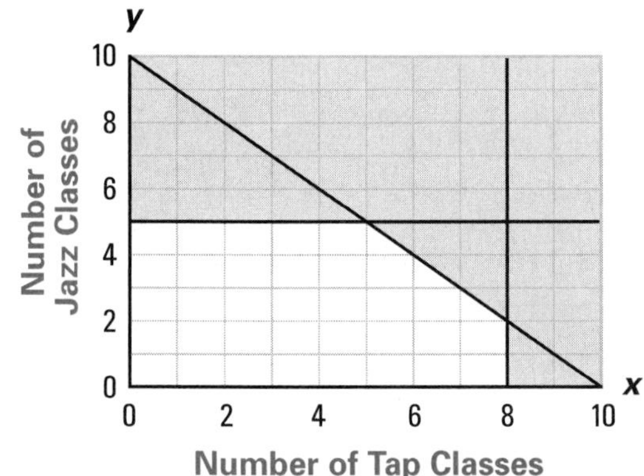

 e. 5 tap classes and 5 jazz classes give the maximum profit of $2,000.

 f. Number of students $= 10x + 15y$

 5 tap classes and 5 jazz classes also give the maximum student participation (125 students).

MORE ASSIGNMENT *pp. 80–85*

Modeling: 3 and choice of one*
Organizing: 1 and 5
Reflecting: 1 and 2
Extending: Choose one*

**When choice is indicated, it is important to leave the choice to the student.*
NOTE: *It is best if Organizing tasks are discussed as a whole class after they have been assigned as homework.*

MORE *continued*

2. a.

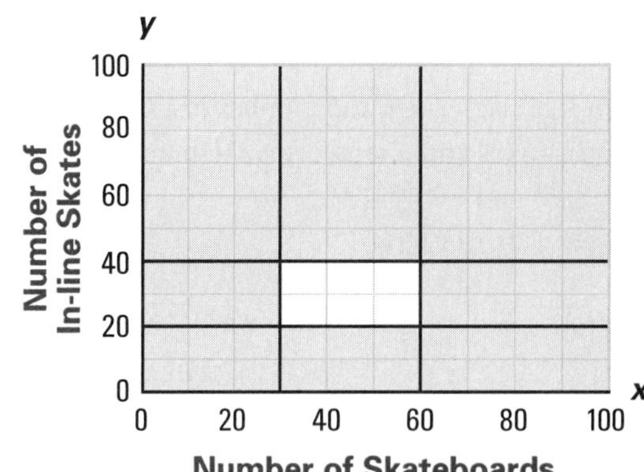

If x represents the number of skateboards produced and y represents the number of in-line skates produced, then the constraints are $x \geq 30$, $y \geq 20$, $x \leq 60$, and $y \leq 40$.

b. There are $31 \cdot 21$ or 651 combinations of in-line skates and skateboards possible.

c.

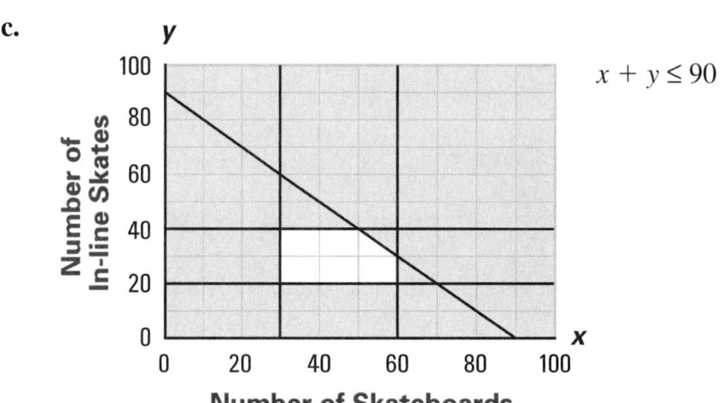

$x + y \leq 90$

d. (30, 40), (50, 40), (60, 30), (60, 20), (30, 20)

e. $Profit = 12x + 18y$

f. The company should make 50 skateboards and 40 in-line skates in order to maximize profit. The profit would be $1,320.

3. If x represents the machine work time (in hours) and y represents the students' work time (in hours), then the constraints are $x \leq 8$, $y \leq 8$, and $30x + 25y \geq 290$. Also, the hours would be greater than or equal to zero, $x \geq 0$ and $y \geq 0$. The coordinates of the corners of the feasible region are (3, 8), (8, 8), and (8, 2). The objective function, $Cost = 15x + 10y$, is minimized when the machine is operated for 3 hours and the students work for 8 hours.

4. a. Let x represent the number of bags of Moonbeam mixture and let y represent the number of bags of Sunshine mixture.

$30x + 60y \leq 300{,}000$

$50x + 20y \leq 260{,}000$

b. $Profit = 2.3x + 2.5y$

c. The vertices of the feasible region are (0, 5,000), (4,000, 3,000), (5,200, 0), and (0, 0). The point (4,000, 3,000) gives the maximum profit of $16,700. Thus, the profit will be maximized if 4,000 Moonbeam mixtures and 3,000 Sunshine mixtures are sold.

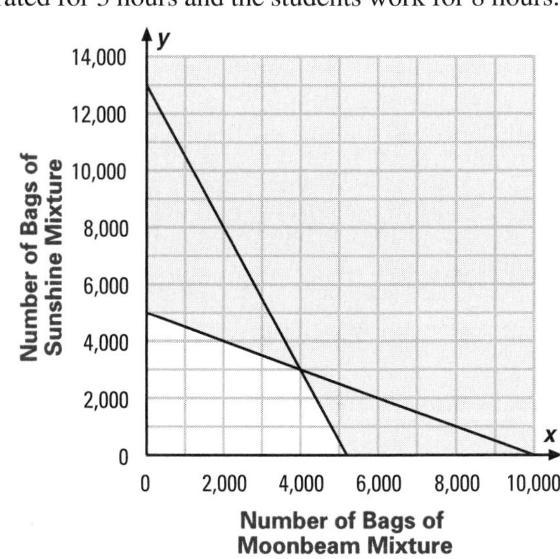

2. A sporting goods manufacturer produces skateboards and in-line skates. Its dealers demand at least 30 skateboards per day and 20 pairs of in-line skates per day. The factory can make at most 60 skateboards and 40 pairs of in-line skates per day.

a. Write and graph inequalities expressing the given constraints on skateboard and in-line skate manufacturing.

b. How many combinations of in-line skates and skateboards are possible?

c. Suppose the total number of skateboards and pairs of in-line skates cannot exceed 90. What inequality expresses this constraint? Graph this new constraint.

d. Find coordinates of corners for the new feasible region.

e. Suppose the profit on each skateboard is \$12 and on each pair of in-line skates is \$18. Write the profit function.

f. How many of each product should the company manufacture to get maximum profit?

3. The manufacturing facility that supplies a chain of Packaging Plus stores received a rush order for 290 boxes. It had to fill the order in eight hours or less.

- The factory has a machine that can produce 30 boxes per hour and costs \$15 per hour to operate.
- The factory can also use two student workers from other, less-urgent tasks; together those students can make 25 boxes per hour at a cost of \$10 per hour.

What combination of machine and student work times will meet the order deadline for least total cost?

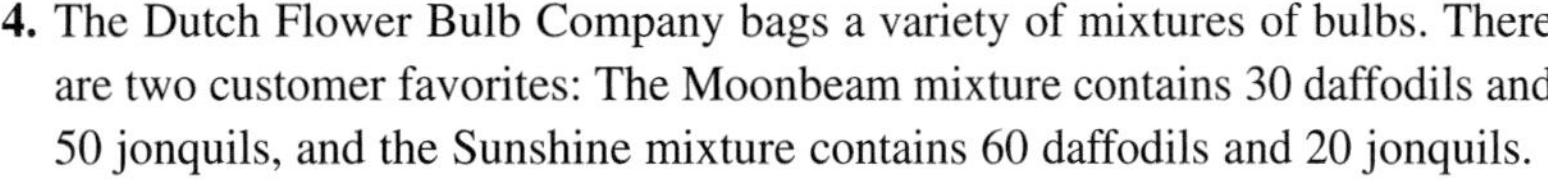

4. The Dutch Flower Bulb Company bags a variety of mixtures of bulbs. There are two customer favorites: The Moonbeam mixture contains 30 daffodils and 50 jonquils, and the Sunshine mixture contains 60 daffodils and 20 jonquils.

The company imports 300,000 daffodils and 260,000 jonquils for sale each year. The profit for each bag of the Moonbeam mixture is \$2.30. The profit for each bag of the Sunshine mixture is \$2.50. The problem is deciding how many bags of each mixture the company should make in order to maximize profit without exceeding available supplies.

a. Write and graph the constraint inequalities.

b. Write the objective function.

c. Find the combination of Moonbeam and Sunshine bags that will maximize profit.

LESSON 4 • LINEAR PROGRAMMING 81

Organizing

1. Give sets of inequalities that define each of the *shaded* regions below. The scales on the coordinate axes are 1.

   a.

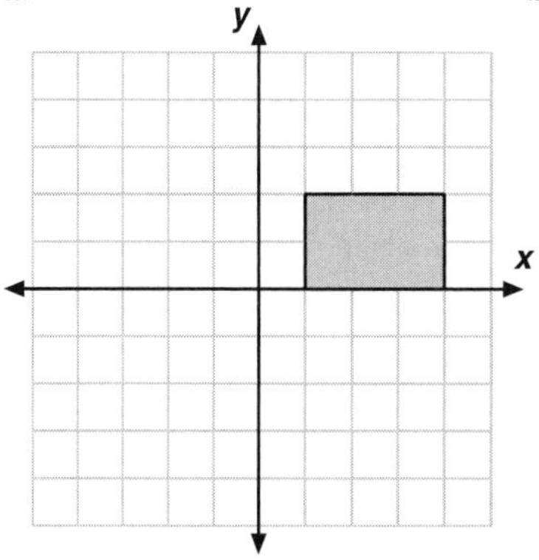

   b.

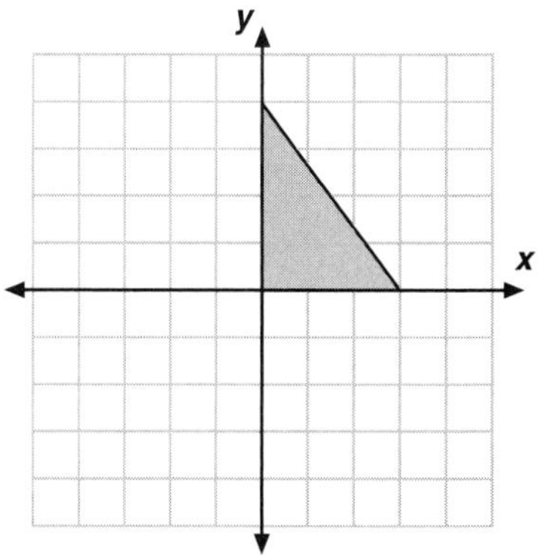

2. Suppose each shaded region in Organizing Task 1 represents the feasible set for a linear programming problem. List the points that you would test in a profit equation. Explain why you picked those points.

3. Sketch the feasible regions defined by the following inequalities. Use the given equations for profit P and cost C to find (x, y) combinations yielding maximum profit or minimum cost within the feasible regions.

   a. $3y - 2x \geq 6$
   $0 \leq x \leq 4$
   $y \leq 5$
   $P = 5x + 3y$

   b. $x \leq 10$
   $2x + y \geq 20$
   $y \leq 14$
   $C = 20x + 5y$

   c. $x + 2y \geq 8$
   $0 \leq x \leq 16$
   $0 \leq y \leq 12$
   $P = 4x + 12y$

4. Describe a situation that could be modeled by the constraint inequalities and the objective function from Part a, b, or c of Organizing Task 3 above.

Organizing

1. a. $x \geq 1, x \leq 4, y \geq 0, y \leq 2$
   b. $x \geq 0, y \geq 0, 4x + 3y \leq 12$
2. a. Since the maximum profit would occur at a corner of the feasible set, consider the following points: (1, 0), (1, 2), (4, 2), and (4, 0). Students' reasons for selection choices may vary.
   b. Since the maximum profit would occur at a corner of the feasible set, test the following points: (0, 4) and (3, 0). Students may also include the point (0, 0), but this point clearly would not give a maximum profit.
3. a. The maximum profit (35) occurs when $x = 4$ and $y = 5$.

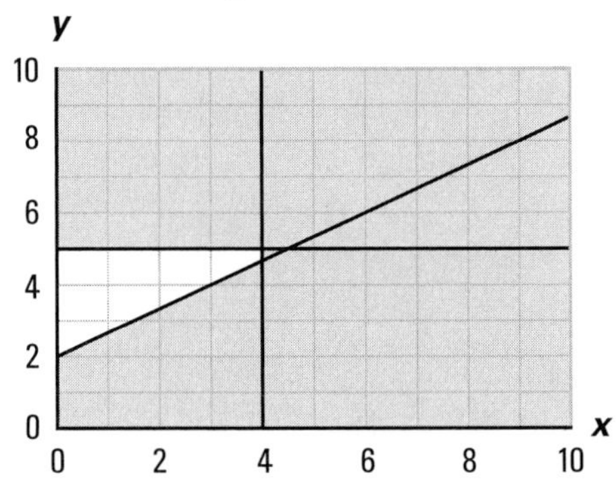

   b. The minimum cost (130) occurs when $x = 3$ and $y = 14$.

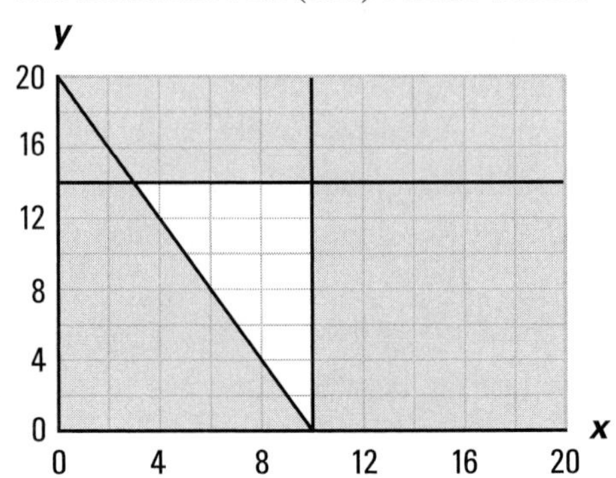

   c. The maximum profit (208) occurs when $x = 16$ and $y = 12$.

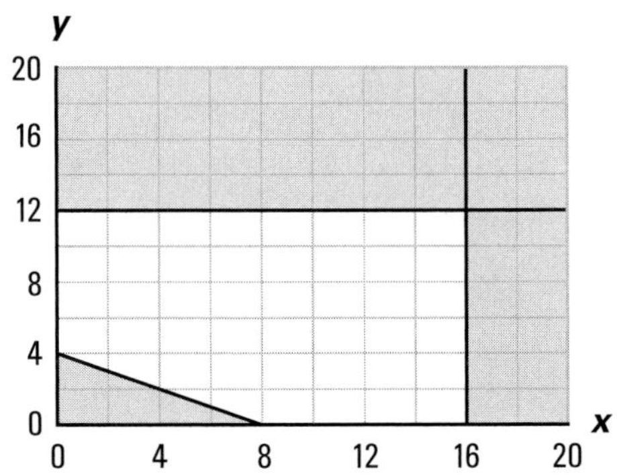

See additional Teaching Notes on page T90S.

Unit 1

MORE *continued*

5. **a.** Angelyn may have been reasoning that, if she could eliminate one of the variables, then she could solve the equation. Students can check the answer by graphing the two equations and finding the point of intersection, or by looking at tables of values and seeing that, when $x = 200$, $y = 300$ for both equations. They can also use some other algebraic method.

   b. Yes, her procedure will always work.

$$x + y = 500$$
$$0.6x + 0.3y = 240$$

Solving the first equation for x in terms of y results in $x = 500 - y$.
Substituting this into the second equation gives

$$0.6(500 - y) + 0.3y = 240$$
$$300 - 0.6y + 0.3y = 240$$
$$300 - 0.3y = 240$$
$$60 = 0.3y$$
$$200 = y$$

If $y = 200$, then $x = 300$.

Reflecting

1. Vertices of a feasible region can be found by solving each equation for y (or x) and setting the expressions equal to each other, solving one equation for x (or y) and substituting into the other equation, or by solving the appropriate system of equations using matrices or linear combinations. Vertices also can be found by graphing the equations and using the intersect option under the CALC menu or by using the tables of values.
2. One graph ($2x + y \leq 6$) would include points on the line $y = 6 - 2x$; the other graph ($2x + y < 6$) would not include the points on the line. The difference could be shown on the graph of $2x + y < 6$ by making the boundary line dotted. Students may think of other ways to show this difference.
3. Students' ways of identifying the necessary pieces for solving a linear programming problem may vary. Some students may think about the objective function first and use that information to determine the variables.
4. Most linear programming problems require the use of computers; only recently have computers been widely available.

5. You often can discover creative ways of carrying out mathematical tasks. For example, Angelyn proposed the following procedure to solve a system of linear equations. To solve the system $0.2x + 0.4y = 160$ and $x + y = 500$, she reasoned as follows:

Angelyn

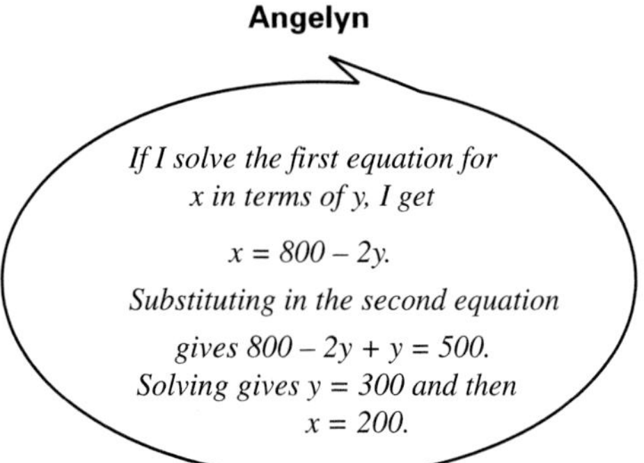
If I solve the first equation for
x in terms of y, I get
x = 800 – 2y.
Substituting in the second equation
gives 800 – 2y + y = 500.
Solving gives y = 300 and then
x = 200.

a. Try to figure out the reasoning used by Angelyn. Check her answer by using a different method to solve the system of equations.

b. Do you think Angelyn's procedure will always work? Try it with the system $x + y = 500$ and $0.6x + 0.3y = 240$.

Reflecting

1. Solving linear programming problems includes finding the boundary of the feasible region. Describe at least three different ways to find the points where the boundary lines defining the region intersect.

2. How would the graphs of the following two inequalities differ?

$2x + y \leq 6$ $\qquad\qquad$ $2x + y < 6$

How could you show their differences in sketches of their graphs?

3. When solving a linear programming problem, how do you identify the variables, constraint inequalities, and objective function?

4. Realistic linear programming problems in business and engineering usually involve many variables and constraints. Why do you think that linear programming was not used much until fairly recently?

Extending

1. A city recreation department offers Saturday gymnastics classes for beginning and advanced students. Each beginner class enrolls 15, and each advanced class enrolls only 10. Available teachers, space, and time lead to these constraints:
   - There can be at most 9 beginner classes and at most 6 advanced classes.
   - The total number of classes can be at most 7.
   - The number of beginner classes should be at most twice the number of advanced classes.

   a. What mix of beginner and advanced classes will give the most children a chance to participate?

   b. Suppose the recreation department director sets new constraints for the schedule of gymnastics classes:
   - The same limits exist for teachers, so there can be at most 9 beginner and 6 advanced classes.
   - The program should serve at least 150 students, with 15 in each beginner class and 10 in each advanced class.

   The new goal is to minimize the cost of the program. Each beginner class costs \$500 to operate, and each advanced class costs \$300. What combination of beginner and advanced classes should be offered?

2. Explain why the minimum or maximum value of the objective function for a linear programming problem seems always to occur near the boundary of the feasible region.

84 UNIT 1 • MULTIPLE-VARIABLE MODELS

Extending

1. **a.** Letting x represent the number of beginner classes and y represent the number of advanced classes, the constraints are $x \le 9$, $y \le 6$, $x + y \le 7$, and $x \le 2y$. The feasible set is shown below.

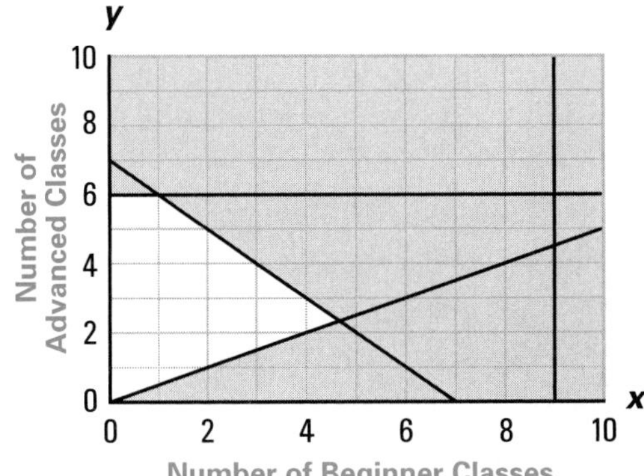

The vertices of the feasible region are (0, 6), (1, 6), (4.67, 2.33), and (0, 0). Since one of the vertices does not intersect at integer values, students need to check the feasible lattice points near that point of intersection. These points are (4, 2) and (4, 3). The objective function is *Participation* $= 15x + 10y$, which is maximized when 4 beginner classes and 3 advanced classes are offered.

b. Letting x represent the number of beginner classes and y represent the number of advanced classes, the constraints are $x \le 9$, $y \le 6$, and $15x + 10y \ge 150$. The feasible set is shown below.

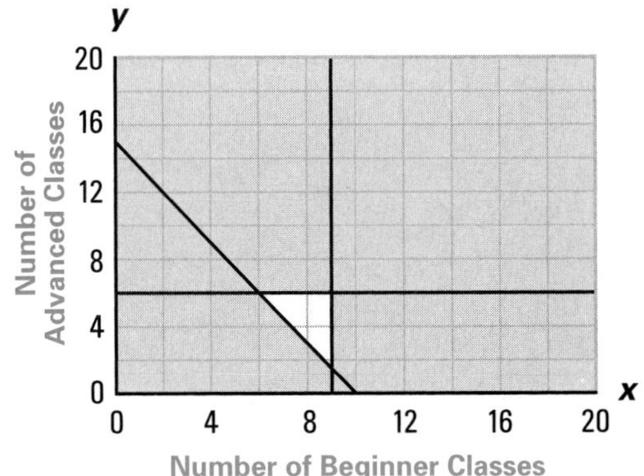

The objective function is *Cost* $= 500x + 300y$, which is minimized when 6 beginner classes and 6 advanced classes are offered.

2. To see that the maximum (minimum) of the objective function will be obtained near the boundary of the feasible region, consider the following argument: If the point is not on the boundary, then it is inside the region. But if this is the case, one could move either horizontally or vertically to the boundary. This increases (decreases) either the x- or y-coordinate and, in turn, will increase (decrease) the value of the objective function. However, if the solution must be integral and the vertices of the feasible region include nonintegral coordinates, the point giving the maximum or minimum may occur close to but not on the boundary.

Assessments 19–22

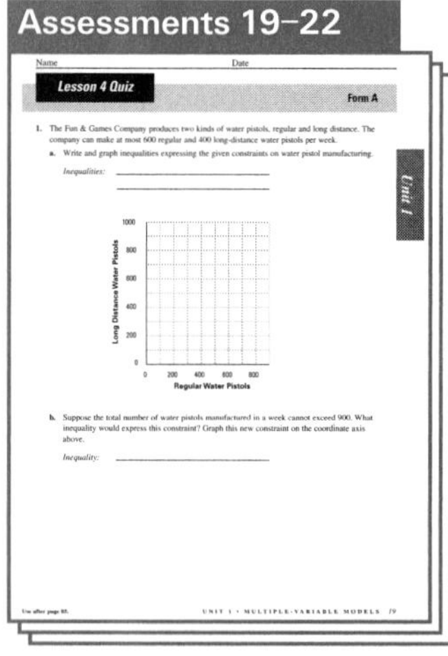

Assessments 23–26

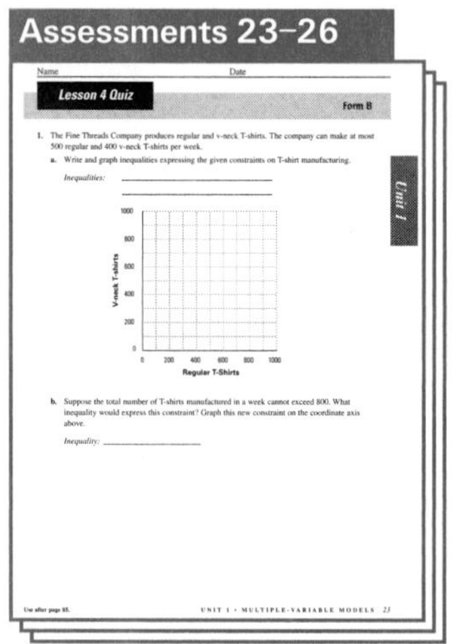

MORE *continued*

3. Letting x represent the number of high school rings made (in hundreds) and y represent the number of college rings made (in hundreds), the constraints are $1.2x + 2y \leq 14$, $0.6x + 3y \leq 15$, and $2x + 2y \leq 20$. The feasible set is shown below.

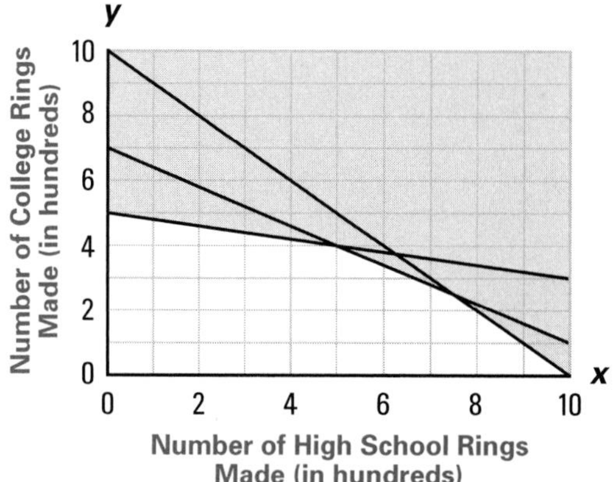

The objective function is $Profit = 500x + 525y$, which is maximized when $x = 7.5$ and $y = 2.5$. That is, the maximum profit of \$5,062.50 occurs when the company produces 750 high school rings and 250 college rings.

4. Letting x represent the number of gallons of Carnival Juice and y represent the number of gallons of Lemon Punch, the restrictions on the available gallons of lemonade and orange juice give the following constraint inequalities: $0.5x + 0.75y \leq 50$ and $0.5x + 0.25y \leq 30$. The objective function is $Profit = 1.60x + 1.92y$, which is maximized when 40 gallons of Carnival Juice and 40 gallons of Lemon Punch are made. The feasible set is shown below.

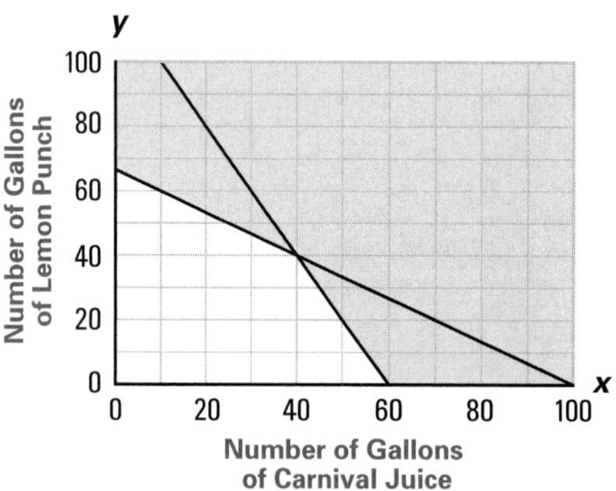

See Assessment Resources pages 19–26.

3. The Bestform Ring Company makes class rings for high schools and colleges all over the country. Production of each ring is a three-step process involving molding, engraving, and polishing. The following chart gives information concerning the time (in hours) that it takes to produce 100 high school rings or 100 college rings and the time that machines and operators are available during one day.

Class Ring Production

Stage in Ring Making	Time to Make 100 High School Rings (in hours)	Time to Make 100 College Rings (in hours)	Machine and Operator Time Available Each Day (in hours)
Molding	1.2	2	14
Engraving	0.6	3	15
Polishing	2	2	20

If the company makes $500 profit on each 100 high school rings and $525 on each 100 college rings, how many of each should be produced to maximize profit, assuming all rings of either type can be sold?

4. The Junior Class of Oakland Mills High School sells juice at the Columbia Fair to raise funds for the Junior-Senior Prom. The students have 50 gallons of lemonade and 30 gallons of orange juice. The juniors mix and sell two drinks: Carnival Juice, which is two quarts orange juice to two quarts lemonade, and Lemon Punch, which is three quarts lemonade to one quart orange juice. If the profit is $1.60 per gallon on the Carnival Juice and $1.92 per gallon on the Lemon Punch, how many gallons of each mixture should the juniors make to maximize their profit?

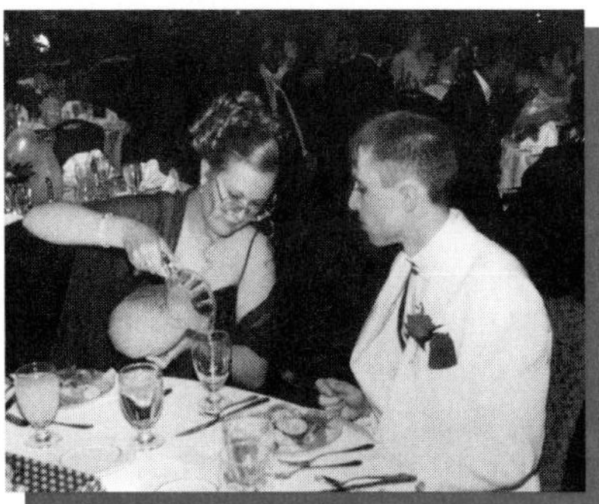

LESSON 4 • LINEAR PROGRAMMING 85

Lesson 5 Looking Back

The lessons in this unit have involved many different situations in which more than two variables were related to each other in important ways. In Lesson 1, you investigated situations that could be modeled by functions with several input variables. Lesson 2 focused specifically on geometric contexts that could be modeled by multiple-variable relations involving trigonometry: the Law of Sines and the Law of Cosines. Situations in Lesson 3 were modeled by systems of equations in which two output variables were linked by a single input variable. In Lesson 4, you examined situations in which there were multiple constraints, modeled by inequalities using two input variables, and an objective function to be maximized or minimized, which involved the same two input variables. The problem contexts that follow will help you organize your thinking on multiple-variable relations, how they can be modeled, and how those models can help in making decisions.

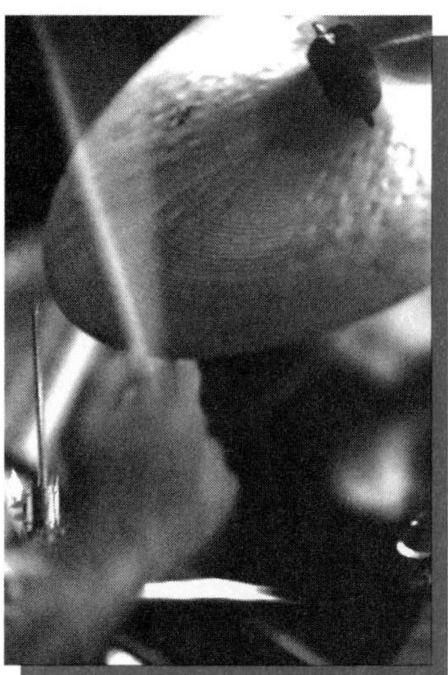

1. The sounds you hear, from musical instruments and human voices to whispering wind and crackling lightning, all are carried by vibrating waves of air. The pitch of a sound is determined by the frequency of vibration; a higher frequency gives a higher pitch. That frequency depends on certain properties of the sound source.

For example, when the drummer in a band hits one of the cymbals, the frequency F of its sound varies directly with the density k of the material and inversely with the square of the cymbal's diameter D.

a. What changes in the variables k and D would lead to higher-pitched sound, and what changes would lead to lower-pitched sound?

86 UNIT 1 • MULTIPLE-VARIABLE MODELS

Lesson 5 *Looking Back*

SYNTHESIZE UNIT IDEAS **small-group activity**

In this lesson, students will again work with various types of multiple-variable equations that they have studied in this unit. Glancing at the final Checkpoint for this unit will allow you to keep in mind the mathematics that will come from the tasks of this lesson and main concepts that students should understand upon completion of this unit.

1. a. Increasing the density k of the sound source or decreasing the diameter D of the sound source would lead to higher-pitched sounds. Decreasing the density of the sound source k or increasing the diameter D of the sound source would lead to lower-pitched sounds.

SYNTHESIZE *continued*

1. b. Responses will vary, but students should be able to discuss how different drum or cymbal sizes affect pitch. You might want to borrow some drums or cymbals from the music department so that students who are not familiar with these variations can experience them.

c. ■ $F = \frac{k}{D^2}$

■ $k = FD^2$

■ $D^2 = \frac{k}{F}$

NOTE: In order to write equations to model the relationships among variables, such as F, k, and D, scientists and engineers may introduce a constant, c, to account for the different kinds of units that may be used to measure frequency, density, and diameter.

---

2. a. Letting x represent the number of traditional windows and y represent the number of modern windows, the constraint inequalities are $x \geq 80$, $y \geq 60$, and $x + y \geq 150$.

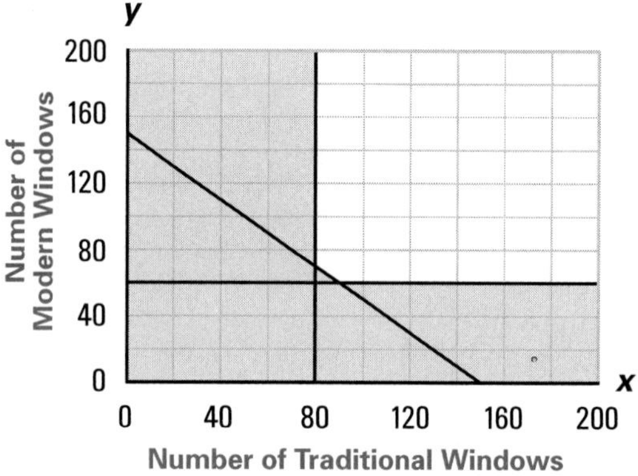

b. Why are the patterns of change you described in Part a reasonable, based on your experience with cymbals, drums, or other similar musical instruments?

c. Write equations showing the relation between F, k, and D. Express the relation in three different ways:

- F is a function of k and D.
- k is a function of F and D.
- D^2 is a function of F and k.

2. When architects design buildings, they have to balance many factors. Construction and operating costs, strength, ease of use, and style of design are only a few.

For example, when architects designing a large city office building began their design work, they had to deal with the following conditions:

- The front of the building had to use windows of traditional style to fit in with the surrounding historic buildings. There had to be at least 80 traditional windows on the front of the building. Those windows each had an area of 20 square feet and glass that was 0.25 inches thick.
- The back of the building was to use modern style windows that had an area of 35 square feet and glass that was 0.5 inches thick. There had to be at least 60 of those windows.
- In order to provide as much natural lighting for the building as possible, the design had to use at least 150 windows.

a. Write the constraint inequalities that match conditions of this situation. Then sketch the region of feasible points.

LESSON 5 • LOOKING BACK 87

b. One way to rate the possible designs is by how well they insulate the building from loss of heat in the winter and loss of air-conditioning in the summer. The heat loss R in Btu's per hour through a glass window can be estimated by the equation $R = \frac{5.8A}{t}$, where A stands for the area of the window in square feet and t stands for the thickness of the glass in inches.

- What are the heat flow rates of the traditional and modern windows?
- Use the results from above to write an objective function if the goal is to choose a combination of traditional and modern windows that minimizes heat flow from the building.
- Find the combination of window types that meets the constraints and minimizes the objective function.

c. Minimizing construction cost is another consideration. The traditional windows cost \$200 apiece. The modern windows cost \$250 apiece.

- Write an objective function if the goal is to minimize total cost.
- Find the combination of traditional and modern windows that will meet the constraints and minimize total cost of the windows.

d. If you were the architect, what combination of traditional and modern windows would you recommend and why?

3. En route to sea, a freighter travels 50 km due west of home port. It then turns, making an angle of 132° with its former path. It travels 80 km before radioing home port.

a. Draw a diagram showing the path of the freighter.

b. How far is the freighter from its home port?

c. If sea conditions permitted, through what angle could the freighter have turned from its original course to go directly from home port to the position at which it radioed the port?

d. Describe a second way in which you could find an answer for Part c.

88 UNIT 1 • MULTIPLE-VARIABLE MODELS

2\. **b.** ■ For the traditional window, $R = 464$ Btu's per hour.
For the modern window, $R = 406$ Btu's per hour.

■ $R = 464x + 406y$

■ In order to minimize heat flow from the building, the architect should use 80 traditional windows and 70 modern windows.

c. ■ $Cost = 200x + 250y$

■ In order to minimize total cost, the architect should use 90 traditional windows and 60 modern windows.

d. Responses will vary depending on whether the student thinks it is more important to minimize heat loss or to minimize the cost of the windows.

3\. **a.**

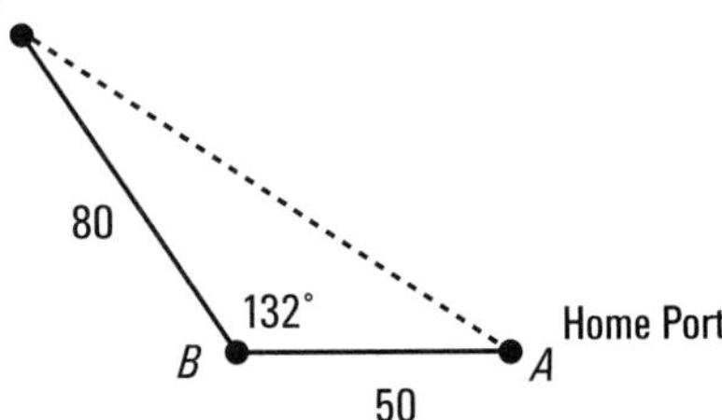

b. Using the diagram and the Law of Cosines:

$$AC^2 = AB^2 + BC^2 - 2 \cdot AB \cdot BC \cos B$$
$$= 50^2 + 80^2 - 2 \cdot 50 \cdot 80 \cdot \cos 132°$$
$$\approx 14{,}253$$
$$AC \approx 119.4 \text{ km}$$

c–d. Either the Law of Sines or the Law of Cosines may be used to compute m$\angle A$. (See page T31 for a short discussion of the ambiguous case.)

Law of Cosines:
$$\cos A = \frac{BC^2 - AC^2 - AB^2}{-2(AC)(AB)}$$
$$\cos A = \frac{80^2 - 119.4^2 - 50^2}{-2(119.4)(50)}$$
$$A \approx 29.8°$$

Law of Sines:
$$\frac{\sin A}{BC} = \frac{\sin B}{AC}$$
$$\sin A = \frac{\sin B \cdot BC}{AC}$$
$$\sin A = \frac{80 \sin 132°}{119.4}$$
$$A \approx 29.9°$$

SYNTHESIZE *continued*

4. **a.** Traveling at a high speed will get the radioactive waste to the storage facility quickly, and the cost of paying the driver will be less since less time is spent on the road. Traveling at a lower speed usually is safer and the truck may get better gas mileage, thereby reducing fuel costs. Students may have other ideas.

   b. The faster the speed, the less time it takes to make the trip. Algebraically, the relationship is $T = \frac{800}{S}$.

   c. $C_D = 25 \cdot \frac{800}{S} = \frac{25 \times 800}{S}$

   As speed increases, the driver cost decreases.

   d. For low speed, the cost of fuel is high. As speed increases, fuel cost decreases to a minimum of $416 at 35 mph. Then it begins to increase as speed increases.

   e. At approximately 46 miles per hour, the cost of fuel is about equal to the cost of paying the driver (about $433).

   f. Total Cost $= \frac{20{,}000}{S} + \frac{6S^2 + 7{,}200}{S}$. To find the driving speed that minimizes costs for each trip, examine either the table or the graph of the Total Cost function. The minimum total cost is about $808. This cost is obtained by driving at a speed of about 67 mph.

5. **a.** First multiply both sides by y to get $zy = 5x$. Then divide both sides by z to get $y = \frac{5x}{z}$.

   b. First multiply both sides by y to get $zy = 5x$. Then divide both sides by 5 to get $x = \frac{zy}{5}$.

   c. First subtract $11y$ from both sides to get $z - 11y = 5x$. Then divide both sides by 5 to get $x = \frac{z - 11y}{5}$.

   d. $d = \frac{88 \sin 100^\circ}{\sin 27^\circ} \approx 190.9$

   e. To graph $3.5x + 1.8y = 2.7$ using the graphing calculator, you must enter the equation in the "$y = \ldots$" form. Students do not have to simplify the equation.

   $y = \frac{(3.5x - 2.7)}{-1.8}$, $y = \frac{3.5x}{-1.8} + \frac{2.7}{1.8}$, or $y = \frac{2.7 - 3.5x}{1.8}$

   f. In the graph below, the shaded portion satisfies the inequality.

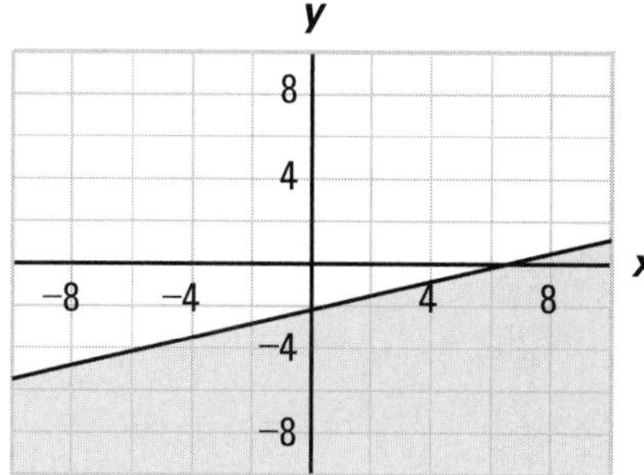

4. On any long trip along American interstate highways, you are sure to meet hundreds of large trucks. They carry cargo of all kinds between nearby cities and across the country from coast to coast. One problem faced by trucking companies is finding the most efficient operating speed. Consider the case of a company that hauls radioactive waste materials from a nuclear power plant to a special storage facility that is 800 miles away.

a. List as many advantages as you can for planning a fairly high speed for the trucks on this job. List advantages for a slower speed.

b. One factor to consider is that pay for the truck driver is related to the time it takes to make the 800-mile trip. How is time T for the 800-mile trip related to speed S in miles per hour?

c. If the truck driver earns $25 per hour, what equation gives the driver cost C_D (in dollars) as a function of speed in miles per hour for the trip? Describe the pattern of change in driver cost as speed increases.

d. Another factor to consider is the cost of fuel for the trip. For trucks owned by the hauling company, the fuel cost C_F (in dollars) for the 800-mile trip is related to the speed of the truck by the equation $C_F = \frac{6S^2 + 7{,}200}{S}$. Describe the pattern of change in fuel cost as truck speed increases.

e. At what speed is the cost of fuel equal to the cost of paying the driver?

f. What equation shows how total operating cost for the trip (fuel and driver pay) changes as driving speed changes? How can that equation be used to find the driving speed that minimizes cost for each trip? What is the minimum cost? At what speed?

5. In your work with multiple-variable models, it often was helpful (1) to rewrite algebraic expressions and (2) to sketch graphs of linear equations and inequalities, and to do both quickly and accurately. Check your level of skill in these areas by completing the following tasks.

a. Solve the equation $z = \frac{5x}{y}$ for y in terms of x and z.

b. Solve the equation $z = \frac{5x}{y}$ for x in terms of y and z.

c. Solve the equation $z = 5x + 11y$ for x in terms of y and z.

d. Solve the equation $\frac{d}{\sin 100^\circ} = \frac{88}{\sin 27^\circ}$.

e. Rewrite the equation $3.5x + 1.8y = 2.7$ so that it can be graphed using a graphing calculator or computer software.

f. Sketch the graph of $2x - 6y \geq 13$.

LESSON 5 • LOOKING BACK 89

Checkpoint

You have investigated several different multiple-variable situations in this unit. In some cases, a single equation can express the relation among several variables. In other cases, more than one equation is needed to show how several output variables depend on a single input variable. And in still other cases, several variables are related by constraint inequalities, and the goal is to find values of the variables that maximize or minimize an objective function.

a Consider the equation $z = \frac{3x}{y}$.

- How does z change as x increases or decreases?
- How does z change as y increases or decreases?
- What equivalent equation shows y as a function of x and z?
- What equivalent equation shows x as a function of y and z?

b Consider the equation $z = 3x + 5y$.

- How does z change as x or y increases? As x or y decreases?
- What equivalent equation shows x as a function of y and z?

c What clues do you use to decide if modeling a problem situation requires the Law of Cosines? If it requires the Law of Sines?

d If two variables y_1 and y_2 are both functions of x, describe how you can use graphs and tables to find values of x for which each of the following is true:

- $y_1 > y_2$
- $y_1 < y_2$
- $y_1 = y_2$

e Describe the roles played by the following elements of linear programming problems:

- Constraints
- Feasible points
- Objective function

f What steps are involved in graphing an inequality like $3x + 5y \leq 10$?

g For each of the following cases, describe what clues you use to decide if a problem situation requires that type of modeling.

- Several variables related by a single equation
- Several equations with the same input variable
- Analysis by linear programming

Be prepared to share your responses and explain your thinking.

SHARE AND SUMMARIZE full-class discussion

Checkpoint

See Teaching Masters 35a–35c.

a ■ If y is positive, then an increase in x causes an increase in z. If y is negative, then an increase in x causes a decrease in z.

■ If x is positive, then an increase in y causes an decrease in z. If x is negative, then an increase in y causes an increase in z.

■ $y = \frac{3x}{z}$

■ $x = \frac{zy}{3}$

b ■ As x or y increases, z increases. As x or y decreases, z decreases.

■ $x = \frac{z - 5y}{3}$

c Students should not memorize these but should be able to reconstruct them from the formulas. The Law of Cosines is useful if you know measures of two sides and the included angle of a triangle, or if you know all three sides of a triangle. The Law of Sines is helpful if you know the measures of two angles and the length of any side, or if you know the length of two sides and the measure of an angle opposite one of them. (Again, it is not advisable to discuss the ambiguous case of the Law of Sines at this time. It will be addressed in Unit 4, "Shapes and Geometric Reasoning.")

d Tables of values can be used to find the indicated relationships. It may be helpful to look at the graphs to get an idea of what is happening with the functions.

■ Plot both functions on the same graph. The values of x for which the graph of y_1 is above the graph of y_2 are the values of x for which $y_1 > y_2$.

■ The values of x for which the graph of y_1 is below the graph of y_2 are the values of x for which $y_1 < y_2$.

■ Where the two graphs intersect is where $y_1 = y_2$.

e ■ The constraints provide the boundaries of the feasible set.

■ The feasible points are all of the (x, y) pairs that satisfy the constraints.

■ The objective function states the relation between the variables and the goal quantity. Usually, solving the problem requires maximizing or minimizing some quantity.

f First, graph the related linear equation, $3x + 5y = 10$. This can be done by putting the equation into "$y = \ldots$" form, and then using the slope and y-intercept to help sketch the graph, or entering the equation into a calculator or computer software. Another method for graphing the line is to find two points on the line, plot them, and draw the line. The x- and y-intercepts are good points to use to help draw the line. Then you must determine which side of the line is the feasible region, either by testing a point or by taking clues from which way the inequality sign points.

g There aren't any hard and fast algorithms for deciding what sort of equation or system models should be applied to given situations. However, it is important for students to review what they've done in this unit to see the big picture of the types of situations they've learned to analyze.

■ Clues might include statements suggesting that the value of one variable depends on or can be calculated from the values of one or more other variables. Sometimes the clue is that two or more variables have some fixed relationship to each other.

■ Clues would include statements that several different quantities depend on or can be calculated from the same quantity.

See additional Teaching Notes on page T90S.

Masters 35a–35c

MASTER 35a — Transparency Master

Checkpoint

You have investigated several different multiple-variable situations in this unit. In some cases, a single equation can express the relation among several variables. In some cases, more than one equation is needed to show how several output variables depend on a single input variable. And in other cases, several variables are related by constraint inequalities and the goal is to find values of the variables that maximize or minimize an objective function.

a Consider the equation $z = \frac{3x}{y}$.
- How does z change as x increases or decreases?
- How does z change as y increases or decreases?
- What equivalent equation shows y as a function of x and z?
- What equivalent equation shows x as a function of y and z?

b Consider the equation $z = 3x + 5y$.
- How does z change as x or y increases? As x or y decreases?
- What equivalent equation shows x as a function of y and z?

Unit 1 Summary

UNIT 1 — Unit Summary

Multiple-Variable Models

Assessments 27–42

In-Class Exam — Form A

NOTE: At the end of the *Teaching Resources* are masters for students to use for summarizing the important ideas developed in each unit.

Unit 1

Looking Back, Looking Ahead

Reflecting on Mathematical Content

The algebra strand of this curriculum has emphasized patterns in tables, graphs, and symbolic rules as various real-life situations involving linear, quadratic, exponential, and power models have been explored. In those situations, students generally were expressing one variable in terms of a second variable. For the students, algebra has been a language with which to express relationships and explore patterns. As students worked through "Multiple-Variable Models," they were confronted with situations involving the need to do more and more symbol manipulation, as they explored more complex rules and relationships, often involving three or four variables. Students have expanded their thinking and reasoning to include inequalities as well as equations, and they continue to use technology as a natural tool to aid them in their thinking and analysis of the algebraic models.

Looking ahead, the next step in the algebra strand challenges students to begin to formalize their algebraic reasoning. What they have handled informally, as they have simplified expressions, solved equations, operated with algebraic symbols, and completed proofs, will be taken to a higher level of sophistication in Unit 3, "Symbol Sense and Algebraic Reasoning." The notion and notation of function is formalized, and the various models studied in the past are revisited. In addition to the concept of function and function notation, transformations of functions will be approached using graphs, tables, and symbolic forms in Unit 6, "Families of Functions."

In Course 4, for college-intending students, the algebra and functions strand continues to develop student understanding of functions including common and natural logarithmic, polynomial, rational, and trigonometric functions. Students also study the fundamental concepts underlying calculus in Unit 1, "Rates of Change." In Unit 7, "Functions and Symbolic Reasoning," students solve logarithmic and trigonometric equations and identities, use rectangular and polar representations of complex numbers, reason with complex numbers and their operations using geometric representation, and find roots of complex numbers. See *Implementing the Core-Plus Mathematics Project* for more information on Course 4.

Unit 1 Assessment

	Assessment Resources
Lesson Quizzes	
Lesson 1 *Linked Variables*	pp. 1–6
Lesson 2 *Algebra, Geometry, and Trigonometry*	pp. 7–12
Lesson 3 *Linked Equations*	pp. 13–18
Lesson 4 *Linear Programming*	pp. 19–26
In-Class Exams	
Form A	pp. 27–32
Form B	pp. 33–36
Take-Home Assessments	pp. 37–38
Unit 1 Projects	
More on Linear Programming	pp. 39–40
Systems and Matrices: A Review	pp. 41–42

Teaching Notes *continued*

Notes continued from page T2

d Some other variables that might be mentioned include the density of the board d, the sharpness of the striking object s, and the width of the board w. (Students also might suggest density by indicating the type of wood.) The equation $E = \frac{kdTw}{Ls}$ captures the relationships among all these variables. While it is not expected that students will arrive at this equation, they should be encouraged to think about how these properties are related. We would expect E to increase as the density or the width of the board increases, and we would expect E to decrease as the sharpness of the striking object increases.

If students suggest the speed or mass of the striking object, you may want to mention that these are the variables that determine the amount of energy produced rather than the amount of energy required.

Notes continued from page T3

Be prepared for this investigation to take a significant amount of time. It sets up all the issues about direct and inverse variation, and it also reviews linear and non-linear relationships. A full-class summary is helpful after Activity 2, when students should have decided that a linear relationship is a good model for the direct relationship between *W* and *T*. Another summary is helpful after Activity 3, to help all students see that some non-linear relationship is a good model for the inverse relationship between *W* and *L*. Yet another is helpful after Activity 4, when students begin to make sense of the particular arrangements of symbols that will give the kind of relationships they are seeking. This investigation introduces many ideas, so do not expect mastery or definitive decisions about all the issues; on the other hand, you should not leave the investigation without at least raising all the appropriate questions regarding the relationships among variables.

1. **See Teaching Master 3.**

   Typical data collected by students might be something like the data in the chart below. It is helpful to put a blank chart up on the board ahead of time and have various groups fill in the data and their models as they collect their measurements. As students complete the experiment, you can keep an eye on their methods and ask them questions that direct their attention to quality control issues. If you want to pool the data, methods should be applied carefully and consistently. If you have more than 5 groups, you may wish to have groups collect data for a 3.5 or 4.5 gap length or to choose a different length.

Number of Strands

Gap Length (in.)	1	2	3	4	5
2	92.5	145.1	188.1	261.6	407.9
3	47.8	109.9	128.4	185.8	333.1
3.5	44.7	84.9	110.3	155.4	205.6
4	38.6	69.9	98.5	124.7	167.6
4.5	33.9	47.1	86.2	112.4	119.3
5	29.6	43.7	79.1	95.9	112.6
6	23.8	28.3	66.5	78.4	90.2

Weight (in grams)

Teaching Notes *continued*

Notes continued from page T4

2\. c. For a gap of 3.5 inches:

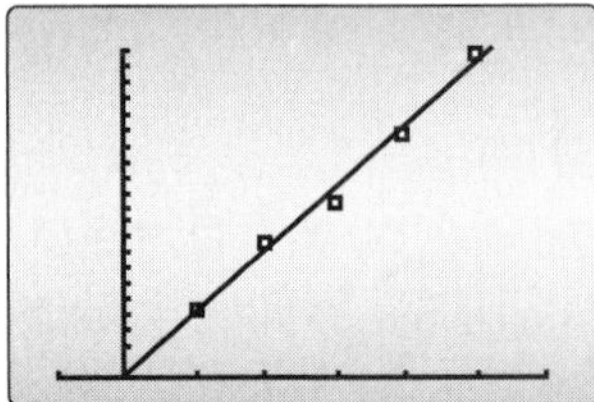

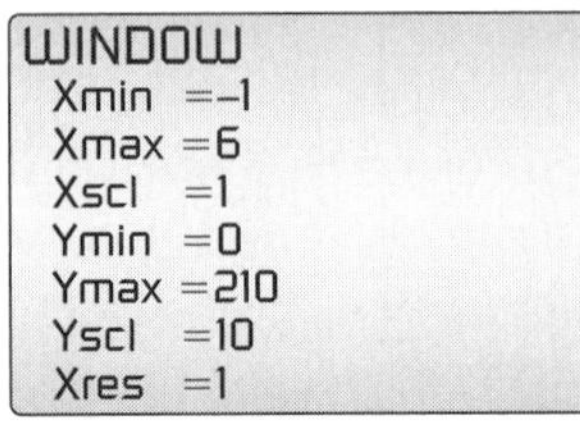

$y = 39.23x + 2.49$

For a gap of 3 inches:

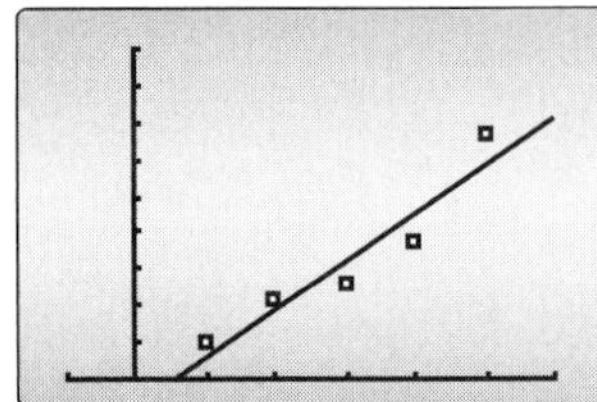

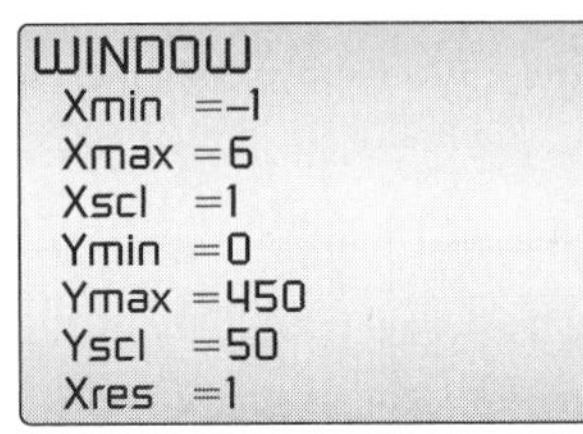

$y = 64.65x - 32.95$

For a gap of 2 inches:

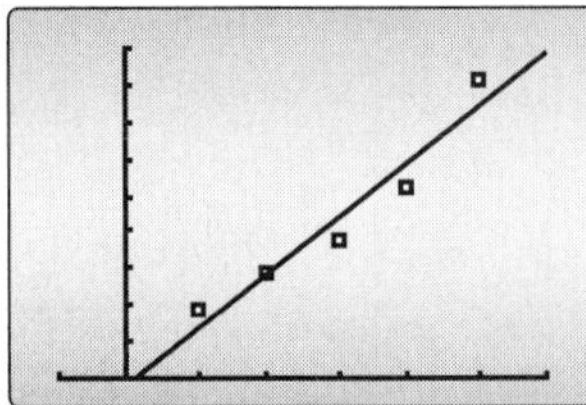

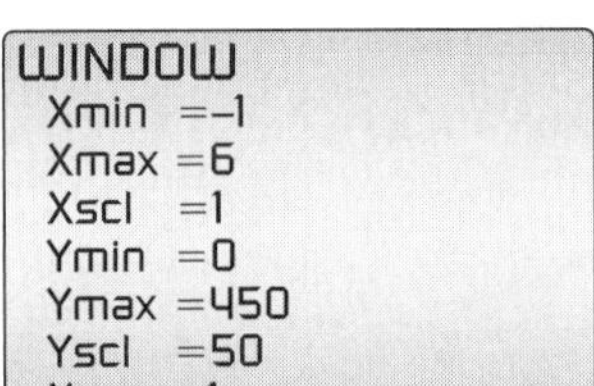

$y = 74.73x - 5.15$

d. When the length of the gap is held constant, breaking weight increases as the thickness, or number of strands, increases. This increase seems to be linear, regardless of the gap length.

3\. **Student responses may vary. An inverse power model is provided for each situation from the sample data in Activity 1. Some students may choose to use exponential models. As you move among the groups, encourage students to discuss their choice of model.**

After this activity, you might pull the class together again to discuss the patterns they see. They should all agree that some decreasing non-linear model is appropriate. If some groups choose an exponential model, ask about the meaning of $W = a \cdot b^L$ if the length of the gap is zero: "Does it make sense to say what weight the bridge will hold if the length is zero? Is an intercept sensible?" If no group suggests an inverse power model, it would be helpful to remind students that $y = \frac{1}{x}$ also has a shape similar to the graphs they are investigating. Ask them to try this kind of model on their data to see if it fits as well as the exponential model they suggested. Returning to the context should convince students that the inverse power model is more appropriate because of the intercept or zero gap issue. If they produce inverse power models, you may need to help them interpret the negative exponents that are produced. Expressions containing negative exponents should be rewritten as fractions.

See additional Teaching Notes on page T90E.

Teaching Notes *continued*

Notes continued from page T4

3. a. For thickness of 1 strand:

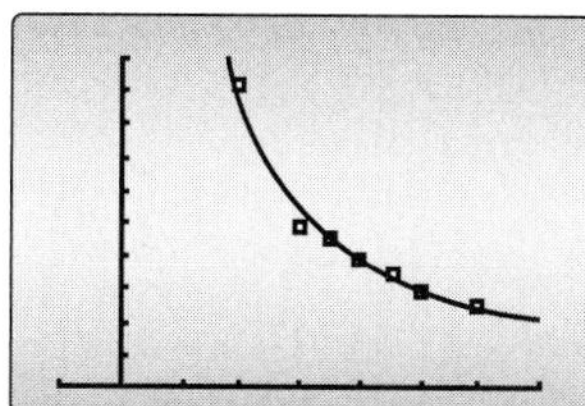
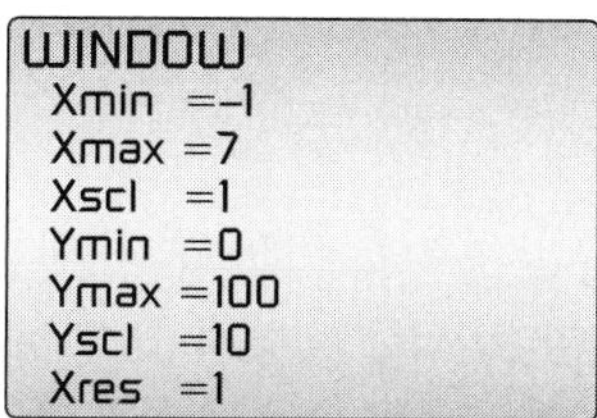

$y = \frac{198}{x^{1.2}}$

b. For thickness of 2 strands:

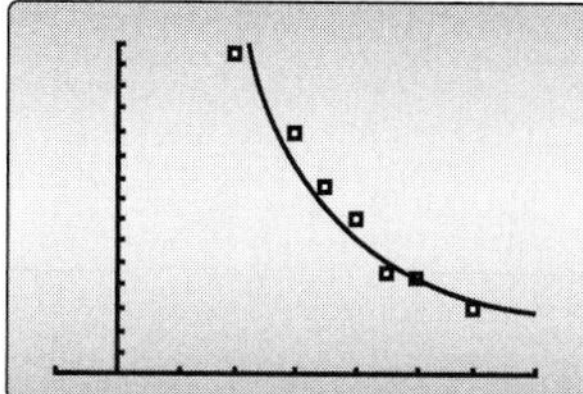
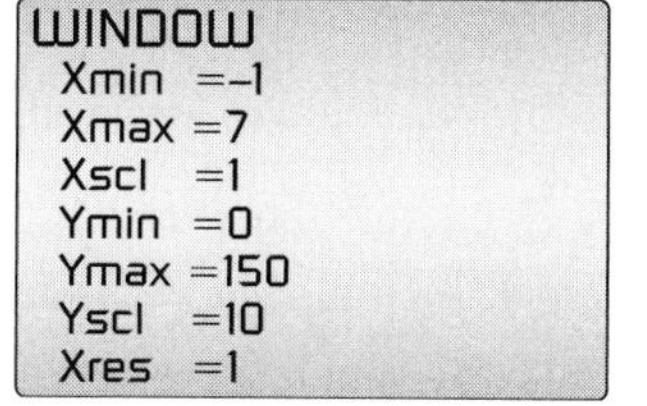

$y = \frac{502}{x^{1.5}}$

For thickness of 3 strands:

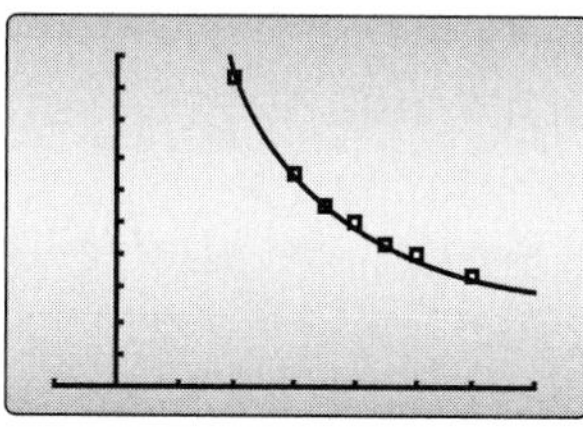
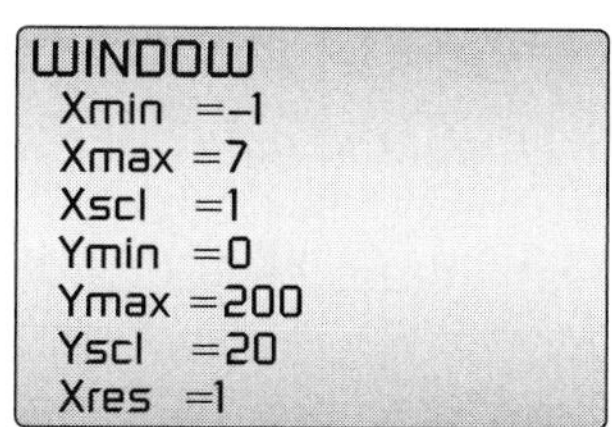

$y = \frac{363}{x^{0.95}}$

For thickness of 4 strands:

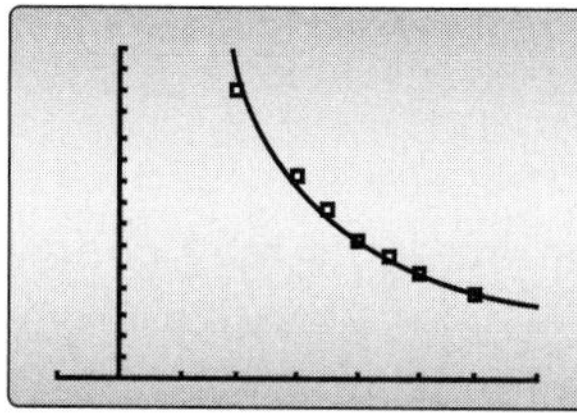
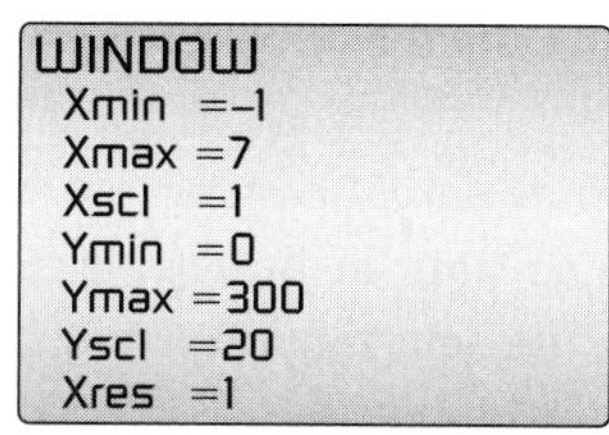

$y = \frac{603}{x^{1.1}}$

For thickness of 5 strands:

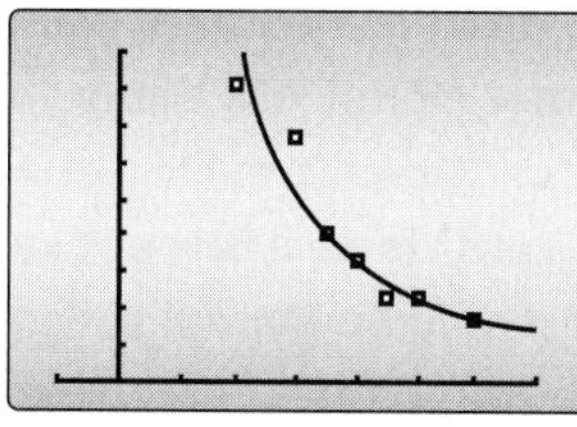
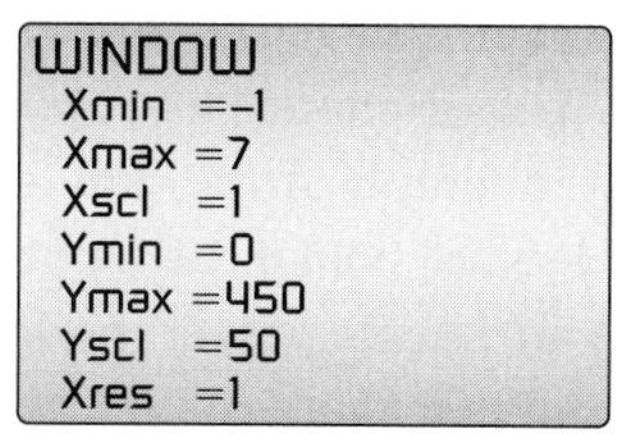

$y = \frac{1,349}{x^{1.5}}$

c. The breaking weight decreases as the gap length increases. The rate of change is not constant.

See additional Teaching Notes on page T90F.

Notes continued from page T4

4. a. Students should understand that they are looking for a model where W increases as T increases and W decreases as L increases. Students should be able to see that $W = 10T + L$ and $W = 10T \times L$ are models where W increases as L increases, and therefore they are not options.

Students might want to test the two remaining models by completing a chart like those below to determine the patterns for both $W = 10T - L$ and $W = \frac{10T}{L}$.

$W = 10T - L$

L \ T	1	2	3	4	5
2	8	18	28	38	48
3	7	17	27	37	47
4	6	16	26	36	46
5	5	15	25	35	45
6	4	14	24	34	44

$W = \frac{10T}{L}$

L \ T	1	2	3	4	5
2	5	10	15	20	25
3	3.3	6.7	10	13.3	16.7
4	2.5	5	7.5	10	12.5
5	2	4	6	8	10
6	1.7	3.3	5	6.7	8.3

By studying the completed charts, students should notice that when $W = 10T - L$, the patterns are all linear because the change is constant. Students should observe that the model $W = \frac{10T}{L}$ is more like the data pattern from the investigation. When L is held constant, $W = \frac{10T}{L}$ is simply a linear equation relating W and T. In this way, the data-fitting rule is similar to the linear models for (*thickness*, *weight*) that students have seen already. Also, when T is held constant, $W = \frac{10T}{L}$ is actually a power model relating W and L.

This rule differs from other algebraic models previously studied in that it has two independent variables instead of one.

b. The students will have different suggestions, and you should spend some time looking at a group's data and their suggestions. This could be done as a class or individually with each group.

After deciding that $W = \frac{10T}{L}$ is the closest model, a group could then modify that model by changing 10 to a value k that better matches their data. They could set up data tables like those below to explore k where $W = \frac{kT}{L}$ or $k = \frac{WL}{T}$. The average of the k values in these tables is approximately 137, so the modified model in this case might be $W = \frac{137T}{L}$.

T	L	W	k
1	3	48	144
2	3	110	165
3	3	128	128
4	3	186	140

T	L	W	k
1	4	39	156
2	4	70	140
3	4	99	132
4	4	125	125

T	L	W	k
1	5	30	150
2	5	44	110
3	5	79	132
4	5	96	120

Teaching Notes *continued*

Notes continued from page T5

APPLY individual task

On Your Own

a. It seems plausible to expect that increasing speed increases the rate of fatal accidents while increasing mass of the car decreases the rate of fatal accidents. Heavier cars tend to offer their passengers more protection in accidents, and they inflict more damage to small cars than the small cars do to them.

b. To test the ideas in Part a requires data on fatalities occurring in cars of various sizes. But it is also important to know how many of each car size were on the road and how many miles were driven by the various kinds of cars. Speeds at which cars in fatal accidents were being driven is also needed. Some of this data could be simulated in crash tests where the mass and speed variables are carefully controlled and systematically varied.

c. Among the symbolic forms offered, that which best matches the relationship described in Part a is $A = 200\frac{s}{m}$. In fact, with speed in kilometers per hour, mass in kilograms, and accident rate in fatalities per 100 million passenger miles, the relationship here gives numbers quite close to those seen recently in U.S. highway data.

Group Processing Suggestions

See *Implementing the Core-Plus Mathematics Curriculum* for suggestions on improving collaborative work. See also Teaching Master 119, which will assist students in evaluating their own group work.

You may wish to give students a group-processing prompt at the beginning of the class period so they know what the focus for the day is to be.

Notes continued from page T15

4. a. $x = \frac{z - by}{a}$

b. $a = \frac{z - by}{x}$

c. $y = \frac{z - ax}{b}$

d. $b = \frac{z - ax}{y}$

e. First, a term is subtracted from each side of the equation, and then both sides of the equation are divided by a variable.

f. As x or y increases, z will increase.

5. a. Multiplying both sides of the equation by bd and then simplifying will produce $ad = bc$. Some students may prefer to look at this in two steps, first multiplying by b and simplifying and then multiplying by d.

b. From Part a, $\frac{a}{b} = \frac{c}{d}$ is equivalent to $ad = bc$. Next divide both sides of the equation $ad = bc$ by ac and simplify. This will give $\frac{d}{c} = \frac{b}{a}$.

Teaching Notes *continued*

Notes continued from page T25

b An altimeter can be used to obtain altitude readings. A hand-held GPS could be used, but would not be as accurate as an altimeter. The Global Positioning System is an array of satellites that can give locations and heights above sea level. To obtain the climbing height of Mount Everest above ground, you would need to get a reading at the top and bottom of the mountain.

c Students might suggest using an altimeter if they can get to the top of the object. Some wristwatches have built-in altimeters and are used by mountain climbers. This method might work easily for a building, but it would not work as well for something like a smokestack or a tree. Measuring the length of the shadow of the object and measuring the height and shadow length of a student might be one method that students would suggest.

$$\frac{\text{height of building}}{\text{shadow length of building}} = \frac{\text{height of student}}{\text{shadow length of student}}$$

SHARE AND SUMMARIZE full-class discussion

Notes continued from page T35

Checkpoint

See Teaching Master 12.

a You would need to know the measure of angle B and the lengths of sides a and c.

$$AC = \sqrt{a^2 + c^2 - 2ac \cos B}$$

b You would need to know the lengths of all three sides.

$$a^2 = b^2 + c^2 - 2bc \cos A$$

$$\cos A = \frac{a^2 - b^2 - c^2}{-2bc}$$

$$m\angle A = \cos^{-1}\left(\frac{a^2 - b^2 - c^2}{-2bc}\right)$$

c If $a^2 + c^2 > b^2$, then $m\angle B$ is less than 90°. If $a^2 + c^2 < b^2$, then $m\angle B$ is greater than 90° (but less than 180°). If $a^2 + c^2 = b^2$, then $m\angle B$ is equal to 90°.

Teaching Notes *continued*

Notes continued from page T37

1. **Division Property of Equality:** If $p = q$, then $p \div r = q \div r$ (if $r \neq 0$).
   - **a.** $100 \div 5 = 10^2 \div 5$
     $48 \div 16 = (6 \cdot 8) \div 16$
     $25 \div 5 = (20 + 5) \div 5$
   - **b.** Dividing both sides of an equation by the same nonzero number maintains equality.

   Square Root Property of Equality: If $p = q$, then $\sqrt{p} = \sqrt{q}$ (if $p, q \geq 0$).
   - **a.** $\sqrt{100} = \sqrt{20 \cdot 5}$
     $\sqrt{22 + 2} = \sqrt{24}$
     $\sqrt{36} = \sqrt{18 \cdot 2}$
   - **b.** Taking the square root of both (nonnegative) sides of an equation maintains equality.

2. **Notice that, since $c^2 = a^2 + b^2$, $c^2 - b^2$ must be nonnegative.**
   - **a.** Start with $c^2 = a^2 + b^2$.

Step 1:	$c^2 - b^2 = a^2$	Inverse of Addition
Step 2:	$\sqrt{c^2 - b^2} = \sqrt{a^2}$	Square Root Property of Equality
Step 3:	$\sqrt{c^2 - b^2} = a$	Inverse of Squaring

   - **b.** Start with $c^2 = a^2 + b^2$.

Step 1:	$c^2 - b^2 = a^2 + b^2 - b^2$	Subtraction Property of Equality
Step 2:	$c^2 - b^2 = a^2$	Adding opposites gives zero.
Step 3:	$\sqrt{c^2 - b^2} = \sqrt{a^2}$	Square Root Property of Equality
Step 4:	$\sqrt{c^2 - b^2} = a$	Inverse of Squaring

Notes continued from page T39

b. **i.** $ZY = \sqrt{18^2 - 16.3^2}$

$ZY \approx 7.6$ in.

ii. $\sin 25^\circ = \frac{ZY}{18}$

$ZY = 18 \sin 25^\circ$

$ZY \approx 7.6$ in.

iii. $\cos 65^\circ = \frac{ZY}{18}$

$ZY = 18 \cos 65^\circ$

$ZY \approx 7.6$ in.

Organizing

Notes continued from page T41

1. **a.** $\frac{f}{5} = \frac{16}{2}$ $\quad \frac{c}{5} = \frac{7}{2}$ $\quad \frac{p}{5} = \frac{8}{2}$

   b. $2f = (16)(5)$ or $f = 40$ grams of fat

   $2c = (7)(5)$ or $c = 17.5$ grams of carbohydrate

   $2p = (8)(5)$ or $p = 20$ grams of protein

   c. They are similar because, just as the sides of similar triangles have a common ratio, the amounts of fat, carbohydrate, and protein in peanut butter will always have a common ratio, even though the amount of peanut butter may vary.

Notes continued from page T44

4. **a.** To find the area of $\triangle ABC$, students need to find h. This can be done by using a right triangle formed by the altitude. If you were given b, c, and $m\angle A$, then $h = b \sin A$, so $Area = \frac{1}{2}ch = \frac{1}{2}cb \sin A$. If you were given a, c, and $m\angle B$, then $h = a \sin B$, so $Area = \frac{1}{2}ch = \frac{1}{2}ca \sin B$.

   b. We know that $h = b \sin A$, but we don't know $m\angle A$. To find $m\angle A$, use the Law of Cosines:

   $$a^2 = b^2 + c^2 - 2bc \cos A$$
   $$\cos A = \frac{a^2 - b^2 - c^2}{-2bc}$$
   $$m\angle A = \cos^{-1}\left(\frac{a^2 - b^2 - c^2}{-2bc}\right)$$

   Now you can substitute the specific values for $m\angle A$ and b into $h = b \sin A$ to find the value of h.

   c. $12.5^2 = 20^2 + 25^2 - 2(20)(25) \cos A$

   $\cos A = 0.8688$

   $m\angle A \approx 29.69°$

   $h = 20(\sin 29.69°) \approx 9.9$ cm

   $Area \approx 0.5(25)(9.9) = 123.75$ square centimeters

Teaching Notes *continued*

Notes continued from page T46

ⓐ Automotive lease plans typically require a down payment and a monthly payment. The leasee is responsible for maintenance and insurance. There is usually a maximum allowable mileage. Exceeding that mileage results in excess charges when the vehicle is returned at the end of the lease period.

ⓑ Students should mention that A-1 Auto Parts should consider such things as how long they will need the truck, how much money they have to spend on the lease each month, how much money they need to put down at the start of the lease, how many miles will be driven and how many are allowed, how much wear and tear there will be on the truck, maintenance costs, whether their cash flow will improve enough to buy a truck eventually, and whether they will need an upgraded truck or even two trucks if business improves.

ⓒ There are many relationships among the above variables. One of these is that, as the down payment increases, the monthly lease payment decreases.

ⓓ *Cost of lease* = *Down payment* + (*Monthly payment*)(*Number of months of the lease*) (Students do not have to come up with this formula at this time. It is the subject of Investigation 1.)

Notes continued from page T48

SHARE AND SUMMARIZE full-class discussion

Checkpoint

See Teaching Master 15.

ⓐ The equations would depend on the down payment, the monthly payment, and the length of time. The down payment corresponds to the y-intercept of the line. The monthly payment is represented by the slope of the line, and the length of time is the independent variable, x.

ⓑ
- $a + bx < c + dx$
- $c + dx < a + bx$
- $c + dx = a + bx$

ⓒ Student responses may vary. Some students may describe a method that depends on using the properties of equality, and others may describe a method that refers back to the graphs or tables.

At this time, it is important to stress how the inequalities and equation from Part b relate to the graph. Plan A is less expensive than Plan B at any time (at any x value) for which the graph of Plan A is below the graph of Plan B. Whenever the graph of Plan B is below the graph of Plan A, then Plan B is the less expensive plan. They cost the same at the time (x value) that corresponds to the point of intersection. It is important that students recognize that a solution involves finding the correct x values for the equation or inequality.

Notes continued from page T49

When groups are working on Activity 4, you may find that some do not use a graph or table to compare these functions. This may be related to the fact that the output variables have quite different meanings. (In the last investigation, the output variables were total payments under Plan A and Plan B, closely connected in meaning.) You may be able to help students see the reasonability of graphing these on the same axes, if you trace with your finger or cursor along the *separate* graphs created by $H = \frac{100{,}000}{P}$ and $A = \frac{P}{10}$, as asked for in Activities 2 and 3. Ask what is happening to H as you proceed: "So at this value of P (or x), the value of H is ...?" Do the same with the other graph: "At this value of P, the value of A is ...? What was H doing at that same value of P?" This may help students see that, instead of going back and forth between *separate* graphs or tables looking for significant points, it is legitimate to put the graphs on the same axes.

For groups who immediately went to the combined graph or table to make comparisons, you might ask what variable is on the horizontal axis (P) and what variable is on the vertical axis (both H and A). You could follow that question with, "Why is it reasonable and helpful to graph both equations on the same axes?"

Notes continued from page T51

b Again, use A for expected number of applicants, H for number of students, and P for pay offered.

$A = \frac{P}{10}$

$H = \frac{100{,}000}{P}$

c The output of both of the modeling equations is dependent on the salary paid to the worker. Both models can be graphed on the same set of axes. The region of the graph where the curve is above the line represents the option in which the number of youth who can be hired is greater than the expected number of applicants. The intersection of the line and curve represents the point at which the expected number of applicants is equal to the number of youths who could be hired. The region of the graph where the line is above the curve represents the situation in which the expected number of applicants is greater than the number who could be hired.

d Students probably solved this system of equations by looking at either the table or the point of intersection of the two graphs. They previously have solved systems of linear equations using both of these methods. You may want to discuss how this system of equations is different from a system of linear equations and the implications of those differences.

Group Processing Suggestions

- Rate yourself on a scale of 1 (low) to 5 (high) for your group participation during this investigation. Then rate each of your group members, and discuss within your group the ratings.
- We did well on checking for understanding by … .

Teaching Notes *continued*

Notes continued from page T55

b *F*: Profit is zero; the number of tickets sold generates just enough income to meet expenses. Determine where the *profit* graph crosses the horizontal axis.

G: Maximum profit. Use the trace capability of a calculator to find the maximum point of the *profit* graph.

H: Profit is zero. Determine where the *profit* graph crosses the horizontal axis.

I: Income is zero. Determine where the *income* graph crosses the horizontal axis.

J: Profit when ticket price is zero. Evaluate the *profit* equation when ticket price is zero, or use the trace capability of a calculator to determine where the *profit* graph crosses the *y*-axis.

c In each of these three problems, there were a number of output variables that were related to a single input variable. In order to analyze the situation, you had to solve systems of equations. This system is different from the others, because some of the graphs intersect in more than one point. The other systems did not have any quadratic equations.

Be sure to discuss the fact that sometimes there are two solutions to a problem, corresponding to two intersection points. For students who are heavily dependent on the table, they should see that the table without a corresponding mental picture of the shapes of the graphs is not much help in determining all the solutions. You might ask if students can think of any other types of algebraic models. They should recall different power models, such as $y = \frac{1}{x^3}$ or $y = x^5$, or they may recall trigonometric models, such as $y = \sin x$. You can then ask how many solutions one might find for a system of linked equations that comprises, for example, a trigonometric function and a linear function. Students should appreciate that one first step is to inspect a graph to help determine the possible number of solutions.

Group Processing Suggestions

- Name ways in which your group works better now than it did two weeks ago.
- We included everyone today by … .

Teaching Notes *continued*

Notes continued from page T60

4. c. There can be either 0, 1, or 2 solutions.

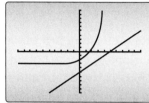

0 solutions | 1 solution | 2 solutions

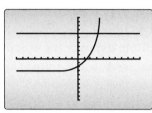

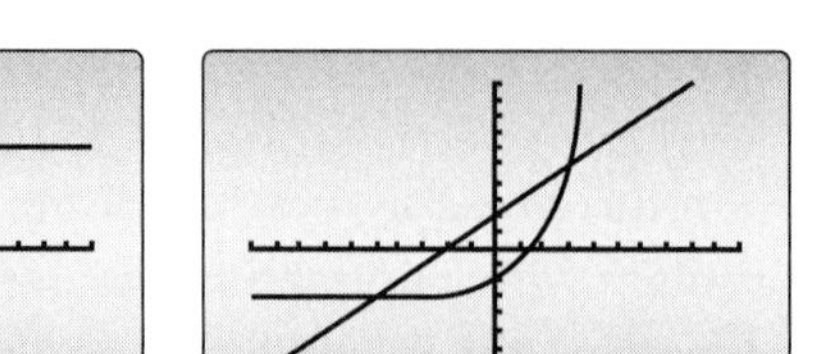

d. Most students will respond with 0, 1, or 2 solutions. Students also might use square inverse examples, in which case there is also the possibility of 3 solutions.

0 solutions | 1 solution | 2 solutions | 3 solutions

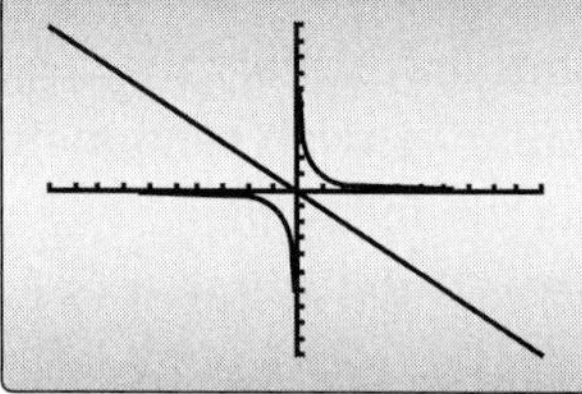

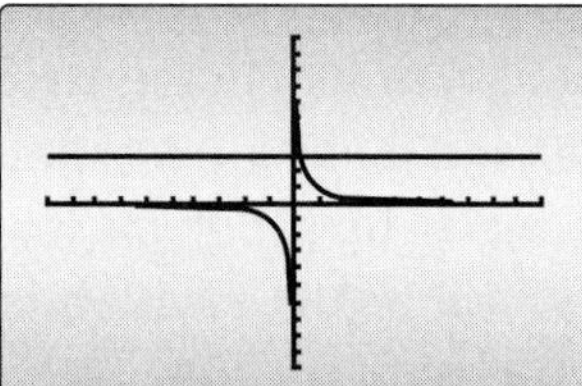

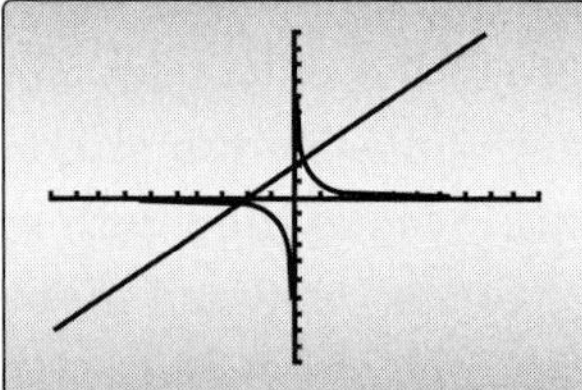

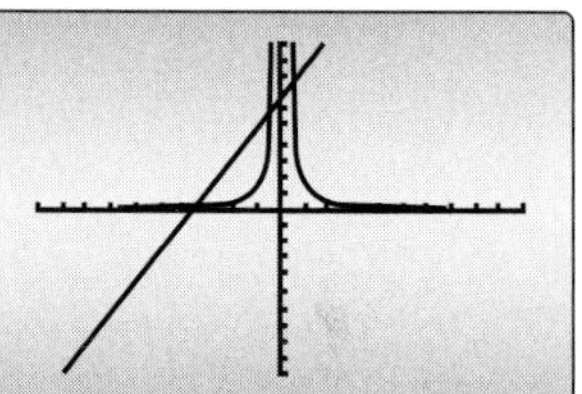

Notes continued from page T61

1. ■ $ax + b = c(d^x)$

0 solutions:	$2x - 10 = 2^x$
1 solution:	$8 = 2^x$
2 solutions:	$2x + 10 = 2^x$

■ $ax + b = \frac{c}{x^2}$

0 solutions:	$-10 = \frac{10}{x^2}$
1 solution:	$2x - 10 = \frac{10}{x^2}$
2 solutions:	$10 = \frac{10}{x^2}$
3 solutions:	$2x + 10 = \frac{10}{x^2}$

Notes continued from page T63

a. Some students may suggest talking to the technicians and asking them to give estimates. Other students may suggest keeping track of the production activities over a period of time to determine an average of how long each activity takes.

b. To determine the profit per model, you have to know how much each product costs to manufacture and market, including capital expenditures as well as advertising, material, labor, and other costs. You also have to know the selling price that the market will bear. Your profit will be the difference between your costs and your income based on sales.

c. Students probably will guess and check, which is okay for now. They should realize that the maximum profit is not found easily by guessing and checking.

Teaching Notes continued

Unit 1

Notes continued from page T68

EXPLORE small-group investigation

INVESTIGATION 2 Using an Algebraic Model

In this investigation, students express the constraints for a linear programming problem with inequalities and use these symbolic expressions to create boundaries separating the feasible and nonfeasible regions. This removes the doubt about the shape of the feasible region and makes it possible in the next investigation to search efficiently for optimal points.

One meaning of the equation $ax + by = c$ is as a description of the set of pairs (x, y) that satisfy this relationship. Students need to recognize that this is a linear relationship and be able to graph it, either by solving the equation for y, which was one of the objectives in Lesson 1, or by finding two points that satisfy the relationship (possibly the intercepts) and joining the points. You may wish to launch into this investigation with some warm-up problems, such as the following:

Solve for y and identify whether the relation is linear. If the relation is linear, sketch a graph of it.

- $y = \frac{x}{2}$
- $x = \frac{y}{2}$
- $x = \frac{2}{y}$
- $x + y = 0.5$
- $2x + 3y = 0$
- $0.6x + 0.3y = 240$

For $y = 0.5x + 3$, what value does y take when x is 0?

For $y = 0.5x + 3$, what value does x take when y is 0?

For $0.6x + 0.3y = 240$, what is the x-intercept? The y-intercept?

For $0.6x + 0.3y = 240$, what is the x-intercept? The y-intercept?

You may wish to have students do Activity 1 as a large group. Certainly you will want to check that all groups are working with the correct inequalities before they go on to Acitivities 2–4. Students who are using calculators to graph the constraints will have few problems showing the separation of the feasible and nonfeasible regions. However, they may have more trouble transferring the graph to paper. Using the intercepts makes this task simpler. The pencil-and-paper copy is useful because it relates the shading of a region to the previous investigation. As you facilitiate the groups, keep checking that students understand what an (x, y) point in a shaded or unshaded region means and that they can test any point against the given constraints.

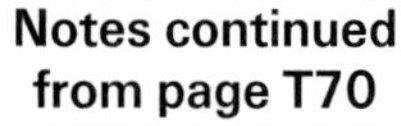
Notes continued from page T70

3. b. Video Game Assembly Time

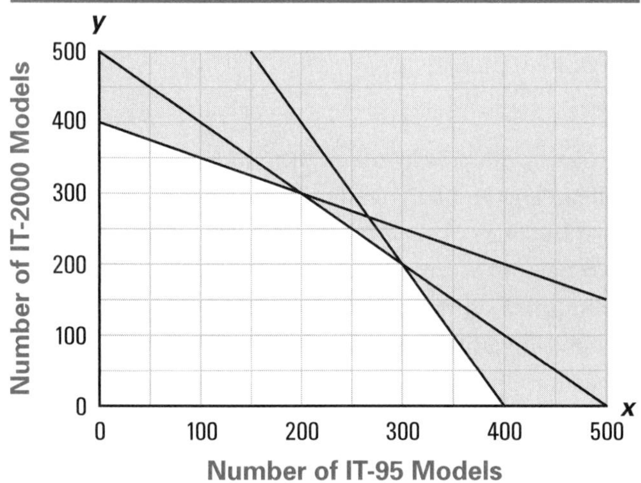

The points that have coordinates that meet all 3 constraints are in a pentagonal region in which all the following are met:

$x \geq 0$
$y \geq 0$
$0.6x + 0.3y \leq 240$
$0.2x + 0.4y \leq 160$
$x + y \leq 500$

The boundary of the feasible set is the boundary of the pentagonal region. It is the pentagon formed by the lines $x = 0$, $y = 0$, $0.6x + 0.3y = 240$, $0.2x + 0.4y = 160$, and $x + y = 500$.

Another description might be that the boundary is the y-axis from $y = 0$ to $y = 400$; $0.6x + 0.3y = 240$ from $x = 0$ to $x = 200$; $x + y = 500$ from $x = 200$ to $x = 300$; $0.2x + 0.4y = 160$ from $x = 300$ to $x = 400$; and the x-axis from $x = 0$ to $x = 400$.

c. Responses will vary. As students proceed through the rest of linear programming, they will need to be able to find such points of intersection. Students can use tables of values, zoom-in on the point of intersection on a graph, or use a variety of algebraic methods. You may wish to encourage the algebraic methods, as they always give exact values. The intersection points are (200, 300) and (300, 200).

d. **See Teaching Masters 26 and 27.**

This activity provides students with another way to solve a system of two equations.

e. Students may find it helpful to return to the grid where they determined the value of the objective function. The largest profit is \$32,500. At this point, students may not realize that this is at a vertex of the pentagon that is the boundary of the feasible region. If students do raise this conjecture, ask them to keep it in mind as they work through the remainder of the lesson.

f. Integrated Technologies should plan to produce 200 IT-95s and 300 IT-2000s each day.

Teaching Notes *continued*

Notes continued from page T76

SHARE AND SUMMARIZE full-class discussion

Checkpoint

See Teaching Master 32.

a. Linear programming involves problems in which there are several limitations or constraints on several variables. The problems in this lesson have dealt with situations in which there have been two variables, such as two video game models, two types of food (bars and drinks), and two types of pizza. In each of these situations, there were several constraints that put certain limits on these variables, making only certain possibilities feasible. There also is an objective function that describes the goal, for example, trying to minimize weight or maximize profit.

b. The first step in solving a linear programming problem is to identify the variables involved in the problem. Next, you need to describe the constraints algebraically; then you need to graph these constraints and determine the feasible region. The next step is to determine the coordinates of the vertices of the feasible region, and the last step is to test these points in the objective function to determine which point is the best solution for the problem.

c. The maximum or minimum value of the objective function always will occur at one of the vertices of the feasible region. See Activity 3 above and the optional extension below.

Optional Checkpoint Extension

If you want to connect the discussion of rates of change to graphical displays of rate of change with interested students, you have only to graph the objective function with a fixed value, for example, for profit. For $P = 50x + 75y$, if the profit is \$15,000, then $15{,}000 = 50x + 75y$, or $y = 200 - \frac{2x}{3}$. This cuts across the unshaded (feasible) region, showing many (x, y) pairs that are feasible for the constraints, and which would give a profit of \$15,000. Increasing the value of the profit does not change the slope of the objective function, but it does move the line closer to the boundaries of the feasible region. Eventually the line will intersect the feasible region only at a vertex (or segment of the boundary). The profit associated with this line is the maximum profit. See the graphs below.

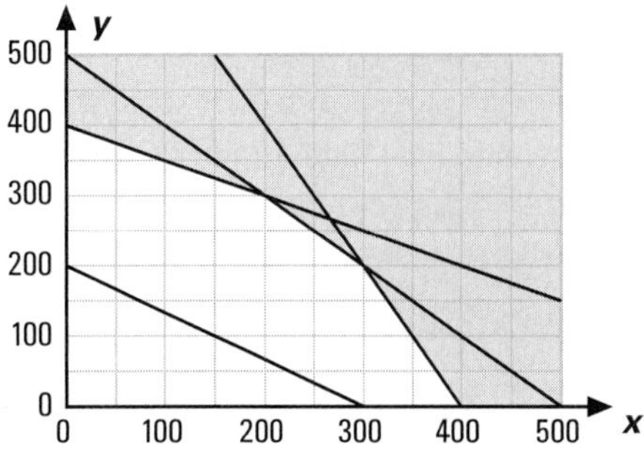

This graph shows the feasible region and the objective function when profit is \$15,000.

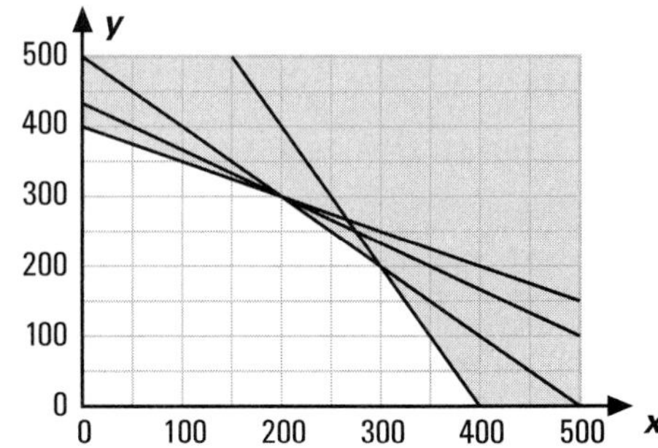

This graph shows the feasible region and the objective function when profit is \$32,500. The objective function only intersects with the feasible region at the point (200, 300).

Notes continued from page T79

5. $x + y \leq 4$ and $x - 2y \geq 6$

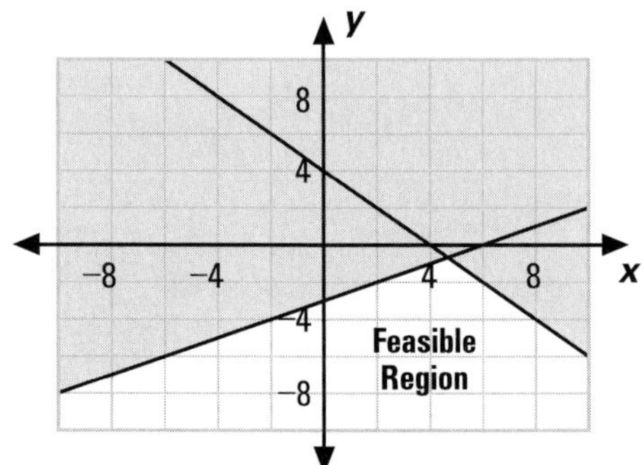

SHARE AND SUMMARIZE full-class discussion

Checkpoint

See Teaching Master 34.

When students are describing their steps for graphing inequalities, you might want to ask them what the graph represents, to keep the focus on making sense of the symbols. For example, rewriting the inequality $ax + by \leq c$, we get a graph of $y \leq (c - ax) \div b$, which represents all the pairs of feasible solutions for the constraint $ax + by \leq c$. Students should be encouraged to check a point to be sure that they are correctly identifying the feasible and nonfeasible regions, especially in those cases in which the coefficient of y is negative. You may want to assign additional practice with such cases to give students the opportunity to spot when the inequality sign seems to reverse.

a Responses will vary. Students should graph the related line first. Some students may do that by determining the x- and y-intercepts for the line. Others may simply enter the non-simplified form in the graphing calculator: $y = (c - ax) \div b$. Still other students may simplify this last form to determine the slope and the y-intercept and use those values to graph the line. After the line is plotted, students may test a point or solve the inequality for y to determine the feasible region.

b Some students may enter the related linear equation in the calculator, while others may use the slope and the y-intercept to graph the line. After they have plotted the related line, students will determine the feasible region, perhaps based on the inequality sign or by testing a point.

See additional Teaching Notes on page T90S.

Teaching Notes *continued*

Notes continued from page T79

APPLY individual task

On Your Own

a. ■ $5x + 2y \geq 6$: Region I is feasible.
■ $5x + 2y \leq 6$: Region II is feasible.

b. One method is to find two points that satisfy the equation, then plot them and draw the line. The intercepts are especially easy points to find. By letting $x = 0$, you can solve to find $y = 3$. By letting $y = 0$, you can solve to determine that $x = \frac{6}{5}$. Then you can plot the points (0, 3) and $\left(\frac{6}{5}, 0\right)$ and draw the line connecting them.

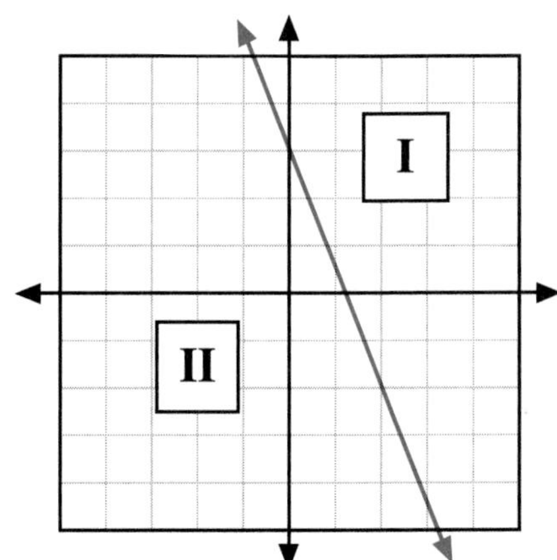

By solving for y, you can enter the new form of the equation in the graphing calculator to graph the line: $y = (6 - 5x) \div 2$. (Remember that it is not necessary to simplify.)

Notes continued from page T82

4. One possible situation for Part b is provided here:

Juan's class is going on a trip, and Juan has been assigned to bring a snack for everybody. On the day of the trip, Juan is so excited that he forgets the snacks at home. There isn't anybody at home who can bring them to him, so he must make do with what the school store has. He decides to purchase packages of granola bars and bags of peanuts. Each package of granola bars will provide a snack for 2 people, and each bag of peanuts will feed one person. There are twenty people in the class. The store is low on stock and only has 10 packages of granola bars and 14 bags of peanuts. If each package of granola bars costs 20 cents and each bag of peanuts costs 5 cents, what should Juan buy in order to get all the snacks he needs and spend the least amount of money?

Notes continued from page T90

■ A linear programming problem has two or more variables with defined constraints (inequalities) and an objective function. Clues would be a description of constraints and a goal to be maximized or minimized.

APPLY individual task

On Your Own

See Unit 1 Summary Masters.

Responses will vary. Above all, preparation of this unit summary should be something that is useful to the individual student. You may wish to have students use the unit summary masters for "Multiple-Variable Models" to help them organize the information.

See Assessment Resources pages 27–42.

Unit 2

Modeling Public Opinion

UNIT OVERVIEW Public opinion plays an important role in any society, influencing politics, education, fashion, television, and many other areas. Thus, it is important for students to learn how public opinion is measured and analyzed. That is the goal of this unit.

The methods of measuring and analyzing public opinion that students will investigate are *surveys* and *elections*. In an election, every person (at least theoretically) votes to express his or her individual opinion. In a survey, you obtain individual opinions from some of the people in a population. In both cases, the problem is to consolidate the individual opinions into public opinion.

In the first lesson of this unit, students will undertake a mathematical analysis of voting. In particular, they will investigate a variety of different methods for analyzing the results of an election carried out using preferential voting (ranking the candidates in order of preference). They will discover that there are drawbacks to all election-analysis methods when there are more than two candidates and that different methods can yield different winners.

In Lessons 2–4, students will investigate surveys. They will learn about sampling, bias, sampling distributions, confidence intervals, and margin of error. They will see how voting methods can play a role in survey design and analysis. There is an emphasis throughout on critical analysis of surveys and elections reported in the media.

While studying this unit, you may wish to bring to class some current newspaper articles or advertisements, or you may wish to have students search the newspapers for instances of voting or surveys.

Modeling Public Opinion

Unit 2

92 • **Lesson 1**
Voting Models

115 • **Lesson 2**
Surveys and Samples

135 • **Lesson 3**
Sampling Distributions: From Population to Sample

153 • **Lesson 4**
Confidence Intervals: From Sample to Population

165 • **Lesson 5**
Looking Back

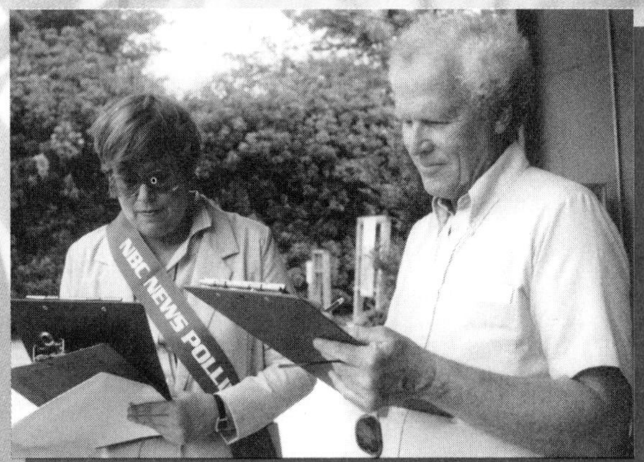

Masters 36a–36d

Unit 2 Objectives

- To measure and analyze public opinion through a mathematical analysis of voting and surveys
- To use and analyze a variety of election analysis methods, particularly those based on preferential voting
- To understand and apply basic ideas related to the design and interpretation of surveys, such as background information, random sampling, and bias
- To construct simulated sampling distributions of sample proportions and to use sampling distributions to identify which proportions are likely to be found in a sample of a given size
- To construct and interpret margin of error and confidence intervals for population proportions
- To critically analyze surveys and elections in everyday life and as reported in the media

See Masters 36a–36d for Maintenance tasks that students can complete after Lesson 1.

Unit 2 Planning Guide

Lesson Objectives	MORE Assignments	Suggested Pacing	Materials
Lesson 1 *Voting Models* • To understand and use voting as a method for measuring and analyzing public opinion • To formulate and investigate sensible ways to choose a winner in an election when voting is done by ranking the candidates (*i.e.*, preferential voting) • To learn and apply some common vote-analysis methods: majority, plurality, points-for-preferences, runoff, pairwise-comparison, and approval • To analyze voting methods in terms of fairness and Arrow's Theorem • To critically analyze elections in everyday life and as reported in the media	**after page 96** Students can begin Modeling Task 3 Parts a–c from p. 106. **after page 98** Students can begin Organizing Task 2 from p. 106. **after page 102** Students can begin Modeling Task 5, Organizing Task 5, any Reflecting task, or Extending Task 2, 3, 4 or 5 from p. 106. **page 106** **Modeling:** 5 and choice of one* **Organizing:** 2 and 5 **Reflecting:** Choose one* **Extending:** Choose one*	5 days	• *Preferential Voting* calculator software • Teaching Resources 37–44 • Assessment Resources 43–48 • Teaching Resources 36a–36d • *Optional*: RAP Book Exercise Set 4
Lesson 2 *Surveys and Samples* • To understand and use surveys as a method for measuring and analyzing public opinion • To understand and identify key elements of a survey and to critically analyze surveys • To understand, identify, and correct bias in a survey • To understand, identify, and design a simple random sample	**after page 120** Students can begin Reflecting task 1 or 3 from p. 128. **after page 124** Students can begin any Extending task from p. 128. **page 128** **Modeling:** 2 and choice of one* **Organizing:** 2 and choice of one* **Reflecting:** Choose one* **Extending:** Choose one*	5 days	• Teaching Resources 45–50 • Assessment Resources 49–52 • *Optional*: RAP Book Exercise Set 5
Lesson 3 *Sampling Distributions: From Population to Sample* • To use a known population parameter to construct a sampling distribution for a sample statistic, particularly the sampling distribution of a sample proportion • To use simulation to construct a simulated sampling distribution and summarize the results with a 90% box plot • To define and investigate the notion of "a likely sample outcome" using 90% box plots • To investigate and describe how changing the population percent or the sample size will change the 90% box plot • To construct and use a chart of 90% box plots for different population percents and a fixed sample size	**after page 143** Students can begin Modeling Task 1 from p. 148. **page 148** **Modeling:** 5 and choice of one* **Organizing:** 2 **Reflecting:** 2 **Extending:** Choose one*	5 days	• Teaching Resources 51–56 • Assessment Resources 53–58 • *Optional*: RAP Book Practice Set 2
Lesson 4 *Confidence Intervals: From Sample to Population* • To use a sample percent and 90% box plots to estimate the population percent • To understand a confidence interval for the population percent as an interval of population percents that are likely to produce the given sample • To construct and interpret a 90% confidence interval for the population percent using 90% box plot charts • To understand, find, and interpret the margin of error • To critically analyze the reporting of survey results, confidence intervals, and margin of error	**page 159** **Modeling:** 1 and 4 **Organizing:** 2 and 3 **Reflecting:** Choose one* **Extending:** 4 and choice of one*	3 days	• Small bags of M&M's® Chocolate Candies • Teaching Resources 57–59b • Assessment Resources 59–64 • *Optional*: RAP Book Exercise Set 6
Lesson 5 *Looking Back* • To review the major objectives of the unit		2–3 days (includes testing)	• Teaching Resources 60a–60b • Unit Summary Master • Assessment Resources 65–82 • *Optional*: RAP Book Practice Set 3

**When choice is indicated, it is important to leave the choice to the student.*

Note: *It is best if Organizing tasks are discussed as a whole class after they have been assigned as homework.*

Lesson 1 Voting Models

Have you ever been asked the question, "What's your opinion?" It seems that on any given issue, there are many different opinions. It is easy enough to discover individual opinions: just listen to talk radio, read the op/ed page of a newspaper, or simply ask people. It's not so easy to determine **public opinion**—the opinion of a group of people. But assessing public opinion is important because it influences many decisions, such as which TV shows should be canceled or which educational programs should be used in your school.

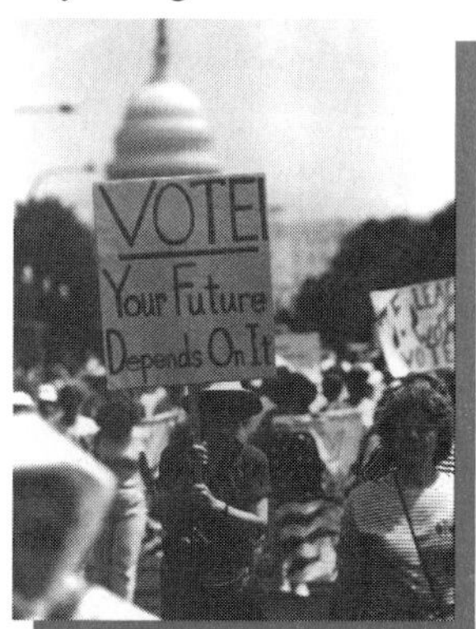

There are two essential steps to determining public opinion: getting individual opinions, and then somehow consolidating the individual opinions into public opinion. In this unit, you will investigate mathematical tools for measuring and analyzing public opinion.

Think About This Situation

An entrepreneur wants to open a new fast-food restaurant franchise. First, she needs to decide which restaurant would be best. The opinions of the community are obviously very important to her planning. Suppose she tries to determine the collective opinion of all students in your school about different fast-food restaurants.

a What are some methods that the entrepreneur could use to determine student opinion?

b Suppose someone suggests taking a survey of some, but not all, students. Do you think this is a good way to measure student opinion? What are some advantages and disadvantages of using a survey like this to determine public opinion?

c Suppose someone else decides to get every student's opinion by having every student vote. What are some advantages and disadvantages of using this method to determine public opinion?

d Describe some situations in which voting is used to determine public opinion. Is there any difference in the way the voting is carried out and analyzed in those situations?

92 UNIT 2 · MODELING PUBLIC OPINION

Lesson 1 *Voting Models*

LESSON OVERVIEW In this unit, students will study two mathematical methods for measuring and analyzing public opinion: voting and surveys. This lesson focuses on voting. Students first do some open-ended explorations designed to provoke thinking about fairness in voting and different voting methods; then they study some specific, commonly used voting methods; and, finally, they briefly consider the fundamental mathematical result in this area, namely, Arrow's Theorem. In subsequent lessons of this unit, students will see that voting methods can be used to gather, summarize, and analyze survey data. For example, by asking people to rank their choices and then analyzing results with the points-for-preferences method, a pollster may be able to improve survey results.

There is a variety of reasonable voting methods, including the commonly used plurality method, runoff, points-for-preferences, pairwise-comparison, and approval voting. All but the last of these methods are based on preferential voting, in which the voter ranks the candidates instead of voting for just one favorite. Ranking the candidates gives you richer data that you can use to more accurately measure and analyze public opinion. Interestingly enough, different voting methods can yield different winners. Arrow's Theorem shows that whenever there are three or more candidates, no voting method always yields fair results (based on Arrow's careful definition of *fairness*). That is, there are drawbacks to all voting methods. In some situations, they can all produce "paradoxical" results. Even though no voting method is perfect, most experts recommend points-for-preferences, in which the point assignments form an arithmetic sequence (such as 4-3-2-1).

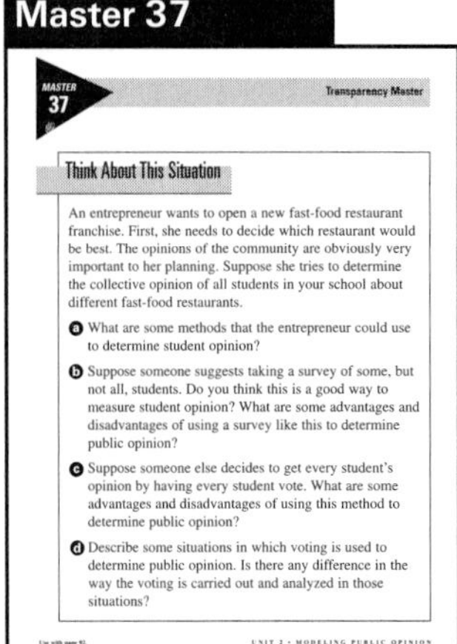
Master 37

MASTER 37 Transparency Master

Think About This Situation

An entrepreneur wants to open a new fast-food restaurant franchise. First, she needs to decide which restaurant would be best. The opinions of the community are obviously very important to her planning. Suppose she tries to determine the collective opinion of all students in your school about different fast-food restaurants.

a. What are some methods that the entrepreneur could use to determine student opinion?

b. Suppose someone suggests taking a survey of some, but not all, students. Do you think this is a good way to measure student opinion? What are some advantages and disadvantages of using a survey like this to determine public opinion?

c. Suppose someone else decides to get every student's opinion by having every student vote. What are some advantages and disadvantages of using this method to determine public opinion?

d. Describe some situations in which voting is used to determine public opinion. Is there any difference in the way the voting is carried out and analyzed in those situations?

Use with page 92. UNIT 2 • MODELING PUBLIC OPINION

Unit 2

Lesson Objectives

- To understand and use voting as a method for measuring and analyzing public opinion
- To formulate and investigate sensible ways to choose a winner in an election when voting is done by ranking the candidates (*i.e.*, preferential voting)
- To learn and apply some common vote-analysis methods: majority, plurality, points-for-preferences, runoff, pairwise-comparison, and approval
- To analyze voting methods in terms of fairness and Arrow's Theorem
- To critically analyze elections in everyday life and as reported in the media

LAUNCH full-class discussion

Think About This Situation

See Teaching Master 37.

The class discussion around these questions will allow you to assess students' knowledge about voting and conducting surveys. They may have been introduced to these ideas in a social studies classroom. Rather than suggesting all the alternatives that follow, if students' background is minimal, you may wish to revisit this "Think About This Situation" during the final unit Checkpoint on page 168.

See additional Teaching Notes on page T168C.

Master 38

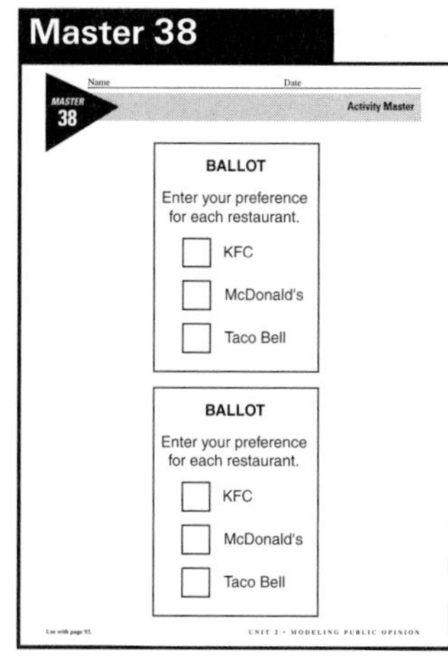
Name
Date
MASTER 38
Activity Master
BALLOT
Enter your preference for each restaurant.
KFC
McDonald's
Taco Bell
BALLOT
Enter your preference for each restaurant.
KFC
McDonald's
Taco Bell
UNIT 2 • MODELING PUBLIC OPINION

Unit 2

EXPLORE small-group investigation

INVESTIGATION 1 Ranking Choices

In this investigation, students will explore different ways of choosing a winner when voting is done by ranking the choices. Students will brainstorm regarding group decision making and will carry out a vote by ranking. In later investigations, they will study other specified voting methods. Many of the methods seen in later investigations may come up informally in this investigation. If so, that is great! In later investigations, you would be able to point out to students that they are building on their own initial ideas. However, do not be concerned if all the voting methods described below do not come up in your class. The key voting methods will be introduced as the lesson progresses.

For Activities 1–5, feel free to substitute other restaurants that may be more relevant to your class. Just be sure that you use consistently ordered ballots and preference tables as the investigation proceeds.

1. a. The class can let each person vote for one choice, and the choice with the largest number of votes wins. The teacher or the committee planning the trip can make the choice. The restaurant nearest to the museum might be chosen. The class can draw a name from a hat.

b. Nonvoting methods include choosing the one nearest to the museum, drawing a name from a hat, conducting a survey, or letting the teacher or committee decide.

c. Voting for your favorite is a common method of voting, but it only indicates your favorite, not how you feel about all of the other options. To get the most information, everyone should rank all of the restaurants by preference. If all of the information in the rankings is taken into account, then more people should be satisfied with the final choice.

2. a. Choices are ranked in some sports standings and in "10 best" or "10 worst" lists. Students will suggest other situations from their own experiences.

b. Possible responses follow: The choice with the most first-rankings can be chosen, or the choice with the fewest last-rankings can be chosen. Another way would be to assign points to each choice and see which has the most points. Students may suggest some of the methods that are considered in the next investigation.

3. See Teaching Master 38.

a. Make sure everyone has a ballot with the "candidates" listed in the same order as shown on the ballot in the text.

b. Eventually, students will be asked to use a preference table (see Activity 6), but for now, encourage them to organize the data in a manner that seems sensible and useful to them. For example, they may simply catalog all responses on the board in a table such as the one below.

Restaurant Preference Rankings

KFC	1	1	1	3	3	1	2	*etc.*
McDonald's	2	3	2	1	1	2	1	*etc.*
Taco Bell	3	2	3	2	2	3	3	*etc.*

Another option is to ask students who ranked the restaurants 1-2-3 to raise their hands, and then take a count. Continue in this manner until there are no new rankings to consider from the class.

INVESTIGATION 1 Ranking Choices

To assess public opinion, you might try to get the opinion of every individual in the group, or you might try to get opinions from just a sample of people in the group. If you ask only a sample, then you have to determine carefully what you can say about the whole group's opinion. Selecting and interpreting data from a sample will be your task in future lessons of this unit. But even if you ask everyone in a group, you still have to combine all the individual opinions to yield a group opinion.

1. Suppose your class is going on a field trip to a nearby math and science museum. One of the most important decisions the class will have to make is where to eat lunch! Everyone will be on the same bus, so you all will have to go to the same restaurant. The choices are McDonald's, KFC, and Taco Bell.
   a. How can you fairly make the decision about where to eat lunch? Working together as a class, list as many decision-making methods as you can.
   b. Did you think about any methods in Part a other than voting? If not, go back and list some nonvoting methods.
   c. Now consider voting. Suppose you decide to choose a restaurant by voting. Everyone could vote for his or her favorite restaurant, or everyone could vote by ranking the restaurants in order of preference. Which voting method do you think will give you the most information and help you make the best decision? Explain.
2. Think about the method of voting by ranking the choices.
   a. What are some situations in which voting is done by ranking the choices?
   b. If voting is done by ranking the choices, how can the winner be chosen? List as many methods for choosing a winner as you can.
3. Now it is time for your class to vote on the three restaurants.
   a. Use a ballot like the one at the right. Vote by ranking the restaurants. Rank them according to your preference by writing "1" next to your favorite restaurant and "2" and "3" next to your second and third preferences.
   b. Based on your ballots, summarize the preferences of everyone in your class.

BALLOT

Enter your preference for each restaurant.

☐ KFC

☐ McDonald's

☐ Taco Bell

Unit 2

LESSON 1 • VOTING MODELS 93

4. Now, analyze the preferences expressed by your class.

a. Did your class use all possible rankings? How many possible rankings are there for three restaurants?

b. How many students in your class chose McDonald's as their first preference?

c. How many voters in your class chose Taco Bell as their first preference?

d. Which restaurant received the most third-preference votes?

5. Think about how to use the class preferences to decide where to eat lunch.

a. Working in small groups, and using all the information on class preferences, decide which restaurant should be the winner. Explain the reasoning you used to choose the winner.

b. Compare your winner, and the method you used, with those of other groups.

6. A class in Iowa organized their individual rankings of restaurants in a **preference table** like the one below:

Restaurant Preference Table

	Rankings					
KFC	1	1	2	2	3	3
McDonald's	2	3	1	3	1	2
Taco Bell	3	2	3	1	2	1
Number of Voters	**6 voters**	**4 voters**	**6 voters**	**7 voters**	**5 voters**	**5 voters**

a. What do the entries in the first "rankings" column mean?

b. How many different rankings were made by this class? Do you think the same number of rankings will appear in all preference tables involving three choices?

94 UNIT 2 • MODELING PUBLIC OPINION

4. The groups should refer to the data summary they did in Part b of Activity 3.

a. Students should spend some time thinking about the number of possible rankings in different situations, but don't get sidetracked into a lengthy discussion. At this point, students should realize that there are 6 possible rankings of 3 candidates. A given class may not include all 6 different rankings.

b–d. Answers will depend on the class data. Also, some groups may discover that the method they used to summarize the class data does not allow them to efficiently answer these questions. If so, they will need to find a better data summary scheme.

5. **Students may very well arrive at a variety of voting methods, and in particular, they may think of the methods that will be discussed in Investigation 2. There are many voting methods that are fairly intuitive, and rather than being told to memorize several methods, it is helpful for students to first see that the methods can arise naturally when analyzing ranking data.**

a. Winners will vary, depending on the vote results and the decision method used. Students should express their reasons carefully and clearly.

b. Students should understand that others may have different winners and different reasons. It is important for them to try to understand other students' reasons even if they do not agree with them.

6. a. The 1-2-3 entries indicate a ranking of 1-2-3 for KFC-McDonald's-Taco Bell. The 6 entry means that 6 voters made the ranking 1-2-3.

b. Six rankings were made by this class. The 6 rankings are all of the possible rankings for 3 candidates with no ties. All 6 rankings will not necessarily appear in all preference tables. In fact, two preference tables may each have 5 rankings that are not the same ones.

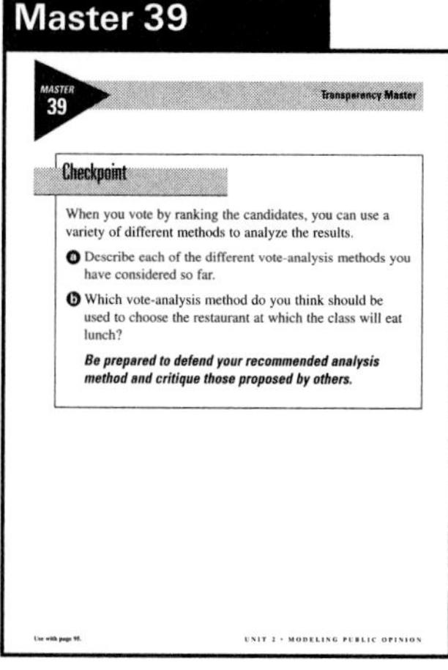

Master 39

MASTER 39 Transparency Master

Checkpoint

When you vote by ranking the candidates, you can use a variety of different methods to analyze the results.

ⓐ Describe each of the different vote-analysis methods you have considered so far.

ⓑ Which vote-analysis method do you think should be used to choose the restaurant at which the class will eat lunch?

Be prepared to defend your recommended analysis method and critique those proposed by others.

Use with page 95. UNIT 2 • MODELING PUBLIC OPINION

EXPLORE *continued*

6. **c.** Students might agree with any of the four, depending on what they consider important about the rankings. For example, Alan considered only students' first preferences. See other responses in Parts d–f.

d. Danita could explain that more students have ranked Taco Bell last, and so choosing Taco Bell would make more students unhappy than any other choice.

e. McDonald's has a total of 11 first-preference votes and Taco Bell has 12 first-preference votes, while KFC has only 10 first-preference votes. If KFC is eliminated from the running (and the votes reassigned based on second preferences), then Taco Bell gets only 16 first-preference votes compared to 17 first-preference votes for McDonald's. Students do not need to completely understand this method at this time. It will be carefully developed in Investigation 2.

f. Colin may be looking at first- and second-preference votes. KFC has a total of 23 first- and second-preference votes compared to 22 for McDonald's and 21 for Taco Bell. He also may be choosing the winner based on fewest last-preference votes.

7. If a preference table was not used to summarize and analyze the class data in Activities 3–5, then students should go back and do so. If a preference table was used, students should now be able to analyze it more thoughtfully.

SHARE AND SUMMARIZE full-class discussion

Checkpoint

See Teaching Master 39.

ⓐ Some possible voting methods that students may have discovered so far are the following: The choice with the most first-preference votes wins. The choice with the most first-preference and second-preference votes wins. The choice with the fewest first-preference votes is eliminated, and there is a *runoff* between the other choices.

There is a variety of other possibilities that students may discover. The point here is for students to see that (1) there is a variety of voting methods possible, (2) there are many voting methods that make sense, and (3) different voting methods can yield different winners.

ⓑ Groups might choose any of the methods but then must give reasons for their choices. For example, using just first-ranked votes gives the most people their first choice; using both first-ranked and second-ranked choices means the fewest students eat at their last-ranked choice; having a runoff allows students to choose between the two most popular restaurants.

c. Examine the opinions below about which restaurant is the winner. With which of these students do you agree? Why?

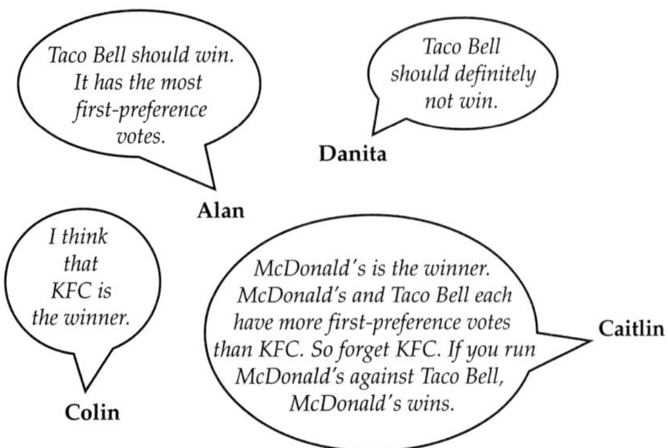

d. How could Danita explain to Alan that Taco Bell should not win?

e. Verify Caitlin's claim that McDonald's and Taco Bell each have more first-preference votes than KFC. Explain why McDonald's is the winner using Caitlin's method.

f. Give a reasonable explanation for Colin's thinking.

7. As a class, use a preference table to reanalyze your preference data from Activity 3. Which restaurant is the winner?

Checkpoint

When you vote by ranking the candidates, you can use a variety of different methods to analyze the results.

a Describe each of the different vote-analysis methods you have considered so far.

b Which vote-analysis method do you think should be used to choose the restaurant at which the class will eat lunch?

Be prepared to defend your recommended analysis method and critique those proposed by others.

Voting based on ranking the candidates, as you have been doing, is sometimes called **preferential voting**. Preferential voting is used for political elections in Australia, Ireland, and South Africa, and it is used in many sports competitions. However, preferential voting is not used in U.S. political elections. By the end of this lesson, you will be able to make some recommendations about whether or not preferential voting should be used more widely.

Unit 2

LESSON 1 • VOTING MODELS 95

On Your Own

Consider the following ballots from an election to determine public opinion about favorite nighttime activities.

Concert 2 Ball game 3 Dance 1	Concert 1 Ball game 2 Dance 3	Concert 3 Ball game 2 Dance 1	Concert 3 Ball game 2 Dance 1	Concert 2 Ball game 1 Dance 3
Concert 2 Ball game 1 Dance 3	Concert 2 Ball game 3 Dance 1	Concert 2 Ball game 1 Dance 3	Concert 2 Ball game 1 Dance 3	Concert 2 Ball game 1 Dance 3
Concert 3 Ball game 2 Dance 1	Concert 1 Ball game 2 Dance 3	Concert 2 Ball game 3 Dance 1	Concert 3 Ball game 2 Dance 1	Concert 2 Ball game 1 Dance 3
Concert 2 Ball game 1 Dance 3	Concert 2 Ball game 1 Dance 3	Concert 1 Ball game 2 Dance 3	Concert 2 Ball game 3 Dance 1	Concert 2 Ball game 3 Dance 1
Concert 1 Ball game 2 Dance 3	Concert 3 Ball game 2 Dance 1	Concert 2 Ball game 1 Dance 3	Concert 1 Ball game 2 Dance 3	Concert 2 Ball game 3 Dance 1

a. Construct a preference table summarizing the results of the balloting.

b. Use the preference table you constructed in Part a to find a winner using two different methods. Describe, in writing, the methods you used.

INVESTIGATION 2 Different Methods, Different Winners

You have seen that there are many ways to analyze the results of preferential voting. In this investigation, you will explore some of the most commonly used vote-analysis methods. Some of these methods may be ones that you have considered already.

For Activities 1 through 5, consider the preference table at the top of the next page, which summarizes voting on preferred athletic shoe brands in one class. The "Number of Voters" row indicates how many voters chose the same ranking. In this case, we have four voter blocks of different sizes.

96 UNIT 2 • MODELING PUBLIC OPINION

APPLY individual task

On Your Own

a. The first step in analyzing election results is organizing the data from the ballots. A preference table is a good way to organize preferential voting data. Below is the preference table for the ballots shown here.

Nighttime Activities Preference Table

	Rankings			
Concert	1	2	2	3
Ball Game	2	1	3	2
Dance	3	3	1	1
Number of Voters	**5 voters**	**9 voters**	**6 voters**	**5 voters**

b. Possible answers are the following: Dance wins if the winner is the candidate that gets the most first-preference votes. Concert wins if the winner is the candidate with the fewest last-preference votes. Ball game wins if the winner is chosen by running off the top two first-preference vote getters (as in Caitlin's method from Activity 6). Other answers are possible, but methods must be carefully described.

MORE ASSIGNMENT *pp. 106–114*

Students can now begin Modeling Task 3 Parts a–c from the MORE assignment following Investigation 3.

Unit 2

EXPLORE small-group investigation

INVESTIGATION 2 Different Methods, Different Winners

In this investigation, five particular voting methods are described and studied. These are some of the most commonly used (or at least proposed) voting methods. Plurality is the one that is the most commonly used, even though, as students will see, it has some serious flaws.

Master 40

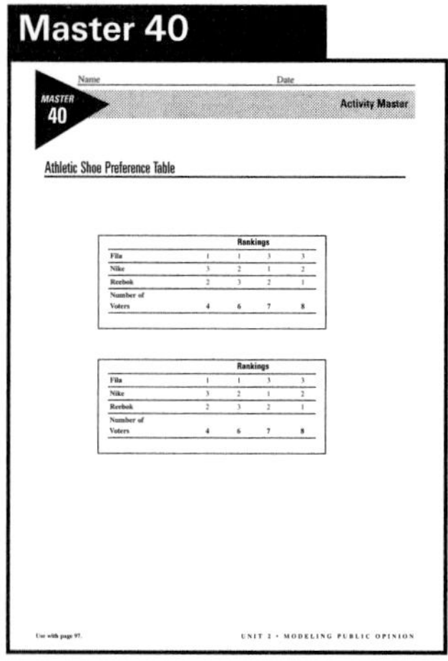

EXPLORE *continued*

1. There is no majority winner since Fila has 10 first-preference votes, Nike has 7 first-preference votes, and Reebok has 8 first-preference votes. There is a total of 25 voters, so 13 first-preference votes are needed for a majority.
2. Fila is the plurality winner with 10 first-preference votes.

The runoff method may be confusing for some students. Teaching Master 40 is helpful for Activities 3 and 4, so that students may scratch out the eliminated row each time they use the runoff method.

3. **a.** Fila received the most first-preference votes (10). Reebok received the next highest number of first-preference votes (8). Students should cross out the row for Nike.

   b. The block of 7 voters prefers Reebok over Fila, so they will now vote for Reebok. Fila gets 10 votes and Reebok gets 15, so Reebok wins.

   c. Some Olympic events use the runoff method. In this country, political elections use the runoff method when no candidate gets a majority and the law requires a majority rather than just a plurality.

   d. Caitlin used the runoff method. Alan used the plurality method.
4. **a.** Pairings are Fila-Reebok, Fila-Nike, and Nike-Reebok.

   b. Nike wins the Fila-Nike runoff, 15 to 10.

Athletic Shoe Preference Table

	Rankings			
Fila	1	1	3	3
Nike	3	2	1	2
Reebok	2	3	2	1
Number of Voters	4	6	7	8

1. A **majority** winner is the candidate that gets more than half of the first-preference votes. Find the majority winner, if there is one.

2. A **plurality** winner is the candidate that receives the most first-preference votes. Find the plurality winner, if there is one.

3. Another common analysis method is the **runoff method**. Using this method, you count the first-preference votes to choose the top two candidates, and then you run off the top two against each other.

   a. Which of the athletic shoe brands received the most first-preference votes? Which brand received the next highest number of first-preference votes? These are the top two candidates. On a copy of the athletic shoe preference table, cross out the row for the brand that is not one of the top two.

   b. Now run off the top two brands against each other. Which brand will be chosen by the block of 7 voters? Why? Which brand is the winner?

   c. What are some other situations in which the runoff method is used to choose a winner?

   d. Look back at the vote-analysis strategies used by Colin, Caitlin, and Alan on page 95. Which student used the runoff method? Who used the plurality method?

4. The **pairwise-comparison method** is based on the runoff method. Developed by the philosopher and social scientist Marie Jean Antoine Nicolas Caritat, the Marquis de Condorcet (1743–1794), this method is sometimes called the *Condorcet method.* (Condorcet is pronounced *con-door-say*.) Using this method, all pairs of candidates are run off against each other. The pairwise-comparison winner, if there is one, is the candidate that beats every other candidate.

The Marquis de Condorcet

   a. In the pairwise-comparison method, each possible pair of candidates will have a runoff. List all possible pairings of athletic shoe brands using Fila, Nike, and Reebok.

   b. Consider the pair Fila and Nike. Run off Fila against Nike. Use a copy of the athletic shoe preference table to help you carry out this runoff. Which candidate wins the runoff?

Unit 2

Unit 2

c. Run off all the other pairs of brands. Write down the winner from each runoff.

d. Find the pairwise-comparison winner, if there is one.

5. Another common vote-analysis method is the **points-for-preferences method**. This method was first proposed by an amateur mathematician, Jean-Charles de Borda, who was a French cavalry officer and naval captain in the eighteenth century. It is sometimes called the *Borda count method.* In this method, points are assigned to each preference, and the winner is the candidate that gets the most total points. For example, 3 points could be assigned to first preference, 2 points to second preference, and 1 point for third preference. There can be many other point assignments.

   a. Using the point assignments above, how many total points does Reebok get?

   b. Find the points-for-preferences winner using the point assignments above.

   c. What are some situations in life in which the points-for-preferences method is used to choose a winner?

Checkpoint

Compare the results of using the five vote-analysis methods in Activities 1 through 5. Which brand do you think should be considered the overall winner? Why?

Be prepared to defend your recommended winner and critique the recommendations of others.

On Your Own

Reproduced below is the restaurant preference table from Activity 6 of Investigation 1. Determine the winner under each of the five vote-analysis methods you have studied.

Restaurant Preference Table

	Rankings					
KFC	1	1	2	2	3	3
McDonald's	2	3	1	3	1	2
Taco Bell	3	2	3	1	2	1
Number of Voters	**6**	**4**	**6**	**7**	**5**	**5**

98 UNIT 2 • MODELING PUBLIC OPINION

4. **c.** Reebok wins the Fila-Reebok runoff, 15 to 10. Nike wins the Nike-Reebok runoff, 13 to 12.
   d. Nike beats each of the other two in pairwise runoffs, so Nike is the pairwise-comparison winner.
5. **a.** Reebok gets 52 points.
   b. Nike is the winner with 53 total points.
   c. Sports competitions, such as gymnastics, may use a modified *points-for-preferences* method; each judge chooses how many points to assign. In some track meets, 3 points are given for first place in an event, 2 points for second place, and 1 point for third place. The winning school is the school with the most points for the meet. In most high school swimming meets, individual events are scored 6 points for first place, and 4, 3, 2, and 1 points for second through fifth place. Relays are scored 9 points for first place, 4 points for second place, and 2 points for third place.

Master 41

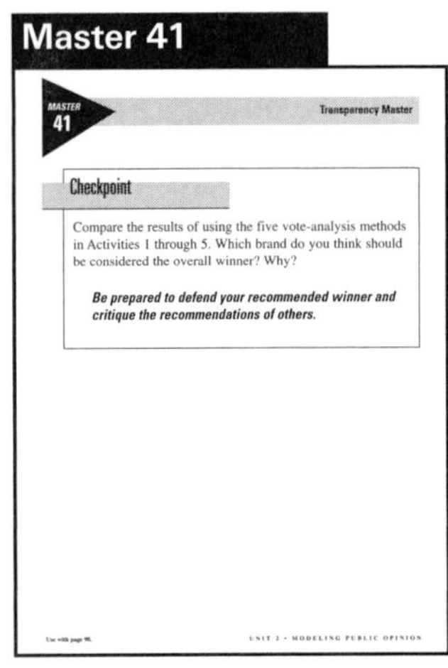
MASTER 41 Transparency Master

Checkpoint

Compare the results of using the five vote-analysis methods in Activities 1 through 5. Which brand do you think should be considered the overall winner? Why?

Be prepared to defend your recommended winner and critique the recommendations of others.

Unit 2

SHARE AND SUMMARIZE full-class discussion

Checkpoint

See Teaching Master 41.

Some groups might choose Nike because it won using two different methods. Other groups may decide that they consider one method to be fairer than the others. In any case, they should give their reasons. The issue of which method is best will be carefully considered in Investigation 3.

APPLY individual task

On Your Own

There is no majority winner. Taco Bell is the plurality winner. McDonald's is the runoff winner. There is no pairwise-comparison winner since no candidate beats both of the others in a runoff. Using 3 points for first preference, 2 points for second preference, and 1 point for third preference, there is no points-for-preferences winner, since each candidate gets a total of 66 points.

MORE

ASSIGNMENT *pp. 106–114*

Students can now begin Organizing Task 2 from the MORE assignment following Investigation 3.

EXPLORE small-group investigation

Students must be careful about entering data too quickly when using the *Preferential Voting* calculator software. The software takes time to accept data. Entering data too fast will result in errors.

6. **a.** More students choose Charnell, the plurality winner, than any other candidate as their first preference.

b. Charnell was ranked last by 74 out of a total of 110 voters. A clear majority ranked Charnell last, yet she wins under the plurality method! This is an example of the flaws or "paradoxes" that can occur in voting.

7. Rodene is the points-for-preferences winner using 5 points for first preference, 4 points for second preference, and so on. By the end of this activity, students should realize that the points-for-preferences winner depends on how the points are assigned and thus can vary greatly.

a. Answers will depend on the point assignments chosen.

b. One way to do this would be to give 1 point for the first preference, 2 for the second preference, and so on, with 5 points going to the last preference.

c. Two examples are

Richard is the winner with a point assignment of 10-9-8-2-1.

Charnell is the winner with a point assignment of 3-1-0-0-0.

d. A reason to declare a points-for-preferences winner the winner of the election is that it seems reasonable to assign points to preferences and thereby 'weight' the preferences. A reason against using a points-for-preferences winner is that different point assignments can result in different winners. Note that if the point assignment is done such that there is a constant difference between point values, such as 9-7-5-3-1, then the winner will always be the same. However, there are many reasonable point assignments where this is not the case.

8. The pairwise-comparison winner is Richard. Some students may consider this a fair choice because Richard wins when running against any other candidate head-to-head. On the other hand, Richard got the fewest first-preference votes of any candidate, so some students may think he is not the fairest choice.

You now know how to analyze a preference table in many ways to help you determine a winner. However, carrying out the various methods can be quite time-consuming. Use of specially designed computer or calculator software considerably reduces the time and effort required and allows you to do a deeper analysis. Use the *Preferential Voting* calculator software, or similar software, to complete Activities 6 through 9. These activities use the preference table below, which shows the results of student voting in an election for junior class president.

PREFERENTIAL VOTING
VERSION 2.0

VOTE AND
ANALYZE RESULTS

PRESS ENTER
TO CONTINUE

Unit 2

Junior Class President Preference Table

	Rankings					
Charnell	1	5	5	5	5	5
Marie	5	1	2	4	2	4
Lamar	4	4	1	2	4	2
Rodene	2	3	4	1	3	3
Richard	3	2	3	3	1	1
Number of Voters	**36**	**24**	**20**	**18**	**8**	**4**

6. Find the winner using the plurality method.

a. Give one reason why the plurality winner is a good choice for the next junior class president.

b. Give one reason why the plurality winner is *not* a good choice for the next junior class president.

7. Next use the points-for-preferences method to determine the winner. Use a point assignment similar to the one described in Activity 5, but for five candidates (5 points for first preference).

a. As a group, decide on another set of point assignments, and then find the points-for-preferences winner using those points.

b. Assign points in such a way that the winner is the choice that gets the *least* total points.

c. Assign points in such a way that Rodene is *not* the winner.

d. Give one reason why a points-for-preferences winner should be declared the winner of this election. Give one reason why a points-for-preferences winner should *not* be declared the winner of this election.

8. Find the pairwise-comparison winner. Do you think the pairwise-comparison winner is a fair choice for the next junior class president? Why or why not?

LESSON 1 • VOTING MODELS 99

9. Find the runoff winner. Did you get the same winner with this method as with any of the other methods? Do you think the runoff winner is a fair choice for the junior class president?

10. Examine the winners you found in Activities 6 through 9. Are there any surprises? Who do you think should be declared the new junior class president?

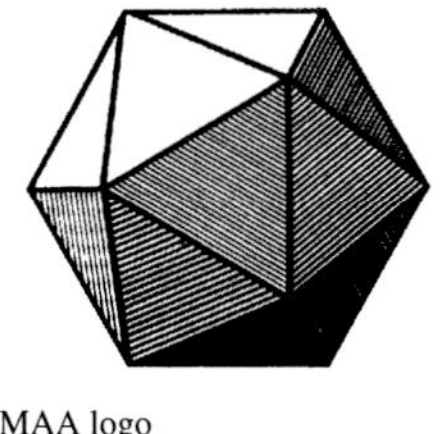

MAA logo

11. Another common voting method is **approval voting**. Since 1987, the Mathematical Association of America (MAA) has elected its officers using approval voting. (The actual 2001 ballot is reproduced below.) The United Nations Security Council also uses approval voting. For this method, every voter selects *all* the candidates he or she approves of. You still can cast only one vote per candidate, but you can vote for as many candidates as you like. For example, if there are five candidates and you approve of three of them, then you can cast a vote for each of the three. The winner in such an election is the candidate that receives the most votes.

The Mathematical Association of America
2001 Ballot
Balloting is by approval voting. For each office,
you are advised to vote for one or two candidates.
One will be elected.

President Elect (2002)	**First Vice-President (2002–03)**
☐ Ronald L. Graham	☐ Carl C. Cowen
☐ John W. Kenelly	☐ Genevieve M. Knight
☐ Hugh L. Montgomery	☐ William Y. Velez
☐ ______________	☐ ______________

a. In the ballot above, why do you think the MAA advises that members vote for one or two candidates?

b. When using approval voting, you don't rank the candidates; you simply cast a vote for all candidates you approve of. Thus, a preference table is not needed. However, to get an idea of how approval voting works, consider again the preference table of votes for a junior class president reproduced below.

Junior Class President Preference Table

	Rankings					
Charnell	1	5	5	5	5	5
Marie	5	1	2	4	2	4
Lamar	4	4	1	2	4	2
Rodene	2	3	4	1	3	3
Richard	3	2	3	3	1	1
Number of Voters	**36**	**24**	**20**	**18**	**8**	**4**

100 UNIT 2 • MODELING PUBLIC OPINION

9. Marie is the runoff winner. This candidate does not win using any other method. We might consider this method fair because we dropped out all those candidates who were not one of the top two in terms of first-preference votes. On the other hand, Marie was ranked either fourth or fifth by more than half of the voters (58 out of 110).

10. Student responses will vary. (The fact that there are different winners with different rating methods is usually surprising to students.)

11. a. Since there are only three candidates listed, voting for more than two candidates would be like not voting at all. This reasoning ignores write-in candidates, since it is unlikely that a write-in candidate will win unless there is a campaign by many of the members.

Master 42

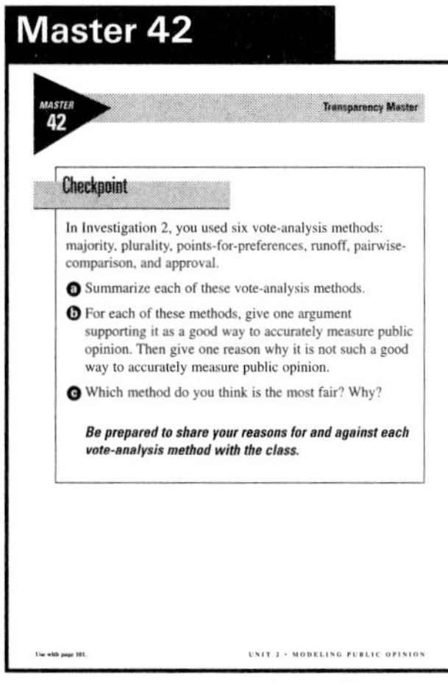
MASTER 42 Transparency Master

Checkpoint

In Investigation 2, you used six vote-analysis methods: majority, plurality, points-for-preferences, runoff, pairwise-comparison, and approval.

(a) Summarize each of these vote-analysis methods.

(b) For each of these methods, give one argument supporting it as a good way to accurately measure public opinion. Then give one reason why it is not such a good way to accurately measure public opinion.

(c) Which method do you think is the most fair? Why?

Be prepared to share your reasons for and against each vote-analysis method with the class.

Use with page 101. UNIT 2 • MODELING PUBLIC OPINION

Unit 2

EXPLORE *continued*

11. b.
- Vote totals are as follows: Charnell–36; Marie–52; Lamar–42; Rodene–90; Richard–110.
- Richard is the winner with 110 approval votes.
- Richard was also the pairwise-comparison winner, but the other winners were different (Charnell, plurality; Rodene, points-for-preferences; and Marie, runoff).

SHARE AND SUMMARIZE full-class discussion

Checkpoint

See Teaching Master 42.

You may wish to have groups discuss and write brief notes on their discussion. Thorough responses should be written in students' Math Toolkits following the discussion.

(a) The **majority** method chooses the candidate who has more than half of the first-preference votes; there may not always be a majority winner. The **plurality** method chooses the candidate with the most first-preference votes. The **points-for-preferences** method gives a certain number of points to each candidate depending on how he or she is ranked by each voter; different point assignments might give different winners. In the **runoff** method, the two candidates with the largest number of first-preference votes are run off against each other. In the **pairwise-comparison** method, each pair of candidates competes in a runoff election, and the candidate who beats everyone else in these elections is chosen as the overall winner. (Note that there may not be a pairwise-comparison winner, as seen in the "On Your Own" on page 98.) With the **approval** method, multiple (unranked) votes are allowed; the winner is the candidate with the most votes.

(b) Responses may vary. Each method has some advantages and some disadvantages.
The **majority** method allows more than half the people to have their first choice win; on the other hand, it does not take into account how people feel about the candidates whom they did not rank first. (In a two-candidate election, the majority winner is the clear and indisputable winner.) The **plurality** method allows more people to have their first choice win, but the plurality winner could actually be the least favorite candidate for the majority of voters. **Points-for-preferences** gives weight to how each voter ranked the candidate, but the outcome could change depending on the weights assigned to the rankings. The **runoff** method lets each voter choose between the two candidates with the most first-preference votes, although it doesn't take into account a candidate with many second-preference votes and few first-preference votes who might satisfy more people. The **pairwise-comparison** method chooses the candidate who beats every other candidate head-to-head, *if* there is one; however, it is possible that the winner is first preference for the fewest number of voters. Under **approval** voting, voters can choose both a mainstream candidate and a long-shot candidate and thus not "throw away" their vote by voting for only the long-shot candidate (see Reflecting Task 4). However, preferences are not as clearly delineated when only approval is given, as opposed to actual rankings.

(c) Students should make a good argument for the method that they think is most fair. (The issues of fairness and finding the best method are considered in the next investigation.)

CONSTRUCTING A MATH TOOLKIT: Following a class discussion, students should write thorough responses to this Checkpoint in their Math Toolkits (See Teaching Master 116).

- Assume that voters will approve of their top three choices. For each group of voters in the table, place a check mark next to the candidates the voters will approve of.
- Compute the approval winner and explain your method.
- Compare the approval winner to the winners you found using the other vote-analysis methods in Activities 6 through 9.

Checkpoint

In Investigation 2, you used six vote-analysis methods: majority, plurality, points-for-preferences, runoff, pairwise-comparison, and approval.

a Summarize each of these vote-analysis methods.

b For each of these methods, give one argument supporting it as a good way to accurately measure public opinion. Then give one reason why it is not such a good way to accurately measure public opinion.

c Which method do you think is the most fair? Why?

Be prepared to share your reasons for and against each vote-analysis method with the class.

On Your Own

Historically, a third-party candidate has had little impact in United States Presidential elections. The 1992 election was a notable exception. The three major candidates were George Bush, Bill Clinton, and Ross Perot. Although Clinton won, both of the other two candidates received a significant share of the popular vote. Of course, the president is elected through the *electoral* college, but think about what the election results might have been if a different voting model were used instead. The final popular vote tallies from the election were as follows:

Clinton	44,908,254
Bush	39,102,343
Perot	19,741,065

Unit 2

LESSON 1 • VOTING MODELS 101

Since voters did not vote by ranking the candidates, there is no exact preference table for this election. However, opinion polls can be used to construct an approximate preference table. (In the next lessons of this unit, you will learn how to analyze opinion polls carefully.) Suppose the opinion polls at the time suggest these three assumptions:

- If a person voted for Clinton, then Perot would have been the second choice.
- If a person voted for Bush, then Perot would have been the second choice.
- For the people who voted for Perot, half would have chosen Clinton as their second choice and half would have chosen Bush.

a. These assumptions, though broad and open to some debate, provide a basis for constructing a reasonable preference table. Complete the preference table below for the 1992 presidential election.

1992 Presidential Election Approximate Preference Table

	Rankings			
Clinton	1			
Bush	3			
Perot	2			
Number of Voters	44,908,254	39,102,343	9,870,532	9,870,532

b. Is there a majority winner?

c. What percent of the total votes does the plurality winner get?

d. Determine the winner using runoff, points-for-preferences, and pairwise-comparison. Are there any surprises?

INVESTIGATION 3 Fair Is Fair, Isn't It?

Looking over all the voting methods you have investigated so far, you'll notice that each one has some drawback. You might be wondering if any voting method is fair. Or, even more fundamental, you might be wondering just what "fair" means. These are very important and difficult questions.

The mathematical approach to answering these questions is first to formulate a mathematical definition of fairness and then to see if any voting method satisfies the definition. In 1949, the Nobel Prize-winning economist Kenneth Arrow did just this. He reached a conclusion about fair voting methods called **Arrow's Theorem**, which is one of the most surprising and famous theorems of this century. In the following activities, you will explore this theorem.

102 UNIT 2 • MODELING PUBLIC OPINION

APPLY individual task

On Your Own

a. Based on the assumptions, the ranking to be entered into the second column is 3-1-2. One of the remaining columns is 2-3-1, and the other is 3-2-1.

b. There is no majority winner.

c. Clinton won the plurality vote with 43%.

d. Clinton would win in a runoff; Perot would win using the points-for-preferences method, in which 3, 2, and 1 points are assigned to first-, second-, and third-preference votes, respectively; and Perot would win in pairwise-comparison. It is surprising that under two very sensible methods, Perot, who was widely considered to be the least-preferred candidate with no chance of winning, would win.

MORE

ASSIGNMENT *pp. 106–114*

Students can now begin Modeling Task 5; Organizing Task 5; any Reflecting task, or Extending Task 2, 3, 4, or 5 from the MORE assignment following Investigation 3.

EXPLORE small-group investigation

INVESTIGATION 3 Fair Is Fair, Isn't It?

This investigation is an important conclusion to the lesson. Students have seen that every voting method considered so far has some drawback. In fact, Arrow's Theorem, which is the focus of this investigation, proposes a definition of a fair method and then proves that no voting method always meets that definition when there are more than two candidates! To understand some of the conditions and how they may be violated, students must engage in some fairly abstract analysis. They may find parts of this investigation challenging, although the concrete examples should help.

EXPLORE ***continued***

1. **a.** The runoff is between A and B. The winner is A with 22 votes to B's 12 votes.
   b. The runoff is now between A and C. The runoff winner is C with 18 votes to A's 16 votes. Candidate A now loses!
   c. Candidate A was the winner in Part a. Then some of the voters (the 4 voters in the last column) change their preferences so that they give even more support to A. It would seem that if A won before and then A gets even more support, then A should win again. But, in fact, A loses in the modified election! This seems unfair. This is an example of a so-called voting paradox. It shows that the runoff method can yield paradoxical (and unfair) results.
2. The situation in Activity 1 violates the "Consistent" condition. Voter preferences changed so that A was raised in some voters' rankings. Although A beat C before this change, after the change A did not beat C.

NOTE: A basic underlying assumption of Arrow's Theorem is that voters are "rational" in the sense that individual voters must give a clear order to their choices. That is, a voter may not prefer A to B, B to C, and C to A. This is like the "Ordered" condition, except it applies to individual voters rather than to the results of an election. This need not be discussed with students unless they somehow mention it themselves.

---

1. Consider the following preference table for three candidates.

Preference Table

	Rankings			
A	1	2	3	2
B	2	3	1	1
C	3	1	2	3
Number of Voters	**12**	**10**	**8**	**4**

a. Determine the runoff winner.

b. Suppose the four voters represented in the last column change their ranking to 1-2-3, so that they now give more support to candidate *A*. Modify the preference table and determine the new runoff winner.

c. What seems unfair about this situation?

2. Arrow proposed six fairness conditions, listed below, that should be satisfied by any fair voting method. Then he *proved* that no voting method can satisfy all six conditions whenever there are more than two candidates! Which of the fairness conditions is violated in the situation from Activity 1?

Fairness Conditions

- **Unanimous** The decision reached using a fair voting method should agree with the unanimous will of the voters. That is, if all voters prefer choice *X* over choice *Y*, then the voting method should pick *X* as the winner over *Y*.
- **Decisive** A fair voting method should be decisive. That is, it should decide for any two choices *X* and *Y* whether *X* beats *Y*, *Y* beats *X*, or there is a tie.
- **Ordered** A fair voting method should establish an order among the candidates, so that if *X* is preferred over *Y*, and *Y* is preferred over *Z*, then *X* is preferred over *Z*.
- **Consistent** Preference trends among the individual voters should be reflected by the results of a fair election. For example, suppose voter preferences change so that *X* is raised in some or all of the voters' rankings. Then if *X* beat *Y* before the change, *X* should still beat *Y* after the change.
- **Relevant** A fair voting method should ignore irrelevant alternatives. That is, for any two candidates *X* and *Y*, the final decision about whether *X* beats *Y* should depend only on how the voters rank *X* versus *Y*, and not on how they rank other candidates.
- **Non-Dictatorship** The decision should not always be based solely on the preference of one voter.

LESSON 1 • VOTING MODELS 103

Unit 2

3. This preference table summarizes voter preferences in an election for class president.

Class President Preference Table

	Rankings			
Jill	1	1	4	4
Sammi	4	3	1	3
Amir	3	4	2	1
Orlando	2	2	3	2
Number of Voters	**45**	**27**	**45**	**36**

a. Who is the runoff winner?

b. Suppose Jill's family moves just after the election. The winner in Part a claims this should have no effect on who wins the election. However, the other candidates demand that Jill be removed from the preference table, and the results recomputed.

- Study the ranking of the 27 voters in the second column who had Jill as their first preference. If Jill is removed, who is their new first preference? Their new second preference? Their new third preference? Update the preference table with your answers.
- Similarly, modify the table to reassign the votes of the block of 45 voters who had Jill as their first preference.

c. According to your new preference table in Part b, who is the runoff winner after Jill drops out? Compare winners before and after Jill drops out.

d. In your opinion, is it fair that a person can win an election when all candidates are on the ballot but loses when a losing candidate drops out?

e. Which of Arrow's fairness conditions is violated in this situation? Explain.

Checkpoint

Fairness and fair voting are important issues in any society.

ⓐ How is fairness of voting methods analyzed mathematically?

ⓑ Discuss why each of Arrow's conditions should be satisfied by any fair voting method.

Be prepared to share your thinking with the entire class.

104 UNIT 2 • MODELING PUBLIC OPINION

Master 43

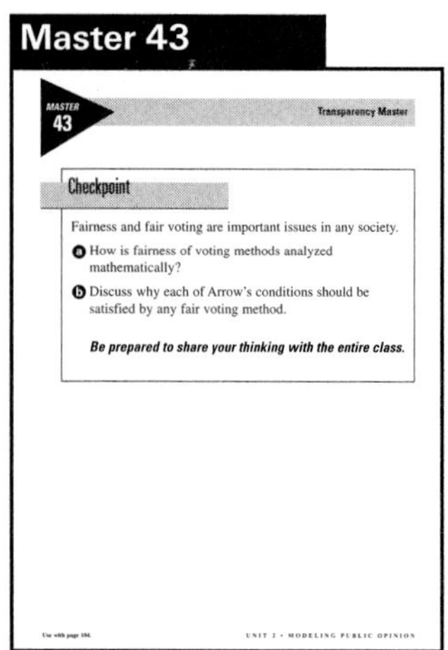

3. **a.** The runoff is between Sammi and Jill. Sammi is the runoff winner with 81 votes to Jill's 72 votes.

b. ■ The 27 voters who had Jill as their first preference now have Orlando as their new first preference. Their new second preference is Sammi, and their new third preference is Amir.

■ The 45 voters who had Jill as their first preference now have Orlando as their first preference, Amir as their second preference, and Sammi as their third preference.

Modified Class President Preference Table

	Rankings			
Sammi	3	2	1	3
Amir	2	3	2	1
Orlando	1	1	3	2
Number of Voters	**45**	**27**	**45**	**36**

c. The runoff after Jill drops out is between Orlando and Sammi. The winner of the runoff is Orlando with 108 votes compared to Sammi's 45 votes. Before Jill dropped out, Sammi won; after Jill dropped out, Orlando won.

d. Some students may feel it is fair, because after a candidate drops out, some voters may be able to transfer their support to a strong alternate candidate. On the other hand, it may seem that whether or not a losing candidate is in the race should have no effect on who wins.

e. This situation violates the "Relevant" condition because the voting method does not ignore Jill, a losing candidate and an "irrelevant alternative." To give a precise explanation of why the "Relevant" condition is violated, you must find a pair of candidates such that the result is influenced by an irrelevant alternative. Consider the situation of Sammi and Orlando. None of the voters changed their relative ranking of Sammi versus Orlando after Jill dropped out. According to the "Relevant" condition, the final decision about whether Sammi is preferred over Orlando should depend only on how the voters rank Sammi versus Orlando. However, Sammi won in one case (before) and lost in the other (after). Thus, the contest of Sammi versus Orlando was *not* decided solely on the basis of the voters' rankings of Sammi versus Orlando.

Some students may reasonably argue that Orlando was a stronger candidate than Sammi, but that is beside the point here. We are explaining only why the contest of Sammi versus Orlando illustrates a violation of the "Relevant" condition.

Some students may also decide that the "Ordered" condition has not been met. While this is true, the condition has not been violated either. You may want to point out to students that the runoff method could be repeated on the losing candidates to establish second, third, and fourth places.

See additional Teaching Notes on page T168D.

APPLY **individual task**

On Your Own

a. Majority is the best method to use with just two candidates. It provides a clear winner (unless there is a tie) with none of the "paradoxes" that plague the other methods when there are more than two candidates.

b. Majority would not be a good method to use, because there may not be a majority winner when there are more than two candidates. Plurality is probably a poor method as well. The two candidates with similar views might split the votes that each could get if in a contest alone against the third candidate. This could leave the third candidate with more votes than either of the first two. Thus, the third candidate wins, even though that person may be the last choice for the majority of students.

Looking at the situation from another angle, the third candidate's supporters may not want plurality voting either. They may feel that their candidate has no real chance to win under the plurality method, since the other two candidates are so popular. Thus, even though they would like to vote for the candidate that best represents their views, they may feel that they would be throwing their vote away. They then may vote for someone who is not their first choice.

Reasonable methods to recommend are approval or points-for-preferences. Points-for-preferences is in general a pretty good method, as stated in the student text on page 105. With approval voting, every student could vote for his or her first choice even if, as described above, some felt their candidate was a long shot. Voting for a long shot would not be throwing a vote away since you could also vote for one of the front-runners as well.

c. Points-for-preferences seems like a good choice. Because these are "finalists," they are "talented," and so it seems reasonable to use a voting scheme that will account for all preferences. Using points-for-preferences, all preferences are accounted for by being "weighted." This is analagous to a sports event with six competitors, and assigning points for different finishing places is a common and effective method in that context. Because there are so many candidates, plurality is not a good method. Also, approval may not work well, since all finalists are probably talented.

You have seen that there are drawbacks to all the voting methods you have considered. Arrow's Theorem proves that when there are more than two candidates, *every* possible voting method violates at least one of his fairness conditions. (Arrow's conditions are widely accepted as a good definition of a fair voting method, but mathematicians continue to look for definitions that may be even better.)

In any case, decisions must be made, and they should be as fair as possible. Although no voting method satisfies all of Arrow's conditions, most experts recommend points-for-preferences, using a point assignment in which there is a common difference between point values, such as 4-3-2-1. But there is no magic formula. You must apply your knowledge of the different voting methods to each particular decision-making situation and then decide on the best voting method to use.

On Your Own

Think about which voting method you would recommend in each of the situations below.

a. There are two choices for a new school mascot. All students will vote to decide which mascot to adopt. Which voting method would you recommend? Why?

b. There are three candidates for president of the junior class. Two candidates have some differences, but their views are generally similar and they are both popular. The remaining candidate has views that are very different from the other two, and those views are shared by a significant group of students. Which voting methods would you *not* recommend for this situation? Which method would you recommend? Justify your recommendations.

c. There are six finalists in the school talent show. All students will vote to choose the overall winner. Choose one voting method that you would recommend. Choose one method other than majority that you would not recommend. In each case, defend your answer.

LESSON 1 • VOTING MODELS 105

Unit 2

MORE

Modeling • Organizing • Reflecting • Extending

Modeling

1. The preference table below summarizes the results of asking all students at a rural high school to rank the importance of four environmental protection policies.

Environmental Protection Preference Table

	Rankings				
Recycle	1	4	4	4	2
Plant Trees	2	3	1	2	3
Conserve Electricity	3	1	3	3	4
Decrease Litter	4	2	2	1	1
Number of Voters	**56**	**48**	**41**	**35**	**29**

a. Using the points-for-preferences method, assigning 3 points to all first-preference votes, 2 points to second-preference, 1 point to third-preference, and 0 points to fourth-preference, which policy should be considered most important to the students?

b. Do you think the point scheme in Part a is reasonable? Why or why not?

c. Does the winner change if you double all the point allocations in Part a? How about if you square all the point allocations in Part a?

d. Hester suggested a modified runoff method. The two policies that get the most first- or second-preference votes undergo a runoff. Find the winner using this method.

2. Some friends and their families are planning a weekend picnic. As part of the day's activities, they want to play a group ball game. Which ball game should they play? They decide to have everyone rank the five different games. The results are shown in the following preference table.

Game Preference Table

	Rankings		
Softball	1	5	5
Soccer	2	1	2
Basketball	3	4	1
Football	4	3	4
Volleyball	5	2	3
Number of Voters	**18**	**16**	**3**

106 UNIT 2 • MODELING PUBLIC OPINION

MORE **independent assignment**

Modeling

1. **a.** Using the points-for-preferences method, planting trees is the winner.
   b. This point scheme is reasonable, because a voter's higher-ranked policies get more points than lower-ranked policies. It might not seem reasonable, because some voters might consider their first choice to be much more important than their other choices and, therefore, deserve many more points.
   c. Doubling all the point allocations does not change the winner, but if you square all the point allocations, then the policy of decreasing litter wins. By squaring, decreasing litter gets 932 points and planting trees gets 810 points.
   d. Under this method, the policy of decreasing litter wins.

MORE

ASSIGNMENT *pp. 106–114*

Modeling: 5 and choice of one*
Organizing: 2 and 5
Reflecting: Choice of one*
Extending: Choice of one*

**When choice is indicated, it is important to leave the choice to the student.*
NOTE: *It is best if Organizing tasks are discussed as a whole class after they have been assigned as homework.*

Unit 2

Master 44

Name Date

MASTER 44 Activity Master

Ballot	Ballot	Ballot	Ballot
Ballot	Ballot	Ballot	Ballot
Ballot	Ballot	Ballot	Ballot
Ballot	Ballot	Ballot	Ballot

Use with page 107. UNIT 2 • MODELING PUBLIC OPINION

Unit 2

MORE *continued*

2. **a.** Softball is the plurality winner. However, softball also receives a majority of last-preference votes. So softball is not a good choice.

b. The pairwise-comparison winner is soccer.

c. The runoff winner is soccer. The points-for-preferences winner, with a point assignment of 5-4-3-2-1, is soccer.

d. Answers may vary. Points-for-preferences is a good method to use, because this method takes into account how each voter ranked each game.

3. **It may be helpful to supply students with blank ballots. (See Teaching Master 44.) When students are studying Lesson 2, you might have them return to this task and reflect on their surveys in terms of randomness and possible bias.**

a. Elections will vary. Other categories could include favorite pet, favorite sport, or least favorite household chore.

b. Lists of "candidates" should include the most common choices that those being polled are likely to choose.

c. Preference tables depend on the data gathered.

d. Winners under the different methods will depend on the preference table. Students should declare an overall winner and justify their choice.

a. Which game is the plurality winner? Do you think the group should choose this game to play? Why or why not?

b. Which game is the pairwise-comparison winner?

c. Find the winners under some other vote-analysis methods.

d. A decision must be made! Which voting method would you recommend to the group? Defend your answer.

3. In Investigation 1, you carried out an election to find your class's favorite restaurant from among McDonald's, KFC, and Taco Bell. Now you will carry out an election in another context of your choice.

a. Choose something about which you can conduct a small election. You might decide to find out about the favorite TV show of some of your friends and family, their favorite soft drink, or their preferred candidate in an upcoming political election.

b. Next, choose three or four "candidates" for the election, make at least 15 ballots like the ballot you completed in Investigation 1, and have friends and family members complete the ballots. (The "candidates" could be different TV shows, different political candidates, different soft drinks, or whatever you are voting on.)

c. Make a preference table summarizing the results of your balloting.

d. Analyze your preference table using each of the six methods from this lesson. Record the winner under each method and discuss which candidate you think should be declared the overall winner.

4. The New Hampshire Primary is the first primary in every U.S. presidential election year. It is an important part of every candidate's campaign. Public opinion throughout the nation can be greatly influenced by how a candidate performs in the New Hampshire Primary. The 1996 New Hampshire Primary provides an interesting case study of the difficulties that can arise in elections involving more than two candidates. In 1996, the major Republican candidates competing in the New Hampshire Primary included Pat Buchanan, Bob Dole, and Lamar Alexander. Pat Buchanan won. This victory contributed to the following events: Dole's campaign faltered, Alexander soon dropped out of the race, and Buchanan gained influence in the Republican party. As in all presidential primaries, the plurality method was used. The final counts are shown below.

Actual Vote Counts for the 1996 New Hampshire Republican Primary

Pat Buchanan	56,923 votes
Bob Dole	54,814 votes
Lamar Alexander	47,214 votes

LESSON 1 • VOTING MODELS 107

By examining exit polls, it is possible to make reasonable assumptions about how voters would have ranked the three candidates. Suppose such a poll resulted in the following preference table.

Primary Election, Estimated Preference Table

	Rankings			
Buchanan	1	3	2	3
Dole	2	1	1	2
Alexander	3	2	3	1
Number of Voters	**56,923**	**27,407**	**27,407**	**47,214**

a. Do you agree that Buchanan was the plurality winner?

b. Compare the actual vote counts to the estimated results shown in the preference table. What assumptions were made to get the estimated results?

c. Determine the winner using runoff, points-for-preferences, and pairwise-comparison.

d. Based on this estimated preference table and your understanding of voting and fairness, who do you think should have been declared the winner of the 1996 New Hampshire Republican Primary? Justify your answer.

e. Do you think the plurality method is the vote-analysis method that should be used in presidential primaries? Why or why not?

5. Sometimes voters vote insincerely to try to change the outcome of an election. Such voting is called **insincere** or **strategic voting**. For example, consider the election for junior class president that you analyzed in Investigation 2 (page 99). Suppose the 20 voters in the third column of the preference table decide to vote strategically (and insincerely) and switch their first and second preferences. The modified preference table is shown below.

Modified Junior Class President Preference Table

	Rankings					
Charnell	1	5	5	5	5	5
Marie	5	1	1	4	2	4
Lamar	4	4	2	2	4	2
Rodene	2	3	4	1	3	3
Richard	3	2	3	3	1	1
Number of Voters	**36**	**24**	**20**	**18**	**8**	**4**

a. Determine the majority, plurality, points-for-preferences, runoff, and pairwise-comparison winners based on this modified preference table.

108 UNIT 2 • MODELING PUBLIC OPINION

4. **a.** Yes, Buchanan was the plurality winner.
   b. Assumptions are as follows:
   - Everyone who voted for Buchanan preferred Dole over Alexander.
   - Everyone who voted for Alexander preferred Dole over Buchanan.
   - Of those who voted for Dole, half preferred Alexander over Buchanan.

   c. The runoff winner is Bob Dole; the points-for-preferences winner is Bob Dole; and the pairwise-comparison winner is also Bob Dole.
   d. Bob Dole should be considered the winner, because he won using three different voting methods that considered the rankings of the candidates. In particular, he won using pairwise-comparison and points-for-preferences, both of which are recommended methods.
   e. Since most presidential primaries involve three or more candidates, Arrow's Theorem tells us that there is no perfect voting method. However, plurality seems to have some pretty serious flaws, more so than points-for-preferences. A basic problem with plurality is that it considers only first-preference votes. It does not take into account the rankings that people have for all candidates. Thus, it makes a choice based on limited information. One common and undesirable result of the plurality method is the situation in which two candidates split the moderate vote and, thereby, an extreme candidate gets the most first-preference votes and wins, even though that candidate may be the least-liked candidate for a majority of voters.
5. **a.** There is still no majority winner, but now the plurality winner is Marie. The points-for-preferences winner, using 5-4-3-2-1 assignment, is Rodene. The runoff winner is Marie, and the pairwise-comparison winner is Richard.

5. **b.** The strategic switch in preference produced a different winner only in plurality voting.

   c. The 20 voters had ranked Charnell, the original plurality winner, as their least-favorite candidate. If they knew the preferences of the other students, they would realize that by switching their preferences in a plurality election, then at least their second-ranked candidate would win, which is preferable to having their least-liked candidate win.

   d. The original runoff winner was Marie. Thus, the only groups of voters who might wish to vote strategically (and insincerely) would be those who really dislike Marie. Consider the group of 18 voters who ranked Marie fourth. If they switch their stated preferences so that Rodene is their second preference and Lamar is their first preference, then the new runoff election is between Lamar and Charnell, and Lamar wins. This is a better result for the block of 18 voters, since they prefer Lamar (the new winner) to Marie (the original winner). Similarly, if the block of 36 voters lists Rodene as their first preference, Rodene will win.

NOTE: Be sure that students do Part d based on the original preference table, not the modified one.

Organizing

1. **a.** Many preference tables will not have a majority winner. Many examples have already been seen.

   b. There will not be a plurality when two or more front-runners receive the same number of first-preference votes; the result is a tie for first place.

   c. If the group of 4 voters rank choice C first, choice B second, and choice A third, then each of A, B, and C will win one of the pairwise elections and there will be no pairwise-comparison winner.

2. **a.** If there is a majority winner, one bar will have a height of 7 or more.

   b. If there is a plurality winner but no majority winner, then there will be a tallest bar, but its height will be no more than 6.

   c. If there is no plurality winner, then there will be two or three tallest bars of equal height.

b. Did this strategic switch in preference produce different winners than those in Investigation 2 for the comparable methods?

c. Give a reason why the 20 voters who switched preferences might have gotten together to plan the switch.

d. Suppose the voters know the election will be analyzed using the runoff method. Find an instance of strategic voting that will benefit one of the groups of voters (using the original, sincere preferences given on page 99).

Organizing

1. You now have experience finding winners with several voting methods. Think about whether those methods always produce winners.

a. Is there a majority winner for all possible preference tables? If not, construct a simple preference table for which there is no majority winner.

b. Is there a plurality winner for all possible preference tables? If not, construct a simple preference table for which there is no plurality winner.

c. Complete the preference table below with a ranking for the group of 4 voters so that there is no pairwise-comparison winner.

Preference Table

	Rankings		
Choice A	1	2	
Choice B	3	1	
Choice C	2	3	
Number of Voters	**8**	**6**	**4**

2. Suppose that a group of 12 students decides to vote to play volleyball, softball, or soccer at their picnic. Each student votes for her or his choice. If the results of the voting are represented in a bar graph, describe the possible shape of the graph in each of the following cases.

a. There is a majority winner.

b. There is a plurality winner but no majority winner.

c. There is no plurality winner.

LESSON 1 • VOTING MODELS 109

3. In this task, you will count the total number of rankings possible (without ties) in a preference table.

   a. With three choices, A, B, and C, there are six possible rankings:

   $$ABC, ACB, BAC, BCA, CAB, CBA.$$

   List all possible rankings if there are four choices. Explain how you know that you have listed all possible rankings.

   b. There are 720 different rankings possible with six choices. Explain how to use this fact to find the number of possible rankings of seven choices.

   c. If *NOW* is the number of rankings possible for a certain number of choices and *NEXT* is the number of rankings possible with one more choice, write an equation showing the relationship between *NOW* and *NEXT*.

   d. **Factorial** notation is an economical way of writing certain products of consecutive integers. For example, $5 \cdot 4 \cdot 3 \cdot 2 \cdot 1 = 5!$ which is read as "5 factorial." Similarly, $8!$ equals $8 \cdot 7 \cdot 6 \cdot 5 \cdot 4 \cdot 3 \cdot 2 \cdot 1$ and is read as "8 factorial." Use factorial notation to write an expression for the number of possible rankings with three choices, four choices, and ten choices.

   e. Use the factorial function on your calculator to compute the number of possible rankings for 5 choices, 10 choices, and 50 choices.

4. When using the pairwise-comparison method, you have to run off all possible pairs of choices. Think about how many possible pairs there could be.

   a. List all the pairs that need to be run off if there are three choices: A, B, and C. How many pairs are there?

   b. List all the pairs that need to be run off if there are four choices: A, B, C, and D. How many pairs are there?

   c. Make a table with the number of choices in one column and the number of possible pairs in another column. Record your results from Parts a and b. Continue the table for the cases of five and six choices.

   d. Describe any patterns you see in your table from Part c. Use your pattern to predict how many possible pairs there are with 10 choices. Predict the number of pairs with n choices.

5. The pairwise-comparison method can be modeled with a digraph, as follows. The vertices represent the candidates, and two vertices are connected by an arrow from one to the other if the one candidate beats the other in their pairwise runoff. For example, if A and B are two of the candidates and A beats B in the A-B runoff, then there is a directed edge from A to B. Draw a digraph representing a pairwise-comparison analysis of each of the preference tables at the top of the next page.

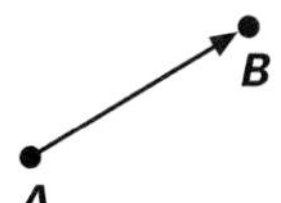

110 UNIT 2 • MODELING PUBLIC OPINION

3. a. With four candidates, *A*, *B*, *C*, and *D*, there are 24 possible rankings: *ABCD*, *ACBD*, *BACD*, *BCAD*, *CABD*, *CBAD*, *ABDC*, *ACDB*, *BADC*, *BCDA*, *CADB*, *CBDA*, *ADBC*, *ADCB*, *BDAC*, *BDCA*, *CDAB*, *CDBA*, *DABC*, *DACB*, *DBAC*, *DBCA*, *DCAB*, and *DCBA*. These are all possible rankings because there are 4 ways to choose first, 3 ways to choose second once first has been chosen, 2 ways to choose third, and 1 way to choose fourth. Another way to see this is that, for each of the original 6 rankings, *D* could be placed in any of 4 positions.

   b. For each of the 720 different rankings possible with 6 choices, the new candidate could be placed in any one of 7 positions. Therefore, there will be $720 \cdot 7$ or 5,040 different possible rankings.

   c. $NEXT = NOW \cdot$ (new number of candidates)

   d. 3!; 4!; 10!

   e. 5! = 120; 10! = 3,628,800. Because 50! is such a large number, some calculators may produce an error message. Others will round 50! and display it in exponential form as 3.04140932E64.

4. a. If there are 3 choices, then there are 3 pairs: *AB*, *AC*, *BC*.

   b. If there are 4 choices, then there are 6 pairs: *AB*, *AC*, *AD*, *BC*, *BD*, *CD*.

   c. **Pairwise Comparisons**

Number of Choices	3	4	5	6
Number of Pairs	3	6	10	15

   d. One pattern: The number of pairs is half the number of choices multiplied by the next smaller integer. With 10 choices, there will be 45 pairs.
   Another pattern: In the table, the number of pairs is found by starting with 3, then adding 3, then adding 4, then adding 5. Continuing in this way, the number of pairs for 10 candidates is 15 + 6 + 7 + 8 + 9 or 45.

MORE *continued*

5. a.

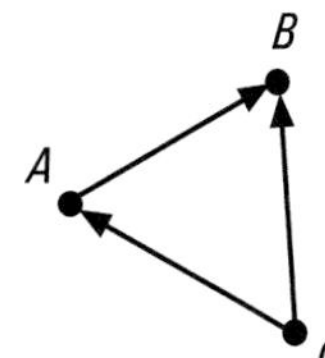

b.

B

A

C

c. A circuit indicates no pairwise-comparison winner. If there is a pairwise-comparison winner, then the vertex for that candidate will have only arrows going out from it (and thus, no incoming arrows).

Reflecting

1. Students should describe difficulties they had understanding the different voting methods. For example, they may say that runoff was the hardest, because they had to eliminate some candidates and reallocate their votes.
2. Be sure that all students see that there are some advantages and some disadvantages. Some of the advantages are that plurality is easy to administer, is easy for everyone to understand, and gives as many people as possible their first preference. Some of the disadvantages are that the winner might be the least favorite candidate for a majority of voters, there is no simple way to resolve a tie, and voters' preferences for candidates other than their top choice are ignored.
3. Mathematics shows us that there are many deeper considerations behind the common belief that voting is fair. Voting is not useless because there are many instances when a choice must be made and people's preferences differ. In these instances, voting is a useful decision-making method. Arrow's Theorem does tell us that it is impossible to find a perfect voting method, but that does not mean that we cannot continue to try to find the best method possible. An understanding of the mathematics of voting can help us set up a voting procedure that is as fair as possible and acceptable to as many voters as possible. Also, Arrow's Theorem does not apply to voting between two choices.
4. Students should discuss approval voting with at least one adult and write a report about the adults' reactions.

a.

Preference Table 1

	Rankings			
Candidate *A*	1	3	3	2
Candidate *B*	3	1	2	3
Candidate *C*	2	2	1	1
Number of Voters	**8**	**6**	**4**	**4**

b.

Preference Table 2

	Rankings		
Candidate *A*	1	2	3
Candidate *B*	3	1	2
Candidate *C*	2	3	1
Number of Voters	**8**	**6**	**4**

c. Can you tell just by looking at a digraph model whether or not there is a pairwise-comparison winner? Explain and illustrate your answer.

Reflecting

1. Which voting model was most difficult for you to understand? Why?

2. Plurality is the most commonly used voting method for political elections in the United States. Do you think this is the best method to use? Write a brief paper explaining the advantages and disadvantages of the plurality method.

3. Does Arrow's Theorem mean that voting is useless and fairness is impossible? Explain.

4. Sometimes in an election there are several candidates, but only two seem to have much chance of winning. The others are called "long shots." This is often the case when there are "third-party" candidates in a presidential election. In such situations, you sometimes hear voters complain that they would like to vote for the long-shot candidate, but they feel that doing so would be throwing their vote away. One advantage of approval voting is that you can vote for a long-shot candidate and yet still vote for one of the front-runners as well. Ask some adults you know who have voted in presidential elections if they ever felt that there was a candidate they wanted to vote for, but didn't because it seemed like they would just be throwing their vote away. Tell these adults how approval voting would solve this problem. Write a paragraph describing whom you talked to, what they said, and how they reacted to your explanation of approval voting.

LESSON 1 • VOTING MODELS 111

5. Discuss what you have learned about voting methods for making fair decisions with some adults. Then interview them by asking the following questions. Write a summary of the interview.
   - Before our conversation, did you know about different voting methods and their advantages and disadvantages?
   - Are you surprised by what I have told you?
   - What are examples in your life in which a group needed to make fair decisions?
   - What methods were used to make those decisions?
   - What do you think is the fairest method to use for electing the President of the United States?

Extending

1. Voting and social decision-making are topics that have intrigued philosophers as well as mathematicians. For example, read the three quotations below. Choose the one that you find most interesting, explain what you think the author meant, and briefly discuss whether you agree or not.

   a. "The principle of majority rule must be taken ethically as a means of ascertaining a real 'general will,' not as a mechanism by which one set of interests is made subservient to another set. Political discussion must be assumed to represent a quest for an objectively ideal or 'best' policy, not a contest between interests." (Jean-Jacques Rousseau, *The Social Contract*, 2nd edition, revised, translated. New York: G.P. Putnam's Sons, 1906.)

   b. "The idealist doctrine then may be summed up by saying that each individual has two orderings, one which governs him in his everyday actions and one which would be relevant under some ideal conditions and which is in some sense truer than the first ordering. It is the latter which is considered relevant to social choice, and it is assumed that there is complete unanimity with regard to the truer individual ordering." (Kenneth Arrow, *Social Choice and Individual Values*, 2nd edition. New Haven: Yale University Press, 1963.)

   c. "[As a basis of political or free society] it is not necessary that everyone subject to the laws should take part in voting them, still less that he should consent to their application to himself, but that it should represent an idea of common good, which each member of the society can make his own so far as he is rational, i.e., capable of the conception of a common good, however much particular passions may lead him to ignore it." (T. H. Green, *Lectures on the Principles of Political Obligation*. New York: Longmans, Green and Co., 1895.)

112 UNIT 2 • MODELING PUBLIC OPINION

5. Students should summarize their interviews with adults about various voting methods.

Extending

1. Responses will vary. Students should discuss one of the passages and support their agreement or disagreement.

MORE ***continued***

2. Methods of voting differ from school to school.
3. Responses will vary depending on the sites accessed.

2. Describe the voting method used in your school for the election of class officers. Discuss the method with your group, and prepare a report for the student government proposing the fairest voting strategy to use in the next election. You might promote one of the methods you studied in this lesson, some combination or modification of those methods, or a method of your own. Point out both advantages and disadvantages of your suggestion and indicate benefits of your strategy over the system currently in use.

3. You can find information about elections and opportunities to vote on the Internet. For example, here are two Internet sites that may be active.

   - *http://www.vote-smart.org/*

     This site has information about current national and state elections in the United States.

   - *http://www.casting-vote.com*

     This site allows you to cast votes on a wide variety of topics including politics, humor, and lifestyles.

   a. Try to visit these sites. Find two other Internet sites that have elections or election information.

   b. Find an Internet site that is conducting an election. Vote in the election. Do people vote for their favorite candidate or do they rank the candidates? What recommendation, if any, would you make to the site manager about the fairest vote-analysis method for the type of election being conducted?

4. Consider the preference table on the next page, showing the results of ranking different types of energy sources. Copy the preference table onto your own paper. You need to do this so that you will have plenty of room to cross things out and make changes.

LESSON 1 • VOTING MODELS 113

Energy Source Preference Table

	Rankings				
Oil	1	4	4	4	2
Solar	2	3	1	2	3
Coal	3	1	3	3	4
Nuclear	4	2	2	1	1
Number of Voters	**37**	**32**	**30**	**21**	**7**

a. Which energy source received the fewest first-preference votes? Eliminate this choice by crossing out its row.

b. Which groups of voters had the energy source you eliminated as their first preference?

c. For each group of voters in Part b, assign a new first preference. Change their most-preferred remaining choice into their new first preference.

d. Repeat Parts a–c for the modified schedule.

e. Continue in this way until there is only one choice left. This remaining choice is the **sequential-elimination** winner. Using this sequential-elimination method, which energy source is the voters' preferred energy source?

ANALYZE ELECTION
1:PLURALITY
2:RUNOFF
3:PAIRWISE
4:POINTS
5:ELIMINATION
6:MAIN MENU

f. The sequential-elimination method is included in some voting software. For example, it is included in the *Preferential Voting* software that runs on your calculator. Use voting software to verify the sequential-elimination winner and compare it to the winners under the other methods included in the software.

g. Explain the connection between the sequential-elimination method and the runoff method when there are only three choices.

5. In this task, you will compare the plurality and sequential-elimination methods (see Extending Task 4).

a. Construct a preference table for which the plurality winner is different from the winner using the sequential-elimination method.

b. Construct a preference table for which the plurality winner is the *same* as the winner using the sequential-elimination method.

c. Can you find conditions under which the plurality winner will always be the same as the sequential-elimination winner?

114 UNIT 2 • MODELING PUBLIC OPINION

4. **a.** Nuclear energy received the fewest first-preference votes.
   b. The last two groups, with 21 voters and 7 voters, had nuclear energy as their first preference.
   c. The group of 21 voters will now have solar energy as their first preference, and the group of 7 voters will now have oil as their first preference.
   d. Coal is eliminated.
   e. Using the sequential-elimination method, solar energy is the winner.
   f. There is no majority winner; the plurality winner is oil; the points-for-preferences winner, using 4-3-2-1 assignment, is solar energy; the runoff winner is coal; the pairwise-comparison winner is solar.
   g. With 3 candidates, the sequential-elimination method and the runoff method are the same: One candidate is eliminated, and, of the remaining two, the one with the most first-preference votes wins.

5. **a.** Tables will vary. In the following example, *B* is the plurality winner, but *A* is the sequential-elimination winner.

	Rankings		
A	1	2	3
B	2	3	1
C	3	1	2
Number of Voters	**4**	**3**	**5**

   b. Again, tables will vary. In the following example, the plurality winner, *B*, is the same as the sequential-elimination winner.

	Rankings		
A	1	2	3
B	2	3	1
C	3	1	2
Number of Voters	**4**	**2**	**8**

   c. The majority winner, the plurality winner, and the sequential-elimination winner will be the same in any election in which there is a majority winner.

See Assessment Resources pages 43–48.

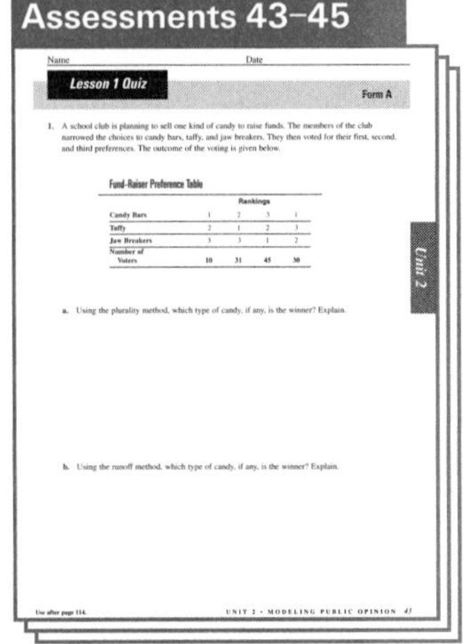

Assessments 43–45

Name Date

Lesson 1 Quiz — Form A

1. A school club is planning to sell one kind of candy to raise funds. The members of the club narrowed the choices to candy bars, taffy, and jaw breakers. They then voted for their first, second, and third preferences. The outcome of the voting is given below.

Fund-Raiser Preference Table

	Rankings			
Candy Bars	1	2	3	1
Taffy	2	1	2	3
Jaw Breakers	3	3	1	2
Number of Voters	10	31	45	30

a. Using the plurality method, which type of candy, if any, is the winner? Explain.

b. Using the runoff method, which type of candy, if any, is the winner? Explain.

Unit 2

Use after page 114. UNIT 2 • MODELING PUBLIC OPINION 43

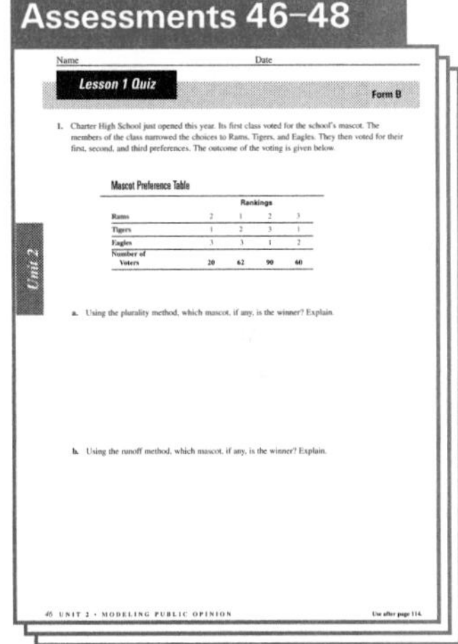

Assessments 46–48

Name Date

Lesson 1 Quiz — Form B

1. Charter High School just opened this year. Its first class voted for the school's mascot. The members of the class narrowed the choices to Rams, Tigers, and Eagles. They then voted for their first, second, and third preferences. The outcome of the voting is given below.

Mascot Preference Table

	Rankings			
Rams	2	1	2	3
Tigers	1	2	3	1
Eagles	3	3	1	2
Number of Voters	20	62	90	60

a. Using the plurality method, which mascot, if any, is the winner? Explain.

b. Using the runoff method, which mascot, if any, is the winner? Explain.

Unit 2

46 UNIT 2 • MODELING PUBLIC OPINION Use after page 114.

Master 45

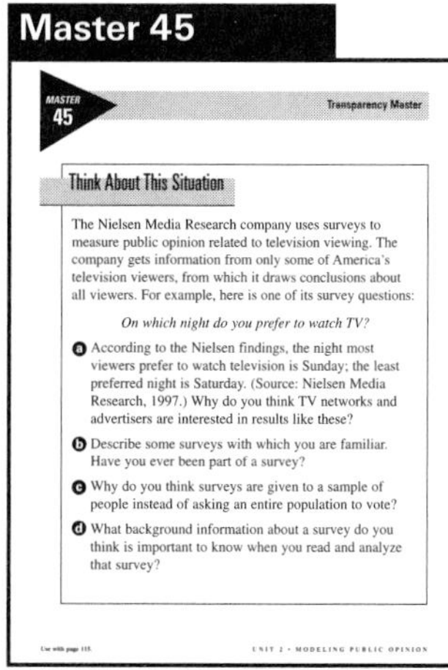
MASTER 45 Transparency Master

Think About This Situation

The Nielsen Media Research company uses surveys to measure public opinion related to television viewing. The company gets information from only some of America's television viewers, from which it draws conclusions about all viewers. For example, here is one of its survey questions:

On which night do you prefer to watch TV?

a. According to the Nielsen findings, the night most viewers prefer to watch television is Sunday; the least preferred night is Saturday. (Source: Nielsen Media Research, 1997.) Why do you think TV networks and advertisers are interested in results like these?

b. Describe some surveys with which you are familiar. Have you ever been part of a survey?

c. Why do you think surveys are given to a sample of people instead of asking an entire population to vote?

d. What background information about a survey do you think is important to know when you read and analyze that survey?

Use with page 115. UNIT 2 • MODELING PUBLIC OPINION

Unit 2

Lesson 2 *Surveys and Samples*

LESSON OVERVIEW **In the last lesson, students learned how to measure and analyze public opinion through voting-analysis methods. In this lesson, students will begin the investigation of surveys as a method for understanding public opinion.**

The first investigation focuses on surveys, voting, and censuses. This investigation is designed to engage students in reading and thinking about surveys and the connection to voting. Voting is often like a census in that data are gathered from all individuals. Voting can also be connected to surveys in interesting and useful ways. In a survey, for example, just as in a voting situation, it may make more sense to ask people to give a ranking rather than just state their favorite. In this way, the voting methods students learned in Lesson 1 can be used to collect, summarize, and report survey data.

Investigation 2 in this lesson focuses on the key issue of bias in surveys, and Investigation 3 is concerned with sample selection and, in particular, random samples.

Lesson Objectives

- **To understand and use surveys as a method for measuring and analyzing public opinion**
- **To understand and identify key elements of a survey and to critically analyze surveys**
- **To understand, identify, and correct bias in a survey**
- **To understand, identify, and design a simple random sample**

LAUNCH **full-class discussion**

Think About This Situation

See Teaching Master 45.

a. Focus students' thinking on their *own* preferred night for viewing TV. Help students realize that this is not a question about when they watch TV or which night has the best TV shows; rather it is a question about when they *prefer* to watch TV. Presumably, it is viewers' preferred nights that determine when the good shows are aired and not vice versa. Networks and advertisers want to be aware of preferred viewing nights so they know when to schedule shows and commercials.

b. Students may have been involved in a variety of surveys, such as market research surveys or surveys at school.

c. It may be impossible or impractical to have everyone vote. Students may suggest cost, difficulty of reaching everyone, and time factor.

d. This question leads into the first investigation. The goal is to get students thinking about the survey instrument before they can confidently accept the results. Many issues are relevant, such as who sponsored the survey, what the population is, how the sample was selected, what the survey questions are, and so on.

Lesson 2

Surveys and Samples

In Lesson 1, you learned how to measure and analyze public opinion in situations where every person has the opportunity to vote. However, it is possible to measure public opinion without getting everyone's opinion. This can be done using *surveys*, which gather opinions from a *sample* of the population.

Surveys are used often by government agencies, the media, and consumer-oriented businesses. With access to computers that easily compile information, more and more data are gathered from surveys to analyze public opinion about issues, products, and people. If surveys are to be efficient and provide accurate information, they must be based on probabilistic concepts and they must be carried out according to standard rules. In this lesson, you will learn some of the mathematics behind surveys, and you will apply what you learn as you analyze surveys reported in the media.

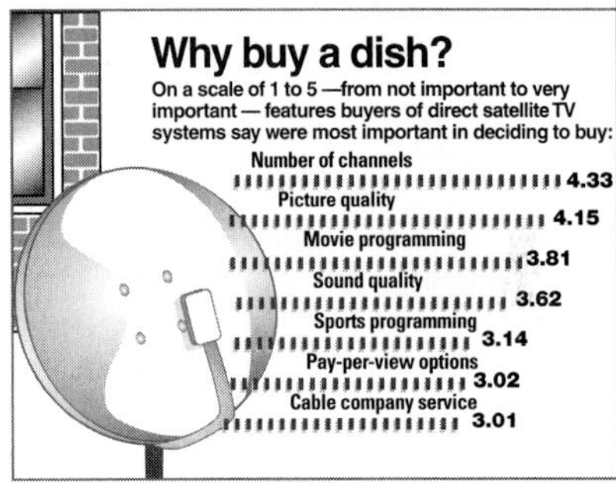

Source: *USA Today*, May 29, 1996.

Think About This Situation

The Nielsen Media Research company uses surveys to measure public opinion related to television viewing. The company gets information from only some of America's television viewers, from which it draws conclusions about all viewers. For example, here is one of its survey questions:

On which night do you prefer to watch TV?

a According to the Nielsen findings, the night most viewers prefer to watch television is Sunday; the least preferred night is Saturday. (Source: Nielsen Media Research, 1997.) Why do you think TV networks and advertisers are interested in results like these?

b Describe some surveys with which you are familiar. Have you ever been part of a survey?

c Why do you think surveys are given to a sample of people instead of asking an entire population to vote?

d What background information about a survey do you think is important to know when you read and analyze that survey?

Unit 2

INVESTIGATION 1 Surveys, Voting, and Censuses

People take surveys about many different things. Sometimes surveys are taken to investigate a trend, such as Internet use or jobless rates, for different segments of the population. One of the most common types of surveys is an *opinion poll*, which is used to describe public opinion on some topic.

1. The Scripps Howard News Service and Ohio University conducted a survey to determine Americans' opinions about heroes. The pollsters defined a *hero* to be "anyone with admirable courage other than family members or biblical figures."

a. Using this definition of "hero," list at least two people whom you consider to be heroes. Compare your list to those of others in your group.

b. Describe how you could use voting methods to report the most popular hero for your class.

c. Suppose you wanted to report the most popular hero according to everyone in your school. Describe how you could do this.

d. Suppose you are given a report of a survey that says Americans' top three heroes are John F. Kennedy, Martin Luther King, and Abraham Lincoln. Describe any doubts you might have about the survey or any questions you would like to ask the people who prepared the report.

2. Read the following excerpt from an article entitled, "The Endangered U.S. Hero."

The Endangered U.S. Hero

By Thomas Hargrove and Guido H. Stempel III
Scripps Howard News Service

President John F. Kennedy was the most commonly named hero in a study of hundreds of adult Americans who indicate that they still have heroes.

He was followed in popularity by civil rights leader Martin Luther King, Abraham Lincoln, Persian Gulf War leader Norman Schwarzkopf and former first lady Jacqueline Kennedy.

But perhaps the real winner was "none-of-the-above."

A survey of 1,000 adults conducted by Scripps Howard News Service and Ohio University found that most Americans said they do not have personal heroes.

And three of the top five—Kennedy, King and Schwarzkopf—have faced intense revisionist criticism in recent years.

The survey asked adults to name up to four heroes whom they admire. The group identified 206, ranging from Socrates to Ralph Nader.

Among the most popular were religious figures like Mother Teresa and political figures such as President Clinton.

The telephone survey was conducted from July 17 to Aug. 1 among 1,000 randomly selected Americans at least 18 years old. Interviews were conducted at the E.W. Scripps School of Journalism at Ohio University.

The survey has a margin of error of 4%.

Source: *Milwaukee Journal,* August 14, 1994.

116 UNIT 2 • MODELING PUBLIC OPINION

EXPLORE small-group investigation

INVESTIGATION 1 Surveys, Voting, and Censuses

This investigation sets the tone for the rest of the unit: We need to be critical consumers of survey results. The issues raised in this investigation include how the sampling process was carried out, who sponsored the survey, and what the purpose was.

NOTE: Activities 1 and 2 are important to set the stage for this lesson. However, do not let students spend too much time on them.

1. a. Students may list political figures, musicians, or leading sports figures.

b. You could decide first on a given list of people to vote for. Then rank the candidates, create a preference table, and use one or more voting methods to analyze the results.

You also might use the list of two heroes that each student already has and declare the most popular to be the one who is on the most lists. (This is somewhat like approval voting.)

c. You might have everyone in the school vote, or you could do a survey of just some of the students. Students should be encouraged to brainstorm about possibilities.

d. Students should think critically about how the survey was conducted, what questions were asked, how the sample was selected, and so on. Students may suggest such questions as who was asked, were the potential heroes given in a list or was the list unspecified, and what were the responses. The goal here is to encourage critical and reasoned analysis of surveys.

2. **a.** Students should engage in a brief discussion. A written response is not necessary.

b. Some of students' doubts and questions should be resolved. The article contains information about the number of people surveyed (1,000 Americans aged 18 and over). The article indicates how the survey was conducted (by telephone), when (July 17 to August 1, 1994), and by whom (E. W. Scripps School of Journalism at Ohio University). Actual numbers or percentages that each "hero" received were not given. A margin of error is given. (What this indicates about the results will be studied in Lesson 4.)

c. Students should list all pertinent information that they would like to know about the survey and see if it is all given in the article. (See the list in Activity 5.) Student responses will depend on their own list. Notice that this survey was given to adults. The class is not from that population, so students' responses are likely to result in a very different list of heroes. For example, most high school students will not relate to Jacqueline Kennedy; Norman Schwarzkopf was a leader in the Persian Gulf War, an event in history that was fresh in people's minds in 1994 but unlikely to be familiar to current high school students.

3. **a.** The article described a sample survey.

b. The population was Americans at least 18 years old who had telephones.

c. The sample was 1,000 randomly selected Americans at least 18 years old who had telephones and answered them.

4. **a.** Unless the population is quite small, you would probably take a survey rather than a census. The population is "all" moviegoers, but the issue is whether you are interested in all moviegoers in the class, in the school, in the region, or in the country or all moviegoers who have seen the new movie. For small populations you could do a census; otherwise, a survey would be used. This leads into Part b, which may have been covered here, depending on how students interpret Part a.

b. The population is the students in class. This population is small and accessible enough that you could do a census.

c. A sample is necessary; a census would be impractical because of time and expense. Also, if you tested each bulb until it burned out, you would destroy all the bulbs and have nothing to sell! The population is all of the lightbulbs produced in a certain time period.

d. A sample or a census; it is important to find out how much food to make, but this information could be obtained either way. The population is all students at school.

e. This question can be interpreted in different ways. If you think that the population is soup eaters, then a survey or census could be used, depending on how large the population is. If you think that the population is the soup, then you would have to take a sample of the soup; otherwise, you would eat all the soup while deciding whether there is enough seasoning.

f. Take a sample; it would be too large a task to ask everyone. The population might be all eligible voters or all those who intend to vote.

5. **a.** Student responses will vary. Some possible answers follow. (Note that it is not necessary for students to write full answers to each question.)

See additional Teaching Notes on page T168E.

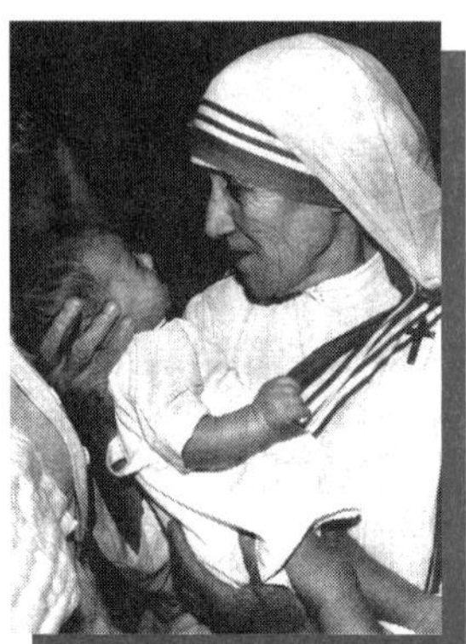

Mother Teresa

a. How did your list of heroes compare to the heroes identified in this article?

b. Were any of your questions or doubts from Part d of Activity 1 resolved? Which ones?

c. It is important to know some details about the survey so that you can judge its validity. For example, who was surveyed and how was the survey conducted? List all the information contained in the article that you think is important for understanding the survey and deciding if it is valid. Is there some important information missing?

3. Individual opinions can be collected by using a census or by using a sample survey. A **census** collects information from every individual in a **population**, which is the entire set of people or objects you would like to describe in some way. A **survey** usually is given to a **sample**, that is, a subset of a population. A survey can be used to form a picture of the entire population without contacting every individual.

a. Did the article which you read in Activity 2 describe a census or a sample survey?

b. Describe the population that was being studied.

c. Describe the sample that was used.

4. Work with a partner to decide whether you would conduct a census or sample survey to answer each of the questions below. Also, describe the population in each case. Compare your answers to those of others in your group.

a. How do people who go to movies feel about a new movie?

b. How do people in your class feel about a particular new movie?

c. Is a manufacturer producing very many defective lightbulbs?

d. How many people are going to eat a hot lunch at school this week?

e. Does the soup you are making have enough seasoning?

f. Who are people going to vote for in the next presidential election?

5. The results of a survey may be interesting, but before the results are accepted, it is important to consider carefully how the survey was constructed and carried out. Some questions you should consider are the following:

- What is the issue of interest or the variable being studied?
- Who sponsored the survey?
- What is the population?
- How was the sample selected?
- How large is the sample?
- What was the *response rate* (percentage of sample responding)?
- How were the responses obtained?
- What were the exact questions asked?

a. Why do you think the answers to the questions above are important to know when you read about a survey?

Unit 2

LESSON 2 • SURVEYS AND SAMPLES 117

b. List other information you think would be important to include in an article describing the results of a survey. For each, indicate why the information might be important.

6. Read the following article, "Textbooks too few, too old, say teachers."

a. Answer the questions given in Activity 5 as they pertain to this article. If the information you listed in Activity 5 Part b is given, record that information as well.

b. Do you think that, based on the information given, you can confidently accept the results in this article?

Textbooks too few, too old, say teachers

By Tamara Henry

Textbook shortages are so severe in some schools that teachers "scrounge, beg, borrow or buy" them, or use books so old that Nelson Mandela is still in jail in South Africa.

A survey of 1,000 elementary and secondary teachers, to be released today at a Miami school by the Association of American Publishers, found:

- 39% say students don't have enough textbooks.
- 42% didn't assign homework because books had to be left at school.
- 52% say kids get wrong information from outdated material; 25% use 10-year-old books.
- 71% use their own money to buy reading materials.

The survey didn't indicate where the problem is most severe, but Michael Casserly, executive director of Council of the Great City Schools, believes it is in urban schools.

"Maybe it's a case of mistaken priorities," says Rick Blake of the AAP. He points to the 1994 Census report that the USA spent $2 billion for textbooks, $16 billion for pet food and $81 billion for alcohol.

Florida Gov. Lawton Chiles, who will be on hand for the survey release, calls for "the most basic kinds of education reform—providing textbooks and resource materials."

Chiles has asked for a $20 million increase in his state textbook budget; education officials estimate $136.4 million is needed to end the shortage.

Source: *USA Today,* February 29, 1996.

7. Examine these results of an Iowa poll on speed limits as reported in the *Des Moines Register*.

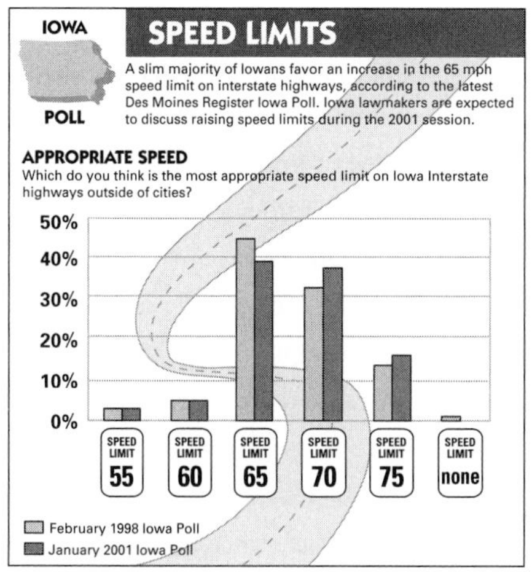
IOWA
POLL
SPEED LIMITS
A slim majority of Iowans favor an increase in the 65 mph speed limit on interstate highways, according to the latest Des Moines Register Iowa Poll. Iowa lawmakers are expected to discuss raising speed limits during the 2001 session.
APPROPRIATE SPEED
Which do you think is the most appropriate speed limit on Iowa Interstate highways outside of cities?
50%
40%
30%
20%
10%
0%
SPEED LIMIT 55
SPEED LIMIT 60
SPEED LIMIT 65
SPEED LIMIT 70
SPEED LIMIT 75
SPEED LIMIT none
February 1998 Iowa Poll
January 2001 Iowa Poll

Source: The Iowa Poll of 800 Iowans conducted by Selzer & Co. has a margin of error +/– 3.5 percentage points.

The Iowa Poll, conducted January 15–21, 2001 asked the following:

The Iowa Legislature sets speed limits for Iowa highways. It is currently 65 miles per hour. Which of the following would be the most appropriate speed limit on Iowa interstate highways outside of cities—55 miles per hour; 60 mph; 65 mph; 70 mph; 75 mph?

The Iowa Poll, conducted for the Des Moines Register by Selzer & Co. of Des Moines, is based on interviews with 800 Iowans age 18 or older. Interviewers contacted households with randomly selected telephone numbers. Percentages based on the full sample may have a maximum margin of error of plus or minus 3.5 percentage points. Republishing the copyrighted Iowa Poll without credit to the Des Moines Register is prohibited.

Source: *Des Moines Register*, January 31, 2001. Copyright 2001 The Des Moines Register and Tribune Company.

118 UNIT 2 • MODELING PUBLIC OPINION

5. b. Students may suggest factual data (male, female), age of the respondents, location of those surveyed, and conclusions reached.

6. a.
   - The issue of interest is whether teachers think there is a shortage of up-to-date textbooks.
   - The survey was sponsored by the Association of American Publishers.
   - The population is not clearly stated. It could be all elementary and secondary teachers in America, all such teachers in Florida, all such teachers in Miami, or some other population.
   - The article does not state how the sample was selected.
   - The sample size was 1,000.
   - The response rate is not given.
   - The method of obtaining responses is not specified.
   - The exact questions asked are not given.

   Students may also include information about their own questions.

   b. Given the relatively high percentages in the responses, there is probably some substance to the conclusions that textbooks are too few and too old. However, more information is needed. In particular, it would be very helpful to know more about the sample of 1,000 teachers: Were they all urban, rural, or suburban, or were they from only a few schools? Also, one must be a little wary of the results since the survey is sponsored by a publishers' association, and publishers will benefit from actions taken based on the stated results.

7. **a.**
- The issue of interest is Iowans' public opinion about increasing interstate highway speed limits.
- The *Des Moines Register* sponsored the poll, and it was conducted by Selzer & Co. of Des Moines.
- The population is adult Iowans.
- The sample was selected by using randomly selected telephone numbers to contact households.
- The sample consisted of 800 Iowans aged 18 or older.
- We know that 800 participants were interviewed. However, the number of phone calls placed or the response rate is not given.
- The responses were obtained through telephone interviews.
- The exact question asked is given in the clipping.

b. There is much more information given in the report of the Iowa Poll than in the report of the textbook poll. Virtually all pertinent information is given in the Iowa Poll, including dates and margin of error, while very little of the pertinent information is given in the textbook poll. In addition, the given information suggests that the Iowa Poll was conducted well. Thus, we would feel much more confident accepting the Iowa Poll results than the textbook poll results.

8. **a.** 740 of 1,000 women approved (voted for) real estate; 670 voted for social work.

b. The plurality winner is real estate; the runoff winner is health care; health care is also the pairwise-comparison winner. Based on the data in the preference table, it seems reasonable to report health care as the top-rated field in this hypothetical sample of 1,000 women.

a. Answer the questions given in Activity 5 as they pertain to this poll. If the information you listed in Activity 5 Part b is given, record that information as well.

b. Do you think that, based on the information given, you can confidently accept the results in this poll?

Information from a sample is often gathered and summarized using methods similar to some of the voting methods you studied in Lesson 1. However, the full potential of voting methods is not always used in surveys. You learned that there are many sensible voting methods and that the method used can greatly influence the results. The results of some of the surveys you have been studying in this lesson may have been improved if the pollsters had used what you know about voting methods.

8. Examine the news item below. To see how different voting methods might be used to gather and summarize the sample data, suppose that the sample consisted of 1,000 working women.

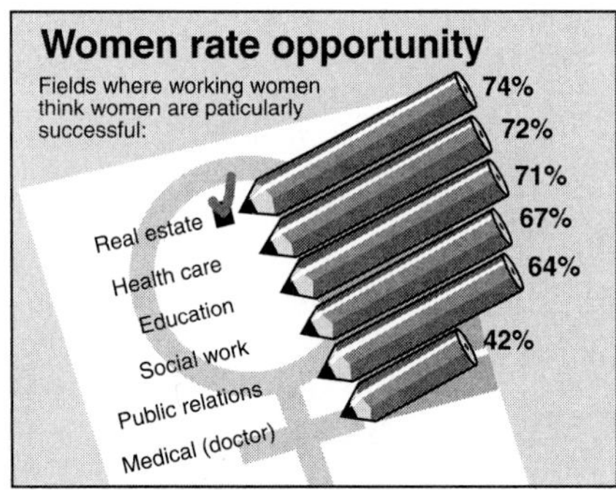

Source: *USA Today*, January 8, 1996.

a. The article states that the respondents could name more than one field. Suppose that, in fact, the 1,000 women in the sample used approval voting to give their opinions on the fields in which women are particularly successful. How many of the 1,000 women approved of (voted for) real estate? How many voted for social work?

b. Suppose that the 1,000 women in the sample ranked the fields. For example, suppose that the rankings for the first three fields are shown in the preference table at the right.

Find the plurality, runoff, and pairwise-comparison winners. Which field do you think should be reported as the top-rated field in this sample of 1,000 working women?

Field Preference Table

	Rankings		
Real Estate	1	2	3
Health Care	2	1	2
Education	3	3	1
Number of Voters	**450**	**300**	**250**

Unit 2

LESSON 2 • SURVEYS AND SAMPLES 119

Unit 2

Checkpoint

Voting, surveys, and censuses can be used to measure and analyze public opinion.

a Describe the difference between taking a sample survey of the students in your school and taking a census of the students.

b What is meant by the "population" when you take a survey?

c List some information you need to know about a survey before you can completely understand and accept the results.

d How can voting methods be used to gather and summarize the individual opinions of people in a sample? Give an example using one survey in this investigation (other than the "Women rate opportunity" survey).

Be prepared to share your responses and thinking with the entire class.

On Your Own

Examine the following article from the October 22, 2001 edition of *USA Today*.

Nike has a ball with hip-hop ads

Ad Track
USA TODAY
HARRIS POLL

A weekly look at how much consumers like a major advertising campaign compared with other ads rated by this poll – and how effective they think the ads are in helping to sell the product.

Today's ad

Nike

Ads for Nike appear to be hip-hop music videos, rather than traditional ads. The first spot opens slowly with basketball players dribbling on a shadowy court. The pace quickly picks up to the sound of dribbling basketballs and a pulsing musical beat, with NBA players Vince Carter and Jason Williams dribbling and passing balls behind their backs. The spot ends with a bouncing basketball and the words: nikebasketball.com.

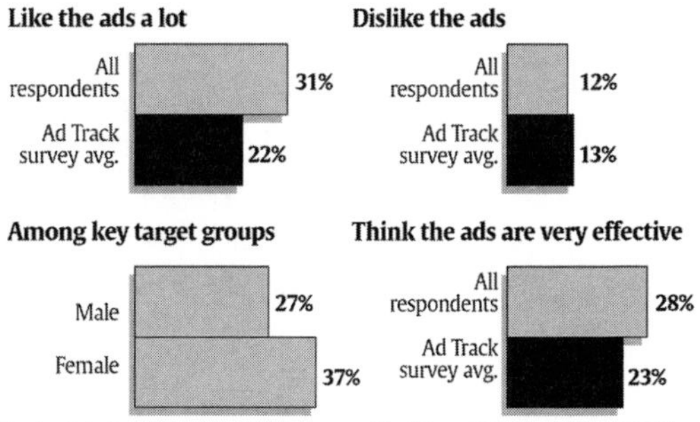

Feel the beat: Ads for Nike feature NBA players moving a basketball to pulsating music.

Like the ads a lot

All respondents	31%
Ad Track survey avg.	22%

Dislike the ads

All respondents	12%
Ad Track survey avg.	13%

Among key target groups

Male	27%
Female	37%

Think the ads are very effective

All respondents	28%
Ad Track survey avg.	23%

To subscribe to Harris Ad Track Research Service, contact David Krane of Harris Interactive at 212-539-9648. Based on a nationwide poll of 611 adults who had seen the Nike ads. Poll was conducted Aug. 24-28; margin of error is ± 4.0 percentage points. Overall average based on 269 ads.

Source: USA TODAY research by Darryl Haralson

USA TODAY

120 UNIT 2 • MODELING PUBLIC OPINION

SHARE AND SUMMARIZE full-class discussion

Checkpoint

See Teaching Master 46.

a A sample survey involves getting information from a subset of the students, while a census involves getting information from all the students.

b The population is the set of all individuals for whom (or for which) you want to determine opinions or get information.

c Responses will vary. They might include exact questions asked or measurements made, method of sample selection, population to be sampled, and so on. Consolidated over members of a group and over all groups in a class, you should expect students to list the items in Activity 5 as well as a few more.

d The voting methods studied in the last lesson can be applied, for example, by using preferential voting or approval voting. With preferential voting, respondents would rank the choices, and then the sample results could be summarized and analyzed using methods like points-for-preferences or pairwise-comparison. For example, in the heroes survey, people could have ranked a given list of potential heroes. Then a preference table could have been constructed and analyzed. In a survey like the Iowa speed limit poll, you could use preferential voting methods as well, but in this case it seems to make more sense to just do as the survey did and ask respondents to choose one. (This is like plurality voting without preference data.)

Master 46

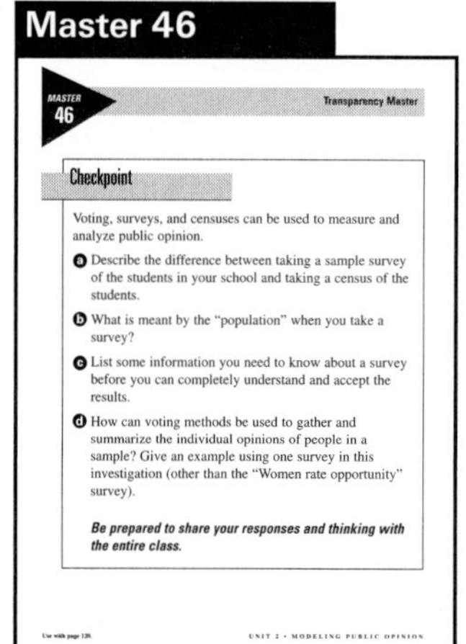
MASTER 46 — Transparency Master

Checkpoint

Voting, surveys, and censuses can be used to measure and analyze public opinion.

a Describe the difference between taking a sample survey of the students in your school and taking a census of the students.

b What is meant by the "population" when you take a survey?

c List some information you need to know about a survey before you can completely understand and accept the results.

d How can voting methods be used to gather and summarize the individual opinions of people in a sample? Give an example using one survey in this investigation (other than the "Women rate opportunity" survey).

Be prepared to share your responses and thinking with the entire class.

Use with page 120. UNIT 2 • MODELING PUBLIC OPINION

CONSTRUCTING A MATH TOOLKIT: Students should indicate in their Toolkits the difference between a census and a sample survey, what is meant by "population," and the information you need to know about a survey before you can understand the results (see Teaching Master 114).

MORE

ASSIGNMENT pp. 128–134

Students can now begin Reflecting Task 1 or 3 from the MORE assignment following Investigation 3.

Unit 2

APPLY individual task

On Your Own

a. The population for the survey would seem to be adults who have seen the Nike ads.

b. The article gives some but not all necessary background information. The article provides information about when the poll was conducted, the margin of error, and the sample size. The questions asked are indicated, but the exact questions are not given. However, the issue of interest is clear, namely, whether consumers like the ads and if they think they are effective. It is not clear how the sample was selected, including if it was a random sample. The article only says that the results are based on a nationwide poll. Also, no information is given about the response rate, how the survey was administered, or the method of obtaining responses. From the source given for the data, it seems that *USA TODAY* sponsored the survey.

c. *USA TODAY* probably sponsored the survey because the editors thought the results would be interesting to readers and thus sales of the newspaper would be enhanced. Others who might find the survey useful include Nike and other athletic apparel companies. In general, many companies planning ads might use the results of the survey to help them decide whether they should create ads that tap into the "hip-hop culture."

d. Advertisers might use preferential or approval voting methods to help track public opinion about different types of ads, like hip-hop musical ads, humorous ads, or "image" ads. They might ask consumers to rank the ads or "vote" for all those of which they approve. This would give useful information about which ads consumers prefer and would help advertisers design more effective ads.

EXPLORE small-group investigation

INVESTIGATION 2 Bias in Surveys

In this investigation, students will explore the important topic of bias in surveys. Your students may equate "bias" with deliberate prejudice and will be surprised to find that bias comes into situations in which no one has any particular motivation to produce particular answers, such as in the activity in Investigation 3 on the average areas of circles or in a survey constructed more for convenience than with an eye to representation.

You can help students identify and analyze bias throughout this investigation by asking them to look for systematic favoritism, systematic deviation from the truth, or systematic errors in the way the sample represents the population.

1. a. The factual questions are the ones on age, gender, and grade. Such questions are used in order to study whether different groups in the population have different opinions.

   b. Item a relates to plurality voting without a preference table, in which voters vote for just their favorite "candidate"; Item c is like preferential voting, and the results could be analyzed using various analysis methods, such as points-for-preferences or pairwise-comparison; Item f is like approval voting, in which voters can vote for (approve of) more than one choice (although the choices are not given).

   c. Students' comments will vary. A precise definition of bias will be presented in the next activity. Student answers might include the following: In Item e, Part i, it was hard to tell what was meant (too many negatives); Item e, Part ii used unfamiliar words; Item d implied that all old people are out of touch with students.

a. What population is the survey on page 120 trying to describe?

b. Does the article give you all the necessary background information about the survey? What additional information would you like to know?

c. Why do you think *USA Today* sponsored the survey? Who else might find the survey useful and how might they use the results of the survey?

d. Describe how advertisers might use vote analysis methods to track public opinion about ads.

INVESTIGATION 2 Bias in Surveys

When interpreting survey results, it is important to consider how the survey was constructed and carried out. In this investigation, you will examine how *bias* may occur in a survey.

1. Study the survey on fast-food restaurants shown below.

a. Responses to some items provide factual information rather than information about someone's opinion. Identify the "fact" items in the survey. Why do you think it is important to include such items in surveys?

b. Several of the items in the survey relate to some of the voting methods you have studied in this unit. Identify these items and the voting method each suggests.

c. Identify items in this survey for which the wording may cause bias and unfairly slant the results. Describe what kind of inaccurate results may be produced.

Survey on Fast-Food Restaurants

Please check the appropriate response.

Age: 14 ____ 15 ____ 16 ____ 17 ____ 18 ____

Male ____ Female ____

Grade ________

a. Name your favorite fast-food place.

b. How many times during a typical week do you eat at a fast-food restaurant?

c. Rank in order the factors that are important to you in choosing a fast-food restaurant.

________ Location

________ Food and price

________ Cleanliness

________ Service

________ Atmosphere

d. Do you think someone old and not in touch with students' preferences should be in charge of fast-food restaurants?

e. Do you agree or disagree with each statement:

i. The menus in fast-food restaurants should not be changed to deny accommodation for senior citizens.

ii. Due to the inveterate nature and intransigent behavior of a segment of the school population, students should not be allowed on the premises of eating establishments after 7:00 P.M.

f. What, in your opinion, are key factors that enable a fast-food restaurant to succeed?

Unit 2

LESSON 2 • SURVEYS AND SAMPLES 121

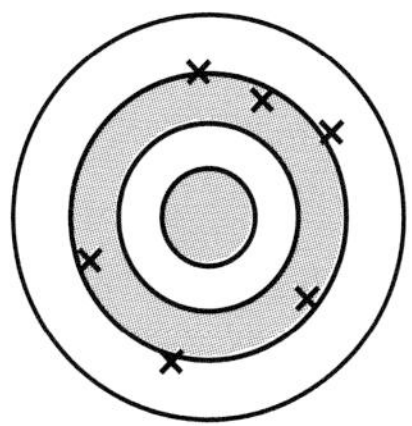

Errors due to chance

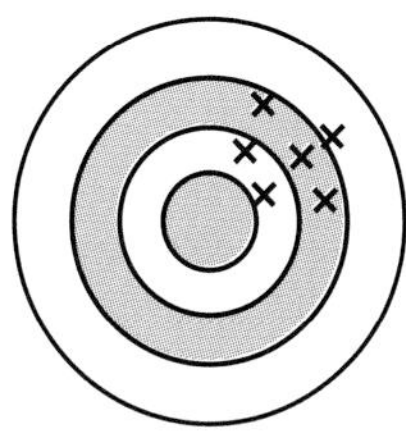

Errors due to bias

Surveys are often used to estimate information about a population. For example, the percentage of "successes" in a sample can be used as an estimate of the percentage of successes in the population. Of course, the sample result probably will not be equal to the true population result. Two possible sources of error are chance and bias. Chance errors are random and tend to cancel each other. **Bias**, on the other hand, tends to push every measurement in the same direction, resulting in systematic deviation from the true population value that you are trying to estimate. Consider possible errors when shooting at a target. The target diagrams to the left illustrate errors in shots due to chance and errors due to bias.

2. The design of a survey is said to be **biased** if it results in systematic deviation from the population value that you want to estimate. Roughly speaking, bias is systematic deviation from the truth. Poor wording is just one of many possible causes of bias. Examine the following situations for ways bias might occur in a survey.

a. Read the article below and briefly summarize it. List at least two possible sources of bias identified in the article. In each case, describe how inaccurate results could have been produced.

Police poll found to be full of flaws

By Diana Griego Erwin

Last April's police union survey blasting the Sacramento Police Department's top brass for poor leadership was "amateurish ... designedly incomplete, misleading and, ultimately, biased."

This is according to a review of the survey by two scholars known for their work in survey research. Their analysis of the Sacramento Police Officers Association survey and its finding found the results of "minimal validity" and "deeply flawed."

SPOA's survey gave Police Chief Arturo Venegas Jr. 1.4 points out of 10.

Commissioned by the Coalition for Community Oriented Policing (CCOP), a community group that embraces Venegas' policing policies, the newest report raises questions about the lengths SPOA leaders will go to undermine public confidence in the chief. It will be distributed Monday to Sacramento Mayor Joe Serna Jr., the City Council and the SPOA.

Information sent out with the original survey questioned the competence of the chief and his top managers and stated the survey would be used for political purposes to improve working conditions for union members.

Other flaws included lack of confidentiality and arithmetic mistakes.

Confidentiality was sacrificed by having officers return the surveys to the union or any SPOA board member. To be valid and confidential, they should have been returned to Trenton West, the firm hired to analyze the survey, the report said.

SPOA President Gene Burchett agreed. He said the SPOA distributed the surveys before hiring the firm, and Trenton West officials had these same criticisms.

"We made it clear that because of the problems there was no scientific validity attached to the survey," Trenton West CEO Dora Kingsley said Saturday. Trenton West's president is Dave Swim, a retired Stockton police captain.

"We still think it's an accurate reflection of those who responded, but—those who responded—maybe that's a problem, too," Burchett said.

The report found that few officers with less than five years of service (or those hired under Venegas' command) responded. Of the 171 union members in that group, only six returned the surveys, the report said.

Source: *The Sacramento Bee*, September 21, 1997.

122 UNIT 2 • MODELING PUBLIC OPINION

2. a. Four sources of possible bias are identified:

- Information sent with the survey putting the chief and managers in a negative light is likely to cause a negative reaction from the respondents. It is also possible it will prompt more of those who agree with the information to respond than might happen otherwise.
- The stated political purpose of the survey may also prompt respondents to respond in a negative manner toward Police Chief Venegas, thus causing bias.
- Lack of confidentiality suggests that some respondents may not be honest when responding. This may cause responses to favor the position of the union officials.
- The article implies that an unusually low proportion of union members with fewer than five years of service responded, implying a bias toward members with more experience. (See Activity 4.)

2. **b.** In some groups, students may be embarrassed to admit that they have cried during a movie, so the results may be too low. In other groups, this may not be the case. The survey has to be carefully designed to elicit truthful answers. (For an example of how this is done in sensitive situations, see Extending Task 1 on page 133.)

c. Surely the results will be too high. People who do not like working for the company are not likely to admit this to their boss in a face-to-face interview.

3. **a.** In this situation, people are self-selected into the sample. Only those people with strong opinions are likely to respond. Thus, the results may be too negative (for those who feel strongly negative about pets) or too positive (for those who love pets).

b. There will be some of the same problems here as in Part a, that is, self-selected respondents and responses only from those with strong opinions. The survey will favor the best player in the final game of the playoffs rather than considering the best player over the entire year, whether or not that player was in the playoffs.

c. Here the results will be too low, because the people who are at home during the hours 5:00 to 7:00 P.M. to answer the phone and respond to the survey are probably at home eating dinner. People who go out to eat are less likely to be home at dinnertime to respond to the survey.

4. **Nonresponse may introduce bias, because those who do not respond often have different opinions from those who do. It is important to understand why some people do not respond and to try to determine how far they are from the respondent group. Nonresponse occurs in three ways: inability to contact a person selected for the sample (*e.g.*, no one home when calling), inability of person to respond to the question (*e.g.*, unfamiliar with subject or lack information, such as when asking how much you paid in taxes 10 years ago), or refusal to answer.**

a. Alumni who are employed in a field other than the one chosen as a university major presumably would have a less-favorable opinion about the usefulness of their education. That is, those who did not respond might be those who were not successful or who have jobs for which they were not prepared, and thus they may think negatively about their university education. This nonresponse may have caused bias. The results may be too positive.

b. Senior citizens in the community may have strong opinions about taxes and about what schools should be doing that are quite different from the opinions of those who have children in the schools. Parents may be willing to spend more money on programs that they think will benefit their own children than the senior citizens would be.

c. In the police poll, very few of the new police officers responded. These less experienced officers (hired under Venegas' command) may have very different opinions than the more experienced officers who have long been union members.

d. In the survey about eating out, it is likely that people who often eat out did not respond since the pollsters called during dinnertime. This could cause bias. The results would be too low.

b. Suppose students in your school are interviewed in groups about whether they have ever cried during a movie. Explain why this survey could be biased.

c. Suppose an employer personally asks employees how they like working for the company. Do you think this survey design is biased? Explain.

3. In Activity 2, the manner in which the information was obtained may have caused bias. Bias can also be introduced by the method of selecting the sample. For each sampling plan described below, explain how bias may occur.

a. In a survey to find out about how people feel about pets, a response form is placed in a newspaper with a request that people cut it out and return it.

b. In a survey about who should be the National Basketball Association (NBA) Player of the Year, television viewers are asked to call in their vote at the end of the final game in the NBA Playoffs.

c. In a survey about how often people go out to eat, interviewers called people at home during the hours 5:00–7:00 P.M.

4. Unfortunately, it often happens that not everyone asked to respond to a survey will do so. This "nonresponse" is another source of bias. For each of the situations below, explain how the nonresponse could cause bias.

a. A university sent out a survey to find out how alumni felt about the usefulness of their education. The results were overwhelmingly positive. Unknown to the university, many alumni were not employed in the profession they chose as a university major, yet few of those alumni returned the survey.

b. A school board sent out a survey to determine public opinion about raising taxes for the public school system. The results indicated strong support for raising taxes to improve public schools. Further analysis showed that there was a significant population of senior citizens in the community, and few of those people responded.

c. Consider again the police poll from Activity 2 Part a. Identify the nonresponse and explain how it could cause bias.

d. Consider again the survey about eating out in Activity 3 Part c. Describe possible nonresponses and explain how this could cause bias.

LESSON 2 • SURVEYS AND SAMPLES 123

Checkpoint

Identify four possible sources of bias in a survey and give an example of each.

Be prepared to explain possible sources of bias and your examples to the class.

On Your Own

Pei and Hugh would like to organize a two-day regional music festival at which members of local high school bands would form ensembles of various sizes and then perform. They decided to survey members of high school bands in the region to determine if they would participate in the festival. They selected 15 band members from each of the 10 schools in their region by getting the names of 15 people from each school band director. On their survey they asked, "Would you be interested in a two-day music festival for our region?"

a. Key elements of a survey that you examined in the last investigation include the following:

- the variable or issue that is being studied
- the population under investigation
- the exact questions asked
- the sample and how it is selected

Identify these key elements in the music festival survey.

b. Identify any possible sources of bias in this survey.

INVESTIGATION 3 Selecting a Sample

An essential part of conducting any survey is selecting a sample. Many different methods can be used to select a sample from a population. But no matter what method is used, the sample must be selected carefully if the survey is to be unbiased. Explore possible ways of selecting a sample and their consequences in the following activities.

124 UNIT 2 • MODELING PUBLIC OPINION

SHARE AND SUMMARIZE full-class discussion

Checkpoint

See Teaching Master 47.

Some sources of bias that students might identify are poor wording, as in the fast-food survey; poor interview methods, as in the example in which the employer personally interviews employees; poor sample selection, as in the examples from Activity 3; and nonresponse, as in the examples from Activity 4. One way to think about bias is in terms of two broad categories: a measurement error, such as poor wording or faulty interview methods, and sample selection error, such as self-selection and high nonresponse rates. It is not necessary that students identify these two categories, but they should be able to list the key sources of bias discussed in the investigation: wording, interview method, sample selection, and nonresponse.

Master 47

MASTER 47 Transparency Master

Checkpoint

Identify four possible sources of bias in a survey and give an example of each.

Be prepared to explain possible sources of bias and your examples to the class.

Use with page 124. UNIT 2 • MODELING PUBLIC OPINION

CONSTRUCTING A MATH TOOLKIT: Students should explain what *bias* means and identify some causes of bias (Teaching Master 114).

APPLY individual task

On Your Own

a.
- The variable or issue that is being studied is not altogether clear. It may be whether or not members of high school bands in the region are interested in a two-day music festival, as indicated by the question asked, or it may be whether or not band members will participate in such a festival, as indicated by the problem statement.
- The population under investigation is all members of high school bands in the region.
- The exact question asked is, "Would you be interested in a two-day music festival for our region?"
- The sample consists of 15 band members from each of the 10 schools in the region. Thus, 150 people are in the sample. Pei and Hugh selected the sample by having each school band director submit 15 names. Presumably, the band directors were free to choose their 15 students in any manner they liked.

b. Some possible sources of bias are the following: The question asked is clearly a source of bias if the issue Pei and Hugh are concerned with is whether or not band members will participate. Band members may be interested and yet not be willing to participate. So the results could be too high. Another possible source of bias is the sampling process. It is not clear how the band directors decided which band members to select for participating in the survey. They may have selected those members who are enthusiastic and most actively involved in the band, in which case the results would probably be too high.

MORE ASSIGNMENT *pp. 128–134*

Students can now begin any Extending task from the MORE assignment following Investigation 3.

INVESTIGATION 3 Selecting a Sample

EXPLORE small-group investigation

In this investigation, students will study one important method of selecting a sample, namely, random sampling. In particular, they will explore simple random samples.

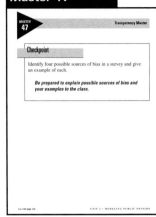

Master 48

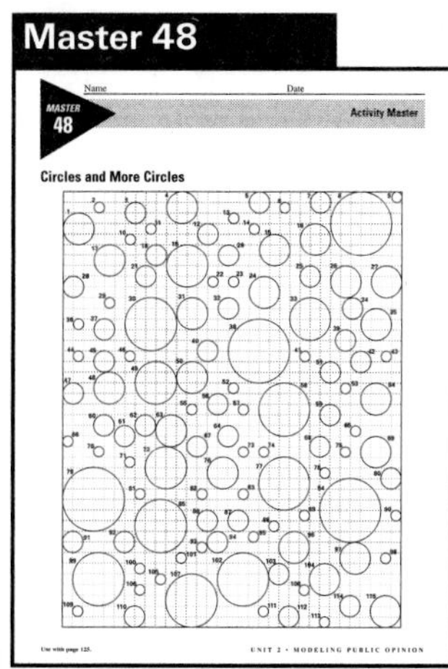

The purpose of the first activity is to introduce students to the differences among guessing, selecting a sample subjectively, and selecting a sample randomly. The potential for bias enters into each of these methods except for the method of using a random sample. Students will see this by examining the distribution of averages under the three different methods.

1. **See Teaching Master 48.**

To save time, you may want to do Parts a and b with the whole class. If so, you could create a number line plot of students' quick educated guesses at this time. Students should be able to complete the remainder of the investigation in their groups.

- **a.** Each student makes and records an educated guess. Encourage students to go with their first impressions.
- **b.** The only precise way to find the average area of all the circles is to compute the average by measuring all circles. Students might think of estimating the average area of all circles by guessing or by taking a sample of circles and finding the average area of all circles in the sample. (The sampling method will be pursued and analyzed in Parts c–h.)

1. Begin by looking carefully at the set of circles shown below.

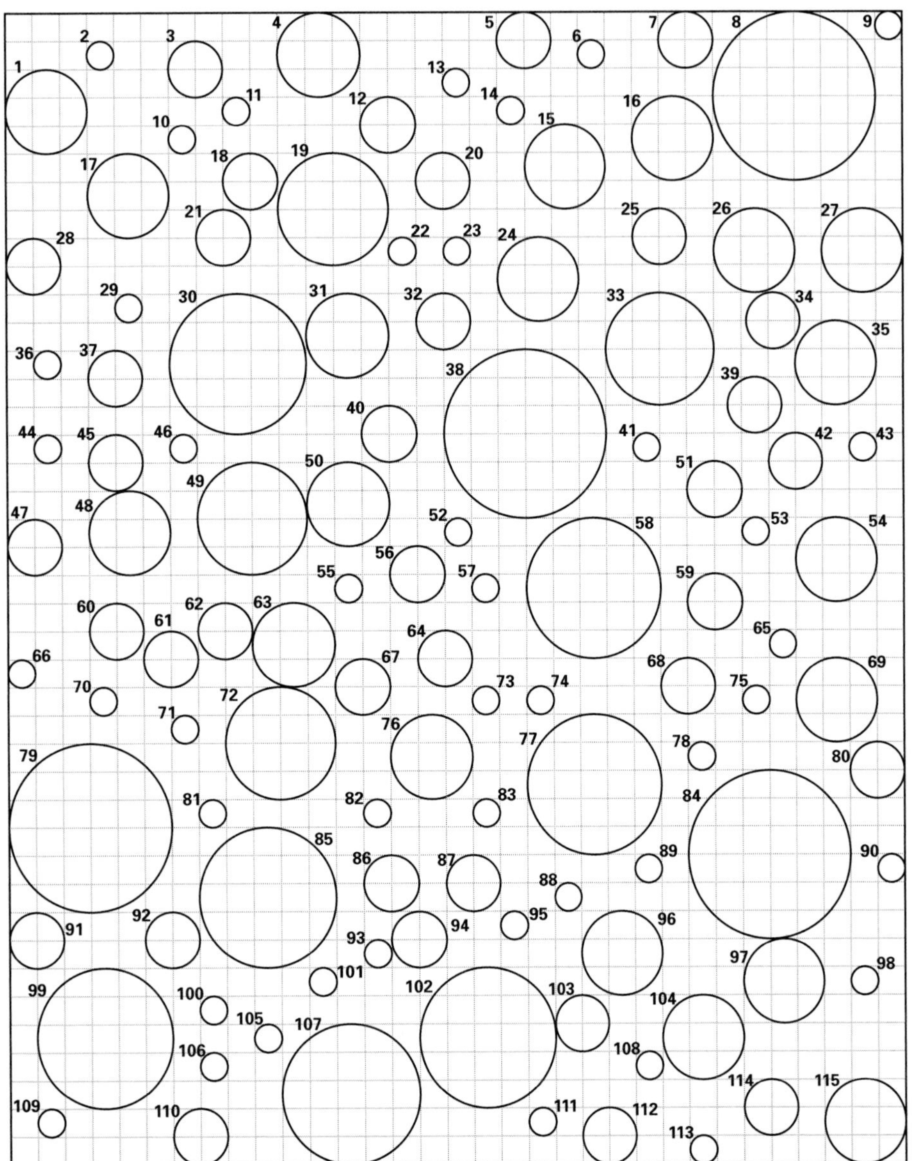

a. Without consulting other group members, quickly make an educated guess for the average area of the circles. Record your guess.

b. How could you find the average area of all the circles? How could you estimate the average area without measuring all the circles?

Unit 2

LESSON 2 • SURVEYS AND SAMPLES 125

c. Each member of your group should select five circles he or she thinks are fairly typical and find the average of the areas of the five circles.

d. Next, each member of your group should generate five random numbers between 1 and 115 inclusive and select the corresponding circles. Find the average area of the five randomly selected circles.

e. Now, pool your data to make three class lists and three number line plots for the averages generated in Parts a, c, and d.

- How do the three plots compare?
- Compute and compare the means for the three lists.

f. Your teacher will tell you the actual average area of the circles on the previous page. Compare that area to the means computed in Part e. Was anything surprising in this comparison? Can you make any conjectures from this experiment?

g. Mark the actual average circle area on the number line plots prepared in Part e. Describe any patterns you see in how the data in each plot are distributed about the actual average.

h. Do you think any of the methods of sample selection in this activity cause bias? Which sampling method do you think is the best? Explain your reasoning.

One of the best methods for sample selection is *random sampling*. Selecting a *simple random sample* is like putting everyone's name in a hat, mixing them up, and then pulling a handful of names out of the hat. More precisely, a **simple random sample** of size n is a collection of n individuals from the population chosen in such a way that every collection of n individuals has an equal chance of being the one selected.

2. You have been examining a population of circles. Now consider the population of students in your school. Suppose you are interested in student opinion about a proposed new school mascot. Describe how you would select a sample of students that you could use to get an estimate of public opinion.

3. Which of the following methods produces a simple random sample of 50 teenaged drivers in a town?

- Go to the high school, ask for a list of students, and select 50 at random using a table of random digits. If any of the 50 students aren't drivers, replace them with different randomly selected students.
- Contact the Department of Motor Vehicles, get a list of all drivers under age 20, and select 50 at random using a table of random digits.
- Contact the Department of Motor Vehicles, get a list of all drivers under age 20, choose a person at random using a random digit table, and then select that person and the next 49 whose names appear on the list.

4. When reading reports of surveys in publications, it is important to consider the sampling process that was used in the survey.

126 UNIT 2 • MODELING PUBLIC OPINION

1. **c.** Students should make a subjective decision about what constitutes a typical circle. The idea here is for them to estimate the average area of all circles by computing the average area of a sample of five circles that seem to be typical or representative.

   d. Each student should generate a random sample of five circles and find the average area of the five circles in the random sample.

   e. **Compile all the class data into three lists of averages, one for each method of estimating the true population average: guessing, subjectively choosing samples of typical circles, and selecting random samples. Also, make the corresponding three number line plots.**

   - The number line plots showing the distributions of averages under the three different methods will vary from class to class. The distribution of guessed averages probably will be skewed high. The averages computed from the subjectively chosen samples of typical circles are likely to be quite variable. The averages for the random samples will probably have less variability and will be clustered around the true population average that you will reveal in Part f. For now, students should describe the patterns they see.
   - The mean of the guessed averages will probably be higher than the other two means.

   f. The actual average of the areas of all 115 circles is approximately 5.13 square units. The mean of the averages from the random samples probably will be very close to the actual average area of all the circles. The other means will not be as close. Students may conjecture that random sampling gives the best estimate. (The reason for this is that the expected value of sample means, using simple random samples, is equal to the population mean. This does not need to be explained to students at this time, but depending on your class, you may wish them to pursue this reason.)

   g. Answers will vary, but you should see the averages from the random samples clustered about the actual average area of all the circles. This is not likely to happen with the other distributions.

   h. Based on the computations and distributions that students have generated, they should see that the random sampling method is the only one that avoids bias. That is, the other methods are more likely to give distributions that are centered above (or maybe below) the actual population mean, while the random sampling method gives a distribution that is centered at the population mean. (This is, in fact, the technical definition of an unbiased estimator: its expected value is the population parameter. Explaining this definition to students is not necessary.) Students should recognize that the guess and the subjective selection of what they identify as "typical" will, in general, cause bias. Random sampling is the best method for eliminating bias. They should begin to recognize that the best way to select a sample is to reduce the possibility for subjectivity to enter into the process. Even if the object is to obtain a "representative" sample, sometimes the choice of what makes a sample representative will produce bias.

TECHNOLOGY NOTE: As you circulate among groups, you may find some that need assistance recalling how to generate random numbers on their calculators. For most calculators, a command like int(115∗rand)+1 will generate numbers in the necessary range. The TI-83 has a randInt feature. It allows you to quickly generate random integers between two specified integers. For example, randInt(1,115,5) produces five random integers between 1 and 115 inclusive.

Unit 2

See additional Teaching Notes on page T168E.

Master 49

MASTER 49 — Transparency Master

Checkpoint

Sample selection is an important part of conducting a survey.

(a) Explain why random sampling is a good method for sample selection.

(b) Explain why choosing a sample according to what you think is "representative" or "typical" is not a good method for sample selection.

(c) Explain why each of the following is *not* an example of simple random sampling:

- The sample consists of those who call in on a toll-free number to state their opinion after a news show.
- The sample consists of those returning a survey in a magazine.
- In a survey of a college's alumni, the sample consists of 50 names randomly selected from the active membership list of the college's alumni association.

Be prepared to share your explanations and thinking with the entire class.

Use with page 127. UNIT 2 • MODELING PUBLIC OPINION

Unit 2

EXPLORE *continued*

4. **a.** This was not a simple random sample, since not every group of Internet users had an equal chance of being the group that filled out the survey. Rather, it was a self-selected sample. As the article states, "Announcements about the survey appeared in Internet-related newsgroups, as banners in search engines, …, advertising networks, and as announcements in newspapers and magazines."

b. Although it is not explicitly stated, we could assume that the Ad Track survey was conducted with random sampling, since it was carried out by a reputable professional pollster, namely, Harris. It is not clear whether the Women Rate Opportunity poll, the textbook poll, or the police poll used a random sample. (In fact, the police poll may have been a census rather than a sample survey.) The Iowa speed limit poll and the hero poll did use random sampling.

SHARE AND SUMMARIZE full-class discussion

Checkpoint

See Teaching Master 49.

(a) Random sampling is a good method for sample selection because it reduces bias. By using a random sample, you get a better estimator of the population characteristics.

(b) By choosing samples according to what you think is representative or typical, you bring subjectivity into the process. Despite your best intentions, subjectivity can lead to bias.

(c)
- The only people in the sample are those who watched the show and who feel strongly enough to make a phone call. This is certainly not a random sample of all people in the population of interest.
- This sample has the same problems as the phone-in survey above.
- If the population is all active members of the college's alumni association, then this is a simple random sample. However, if the population is all college alumni, then it is not a simple random sample because not all groups of 50 alumni have an equal chance of being selected, since only active members are chosen.

CONSTRUCTING A MATH TOOLKIT: Students should explain what a simple random sample is and why random sampling is a good method of sample selection.

a. Read the article below on Internet use and describe how the sample was selected.

Who Are Internet Users?

By Michael J. Martinez

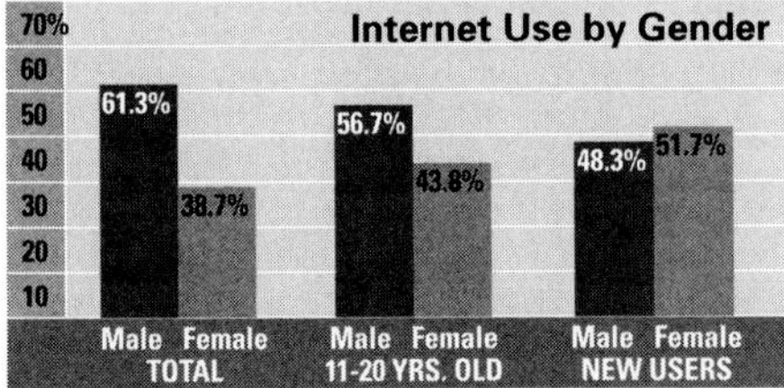

The Web remains a male domain, these figures show. But look at the graph on the right: New Web users are slightly more likely to be women.

For the first time, women outnumber men among new Internet users, according to a new survey from Georgia Tech.

Among those Internet users who have been online for less than a year, nearly 52 percent were female, found the poll by the college's Graphics, Visualization, & Usability Center. Survey administrator Colleen Kehoe said it's the first time that women have taken a statistical lead over men in the nine years the survey has been done.

"Lots of people have predicted that women will catch up to men as far as Internet use goes, and we're seeing that come true here," Kehoe says.

And there are more younger women getting online. The survey, conducted among 12,591 Internet users in April, shows that females accounted for nearly 44 percent of users between the ages of 11 and 20.

Among the survey's findings are:

- 38.7% of the respondents were female which is up from the previous two surveys.
- Users' average age was 35.1, about the same as past surveys.
- The largest category of users (45%) has used the Internet for 1 to 3 years.
- 62.6% of respondents access the Web from home.
- 67.2% of respondents pay for their own Internet access.

GVU's survey is conducted over the Web: participants respond to a questionnaire posted on the Web. Announcments about the survey appeared in Internet-related newsgroups, as banners in search engines (e.g. Yahoo, Excite) and advertising networks, and as announcements in newspapers and magazines.

Source: www.abcnews.com/;
www.gvu.gatech.edu/user_surveys/

b. Now look back at the other articles you read in this lesson. Which articles describe surveys that use random sampling?

Checkpoint

Sample selection is an important part of conducting a survey.

a Explain why random sampling is a good method for sample selection.

b Explain why choosing a sample according to what you think is "representative" or "typical" is not a good method for sample selection.

c Explain why each of the following is *not* an example of simple random sampling:

- The sample consists of those who call in on a toll-free number to state their opinion after a news show.
- The sample consists of those returning a survey in a magazine.
- In a survey of a college's alumni, the sample consists of 50 names randomly selected from the active membership list of the college's alumni association.

Be prepared to share your explanations and thinking with the entire class.

LESSON 2 • SURVEYS AND SAMPLES 127

On Your Own

Suppose you plan to use a survey to find out how students in your school feel about permitting seniors to leave campus for lunch.

a. How could you get a random sample? Explain why your method will give you a random sample.

b. Describe a good way to administer the survey, and explain why your method will not result in any bias.

MORE

Modeling • Organizing • Reflecting • Extending

Modeling

1. Critique the survey reported in the article below, based on the issues identified on page 117. Also, identify any possible sources of bias in the survey.

Nicolet High School
Alumni suggest emphasis on job-seeking skills

By David Thome of The Journal Staff

Glendale—Five years after leaving Nicolet High School, most graduates say they were well-prepared for college and work, but would have liked more information on conducting job interviews and on which jobs had the best prospects.

The school's second five-year survey of graduates also indicates that while former students felt they have developed good work habits at Nicolet, more than half changed their career plans since graduation.

Associate Principal Mike Salkowski said some courses and activities will be refined to address deficiencies identified by the grads. Guidance counselors, for example, will be asked to provide more information on which careers are likely to have more or fewer opportunities in the future.

About a fourth of all grads from the classes of 1986 and '87 responded to surveys the school sent out in 1991 and '92.

More than 80% of respondents from both classes said at Nicolet they learned to work well with others, solve problems, accept responsibility and meet deadlines.

"I'm glad they gave high marks to 'problem solving' and 'working with others,'" Salkowski said. "People who do hiring tell us that those things are very much on their minds. The days of working in your own cubicle on your own, narrow things are gone."

He said that he was surprised that three-fourths of the responding grads said they hadn't received enough information on job interviewing and resumes.

Since 1987, however, Nicolet had added classes and other activities that emphasize job-seeking skills, including a simulated job interview for all sophomores.

Salkowski said he also was intrigued that only 42% of the '87 grads were working in or studying toward the same career they planned on in high school. While there's no way to determine whether 42% is high or low compared with other high schools, Salkowski said he would be concerned if the figure dropped in subsequent years.

Half of the '86 grads said in their five-year study that they had the same career plans as they had during high school. Salkowski noted that the state of the economy may have caused part of the difference.

According to the five-year surveys:

- 38% of '87 and 43% of the '86 grads still were in school after five years.
- 62% of '87 grads had full-time jobs after five years, compared with 52% of '86 grads.
- 19% of the Class of '87 and 18% of the Class of '86 have gone to graduate school.
- 63% of '87 grads and 60% of '86 grads felt Nicolet offered adequate instruction in using computers

Source: *Milwaukee Journal*, December 15, 1993.

128 UNIT 2 • MODELING PUBLIC OPINION

APPLY **individual task**

On Your Own

a. If you get a numbered list of students and randomly generate numbers to select a sample, then you will get a simple random sample. Students might explain how chance has been used to make the selection, not convenience or self-selection. Be sure that students do not consider a random sample to be one that is "accidental," such as selecting the first 10 students they meet when walking at random through the halls. (Some students will spend more time in particular areas of the school.) Also be sure that they do not think giving the survey to their friends produces results that can be generalized to all students.

b. Students may suggest using phone, mail, in-person interviews or handing out a written survey. They should avoid sources of bias like poor wording, poor interview methods, and high nonresponse rates. Thus, for example, the questions should be worded carefully, the survey should be administered so that all responses are confidential, and every effort should be made to get a response from every person in the random sample.

Unit 2

MORE **independent assignment**

Modeling

1.
- **Issue of interest:** The surveys were designed to find out what graduates were doing and how satisfied they were with their high school education.
- **Sponsor:** Nicolet High School
- **Population:** The population is all graduates of Nicolet High School from the classes of 1986 and 1987 after they had been out of school for five years.
- **Sample selection:** The sample is the same as the population. The survey was sent to everyone in the population, so this was actually an attempt to take a census.
- **Sample size:** The sample is the same as the population.
- **Nonresponse:** There was a 75% nonresponse rate.
- **Exact questions:** The exact questions were not given.
- **Method of obtaining responses:** Nicolet High School sent out surveys to all graduates after they had been out for five years.
- **Bias:** There could have been bias as a result of the nonresponse. Nonresponse is an important factor here, because those who returned the surveys might be those who felt they owed something to their high school because it did a relatively good job preparing them. The 80% of those who said they learned to work well with others, to solve problems, and to meet deadlines actually represents less than a fourth of the graduates. The other 75% who did not respond might have opposing views. Since the exact questions were not given, we cannot judge if they could have caused bias.

MORE
ASSIGNMENT *pp. 128–134*

Modeling: 2 and choice of one*
Organizing: 2 and choice of one*
Reflecting: Choose one*
Extending: Choose one*

**When choice is indicated, it is important to leave the choice to the student.*
NOTE: *It is best if Organizing tasks are discussed as a whole class after they have been assigned as homework.*

2. **a.** The federal job survey was revised because the Bureau of Labor Statistics (BLS) wanted to get a more accurate estimate of unemployment. The BLS claimed that the 1993 survey was biased, resulting in an unemployment rate that was too low. The BLS said it has improved definitions of what it means to be laid off, working part-time, and too discouraged to look for work. The new survey also more accurately counts women as part of the workforce.

   An example was given of how one key question was reworded. The BLS says that the current question leads some women to classify themselves as homemakers even though they may also be working for pay or looking for work. Certainly, the question would seem to have that effect, particularly because of the phrase "most of last week." If a woman was keeping house most of the week but also did some work for pay, she would still classify herself as "keeping house." It takes a bit more reasoning to see why this would bias the results toward a jobless rate that is too low.

   The key point is that homemakers are not considered part of the workforce, but those who work for pay or profit are considered part of the workforce. Consider this hypothetical scenario: Suppose 2 out of 8 people in the workforce are jobless. This yields a 25% jobless rate. Suppose that by using the new question, 2 women who were previously categorized as homemakers answer "yes" to the new question and thus are now considered part of the workforce. So now the workforce is 10 people. The women added to the workforce in this way are probably more likely to be looking for work and, therefore, be classified as jobless. The jobless rate could go up to 3 out of 10 or 4 out of 10, resulting in a rate that is higher than the original 25% rate. The new question should remove the bias and increase the jobless rate.

   b. Students might list things like how the survey is administered, what is the response rate, more clarification on the questions asked, and more explanation of the conclusions claimed.

2. Carefully read the article below.

Federal job survey revised

By Mark Memmott

Washington—The nation's unemployment rate could jump next year, when the Bureau of Labor Statistics changes the way it collects information on unemployment.

Tests indicate BLS' estimate of the jobless rate might rise half a percentage point in January, compared with December, because of revisions in its monthly survey of 60,000 households. The unemployment rate now is 6.8%. BLS will report the January rate Feb. 4.

There's also a chance the rate might not rise at all. Despite the test results, "we want to make it very clear we really have no idea what will happen" to the January estimate, says Jack Bregger, assistant BLS commissioner.

No matter what happens, investors and the public must realize "it's not a big change, it's not a small change," says BLS Commissioner Katharine Abraham. "It's a different measurement based on a redefined survey. You can't compare it to the old numbers."

BLS has been working since 1986—and has spent $40 million—on its first major change in the unemployment survey since 1967. The goal is a more accurate estimate of unemployment. BLS says it has improved definitions of what it means to be laid off, working part time and too discouraged to look for work.

The revisions won't affect BLS' monthly survey of businesses, from which it estimates the number of jobs on payrolls.

Abraham and other top BLS officials said Tuesday that a September '92 through August '93 test of the new survey showed the average jobless rate those 12 months was 7.6%. Average based on the current survey: 7.1%. A major reason for the difference, BLS says, is that the new survey more accurately counts women as part of the labor force.

BLS says the current survey leads some women to classify themselves as homemakers even though they may also be working outside the home or looking for work. By including those women as part of the would-be workforce, the new survey raised the average jobless rate for women over the 12-month test to 6.8%, from the current survey's 6%.

Katharine Abraham
(Photo by Tom Horan, GPN)

Source: *USA Today*, November 17, 1993.

Change ends homemaker bias

A key question will be reworded to avoid steering women toward saying they are "keeping house":

Current question

What were you doing most of last week?

- Working or something else?
- Keeping house or something else?
- Going to school or something else?

New question

Last week, did you do any work for either pay or profit?

a. How was the federal job survey revised? Why was the revision considered necessary?

b. The article does not fully describe the federal job survey. What additional information do you think is needed in order to completely understand the survey?

LESSON 2 • SURVEYS AND SAMPLES 129

3. Examine each of the following survey situations. Do you think the survey design is biased? Explain your reasoning in each case.

a. The following question was asked on an opinion poll about taxes: "Do you agree that the current high tax structure is excessive?"

b. The following instructions were given for an opinion poll about movies: "Rate the movies 1 to 10, where 1 is best."

c. The survey results were obtained from those who called the network office after hearing the debate on television.

d. To determine the number of people looking for jobs, an interviewer asked survey respondents, "Are you unemployed?"

4. The following is an excerpt from an article in the *Pittsburgh Tribune-Review*.

Teen survey: Freedom—with limits

By Gerard DeFlitch
Tribune-Review

They feel that adults—especially their parents—have been a bit slow in granting the freedom they deserve. They understand the need for some restraints, but plan to be less strict when it comes time to raise their own families. They are the teen-agers of western Pennsylvania, and a survey shows them to be in general agreement with but slightly more conservative than the average American youth.

More than 250,000 of their peers in grades six through 12 participated in the survey, whose central question was: "Do you have enough freedom?" The poll was conducted by USA Weekend magazine and the Sunday newspapers—including this one—that carry it each week. Results of the national survey, detailed in today's issue of the magazine, provide a fascinating look at a subject of extreme importance to these almost-adults.

Just as fascinating are the responses from teens who read the Tribune-Review. Nationally, 47 percent say they don't have enough freedom, 37 percent say they have the right amount, and 16 percent say they have too much. Among 107 Tribune-Review respondents 45 (42 percent) say they have the right amount, 34 (32 percent) say they don't have enough, and 28 (26 percent) say they have too much.

Source: Gerard DeFlitch, *Pittsburgh Tribune-Review*, May 4, 1997.

a. What is the population for the survey?

b. Does the excerpt indicate how the sample was selected?

c. How could the surveyors have selected a simple random sample?

130 UNIT 2 • MODELING PUBLIC OPINION

3. a. This survey design is biased because the question is worded in a way that promotes "yes" answers. By saying that the tax structure is high, it is more likely that respondents will say that it is excessive.
   b. No apparent bias.
   c. Bias may be introduced by the sampling process since usually only people who have a special interest or who feel strongly about their point of view will call. Others will not be represented.
   d. This survey design is biased since the question asked will probably produce systematic deviation from the truth. This is because the question asked does not clearly address the objective of determining the number of people looking for jobs. When asked, "Are you unemployed?", someone might say "yes" and yet not be looking for a job. On the other hand, someone could answer "no" and be looking for a job.
4. a. Two populations are discussed: American teenagers in grades 6 through 12 and the portion of those students living in western Pennsylvania (whose household reads the *Pittsburgh Tribune-Review*).
   b. The sample consisted of more than 250,000 students nationwide and 107 students in the region. The article does not indicate how the sample was selected. However, because the survey was sponsored by the newspapers and the excerpt refers to "*Tribune-Review* respondents," it's likely that the survey was printed in the newspaper and readers were asked to mail completed surveys.
   c. The surveyors could have generated a numbered list of all students in the target population and then generated a random number for each student to be surveyed. This is impractical for a large population like the nationwide population. Students may suggest randomly selecting a certain number of school districts and then randomly selecting students from those districts. Although this is a type of random sampling, it does not generally yield a simple random sample, because differences in district sizes make it more difficult to ensure that each group in the nation has an equal chance of being chosen. Furthermore, using this method it would be impossible to select a group that contained students from more districts than the number randomly selected.

Master 50

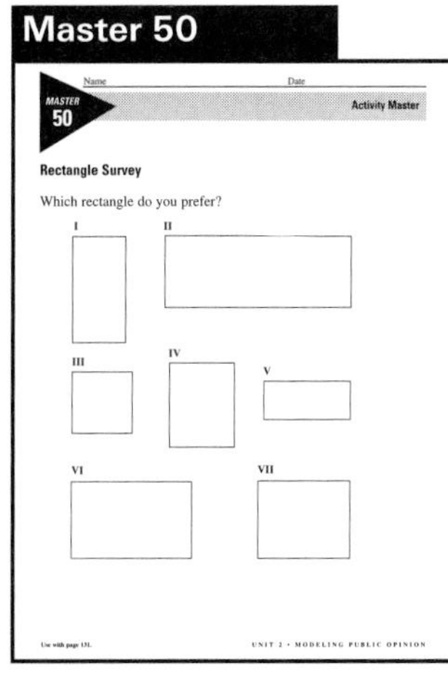

MORE *continued*

Organizing

1. **See Teaching Master 50.**

   The set of rectangles contains one rectangle (VI) that is made using the golden ratio. That is, the ratio of length to width is about $\frac{1 + \sqrt{5}}{2}$. This ratio seems to be found in nature in such places as the chamber of the nautilus snail, as well as in some works of art and architecture. The question of interest is whether people actually prefer rectangle VI to any of the others.

   a. Student summaries will vary depending on their particular sample survey. You may want to encourage them to try the survey on a couple of test subjects first to help discover any problems that might arise or any clarification they may need to provide. Those test subjects should not be included in the survey of 40 people. Also, you might encourage students to cut out the rectangles on Teaching Master 50 so that they can be presented each time in a random order.

   b. Respondents could be asked to rank the rectangles in order of preference.

   c. The ratios calculated will be approximate.

   - Rectangle VI has a ratio of about 1.62, which is closest to a golden rectangle.
   - Students should describe any preference they see in their survey for the golden rectangle.

Unit 2

Organizing

1. Below is a group of rectangles.

   a. Show this page to 40 people and ask them: "Which rectangle do you prefer?" Write a brief summary of your survey results.

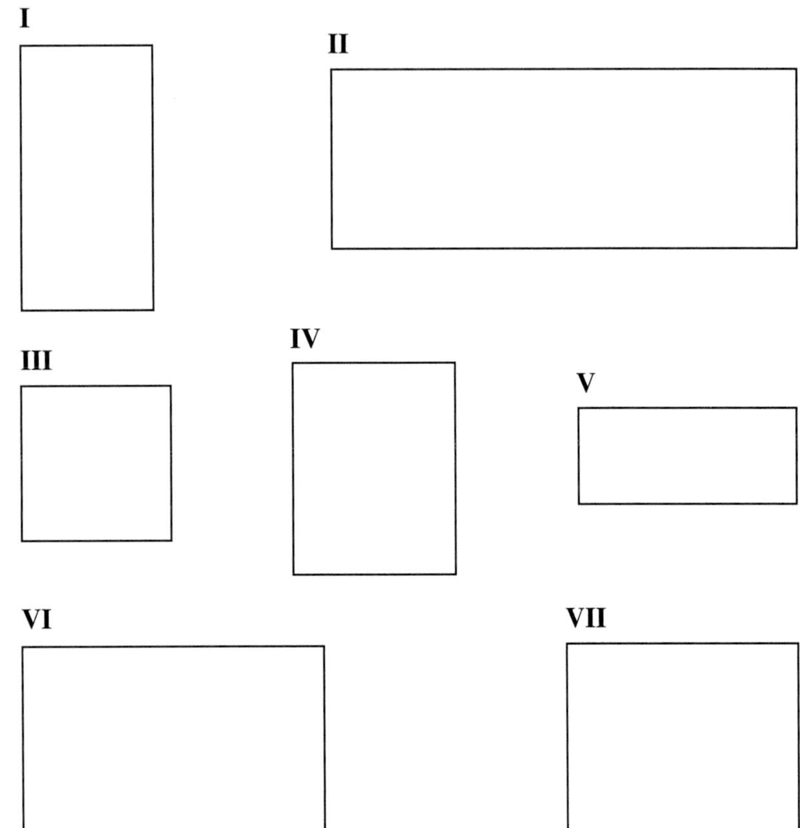

   b. Explain how you would modify the survey so that people could respond by preferential voting.

   c. A **golden rectangle** is a rectangle where the ratio of the length to the width is $\frac{1 + \sqrt{5}}{2}$ or approximately 1.618. Such a rectangle is believed to be one of the most visually pleasing rectangular shapes.

   - Which rectangle on the survey is closest to being a golden rectangle?
   - Is there a relation between the rectangle most preferred in your survey and a golden rectangle?

Unit 2

2. In Activity 1 of Investigation 3 (page 125), you considered the average area of a collection of circles. Think about some characteristics of "average circles."

   a. Does a circle of average radius have average circumference? Justify your answer.

   b. Does a circle of average radius have average area? If so, explain why. If not, give an example of a small collection of circles such that a circle of average radius does not have average area.

3. Examine the news item below entitled, "Small-business help wanted."

Source: *USA Today*, February 20, 1996.

   a. According to the news item, small-business owners were asked what they wanted most in a new employee. What method of voting is indicated by this question and the way the results are reported?

   b. As you discovered in Lesson 1, you can get more information about public opinion if you ask people to rank their choices, rather than just vote for their favorite. Design a questionnaire that you could use to get each person's ranking of the four given employee characteristics: dependability, honesty, good attitude, and competence.

   c. Suppose that the sample consisted of 200 small-business owners and their rankings are summarized in the following preference table.

Employee Characteristics Preference Table

	Rankings				
Dependability	1	1	3	4	4
Honesty	4	3	1	3	3
Good Attitude	3	4	4	1	2
Competence	2	2	2	2	1
Number of Voters	27	43	54	38	38

132 UNIT 2 • MODELING PUBLIC OPINION

2. **a.** Yes. Circumference $C = 2\pi r$, so the circumference of a circle with average radius is given by

$$C = 2\pi r_{avg} = 2\pi\left(\frac{\sum_{i=1}^{n} r_i}{n}\right) = \frac{\sum_{i=1}^{n} 2\pi r_i}{n}$$

which is the average circumference. Students do not need to give a general proof, but they should explain, perhaps illustrating their reasoning using a collection of at least 2 or 3 circles.

b. No. Area $A = \pi r^2$. Suppose you have two circles. One circle has radius 1, and the other has radius 5. Thus, the average radius is 3. Therefore, the area of a circle with average radius is 9π. However, the average area of the two circles is $\frac{\pi + 25\pi}{2} = 13\pi$. Thus, the circle of average radius does not have average area.

3. **a.** Note that the percents sum to 100% and the business owners identified what they wanted *most*. Thus, from the viewpoint of voting, it looks like the respondents were given a list of four choices and were told to vote for their favorite. Then the results were presented as if the plurality method was used. There is certainly no indication of approval or preferential voting.

b. Make a ballot that lists the four choices with a box next to each. The instructions at the top of the ballot should read, "Rank the following four characteristics according to how much you want a new employee to have each characteristic. Indicate your most-valued characteristic with a 1, your next most-valued characteristic with a 2, and so on."

3. c. ■ Dependability–70; Honesty–54; Good Attitude–38; Competence–38. These results match the results shown in the actual clipping.
   ■ Plurality winner–Dependability
   Runoff winner–Honesty
   Points-for-preferences winner (using points 4-3-2-1)–Competence
   ■ The pairwise-comparison winner is competence as well. Thus, competence, as the points-for-preferences winner and pairwise-comparison winner, would be a reasonable choice to declare as the characteristic most valued by this hypothetical sample of small-business owners, even though competence has only 19% of the first-preference votes.

Reflecting

1. Students may suggest many different surveys, such as surveys about preferred lunches, different ways to schedule classes and extracurricular activities, number of hours in the school day, or preferred candidates for student government office.
2. Be sure that students discuss key issues, such as population, sample, procedure, sponsor, and bias.
3. In general, when a survey offers several choices and the respondents are asked to give their opinion, preferential voting can provide a way to gather richer data on preferences. Then the sample data can be summarized and the results reported using different analysis methods, such as points-for-preferences or pairwise-comparison. As students discovered in Lesson 1, such an approach can provide a better measure of public opinion than the commonly used method of "vote for your favorite," which is like finding a plurality winner.
4. Students should report that they are more aware of important issues related to surveys and that they have learned to read and analyze reports of surveys more critically.

- How many first-preference votes does each characteristic get? Does this match with the data reported in the news item on the previous page?
- Find the winner using the plurality, runoff, and points-for-preferences methods.
- Which characteristic would you report as the one most valued by the 200 small-business owners in this sample? Give an argument justifying your choice. If you feel it would strengthen your argument, determine the winner using other vote-analysis methods.

Reflecting

1. Think of two examples at school in which it would be useful to give a survey to determine public opinion. In each case, briefly describe the issue of interest and why the survey would be useful.

2. Find an example of a survey on TV, in the newspaper, or on radio. Write a brief summary of the survey which includes a discussion of the key issues you have studied in this lesson.

3. In Lesson 1, you studied voting and methods of vote analysis. In this lesson, you studied surveys and investigated some examples in which vote-analysis methods were used to gather and summarize sample data. Do you think that the use of vote-analysis methods in surveys can improve surveys? Explain your reasoning.

4. The age in which we live has been called the Information Age. We are bombarded with information every day—on TV and the radio, in newspapers, magazines, and books, and on the Internet. Surveys are one common source of information. After having completed this lesson, do you feel that you are a better "consumer" of the information given in surveys? Explain.

Extending

1. Suppose you want to survey your class for some very personal information. If you ask students directly, they might not tell the truth. This would create bias in your survey. Getting honest answers to sensitive questions is a common problem for pollsters. One way to solve this problem is to use a *randomized response technique*.

Unit 2

LESSON 2 • SURVEYS AND SAMPLES 133

Using this technique, the survey designer pairs a sensitive question (to be answered "yes" or "no") with a harmless question, to which the interviewer could not possibly know the answer and which has a known proportion of "yes" responses. For example, the harmless question might be "Is the coin you just (secretly) tossed a head?" When the respondent comes to the sensitive question, he or she secretly rolls a standard die and flips a coin. If the result of the die roll is 1 or 2, then the respondent answers the harmless question about the coin flip. If the result of tossing the die is 3, 4, 5, or 6, then the respondent answers the sensitive question. The interviewer records the number of "yes" answers.

a. Explain why only the respondent knows which question is being answered.

b. Explain why the interviewer does not know the correct answer to either question.

c. Write an equation showing how the proportion of all "yes" responses is related to the proportion of "yes" responses to the sensitive question and to the proportion of "yes" responses to the harmless question.

d. Suppose in a sample of 40 people there were 31 "yes" responses. Estimate the proportion of "yes" responses to the sensitive question.

2. Write a brief report on the United States Census. You may find a source in a library, call the Bureau of the Census in Washington, D.C., or find the information on the Internet. Your report should include answers to the following questions as well as any other interesting facts you find.

a. How often is the Census given?

b. When did the Census start and why?

c. What is done with the information collected by the Census?

d. What questions does the Census ask?

e. Explain why a census may be biased because of nonresponse.

3. Select a topic that is of interest to students at your school. Write a question about the topic in a way that you think will cause bias. Then rephrase the question in a way that you think will cause bias in a different direction. Give each question to at least 30 different people. Collect responses and compare the results. Did the difference in wording have the effects you thought it would? Explain.

134 UNIT 2 • MODELING PUBLIC OPINION

Assessments 49–50

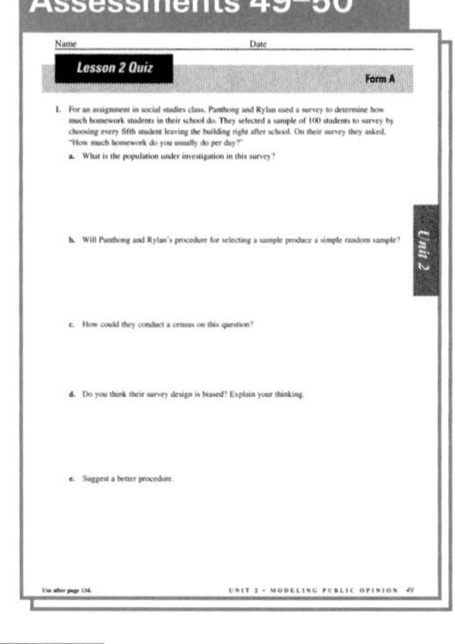
Lesson 2 Quiz

Form A

Extending

1. **a.** The question is determined by a secret die roll, and only the respondent knows the result of the roll.

   b. The respondent secretly chooses, based on the die roll, which question to answer honestly. Since the coin flip is also secret, the interviewer does not know the correct answer to either question before the respondent answers. Even when the respondent does answer either "yes" or "no," the interviewer has no way of knowing to which question the answer refers.

   c. You can determine the proportion of "yes" answers to the sensitive question by solving this equation:

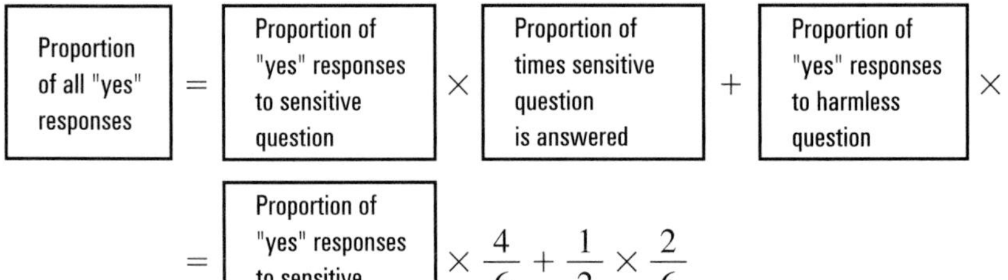

Assessments 51–52

Lesson 2 Quiz

Form B

The "yes" responses refer to either the sensitive question or the harmless question. The harmless question is answered about $\frac{2}{6}$ of the time, because that is the probability of getting 1 or 2 when rolling a die. When the harmless question is answered, about $\frac{1}{2}$ of the answers will be "yes," because that is the probability of getting heads when tossing a fair coin. Thus, the proportion of "yes" answers that refer to the harmless question is $\frac{1}{2} \times \frac{2}{6}$. Similar reasoning applies to the first term on the right-hand side of the given equation, which therefore gives the proportion of "yes" answers that refer to the sensitive question. Adding the two terms together gives the proportion of all "yes" responses.

   d. If p represents the proportion of "yes" answers to the sensitive question, then

$$\frac{31}{40} = \left(p \cdot \frac{4}{6}\right) + \left(\frac{1}{2} \cdot \frac{2}{6}\right)$$

$$p \approx 0.9125$$

An alternate solution is the following: The expected number of "yes" answers to the harmless question is $40 \cdot \frac{1}{2} \cdot \frac{2}{6}$, or about 6.667. So the number of "yes" answers that refer to the sensitive question is approximately 31 – 6.667 or 24.333. This is the number of "yes" answers to the sensitive question, but not all respondents answered the sensitive question. In fact, only $\frac{4}{6} \cdot 40$ or about 26.667 respondents were expected to answer the sensitive question. Thus, the proportion is $\frac{24.333}{26.667}$, or about 0.9125. (Note that the proportion of "yes" responses to the sensitive question is not equal to $\frac{24.333}{40}$, as some students may report.)

2. **Reports should include the following, but students are not limited to this information:**

   a. The Census is taken every 10 years in the "0" years.

   b. The Census was mandated by the United States Constitution because the number of people in a state determines the number of people a state can have in the House of Representatives. The first Census was taken in 1790.

See additional Teaching Notes on page T168F.

Master 51

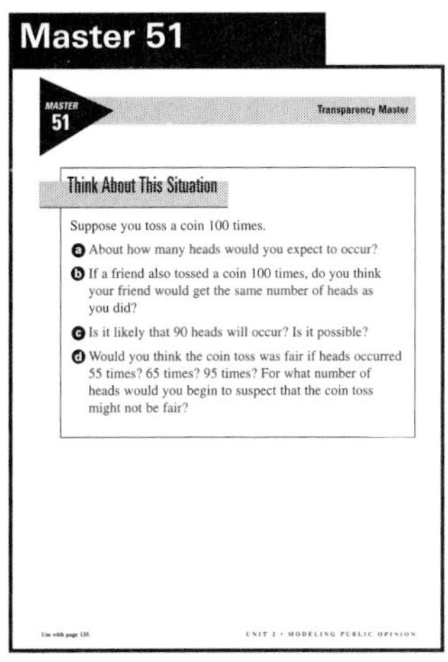
MASTER 51

Transparency Master

Think About This Situation

Suppose you toss a coin 100 times.

a. About how many heads would you expect to occur?

b. If a friend also tossed a coin 100 times, do you think your friend would get the same number of heads as you did?

c. Is it likely that 90 heads will occur? Is it possible?

d. Would you think the coin toss was fair if heads occurred 55 times? 65 times? 95 times? For what number of heads would you begin to suspect that the coin toss might not be fair?

Use with page 135.

UNIT 2 • MODELING PUBLIC OPINION

Unit 2

Lesson 3 Sampling Distributions: From Population to Sample

LESSON OVERVIEW In the last lesson, students learned to analyze surveys critically. They learned some of the important issues related to surveys, such as bias, random sampling, and some connections to voting methods. One key idea they have yet to learn about is *margin of error*. Margin of error was mentioned in many of the surveys students read in Lesson 2, and now they will begin to learn what it means. To arrive at an understanding of margin of error, students first learn about sampling distributions. Then in Lesson 4, they apply their knowledge of sampling distributions to study confidence intervals and margin of error.

The main goal of a survey is to use information collected from a sample to make inferences about the whole population. One way such inferences are stated is through the use of *confidence intervals*. When making population inferences, you are working "from sample to population." However, the first step in studying confidence intervals is, in essence, to reverse this process. In order to understand confidence intervals, students must first understand *sampling distributions*. To create a sampling distibution, the population parameter must be known; you construct the distribution of a statistic that estimates the known parameter. Thus, with sampling distributions, in a sense, you are working from the population to a sample.

Students will investigate random samples of a given size drawn from a given population. They will compute different sample outcomes from these samples, such as sample total, sample proportion, and sample percent. They will study the sampling distributions of these sample outcomes. (Such sampling distributions are the focus of this lesson.) They will construct a type of box plot, called a *90% box plot*, that summarizes some of the characteristics of a sampling distribution. In particular, the 90% box plots will be used to define what is meant by a likely sample outcome. Based on the idea of likely sample outcome, students will construct and apply confidence intervals in Lesson 4.

The development of ideas in this lesson is as follows: First establish a criterion for deciding whether a sample outcome is likely. The use of 90% box plots helps students make these decisions quickly. Then investigate 90% box plots in situations with different population percents and different sample sizes. Finally, combine these box plots into charts, which will be used in the next lesson to construct confidence intervals.

Lesson Objectives

- To use a known population parameter to construct a sampling distribution for a sample statistic, particularly the sampling distribution of a sample proportion
- To use simulation to construct a simulated sampling distribution and summarize the results with a 90% box plot

See additional Teaching Notes on page T168G.

Lesson 3

Sampling Distributions: From Population to Sample

Unit 2

Perhaps you've wondered about the "margin of error" that is reported in many of the surveys you have read about. Or maybe you're wondering how a pollster can make such precise claims about an entire population based on just a sample from that population, even if the sample is random, the sample size is large, the questions are worded well, and the survey design is unbiased, in general. These are important things to wonder about! In the next two lessons, you will develop the mathematics needed to relate samples to populations. This mathematics will allow you to model public opinion more effectively.

The first step is to understand both how likely a sample outcome is and how much variability there is among samples. You may have noted this type of variability in your exploration of distributions in "Simulation Models" from Course 1 and "Patterns in Chance" from Course 2. In this lesson, you will investigate proportions and totals obtained from samples and study the likelihood and variability of those sample outcomes. You will begin by considering experiments involving tossing a coin.

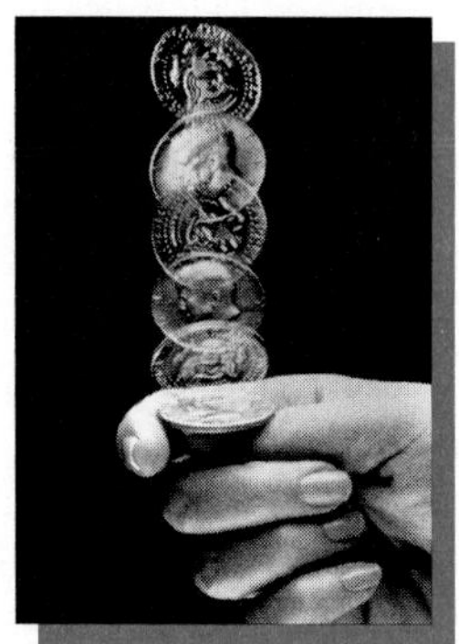

Think About This Situation

Suppose you toss a coin 100 times.

a About how many heads would you expect to occur?

b If a friend also tossed a coin 100 times, do you think your friend would get the same number of heads as you did?

c Is it likely that 90 heads will occur? Is it possible?

d Would you think the coin toss was fair if heads occurred 55 times? 65 times? 95 times? For what number of heads would you begin to suspect that the coin toss might not be fair?

LESSON 3 • SAMPLING DISTRIBUTIONS: FROM POPULATION TO SAMPLE 135

INVESTIGATION 1 Is It Likely or Unlikely?

One way to understand the likelihood and variability of sample outcomes is to examine the *sampling distribution*. A **sampling distribution** is the distribution of the outcomes from all possible samples of the same size taken from a given population.

1. Consider an experiment in which you toss a coin 50 times and record the number of heads. Tossing the coin 50 times is like taking a sample of size 50 from the population of all possible coin tosses. For this experiment, the number of heads in 50 tosses is the sample outcome of interest.

a. In general, how many heads would you expect to get in 50 tosses?

b. Work together in your group to toss a coin 50 times and record the number of heads.

c. Describe how you could simulate this experiment using random numbers. Each member of your group should simulate the experiment two times using a random number generator or a table of random digits. Remember that one experiment consists of tossing a coin 50 times and counting the number of heads. Record your results.

d. Pool the results of this simulation from all groups, and make a number line plot of the number of heads in 50 tosses. Describe this simulated sampling distribution.

e. Which outcomes are most likely? Where do these outcomes appear in the number line plot? Which outcomes are very unlikely? Where do the unlikely outcomes appear in the number line plot?

2. Another class performed this experiment of tossing a coin 50 times and recording the number of heads. They repeated the experiment 60 times. The plot at the right shows the observed distribution of the number of heads in the 60 samples.

a. Describe how this simulated sampling distribution is similar to and different from the distribution your class constructed in Activity 1. Explain why your class did not get exactly the same sample outcomes as this class.

b. What numbers of heads are unlikely? Where do the unlikely outcomes appear in the distribution? Where do the likely outcomes appear?

Number of Heads	Number of Samples
18	◆◆
19	◆
20	◆◆◆
21	◆◆◆◆◆
22	◆◆◆◆
23	◆◆◆
24	◆◆◆◆◆◆
25	◆◆◆◆◆◆◆◆
26	◆◆◆◆◆◆◆
27	◆◆◆◆◆◆◆◆◆
28	◆◆◆◆
29	◆◆
30	◆◆◆◆
31	◆◆

136 UNIT 2 • MODELING PUBLIC OPINION

EXPLORE small-group investigation

INVESTIGATION 1 Is It Likely or Unlikely?

In this investigation, students explore what it means for the outcome of a sample to be considered "likely." Roughly, the criterion for "likely" is that the outcome falls in the middle 90% of the sampling distribution. First, students construct simulated sampling distributions, then they represent the distributions with 90% box plots, and finally they recognize that likely outcomes are those that are in the 90% box.

While students are collecting the results of many experiments, each of which consists of tossing a coin 50 times, you can set up a chart on the board to display accumulated data. It is worthwhile to set up the chart so that it shows all possibilities from 0 heads to 50 heads, even though the data will be concentrated in the middle. By the end of Activity 2, students should have established that the sampling distribution is centered around the expected number of heads. They may disagree about classifying specific samples as unlikely; if this happens, they will probably be ready for a fixed criterion. To help students become familiar with the vocabulary "sampling distribution," you can connect the words to more colloquial language as you circulate. For example, you might say, "How did your samples turn out? Show me your sampling distribution." "What were the fewest and greatest numbers of heads? Was your sampling distribution spread evenly between this minimum and maximum?" "What shape is your sampling distribution? What does this say about how the samples turned out?" "If you drew a histogram of the frequency table in Activities 1 and 2, how should you label the axes? From the histogram, what can you say about how the sample statistic is distributed?"

1. a. You would expect to get 25 heads in 50 tosses.

b. Students should record the results of 50 consecutive tosses.

c. Be sure students realize that one experiment consists of tossing a coin 50 times and recording the number of heads. One experiment is *not* just one toss of a coin. An odd random integer could be heads, and an even random number could be tails, or vice versa. Other methods are possible. For example, the following command on a TI-82 or TI-83 calculator will simulate 50 coin tosses, in which 0 is counted as a head and 1 as a tail (or vice versa):

```
seq(iPart(2*rand),X,1,50,1)
```

The rand command gives a random number between (but not including) 0 and 1. Multiplying this result by 2 gives a number between (but not including) 0 and 2. Taking the integer part with the iPart command (or the int command since the number is greater than 0) truncates the number so that it is either 0 or 1. The seq command (under LIST OPS) does this operation 50 times. (The operation is iterated for values of x going from 1 to 50 in steps of 1; there is no x in the calculation, so the same operation is done 50 times.) It is also possible to put this sequence of values into a list and sort the list. Then it is only a matter of highlighting the last zero in the list and noticing its numbered entry in the list. Counting the zeros is not necessary and may introduce errors. A simpler command for the TI-83:

```
randInt(0,1,50)
```

d. The sampling distribution should have more outcomes in the center, around 25, and fewer toward the ends. (See Activity 2, page 136, for a sample plot.)

TECHNOLOGY NOTE: Texas Instruments has developed probability simulation software for the TI-83 Plus. The program is available at the TI calculator Web site: www.ti.com/calc/.

See additional Teaching Notes on page T168G.

Unit 2

2. **c.** Based on this simulated sampling distribution, 35 heads is an unlikely outcome since it is beyond the highest outcome in the distribution. 27 seems to be a likely outcome since it is in the middle of the distribution. 30 heads is a borderline case in which some students might say "likely" and others might say "unlikely." Again, we adopt a precise criterion for "likely" following this activity.

3. **a.** 5% of 60 is 3, so look for the three lowest outcomes. The outcomes of 18 and 19 heads are in the lowest 5% of all outcomes in the distribution. The lower cutoff point for likely outcomes is 20; that is, 20 is considered likely, but outcomes smaller than 20 are considered unlikely. Outcomes of 30 and 31 heads are in the highest 5%. Notice that three outcomes constitute 5% of outcomes and that the three highest outcomes are 31, 31, and 30. But there are several 30s. If all of them are included, then there will be more than 5% in the unlikely range. The cutoff is not clean the way it was for the lower outcomes. The issue then is whether to classify 30 as likely or unlikely. The convention students should use is always to classify "in favor of likely." That is, never have more than 5% of the outcomes be unlikely. In this case, 30 must be the upper cutoff point for likely outcomes; otherwise, there would be six unlikely outcomes, which is more than 5%.

b. The interval of likely outcomes is from 20 to 30 heads, inclusive.

4. **a.** The 90% box plot will look similar to the one below:

Number of Heads	Number of Samples
18	◆◆
19	◆
20	◆◆◆
21	◆◆◆◆◆
22	◆◆◆◆
23	◆◆◆
24	◆◆◆◆◆◆
25	◆◆◆◆◆◆◆◆
26	◆◆◆◆◆◆◆
27	◆◆◆◆◆◆◆◆◆
28	◆◆◆◆
29	◆◆
30	◆◆◆◆
31	◆◆

b. The outcome of 19 heads is classified as unlikely. An outcome of 28 heads is classified as likely.

c. An outcome of 30 heads would be considered likely.

5. Assuming that this is a simulated 90% box plot, about 10% (no more than 10%) of the simulated samples gave outcomes that were outside the interval 3 to 9. Note that numbers on the edge of the box are considered to be within the box and thus are considered likely outcomes. Alternatively, if this is a theoretical 90% box plot (based, theoretically, on all possible samples) or if this is a simulated box plot using a very large number of simulated samples (thereby being essentially identical to the theoretical box plot), then any sample we draw has a 10% chance of being outside the box, that is, outside the interval 3 to 9.

c. If someone else tossed a coin 50 times, do you think 35 heads would be a likely outcome, based on this sampling distribution? Would 27 heads be likely? Would 30 heads?

While working through the previous two activities, you and your classmates probably had some debates about which outcomes should be considered "likely." In fact, there are many reasonable criteria you might use for deciding if an outcome is likely or not. We will adopt a common and useful criterion: from now on, a **likely outcome** is one that occurs in the middle 90% of the sampling distribution. **Unlikely outcomes** are those in the upper or lower 5% of the distribution. Using these definitions, you will be able to analyze surveys and samples systematically, and everyone will get consistent results.

Unit 2

3. Now look back at the distribution in Activity 2.

a. Which outcomes are in the lowest 5% of the distribution? Which outcomes are in the highest 5%? (If there is no clean cutoff point, you should choose a cutoff point that leaves *fewer* than 5% of the outcomes in the unlikely range.)

b. What is the interval of likely outcomes?

4. A useful representation of a sampling distribution that highlights the likely and unlikely outcomes is a modified box plot. Again, refer back to the distribution in Activity 2.

a. Draw a box around the likely outcomes in the distribution. A plot like this is called a **90% box plot**. The likely outcomes are in the box (including the edges of the box), and the unlikely outcomes are those outside the box.

b. Based upon your 90% box plot, is the outcome of 19 heads classified as likely or unlikely? How about an outcome of 28 heads?

c. Suppose the coin-tossing experiment is conducted one more time and 30 heads occur. Based upon your 90% box plot, is this considered a likely or unlikely outcome?

5. Consider the 90% box plot shown below.

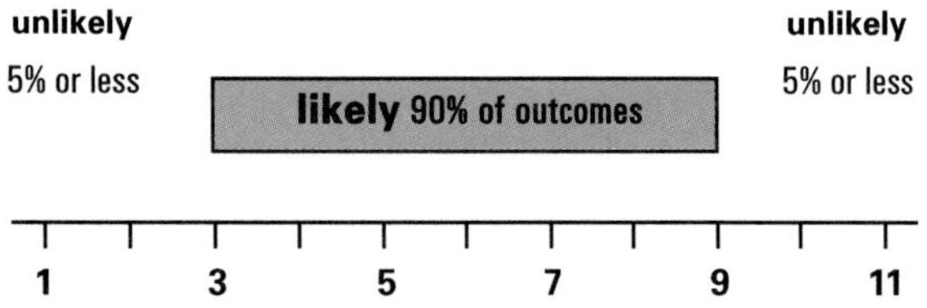

Explain this sentence: "The probability of getting an outcome outside of the interval from 3 to 9 is about 0.1."

LESSON 3 • SAMPLING DISTRIBUTIONS: FROM POPULATION TO SAMPLE 137

6. According to the United States Bureau of the Census, in 1998 approximately 40% of those who purchased sneakers were under 14 years old. (Source: United States Bureau of the Census, *Statistical Abstract of the United States: 2000* (120th edition.) Washington, D.C., 2000.)

   a. What is the population in this situation?

   b. Carry out a simulation of selecting a random sample of 30 people from this population and recording how many are under 14 years old.

   c. Another class simulated 60 samples of size 30 from the population. Each sample represented 30 sneakers buyers. For each of these samples, they recorded the number of buyers under 14 years old. The results are shown in the histogram below. Make a 90% box plot summarizing this simulated sampling distribution.

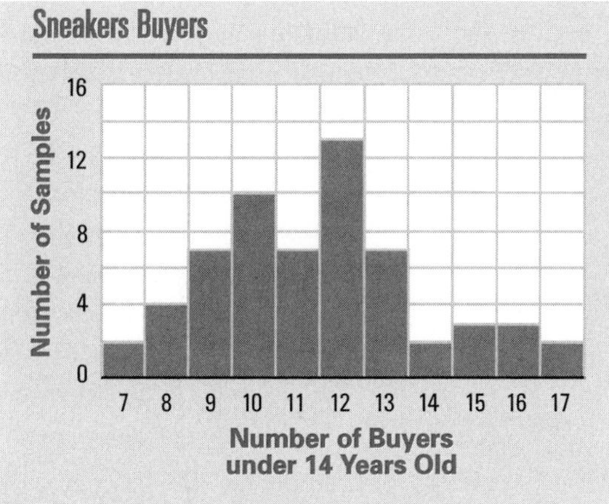

   d. Which sample outcomes are considered likely?

   e. According to this sampling distribution, what percentage of the samples have more than 16 buyers under 14 years old?

   f. Suppose a friend reports that he sampled 30 sneakers buyers and found that only 7 were under 14 years old. According to your 90% box plot, is this a likely outcome? Suppose you suspect that this outcome did not occur simply due to chance. List several reasons that might account for this unusually low sample outcome.

138 UNIT 2 • MODELING PUBLIC OPINION

6. **a.** The population is all people who purchased sneakers in 1998.

b. Responses may vary. One way would be to choose 30 random numbers, each an integer between 1 and 5 inclusive. Numbers 1 and 2 could correspond to people under 14 years old, since this would be $\frac{2}{5}$ or 40% of the 5 different possible random numbers. Numbers 3, 4, and 5 could correspond to people 14 years old or older.

c. Sneaker Buyers

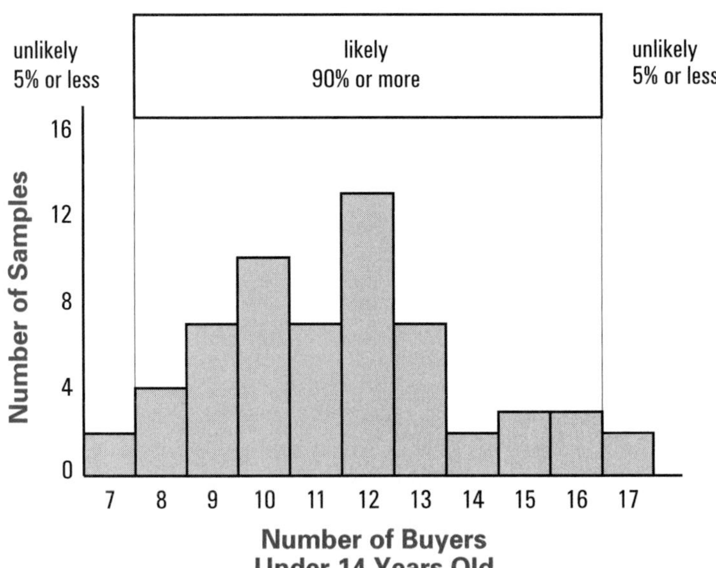

d. Sample outcomes of 8 to 16 sneakers buyers under 14 years old are considered likely.

e. In this sampling distribution, only 2 samples have more than 16 buyers under 14 years old, which is about 3.3% of the total number of sample outcomes.

f. An outcome of 7 is unlikely, based on this 90% box plot. Even though unlikely, it is a possible result that could have occurred just by chance. On the other hand, some reasons that might account for this unusually low number are the following:
The survey was done while school was in session.
The survey was done while many young people were away at a community track meet.
The survey was done during curfew hours.
The sample was not a simple random sample.

Master 52

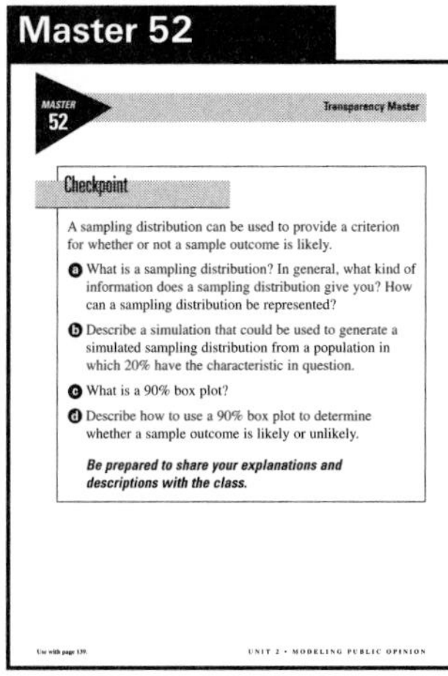
MASTER 52

Transparency Master

Checkpoint

A sampling distribution can be used to provide a criterion for whether or not a sample outcome is likely.

(a) What is a sampling distribution? In general, what kind of information does a sampling distribution give you? How can a sampling distribution be represented?

(b) Describe a simulation that could be used to generate a simulated sampling distribution from a population in which 20% have the characteristic in question.

(c) What is a 90% box plot?

(d) Describe how to use a 90% box plot to determine whether a sample outcome is likely or unlikely.

Be prepared to share your explanations and descriptions with the class.

Use with page 139.

UNIT 2 • MODELING PUBLIC OPINION

Unit 2

SHARE AND SUMMARIZE full-class discussion

Checkpoint

See Teaching Master 52.

(a) Students should be able to state the basic idea of a sampling distribution, that it is the distribution of the outcomes from all possible samples. More precisely, a (theoretical) sampling distribution is the distribution of the outcomes from all possible samples of the same size from the same population. As students work with standard box plot charts in Investigation 3, you should help them see the difference between the theoretical sampling distribution, based on all possible samples, and the *simulated* sampling distributions they constructed by simulating some samples.

Another point you may need to clarify is the difference between a sampling distribution and a 90% box plot. A 90% box plot is not the sampling distribution; rather it is a graphical way to summarize and represent some of the information in a sampling distribution. A sampling distribution can be represented, for example, by a histogram or a number line plot. A sampling distribution gives information about how the sample outcomes are distributed, including for example, the center of the distribution, the spread, or any outliers.

(b) Find a random process that has a 20% chance of one outcome, corresponding to an individual in the population having the characteristic, and an 80% chance of another outcome, corresponding to an individual not having the characteristic. (For example, use a calculator or computer to generate random numbers between 1 and 10; let a 1 or 2 represent an individual with the characteristic and the numbers 3–10 represent an individual that does not have the characteristic.) Then, simulate drawing a random sample of a particular size from the population by repeating the process the appropriate number of times. (For our example, generating 30 random numbers would give a sample of size 30.) Simulate many random samples in this way. For each random sample, keep track of the number of individuals in the sample who have the target characteristic. (For our example, this would be the number of 1s or 2s in each sample of 30 numbers.) The distribution of all these sample outcomes is the simulated sampling distribution.

(c) A 90% box plot is a box that contains the middle 90% (or more) of the sample outcomes. More precisely, a 90% box plot is a box, usually drawn above a horizontal scale such that from edge to edge the box spans a range of values that account for the middle 90% of all sample outcomes. Values in the bottom 5% and the top 5% of sample outcomes are not included in the box.

(d) You just look at the horizontal scale to see if the sample outcome is in the 90% box or not.

APPLY individual task

On Your Own

TECHNOLOGY NOTE: You may wish to introduce students to the randBin feature on the TI-83. See the note on page T168H. For this simulation, use randBin(30,.68,1).

a. Since outcomes of more than 24 households are outside the 90% box, the percentage is no more than 5% (although it could be less).

b. These results are likely because the outcome of 23 households is in the likely range.

c. Responses will vary. For example, generate 30 random numbers between 1 and 100, inclusive, and then count the number of occurrences of 1–68. This will be the sample outcome. If the number of occurrences is between 16 and 24, inclusive, then it is considered to be a likely outcome.

Checkpoint

A sampling distribution can be used to provide a criterion for whether or not a sample outcome is likely.

a What is a sampling distribution? In general, what kind of information does a sampling distribution give you? How can a sampling distribution be represented?

b Describe a simulation that could be used to generate a simulated sampling distribution from a population in which 20% have the characteristic in question.

c What is a 90% box plot?

d Describe how to use a 90% box plot to determine whether a sample outcome is likely or unlikely.

Be prepared to share your explanations and descriptions with the class.

Unit 2

On Your Own

In 1999, 68% of United States households had cable television. The following 90% box plot shows the results of simulating a large number of random samples of 30 U.S. households and recording the number in each sample with cable television. (Source: *The World Almanac and Book of Facts 2001*. Mahwah, NJ: World Almanac, 2001.)

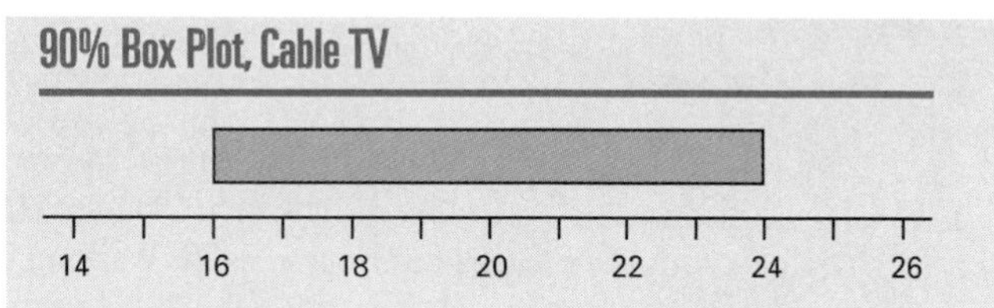

a. About what percentage of samples had more than 24 households with cable television?

b. Suppose you simulated a new random sample of 30 households in this situation and found that 23 have cable television. Are your results likely or unlikely according to the box plot? Explain.

c. Simulate a random sample of 30 households and find the number that have cable television. Describe how you simulated your sample outcome. Based on the 90% box plot, is your sample outcome likely or unlikely?

LESSON 3 • SAMPLING DISTRIBUTIONS: FROM POPULATION TO SAMPLE 139

INVESTIGATION 2 Box Plot Charts for a Fixed Sample Size

In Investigation 1, you learned how to classify sample outcomes as likely or unlikely. You found that a 90% box plot is a convenient way to summarize a sampling distribution in terms of the likely and unlikely sample outcomes. You investigated situations involving a variety of sample sizes and populations. In this investigation, you will systematically study 90% box plots of likely sample outcomes for samples of size 30, taken from different populations.

1. Divide Parts a, b, and c below among groups in your class. For your assigned part, do the following.

- Design a simulation to model the given situation, conduct the simulation 60 times, and construct a 90% box plot. It may be helpful to use special functions on a graphing calculator or software like the SIMBOX option of the *Sampling* calculator software.

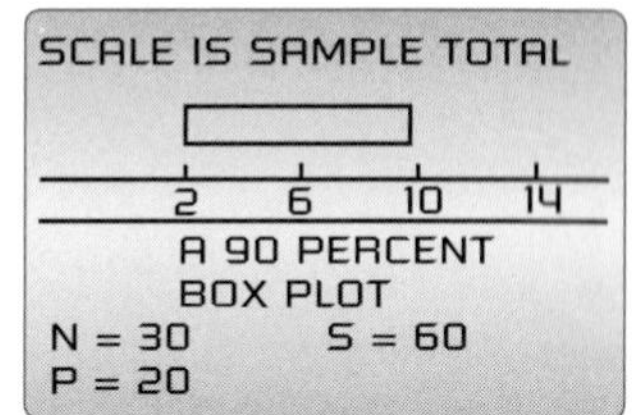

- Use the box plot to answer the given question.
- If you use software or a special function on a calculator, explain what the software or special function does.

a. About 20% of the 1999 U.S. adult population did not have a high school diploma. (Source: U.S. Census Bureau, *Statistical Abstract of the United States*, Washington, D.C., 2000.) In a random sample of 30 U.S. adults taken in 1999, how many people would you be likely to find who do not have a high school diploma?

b. About 20% of the students at a particular school are absent at least 10 days a semester. If you took a random sample of 30 students from this school, about how many would be likely to have been absent at least 10 days last semester?

c. In 1997, about 20% of Americans aged 55 years and older lived in households that had a computer. (Source: U.S. Census Bureau, *Population Profile of the United States: 1999*, Washington, D.C., March 2001.) In a random sample taken in 1997 of 30 Americans aged 55 or older, how many would you be likely to find who lived in a household that had a computer?

2. Compare your answers and box plots from Activity 1 to those of groups that worked on different parts of that activity. Describe and explain the similarities and differences.

140 UNIT 2 • MODELING PUBLIC OPINION

EXPLORE small-group investigation

INVESTIGATION 2 Box Plot Charts for a Fixed Sample Size

In Investigation 1, students explored 90% box plots as a way to classify sample outcomes as likely or unlikely. In this investigation, students will construct 90% box plots "from scratch" using simulation. It is important for students to do this construction so that they get a good understanding of sampling distributions, in general, and 90% box plots, in particular. An important factor to keep in mind when simulating 90% box plots is that the number of samples simulated will generally be rather small thus, the box plot generated will be only an approximation of the actual theoretical box plot. Therefore, while simulated box plots are very useful for developing understanding, they have limited use for answering statistical questions. In Investigation 3, students will use "standard" 90% box plots that are created by theoretical means. The standard box plots will be used in Lesson 4 to construct confidence intervals.

There are two key factors that affect 90% box plots—population percent and sample size. In this investigation, students use a fixed sample size of 30 and examine how 90% box plots vary for different population percents. (In Investigation 3, different sample sizes are explored.)

The goals of Activity 1 are i) to generate many samples and notice how the samples drawn from the same population will vary with respect to how many in a sample have a high school diploma; ii) to summarize this variability with a 90% box plot; and iii) to use the box plot to answer questions about likelihood of outcomes.

The SIMBOX feature of the *Sampling* calculator software quickly simulates up to 99 samples and can display a 90% box plot. For this activity, students should select SIMBOX, enter the sample size *N*, the population percent *P*, and the number of samples *S*.

MAIN MENU
SIMBOX
2:STDBOX
3:BOXCHART
4:INTRODUCTION
5:QUIT

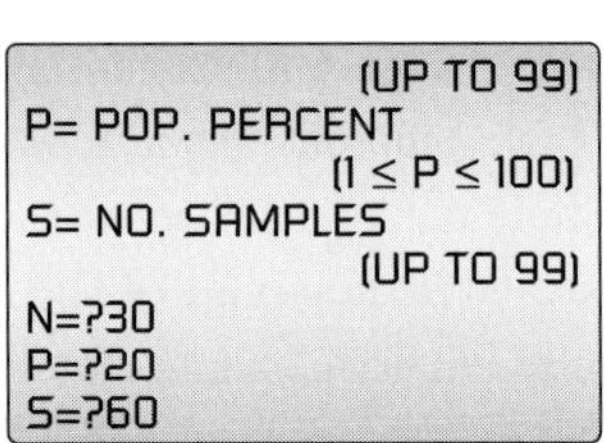

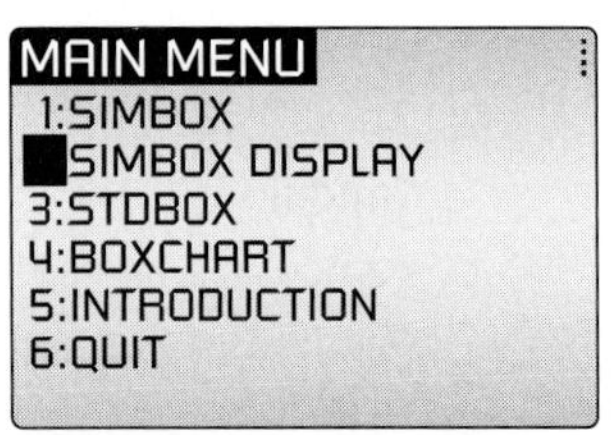

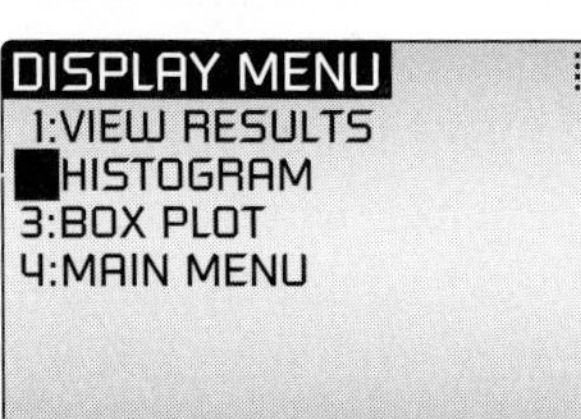

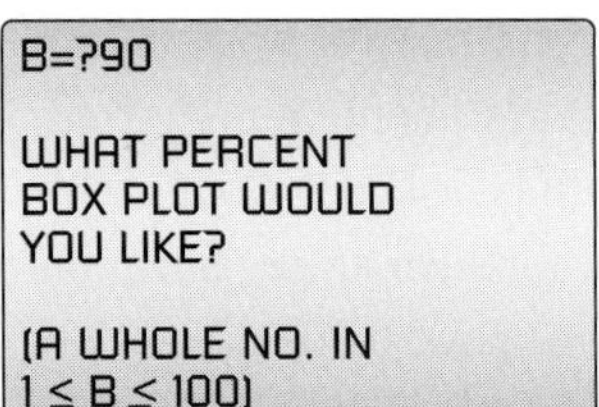

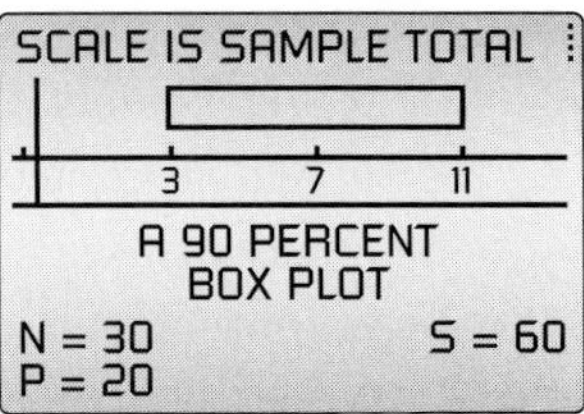

If your students are using TI-83 calculators, you may want to point out the randBin function, located in the MATH PRB menu. For Activity 1, the command would be randBin(30,.2,60).

See additional Teaching Notes on page T168H.

Unit 2

EXPLORE *continued*

For a transition from Activity 2 to Activity 3, you can bring students together to discuss the box plots. Ask if there was anything in the various simulations that would have caused the box plots to be different from each other. Students should focus on the essentials: The underlying probability was the same each time, the sample size was the same each time, and the number of repetitions was the same each time. Random chance was the only mathematical difference among the simulations.

Next, you can ask your students how they think the box plots would change if a different population percent were used. They may be unsure about the effect of changing the population percent. You can take all suggestions and ask for reasons. You do not have to correct all misconceptions at this time, since the next two activities will address this issue.

In Activities 3–6, students construct and use 90% box plots based on various underlying population percents. As students explore, you can use the vocabulary of this lesson to engage them in conversation: "How do you think your 90% box plot will turn out this time? What is the sample outcome of interest that you are recording this time? What probability does your model represent?" You can also check on the mechanics of constructing 90% box plots. Again, you might want to have scales on the board for each group to record its box plot in Activity 3, Part b.

3. You might want to assign subject areas for the groups to study, rather than allowing them to choose for themselves. If you do not have enough groups to complete all areas, you may omit Music, English, Technical Education, and Science (in that order). The remaining percentages will be needed in Activities 4–6. Note that in Part b of this activity, each group will be expected to display a copy of its 90% box plot in the classroom. You might want to announce this in advance so that the groups will be sure to create a large, neat plot.

Subject	Theoretical Likely Range
English	24–29
Mathematics	20–27
Social Studies	17–25
Science	14–22
Foreign Language	11–19
Physical Education	8–16
Technical Education	5–13
Music	3–10
Art	1–6

   a. Results will depend on students' simulations. Theoretical likely ranges are given on the left. Students should construct a simulated 90% box plot by running at least 60 trials. One way to do this, using the subject Mathematics as an example, is as follows. Generate 30 random integers from 1 to 10 and count the number of occurrences of 1–8. This total is the sample outcome. Then repeat this process 60 times. Find the middle 90% of these sample outcomes. The interval spanned by the middle 90% of outcomes gives the simulated 90% box plot. The likely sample outcomes are those outcomes that fall within the interval spanned by the simulated 90% box plot.

   b. The 90% box plots from all the groups should be displayed somewhere in the classroom where all students can easily see them. In Activity 4, students will need to use these box plots. Don't worry about an organized display of the box plots right now. In Activity 5, students will be asked to organize the box plots into a chart, but it's best if they first see the need for such an organization. If they decide to display the plots in some organized manner now, that's great. Otherwise, just get all boxes displayed so that they can be used in the next activities.

4. **a.** Using the box plot for Physical Education courses, you will probably see that it is likely that 15 of these people own a midsize car. Keep in mind that by simulating the box plots, you will get some variability in results. Therefore, sometimes 15 might be classified as an unlikely outcome.

   b. Using the box plot for Social Studies courses, you will probably see that it is unlikely for only 10 out of 30 people to have cable TV service.

   c. Using the box plot for Foreign Language courses, you will probably find that this result is also unlikely.

3. In Activity 1, your class generated 90% box plots for different situations in which the characteristic in question occurred in 20% of the population. Although there was some variability among the box plots, they were all reasonably similar. It will be useful to generate box plots for other population percents. For example, consider the population percents below, showing the portion of students enrolled in each academic area for the 2001–2002 school year at Libertyville High School.

Current Enrollment, Libertyville High

Subject	Percentage
English	90%
Mathematics	80%
Social Studies	70%
Science	60%
Foreign Language	50%
Physical Education	40%
Technical Education	30%
Music	20%
Art	10%

Each group should choose at least one of the subject areas, but make sure that each subject area is covered by at least one group. You can omit Music since you have already worked with situations involving 20% populations. (Your teacher may wish to assign subject areas.)

a. Suppose you take a random sample of 30 Libertyville students and find the number who are enrolled in your chosen subject area. Construct and explain how to use a simulated 90% box plot to find the likely sample outcomes in this situation. Run at least 60 trials of your simulation.

b. Display a copy of your 90% box plot in your classroom.

4. Based on your class's box plots from Activity 3, answer the following questions.

a. Forty percent of all car owners own a midsize car. If you randomly sample 30 car owners, is it likely that 15 of these people own a midsize car?

b. According to the United States Bureau of the Census, about 70% of U.S. households in 2000 had cable TV. (Source: Television Bureau of Advertising, Inc., *Trends in Television*, 2000.) Suppose a random sample of 30 households was taken that year, and only 10 had cable service. Is this surprising?

c. About 50% of the population in 1999 was 36 years or older. (Source: U.S. Census Bureau, *Profile of the United States: 1999*, Washington, D.C., March 2001.) Suppose that in 1999, a random sample of 30 people included only 10 who were 36 years or older. Is this likely?

LESSON 3 • SAMPLING DISTRIBUTIONS: FROM POPULATION TO SAMPLE 141

Unit 2

5. It will be easier to use the box plots that your class has constructed if you organize them all into one chart.

   a. On a copy of the chart below, carefully draw in the box plots that your class constructed so that there is a box plot opposite each population percent indicated on the vertical axis.

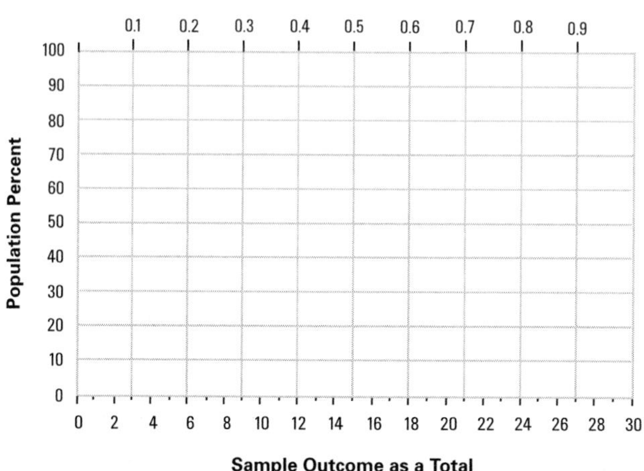

   b. For what size samples can the chart be used?

   c. Describe any patterns you see in the chart.

6. Use the chart from Activity 5 to help answer each of the following questions.

   a. Approximately 10% of the population is left-handed. If 18 of 30 injured people in a hospital ward are left-handed, what conclusions might you draw?

   b. Approximately 50% of all children born are girls. In some communities, newborns are listed in the newspaper. If you took a random sample of 30 newborn children listed in the paper, what would be likely results for the number of girls you would find?

   c. Is 17 a likely sample outcome for a population percent of 40% and a sample size of 30? Explain why or why not.

   d. Eighty percent of all students in a school participate in an extracurricular activity. In a random sample of 30 students from the sophomore class, only 18 students participated in an extracurricular activity. Do you think the sophomores are very different from the rest of the school? Explain why or why not.

142 UNIT 2 • MODELING PUBLIC OPINION

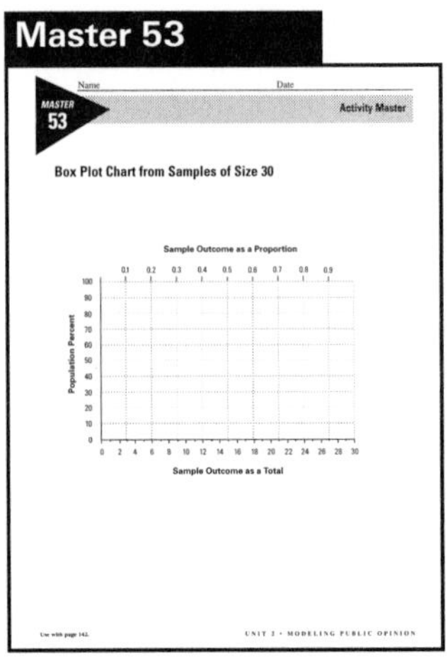

5. **See Teaching Master 53.**
   a. Each student can construct a box plot chart by simply copying the displayed charts from the previous activities onto one like the sample in the text. (Some students may notice that the chart has a scale of "sample outcome as a proportion" on the top. This scale will be studied explicitly in the next investigation, so don't spend time on it now. The "sample outcome as a total" scale is the scale that matches all the work done up to now. In all activities so far, the sample outcome has been the total number of "successes," such as 10 people in the sample who have cable or 25 people who watch at least two hours of TV. Thus, the sample outcome has always been the sample total.)
   b. The chart can be used for samples of size 30.
   c. Students may describe the following patterns: The width of the boxes varies, with larger boxes for population percents close to 50% and smaller ones for more extreme population percents. The approximate center of each box seems to equal 30 × *the population percent.* (However, this is only an approximate relationship. These sampling distributions are not symmetrical except for $p = 0.5$, so the distributions won't be centered at this value. In any case, the simulations will result in some variability.)

You might want to do Activity 6 as a full-class discussion. At this point, you probably have a lot of board space dedicated to the box plots that have been recorded for Activities 1–5. Some students may have trouble relating the questions in Activity 6 to the box plots they have recorded. If they do not make the connection, you can ask them how we would go about setting up a simulation to answer Activity 6, Part a. This should alert them to the fact that this work has already been done in the guise of the sampling distribution of numbers of students in Art classes.

6. **a.** This is an unlikely outcome (too high) for a random sample chosen from a population in which 10% are left-handed. Based on this evidence, you might conclude that left-handed people are more likely to have accidents than right-handed people. Or you might look for some bias in the survey, such as a nonrandom sample, that would cause the survey to give results that tend to be too high.
   b. Assuming the community has the same percentage of girl babies as the population at large, you would be likely to find between 11 and 19 girls. Responses may vary slightly, depending on the simulation results.
   c. No, 17 is not a likely sample outcome, since the likely region is, approximately, from 8 to 16. Answers may vary slightly, depending on the simulation results.
   d. Eighteen students is an unlikely outcome for a random sample drawn from a population in which 80% participate in extracurricular activities; from 20 students to 27 students would be likely. (Again, the 90% box plot you have in your class may be slightly different because it was created using simulation.) Based on this evidence, the sophomores seem to be different from the rest of the school in terms of their participation in extracurricular activities.

Unit 2

Master 54

MASTER 54 Transparency Master

Checkpoint

A 90% box plot provides a useful summary of a sampling distribution.

a Describe how to construct a 90% box plot chart using simulation.

b Describe how 90% box plots change as population percent changes from 0% to 50% and then from 50% to 100%.

c Suppose you toss a coin 200 times and record the number of heads. Describe how you could use simulation to find the likely outcomes in this situation.

Be prepared to share your descriptions and thinking with the entire class.

Use with page 143. UNIT 2 • MODELING PUBLIC OPINION

SHARE AND SUMMARIZE full-class discussion

Checkpoint

See Teaching Master 54.

a To construct a 90% box plot chart, use a random process in which the probability of "success" is the given population percent. Simulate the outcomes from many random samples of a given size using this random process. Find the range where at most 5% of the highest outcomes fall, and find the range where at most 5% of the lowest values fall; these are the unlikely regions. The interval between these regions is the likely interval, which is the interval spanned by the 90% box plot.

b The center of the box of "likely outcomes" moves to the right as the population percent increases. Students might also note that the box is widest for the population percent of 50%, indicating that the variability of the sampling distribution depends on the population percent: It is a maximum when the underlying population percent is 50%, and it is a minimum when the population percent is closest to 0% or 100%. (Since the box plots are the results of student-generated simulations, the pattern in the widths of the "likely" box might not be apparent. You might want to return to this discussion when students have seen standard charts.)

c Since the expected value is 100 heads, some students may suggest that it is more reasonable to estimate with this exact number. However, the key word to focus on here is "likely." Since there is variability in the number of heads in 200 tosses over many trials of 200 tosses and since "likely" has been technically defined in this lesson, a better answer is to estimate with an interval, namely, the interval of likely outcomes. You could construct an approximate interval of likely outcomes by constructing a simulated 90% box plot, as described in Part a.

Another perspective on this question of point estimate versus interval estimate is the following: although you would "expect" to get 100 heads (since that is the mean), the probability of getting exactly 100 heads is quite small (only 0.056). However, by giving an interval around 100 for what we are likely to expect, we can have a high probability of getting a result in that interval.

NOTE: Students may at first describe the 90% interval as either the length or the width of the box (interval). For example, an interval from 3 to 9 can be described as having either width 6 or length 6. The term *width* is used in this unit because that is the more common term in statistics when referring to confidence intervals. If you wish to formalize this idea see Organizing Task 1 on page 150.

APPLY individual task

On Your Own

Students should conduct a simulation using a 85% success rate and many trials. Then they should construct the simulated 90% box plot. The theoretical 90% box plot spans the interval 22 to 28. Student simulated box plots might yield the interval 22 to 28 or something similar.

MORE

ASSIGNMENT *pp. 148–152*

Students can now begin Modeling Task 1 from the MORE assignment following Investigation 3.

See additional Teaching Notes on page T168H.

Checkpoint

A 90% box plot provides a useful summary of a sampling distribution.

a Describe how to construct a 90% box plot chart using simulation.

b Describe how 90% box plots change as population percent changes from 0% to 50% and then from 50% to 100%.

c Suppose you toss a coin 200 times and record the number of heads. Describe how you could use simulation to find the likely outcomes in this situation.

Be prepared to share your descriptions and thinking with the entire class.

On Your Own

In 2001, about 85% of households in the United States had a VCR. (Source: Television Bureau of Advertising, Inc., http://www.tvb.org/tvfacts/index.html.) Suppose you have a random sample of 30 U.S. households taken in 2001, and you find the number of households that have a VCR. Use simulation to find the likely sample outcomes in this situation.

Unit 2

INVESTIGATION 3 Standard Charts for Different Sample Sizes

In the previous investigation, you studied 90% box plots for a variety of population percents, but always with a sample size of 30. Of course, sample sizes will not always be 30! In this investigation, you will explore situations involving different sample sizes.

1. Examine the 90% box plot chart for a sample size of 30 that you constructed in Activity 5 of the last investigation. That chart shows 90% box plots for different population percents, but always with a sample size of 30. How do you think that chart would change if you used a sample size of 20?

LESSON 3 • SAMPLING DISTRIBUTIONS: FROM POPULATION TO SAMPLE 143

2. Standard box plot charts have been made for many different sample sizes. The box plots in the standard charts are constructed using a very large number of simulated samples or using theoretical methods from probability. Below are standard charts for random samples of sizes 20, 40, 80, and 100.

90% Box Plots from Samples of Size 20

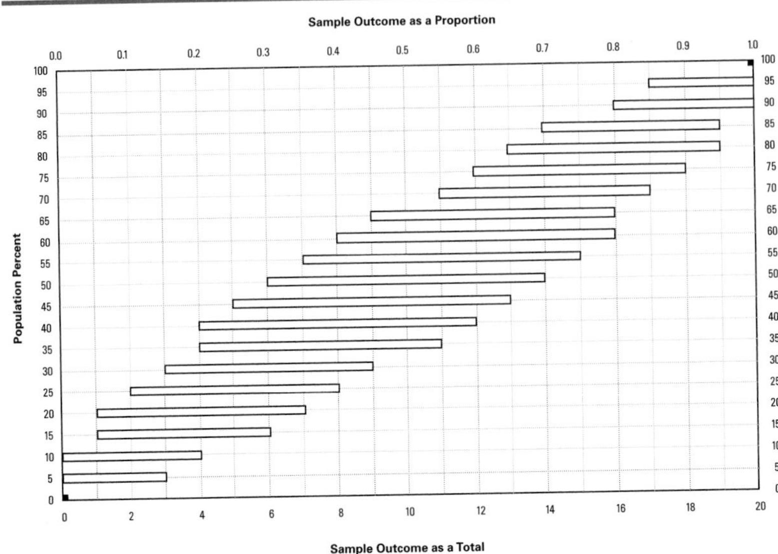

90% Box Plots from Samples of Size 40

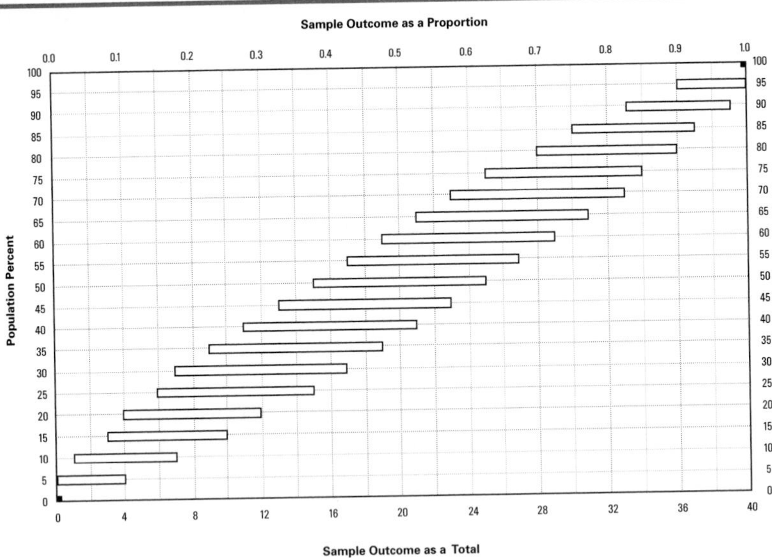

144 UNIT 2 • MODELING PUBLIC OPINION

EXPLORE *continued*

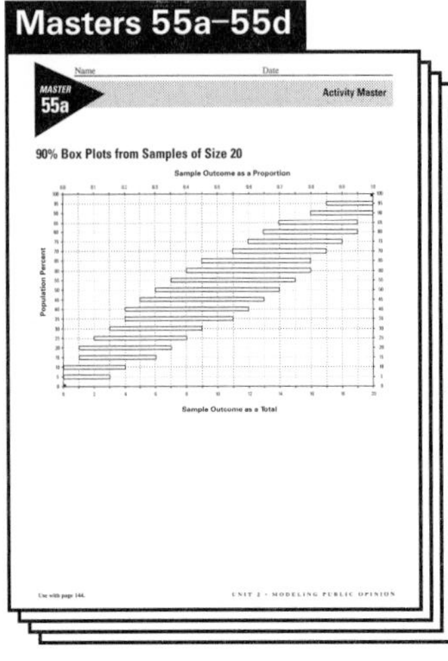

2. **See Teaching Masters 55a–55d.**
Students might describe some of the following patterns. As the sample size increases, the width of the 90% box increases in terms of sample total but decreases in terms of sample proportion. (If students simply say the boxes get smaller, you might want to press them to consider the two scales.) All 90% box plots move to the right as the population increases. For a fixed sample size, the box plot for a 20% population is the same width as the box plot for an 80% population, likewise for a 40% population compared to a 60% population, and so on. Box plots in the center of the chart are wider than those at the edges.

Unit 2

Unit 2

Compare these charts to each other and to the chart you constructed for sample size 30. Describe at least two patterns you see in individual charts or between charts.

90% Box Plots from Samples of Size 80

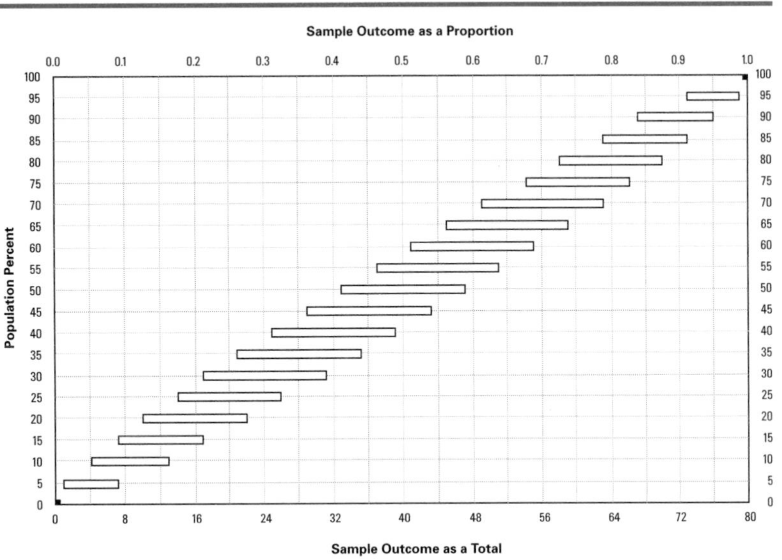

90% Box Plots from Samples of Size 100

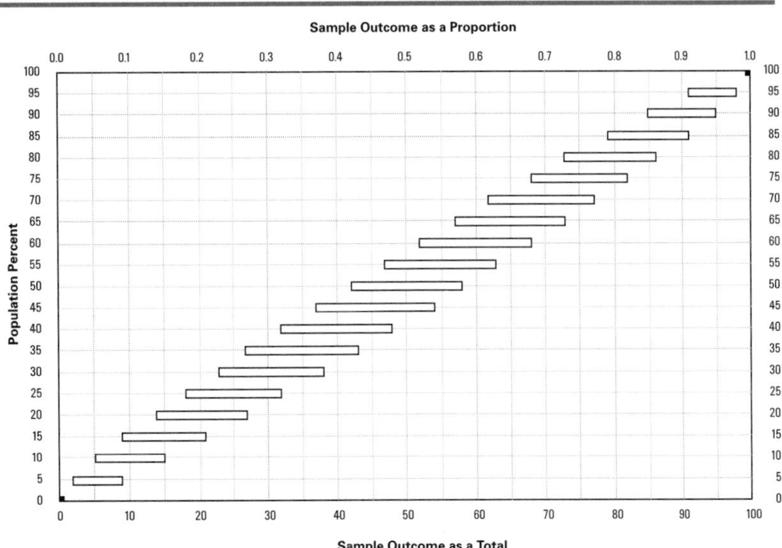

LESSON 3 • SAMPLING DISTRIBUTIONS: FROM POPULATION TO SAMPLE 145

3. Notice that the standard charts have a scale showing sample outcomes as proportions along the top and a scale showing sample outcomes as totals along the bottom.

a. Suppose 80% of students in a school ride the bus to school. Find the interval of likely values for the number of bus-riding students in a random sample of 40 students from that school. Find the interval of likely values for the *proportion* of bus-riding students in a random sample of 40 students.

b. Assume that approximately 10% of the population is left-handed. Suppose you take a random sample of 80 people and find the proportion who are left-handed. What are the likely values for this proportion?

c. Compare the top and bottom scales on the charts for different sample sizes. Explain why, as you go from chart to chart, one of these scales changes while the other does not.

4. In 1999, approximately 20% of all U.S. residents lived in the nine Northeastern states. (Source: U.S. Census Bureau, *Population Profile of the United States: 1999*, Washington, D.C., March 2001.) Assign one person in your group to consider samples of size 20, another to consider samples of size 40, one to consider samples of size 80, and one to consider samples of size 100. Based on your assigned sample size, answer each question below, using the standard 90% box plot charts.

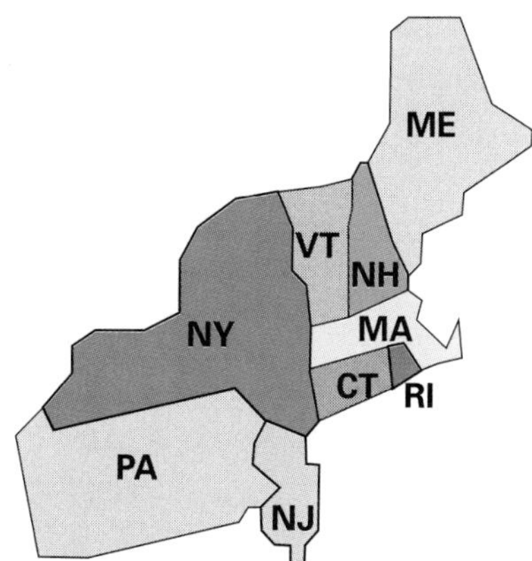

a. In a random sample of U.S. residents in 1999, where the sample size is equal to your assigned sample size, about what *proportion* of people in the sample would be likely to have been living in the northeastern states? Record your sample size and the interval of likely values for the sample proportion.

b. Suppose that 14 people lived in the Northeast in your sample. Is this a likely sample outcome?

c. Compare your answer to Part b to the answers of others in your group. Explain why it makes sense that 14 northeastern residents could be likely for some sample sizes but not for others.

d. Compare your interval in Part a to the intervals of others in your group.

- Describe any patterns you see.
- As the sample sizes get larger, what happens to the width of the 90% box plots? Explain why this relationship makes sense. (To investigate the precise relationship, see Extending Task 3 on page 152.)

146 UNIT 2 • MODELING PUBLIC OPINION

3. a. The interval of likely values for the number of bus-riding students is 28 to 36. The interval of likely values for the proportion of bus-riding students is 0.7 to 0.9.

b. The likely values for the proportion range from 0.05 to 0.1625. (It is not possible to read the proportion 0.1625 directly from the sample proportion of the chart, since the chart is not calibrated finely enough. However, it is possible to read the sample total scale with reasonable accuracy. Thus, you could read the chart to get sample totals of 4 to 13, and then divide these numbers by 80 (the sample size) to get sample proportions of 0.05 to 0.1625.)

c. The "sample outcome as a total" scale shows the different possible values for the total number of "successes" in a sample. The numbers on the "sample outcome as a proportion" scale are found by dividing the sample total by the sample size. The sample total will range from 0 to the sample size, while the sample proportion always ranges from 0 to 1, no matter what the sample size is. The sample outcome can be measured or reported as a total number or as a proportion.

4. a. The intervals of likely values for the sample proportion are given below. (See Activity 3, Part b regarding how to find the sample proportions.)
For samples of size 20: between 0.05 and 0.35 (or from 1 to 7)
For samples of size 40: between 0.10 and 0.30 (or from 4 to 12)
For samples of size 80: between 0.13 and 0.275 (or from 10 to 22)
For samples of size 100: between 0.13 and 0.27 (or from 14 to 27)

b. An outcome of 14 is likely for sample sizes of 80 and 100.

c. Since the rate is about 20% for the whole population, 20% of larger sample sizes will be more than 20% of smaller sample sizes.

d.
- Students may notice patterns based on sample totals or sample proportions. Students may note that the width gets larger as measured by sample totals. This is fine to notice, but ask them to look also at the width in terms of sample proportions.
- As the sample size gets larger, the width of the 90% box plot interval, measured in terms of sample proportions, gets smaller. This is because there is less variability with larger sample sizes. To make a comparison using sample totals that takes into account the differing sample sizes, see Organizing Task 1 on page 150, where the idea of relative width is considered.

Unit 2

Master 56

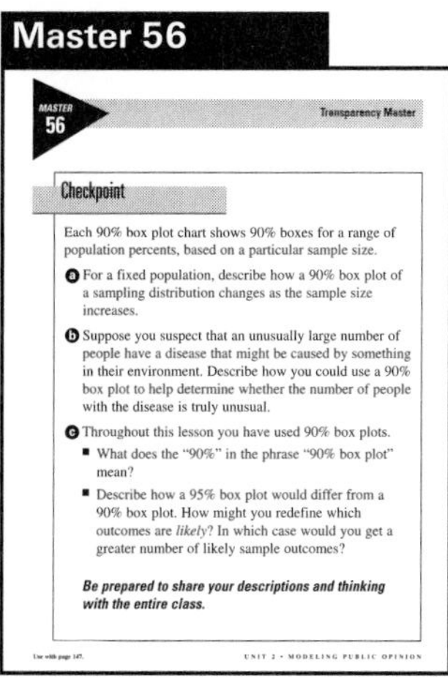

MASTER 56 Transparency Master

Checkpoint

Each 90% box plot chart shows 90% boxes for a range of population percents, based on a particular sample size.

ⓐ For a fixed population, describe how a 90% box plot of a sampling distribution changes as the sample size increases.

ⓑ Suppose you suspect that an unusually large number of people have a disease that might be caused by something in their environment. Describe how you could use a 90% box plot to help determine whether the number of people with the disease is truly unusual.

ⓒ Throughout this lesson you have used 90% box plots.

- What does the "90%" in the phrase "90% box plot" mean?
- Describe how a 95% box plot would differ from a 90% box plot. How might you redefine which outcomes are *likely*? In which case would you get a greater number of likely sample outcomes?

Be prepared to share your descriptions and thinking with the entire class.

Use with page 147. UNIT 2 • MODELING PUBLIC OPINION

Unit 2

EXPLORE *continued*

5. **a.** Sam's assertion is reasonable; for a population percent of 70%, it is likely that between 62 and 77 students would have scored 3 or better (based on a 90% box plot), but only 60 scored 3 or better in the reported district. On the other hand, the district could be typical and the unlikely outcome is just the result of chance. Students should not forget that about 10% of sample outcomes from a given population will fall in the unlikely range. This possibility must always be considered. (To decide statistically which is the correct interpretation requires a formal analysis using hypothesis testing, which is a topic to be studied in Course 4.)

   b. A likely number of remissions in a random sample of 100 people from a population that has a 10% remission rate is between 5 and 15 (based on a 90% box plot). Thus, it is reasonable to conclude that the drug is somewhat effective since 20 remissions is an unlikely (high) outcome. On the other hand, the drug might have no effect and the unlikely outcome is just the result of chance. (See the comments in Part a above.)

   Another factor to be considered here is whether the sample was a random sample. If not, that could be a source of bias, which might explain the unusually high sample outcome.

   c. With a 20% rate of cancer (1 in 5) statewide, a likely number of cancer cases in a random sample of size 100 from the state population is between 14 and 27. In this town, 30 people in a random sample of 100 had cancer, which is an unlikely outcome. Thus, the residents of the town do have grounds for concern. It may be that the cancer rate in the town is higher than the state cancer rate. On the other hand, the town could be typical, with the same cancer rate as the rest of the state, and the unlikely outcome is just the result of chance. (See the comments in Part a above.)

SHARE AND SUMMARIZE full-class discussion

Checkpoint

See Teaching Master 56.

ⓐ As the sample size increases, the width of the 90% box increases as measured by sample total but decreases as measured by sample proportion. The measurement in terms of sample proportion is more meaningful here, since it gives the width relative to the sample size. The narrower boxes for larger sample sizes reflect the fact that there is less variability in the sample proportions as the sample size increases.

ⓑ Find the usual rate of the disease from state or national records. Take a random sample from the local population, and determine how many individuals have the disease. Make or find a 90% box plot for the state or national rate and for the sample size that you used. If the number of cases of the disease in your sample is high and unlikely (that is, if the number is greater than the upper limit of the 90% box plot), then you have grounds to suspect that there may be a local environmental cause for the disease. Of course, this would not be definitive evidence since an unlikely outcome can occur just as the result of chance.

See additional Teaching Notes on page T168I.

5. By using 90% box plots, you can decide whether sample outcomes from a known population are likely. However, there can be many explanations for an unlikely sample outcome. Consider the three following situations.

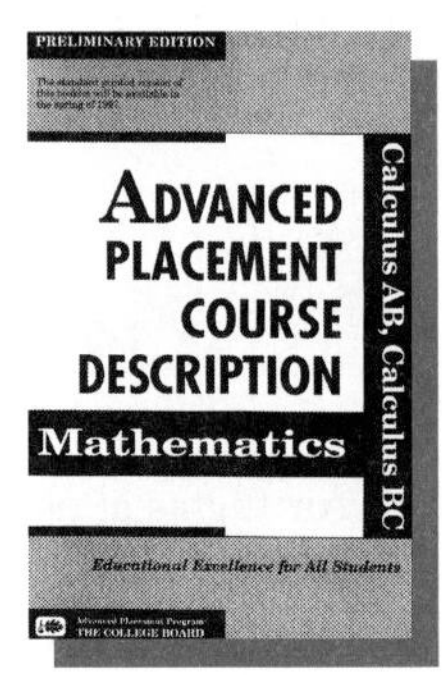

a. According to the *AP National Summary Reports* from the College Board, about 70% of the students who took an Advanced Placement Calculus test in March 2000 scored 3 or better on a scale of 1 to 5, where 5 is best. (Source: http:/www.collegeboard.org/ap/library/state_nat_rpts_00.html) Sam chose a random sample of 100 students in a nearby district who took an AP Calculus test and found that only 60 of them scored 3 or better. He reported to his class that "the results of my survey clearly indicate that students in this district do not score as well as students nationwide." Do you agree with Sam's statement? Why or why not?

b. Suppose a study is done on the effects of a drug used to treat people with Lou Gehrig's disease. In a sample of 100 people with Lou Gehrig's disease, 20 of them had a remission when they used the drug. Without the drug, only 10% of the population had a remission. What do you think about the effectiveness of the drug?

c. There is concern in a small Texas town about the rate of cancer among those who live there. According to health records, only 1 person in 5 people in the state will have cancer. In a random sample of the records of 100 residents in the town, 30% had cancer. Do you think the town residents have grounds for concern?

Checkpoint

Each 90% box plot chart shows 90% boxes for a range of population percents, based on a particular sample size.

a For a fixed population, describe how a 90% box plot of a sampling distribution changes as the sample size increases.

b Suppose you suspect that an unusually large number of people have a disease that might be caused by something in their environment. Describe how you could use a 90% box plot to help determine whether the number of people with the disease is truly unusual.

c Throughout this lesson you have used 90% box plots.

- What does the "90%" in the phrase "90% box plot" mean?
- Describe how a 95% box plot would differ from a 90% box plot. How might you redefine which outcomes are *likely*? In which case would you get a greater number of likely sample outcomes?

Be prepared to share your descriptions and thinking with the entire class.

On Your Own

In 2000, about 70% of the flights run by USAir arrived on time, according to the Air Travel Consumer Report from the Office of Aviation Enforcement and Proceedings (February, 2001).

a. In a random sample of 40 USAir flights, give an interval that indicates how many would be likely to arrive on time.

b. A consumer group selected a random sample of 40 USAir flights at one airport and found that 32 were on time. Does this mean that arrivals at that airport were better than usual in terms of being on time? Explain why or why not.

c. Describe how the interval of likely sample outcomes would change if the sample size is increased. Check your answer by finding the interval for a random sample of 80 flights and comparing it to the interval you found in Part a.

MORE

Modeling • Organizing • Reflecting • Extending

Modeling

1. A number of students each surveyed a random sample of 30 people from the same population to determine how many families had pets. Their results are represented in the distribution on the right.

a. Explain what the 6 tallies after 7 represent.

b. How many students were involved in collecting the data?

c. Make a 90% box plot from the distribution.

Number of Families With Pets	Number of Samples
3	
4	♦♦
5	
6	♦♦♦
7	♦♦♦♦♦♦
8	♦♦♦♦♦♦♦
9	♦♦♦♦♦♦♦♦♦♦♦♦
10	♦♦♦♦♦♦
11	♦♦♦♦♦♦♦♦
12	♦♦
13	♦♦♦
14	♦

148 UNIT 2 • MODELING PUBLIC OPINION

APPLY individual task

On Your Own

a. These data are available at http://www.dot.gov/airconsumer/index1.htm. By examining a 90% box plot, you can see that, in a random sample of 40 USAir flights, the likely number of on-time flights is 23 to 33.

b. Since 32 on-time arrivals is a likely outcome, this is not strong evidence that the arrivals at that airport were better than usual in terms of being on time.

c. If the sample size increased, the interval of likely sample totals would be larger and the interval of likely sample proportions would be smaller. For example, for a random sample of 80 flights, the interval of likely sample totals is 49 to 63. In terms of sample outcomes as proportions, the interval of likely values is 0.613 to 0.788. For a sample size of 40, the interval of likely sample totals is 23 to 33 and the interval of likely proportions is 0.575 to 0.825. Thus, the interval of likely sample proportions for a larger sample size is smaller.

MORE ASSIGNMENT pp. 148–152

Modeling: 5 and choice of one*
Organizing: 2
Reflecting: 2
Extending: Choose one*

**When choice is indicated, it is important to leave the choice to the student.*
NOTE: *It is best if Organizing tasks are discussed as a whole class after they have been assigned as homework.*

Unit 2

MORE independent assignment

Modeling

1. a. Six samples of 30 had 7 families with pets.
   b. There are 50 samples represented in the distribution. Since each student selected one sample, 50 students were involved in collecting the data.
   c. The 90% box plot would range from 6 to 13.

Number of Familes With Pets	Number of Samples
3	
4	◆◆
5	
6	◆◆◆
7	◆◆◆◆◆◆
8	◆◆◆◆◆◆◆
9	◆◆◆◆◆◆◆◆◆◆◆◆
10	◆◆◆◆◆◆
11	◆◆◆◆◆◆◆◆
12	◆◆
13	◆◆◆
14	◆

1. **d.** Sallee's results are in the unlikely range. Thus, students may think that she did not really do the survey and that she just made up her sample outcome. However, she may have done the survey and just by chance gotten an unlikely sample outcome. Or, maybe she did the survey but did not have a random sample. For example, maybe Sallee lives in an apartment complex that does not allow pets, and she drew her sample from neighbors.

   e. You would expect to find an unlikely outcome in about 10% of all random samples. This is because a *likely* outcome is defined as one in the middle 90% of all possible sample outcomes.

2. Since the 90% box plot ranges from 7 to 17 for the 30% row on the standard chart for samples of size 40, an outcome of 11 accidents for a 30% accident rate is not unlikely, so this does not seem to be a substantial reduction.

3. In a random sample of size 40 from a population in which the population percent is 35%, 10 is a likely sample outcome. So we cannot conclude on the basis of this evidence that the first school has an unusual number of students working. Considering the situation at the second school, in a random sample of size 100, 41% is a likely outcome; thus, there is also nothing unusual to report about this school. However, at the third school, a sample total of 36 is an unlikely (high) outcome. Thus, evidence suggests that an unusually high number of students in this school are employed.

4. **a.** You would expect to find from 37 to 53 women.

   b. Since 40 is in the likely range, there is no reason to suspect discrimination in hiring practices based on this evidence.

5. **a.** For the age group 45 to 64, use a random process that would yield 1 success out of 10; for example, generate a random integer between 0 and 9, inclusive, and count 0 as an occurrence of heart disease. To simulate one sample of size 20, generate 20 of these random integers and count the number of 0s. For the age group 65 and over, use a random process that would yield 3 successes out of 10.

d. Sallee was absent the day the students brought in and analyzed their results. She added hers to the table the next day, claiming that in her random sample of 30 people she found only 3 people that have pets in their family. Do you think she really took a random survey of 30 people?

e. In approximately how many random samples would you expect to get an outcome that is unlikely?

2. Past records show that 30% of all automobile accidents in a certain community are caused by drivers under the age of 19. A local school district decided to conduct a large campaign on driving safely. Several months after the campaign was underway, a random sample of 40 police accident reports was selected. Only 11 of the 40 accidents were caused by someone under the age of 19. Does this seem to be a substantial reduction or not? Explain.

3. In 1995, approximately 35% of high school students in the United States had jobs. (Source: U.S. Census Bureau, *Statistical Abstract of the United States: 1996* (116th edition). Washington D.C., 1996.) Suppose that, at that time, a research team was investigating three schools in your area to determine whether the number of students employed was typical. In the first school, they found that 10 students from a random sample of 40 held jobs. They randomly sampled 100 students in the second school and found that 41% had jobs. In the third school, they randomly sampled 80 students and found that 36 had jobs. How do these schools compare? Did any of them have an unusual number of employed students? Explain.

4. Women comprised about 45% of the U.S. workforce in 2000. (Source: *The World Almanac and Book of Facts, 2001*. Mahwah, NJ: World Almanac 2001.) Suppose you took a random sample of 100 working people in the United States in 2000, and you counted the number of women in the sample.

a. Use one of the standard 90% box plot charts to find the likely sample outcomes in this situation.

b. If you found that in a sample of 100 employees at a given company, only 40 of them were women, would you consider you had possible grounds for discrimination in hiring practices? Explain why or why not.

5. In 1993, approximately 10% of women in the age group 45 to 64 had heart disease, and 30% of women aged 65 and over had heart disease. (Source: United States Bureau of the Census, 1994.)

a. For each age category, describe how you could simulate the process of selecting a random sample of 20 women from 1993 and finding the number of women in the sample who had heart disease.

LESSON 3 • SAMPLING DISTRIBUTIONS: FROM POPULATION TO SAMPLE 149

b. Use simulation to create a 90% box plot for each age category. Compare them to the standard box plots. Explain any differences.

c. Suppose you found that 5 of the women in a random sample of 20 women aged 45 to 64 had heart disease. Is this unusual? Would your answer change if the sample was selected from women over the age of 64? Explain how you made your decisions.

Organizing

1. In Activity 4 of Investigation 3, you examined the effect of different sample sizes on the width of 90% box plots, when the width was measured on the sample *proportion* scale of box plot charts. Now consider the sample *total* scale.

a. Find the width of the 90% box plot for a population percent of 30% for sample sizes 20, 40, 80, and 100, as measured on the sample total scale.

b. Compute the ratio of the width of each interval to the sample size. That is, compute $\frac{\text{width of interval}}{\text{sample size}}$. This is called the *relative width* of the interval.

c. As the sample sizes get larger, what happens to the relative width of the intervals? Explain why this pattern makes sense. Compare this pattern to what you found about how width changes when it is measured on the sample proportion scale.

2. Discuss whether the following statements are true. In each case, give a justification for your claim.

a. The interval of likely outcomes for samples from an 80% population is closely related to the interval of likely outcomes for samples of the same size from a 20% population.

b. As the sample size increases, the size of the interval of likely values for the sample *total* decreases.

c. As the sample size increases, the size of the interval of likely values for the sample *proportion* decreases.

d. It is reasonable that an unlikely outcome will occur in about 1 out of every 10 random samples.

3. The manufacturer of a multicolored hard candy announced that 20% of the candy it makes is cherry flavored. Eighty students were each given a sample of 20 of the hard candies. Of the 80 samples, 20 had over 8 cherry-flavored candies. Set up a simulation or use your box plot charts to determine what conclusions you might make based on this sample evidence.

150 UNIT 2 • MODELING PUBLIC OPINION

5. **b.** The simulated box plots will be similar to the standard box plots. Thus, the simulated box plot for the age group 45 to 64 should range from 0 to 4, approximately. The simulated box plot for the age group 65 and over should range from 3 to 9, approximately. There may be some difference between the range of the simulated box plots and the range of the standard box plots because of the process of simulating with a rather small number of samples; the more samples simulated, the better the simulated box plot will approximate the standard box plot.

   c. In a random sample of 20 women aged 45 to 64, 5 is an unlikely sample total. It is too high. However, if the sample were selected from women aged 65 and over, then 5 would be likely. These decisions are made by looking to see whether or not 5 is in the appropriate 90% box.

Organizing

1. **a.** For sample size 20, the width is 6 (that is, $9 - 3$).
   For sample size 40, the width is 10 (that is, $17 - 7$).
   For sample size 80, the width is 14 (that is, $31 - 17$).
   For sample size 100, the width is 15 (that is, $38 - 23$).

   b. For sample size 20, the relative width is $\frac{6}{20}$ or 0.3.
   For sample size 40, the relative width is $\frac{10}{40}$ or 0.25.
   For sample size 80, the relative width is $\frac{14}{80}$ or 0.175.
   For sample size 100, the relative width is $\frac{15}{100}$ or 0.15.

   c. As the sample sizes get larger, the relative width of the intervals gets smaller. This agrees with how width changed when measured on the sample proportion scale, because the relative width is exactly the same as the width in terms of sample proportions. This pattern in interval width makes sense, because with larger samples there is less variability in the sample proportions.

2. **a.** True. They are the same length and the same distance from the nearest edge of the chart.

   b. False. As the sample size increases, so does the range of likely sample totals. You can check the standard box plot charts to verify this. Be sure to contrast this with Part c below.

   c. True. A larger sample size results in narrower boxes, as measured by the scale of sample proportions.

   d. True. Since likely outcomes are about 90% of all outcomes, about 10% of all outcomes will be unlikely.

3. In a sample of 20 candies taken from a population in which 20% of all candies are cherry flavored, we are likely to get from 1 to 7 cherry-flavored candies (using the standard box plot chart for sample size 20). Of the 80 samples, 25% or one-quarter had an unlikely number of cherry-flavored candies. One would expect about 5% of samples would have an unlikely number larger than 7. There are at least two possible conclusions: (1) the given population percent was not correct; it is actually higher, and (2) the sampling process is biased. For example, maybe the samples were not random, and this caused inaccurate results.

4. **Of course, this task should not be applied to classes that are purposely same-gender.**
   a. The likely interval depends on the school's percentage of girls.
   b. If the results show that the number of girls in the sample is not likely, (too low, for example), then students may argue that there is a low participation rate for girls in advanced math at the school. They should think about what might cause this and whether it is a local cause or a more widespread issue. (You may want to suggest that students do research into gender bias studies.)
   c. Students might want to experiment with courses that they think might have unlikely numbers of boys and girls.

Reflecting

1. It is important to emphasize that the population proportion must be known in order to create a sampling distribution. To find the likely interval, use the standard charts or conduct a simulation.
2. a. All the box plots will be similar, since they are all based on random samples of the same size (30) from populations with the same population percent. There probably will be some differences, however, because of the chance nature of simulations and the fact that the number of simulated samples is rather low (40) for two of the students. Henrique's simulation will likely be closer to the theoretical since he used 200 random samples rather than 40.
   b. Since each population has the same population percent, namely 60%, we could consider using any of the three box plots to determine likelihood. The real-world context of the population is not important; the sample size and population percent are the only essential factors. However, these simulated box plots are only approximations of the standard box plot, which is theoretical, based on all possible samples. Ideally, the standard box plot should be used to judge the likelihood of the two new samples. Since the simulated box plot based on the largest number of samples is the best approximation of the standard box plot, the simulated box based on 200 samples would be the best to use.

NOTE: In general, the more simulated samples, the better the box plot, that is, the closer the box plot is to the standard box plot and the less variability there is among simulated box plots. But you need a substantial increase in the number of samples to see a significantly more reliable box plot.

---

3. ■ The 90% refers to the middle 90% of all possible sample outcomes.
   ■ This means that 90% of individuals in a population have this characteristic. This 90% refers to a particular row on a standard box plot chart.
   ■ This is a sample outcome. The proportion in the random sample that has the characteristic is 0.9. This refers to the horizontal scale of the box plot chart.

4. Obtain the number of male and female students in your school from the attendance office. Use this to establish the percentage of each for your school. (You may have to estimate a percentage to use with your box plot charts.)

a. Based on this percentage, how many females are likely to be in a random sample of 20 students in your school?

b. Take a random sample of 20 students enrolled in advanced mathematics courses. How many females were in your sample? Is this number unusual? What might explain your results?

c. Choose another course and take a random sample to determine whether the number of males in the course is unlikely.

Reflecting

1. Think of a situation in your community or at school for which you know the population percent. Describe the situation and explain how you could find an interval of likely outcomes for samples from the population.

2. Kodjo simulated 40 random samples of size 30 from a population in which 60% of the individuals have a certain characteristic. Toni simulated 40 random samples of size 30 from a different population in which 60% of the population have a different characteristic. Henrique simulated 200 random samples of size 30 from the same population as Toni. Each of the three students made a 90% box plot based on their results.

a. Will any of the box plots be the same? Will any be similar?

b. There are two different populations referred to in this situation. Suppose a new sample of size 30 is generated from each population. Would it be reasonable to use any one of the box plots to judge the likelihood of these two new sample outcomes? Explain.

3. Percents are involved in different parts of the activities and tasks in this lesson. Explain the differences in the following uses of percent:

- 90% box plots
- 90% of the population has a given characteristic
- 90% of a random sample has a certain characteristic

LESSON 3 • SAMPLING DISTRIBUTIONS: FROM POPULATION TO SAMPLE 151

Extending

1. Discuss whether the following statements are true. In each case, give a justification for your claim.

   a. The interval of likely sample outcomes for samples of size 80 is half as big as that for samples of size 40.

   b. For all purchases of running shoes in 1998, about 30% were for consumers who were 17 years old or younger. (Source: U.S. Census Bureau, *Statistical Abstract of the United States: 2000* (120th edition). Washington, D.C., 2000.) Suppose you select a sample of 40 running-shoe purchases in 1998 and find that only 5 of them were for consumers aged 17 years or less. You can definitely conclude that your sample came from an environment in which a disproportionate number of purchases was for youths.

2. In Investigation 3, when you first started using standard box plot charts, it was stated that the box plots in the standard charts were constructed using a very large number of simulated samples or using theoretical methods from probability.

   a. Consider a 90% box plot for samples of size 20 from a population with a percent of 30%. Construct such a box plot using at least 1,000 samples. Compare it to the box plot on your standard chart. Explain any differences.

   b. *Challenge*: Construct the box plot in Part a using theoretical methods from probability. To do this you might want to consult a reference book or someone familiar with theoretical probability methods. Write a complete description of how to construct the box plot. Compare your box plot to the box plot on the standard chart.

3. In Activity 4 Part d of Investigation 3 (page 146), you found a relationship between sample size and the width of 90% box plots. Now you will use software to examine that relationship more closely. Using software like the STDBOX option of the *Sampling* calculator software, carry out the following experiment. Consider 90% box plots and 95% box plots for sample proportions.

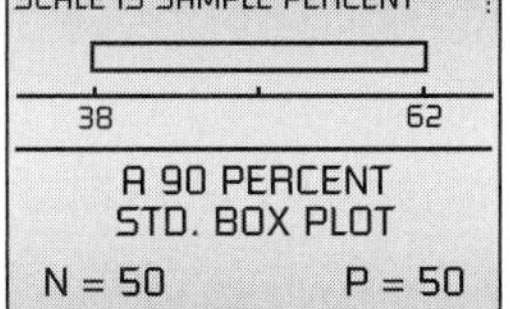

   a. Using the software to construct standard box plots, compare widths of box plots when a sample size is increased by factors of 2 and 4. Use a population percent of 50%, and use the largest sample sizes accepted by the software.

   b. Look for patterns and state the relationship between box plot width and sample size as precisely as you can.

   c. Use the relationship in Part b to predict what happens to the width of box plots when the sample size is increased by a factor of 5 and by some other factors. Check your predictions by using the software to construct the box plots.

152 UNIT 2 • MODELING PUBLIC OPINION

Extending

1. a. This is not true. The interval of likely sample outcomes for sample size 80 is smaller (when measured in terms of sample proportion), but not half as big. In fact, the width of the interval for sample size 80 will be the width of the interval for sample size 40 multiplied by $\frac{1}{\sqrt{2}}$. See Extending Task 3 for a more thorough investigation of this relationship.

   b. False. The interval of likely sample outcomes is 7 to 17. Thus, 5 is an unlikely outcome. However, there are several possible interpretations. This "environment" could indeed be such that the population percent is 30% and this unlikely sample outcome is simply due to chance. On the other hand, it is reasonable, although not beyond all doubt, that the sample came from an environment where a disproportionate number of youths bought running shoes. Finally, this survey may have been flawed in some way, in which case the results cannot be given much credence.

2. a. Increasing the number of simulated samples will result in less variability among simulated box plots and will yield box plots closer to the standard box plot. With 1,000 samples, there should be very little difference between the box plot constructed through simulation and the standard box plot.

   b. Use binomial probabilites. Compute the probability of 0 "successes." Add this to the probability of 1 success. Keep adding sequentially in this way until you reach the point at which the cumulative probability first exceeds 0.05. This gives the lower cutoff point for the 90% box plot. Continue in a similar manner to find the upper cutoff point. For example, the calculation needed to compute the probability of 2 successes is the following:

   $$C(20, 2) \times 0.3^2 \times 0.7^{18}$$

   where $C(x, y)$ is the number of possible combinations of x objects taken y at a time. This method produces the interval 3 to 9, which agrees with the standard chart.

3. The width of a box plot is approximately inversely proportional to the square root of the sample size when dealing with sample proportions. For example, if the sample size increases by a factor of 4, then the box plot width will decrease by a factor of about $\frac{1}{2}$. This relationship holds for 90% box plots and 95% box plots, as long as the sample size is large. The larger the sample size, and the closer the population percent is to 50%, the better the approximation. (This is because the sampling distribution is approximately normal under those conditions.)

See Assessment Resources pages 53–58.

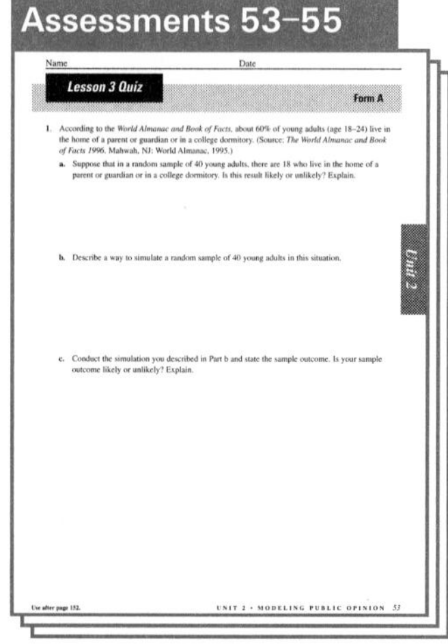

Assessments 53–55

Name Date

Lesson 3 Quiz Form A

1. According to the *World Almanac and Book of Facts*, about 60% of young adults (age 18–24) live in the home of a parent or guardian or in a college dormitory. (Source: *The World Almanac and Book of Facts 1996*. Mahwah, NJ: World Almanac, 1995.)
   a. Suppose that in a random sample of 40 young adults, there are 18 who live in the home of a parent or guardian or in a college dormitory. Is this result likely or unlikely? Explain.
   b. Describe a way to simulate a random sample of 40 young adults in this situation.
   c. Conduct the simulation you described in Part b and state the sample outcome. Is your sample outcome likely or unlikely? Explain.

Unit 2

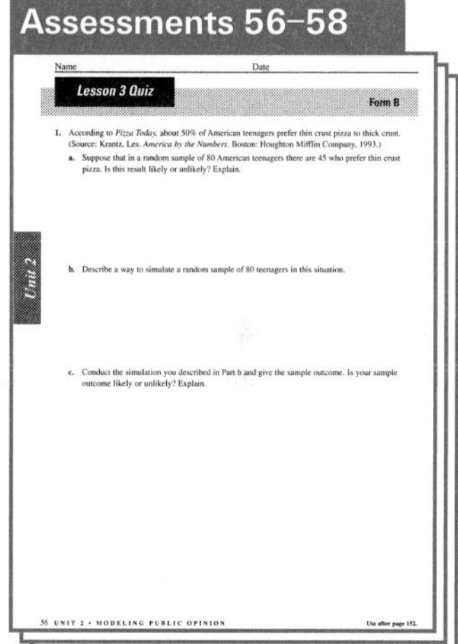

Assessments 56–58

Name Date

Lesson 3 Quiz Form B

1. According to *Pizza Today*, about 50% of American teenagers prefer thin crust pizza to thick crust. (Source: Krantz, Les. *America by the Numbers*. Boston: Houghton Mifflin Company, 1993.)
   a. Suppose that in a random sample of 80 American teenagers there are 45 who prefer thin crust pizza. Is this result likely or unlikely? Explain.
   b. Describe a way to simulate a random sample of 80 teenagers in this situation.
   c. Conduct the simulation you described in Part b and give the sample outcome. Is your sample outcome likely or unlikely? Explain.

Unit 2

Lesson 4 Confidence Intervals: From Sample to Population

LESSON OVERVIEW In this lesson, students will learn how to make inferences about a population based on information from a sample (thus the title, "From Sample to Population"). In particular, students will use the sample percent to estimate the population percent, and they will describe the confidence level of their estimates. They will do all this by constructing, applying, and interpreting a *90% confidence interval* for the population percent.

Roughly speaking, this lesson involves the reverse of the process used in Lesson 3. In that lesson, students determined an interval of likely sample outcomes based on a known population percent. In this lesson, students will find an interval of likely population percents based on a particular sample outcome. Such an interval of likely population percents is a confidence interval for the actual population percent. A confidence interval provides a way to estimate the actual population percent when it is unknown. The approach is based on the work with 90% box plots from the last lesson. This general approach, which is concrete, accessible, and theoretically sound, was originally developed by Jim Swift, a high school mathematics teacher in British Columbia.

Lesson Objectives

- To use a sample percent and 90% box plots to estimate the population percent
- To understand a confidence interval for the population percent as an interval of population percents that are likely to produce the given sample
- To construct and interpret a 90% confidence interval for the population percent using 90% box plot charts
- To understand, find, and interpret the margin of error
- To critically analyze the reporting of survey results, confidence intervals, and margin of error

See additional Teaching Notes on page T168I.

Lesson 4 Confidence Intervals: From Sample to Population

In this lesson, you will investigate two important related questions:

- How can you make inferences about an entire population based on information from just a sample?
- How confident can you be about such inferences?

For example, how can a pollster confidently report public opinion on such issues as crime or genetic engineering when only a few people are polled? In situations like these, the pollster uses a sample to estimate an unknown population characteristic, such as the percent of all people who favor a tougher stance on crime. In this lesson, you will learn how to estimate an unknown population percent using a *confidence interval*.

Interestingly enough, in order to develop this method for estimating an *unknown* population characteristic, you first need to investigate sampling from populations with a *known* characteristic, as you did in Lesson 3. In that lesson, you started with a known population characteristic, such as the percent of women workers in the population or the percent of all students who scored well on the Advanced Placement Calculus examination. Knowing the population percent, you used a 90% box plot to decide whether a particular sample outcome was likely.

Now you are going to reverse the process. You will learn how to use information about samples and sampling distributions to estimate the unknown population percent. For example, information about how a few voters feel about a political candidate can be used to describe how all voters feel, as seen in the following newspaper article about the 2000 United States presidential campaign.

Gore leading Bush by 10%, new poll shows

By Richard Benedetto

Democratic presidential candidate Al Gore moved into a clear lead over Republican George W. Bush in the latest USA TODAY/CNN/Gallup Tracking Poll. The poll, released Thursday, showed the vice president ahead by 10 percentage points, 51%–41%.

It marks the first time that the vice president has gone over 50% support and the first time he has had a double-digit advantage over the Texas governor. The lead is also outside the poll's +/−4 percentage-point margin of error. That suggests that the Gore lead is more than just a statistical tossup.

The Gore lead is driven by independent voters. While 88% of Republicans support Bush and 88% of Democrats support Gore, the vice president leads among independents 46%-33%.

The numbers have to be disappointing to Bush strategists, who had hoped that an appearance on the *Oprah Winfrey Show* and a shift back to an emphasis on issues would help stem the vice president's momentum.

The USA TODAY/CNN/Gallup Tracking Poll interviews 250 likely voters each night. The last three nights of polling are combined to produce the latest results.

Source: *USA Today*, September 22, 2000.

LESSON 4 • CONFIDENCE INTERVALS: FROM SAMPLE TO POPULATION 153

Unit 2

Think About This Situation

The USA TODAY/CNN/Gallup Tracking Poll reported in the article "Gore leading Bush by 10%, new poll shows" measured public opinion about the two candidates for President of the United States in September 2000.

a Based on the information given in the article, what is your estimate for the percentage of likely voters who supported Al Gore at the time the poll was taken?

b Do you think that with another sample of the same size, the pollsters would have gotten the same results?

c Do you think it is probable that exactly 51% of all likely voters in the country supported Vice President Gore at that time? Is it possible?

d The article reports a margin of error of plus or minus 4 points. What do you think that means?

e Do you think it is possible that only 45% of all likely voters in the country supported Vice President Gore at the time of the poll?

INVESTIGATION 1 Likely Populations

Politicians want to know how the public feels about certain political issues. Manufacturers want to know how the public feels about their products. It is important in many contexts to determine public opinion. But in most cases, you have to measure public opinion about an issue using only a sample. In this investigation, you will learn how to use your knowledge of likely sample outcomes and 90% box plots to do this.

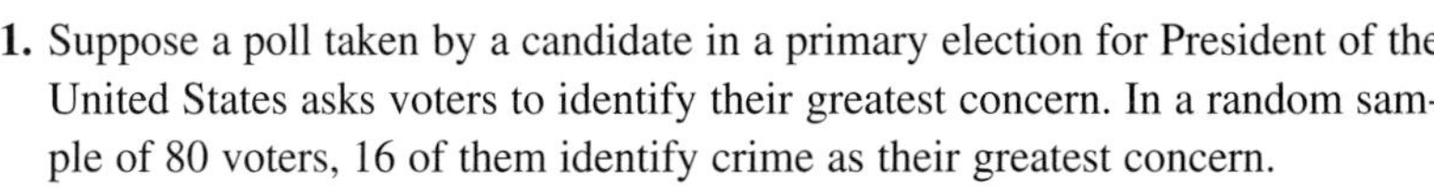

1. Suppose a poll taken by a candidate in a primary election for President of the United States asks voters to identify their greatest concern. In a random sample of 80 voters, 16 of them identify crime as their greatest concern.
   - **a.** Based on the sample outcome of 16 out of 80, what is your estimate for the percent of all voters in the entire population who identify crime as their greatest concern? Describe the reasoning you used to get your estimate.
   - **b.** If you haven't already done so, think about how you could state your estimate as an interval of likely population percents. Try to describe a method for determining such an interval.

In Activity 1, you estimated an unknown population percent based on the outcome from a particular sample selected from that population. In Part b of that activity, you worked on constructing an interval of likely population percents. This is the basic idea behind what is called a *confidence interval*. In the following activities, you will investigate confidence intervals in a more precise and systematic manner.

154 UNIT 2 • MODELING PUBLIC OPINION

Think About This Situation

See Teaching Masters 57 and 58.

Ⓐ The article states that 51% of likely voters supported Gore. So students might use 51% as their estimate. However, they should be encouraged to recognize 51% as the sample percent, which is not necessarily the population percent. They may consider the margin of error and give their estimate as an interval, 47%–55%. They are specifically asked about margin of error in Part d.

Ⓑ No; it is likely that, with another sample of the same size, the pollsters would have gotten slightly different results.

Ⓒ It is unlikely that exactly 51% of all likely voters in the entire country supported Vice President Gore at that time, even though the percent was probably close to 51%. However, it is possible that the percentage was exactly 51%.

Ⓓ Students will probably have a rough idea what margin of error means. By the end of the lesson, they will be able to explain its meaning more precisely. For now, they will probably suggest that the true percentage of likely voters who support Gore is somewhere between 47% and 55%. This is not quite correct, but the goal here is to start them thinking that an estimate based on a sample may not be exact and that an interval may be a reasonable way to state the estimate. There is no information given in the article about the confidence level for this estimate. This is an important issue that will be investigated in the lesson.

Ⓔ This question is designed to focus the discussion on margin of error and population estimates. Some students, if not many, may think that since 45% is outside of the interval 51% plus or minus 4 points, 45% cannot be the true population percent. In fact, it could be the true population percent, and this is one of the points that will be investigated in the lesson. At this time, the goal is simply to generate some discussion, raise some issues, and establish the need for a more careful mathematical analysis.

Master 57

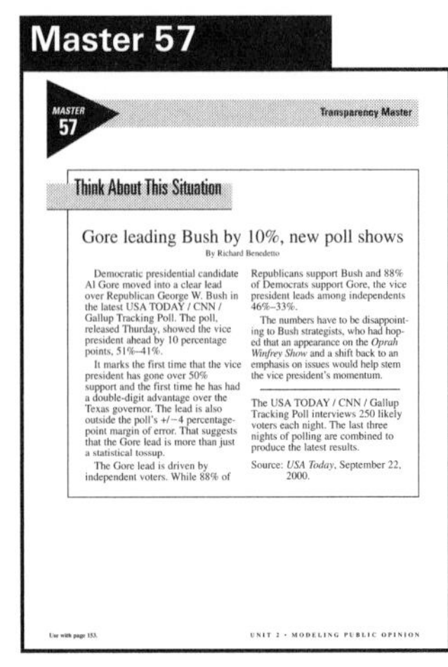
MASTER 57 Transparency Master

Think About This Situation

Gore leading Bush by 10%, new poll shows

By Richard Benedetto

Democratic presidential candidate Al Gore moved into a clear lead over Republican George W. Bush in the latest USA TODAY / CNN / Gallup Tracking Poll. The poll, released Thurday, showed the vice president ahead by 10 percentage points, 51%–41%.

It marks the first time that the vice president has gone over 50% support and the first time he has had a double-digit advantage over the Texas governor. The lead is also outside the poll's +/−4 percentage-point margin of error. That suggests that the Gore lead is more than just a statistical tossup.

The Gore lead is driven by independent voters. While 88% of Republicans support Bush and 88% of Democrats support Gore, the vice president leads among independents 46%–33%.

The numbers have to be disappointing to Bush strategists, who had hoped that an appearance on the *Oprah Winfrey Show* and a shift back to an emphasis on issues would help stem the vice president's momentum.

The USA TODAY / CNN / Gallup Tracking Poll interviews 250 likely voters each night. The last three nights of polling are combined to produce the latest results.

Source: *USA Today*, September 22, 2000.

Use with page 153. UNIT 2 • MODELING PUBLIC OPINION

Master 58

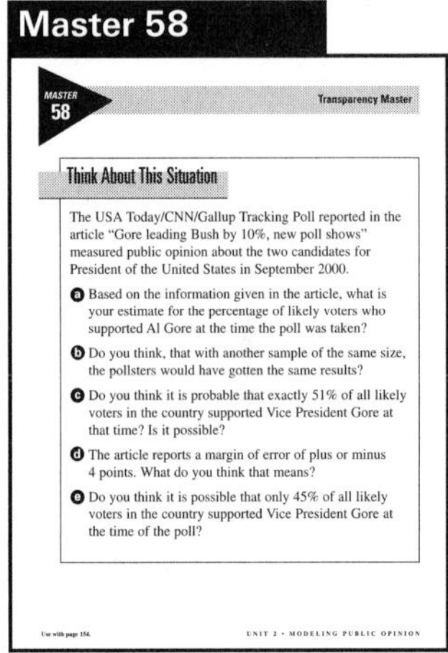
MASTER 58 Transparency Master

Think About This Situation

The USA Today/CNN/Gallup Tracking Poll reported in the article "Gore leading Bush by 10%, new poll shows" measured public opinion about the two candidates for President of the United States in September 2000.

Ⓐ Based on the information given in the article, what is your estimate for the percentage of likely voters who supported Al Gore at the time the poll was taken?

Ⓑ Do you think, that with another sample of the same size, the pollsters would have gotten the same results?

Ⓒ Do you think it is probable that exactly 51% of all likely voters in the country supported Vice President Gore at that time? Is it possible?

Ⓓ The article reports a margin of error of plus or minus 4 points. What do you think that means?

Ⓔ Do you think it is possible that only 45% of all likely voters in the country supported Vice President Gore at the time of the poll?

Use with page 154. UNIT 2 • MODELING PUBLIC OPINION

Unit 2

EXPLORE small-group investigation

INVESTIGATION 1 Likely Populations

1. a. Since 16 out of 80 is 20%, it is reasonable to estimate that about 20% of voters in the entire population identify crime as their greatest concern. At this point, students may give 20% as their answer, they may give an interval, or they may say "about 20%." Their answers to questions like this one will get much more precise as the lesson progresses.

   b. This question gives students a chance to generate an interval in a way that seems sensible to them before we develop the specific 90% box chart method in this lesson. It may be that some students, on their own, will use a 90% box chart to generate an interval. Other students may give just a "seat of the pants" interval of 20% ± (something). In any case, students should think about how to form an interval estimate and explain how they did it.

2. **The goal of this activity is to have students think about this question: For which population percents is 16 a likely sample outcome? The interval of such population percents is the confidence interval students will learn to determine.**
   - **a.** If the population percent is 25% and the sample size is 80, then a sample outcome of 16 is a likely outcome because 16 falls in the 90% box plot for a 25% population. This problem is just like the problems students did in the previous lesson.
   - **b.** The sample outcome of 16 is not a likely outcome if the population percent is 30%, because 16 is not in the 90% box plot for a sample size of 80 and a population percent of 30%.
   - **c.** Look at 16 on the lower scale of the standard box plot chart for sample size 80, and then find all the 90% box plots that include 16. On the standard chart for sample size 80, 16 is a likely outcome for population percents 15%, 20%, and 25%.
     - This range of population percents can be expressed by the interval 15%–25%. (To the precision we are using here, this is the 90% confidence interval that will be defined formally after Activity 3.)
     - The best single number estimate to report is the sample percent of 20%. This is reasonable, because it is the exact percent from the sample and it lies in the center of the interval just found.
     - Another way to express the interval is 20% ±5%. (This shows the margin of error, which is introduced formally after Activity 3.)

NOTE: Here, and throughout this lesson, all intervals students should calculate are given using 5% increments, because that is the increment on the box plot charts that they are using. An interval given as 15%–25% might actually be 14%–28%, but, for our purposes, 15%–25% will suffice.

---

d.

Interval	This shows the range, but it does not highlight the sample outcome, which is the best single number estimate.
Single number	This highlights the sample outcome, which is the best single number estimate, but it does not indicate the variability in the estimate.
Value ±	This shows both the single number estimate and the variability.

NOTE: Be aware that use of margin of error generally assumes that the confidence interval is symmetric about the sample outcome. That is, the confidence interval is of the form (sample outcome) ±(margin of error), and the sample outcome is in the center of the confidence interval. This will *not* always be true for confidence intervals constructed by the 90% box plot method. It will be true if the sample proportion is close enough to 0.5, but not necessarily when the proportion is very high or very low. The activities in this lesson involving margin of error use proportions near enough to 0.5 so that this issue is not likely to come up. It is probably best not to mention it. If a student notices this issue, you can make an analogy to error tolerances in engineering in which an interval may be stated, for example, as 15 (+3, –2). Or, you could tell students that, in this context, margin of error gives an approximation of a confidence interval.

See additional Teaching Notes on page T168I.

2. Consider again the poll from Activity 1, in which 16 voters out of a random sample of 80 identify crime as the issue that concerns them the most. Think about how to use this sample information to estimate the percent of all voters in the population who identify crime as their greatest concern.

   a. Suppose the population percent is 25%. Is the sample outcome of 16 a likely outcome for that population percent? How can you tell?

   b. Suppose the population percent is 30%. Is the sample outcome of 16 a likely outcome for that population percent?

   c. Describe how you could use a box plot chart to find all the population percents for which 16 is a likely sample outcome.

   - Express this range of population percents as an interval.
   - If you wished to report a single value as an estimate of the population percent, which value from the interval would you report? Why is that percent a reasonable estimate?
   - State the interval of population percents for which 16 is a likely sample outcome as one value plus or minus a number of percentage points.

   d. Consider all three ways of reporting the population percents for which 16 is a likely sample outcome from Part c. Do any of these match your estimate for the population percent from Activity 1? What are some advantages and disadvantages of each way of reporting?

3. In a random sample of size 40 from the same population, 22 people identified the economy as their greatest concern. A 90% box plot chart for sample size 40 follows.

   a. Determine an interval of population percents for which this sample outcome of 22 is a likely outcome. Explain why this interval provides a reasonable estimate for the unknown population percent of all voters who identify the economy as their greatest concern.

90% Box Plots from Samples of Size 40

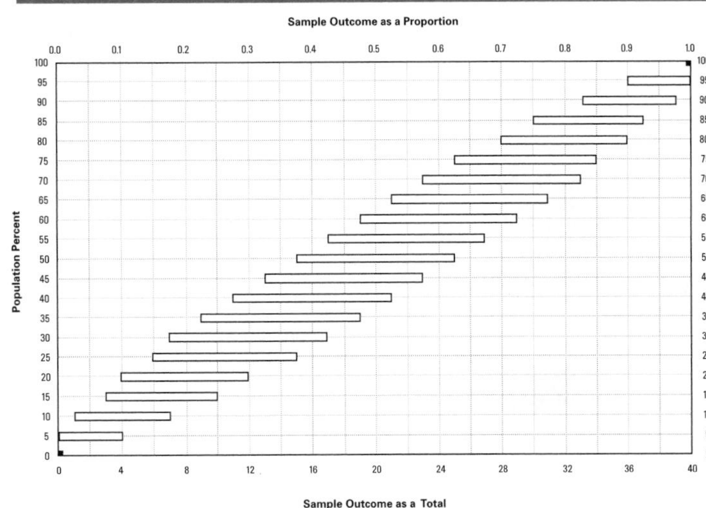

Unit 2

LESSON 4 • CONFIDENCE INTERVALS: FROM SAMPLE TO POPULATION 155

b. Marita drew a vertical line from the sample outcome of 22 up through the boxes. Make a sketch of the box plot chart and show the vertical line Marita drew. Describe how this vertical line can be used to find the interval of population percents for which 22 is a likely sample outcome. How does Marita's method compare to the method you described in Part b of Activity 1?

c. State an estimate for the unknown population percent as one value plus or minus another value.

The intervals that you found in Activities 1 through 3 are called *90% confidence intervals* for the actual unknown population percent. *Roughly, a confidence interval for the actual population percent is an interval of likely population percents.* More precisely, a **90% confidence interval** for the actual population percent is the interval of all population percents for which the given sample outcome is a likely outcome, where "likely outcome" is defined in terms of 90% box plots. For a confidence interval such as 15% to 25%, expressed in the form 20% ± 5%, the 5% is called the **margin of error**.

4. For each of the situations below, use confidence intervals to help answer the question posed.

a. In 1995, there was a federal proposal to replace paper dollars with coins, because coins last longer and are cheaper to circulate. Before implementing the proposal, the federal government wanted to know what percentage of Americans opposed this policy. To help find out, the Gallup organization questioned a random sample of Americans. Almost 75% of the people in the Gallup Poll opposed the proposal. (Source: *USA Today*, June 14, 1995.) The Gallup Poll used a large sample. To make the computations simpler, suppose 75% of the people in a random sample of 80 adults in Greenback County oppose the proposal. What percentage of all adults in Greenback County is likely to oppose the proposal?

b. A school board wants to find out how the people in their district feel about discipline in the schools. In a random sample of 40 people in the school district, 18 of them say they think the schools are not tough enough. About what percentage of all people in the district think the schools are not tough enough?

c. A candidate for a local election took a random survey of 100 people in her district and found that 52% of them intended to vote for her. Should she assume she has a majority and will win the election? Why or why not?

5. In a random sample of 100 people in a certain community, 73% of the people said they always wear seat belts.

a. What percentage of people in the entire community from which the sample was selected do you think always wear seat belts?

3. b. **90% Box Plots from Samples of Size 40**

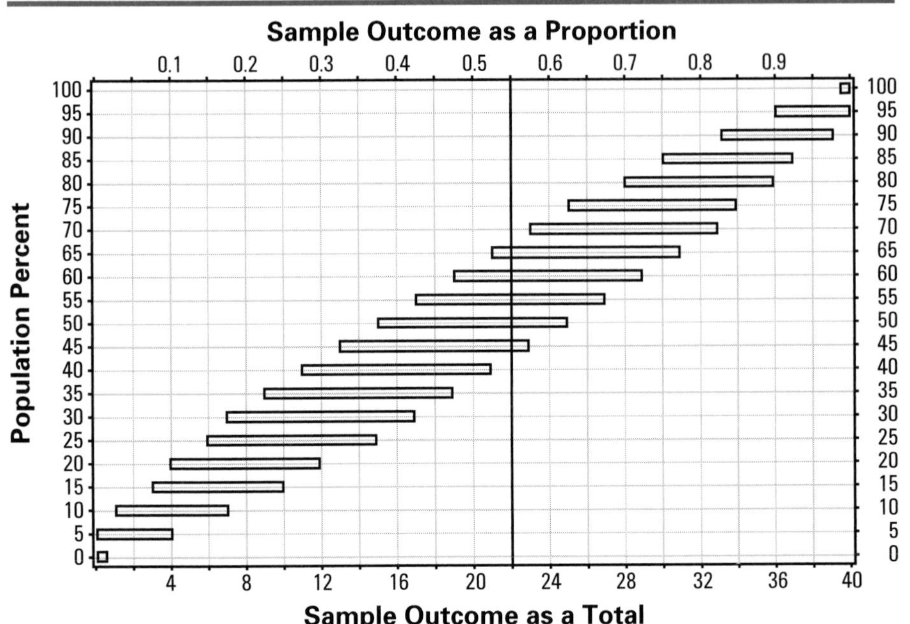

Look at the 90% box plots that this vertical line intersects. Since 22 is a likely sample outcome for those population percents, those percents give the interval of population percents for which 22 is a likely sample outcome. Students may have used a method similar to this one when they did Part b of Activity 1.

c. This could be reported as 55% ±10%.

4. a. We can use a confidence interval to estimate the percentage of the population who oppose the proposal. A 90% confidence interval for the actual population percent is 70%–80%. (Be sure that students use the top scale of the box plot chart, which gives the sample proportion when they are using the chart to find the confidence interval for this problem or find 75% of 80 which is 60 and use the sample outcome as a total on the bottom of the chart.)

b. About 35% to 55% of all people in the district think the schools are not tough enough. That is, a 90% confidence interval for the actual population percent is 35%–55%.

c. The confidence interval in this case starts at 45%. The candidate should not assume that she will win based on these results, because a sample outcome of 52% is likely from population percents below 50% and she needs more than 50% in order to win (assuming that she has only one opponent).

5. a. A 90% confidence interval for the true population percent is 65%–80%. (Note that, because of the limited accuracy of the box plot chart, some students might describe a slightly different interval.)

5. b. No, the 90% confidence interval for the population percent is not guaranteed to contain the actual percentage of people in the population who always wear seat belts. This is because of the nature of the random sampling process and the chance that a given sample outcome could be an unlikely outcome. If we happen to get a random sample that has a proportion of "successes" in the outer 10% of the sampling distribution, the confidence interval won't contain the true population percent.

A more detailed explanation follows: because people were chosen at random to participate in the survey, the sample chosen could have been very different from the whole population, either with many more people using seat belts or with many fewer people using seat belts. The population percents in the confidence interval are those population percents for which the sample outcome of 73% is likely. If, in fact, 73% is an *unlikely* sample outcome from the given population, then the actual percentage for the given population will not be in the range of likely population percents; that is, it will not be in the confidence interval. This subtle but important point will be investigated in Activity 6.

6. This experiment is designed to help students understand the important point that about 90% of confidence intervals constructed by sampling from a given population will contain the actual population percent.

As of June 2002, the actual population percents for M&M's® Plain Chocolate Candies were as follows:

30% brown	**10% green**
20% yellow	**10% orange**
20% red	**10% blue**

There are other varieties of M&M's Chocolate Candies, and they have different percents. You can get the latest information on the Internet at http://www.m-ms.com/cai/mms/faq.html.

a. Answers will depend on the students' samples. Each student should select a random sample of 20 candies, find the percentage of red candies in the sample, and use that sample percent to construct a 90% confidence interval for the population percentage of red candies.

b. The confidence intervals will probably vary slightly. Each student is selecting a random sample, so it is certainly possible that different students will have different sample percents, and those sample percents could generate different confidence intervals.

c. It is possible that some confidence intervals will not contain the actual population percent. (In fact, about 10% of the confidence intervals in a large collection of confidence intervals will not contain the actual population percent.) This may be quite surprising to some students.

NOTE: It is important to have a reasonably large collection of confidence intervals in order to see the desired pattern. Your class should produce at least 30 confidence intervals. More is better, subject to time limitations, of course. You may want to ask all or some students to sample twice and produce intervals for each sample.

See additional Teaching Notes on page T168J.

b. Do you think a 90% confidence interval for the population percent is guaranteed to contain the actual population percentage of people who always wear seat belts? Explain why or why not. Assume that the survey was properly conducted.

6. Now that you know how to construct a confidence interval, explore some of the properties of confidence intervals by completing the following activity. To begin, each student in your class should have a small bag of "M&M's"® Chocolate Candies.

a. Select a random sample of 20 candies from your bag. Use the sample to find a 90% confidence interval for the actual population percent of red candies.

b. Compare your confidence interval to those of other members of your group. Are they all the same? Should they be the same? Explain.

c. For M&M's® Chocolate Candies in June 2002, the population percent for red candies was 20%. Check the M&M's Web site to get the current percent. Does the confidence interval you produced from your sample contain the actual population percent?

d. Your class should produce at least 30 confidence intervals. (If there are fewer than 30 students in your class, your teacher may ask you to use another sample of 20 candies from a new bag to construct another confidence interval.) How many confidence intervals produced by students in your class contain the actual population percent? Explain the results.

Unit 2

7. Now consider the following three statements as you look back at your work in the previous activities. For each statement, discuss and give an example that illustrates the statement.

a. Two different samples of the same size from the same population can generate two different confidence intervals for the population percent.

b. Not all confidence intervals contain the actual population percent.

c. Suppose you draw many samples from a given population, and for each sample you generate a 90% confidence interval for the population percent. You would expect that about 90% of these confidence intervals will contain the actual population percent.

8. Suppose someone surveyed a random sample of students in your school. The person reported a 90% confidence interval of 50% to 70% for the percent of all students for whom basketball is their favorite sport.

a. Based on the box plot charts you have, about what sample size do you think was used in the survey? Explain how you made your choice.

b. The athletic director at the school decided, based on the results of the survey, to show videos of the school's basketball games during lunch and study halls for a small fee to each viewer. Do you think this will be a successful endeavor?

LESSON 4 • CONFIDENCE INTERVALS: FROM SAMPLE TO POPULATION 157

9. Most major polls use a 95% confidence level to report results.

a. In Activity 2, you found a 90% confidence interval based on a poll in which 16 voters in a random sample of 80 identified crime as their greatest concern. How would a 95% confidence interval differ from the 90% confidence interval? Use software such as *Sampling* to determine a 95% confidence interval for this poll to check your conjecture.

b. Refer to the article about the 2000 U.S. presidential campaign, page 153. How would you interpret the USA TODAY/CNN/Gallup Tracking Poll results for registered voters now?

Checkpoint

In this investigation, you explored the use of confidence intervals to interpret sample statistics.

a Describe the connection between the two topics in each item below:

- Confidence interval and the informal idea of likely populations
- Confidence interval and margin of error

b Describe how to construct a 90% confidence interval.

c Explain what happens to the width of a 90% confidence interval as sample size increases.

d In Lessons 3 and 4, you studied two related but very different problems. In one type of problem, you use a known population percent to find the likely sample outcomes. In the other type, you use a particular sample outcome to estimate the unknown population percent. Which of these two problems can be solved using confidence intervals? Explain how to solve the other type of problem.

e Suppose 32 people in a randomly selected sample of 80 people answer "yes" to a question. Then the 90% confidence interval for the actual percent of people in the population who would answer "yes" is 35% to 45%. For each statement below, do you think it is a good explanation of what "90% confidence" means in this situation? Why or why not?

- There is a 90% chance that the actual population percent is between 35% and 45%.
- The given interval was determined using a method that gives a correct result 90% of the time.
- The sample outcome of 32 out of 80 is a likely sample outcome from populations with percents from 35% to 45%.
- If we draw many random samples of size 80 from this population and generate a 90% confidence interval for each, then about 90% of these confidence intervals will contain the actual population percent.

Be prepared to share your descriptions and thinking with the entire class.

158 UNIT 2 • MODELING PUBLIC OPINION

9. **a.** The 95% confidence interval would be wider. In intuitive terms, if you want to be more confident about your interval estimate, then you have to have a wider interval. In more technical terms, 95% boxes are wider than 90% boxes, because they contain 95% of possible sample outcomes instead of just 90% of outcomes. Thus, when using the box-chart procedure for constructing a confidence interval, you will hit more boxes. This generates a wider confidence interval.

   The 95% confidence interval for this poll is 15%–30%, using 5% increments in the box chart. Recall that the 90% confidence interval is 15% to 25%, which is a narrower interval.

   b. The USA TODAY/CNN/Gallup Tracking Poll probably used a 95% confidence interval. The reported result for registered voters is 53% with a margin of error of 3%. So the 95% confidence interval is 50%–56%. Thus, if many confidence intervals were constructed from many random samples, about 95% of the confidence intervals would contain the actual population percent. Note that a 90% confidence interval would be narrower and thus give a more focused estimate of the population percent, but there would be a greater chance that the interval would not contain the actual population percent.

Masters 59a-59b

MASTER 59a — Transparency Master

Checkpoint

In this investigation, you explored the use of confidence intervals to interpret sample statistics.

ⓐ Describe the connection between the two topics in each item below:

- Confidence interval and the informal idea of likely populations
- Confidence interval and margin of error

ⓑ Describe how to construct a 90% confidence interval.

ⓒ Explain what happens to the width of a 90% confidence interval as sample size increases.

ⓓ In Lessons 3 and 4, you studied two related but very different problems. In one type of problem, you use a known population percent to find the likely sample outcomes. In the other type, you use a particular sample outcome to estimate the unknown population percent. Which of these two problems can be solved using confidence intervals? Explain how to solve the other type of problem.

Use with page 158. UNIT 2 • MODELING PUBLIC OPINION

Unit 2

SHARE AND SUMMARIZE full-class discussion

Checkpoint

See Teaching Masters 59a–59b.

ⓐ
- A confidence interval is a range of "likely populations," that is, populations for which the sample outcome is likely.
- A confidence interval can often be expressed as (sample outcome) $\pm$(margin of error).

ⓑ To construct a 90% confidence interval, look at the standard 90% box plot chart for the given sample size. Draw a vertical line through the sample proportion or the sample total. See which 90% box plots are hit by that line. The interval of population percents corresponding to the boxes that are hit is the 90% confidence interval.

ⓒ As sample size increases, the width of the 90% boxes decreases, because there is less variability in the sample proportions. Since the boxes are narrower, fewer boxes are hit when using box plot charts to construct a confidence interval. Therefore, the confidence intervals are narrower.

ⓓ This is an important discussion. Students need to explicitly discuss the differences and connections between the sampling distribution problems studied in Lesson 3 and the confidence interval problems studied in Lesson 4. Confidence intervals are used to solve the second type of problem; that is, you use a confidence interval, which is constructed from a particular sample outcome, to estimate an unknown population percent. In the first type of problem, which was studied in Lesson 3, you know the population percent, and you want to find the sampling distribution. More specifically, you want to find the likely sample outcomes. For example, assume 10% of all people in the United States are left-handed. Suppose you draw a random sample of 40 people from the population and count the number who are left handed. The range of likely values for this sample outcome is the range of a 90% box plot for samples of size 40 drawn from a population with population percent of 10%, that is, 1–7.

See additional Teaching Notes on page T168K.

Unit 2

APPLY individual task

On Your Own

a. For this situation, the interval of likely population percents is 25%–45%.

b. If the survey was given to 100 randomly selected people, the 90% confidence interval would be 30%–40%.

c. The confidence level is 90%. That means that, roughly 90% of the time, the constructed confidence interval will contain the actual population percent. More precisely, if you draw many samples from this population and generate a confidence interval for each sample, then about 90% of those confidence intervals will contain the actual population percent.

d. In Part a, the confidence interval can be written as 35% ±10%, so the margin of error is 10%. In Part b, the confidence interval can be written as 35% ±5%, so the margin of error is 5%.

MORE ASSIGNMENT *pp. 159–164*

Modeling: 1 and 4
Organizing: 2 and 3
Reflecting: Choose one*
Extending: 4 and choice of one*

**When choice is indicated, it is important to leave the choice to the student.*
NOTE: *It is best if Organizing tasks are discussed as a whole class after they have been assigned as homework.*

MORE independent assignment

Modeling

1. a. ■ If there were 40 people in the sample, it is likely that 50% to 70% of young people think brands are important, since the confidence interval is 50%–70%.

■ If there were 100 people in the sample, the confidence interval would be 55%–65%.

b. For samples of size 20: 25%–55%. For samples of size 40: 30%–50%.

c. When the sample size is smaller, the confidence interval is wider. (See Checkpoint Part c on page 158.)

On Your Own

According to a survey conducted by the National Pasta Association, about 35% of people surveyed indicated that spaghetti was their favorite pasta. (Source: National Pasta Association, *Pasta Home Page*, *http://www.ilovepasta.org/press_room.html*)

a. Assuming the survey was given to a random sample of 40 people, determine an interval of population percents that you think are likely. (Use 90% box plots as your criterion for likely.)

b. Assuming the survey was given to 100 randomly selected people, find a 90% confidence interval for the percent of people in the whole population who indicate spaghetti is their favorite pasta.

c. How confident are you that the intervals you determined in Parts a and b will contain the actual percent of people who indicate spaghetti is their favorite pasta? Give a careful explanation of your answer.

d. Express your answers to Parts a and b in terms of margin of error.

MORE
Modeling • Organizing • Reflecting • Extending

Modeling

1. According to the International Mass Retail Association, 60% of consumers age 8 to 17 surveyed think it is important to consider brands when they buy sneakers. (Source: *USA Today*, July 21, 1995.)

a. Brand name recognition and purchases are very important in some segments of the retail industry.

- If there were 40 people in the sample, what is your estimate of the percentage of all consumers aged 8 to 17 who think brands are important in buying sneakers?
- How would this estimate change if there were 100 people in the sample?

b. About 40% of those polled think brand names are important in buying toys and games. Find a 90% confidence interval for the actual percentage of the population who think brand names are important in buying toys and games. Use samples of size 20 and size 40.

c. Describe and explain any patterns shown in this task between sample size and width of the confidence interval.

Unit 2

LESSON 4 • CONFIDENCE INTERVALS: FROM SAMPLE TO POPULATION 159

2. A poll taken before the presidential election of 2000 reported the following: "The poll had Gore ahead of Republican George W. Bush, 48%–43%. ...So the race remains statistically deadlocked." (margin of error: 4 points). Why did the newspaper choose not to say one of the candidates was ahead? (Source: *USA Today*, September 19, 2000.)

3. Find a poll or survey that is reported in a newspaper. Identify the margin of error. Explain what it means in terms of the survey results.

4. Cellular phones were once a novelty. Now they are becoming more and more commonplace.

   a. Twenty percent of people who owned a cellular phone in 1999 did not own one in 1998 (Source: *The World Almanac and Book of Facts 2001*. Mahwah, NJ: World Almanac 2001.) Suppose you took a random sample of 40 teachers in your school who owned a cellular phone in 1999 and found that only 4 of them did not own one in 1998. Does this mean that teachers in your school are not typical?

   b. Suppose you took a random sample of 40 people in your town who owned a cellular phone in 1999 and found that 13 of them did not own one in 1998. What conclusion could you draw about the percentage of people in your town who owned a cellular phone in 1999 but not in 1998? Defend your conclusion by using confidence intervals.

Organizing

1. What relationship, if any, is there between margin of error and sample size? How is this relationship connected with box plots for various sample sizes?

2. The line plot on the next page shows a month-by-month pattern of change in one region's public opinion about the baseball strike in 1994–1995, much as it would have looked in a newspaper article. The plot shows the estimated percentage of people in the population supporting the strike. The opinion poll each month had a margin of error of 4%.

   a. On a copy of the graph, for each month, plot points illustrating the margin of error and sketch a vertical line segment showing the confidence interval.

   b. Shade a band through the graph that illustrates the changing confidence intervals for the actual percentage of people in the population supporting the strike.

160 UNIT 2 • MODELING PUBLIC OPINION

2. The survey says that Gore is favored by 48% ±4% of the voters and that Bush is favored by 43% ±4%. Gore's actual population percentage is likely to be between 44% and 52%; similarly, Bush's percentage is likely to be between 39% and 47%. There is considerable overlap in these two intervals, which means that the actual percentages could be the same or either one could be ahead.
3. Students will discover that some polls are reported without mention of the margin of error. They should find one that states the margin of error (or they may be able to compute the margin of error using the formula in Organizing Task 3 or Extending Task 2).
4. **a.** Students now have two ways of analyzing this situation. First, use the perspective of likely sample outcomes as in Lesson 3. The interval of likely sample outcomes for random samples of size 40 from the population of all people who owned a cell phone in 1999 is 4 to 12 (using a 90% box plot). Since the given sample outcome of 4 is in this interval, it is considered a likely sample outcome from such a population. Thus, there is no evidence to suggest that teachers in your school are not typical.

   A second perspective on this problem comes from the study of confidence intervals in this lesson. Use a 90% confidence interval to estimate the population percent for the population of all teachers in your school who owned a cellular phone in 1999, then compare this to the overall population percent. In a random sample of 40 teachers, the sample outcome is 4. This yields a confidence interval of 5% to 20% for the actual population percent for the population of teachers in your school who owned a cellular phone in 1999. The overall population percent, from the World Almanac data, is 20%. Since 20% is in the confidence interval, there is no evidence to suggest that the teachers in your school are not typical.

   b. You don't know the population percent, and you will try to estimate it using a sample outcome. Using the sample total of 13, the 90% confidence interval is 25%–45%. Thus, we are 90% confident that the actual percentage of all people in your town who owned a cell phone in 1999 but not in 1998 is between 25% and 45%. Students may notice that the overall population percent from the World Almanac is 20%, which is not in the confidence interval. This provides evidence that the town population in this problem is not typical.

Organizing

1. As sample size increases, there is less variability in the sample proportions, so the 90% box plots get narrower (have a shorter interval length). Narrower box plots are harder to "hit" in the process of constructing confidence intervals. So the confidence intervals get smaller, which means the margin of error gets smaller. Thus, as sample size increases, margin of error decreases. See Organizing Task 3 for a more technical analysis of margin of error and sample size.
2. **a–b.** See the graph at the right.

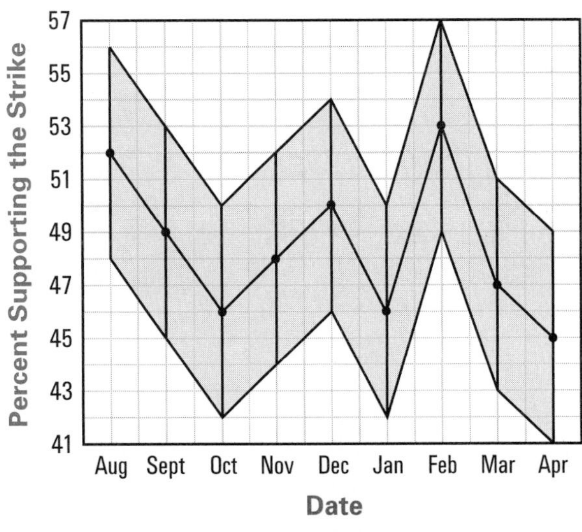

2. **c.** During the period from August to April, values within the confidence intervals went as high as 57% and as low as 41%. The percentage reported went down, then up, then down, then up, and then down again. Also, by having the scale as shown, the peaks and valleys are accentuated and the visual appearance of the graph shows lots of fluctuation, much more so than if the scale went from 0 to 100.

   d. During the entire period shown, 49% was in the confidence interval region. It is possible that, during the entire strike, public opinion never changed from 49%.

3. **a.**
   - As sample size increases, margin of error decreases. Since n (sample size) is in the denominator, as n gets larger the fraction gets smaller, thus, the margin of error gets smaller. Alternatively, as sample size increases, there is less variability in the sample proportions, so the 90% box plots get narrower (or shorter). Narrower box plots are harder to "hit" in the process of constructing confidence intervals. So the confidence intervals get smaller, which means the margin of error gets smaller.
   - Sample proportions closer to 0.5 have a larger margin of error. You can see this from the formula. The numerator is $\hat{p}\hat{q}$, but $\hat{q} = 1 - \hat{p}$, so $\hat{p}\hat{q} = \hat{p}(1 - \hat{p})$. This quadratic function has its maximum when $\hat{p} = \frac{1}{2}$. So the fraction in the formula is maximum when $\hat{p} = 0.5$, that is, when the sample proportion is 0.5.

   b. Note that in both cases, $n\hat{p} \geq 10$ and $n\hat{q} \geq 10$, so the conditions for when to use the formula are met.

Margin of Error, as Percentage

	Sample Size 20	Sample Size 80
Formula	18	9
Standard Box Plot Charts	15	5
Software	18	8

   c. The following focuses on the methods rather than the values given in Part b; students may choose to respond more concretely. Students are not expected to explain the formula, but they should be able to reason about the other two methods.

   All three methods yield approximations. The formula is based on a normal approximation of the sampling distribution for the sample proportion. For these examples, this approximation is quite good, so the results from the formula are the best results. The standard box plot charts do not give exact results because they step up in intervals of 5% for the population percents. Using the software with 2% intervals, the answers are closer to exact but still can be slightly off. To get the exact answers, we would need to use the binomial distribution, which will be developed in Course 4.

   d. As the sample size is increased by a factor of 4, from 20 to 80, the margin of error is decreased by about a factor of $\frac{1}{2}$, from 18 to 9. This pattern is explained by the formula, which shows that the approximate margin of error is inversely proportional to the square root of the sample size.

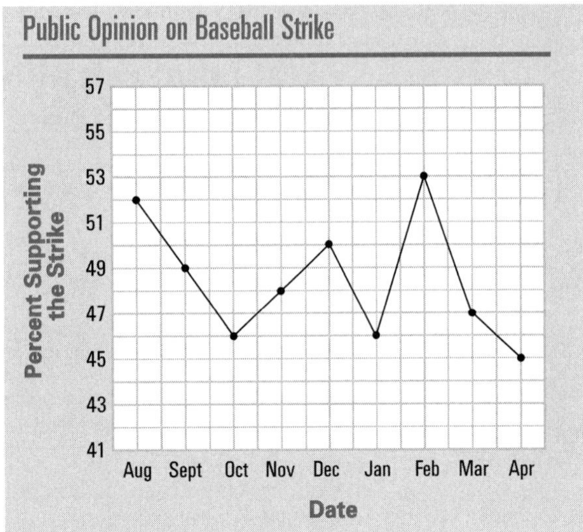

c. Suppose you represented the owners of a striking team and you wanted to use this information to claim that public support for the strike fluctuated widely over the given time span. Give an argument supporting that claim.

d. Suppose you represented the players and you wanted to claim that public support never wavered. Give an argument supporting that claim.

3. The following formula can be used to estimate the margin of error for a 90% confidence level:

$$\textit{margin of error} = 1.645\sqrt{\frac{\hat{p}\hat{q}}{n}}$$

where $\hat{p}$ (read "*p* hat") is the sample proportion, $\hat{q}$ is $1 - \hat{p}$, and n is the sample size. (This formula should be used only if $n\hat{p} \geq 10$ and $n\hat{q} \geq 10$.)

a. Describe how the margin of error changes in the following cases:

- The sample size increases.
- The sample proportion increases.

b. Find the margin of error for samples of sizes 20 and 80 when $\hat{p} = 0.5$ using the following three methods.

- The above formula
- Your standard box plot charts
- Software, such as the BOXCHART feature of the *Sampling* calculator software, with population percent intervals of 2%

c. Describe and explain any differences among the answers you get using the three different methods.

d. Describe the pattern in the margin of error results for sample size 20 and sample size 80.

Unit 2

4. Read the article below, which appeared in a college campus newspaper.

Cut administration salaries, poll says

Students want top UI (University of Iowa) administrators to reduce their salaries by 6 percent to aid the university in potential budget cuts, the UI Student Government president said Thursday.

That was the most frequent suggestion students voiced to the UISG in response to a mass e-mail last week soliciting input on how to cut the university budget, UISG President Nick Klenske announced Thursday.

From the 20 responses, the most reported recommendation was for the administration to take a 6 percent salary reduction, a gesture in response to the proposed 6 percent (budget) cut. Some students also called on coaches and other workers in the Athletics Department to take similar cuts from the portions of their salaries that are state-funded.

Administrations, who don't interact face-to-face with the students, should take the cut instead of teaching assistants and professors, Klenske said

"Those who directly teach the students shouldn't suffer," he said. "When we need to make cuts we should target non-educational aspects of the UI first."

Source: *The Daily Iowan*, April 27, 2001.

a. Critique this poll and the conclusion stated in the headline. Use at least two big ideas that you have learned about surveys, samples, and confidence intervals.

b. Would any of the voting models you learned about in Lesson 1 be useful for measuring and analyzing public opinion on the issues in this article? Explain.

5. In Lessons 3 and 4, you considered two basic questions: "Which sample outcomes are likely?" and "What is the population percent?" Explain how to answer each question.

Reflecting

1. Suppose you selected a random sample of 90 registered voters from your town or city, and 90% of the sample preferred candidate A in the local school board election. A 90% confidence interval for the percentage of all registered voters in town who prefer candidate A can be expressed as 90% ± 5%. There are a lot of 90s in this problem! Explain the meaning of each "90."

2. Suppose you read about a survey in the newspaper, but no margin of error nor sample size is given. What conclusions can you draw?

3. Describe two situations in which the margin of error would make you question the conclusions drawn from a survey.

4. Jeri said that confidence intervals were difficult for her to understand at first. She said it took her a while to realize that what you are confident in is not really a particular interval, but rather a method of generating intervals. Explain what you think she means by this statement.

5. Refer to Activity 7 Part c, page 157. Draw a diagram that you think illustrates that statement.

162 UNIT 2 • MODELING PUBLIC OPINION

4. **a.** The procedure does not reflect any of the properties of a well-designed survey. Sampling bias is introduced by having people respond by e-mail rather than taking a random sample. The response was to a survey question, but we don't know the exact wording. There is no way to assume that the UI student population, particularly those who do not regularly use e-mail, had any opportunity to respond. There is no indication as to whether the respondents were undergraduate students, graduate students, or students at large. The number in the sample is too low (20) to give a very reliable result. The confidence intervals would be quite wide and thus of little use in estimating the population percent.

   b. In general, preferential voting methods can be used by asking people to rank their choices, or approval voting methods can be used by letting people choose more than one, that is, choose all those of which they approve.

5. These are the two fundamental questions from Lessons 3 and 4, respectively. You can answer the question, "Which sample outcomes are likely?", by using a 90% box plot, which represents the middle 90% of outcomes from all possible samples of the same size from the given population (for which you know the population percent). A sample outcome is defined to be likely if it falls within this 90% box. You can answer the question, "What is the population percent?", by selecting a random sample from the population in question, finding the sample outcome, and constructing a 90% confidence interval based on the sample outcome. A confidence interval is, roughly speaking, the range of likely population percents. That is, populations that have percents within the range of the confidence interval are those populations for which the specific sample outcome is a likely sample outcome. If this confidence interval is constructed based on 90% box plots, then it is called a 90% confidence interval.

Reflecting

1. The sample size is 90, since the random sample consisted of 90 registered voters. The sample percent is 90%, since 90% of the sample (81 voters) preferred candidate A. A 90% confidence interval was used to estimate the actual population percent. The confidence interval was from 85% to 95%, with the 90% indicating the center of the interval.
2. It would not be good to base any conclusions on such a survey. You need more information. It may be that the people who designed and conducted the survey did not do a careful job. But even if the design was well done, the sample size and margin of error can greatly influence how the results should be interpreted.
3. Answers may vary. For examples in the lesson, see Part c of Activity 4 (page 156) and Organizing Task 3 (page 161).
4. Jeri may mean that even though you construct and report one particular confidence interval, in order to interpret the result correctly, you have to be thinking about the process of theoretically generating all possible confidence intervals. That is, if you draw all possible samples of a given sample size from a given population and generate all possible confidence intervals, then 90% of the confidence intervals will contain the actual population percent. You are, therefore, confident in the process of generating confidence intervals; you are confident that 90% of the confidence intervals generated by the process will be "on target."

See additional Teaching Notes on page T168L.

Extending

1. The phrase "chances are 19 out of 20" indicates that they used a 95% level of confidence. That is, they constructed a 95% confidence interval. The phrase "no more than 2.2 percentage points in either direction" indicates a margin of error of 2.2%. When the article mentions all adults with telephones, that refers to the population. If all adults with phones had been surveyed, the surveyors would have found the population percent, which is likely to be in the confidence interval defined by ±2.2%. Thus, the statement made in the article is a reasonable way to state the confidence level of the survey.
2. **a.** The article reports that 51% of the 750 likely voters in the sample supported Gore. The computed margin of error for this sample percent and sample size is about 0.036 or about 4%. The computed margin of error for this sample percent and sample size is about 0.036. To the nearest percent, the margin of error is 4%, which matches what is stated in the article.

   b. The criteria for using the formula are met. The computed margin of error is about 0.015 or about 1.5%.

   c. The computed margin of error is about 0.030 or about 3.0%, so the confidence interval is about 47.0% to 53.0%.

   d. The margin of error using the given formula is about 0.029 or about 2.9%. This is a little lower than the 3% margin of error reported in the newspaper. It seems that the reporter decided to round to the nearest whole percentage point.

Extending

1. In an article entitled "White House assertions on FBI files are widely rejected, survey shows" from the *Wall Street Journal* (June 6, 1996), the following statement is made:

"Chances are 19 of 20 that if all adults with telephones in the U.S. had been surveyed [instead of surveying just a sample of adults with telephones], the finding would differ from these poll results by no more than 2.2 percentage points in either direction among all adults… ."

Explain the meaning of this statement. Do you think that this is an accurate way to state the "confidence level" of the survey? Your answer and explanation should include a discussion of how the statement relates to the ideas of confidence interval and margin of error.

2. Organizing Task 3, page 161, introduces the margin-of-error formula for a 90% confidence level. If you use a 95% confidence level instead of a 90% level, the margin of error can be estimated using the following formula:

$$\textit{margin of error} = 1.96\sqrt{\frac{\hat{p}\hat{q}}{n}}$$

where $\hat{p}$ is the sample proportion, $\hat{q}$ is $1 - \hat{p}$, and n is the sample size. (This formula should be used only if $n\hat{p} \geq 10$ and $n\hat{q} \geq 10$.)

a. Use this formula to compute the margin of error for the survey reported in the article on the 2000 U.S. presidential campaign at the beginning of the lesson, page 153. Explain any differences between the margin of error stated in the article and the margin of error computed using the above formula.

b. In 1997, the Odyssey company conducted a survey about online services. 18% of 2,500 adults who had computers at home and were at least aware of the online services America Online® and Microsoft Network® rated these services as good or very good. (Source: *New York Times on the Web*, *http://www.nytimes.com*, September 8, 1997.) Are the criteria of $n\hat{p} \geq 10$ and $n\hat{q} \geq 10$ satisfied in this situation? What is the margin of error at a 95% confidence level?

c. A Gallup Poll immediately following the 2000 Democratic National Convention found that 50% of 1,043 adults say that the Democratic Party better represents their values. (Source: The Gallup Organization, August 22, 2000. Available: www.gallup.com/poll/releases) What is a 95% confidence interval for the percentage of all adults at that time who said the Democratic Party better represents their values?

d. In June 2001, the Gallup organization conducted a survey of 1,004 adults about job equity. The organization reported that 32% of the women in the survey believe that men and women enjoy equal job opportunities in the United States. The survey had a margin of error of 3 percentage points. Is this stated margin of error consistent with the formula for margin of error given above? Explain. (Source: The Gallup Organization, June 29, 2001. Available: www.gallup.com/poll/releases)

Unit 2

LESSON 4 • CONFIDENCE INTERVALS: FROM SAMPLE TO POPULATION 163

3. Refer to the formula for the margin of error for a 95% confidence level in Extending Task 2.

   a. Use a sample proportion of 0.5. Describe what happens to the margin of error as the sample size increases. Compare your results here to those you got for a 90% confidence interval in Organizing Task 3 on page 161.

   b. Use a sample proportion of 0.8. How does this affect the change in the margin of error as the sample size increases?

   c. If the sample size increases by factors of 4, 5, and 9, what happens to the margin of error?

4. In an article in *USA Today* about the height of today's athletes, the following statements appeared: "Average heights have leveled, but that doesn't show what's happening in the very tall segment ... 'Though the group has not, on average, increased you may see shifts at the extreme percentile. More people get a chance to reach their maximum,' says [Robert] Malina, [professor of anthropology and kinesiology at the University of Texas]." (Source: *USA Today*, June 6, 1995.) Does this make sense? Can you explain what is meant by the quoted statements?

5. Examine the following chart and read the summary of the poll.

IOWA POLL

Politicians

■ **Iowa's highest-ranking** elected officials are winning strong approval, the Iowa Poll shows.

▶ *Do you approve of the job being done by. . .*	U.S. Sen. Charles Grassley	U.S. Sen. Tom Harkin	Gov. Terry Branstad
Yes	**75%**	**71%**	**70%**
No	**10%**	**16%**	**23%**
Unsure	**15%**	**13%**	**7%**

Based on interviews with 800 Iowa adults.

MARY ELLEN KELLEY / THE REGISTER

Source: *Des Moines Register*, February 24, 1998. Copyright 1998 the Des Moines Register and Tribune Company. Reprinted with permission.

The Iowa Poll, conducted Jan. 31–Feb. 4, asked the following:

I'd like to begin by mentioning the names of some current public figures who hold office. For each, please tell me if you approve or disapprove of the job they are doing. Bill Clinton as president. Al Gore as vice president. Charles Grassley as U.S. senator. Tom Harkin as U.S. senator. Terry Branstad as governor.

The Iowa Poll, conducted for The Des Moines Register by Selzer and Co. Inc. of Des Moines, is based on interviews with 800 Iowans age 18 or older. Interviewers contacted households with randomly selected telephone numbers. Percentages based on the full sample may have a maximum margin of error of plus or minus 3.5 percentage points. Republishing the copyrighted Iowa Poll without credit to The Des Moines Register is prohibited.

   a. Does the summary of the poll provide enough information for you to accept the results with confidence? Explain, based on the analysis of background information you carried out in Lesson 2.

   b. Based on this poll and the information given, estimate the confidence interval for the percentage of all adults in Iowa who approve of Senator Grassley. Explain how you determined the confidence interval.

   c. A major poll like this typically uses a large sample size and a 95% confidence level. However, consider a simpler situation. Suppose that, in a random sample of 100 Iowa adults, 75% approved of Senator Grassley. Based on such a poll, what is a 90% confidence interval for the percentage of all adults in Iowa who approve of Senator Grassley?

   d. Compare the confidence intervals in Parts b and c. Explain any similarities and differences.

164 UNIT 2 • MODELING PUBLIC OPINION

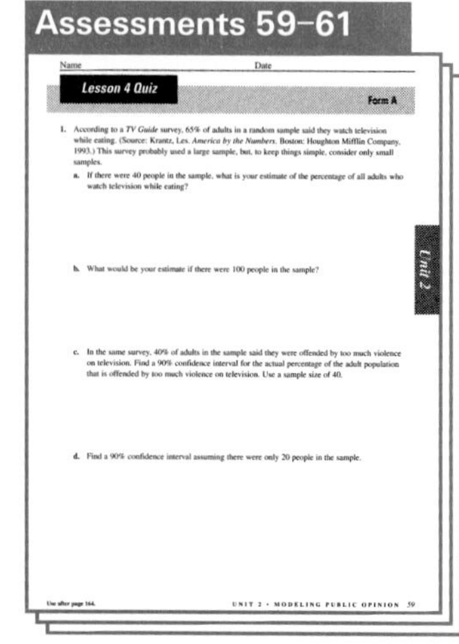

Assessments 59–61

Name Date

Lesson 4 Quiz **Form A**

1. According to a *TV Guide* survey, 65% of adults in a random sample said they watch television while eating. (Source: Krantz, Les. *America by the Numbers*. Boston: Houghton Mifflin Company, 1993.) This survey probably used a large sample, but, to keep things simple, consider only small samples.
   a. If there were 40 people in the sample, what is your estimate of the percentage of all adults who watch television while eating?
   b. What would be your estimate if there were 100 people in the sample?
   c. In the same survey, 40% of adults in the sample said they were offended by too much violence on television. Find a 90% confidence interval for the actual percentage of the adult population that is offended by too much violence on television. Use a sample size of 40.
   d. Find a 90% confidence interval assuming there were only 20 people in the sample.

Unit 2

Use after page 164. UNIT 2 • MODELING PUBLIC OPINION 59

3. **a.** When $\hat{p} = 0.5$ in the formula, the margin of error becomes very close to $\sqrt{\frac{1}{n}}$. Thus, as sample size increases, margin of error decreases. This is the same conclusion as in Organizing Task 3.
   b. When $\hat{p} = 0.8$, the formula for margin of error is different than for $\hat{p} = 0.5$, but the pattern is still the same because of the n in the denominator of the fraction. That is, as sample size increases, margin of error decreases.
   c. Looking more closely at the formula, you see that it can be rewritten as $\frac{1}{\sqrt{n}} \cdot 1.96\sqrt{\hat{p}\hat{q}}$. This shows that the margin of error varies inversely with the square root of the sample size. Thus, if the sample size increases by factors of 4, 5, and 9, then the margin of error decreases by factors of $\frac{1}{2}$, $\frac{1}{\sqrt{5}}$ or approximately 0.45, and $\frac{1}{3}$, respectively.
4. The speaker seems to be saying that although the average height of an athlete has remained at the same level, those in the highest percentiles may be taller than ever. This should cause one to wonder how the tallest group can grow taller if the average stays the same. If the average used is the mean, this can happen only if the other groups are shorter. If the average used is the median, then it would not change if only the tallest group got taller. It's not clear what is meant by the last statement. Perhaps the speaker meant that through better nutrition, or for some other reason, more athletes grow as tall as they possibly can. Again, this would cause one to wonder why the average has not been raised as other groups are allowed to reach their maximum as well.

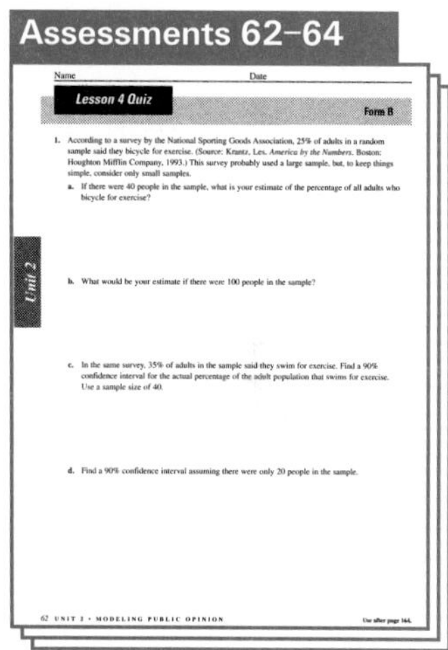

Assessments 62–64

Name Date

Lesson 4 Quiz **Form B**

1. According to a survey by the National Sporting Goods Association, 25% of adults in a random sample said they bicycle for exercise. (Source: Krantz, Les. *America by the Numbers*. Boston: Houghton Mifflin Company, 1993.) This survey probably used a large sample, but, to keep things simple, consider only small samples.
   a. If there were 40 people in the sample, what is your estimate of the percentage of all adults who bicycle for exercise?
   b. What would be your estimate if there were 100 people in the sample?
   c. In the same survey, 35% of adults in the sample said they swim for exercise. Find a 90% confidence interval for the actual percentage of the adult population that swims for exercise. Use a sample size of 40.
   d. Find a 90% confidence interval assuming there were only 20 people in the sample.

Unit 2

62 UNIT 2 • MODELING PUBLIC OPINION Use after page 164.

5. **a.** This poll seems to have been carried out and reported well. For example, the following important questions from Lesson 2 are adequately answered and reported: What is the issue of interest? [approval ratings] Who sponsored the survey? [*The Des Moines Register*] What is the population? [Iowans age 18 or older] How was the sample selected? [randomly selected phone numbers] How large is the sample? [800] What was the response rate? [not stated] How were the responses obtained? [telephone interviews] What were the exact questions asked? [exact interview script is given]
   b. The article states that the "maximum margin of error" is 3.5 percentage points. Based on this given margin of error, an estimate for the confidence interval for Grassley is 71.5%–78.5%. (Note that by using the formula given in Extending Task 2 on page 163 to estimate the margin of error at a 95% confidence level, we get that the margin of error for Grassley is about 0.03; for Harkin the margin of error is about 0.031; and for Branstad it is about 0.032. Approval of Al Gore was also reported, although not included in the excerpt in the text, and the margin of error for Gore would be about 0.034. It is common practice to report the largest margin of error, as indicated by the statement of the "maximum margin of error plus or minus 3.5 percentage points" in the article, but this is still higher than 0.034. One would need more information to resolve this small discrepancy.)
   c. Based on such a poll and a 90% box plot chart (Teaching Master 55d), the 90% confidence interval would be 70%–80%. If students use the formulas in Organizing Task 3 and Extending Task 2 they will find a margin of error of about 7% for the 90% confidence level and about 3% for the 95% confidence level.
   d. The confidence interval in Part b is narrower. In Part b, there is a higher confidence level and a larger sample size. In general, a higher confidence level produces a wider confidence interval, while a larger sample size produces a narrower confidence interval. In this case, these two conflicting effects resulted in a narrower confidence interval, because the sample size was so much larger.

See Assessment Resources pages 59–64.

Unit 2

Lesson 5 *Looking Back*

SYNTHESIZE UNIT IDEAS small-group activity

1. Student work will vary. Be sure students choose questions that involve just two alternatives, preferably "yes" and "no." It helps to have students critique each other's questions or poll several people with their questions in order to ensure that the respondents interpret the questions in the way intended by the author. The two questions in the surveys are examples of the major topics and different points of view in Lessons 3 and 4. In Lesson 3, students worked "from population to sample" as they investigated sampling distributions and likely sample outcomes. This corresponds to the question about left-handedness. The population percent is already known, and students can analyze their survey results in terms of how likely their sample outcome is. In Lesson 4, students worked "from sample to population" as they investigated confidence intervals and margin of error. This corresponds to the students' own questions. In this situation, students can use a confidence interval to estimate the population percent from a sample percent.

Lesson 5

Looking Back

In this unit, you have studied two mathematical methods for measuring and analyzing public opinion: voting and surveys. You learned about different methods of voting, such as preferential voting and approval voting. Using preferential voting, you found that different vote-analysis methods, such as plurality and points-for-preferences, can yield different winners. These methods also can be applied to help gather and summarize survey data. While voting is used in situations in which every person has the opportunity to vote, sample surveys are used to estimate public opinion based on the opinions of just a few individuals in the population. You used confidence intervals and margin of error to make such estimates and to describe the level of confidence in the estimate. In this lesson, you will review and pull together all these key ideas related to voting and surveys.

1. Conduct and interpret the results of a survey as described below.

a. Working with a partner, prepare a two-question survey.

- For the first question, think of a school-related question about which you would like to gather information. Design your question so that it has a "yes" or "no" answer. (For example: *Should the winter dance be formal? Should the school change its mascot? Are you in favor of the new library policy?*)
- For the second question, assume that approximately 10% of the population is left-handed. Your question is: *Are you left-handed?*

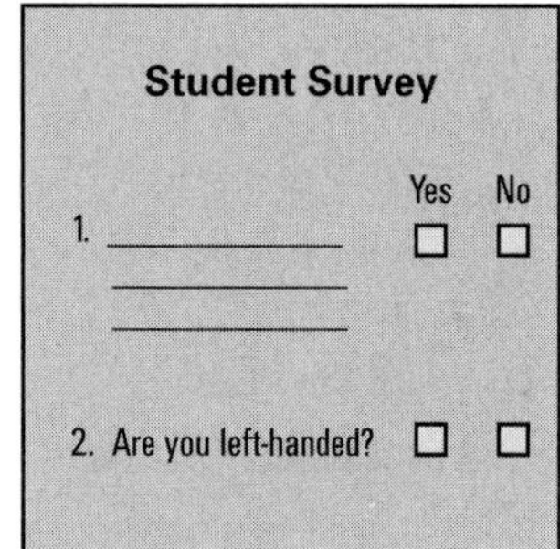

b. Randomly select 20 students and ask them your two questions.

c. Summarize the results of your survey for each question. Draw any conclusions that you think are reasonable. Explain your conclusions.

d. Describe the differences in the conclusions you drew, the reasoning you used, and your methods of analysis for the two different questions.

LESSON 5 • LOOKING BACK 165

2. Examine this *Fan Favorites* clipping from *USA Today*.

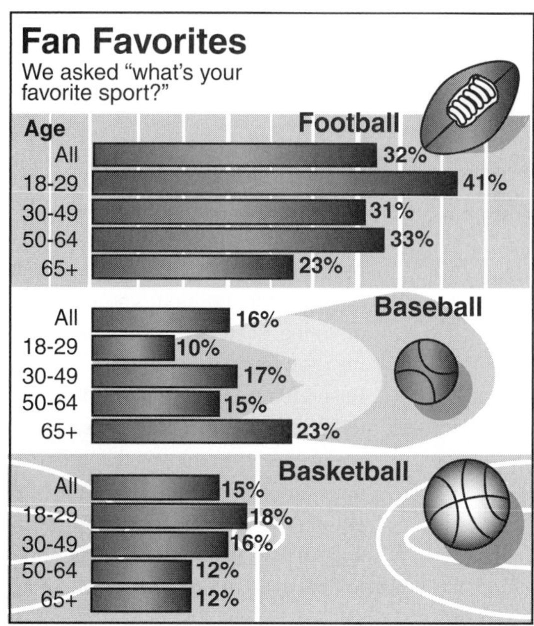

Source: *USA Today,* May 26, 1995.

a. Describe two trends in the data that are interesting or surprising to you.

b. In Lesson 2, you analyzed surveys based on several basic questions and criteria. Referring to those questions, do you think you have been given enough information to understand and accept the results of the *Fan Favorites* survey? Explain.

c. Suppose the results shown for 18- to 29-year-olds are based on a random sample of 100 people aged 18 to 29 in Akron, Ohio. About what percent of all 18- to 29-year-olds in Akron would indicate football as their favorite sport? Express your answer as a confidence interval.

d. The question asked in the poll was "What's your favorite sport?" What kind of voting method does this suggest? Reword the question so that preferential voting methods could be used to gather and summarize the sample data.

166 UNIT 2 • MODELING PUBLIC OPINION

2. a. Possible trends include: the age distributions vary greatly from sport to sport. Of those over the age of 64, only 58% had favorites in these three sports, while 69% of those aged 18–29 chose one of the three. Overall, the sports are ranked football-baseball-basketball.

b. Following are some of the questions that should be considered:

- What is the population being studied?
- How were the people who were polled chosen from that population?
- How many people were polled?
- What was the question they were asked? (In particular, were any other sports listed as responses?)
- Were people allowed to give more than one choice if they had two favorite sports?
- What is the margin of error?
- Who sponsored the survey, and what interests does the sponsor have in the outcome of the survey?
- In cases in which the percentages do not add up to 100, what were the other responses?

Very few of these questions have been answered. The survey results may be interesting, but there is not enough information given about the survey for the results to be accepted as general facts or for the results to be used in any substantive way.

c. If the results shown for 18- to 29-year-olds are based on a random sample of 100 18- to 29-year-olds in Akron, then a 90% confidence interval for the percent of all 18- to 29-year-olds in Akron who indicate football as their favorite sport is 35%–45%. This can be seen by the three boxes above 41 on the 90% Box Plots from Samples of Size 100.

d. The question suggests the plurality method of voting, in which voters vote for their favorite and the candidate with the most votes wins. If the survey had asked, "List your first three favorite sports in order of preference" or "Rank football, baseball, and basketball in order of your preference," then the surveyors could have used, for example, points-for-preferences or pairwise-comparison methods to summarize the sample data.

3. **a.** Here, you know the population percent (15%) and need to decide whether a particular sample total (10) is likely. Check to see if the sample outcome is in the 90% box plot for the given population and the given sample size. The range of this box plot is approximately 3 to 10. Since 10 is in this range, it is a likely sample outcome.

   b. Answers will vary, depending on the simulation. You could simulate selecting a random sample by generating 20 random integers, each between 1 and 100 inclusive. The number of people in the sample not covered by health insurance corresponds to the number of occurrences of the numbers 1 through 15 in the 20 random numbers. The range of the 90% box plot for samples of size 20 from a population with population percent of 15% is 1 to 6. The simulated sample outcome is likely if it is in this range.

   c. About 90% of the samples would yield likely sample outcomes. So about 450 of the simulated sample outcomes would be likely.

4. The "winners" under various voting methods are as follows:
   - Majority: no winner
   - Plurality: Calaveras, with 6,692 first-preference votes out of a total of 13,386 votes
   - Points-for-preferences: Jefferson, with 41,397 points using a 4-3-2-1 point assignment
   - Runoff method: Jefferson, with 6,694 votes to Calaveras's 6,692 votes
   - Pairwise-comparison method: Jefferson, with 3 pairwise wins
   - Approval voting (assuming each person votes for his or her first two choices): Jefferson, with 10,352 approval votes

   Students might choose Jefferson or Calaveras as the winner. However, the evidence very strongly favors Jefferson as the winner since Jefferson wins under so many methods other than plurality. In particular, Jefferson wins under points-for-preferences and pairwise-comparison, which are the methods most widely recommended by experts.

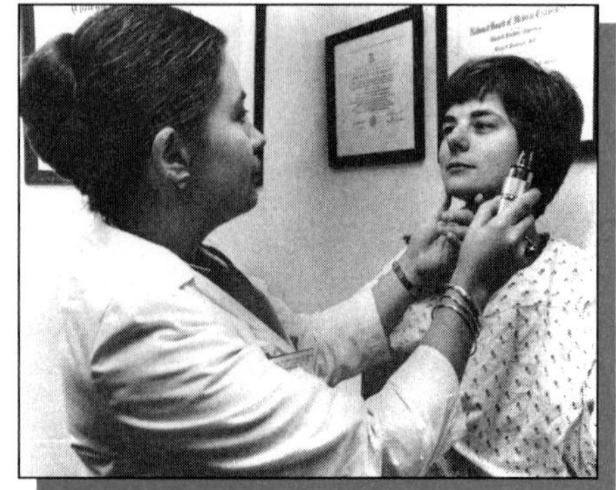

3. Approximately 15% of all people in the United States were not covered by health insurance in 1998. (Source: U.S. Census Bureau, *Statistical Abstract of the United States: 2000*. Washington, D.C., 2000.) Assume that figure is still valid today.

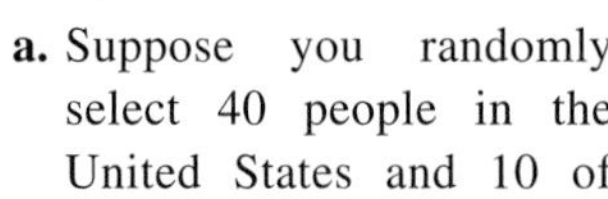

   a. Suppose you randomly select 40 people in the United States and 10 of them are not covered by health insurance. Is this a likely sample outcome? Explain.

   b. Simulate a random sample of 20 people from this population and find the number of people in the sample who are not covered by health insurance. Is your simulated sample outcome likely?

   c. Imagine simulating 500 random samples of size 80. (Don't actually do it!) How many of the simulated sample outcomes will be likely outcomes?

4. A new sanitary landfill is to be located in one of four neighboring counties: Calaveras, Montclair, Jefferson, or King. All residents voted on where they thought it should be located, with the results shown in the following preference table.

Landfill Preference Table

	Rankings				
Calaveras	1	1	3	4	4
Montclair	3	4	4	1	3
Jefferson	2	3	1	2	1
King	4	2	2	3	2
Number of Voters	3,658	3,034	2,518	2,421	1,755

If the location of the landfill is to be decided based on these data, in which county should the landfill be built? Justify your answer. Your analysis should include finding the "winner" using at least two different vote-analysis methods.

LESSON 5 • LOOKING BACK 167

Unit 2

Checkpoint

In this unit, you have studied a variety of concepts and techniques for measuring and analyzing public opinion.

a List and explain two or three important points you have learned about voting. Give an example illustrating each point.

b When public opinion is estimated by sample surveys, issues of bias, sample selection, and interpretation need to be carefully considered.

- What does it mean for the design of a survey to be biased? Give an example of a source of bias in a survey.
- Describe and give an example of a simple random sample. Why is random sampling a good method of sample selection?
- List and discuss at least four key questions that you should ask when analyzing any survey.

c Describe connections and differences between 90% box plots and 90% confidence intervals. Give an example of a question that can be answered using a single 90% box plot. Give an example of a question that can be answered using a 90% confidence interval.

d In this unit, you learned how to draw conclusions about samples based on information about the population. You also learned how to reason in the opposite direction, that is, how to make inferences about a population based on information about a sample.

- Lesson 3 is entitled, "Sampling Distributions: From Population to Sample." Explain how finding sampling distributions and 90% box plots involves reasoning "from population to sample."
- Lesson 4 is entitled, "Confidence Intervals: From Sample to Population." Explain how finding confidence intervals involves reasoning "from sample to population."

Be prepared to share your descriptions and thinking with the entire class.

On Your Own

Write, in outline form, a summary of the important mathematical concepts and methods developed in this unit. Organize your summary so that it can be used as a quick reference in future units and courses.

168 UNIT 2 • MODELING PUBLIC OPINION

SHARE AND SUMMARIZE full-class discussion

Checkpoint

See Teaching Masters 60a–60b.

Masters 60a–60b

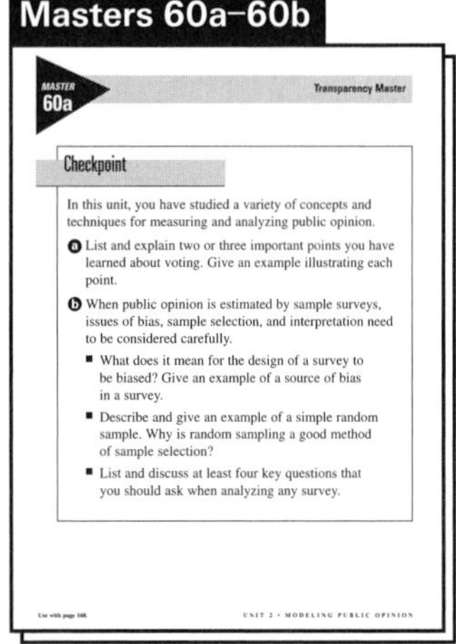

MASTER 60a — Transparency Master

Checkpoint

In this unit, you have studied a variety of concepts and techniques for measuring and analyzing public opinion.

a List and explain two or three important points you have learned about voting. Give an example illustrating each point.

b When public opinion is estimated by sample surveys, issues of bias, sample selection, and interpretation need to be considered carefully.

- What does it mean for the design of a survey to be biased? Give an example of a source of bias in a survey.
- Describe and give an example of a simple random sample. Why is random sampling a good method of sample selection?
- List and discuss at least four key questions that you should ask when analyzing any survey.

a Students might list some of the following points:

There is a variety of reasonable voting methods, including plurality, runoff, points-for-preferences, pairwise-comparison, and approval voting. All but the last of these methods are based on preferential voting, in which voters rank the candidates instead of voting for just their favorite. This gives richer data that can be used to measure and analyze public opinion. Different voting methods can produce different winners. Whenever there are three or more candidates, Arrow's Theorem shows that no voting method will always yield fair results, using Arrow's definition of "fair." That is, there are drawbacks to all voting methods. In some situations, they can all produce "paradoxical" results. Even though no voting method is perfect, the most widely recommended voting method is points-for-preferences, in which the point assignments form an arithmetic sequence (like 4-3-2-1).

Voting methods can also be used to gather, summarize, and analyze survey data. By using voting methods in surveys, for example, asking people to rank their choices, and then analyzing results with the points-for-preferences method, you may be able to improve survey results.

Unit 2 Summary

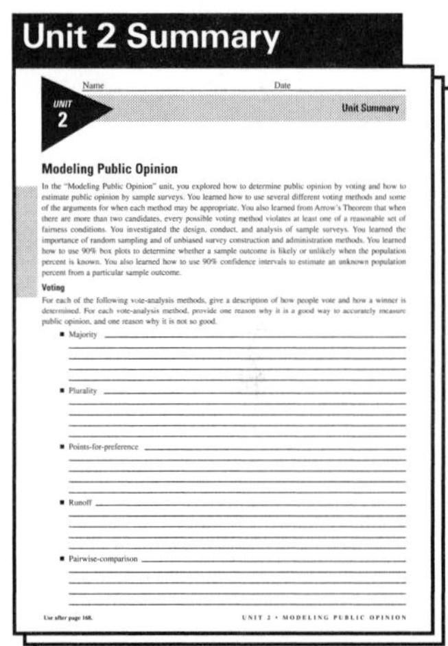

Name Date

UNIT 2 — Unit Summary

Modeling Public Opinion

In the "Modeling Public Opinion" unit, you explored how to determine public opinion by voting and how to estimate public opinion by sample surveys. You learned how to use several different voting methods and some of the arguments for when each method may be appropriate. You also learned from Arrow's Theorem that when there are more than two candidates, every possible voting method violates at least one of a reasonable set of fairness conditions. You investigated the design, conduct, and analysis of sample surveys. You learned the importance of random sampling and of unbiased survey construction and administration methods. You learned how to use 90% box plots to determine whether a sample outcome is likely or unlikely when the population percent is known. You also learned how to use 90% confidence intervals to estimate an unknown population percent from a particular sample outcome.

Voting

For each of the following vote-analysis methods, give a description of how people vote and how a winner is determined. For each vote-analysis method, provide one reason why it is a good way to accurately measure public opinion, and one reason why it is not so good.

- Majority
- Plurality
- Points-for-preference
- Runoff
- Pairwise-comparison

b
- Bias is, roughly, systematic deviation from the truth. For example, the design of a survey that measures the percentage of people having some characteristic is biased if, under repeated sampling, the average of the percentages is above or below the actual population percent. Some sources of bias are poor wording of questions, poor interview methods, poor sample selection, and nonresponse.
- Selecting a simple random sample is like drawing a handful of names out of a hat. More precisely, a simple random sample of size n is a collection of n individuals from a population chosen in such a way that every collection of n individuals has an equal chance of being the one selected. For example, you could select a random sample of students from your school by getting a numbered list of all students in the school and then choosing students based on random numbers. Random sampling is a good way to reduce bias.
- Important questions that need to be asked and answered when analyzing surveys include the following: What is the issue of interest? Who sponsored the survey? What is the population? How was the sample selected? How large is the sample? What was the response rate? How were the responses obtained? What were the exact questions asked?

As students discuss these questions, they might include such things as the importance of random sampling when selecting a sample (to reduce bias), carefully worded survey questions (to reduce bias), and large samples whenever possible (to reduce variability).

Assessments 65–82

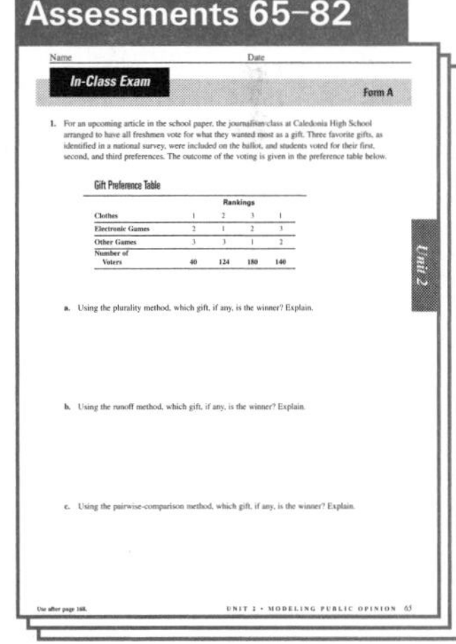

Name Date

In-Class Exam — Form A

1. For an upcoming article in the school paper, the journalism class at Caledonia High School arranged to have all freshmen vote for what they wanted most as a gift. Three favorite gifts, as identified in a national survey, were included on the ballot, and students voted for their first, second, and third preferences. The outcome of the voting is given in the preference table below.

Gift Preference Table

	Rankings			
Clothes	1	2	3	1
Electronic Games	2	1	2	3
Other Games	3	3	1	2
Number of Voters	40	124	180	140

a. Using the plurality method, which gift, if any, is the winner? Explain.

b. Using the runoff method, which gift, if any, is the winner? Explain.

c. Using the pairwise-comparison method, which gift, if any, is the winner? Explain.

Unit 2

See additional Teaching Notes on page T168M.

Looking Back, Looking Ahead

Unit 2

Reflecting on Mathematical Content

In this unit, students have investigated ways to measure and analyze public opinion. They have used two methods to do this: voting and sample surveys. Thus, this unit has provided a unique opportunity to blend the mathematical analysis of two different, yet related, topics.

With regard to voting, students learned that in many situations it makes sense to use preferential voting (rank the candidates) or approval voting (vote for all candidates of whom you approve), in addition to the commonly used method of simply voting for your favorite candidate. Also, they discovered that there are many reasonable ways to analyze the results of preferential voting and that different methods can produce different winners. Furthermore, they saw that whenever there are more than two candidates, all voting methods have drawbacks and can yield results that seem unfair.

With regard to sample surveys, students developed an understanding of basic ideas related to survey design, such as bias and random sampling; they learned how to define and analyze likely sample outcomes using sampling distributions and 90% box plots; and they learned how to use a sample to make an inference about a population, using confidence intervals and margin of error. Voting methods were seen to be useful in terms of collecting and summarizing sample data.

This unit continued the development of such important ideas as simulation and variability, previously developed in the Course 1 units "Patterns in Data" and "Simulation Models" and in the Course 2 unit "Patterns in Chance." Subsequent units in the *Contemporary Mathematics in Context* curriculum will continue some of the analysis begun here. In Unit 5, "Patterns in Variation," students will study the normal distribution as a model of variation, measure variation by the number of standard deviations from the mean, and are introduced to the probability and statistical inference involved in control charts used in industry for statistical process control. The sampling distributions studied in this unit are examples of an important type of distribution called the *binomial distribution*, which will be examined carefully in Course 4 Unit 5. Also, finding a confidence interval is one aspect of the process of statistical inference, whereby you use a sample to make inferences about a population; this process, too, will be studied further in Course 4 Unit 5 when students learn additional methods for finding confidence intervals and also learn about hypothesis testing.

Unit 2 Assessment

Lesson Quizzes	Assessment Resources
Lesson 1 *Voting Models*	pp. 43–48
Lesson 2 *Surveys and Samples*	pp. 49–52
Lesson 3 *Sampling Distributions: from Population to Sample*	pp. 53–58
Lesson 4 *Confidence Intervals: from Sample to Population*	pp. 59–64
In-Class Exams	
Form A	pp. 65–70
Form B	pp. 71–76
Take-Home Assessments	pp. 77–78
Unit 2 Projects	
The Presidential Election	pp. 79–80
A Survey of Your Choice	pp. 81–82

Notes continued from page T92

a A survey of students might be conducted. In this case, there may be some discussion about how to conduct the survey, for example, at lunchtime when a cross section of the students is readily available or by selecting a random sampling. Other options are to conduct a census or hold an election. For an election, students could vote for their favorite or rank the candidates. Encourage a variety of responses, but students needn't mention all of the options above.

b One advantage is that it requires less time to sample some students than to question all students. It's also easier to count and tabulate the results. A disadvantage is that not all opinions are considered. It might be difficult to decide fairly which students to survey.

c An advantage is that everyone's opinion is taken into account. It might be easier to hand out a ballot to every student than to choose which students fill out a survey. A disadvantage is that more time is required to conduct the voting and evaluate the results. The opinions of people who don't go to fast-food restaurants would count as much as those who do.

d Voting is used in political elections. A family may vote on where to go for a vacation. The class may vote by a show of hands to elect a student representative. Judges of a sporting event may vote by evaluating each contestant and then averaging the scores. Voting is carried out and analyzed in different ways in these different situations. For example, voters may vote for their favorite candidate or rank the candidates. The results may be analyzed by tally, weighted total, averaging, or other methods. (You may wish to return to this item at the end of the unit when students will be able to better identify voting methods.)

Notes continued from page T104

SHARE AND SUMMARIZE full-class discussion

Checkpoint

See Teaching Master 43.

a. First, a definition of fairness must be written, including axioms, or conditions to be met. Then a voting method is considered fair if it satisfies all of the axioms.

b. **Encourage students to express their own ideas about what fairness is. They may find that, by listening to the ideas of others, they will want to change their own ideas. One informal way to analyze Arrow's fairness conditions is in terms of public opinion. A fair voting method should yield results that accurately reflect public opinion.**

- **Unanimous** Certainly if every voter prefers candidate *X*, then a fair voting method should produce the result that *X* is preferred. Otherwise, every voter would have his or her preference violated, and the result would in no way reflect public opinion.
- **Decisive** This condition is necessary to assure that there is an outcome.
- **Ordered** It is natural to think that if *X* is preferred over *Y* and *Y* is preferred over *Z*, then *X* is preferred over *Z*. Otherwise, there is no way to establish an ordering of candidates.
- **Consistent** This seems fair because voter opinion should determine the winner. Thus, if voter preferences change and are even more strongly in favor of the original winner, then that candidate should still be the winner.
- **Relevant** Given the opinions of the people with regard to *X* versus *Y*, the voting method should produce a result that reflects those opinions. **Although this sounds reasonable, it has been suggested that this condition in particular does not contribute adequately to the definition of fairness. For more information, see "Are Individual Rights Possible?" by Donald G. Saari (*Mathematics Magazine* 70, No. 2 (April 1997): 83–92).**
- **Non-Dictatorship** Our understanding of fairness is that the opinions of everyone should be taken into account; no one person is more important than any other person, and certainly no one person should dominate all others.

Notes continued from page T117

- The issue of interest or variable being studied tells you what the goal of the survey was.
- The sponsors of a survey can word questions or structure the process to bias the outcomes toward their special interest.
- The population tells to whom the survey results are supposed to apply.
- The way the sample was selected tells you if reliable conclusions can be drawn about the population. For example, in a survey concerning public opinion about a presidential candidate, you would not want to ask only women or only men, and asking only your friends is not likely to give a representative response.
- The number of people in your sample is important to know because if the sample is too small relative to the size of the population, the results are not likely to be representative of the entire population.
- If the response rate isn't high, then it's possible that the people who chose to respond are different in a significant way from the others.
- The method of obtaining the responses can affect the results. For example, if people watching a news show respond to a question about a particular news story by calling a toll-free telephone number, then only those watching and those motivated enough to call will influence the results.
- Often the questions asked can be interpreted several ways. It is important to know exactly to what people thought they were responding. Thus, you need to know the exact questions asked so that you can decide how to interpret the results. For example, there is a difference between the questions, "Do you think the extreme violence in movies today is too much?" and "Do you think today's movies have too much violence in them?"

Notes continued from page T126

2. You should get a random sample. This might be done as follows: Suppose there are 426 students in the school. You could get an ordered list of all the students; then generate 30 random numbers between 1 and 426 and choose the students with those numbers to be in the sample.

3.
- This is not a simple random sample, since no group of 50 that contains a teenaged driver who doesn't attend high school has a chance of being selected.
- This is a simple random sample. All groups of size 50 have an equal chance of being selected.
- This is not a simple random sample since, for example, the sample of size 50 that consists of drivers #2, #4, #6, …, #100 cannot be chosen.

Notes continued from page T134

2. c. The information collected by the Census is privileged information, and, by Federal law, individual personal information cannot be given to any individual or organization, including the rest of the government. (At times, other governmental agencies have wanted access to this information but consistently have lost the argument. The Census Bureau realizes that people will be less likely to respond if they know that the IRS, for example, could also use the information.)

   Census information is used by other branches of the government to make decisions and plan policy. It also is released in summary form to others who are interested and can use the information, such as businesses, city governments, hospitals, and those tracking health and disease trends.

   d. There are seven basic questions that people must answer: name and address, age, sex, race, relationship to head of household, marital status, and visitors in the home when the Census is taken. A subgroup is given a "long form" that contains other questions of interest for that particular Census.

   e. Because it is difficult to take a census of those who are homeless or who are illegal immigrants, the Census tends to undercount some groups. These individuals may not be typical of the number of people residing in a household and relying on a given income. In addition, African-American and Hispanic people traditionally have been underrepresented in the Census. The results can make a difference in a city's population, which will affect the representation in Congress as well as federal money for social programs, and so on.

   (Source: Wallechinsky and Wallace. *The People's Almanac*. Garden City, New York: Doubleday & Company, Inc., 1975.)

3. Students can use any question they think might be of interest and introduce bias, for example, by using leading words ("Wouldn't you like ..." or "Doesn't it seem unreasonable that ..."), double negatives, or vocabulary that sounds positive or negative.

See Assessment Resources pages 49–52.

Notes continued from page T135

- To define and investigate the notion of "a likely sample outcome" using 90% box plots
- To investigate and describe how changing the population percent or the sample size will change the 90% box plot
- To construct and use a chart of 90% box plots for different population percents and a fixed sample size

LAUNCH full-class discussion

Think About This Situation

See Teaching Master 51.

a You would expect about 50 heads out of 100 coin tosses.

b It would be unlikely that a friend would get exactly the same number of heads.

c It is unlikely that 90 heads will occur, but it is possible.

d Responses may vary. There is no reason to assume that a coin that gives 55 heads out of 100 tosses is unfair. A coin that gives 95 heads out of 100 tosses has a good chance of being unfair. The conclusion is less certain for a coin that gives 65 heads in 100 tosses. One of the things students will learn is a way to determine if 65 heads out of 100 tosses could have occurred, if the coin is really fair.

Notes continued from page T136

1. e. The outcomes in which the number of heads is near 25 are most likely. These outcomes appear in the center of the number line plot. The outcomes in which there are very few heads or close to 50 heads are very unlikely. The unlikely outcomes appear in the left and right "tails" of the number line plot. The exact cutoff between likely and unlikely outcomes may cause much debate. Such debate is good, but you shouldn't allow it to take up too much class time. A definite criterion for this cutoff will be given after Activity 2.

2. a. This distribution is similar in that most of the samples occurred in the center of the range. It is probably different from the class's distribution in the exact number of samples for each outcome and the values of the different outcomes. (Unless your class consists of 30 students, the class will not have 60 sample outcomes.) Since the outcome of a coin toss is random and unpredictable, we would not expect that two different sets of 60 sample outcomes would be exactly the same.

b. Large numbers of heads (near 50) and small numbers of heads (near 0) are unlikely. The unlikely outcomes appear at the edges (top and bottom or left and right) of the distribution. The likely outcomes appear near the center of the distribution.

Notes continued from page T140

1. The theoretical likely range is 3 to 10. A given group of students should work on just one of Parts a, b, and c. They should work together to figure out how to construct a 90% box plot using simulation. Each of the three situations in this activity has the same sample size (30) and the same population percent (20%). Thus, they are mathematically equivalent. However, students may not see this. They may see three different contexts, and, therefore, three very different problems. One goal of this activity is for students to understand that the three problems are "the same." However, because students are simulating small numbers of samples, the three box plots generated will probably be slightly different.
2. Perhaps the most efficient way for students to compare plots is to place them above a scale on the board or wall. The 90% box plots will be very similar for the different situations, because each situation has the same sample size and population percent. There will be small differences because of the random nature of the simulation process and the relatively small number of samples. It is most important at this time to focus on the similarities and not the differences.

EXPLORE small-group investigation

Notes continued from page T143

INVESTIGATION 3 Standard Charts for Different Sample Sizes

In this investigation, the analysis moves from box plots constructed by simulation to standard box plots constructed by mathematical theory. The advantage of using standard box plots is that the variability among box plots that you encountered with small number simulations is eliminated. (Of course, box plots constructed by simulation with a large number of samples should be close to the theoretical ones.) Also in this investigation, sample outcomes will include sample proportions, as well as sample totals.

1. The centers of the boxes would be in different places, and the boxes would have different widths. Students need not describe precise changes at this time.

Notes continued from page T147

C
- The "90%" in the phrase "90% box plot" means that 90% of all possible samples of the same size from the same population will have a sample outcome that falls in the box. As an example, if the 90% box plot ranges from 8 to 16, then 90% of samples will have a sample total between 8 and 16, inclusive.
- A 95% box plot would give an interval that includes the sample outcomes from 95% of all possible samples. This would be a larger interval than the one given by a 90% box. Thus, if we redefine a likely outcome to be one in the middle 95% of all possible sample outcomes, there would be a greater number of likely sample outcomes based on a 95% box plot.

Notes continued from page T153

LAUNCH full-class discussion

In launching this lesson, you may wish to read over the article about the 2000 presidential election with students. Ask them what observations they can make about this poll. They should be able to identify ideas that they learned in the previous three lessons, but they may need prompting to find new ideas. Students may mention the implied associated voting method, the size of the sample, the population being represented, the apparent questions asked, and the sample proportion. You may want to point out the language about "error" as a new idea. You also may want to have other examples of polls that quote margins of error other than 4%. (*USA Today* often has polls that can be used.) After discussing the "Think About This Situation" questions, you might ask, "Do we know the proportion of the population that will vote for Gore? Do we know the proportion of the sample that will vote for Gore?" Tell students that this is an important distinction between the things we know and the things about which we are going to make probabilistic judgments.

Notes continued from page T155

3. a. This sample outcome is a likely outcome for samples drawn from populations with the following percents: 45%, 50%, 55%, 60%, and 65%. Thus, the interval of likely population percents is 45%–65%. It seems reasonable that if we find all the population percents for which the sample outcome is likely, then the actual population percent will probably be one of those percents. Thus, the interval of all such population percents provides a reasonable estimate for the actual (unknown) population percent.

Notes continued from page T157

6. **d.** About 90% of the confidence intervals will contain the actual population percent. Of course, the results from class to class will vary, so you should be prepared to deal with results that may not be very close to 90%. An explanation is given below; also see the comments in Part b of Activity 5.

   This empirical experiment should help students understand the important point that a given confidence interval may not contain the actual population percent. In fact, only about 90% of all possible confidence intervals will contain the actual population percent. This can be explained as follows.

   You begin with a given target population. Then you draw a random sample from that population. Ninety percent of the time, the sample you draw is a likely sample. That is, the sample outcome is in the 90% box for that population. In this case, the confidence interval will contain the actual population percent because in implementing the box-chart procedure for constructing a confidence interval, you will "hit" the target population's 90% box. But 10% of the time, you will get a sample that yields an unlikely sample outcome. In this case, the sample outcome will not be in the 90% box for the given target population. So the confidence interval will not contain the actual population percent because now when you use the box-chart procedure to find a confidence interval, you will not hit the target population's 90% box. Hence, if you select many random samples from the target population and construct a confidence interval based on each sample, then about 10% of those confidence intervals will not contain the actual population percent.

NOTE: There is a fine point that you may or may not decide to discuss with your students. It's not precisely true, even theoretically, that 90% of all possible confidence intervals will contain the actual population percent. This is because the 90% boxes contain 90% *or more* of all possible sample outcomes. In fact, they typically do contain more than 90% because the sample totals are integers and so the cutoff points cannot typically be at exactly 5% and 95%.

7. **a.** The two samples can have very different outcomes (totals or proportions), which will result in two different confidence intervals. Students should have seen this happen as they compared confidence intervals in Activity 6.

   b. Some samples can be very unusual because of the random nature of the sampling process. Thus, the sample outcome can be unlikely, thereby generating a confidence interval that does not contain the actual population percent. This can be very surprising to students and should be emphasized. Students should have seen this happen as they examined all the intervals generated in Activity 6.

   c. This is an important conclusion. It explains what is meant by "90% confidence." Students should have seen this happen in Activity 6. For an explanation, see Part d of Activity 6. For an illustrative diagram, see Reflecting Task 5 on page 162.

8. **a.** Sample size 40 will work because it is possible for a vertical line to simultaneously hit exactly those boxes in the 50%–70% range. For example, look at the vertical line drawn from the sample total of 24. It can't be sample size 100, because if you go up from the far right edge of the 50% box, the highest box you hit is 65%. The same is true with sample size 80. Sample size 20 will not work because any vertical line that hits both the 50% box and the 70% box also hits boxes above 70% or below 50%.

   b. On the one hand, it seems like a good idea because it is likely that basketball is the favorite sport for more than half of the students. However, just because basketball is a student's favorite sport does not mean that he or she will pay to sit and watch basketball videos at lunch.

Notes continued from page T158

e
- This is not a good description. The population percent is some fixed (although unknown) value. Also, the interval 35%–45% is a fixed interval. Either the fixed population percent is in this particular interval or not. It doesn't make sense to say that there is a 90% chance that it is in the interval. The phrase "90% chance" implies that some chance or probability is involved. But this is not the case. Once you have a particular confidence interval, there is no longer any probability about the actual population percent being in the confidence interval; it is either in the particular interval or it is not.
- This is a reasonable explanation. The method we use for constructing confidence intervals may or may not produce an interval that contains the true population percent. But 90% of the time it will produce a "correct result," that is, a confidence interval that does contain the actual population percent. See the final statement in this part for another perspective on this idea.
- This is an accurate statement, but it does not directly explain the meaning of "90% confidence."
- This is a good explanation.

Notes continued from page T162

5.

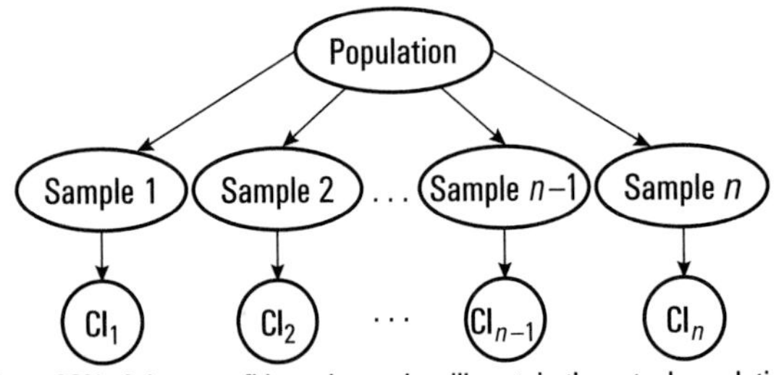

About 90% of these confidence intervals will contain the actual population.

Notes continued from page T168

c There are many connections and differences between 90% box plots and 90% confidence intervals that students should discuss. Some are listed below.

- We use the middle 90% of the sampling distribution to define likely sample outcomes. A 90% box plot for a sampling distribution is a box that shows the range within which the middle 90% of sample outcomes fall, when drawing all possible samples of the same size from a given population. Outcomes that fall in the box are considered likely outcomes.
- A 90% confidence interval is constructed using 90% box plots. In particular, the 90% box plots for different population percents can be put into one chart for a given sample size. The chart can be used to construct a 90% confidence interval. To do this, you first select a random sample and find the sample outcome; then you find all populations such that their 90% boxes contain the sample outcome.
- Though closely connected, a 90% box plot and a 90% confidence interval are very different, and they are used to solve different types of problems. If the problem is to decide whether or not a particular sample outcome from a known population is likely or not, then use a 90% box plot. If the problem is to find an interval estimate for an unknown population, then use a confidence interval.

d
- To find sampling distributions and 90% box plots, you work "from population to sample," starting with a known population percent and then selecting samples from that population. The sampling distribution is the distribution of the outcomes from all possible samples of the same size from the given population. A 90% box plot contains the middle 90% of all these sample outcomes. A sample outcome is defined to be likely if it is in the 90% box plot.
- To find a confidence interval, you work "from sample to population," using a sample percent (or total) to estimate an unknown population percent. Suppose you have a population for which you want to know the percentage of a particular characteristic. Rather than asking every individual in the population, you can select a random sample and find the sample percent. The population percent won't be exactly the same as the sample percent, but an interval around the sample percent will be a good estimate for the population percent. Such an interval is called a confidence interval. A confidence interval is the interval of population percents for which the sample outcome is likely.

APPLY individual task

On Your Own

See Unit 2 Summary Masters.

Responses will vary. Above all, preparation of this unit summary should be something that is useful to the individual student. You may wish to have students use the unit summary masters for "Modeling Public Opinion" to help them organize the information.

See Assessment Resources pages 65–82.

Unit 3 Symbol Sense and Algebraic Reasoning

Masters 61a–61d

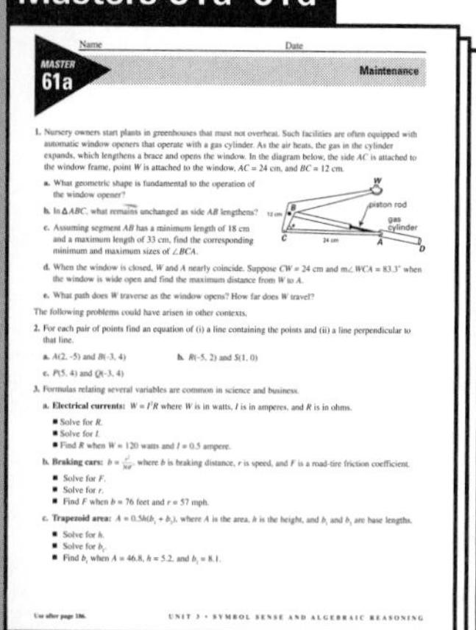

Name Date

MASTER 61a **Maintenance**

1. Nursery owners start plants in greenhouses that must not overheat. Such facilities are often equipped with automatic window openers that operate with a gas cylinder. As the air heats, the gas in the cylinder expands, which lengthens a brace and opens the window. In the diagram below, the side AC is attached to the window frame, point W is attached to the window, $AC = 24$ cm, and $BC = 12$ cm.
   a. What geometric shape is fundamental to the operation of the window opener?
   b. In $\triangle ABC$, what remains unchanged as side AB lengthens?
   c. Assuming segment AB has a minimum length of 18 cm and a maximum length of 33 cm, find the corresponding minimum and maximum sizes of $\angle BCA$.
   d. When the window is closed, W and A nearly coincide. Suppose $CW = 24$ cm and $m\angle WCA = 83.3°$ when the window is wide open and find the maximum distance from W to A.
   e. What path does W traverse as the window opens? How far does W travel?

The following problems could have arisen in other contexts.

2. For each pair of points find an equation of (i) a line containing the points and (ii) a line perpendicular to that line.
   a. $A(2, -5)$ and $B(-3, 4)$ b. $R(-5, 2)$ and $S(1, 0)$
   c. $P(5, 4)$ and $Q(-3, 4)$
3. Formulas relating several variables are common in science and business.
   a. **Electrical currents:** $W = I^2R$ where W is in watts, I is in amperes, and R is in ohms.
      - Solve for R.
      - Solve for I.
      - Find R when $W = 120$ watts and $I = 0.5$ ampere.
   b. **Braking cars:** $b = \frac{r^2}{30F}$ where b is braking distance, r is speed, and F is a road-tire friction coefficient.
      - Solve for F.
      - Solve for r.
      - Find F when $b = 76$ feet and $r = 57$ mph.
   c. **Trapezoid area:** $A = 0.5h(b_1 + b_2)$, where A is the area, h is the height, and b_1 and b_2 are base lengths.
      - Solve for h.
      - Solve for b_1.
      - Find b_1 when $A = 46.8$, $h = 5.2$, and $b_2 = 8.1$.

Use after page 186. UNIT 3 • SYMBOL SENSE AND ALGEBRAIC REASONING

UNIT OVERVIEW This unit is designed to cover the essential topics of functions, function notation, algebraic operations, polynomials, solving algebraic equations and inequalities, and algebraic proofs. These ideas have been developed in earlier units through work on a variety of problems in science and business contexts. In this unit, students will be learning and practicing the mathematical notation and principles that are used to express that intuitive understanding and reasoning in the formal language of standard mathematics.

Unit 3 Objectives

- **To develop a more formal understanding of functions and function notation**
- **To reason about algebraic expressions by applying the basic algebraic properties of commutativity, associativity, identity, inverse, and distributivity**
- **To develop greater facility with algebraic operations with polynomials, including adding, subtracting, multiplying, factoring, and solving**
- **To solve linear and quadratic equations and inequalities by reasoning with their symbolic forms**
- **To prove important mathematical patterns by writing algebraic expressions, equations, and inequalities in equivalent forms and applying algebraic reasoning**

Investigations to help students reach these learning goals are organized in five lessons. The first lesson covers a formal treatment of functions and function notation as algebraic models studied in previous units. In Lesson 2, algebraic expressions and functions are written in various equivalent forms, which leads into an exploration of the basic properties of numbers and operations. The focus of Lesson 3 is to multiply binomial factors, to factor quadratic expressions, and to simplify algebraic fractions. Students also investigate the relationship between the axis of symmetry of the quadratic polynomial and the roots of the polynomial, as well as the relationship between the axis of symmetry and the minimum or maximum value of the quadratic polynomial. In the fourth lesson of the unit, students solve equations and inequalities by algebraic manipulation. They also learn how to apply the quadratic formula. The final lesson of the unit involves proving mathematical patterns by using a variety of algebraic properties, operations, and reasoning strategies. Various identities involving coordinate geometry, statistics, and trigonometry will be proven by the students.

See Teaching Masters 61a–61d for Maintenance tasks that students can work on after Lesson 1.

Symbol Sense and Algebraic Reasoning

Unit 3

170 • **Lesson 1**
Algebra and Functions

187 • **Lesson 2**
Algebraic Operations: Part 1

208 • **Lesson 3**
Algebraic Operations: Part 2

225 • **Lesson 4**
Reasoning to Solve Equations and Inequalities

240 • **Lesson 5**
Proof through Algebraic Reasoning

253 • **Lesson 6**
Looking Back

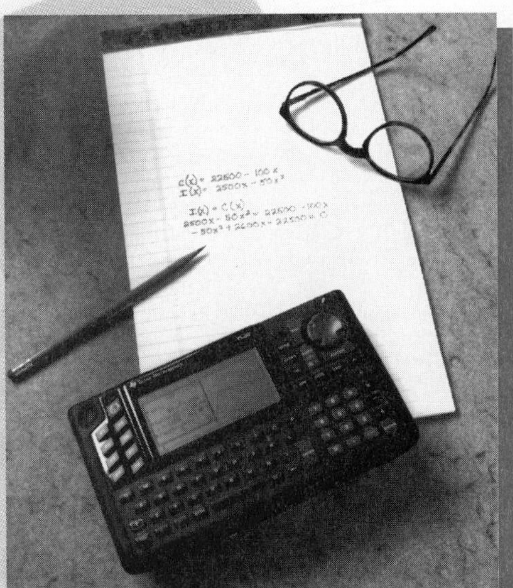

169

Unit 3

Unit 3 Planning Guide

Lesson Objectives	MORE Assignments	Suggested Pacing	Materials
Lesson 1 *Algebra and Functions* • To write algebraic rules as functions • To describe the table and graph patterns expected, given an algebraic rule in function form • To evaluate and interpret the meaning of expressions involving function notation • To understand the meaning of *domain* and *range* and to understand the relationship between those sets and input and output values, respectively • To determine practical and theoretical domains and ranges for various functions that model real-world situations • To determine whether a relation is a function by inspecting its graph or table	**after page 174** Students can begin Modeling Task 1 or 2 or Reflecting Task 4 from p. 179. **page 179** **Modeling:** 1 or 2, and 4 or 5* **Organizing:** 1, 2, and 4 **Reflecting:** 4 **Extending:** Choose one*	3 days	• Teaching Resources 62–64 • Assessment Resources 83–88 • *Optional*: HOT WHEELS® or similar racing track • *Optional*: RAP Book Exercise Set 7
Lesson 2 *Algebraic Operations: Part 1* • To determine the equivalence of different forms of symbolic rules by examining tables of values, by graphing, and by rewriting rules • To recognize and apply the commutative and associative properties of addition and multiplication • To recognize and apply the distributive property of multiplication over addition (subtraction) • To simplify algebraic expressions	**after page 192** Students can begin Modeling Task 1 or 4 from p. 201. **after page 197** Students can begin Organizing Task 1, 4, or 5; Reflecting Task 1; or Extending Task 2 from p. 201. **page 201** **Modeling:** 3, 4, and choice of one* **Organizing:** 3, 5, and choice of one* **Reflecting:** 1 and 3 **Extending:** Choose one*	6 days	• Teaching Resources 61a–61d, 65–72 • Assessment Resources 89–94 • *Optional*: RAP Book Exercise Set 8
Lesson 3 *Algebraic Operations: Part 2* • To determine, by simplifying algebraic rules, by examining tables of values, and by graphing, that different forms of symbolic rules can express the same relation between variables • To simplify algebraic fractions, multiply factors, and factor quadratic expressions • To recognize the relationship between the factors and the zeroes of a polynomial function • To recognize the relationship between the zeroes of a quadratic function and the line of symmetry of its graph and to use this relationship to determine the equation for the axis of symmetry and the extrema • To write a function rule of a polynomial, given its zeroes	**after page 212** Students can begin Modeling Task 1, Organizing Task 1 or 2, or Reflecting Task 2 from p. 218. **after page 214** Students can begin Modeling Task 4 or Extending Task 1, 2, or 4 from p. 218. **page 218** **Modeling:** 3 and choice of one* **Organizing:** 1, 2, and 3 **Reflecting:** 2 and 4 **Extending:** Choose one*	7 days	• Scissors • Teaching Resources 73–76 • Assessment Resources 95–102 • *Optional*: RAP Book Practice Set 4
Lesson 4 *Reasoning to Solve Equations and Inequalities* • To solve linear equations and inequalities using algebraic reasoning • To identify whether a quadratic function has 0, 1, or 2 zeroes and to describe the graph of the function • To solve quadratic equations and inequalities by using the quadratic formula • To understand that for the quadratic function $f(x) = ax^2 + bx + c$ $(a \neq 0)$, $x = \frac{-b}{2a}$ is the equation for the axis of symmetry and the value $\frac{\sqrt{b^2 - 4ac}}{2a}$ is the distance between the zeroes of the function and the axis of symmetry • To solve quadratic equations and inequalities by using the solve feature of a calculator or computer software	**after page 229** Students can begin Modeling Task 1 or 3 or Organizing Task 1, 2, or 3 from p. 234. **page 234** **Modeling:** 3 and 4 **Organizing:** 1, 2, and 3 or 4* **Reflecting:** 5 **Extending:** Choose one*	7 days	• Teaching Resources 77–81 • Assessment Resources 103–108 • *Optional*: RAP Book Exercise Set 9

Unit 3 Planning Guide *continued*

Lesson Objectives	MORE Assignments	Suggested Pacing	Materials
Lesson 5 *Proof through Algebraic Reasoning* • To prove mathematical patterns by using a variety of algebraic properties, operations, and reasoning strategies • To write expressions, equations, and inequalities in equivalent symbolic forms to prove relationships • To prove the Pythagorean Theorem • To prove the Law of Cosines	**after page 243** Students can begin Modeling Task 1 or Organizing Task 1 or 4 from p. 247. **page 247** **Modeling:** 1 and 3 **Organizing:** 1 and 4 **Reflecting:** 3 and 4 **Extending:** Choose one*	5 days	• Teaching Resources 82–84 • Assessment Resources 109–114 • *Optional*: RAP Book Exercise Set 10
Lesson 6 *Looking Back* • To review the major objectives of the unit		3–4 days (includes testing)	• Teaching Resources 85a–85b • Unit Summary Master • Assessment Resources 115–157 • *Optional*: RAP Book Practice Set 5

**When choice is indicated, it is important to leave the choice to the student.*
***Note:** It is best if Organizing tasks are discussed as a whole class after they have been assigned as homework.*

Unit 3

Lesson 1 Algebra and Functions

Are you a bicyclist, a skater, a skateboarder, a skier, or a snowboarder? Do you enjoy high and fast roller coasters at amusement parks? Many popular sports and recreations like these involve rolling or sliding down and up hills.

For example, when you ride a roller coaster, there is a motor that pulls you to the top of the first hill. But then gravity pulls you down, momentum carries you up to the top of the next hill, and so on. The big question is how far the energy gained on a downhill ride or slide will carry you uphill on the other side.

Think About This Situation

Suppose that you were asked to design an exciting, but safe, roller coaster for an amusement park.

a What variables would you have to consider in designing the first hill so that downhill momentum would carry the cars up and over the second hill without a pull?

b What changes in the design would be needed if you wanted to put a loop in the track so that the cars and riders turn upside down in a 360° turn?

If possible, test your ideas with simulations of roller coaster designs using flexible, grooved track and small cars like those that come with HOT WHEELS® setups.

170 UNIT 3 • SYMBOL SENSE AND ALGEBRAIC REASONING

Lesson 1 *Algebra and Functions*

LESSON OVERVIEW **Students will gain a better understanding of functions from a formal point of view as they study this first lesson of the unit. The concept of a function is introduced through tables and graphs. Students study formal function notation with an emphasis on explaining the meaning of the symbols as they relate to real-world situations. Students revisit functions with symbolic rules involving many of the algebraic models they have previously studied. They are given many opportunities to find symbolic rules that model common data patterns and conversely, to estimate the patterns in graphs and tables by studying the rules used to generate them. Also, real-world problem situations allow students to compare theoretical and practical meanings for the symbolic rules.**

Lesson Objectives

- To write algebraic rules as functions
- To describe the table and graph patterns expected, given an algebraic rule in function form
- To evaluate and interpret the meaning of expressions involving function notation
- To understand the meaning of *domain* and *range* and to understand the relationship between those sets and input and output values, respectively
- To determine practical and theoretical domains and ranges for various functions that model real-world situations
- To determine whether a relation is a function by inspecting its graph or table

LAUNCH **full-class discussion**

Think About This Situation

See Teaching Master 62.

ⓐ Responses will vary. In general, students might talk about the steepness needed to gain enough momentum to carry the car up the next hill. The variables that might be involved in such a discussion would be the slope of the track, length of the track, mass of the car, mass of the riders, height of the first hill, height of the second hill, and initial speed of the car.

ⓑ Responses will vary. Students might discuss the fact that putting a loop in the track will require considerable steepness in the approach so that the car will be able to gain enough momentum to complete the uphill portion of the loop.

Master 62

MASTER 62 — Transparency Master

Think About This Situation

Suppose that you were asked to design an exciting, but safe, roller coaster for an amusement park.

ⓐ What variables would you have to consider in designing the first hill so that downhill momentum would carry the cars up and over the second hill without a pull?

ⓑ What changes in the design would be needed if you wanted to put a loop in the track so that the cars and riders turn upside down in a 360° turn?

If possible, test your ideas with simulations of roller coaster designs using flexible, grooved track and small cars like those that come with HOT WHEELS® setups.

Use with page 170. UNIT 3 • SYMBOL SENSE AND ALGEBRAIC REASONING

Unit 3

EXPLORE small-group investigation

INVESTIGATION 1 Defining Functions

In previous units, students have been asked to "solve for *y* in terms of *x*" or to write a relationship that shows, for example, "income as a function of price." They have created expressions to show that weight, for example, is dependent on the width and thickness of a bridge. In this investigation, they will learn the formal definition and notation for functions.

As students work in groups on this investigation, you may want to urge them to use such phrases as "*h* of 8 equals 12" in the prescribed way and to tell you what the phrases mean. Some students retain a persistent misconception that "*h*(8)" or "*h* of 8" means "a height of 8," rather than "the height when the input variable is 8." Whenever you hear this mistake, point out how the English usage may be causing the error, and have students identify the input and output variables. If students have used list capabilities on their graphing calculators, they may already be familiar with defining a list as $Y_1(L_1)$ and, therefore, have less trouble determining input and output variables.

Unit 3

INVESTIGATION 1 Defining Functions

When students at a Colorado high school considered the "down and up" questions about roller coasters, they thought about ski and dirt bike jumping. They wondered about the relationship between length and steepness of the run leading to a jump ramp and length of the jumps from the end of that ramp. Using HOT WHEELS® track set pieces, they collected data relating *length of run* to *length of jump* by various HOT WHEELS® cars.

For one of their setups and cars, they collected the following data and produced the accompanying graph. You might get different results with a different track and jump-ramp setup.

Jump Ramp Experimental Data

Run Length (cm)	Jump Length (cm)
15	0
30	0
60	20
90	45
120	70
150	90
180	105
210	115
240	120

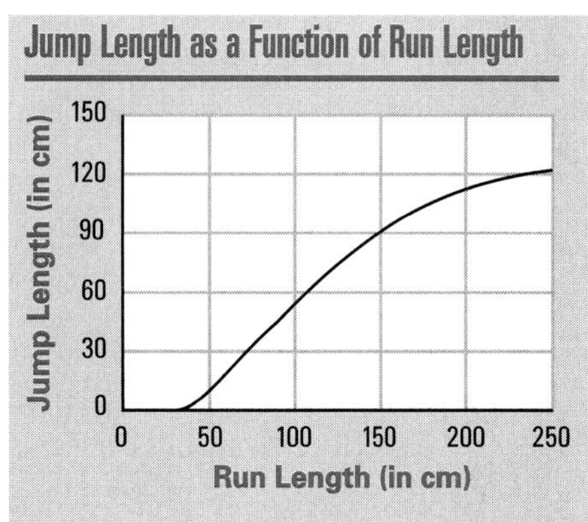

The graph shows the relationship between run length x and jump length y. *For each x value, there is exactly one corresponding value of y.* When this happens, we say that the variable *y is a function of x* or that *the relation between run length x and jump length y is a function.*

This sort of functional relationship between variables is often written using symbolic shorthand. To show that y is a function of x, mathematicians and other professional users of mathematics commonly write "$y = f(x)$." Then facts and questions about the function can also be written in symbolic shorthand form.

Unit 3

LESSON 1 • ALGEBRA AND FUNCTIONS 171

For example, to express the fact that a run of 90 centimeters will give a jump of 45 centimeters, you could write "$f(90) = 45$." Similarly, you could write "$f(180) = 105$" to show that a run of 180 centimeters leads to a jump of 105 centimeters. These function equations are usually read "f of 90 equals 45" and "f of 180 equals 105." Written in this form, the "$f(90)$" does *not* mean "f times 90."

1. Refer to the function graph relating run length to jump length.

a. What is meant by $f(75) = 30$? How is that fact shown on the graph?

b. What value of y satisfies the equation $y = f(120)$, and what does that information tell about jump length?

c. What values of x satisfy the equation $100 = f(x)$, and what does that information tell about jump lengths?

d. What value of y satisfies the equation $y = f(210)$, and what does that information tell about jump length?

e. What values of x satisfy the equation $0 = f(x)$, and what does that information tell about jump lengths?

In previous units and courses, you've studied a variety of other functions relating variables. For example, you might recall this graph showing how the height of a bungee jumper varies during the ups and downs of a jump.

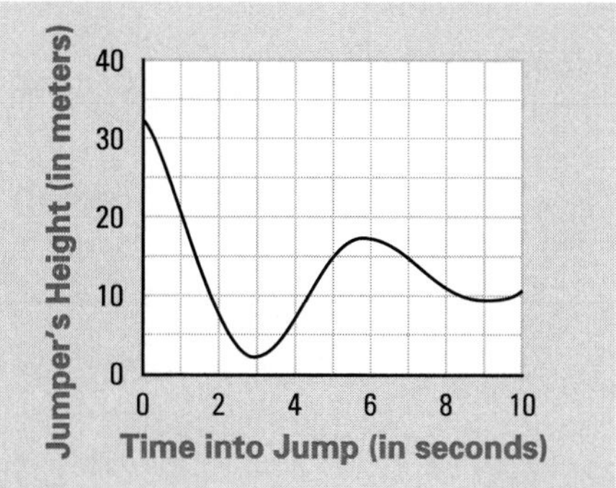

In this situation, the jumper's height is a function of time. It is common to choose letter names for functions that remind us of the quantities involved. In this case, it would be helpful to use the letter h, for height, to name the function. Then we would write $y = h(x)$.

2. Use the graph above to answer these questions about the function relating jump time and height.

a. What information is expressed by $h(8) = 12$?

b. What value of y satisfies $y = h(4)$, and what does the answer tell you about the jump?

c. What values of x satisfy $15 = h(x)$, and what do they tell you about the jump?

172 UNIT 3 • SYMBOL SENSE AND ALGEBRAIC REASONING

EXPLORE *continued*

1. **a.** A run of 75 cm results in a jump of 30 cm. The point (75, 30) is located on the graph.
   b. $y \approx 70$. This means that a run of 120 cm resulted in a jump of about 70 cm.
   c. $x \approx 175$. This means that a run of about 175 cm resulted in a jump of 100 cm.
   d. $y \approx 115$. This means that a run of 210 cm resulted in a jump of about 115 cm.
   e. $0 \leq x \leq 35$. This means that when the run length is less than or equal to approximately 35, the car was not able to jump.
2. **a.** At 8 seconds, the height of the jumper was 12 meters.
   b. $h(4) \approx 7$, which tells us that the height of the jumper at 4 seconds is about 7 meters.
   c. For $x \approx 1.4$, 5.0, and 7.0, $15 = h(x)$. This means that at about 1.4, 5.0, and 7.0 seconds, the jumper's height was 15 meters. The values also indicate that the jumper was bouncing up and down.

Unit 3

3. **a.** Graph i. There are 20 discrete data points in a pattern showing that as children become older they grow taller.

   b. Graph iii. Although there are again 20 discrete data points, there is no pattern connecting age and IQ.

   c. Graph ii. This is basically the same pattern as the first graph, but the graph is continuous. For each age, there is only one average height.

4. Only Graph ii represents a function. For the other two graphs, there is at least one age value for which there are several height or IQ values. However, in Graph i, there is a clear trend that is close to a functional relation.

In a relation between two variables x and y, y is a **function of** x when there is exactly one y value corresponding to each given x value. The notation "$y = f(x)$" indicates a clear prediction of y from x. You might have noticed in the bungee example that the correspondence doesn't always have the same property when viewed in the opposite direction, from y to x. For instance, the jumper is 15 meters above the ground at several times in the jump.

3. The graphs below illustrate three different relations between variables. Match each graph with the following relation that it seems most likely to represent. Be prepared to explain your reasoning.

a. Age and height (in centimeters) for a group of 20 young people of various ages

b. Age and IQ for the same group of 20 young people

c. Average height (in centimeters) for young people at various ages

i.

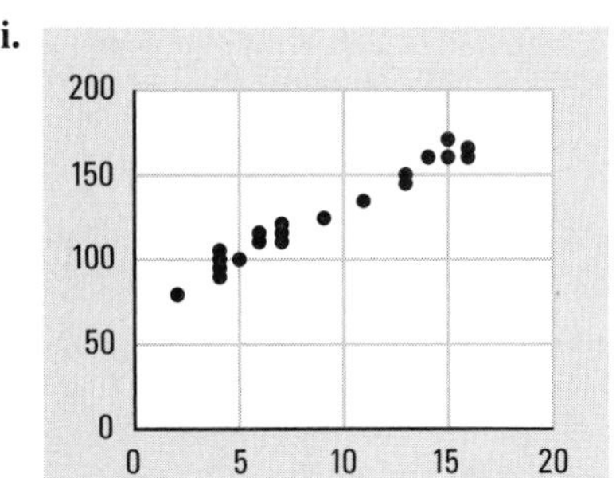

ii.

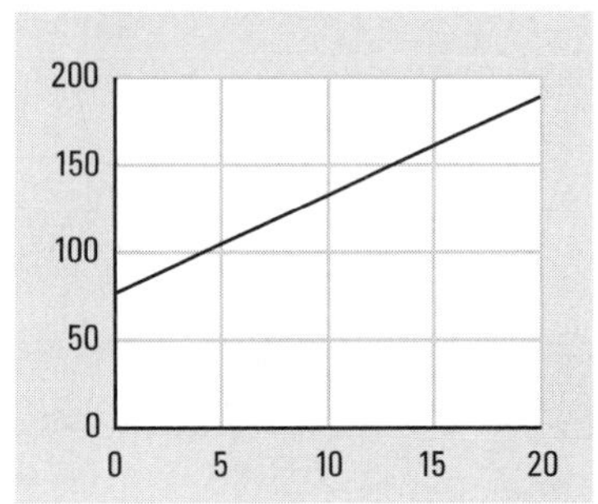

iii.

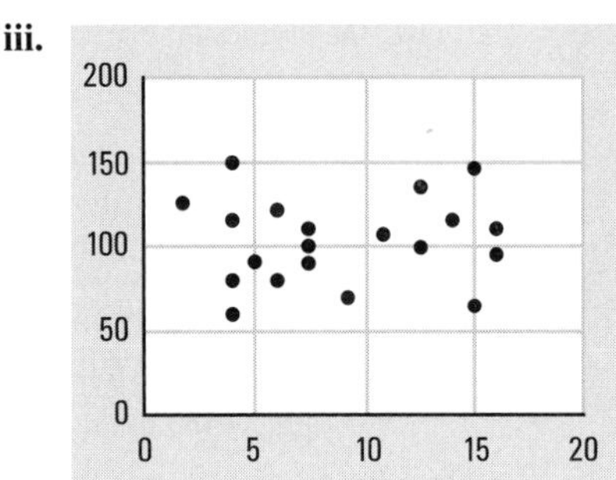

4. Determine whether or not each of the graphs in Activity 3 represents a function relating two variables. Explain your reasoning in each case.

LESSON 1 • ALGEBRA AND FUNCTIONS 173

Unit 3

Checkpoint

Investigation 1 focused attention on relations between variables that are called *functions*.

a What examples would you use to illustrate situations in which one variable is a function of another?

b What are some examples of relations between variables that are not functions?

c Suppose x and y are labels for two related variables.

- When is it proper to say that a relation between variables y and x is a function, with y a function of x?
- How can you tell from a graph of (x, y) data whether y is a function of x?
- What does an equation like $f(5) = 12$ tell about the relation between variables x and y when $y = f(x)$?

Be prepared to share your ideas with the entire class.

On Your Own

The graph below shows the *height* of a baseball in flight as *time* passes.

a. Why is it correct to say that *height* of a baseball is a function of *time* in flight?

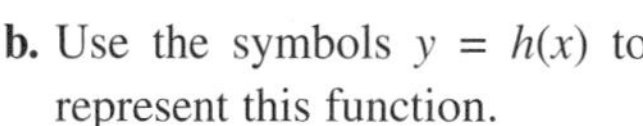

b. Use the symbols $y = h(x)$ to represent this function.

- What does the equation $h(1.5) = 18$ tell about the flight of the ball?
- What is the value of $h(3)$, and what does it tell about the flight of the ball?

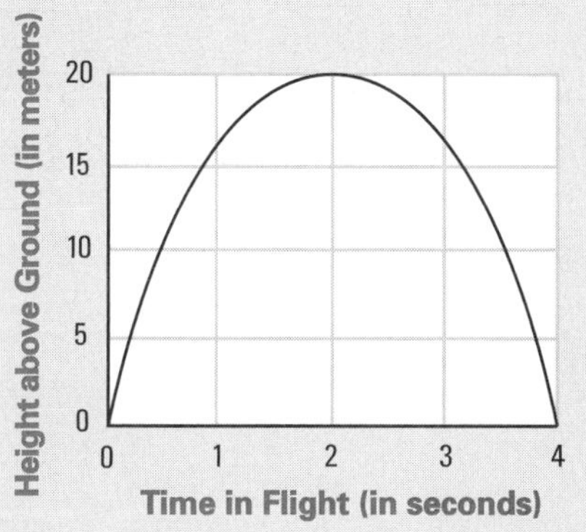

- What values of x satisfy the equation $10 = h(x)$, and what do those values tell about the flight of the ball?

c. Why do you think the notation $h(x)$ was used instead of $f(x)$?

174 UNIT 3 • SYMBOL SENSE AND ALGEBRAIC REASONING

SHARE AND SUMMARIZE full-class discussion

Checkpoint

See Teaching Master 63.

a Examples might include someone's height over time, weight over time, or foot length over time.

b Examples of relations that are not functions might include age versus family size for all the students in a school or age versus grade point average for all the students in a school.

c
- It is proper to call a relation a function when, given a value of x, you can find the corresponding value for y. This is possible when there is only one y value for each x value.
- If there are no two points on the same vertical line, then for that graph, y is a function of x.
- $f(5) = 12$ tells you that y is a function of x containing the point (5, 12), or when $x = 5$, $y = 12$.

Master 63

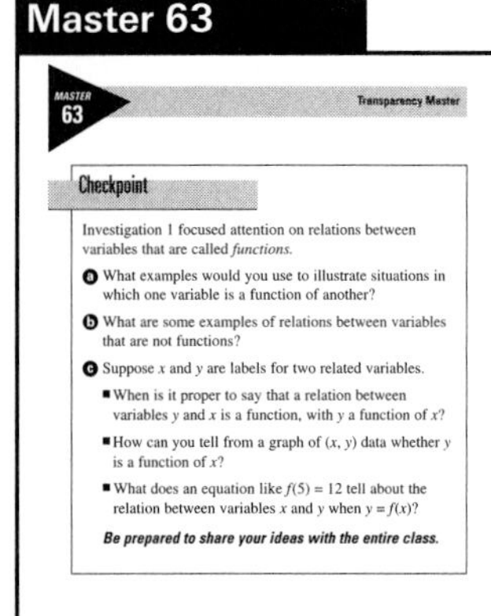
MASTER 63 Transparency Master

Checkpoint

Investigation 1 focused attention on relations between variables that are called *functions*.

a What examples would you use to illustrate situations in which one variable is a function of another?

b What are some examples of relations between variables that are not functions?

c Suppose x and y are labels for two related variables.
- When is it proper to say that a relation between variables y and x is a function, with y a function of x?
- How can you tell from a graph of (x, y) data whether y is a function of x?
- What does an equation like $f(5) = 12$ tell about the relation between variables x and y when $y = f(x)$?

Be prepared to share your ideas with the entire class.

Use with page 174 UNIT 3 • SYMBOL SENSE AND ALGEBRAIC REASONING

CONSTRUCTING A MATH TOOLKIT: Students should record a definition of function and then indicate how they can determine whether or not a given relationship is a function.

APPLY individual task

On Your Own

a. This is a function because, for any value of time in flight, there is one and only one value for height. In other words, if you know the time, then you can find the height.

b.
- The height of the ball at 1.5 seconds is 18 meters.
- $h(3) \approx 16$, which means that at 3 seconds, the height of the ball is approximately 16 meters.
- $10 = h(x)$ when $x \approx 0.5$ and $x \approx 3.5$. The ball is at a height of 10 meters at 0.5 seconds and again at 3.5 seconds. From this, we know that the ball went up and came down and that the maximum height of the ball was greater than 10 feet.

c. This function is showing the height of the baseball; therefore, $h(x)$ uses h to stand for height.

MORE

ASSIGNMENT *pp. 179–186*

Students can now begin Modeling Task 1 or 2 or Reflecting Task 4 from the MORE assignment following Investigation 2.

Unit 3

EXPLORE small-group investigation

INVESTIGATION 2 Functions with Symbolic Rules

In this investigation, students review several types of functional relationships they have investigated in previous units, and they examine the effect the parameters in the equations have on the graphs and tables. They are introduced to the terms *domain* and *range* and make sense of these in practical and theoretical terms.

Students will have lots of practice with the new notation as they evaluate linear, exponential, quadratic, and trigonometric functions at various points. They will probably use the table function on a calculator to do this, but some will use the home screen. You may want to include a full-class discussion after Activity 4 so that students can share their ideas for questions that ask which numbers make sense as input and output values. This becomes the explicit focus of Activities 5 and 6. Some students may find it difficult to leave context behind and move to the theoretical domain and range. If you find a group having trouble, you might ask if students can predict the shape of the graph from the symbolic rule; that is, without knowing what the variables represent, can they predict the shape of the graph? Then ask them which part of the graph actually represents the contextualized relationship. These questions may help direct their attention toward the idea that the practical domain is a subset of the theoretical domain.

1. **a.** ■ $C(100) = 21{,}000$, which means that if 100 pairs of shoes are bought, the monthly operating cost is $21,000.
■ $C(250) = 26{,}250$, which means that if 250 pairs of shoes are bought, the monthly operating cost is $26,250.
■ $C(0) = 17{,}500$, which means that if 0 pairs of shoes are bought, the monthly operating cost is $17,500.

b. The fixed costs each month are $17,500, and 35 represents the cost for each pair of shoes bought.

c. $C(200) = 24{,}500$, which tells you that when 200 pairs of shoes are bought, the monthly operating cost is $24,500.

d. You would expect the change in a table of values to be constant. For each additional pair of shoes bought, there is a $35 increase in cost. In the table, each 1-unit increase in x corresponds to a 35-unit increase in y. The graph would be a straight line with slope of 35 and y-intercept of 17,500.

e. Since x represents the number of pairs of shoes bought, only nonnegative integer values make sense as input values. Considering the specific model, the realistic output values $C(x)$ are numbers greater than 17,500. (In Activity 5, students refine the range for this function.)

Unit 3

INVESTIGATION 2 Functions with Symbolic Rules

In previous work, you've investigated tables, graphs, and symbolic rules for several of the most common patterns of change: linear, exponential, power (direct and inverse), quadratic, and trigonometric models. You've written the symbolic rules for those patterns as equations. Those rules can also be written using "$f(x)$" notation.

For example, in stores that sell athletic shoes of various kinds, the cost of doing business includes fixed expenses (like rent and pay for employees) and variable expenses (like the number of pairs of shoes bought from manufacturers). Operating costs of any store will be a function of those two main factors.

The typical American now owns two or three pairs of athletic shoes, which range in price from a $20 pair of old-fashioned sneakers at a discount store to $135 for top-of-the-line basketball shoes. One big seller has been Nike's Air Pegasus, which, like nearly all athletic shoes, is manufactured by suppliers in Asia. This accounting is based on a sale at an outlet of a large national retailer.

—By Steven Pearlstein

Production labor	$2.75
Materials	9.00
Rent, equipment	3.00
Supplier's operating profit	1.75
Duties	3.00
Shipping	.50
Cost to Nike	**$20.00**
Research/development	$.25
Promotion/advertising	4.00
Sales, distribution, administration	5.00
Nike's operating profit	6.25
Cost to retailer	**$35.50**
Rent	$9.00
Personnel	9.50
Other	7.00
Retailer's operating profit	9.00
COST TO CONSUMER	**$70.00**

SOURCES: Nike Inc., Reebok International Inc., The Finish Line Inc., Just for Feet Inc., Melville Corp., U.S. Customs Service, Athletic Footwear Assn., industry consultants and executives. *The Washington Post*

1. At All Sport Shoes, the manager estimates the monthly operating cost for the store (in dollars) using a function of the number of pairs of shoes that the store purchases from its suppliers. The rule for that function is $C(x) = 17{,}500 + 35x$.

a. Evaluate and explain the meaning of each of the following:

- $C(100)$
- $C(250)$
- $C(0)$

b. What do the numbers 17,500 and 35 tell about the relation between the number of pairs of shoes purchased from the manufacturer and the total cost of doing business at the store for one month?

c. What values of x satisfy $C(x) = 24{,}500$, and what do those values tell about the store's monthly business costs?

d. What table and graph patterns do you expect for this cost function?

e. What numbers make sense as input values for the variable x? What numbers are realistic as output values for the function $C(x)$?

LESSON 1 • ALGEBRA AND FUNCTIONS 175

2. The population of the United States over several years can be estimated by the function model $P(x) = 276(1.009)^x$, where x is the number of years after 2000 (so 2000 is represented by $x = 0$) and $P(x)$ is U.S. population in millions.

   a. Evaluate and explain the meaning of each of the following:

      - $P(0)$
      - $P(5)$
      - $P(15)$
      - $P(100)$

   b. What table and graph patterns do you expect for this population function?

   c. What do the numbers 276 and 1.009 tell about the estimated relation between time and population? How do these two numbers affect tables and graphs of the function?

   d. What values of x satisfy the equation $P(x) = 400$, and what does your answer tell about U.S. population growth?

   e. What numbers make sense as input values for the variable x? What numbers are realistic as output values for the function $P(x)$?

3. If you bounce up from a trampoline, your height above the trampoline surface varies over time on each bounce. The pattern for a single bounce might be given by a function model $h(t) = -16t^2 + 24t$. (Here, time t is in seconds, and height $h(t)$ is in feet.)

   a. Evaluate and explain the meaning of each of the following:

      - $h(0)$
      - $h(0.5)$
      - $h(1.2)$

   b. What table and graph patterns do you expect for this function rule?

   c. What do the numbers –16 and 24 tell about the relation between height above the trampoline and time? How do these two numbers affect tables and graphs of the function?

   d. According to this model, when would you reach your maximum height above the trampoline? What height would that be?

   e. After how much time would you return to the surface of the trampoline?

   f. What numbers make sense as input values for the variable t? What numbers make sense as output values for the function $h(t)$?

Unit 3

176 UNIT 3 • SYMBOL SENSE AND ALGEBRAIC REASONING

2. **a.** ■ $P(0) = 276$, which means that in 2000 the population was 276 million.

■ $P(5) \approx 289$, which means that the estimated population for the year 2005 is approximately 289 million.

■ $P(15) \approx 316$, which means that the estimated population for the year 2015 is approximately 316 million.

■ $P(100) \approx 676$, which means that the estimated population for the year 2100 is approximately 676 million.

b. From the table, you would expect that as x increases at a constant rate, y would increase at an increasing rate. You would expect the graph to curve upward. The graph will have a y-intercept of 276.

c. The initial population, when $x = 0$, is 276 million; each year the population increases by 0.9%, which is reflected by the base of 1.009. The table contains the point (0, 276), and as x increases by increments of 1, y increases by a factor of 1.009. In the graph, this is shown by a curve with a y-intercept of 276 that curves up as x increases in value.

d. $P(41.4) \approx 400$, which tells us that during the year 2041, the population is expected to reach 400 million. This indicates that the population is continuing to grow; whether it is doing so at an alarming rate could be debated.

e. Any nonnegative decimal number makes sense as an input value x. However, the model will probably not be very accurate in predicting population for even 100 years in the future. Thus, the input values should be limited, possibly to decimal values between 0 and 100. Considering the specific model, the realistic output values $P(x)$ are positive numbers greater than 276 and less than the largest functional value of the restricted domain, in this case, $P(100)$ or approximately 676. Negative values of x allow backward population estimates.

3. **a.** ■ $h(0) = 0$, which means that at time 0 the height is 0 feet.

■ $h(0.5) = 8$, which means that at 0.5 second the height is 8 feet.

■ $h(1.2) = 5.76$, which means that at 1.2 seconds the height is 5.76 feet.

b. The table and graph should show that the height is increasing (up to 0.75 second) and then decreasing (from 0.75 second on).

c. As the students learned in the Course 2 unit "Power Models," –16 is the effect of gravity in terms of feet per second squared, and 24 is the initial velocity in terms of feet per second. The coefficient –16 inverts the standard quadratic graph, and the $24t$ term increases the maximum value and shifts the graph to the right.

d. The maximum height for the gymnast is 9 feet at 0.75 second.

e. It takes 1.5 seconds to return to the trampoline.

f. Nonnegative times make sense as input values. The specific equation further limits times to 0 to 1.5 seconds as input values for t. Output values $h(t)$ would then range from 0 to 9 feet. (Some students may wish to discuss input and output values that allow for heights below the trampoline.)

4. a. ■ $h(0) = 35$, which means that height at time 0 seconds is 35 feet.
   ■ $h(1.6) \approx 65$, which means that height at time 1.6 seconds is approximately 65 feet.
   ■ $h(3) \approx 39.2$, which means that height at time 3 seconds is approximately 39.2 feet.
   ■ $h(4.7) \approx 5.0$, which means that height at time 4.7 seconds is approximately 5.0 feet.
   ■ $h(6.28) \approx 34.9$, which means that height at time 6.28 seconds is approximately 34.9 feet.
   ■ $h(7.85) \approx 65$, which means that height at time 7.85 seconds is approximately 65 feet.

   b. When the input value for t is 0 or any multiple of $\frac{6.28}{2}$ (that is, a multiple of π, although students probably will not realize this), then $h(t) \approx 35$.

   c. The 30 tells us that the radius of the Ferris wheel is 30 feet. The 35 tells us that the starting height (middle seat) or the center of the Ferris wheel is 35 feet. So at its lowest point, the Ferris wheel is 5 feet off the ground.

   d. In the table, the values for the function first increase, then decrease, then increase again. In the graph, the curve rises, falls, and then rises again. This pattern is demonstrated in the motion of the Ferris wheel. First the seat of the Ferris wheel goes up, and then it comes down on the other side; it repeats the rising and falling as it rotates around with the wheel.

   e. Any positive decimal number makes sense as an input value. However, students may want to impose a limit so that the largest input value is the length of the ride (say 5 minutes or 300 seconds). The output values specific to this situation will be between 5 and 65 feet, inclusive.

5. a. For the domain, you will not have negative numbers of shoes and you will have only integer values for x, since 1.62 pairs of shoes is not reasonable. Also, the numbers in the range include 17,500 and all numbers equal to 17,500 plus a positive multiple of 35.

4. If you ride on a Ferris wheel, your height above the ground will vary as the wheel turns. Suppose the wheel starts spinning for a ride when you are in the same position as the seat marked with an asterisk (*) in the diagram at the right.

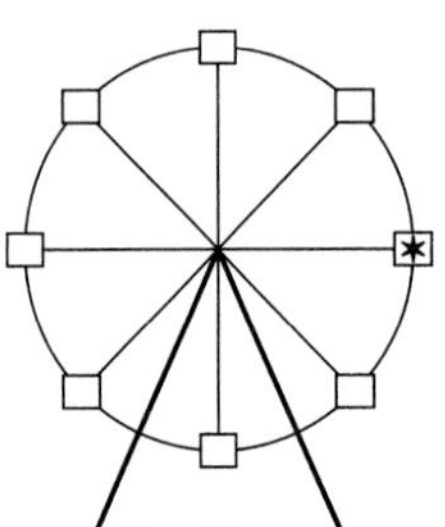

If the wheel has a radius of 30 feet and spins so that you first move up from the indicated position, making a full turn every 6.28 seconds, your height (in feet) at any time during the ride (in seconds) could be estimated by the function model $h(t) = 30 \sin t + 35$. (Since t is not a degree measure, this equation assumes that the input variable is measured in radians.)

a. Evaluate and explain the meaning of each of the following:

- $h(0)$
- $h(1.6)$
- $h(3)$
- $h(4.7)$
- $h(6.28)$
- $h(7.85)$

b. For what values of the input variable t is $h(t)$ equal to 35?

c. What do the numbers 30 and 35 in the function rule tell about the situation being modeled?

d. What patterns will you find in tables and graphs of this function rule, and how do they relate to the motion of the Ferris wheel?

e. What numbers make sense as input values for the variable t? What numbers would you expect as output values for the function $h(t)$?

For any function $f(x)$ relating two (or more) variables, it is customary to refer to the variable x as the *input* and the second variable as the *output*. In many situations and for many function rules, only some numbers make sense as inputs. Those numbers make up what is called the **domain** of the function. In a similar way, only some numbers will occur as outputs of the function. Those numbers make up what is called the **range** of the function.

There are two ways to think about domain and range for a function that models a real-world problem situation. On one hand, you might ask what numbers are realistic or *practical* as inputs and outputs. On the other hand, you might ask what numbers *theoretically* can be used as inputs for the given algebraic rule (regardless of whether they make sense in the problem situation).

5. The function predicting monthly business costs for All Sport Shoes had the rule $C(x) = 17{,}500 + 35x$, where x was the number of pairs of shoes ordered from the manufacturer and $C(x)$ was the monthly operating cost in dollars.

a. A table of (*number of pairs of shoes*, *cost*) data might begin like this:

x	0	1	2	3	4
$C(x)$	17,500	17,535	17,570	17,605	17,640

What does this pattern suggest about the *practical domain* and *range* of the cost function?

Unit 3

LESSON 1 • ALGEBRA AND FUNCTIONS 177

b. For what input values of x can you use the rule $C(x) = 17{,}500 + 35x$ to calculate an output value (regardless of whether the input or output makes sense in the shoe business)? What is the range of output values that will occur as all possible values of x are used? What do your answers say about the *theoretical domain* and *range* of this function?

6. Look back at your work with the other function models in this investigation.

a. Describe the *theoretical* domains and ranges for the functions below.

- $P(x) = 276(1.009)^x$
- $h(t) = -16t^2 + 24t$
- $h(t) = 30 \sin t + 35$

b. Describe the *practical* domains and ranges for the functions in Part a when they are used as models to predict their respective relations:

- Estimated U.S. population as a function of time in years after 1995
- Height of a trampoline bouncer as a function of time into a bounce
- Height of a Ferris wheel rider as a function of time into the ride

Checkpoint

In Investigation 2, you explored the use of function notation to express symbolic rules for several types of algebraic models.

a Which of those situations (if any) involved the following function types?

- Linear models
- Exponential models (growth or decay)
- Power models (direct or inverse)
- Quadratic models
- Trigonometric models

b For each of the five function types listed in Part a, what general patterns do you expect in the following?

- Graphs
- Tables of (x, y) values
- Symbolic rules

c What are the theoretical domains and ranges of the various models listed in Part a? How are the domains of those models sometimes limited by practical considerations?

Be prepared to share your ideas with the class.

Unit 3

178 UNIT 3 • SYMBOL SENSE AND ALGEBRAIC REASONING

5. b. Outside of the context, the input values for the rule can be all real numbers, and the output can also be all real numbers. The theoretical domain and range are much larger than the practical domain and range, because they do not take into consideration the constraints of the problem situation.

6. a.
- ■ $P(x) = 276(1.009)^x$ **Domain:** x is any real number. **Range:** $P(x) > 0$
- ■ $h(t) = -16t^2 + 24t$ **Domain:** t is any real number. **Range:** $h(t) \leq 9$
- ■ $h(t) = 30 \sin t + 35$ **Domain:** t is any real number. **Range:** $5 \leq h(t) \leq 65$

b.
- ■ $P(x) = 276(1.009)^x$ **Domain:** $0 \leq x \leq 100$ (This upper limit is debatable.) **Range:** $P(x) \geq 276$ Negative values of x are suitable for time in past. Then population values will be less than 276.
- ■ $h(t) = -16t^2 + 24t$ **Domain:** $0 \leq t \leq 1.5$ **Range:** $0 \leq h(t) \leq 9$
- ■ $h(t) = 30 \sin t + 35$ **Domain:** $t \geq 0$ or $0 \leq t \leq 300$ (about a 5-minute ride) **Range:** $5 \leq h(t) \leq 65$

Master 64

MASTER 64 Transparency Master

Checkpoint

In Investigation 2, you explored the use of function notation to express symbolic rules for several types of algebraic models.

a Which of those situations (if any) involved the following function types?
- Linear models
- Exponential models (growth or decay)
- Power models (direct or inverse)
- Quadratic models
- Trigonometric models

b For each of the five function types listed in Part a, what general patterns do you expect in the following?
- Graphs
- Tables of (x, y) values
- Symbolic rules

c What are the theoretical domains and ranges of the various models listed in Part a? How are the domains of those models sometimes limited by practical considerations?

Be prepared to share your ideas with the entire class.

Use with page 178. UNIT 3 • SYMBOL SENSE AND ALGEBRAIC REASONING

SHARE AND SUMMARIZE full-class discussion

Checkpoint

See Teaching Master 64.

This Checkpoint provides an excellent opportunity to review the major algebraic models and make connections to more formal notation and ideas of domain and range. The activities in the investigation have given students an opportunity to remind themselves of characteristics of all these functions, except for inverse power. If your students need to be reminded of this type of function, you may wish to assign some inverse power examples to be graphed by students so that, in a large group setting, students' answers for the section on inverse power can be augmented or refined as necessary. The inverse power relation is actually investigated in the "On Your Own" following the Checkpoint.

In general, it is helpful to have students make sense of the symbols in terms of the patterns they see in tables and graphs. You may have to add some probing questions of your own to get full answers from students, such as, "Why does the exponential curve never cross the *x*-axis? What characteristics of the function $f(x) = \frac{1}{x^2}$ guarantee that the two branches of the curve never cross the *y*-axis? That they never have negative output values?"

a
- ■ Linear models: Monthly operating costs of athletic shoe sales
- ■ Exponential models: U.S. population problem
- ■ Power models: None
- ■ Quadratic models: Bouncing on the trampoline
- ■ Trigonometric models: Ferris wheel

See additional Teaching Notes on page T257C.

CONSTRUCTING A MATH TOOLKIT: Students should describe how to find the theoretical domain and range of a function and explain function notation.

Unit 3

APPLY individual task

On Your Own

a.
- At a distance of 1 meter, the intensity is 20 watts per square meter.
- At a distance of 2 meters, the intensity is 5 watts per square meter.
- At a distance of 3 meters, the intensity is approximately 2.22 watts per square meter.
- At a distance of 0.5 meters, the intensity is 80 watts per square meter.
- At a distance of 10 meters, the intensity is 0.2 watts per square meter.

b. As the distance increases, the intensity decreases. As the distance decreases, the intensity increases. One can see this from the function: When the denominator increases, the value of the function decreases; when the denominator decreases, the value of the function increases.

c. Since it doesn't make sense for distance to be negative, the practical domain is $d > 0$. The practical range is $I(d) > 0$.

d. Theoretically, d could be any real number except 0. The theoretical range includes all positive real numbers.

On Your Own

In Course 2, the relation between sound *intensity* and *distance* from the source of that sound (like a stereo system) was explored using the function with rule $I(d) = \frac{20}{d^2}$. This symbolic rule gives intensity in watts per square meter as a function of distance (in meters) from the source.

a. Evaluate and explain the meaning of each of the following:

- $I(1)$
- $I(2)$
- $I(3)$
- $I(0.5)$
- $I(10)$

b. What patterns of change occur in tables and graphs of this function? How can those patterns be predicted from the function rule without any calculations?

c. What are the practical domain and range of this function? Explain your reasoning.

d. What are the theoretical domain and range of this function? Explain your reasoning.

MORE

Modeling • Organizing • Reflecting • Extending

Modeling

1. In a wildlife experiment, all fish were removed from a lake and the lake was restocked with 1,000 new fish. The population of fish then increased over the years. Fish population in a newly stocked lake is a function of time t since the first fish were deposited in the lake. Let $y = P(t)$ represent that function, and use information from the graph below to complete the following tasks.

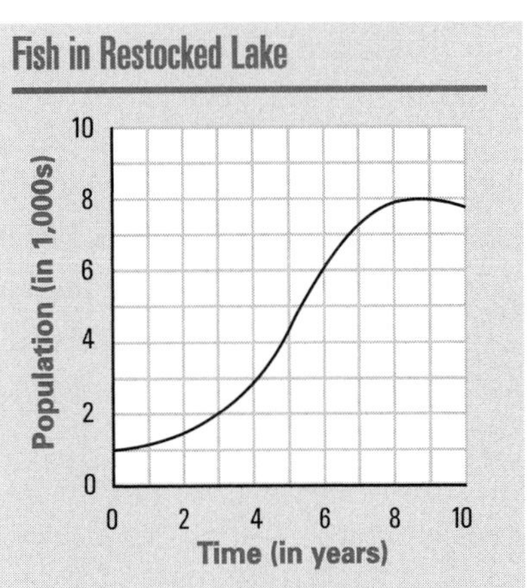

LESSON 1 • ALGEBRA AND FUNCTIONS 179

a. Estimate and explain the meaning of $P(6)$.

b. Estimate and explain the meaning of $P(4)$.

c. Estimate and explain the meaning of the t value for which $P(t) = 7$.

d. Use function notation to express the following statement: "The fish population after five years will be 4,500."

e. Estimate and explain the meaning of $P(5) - P(4)$.

2. The depth of water at an ocean pier changes over time as tides go in and out. Let $y = D(t)$ represent the function giving water depth as a function of time t during one 24-hour day, and use information from the graph below to complete the following tasks.

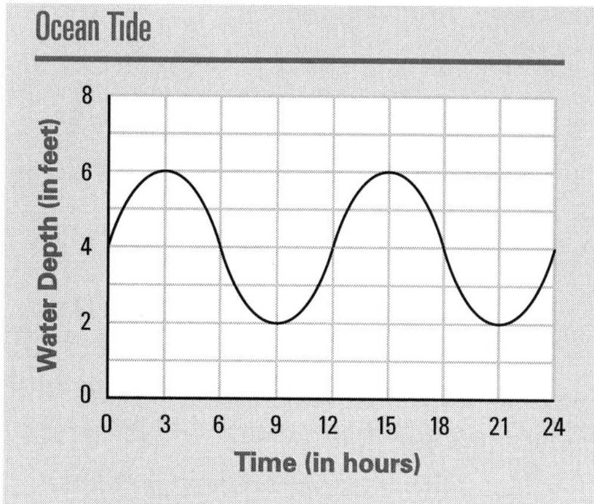

a. Use function notation to express the following statement: "Water depth after three hours is six feet."

b. Estimate and explain the meaning of $D(9)$.

c. Estimate and explain the meaning of $D(15)$.

d. Estimate and explain the meaning of $D(22)$.

e. Estimate and explain the meaning of the t values for which $D(t) = 4$.

180 UNIT 3 • SYMBOL SENSE AND ALGEBRAIC REASONING

MORE independent assignment

Modeling

1. a. $P(6) \approx 6.1$, which means that in 6 years, there will be approximately 6,100 fish in the lake.
   b. $P(4) \approx 2.9$, which means that in 4 years, there will be approximately 2,900 fish in the lake.
   c. $P(t) = 7$ when $t = 6.6$, which means that in 6.6 years, there will be 7,000 fish in the lake.
   d. $P(5) = 4.5$
   e. $P(5) = 4.5$ and $P(4) \approx 2.9$, so $P(5) - P(4) \approx 1.6$. This means that the fish population will grow by approximately 1,600 fish between years 4 and 5.
2. a. $D(3) = 6$
   b. $D(9) = 2$, which means that the water depth at 9 hours is 2 feet.
   c. $D(15) = 6$, which means that the water depth at 15 hours is 6 feet.
   d. $D(22) \approx 2.3$, which means that the water depth at 22 hours is about 2.3 feet.
   e. $D(t) = 4$ when $t = 0, 6, 12, 18,$ and 24. At the 0-, 6-, 12-, 18-, and 24-hour marks, the depth of the water is 4 feet.

MORE
ASSIGNMENT *pp. 179–186*

Modeling: 1 or 2, and 4 or 5*
Organizing: 1, 2, and 4
Reflecting: 4
Extending: Choose one*

**When choice is indicated, it is important to leave the choice to the student.*
NOTE: *It is best if Organizing tasks are discussed as a whole class after they have been assigned as homework.*

Unit 3

3. **a.** $c(15) = 6{,}250$, which means that if the admission price is $15, there will be 6,250 customers per day.

$c(30) = 2{,}500$, which means that if the admission price is $30, there will be 2,500 customers per day.

b. For $x = 24$, $c(x) = 4{,}000$, which means that if the admission price is $24, there will be 4,000 customers per day.

c. The practical domain is $0 \le x \le 40$, and x should have at most two decimal places. The practical range is integers in $0 \le c(x) \le 10{,}000$.

d. Both the theoretical domain and range are all real numbers.

4. **a.** $i(5) \approx 7.7$, which means that there will be approximately 7.7 units of insulin left in the person's system after 5 minutes.

$i(20) \approx 3.6$, which means that there will be approximately 3.6 units of insulin left in the person's system after 20 minutes.

b. $i(45) \approx 1$, which means that there will be approximately 1 unit of insulin left in the person's system after about 45 minutes.

c. The practical domain is $t \ge 0$. Some students may argue that after a long time the amount of insulin will become undetectable and at that time the model is no longer appropriate. The practical range is $0 < i(t) \le 10$.

d. The theoretical domain is all real numbers, and the theoretical range is all positive real numbers.

5. **a.** $h(25) = 11.25$, which means that 25 feet from the left end of the bridge, the cable is 11.25 feet above the surface of the bridge.

$h(65) = 7.25$, which means that 65 feet from the left end of the bridge, the cable is 7.25 feet above the surface of the bridge.

b. $h(x) = 13$ when $x \approx 21.7$ and $x \approx 78.3$, which means that the cable is 13 feet above the surface of the bridge at distances of approximately 21.7 and 78.3 feet from the left end of the bridge.

c. Practical domain: $0 \le x \le 100$

Practical range: $5 \le h(x) \le 30$

d. Theoretical domain: all real numbers

Theoretical range: $h(x) \ge 5$

3. Planners of an amusement park estimate that the number of daily customers will be related to the chosen admission price x (in dollars) by the function $c(x) = 10{,}000 - 250x$.

   a. Calculate and explain the meaning of $c(15)$ and $c(30)$.

   b. Find the value of x satisfying the equation $c(x) = 4{,}000$, and explain what it tells about the relation between admission price and number of customers.

   c. Describe the practical domain and range of the function $c(x)$.

   d. Describe the theoretical domain and range of the function $c(x)$.

4. Insulin is an important hormone produced by the body. In 5% to 10% of all diagnosed cases of diabetes, the disease is due to the body's inability to produce insulin; the people with this form of diabetes must take medicine containing insulin. Once the insulin gets to the bloodstream, it begins to break down quickly. When 10 units of insulin are delivered to a person's bloodstream, the amount remaining after t minutes might be modeled by an equation like $i(t) = 10(0.95)^t$.

   a. Calculate and explain the meaning of $i(5)$ and $i(20)$.

   b. Find a value of t satisfying the equation $i(t) = 1$, and explain what it tells about the relation between time and amount of insulin in the person's bloodstream.

   c. Describe the practical domain and range of the function $i(t)$.

   d. Describe the theoretical domain and range of the function $i(t)$.

5. The following sketch shows a 100-foot bridge suspended from cables between two towers, each 30 feet high. The height of the suspension cable above the bridge surface is a function of distance x from the left end of the bridge with rule $h(x) = 0.01x^2 - x + 30$. All distances are measured in feet.

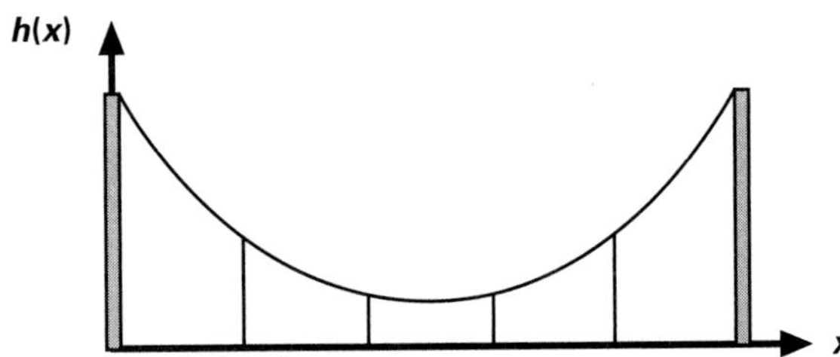

   a. Calculate and explain the meaning of $h(25)$ and $h(65)$.

   b. Find the value of x satisfying $h(x) = 13$, and explain what it tells about the relation between distance along the bridge and height of the suspension cable.

   c. Describe the practical domain and range of the function $h(x)$.

   d. Describe the theoretical domain and range of the function $h(x)$.

Unit 3

LESSON 1 • ALGEBRA AND FUNCTIONS 181

6. When a shoe company launches a new model, it has certain startup costs for design and advertising. Then it has production costs for each pair of shoes that is made. When the planning department of Start Line Shoes estimated costs of a proposed new model bearing a popular athlete's name, it reported that the average cost per pair of shoes (in dollars) would depend on the number made, with the equation $C(x) = 29 + \frac{25{,}000{,}000}{x}$.

   a. Calculate and explain the meaning of each of the following:
   - $C(1)$
   - $C(1{,}000{,}000)$
   - $C(2{,}500{,}000)$

   b. For what value of x is $C(x) = 40$, and what does this value tell about the business prospects of the new shoe line?

   c. Sketch a graph of $C(x)$ using $0 \leq x \leq 10{,}000{,}000$ and $0 \leq y \leq 100$. Then explain what the shape of that graph shows about change in average production cost for the shoes as numbers produced increase. Try graphing over a larger interval of x values. What do you think is the lowest production cost per pair possible for Start Line Shoes?

   d. What connection is there between the graph of $C(x)$ and one of the basic function types you've studied in earlier units?

Organizing

1. Examine the tables below, each of which describes a relation between y and x. In which of these tables is y a function of x? If the relation described by a table is not a function, explain why not.

a.

x	1	2	3	4	5	6	7	8	9
y	3	5	7	9	11	13	15	17	19

b.

x	1	2	3	4	5	6	7	8	9
y	3	5	7	9	11	9	7	5	3

c.

x	1	2	3	4	5	4	3	2	1
y	3	5	7	9	11	9	7	5	3

d.

x	9	4	1	0	1	4	9	16	25
y	–3	–2	–1	0	1	2	3	4	3

182 UNIT 3 • SYMBOL SENSE AND ALGEBRAIC REASONING

6. a. ■ $C(1) = \$25,000,029$, which means that if only one pair of shoes is produced, the cost will be \$25,000,029.
   ■ $C(1,000,000) = \$54$, which means that if 1,000,000 pairs of shoes are produced, the cost will be \$54 per pair.
   ■ $C(2,500,000) = \$39$, which means that if 2,500,000 pairs of shoes are produced, the cost will be \$39 per pair.

   b. $C(x)$ will be 40 when $x \approx 2,272,727$. This means that if the company wants the production cost to be \$40 per pair of shoes, it must produce 2,272,727 pairs of shoes. It takes a large number of sales to keep the price low because of the high startup costs.

   c. This graph shows that, as the number produced increases, the price drops, quickly at first and then very slowly. If students extend the graph (or analyze the equation), they should see that the production cost per pair will never go below \$29. Although there really isn't a lowest number possible, you can get as close to \$29 as you like by choosing a high-enough number of shoes made.

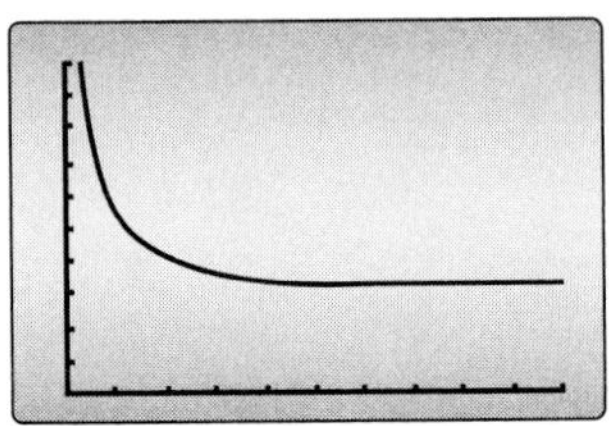

WINDOW
Xmin =0
Xmax =10000000
Xscl =1000000
Ymin =0
Ymax =100
Yscl =10
Xres =1

   d. This is an inverse power model translated up 29 units.

Organizing

1. a. y is a function of x.
   b. y is a function of x.
   c. y is a function of x.
   d. y is not a function of x. Several of the x values given have more than one corresponding y value. For example, the x value of 1 has y values of both –1 and 1.

Unit 3

2. **a.** y is not a function of x. A vertical line can be drawn that intersects the graph more than one time, and this indicates that there is at least one x value that has more than one y value.

b. y is a function of x.

c. y is not a function of x. There are many x values that have more than one associated y value.

d. y is not a function of x. The beginning of one segment has the exact same x value as the segment above it. Thus, these x values have two different y values associated with them.

3. **a.** As the measure of the acute angle at A increases, the sine ratio increases, the cosine ratio decreases, and the tangent ratio increases.

b. Yes, each ratio is a function of the measure of $\angle A$. Each ratio has only one value for a given angle measure.

c. $\sin A = 0.5$ means that the value of sine associated with the measure of $\angle A$ is 0.5. This notation is similar to function notation in that A stands for the variable angle and "sin" tells us to find the value of the sine of $\angle A$.

2. Examine each of the graphs below describing a relation between y and x. In which of these graphs is y a function of x? If the relation described by a graph is not a function, explain why not.

a.

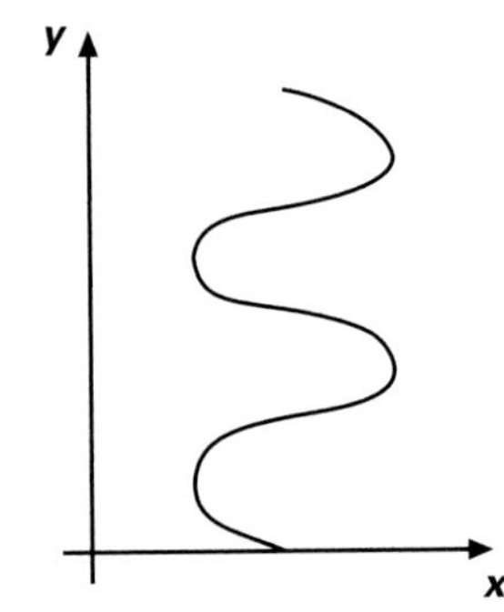

b.

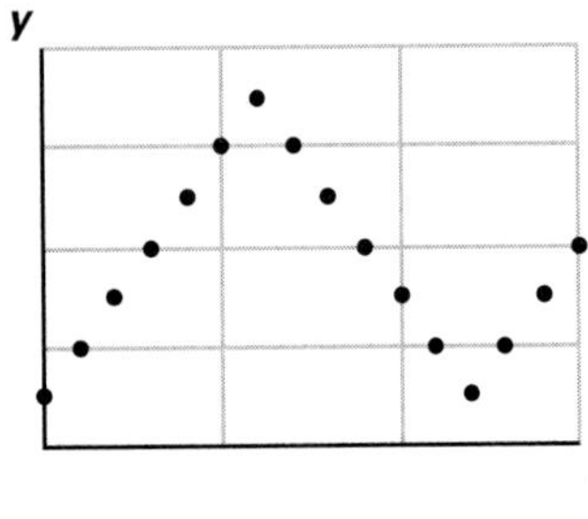

c.

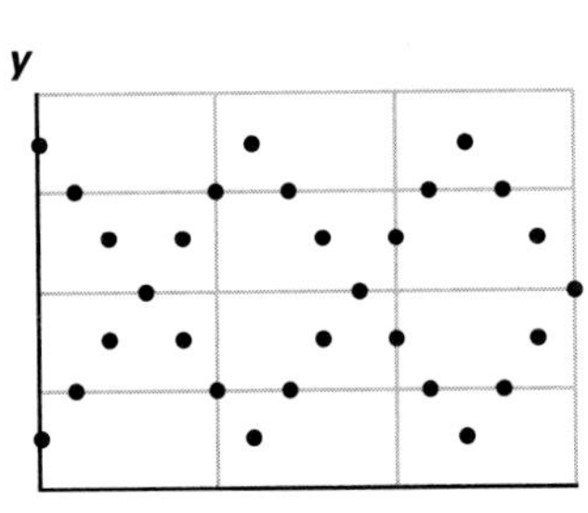

d.

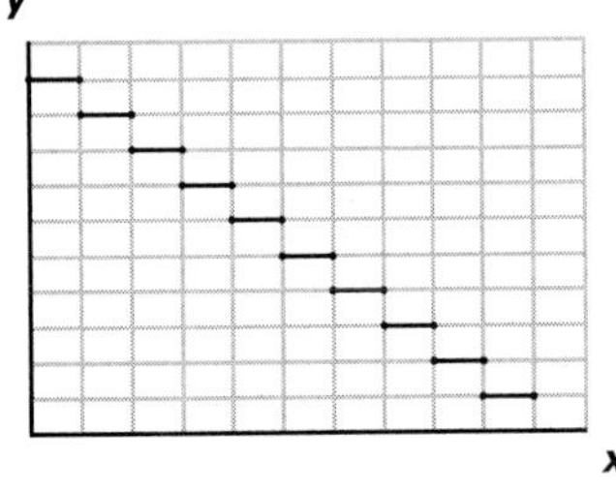

3. The diagram below shows three right triangles with a common right angle at C. Think back to your work with the trigonometric ratios: sine, cosine, and tangent.

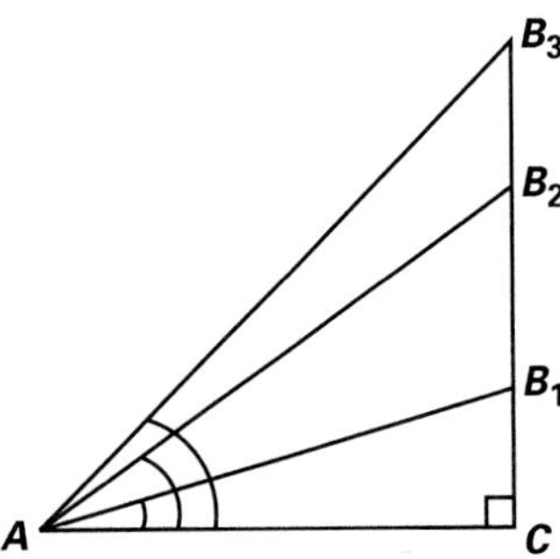

a. As the acute angle at A changes, what happens to each of these ratios?

b. Is each ratio a function of the measure of $\angle A$? Explain your reasoning.

c. What does $\sin A = 0.5$ mean? How is this notation similar to the function notation introduced in this lesson?

Unit 3

LESSON 1 • ALGEBRA AND FUNCTIONS 183

4. In previous units, you calculated absolute values and may have calculated square roots to measure variation in sets of numerical data.
   a. Is the relation between each real number and its absolute value a function? Explain your reasoning.
   b. Is the relation between each nonnegative real number and its square root a function? Explain.
   c. What symbolic notation indicates that a variable y is the absolute value of x?
   d. What symbolic notation indicates that a variable y is the square root of x?

Reflecting

1. In previous courses, you've studied a variety of patterns relating variables. Give some examples of *linear models*, *exponential models*, or *power models* to illustrate the importance of being able to predict values of one variable y from another variable x in the way that functions do.
2. Scatterplots often show the trend of a relation between variables, but they don't allow you to predict y exactly from x. For example, both the scatterplot and linear model on the diagram below show how *weight* of a bungee jumper is related to *stretch* of the bungee cord.

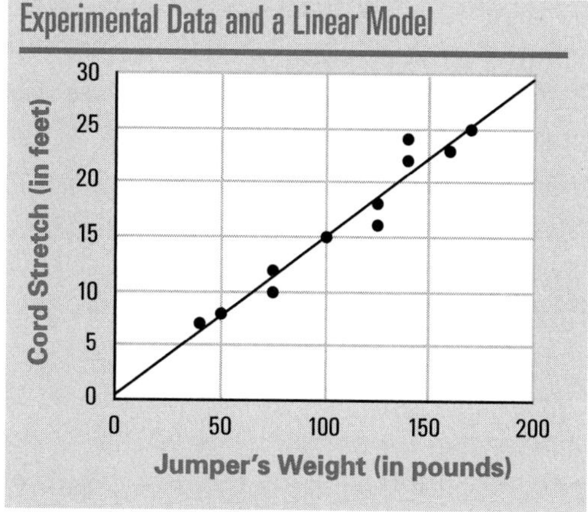

   a. In what ways is the linear model more useful than the scatterplot?
   b. In what ways does the scatterplot give more useful information about the relation?

184 UNIT 3 • SYMBOL SENSE AND ALGEBRAIC REASONING

4. **a.** Yes, absolute value is a function. There is only one possible value for the absolute value of any number.
   b. Yes, finding the square root of a nonnegative number is a function. Every nonnegative number has only one square root.
   c. $y = |x|$
   d. $y = \sqrt{x}$

Reflecting

1. Responses will vary. Students may remember examples of linear models for (*price*, *ticket sales*), (*time*, *distance*), (*cases of soft drinks sold*, *monthly profit*); exponential models for (*time*, *bacteria count*), (*time*, *units of insulin in blood*), (*time*, *population*), (*time*, *number of AIDS cases*); and power models for (*time*, *height of a ball*), (*time*, *height of a diver*), (*distance from light*, *light intensity*). In all these examples, it is important to have exactly one y value for any given x value.
2. **a.** The linear model allows you to estimate the amount of cord stretch for weight values other than the ones given.
   b. The data given in the scatterplot are actual measurements. Rather than estimating the amount of stretch, which could be inaccurate, these data give actual stretches for particular weights. In a scatterplot, it is possible to have different stretches for the same weight values.

3. **a.** $h(16)$ represents Judy's height in centimeters when she is 16 years old.
   b. $h(14) - h(13)$ represents how many centimeters Judy grew between the ages of 13 and 14.
   c. Responses may vary. The symbolic notation is very concise. However, one disadvantage is that not everybody will be able to interpret it.
4. Responses may vary. Many calculators have built-in functions for finding the sine, cosine, and tangent of an angle and also for finding the absolute value, square, and square root of a number. We say that these are built-in because we don't have to input the rule. All we need to do is give the calculator the input value and choose the function, and it will use the correct rule to produce an output value.
5. Responses will vary. Some students may mention that, frequently, the real-world situations have domains and ranges in the first quadrant. They might also examine minimum and maximum values for the function to determine the physical limitations. To determine the theoretical range and domain, students might mention such restrictions as not having a zero in the denominator of a fraction. Some students might use a table to examine the pattern of the function.

Extending

1. **a.**

x	0	1.3	2.9	–4.5	–3.88	4.78	5	100	–0.02
$f(x)$	0	1	2	–5	–4	4	5	100	–1
$c(x)$	0	2	3	–4	–3	5	5	100	0

   b. The rule $s(x) = 1.50c(x)$ gives the cost for shipping a package weighing x pounds.

Unit 3

3. Suppose the relation between Judy's height in centimeters and age in years is given by a function $y = h(x)$, where x is her age and y is her height.

   a. What does $h(16)$ represent?

   b. What does $h(14) - h(13)$ represent?

   c. Look back at the notation in Parts a and b and consider what each expression represents in words. What advantage is there to using function notation? Are there disadvantages? Explain.

4. It often is said that calculators have "built-in" functions. Explain what this means in terms of particular functions on your calculator.

5. What strategies have you used to find the practical domain and range of a function rule that is used to model some real-world situation? What strategies have you used to find the theoretical domain and range?

Extending

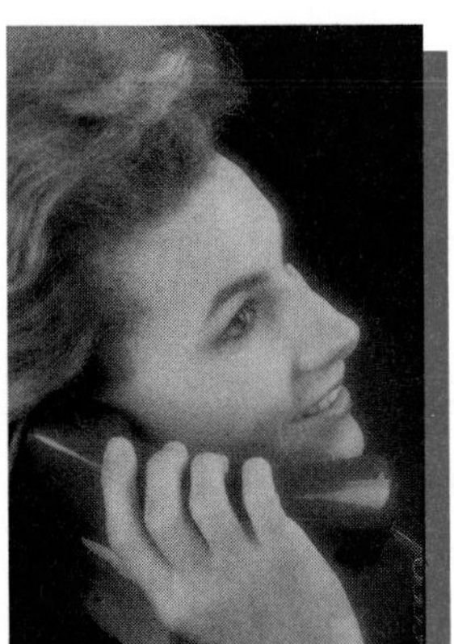

1. Many services that we use on a daily basis are priced with rules that ignore fractions. For example, a long-distance telephone call might cost $1.25 per minute or any fraction of a minute. This means that calls lasting any part of one minute will cost $1.25, calls of any length between one and two minutes will cost $2.50, and so on.

   There are two functions that are particularly helpful in modeling situations in which that kind of rounding is involved. One is the **floor function**, $f(x)$, and the other is the **ceiling function**, $c(x)$. The floor function always gives the greatest integer less than or equal to x. The ceiling function always gives the smallest integer greater than or equal to x.

   a. Use these definitions to complete a table like the one below.

x	0	1.3	2.9	−4.5	−3.88	4.78	5	100	−0.02
$f(x)$									
$c(x)$									

   b. The cost of shipping a package from one city to another is often a function of the weight of that package. Suppose one company charges $1.50 for each pound or fraction of a pound. What rule, involving the ceiling or floor function, gives the cost for shipping a package of exact weight x (in pounds)?

Unit 3

LESSON 1 • ALGEBRA AND FUNCTIONS 185

c. The cost of a cellular telephone call is \$1 for the first minute and \$0.25 for each minute or part of a minute beyond the first. What rule, involving the ceiling or floor function, gives the cost for a call that lasts x minutes? (Again, x might be a fractional number.)

d. The managers at Computer World decided to reward each salesperson based upon the dollar value of the merchandise sold during the month. At the end of each month, the managers will award \$10 of store credit for every \$5,000 worth of sales. What rule involving the ceiling or floor function will give the amount of store credit C for monthly sales of m dollars?

2. Suppose $g(x)$ is defined *piecewise* as follows:

$$g(x) = \begin{cases} 4 - x^2 & \text{if } x < 2, \\ x - 3 & \text{if } x \geq 2 \end{cases}$$

a. Give numerical values for $g(-2)$, $g(0)$, $g(2)$, and $g(10)$.

b. Sketch the graph of $y = g(x)$.

c. Explain why $y = g(x)$ is or is not a function.

d. Investigate how you might use your calculator or computer software to graph piecewise-defined rules. Write a report of your findings.

3. The function $F(x) = \frac{1}{12}x$ converts measurements from inches to feet, and the function $Y(x) = \frac{1}{3}x$ converts from feet to yards.

a. How can you use these functions to find the number of yards in 48 inches?

b. Explain the meaning of $Y(F(x)) = \frac{1}{36}x$.

c. If we define $f(x) = 2x$ and $g(x) = x^2$, then what are $f(g(x))$ and $g(f(x))$?

d. If we define $f(x) = 3x + 5$ and $g(x) = \frac{x-5}{3}$, then what are $f(g(x))$ and $g(f(x))$?

186 UNIT 3 • SYMBOL SENSE AND ALGEBRAIC REASONING

1. c. The function $t(x) = 1 + 0.25c(x - 1)$ gives the cost for a call that lasts x minutes if $x \geq 1$.

d. The function $C(m) = 10f\left(\frac{m}{5{,}000}\right)$ gives the store credit for monthly sales of m dollars.

2. a. $g(-2) = 4 - (-2)^2 = 4 - 4 = 0$
$g(0) = 4 - 0^2 = 4$
$g(2) = 2 - 3 = -1$
$g(10) = 10 - 3 = 7$

b.

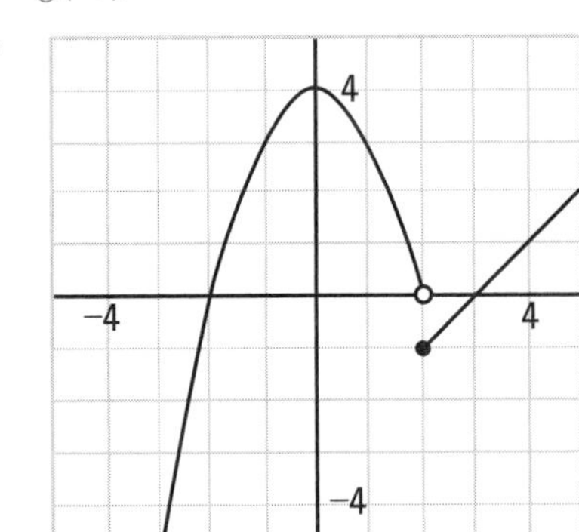

c. $y = g(x)$ is a function. The only x value that might cause difficulty is $x = 2$, but the piecewise definition clearly tells us that for $x = 2$, $g(2) = 2 - 3 = -1$.

d. Responses may vary, depending on the technology used. On the TI-82 or TI-83, logical operators can be included in the definition of the function in order to create a piecewise-defined function. However, if you don't want the "pieces" connected, you will need to use dot mode rather than connected mode. The command for this function could be $Y_1 = (4 - X^2)(X < 2) + (X - 3)(X \geq 2)$ and will produce the graph below.

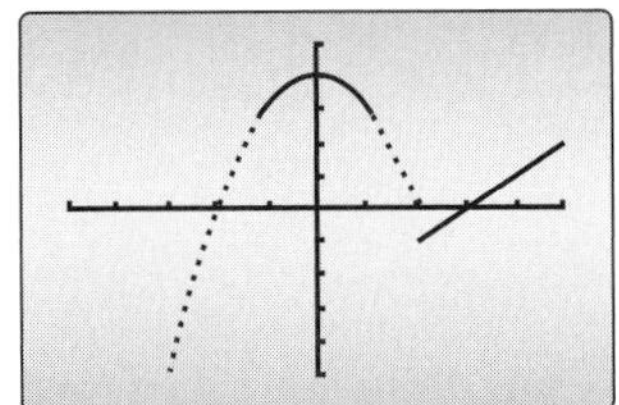

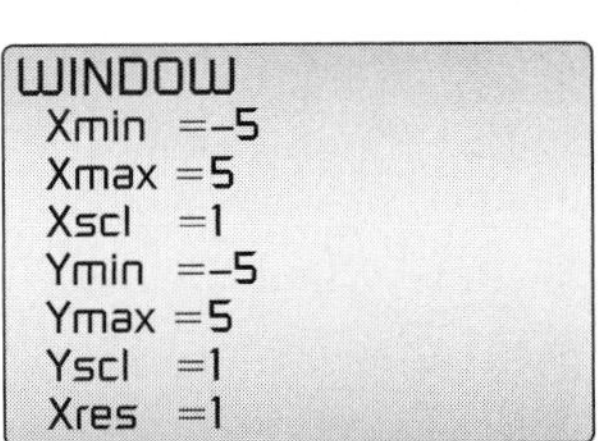

WINDOW
Xmin =-5
Xmax =5
Xscl =1
Ymin =-5
Ymax =5
Yscl =1
Xres =1

3. a. First calculate $F(48)$ to find the number of feet in 48 inches. Then, since $F(48) = 4$, you can evaluate $Y(4)$ to find the number of yards. Since $Y(4) = \frac{4}{3}$, there are $\frac{4}{3}$ yards in 48 inches.

b. $Y(F(x)) = \frac{1}{36}x$ converts from inches to yards.
Since $F(x) = \frac{1}{12}x$, $Y(F(x)) = Y\left(\frac{1}{12}x\right) = \frac{1}{36}x$.

c. $f(g(x)) = f(x^2) = 2x^2$

$g(f(x)) = g(2x) = (2x)^2 = 4x^2$

d. $f(g(x)) = f\left(\frac{x-5}{3}\right) = 3\left(\frac{x-5}{3}\right) + 5 = x$

$g(f(x)) = g(3x + 5) = \frac{(3x+5) - 5}{3} = x$

NOTE: This problem can be further explored with an advanced group to consider why in Part c both $f(g(x))$ and $g(f(x))$ are equal to x.

See Assessment Resources pages 83–88.

Assessments 83–85

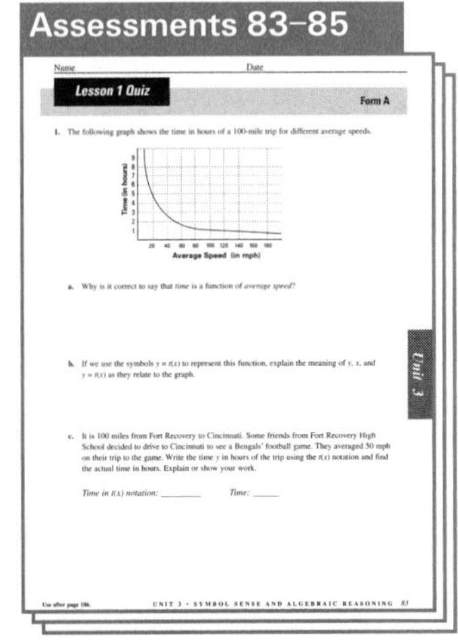

Assessments 86–88

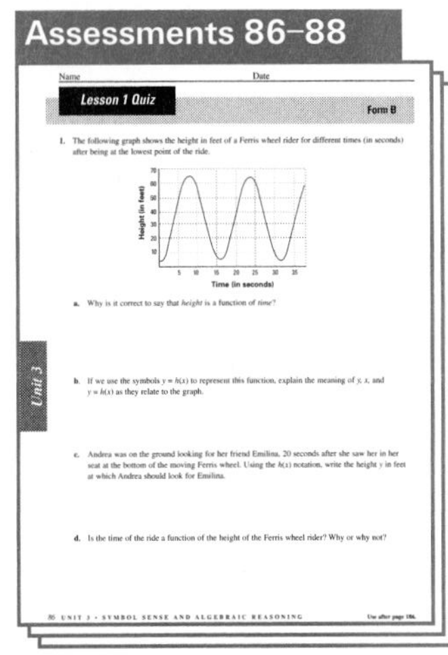

Unit 3

Lesson 2 *Algebraic Operations: Part 1*

LESSON OVERVIEW The business constraints of a band provide the expressions and functions needed to explore equivalent algebraic forms and the basic properties of numbers and operations in this lesson. The band situation actually allows students to manipulate expressions that have meaning. It also enables them to understand that, in some cases, certain forms are more convenient to use than others.

Lesson Objectives

- To determine the equivalence of different forms of symbolic rules by examining tables of values, by graphing, and by rewriting rules
- To recognize and apply the commutative and associative properties of addition and multiplication
- To recognize and apply the distributive property of multiplication over addition (subtraction)
- To simplify algebraic expressions

Lesson 2

Algebraic Operations: Part 1

Music is a major form of entertainment in our society. Production and sale of music are also big businesses. All across the country, there are thousands of individuals and groups practicing hard and hoping to make it big with a best-selling single or album. Unfortunately, as the following information shows, even a big hit might not bring much profit to the musicians.

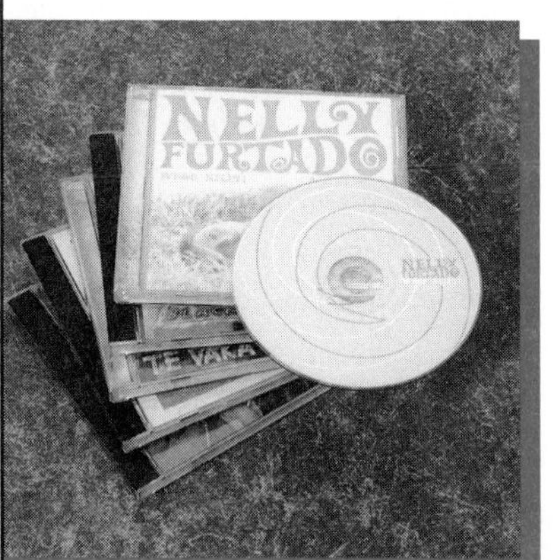

What an Unknown Band Might Expect for Its First Album on a Major Label

ADVANCES and RECOUPABLE COSTS

The label advances money to the band, and it also deducts some of its own expenses from initial royalties:

■ Recording advance	\$200,000
■ One video	\$75,000
■ Touring	\$40,000
■ Independent promotion	\$50,000
Total advances and recoupable costs	**\$365,000**

EARNINGS (based on 200,000 CDs sold)

A CD might cost \$15, but the label makes deductions before calculating band royalties.

Original CD price	\$15.00
■ 25 percent off for packaging and pressing cost	–\$3.75
■ 10 percent off for discounts to retailers	–\$1.50
■ Other discounts (11 percent)	–\$1.65
Base CD price	**\$8.10**

The typical band earns 10 percent per CD.

\$8.10 × 0.1 = \$0.81 per CD	
\$0.81 per CD × 200,000 CDs sold =	**\$162,000**
If the band writes all of its own songs, it can expect another \$0.52 per CD for publishing rights	**\$104,000**

THE BOTTOM LINE (for 200,000 CDs sold)

Total band income from CD sales	\$266,000
Minus label's advances and costs	–\$365,000
Amount needed before band sees profit	**\$99,000**

Source: Maggie Lange, Esquire; Perkins, Smith and Cohen, LLP. Boston, Massachusetts.

LESSON 2 • ALGEBRAIC OPERATIONS: PART 1 187

Think About This Situation

The table on the previous page shows how a band can sell 200,000 compact discs and make no profit at all.

a. How much money is taken in from the sale of the CDs?

b. Who makes profit from these sales?

c. How would the band's profit or loss change if sales were more or less than 200,000 copies?

d. Why would a band enter a business deal like this?

INVESTIGATION 1 How to Succeed in Business

The table on the previous page showed profit (actually, loss!) prospects for a band whose compact disc sold 200,000 copies. It's interesting to see what the story would be for a band if only 50,000 or 100,000 copies of a CD were sold, or if the CD became a hit and at least 500,000 copies were sold.

1. Suppose that when a new band recorded its first album with a major label, it had to deal with these business conditions:

- Expenses of $365,000 for the recording advance, video production, touring, and promotion (to be repaid out of royalties)
- Income of $0.81 per CD from royalties
- Income of $0.52 per CD for publishing rights

The band's profit on the CDs would depend on sales. The group's business manager could express the profit function in several different ways. Here are two possibilities:

$$P_1(x) = (0.81x + 0.52x) - 365{,}000$$

$$P_2(x) = 1.33x - 365{,}000$$

Unit 3

188 UNIT 3 • SYMBOL SENSE AND ALGEBRAIC REASONING

LAUNCH full-class discussion

Think About This Situation

See Teaching Masters 65 and 66.

For some students, the table on student page 187 may be hard to understand. Having a transparency of the table (Teaching Master 65) may aid in the discussion. You may have to help with some of the vocabulary. You might ask the class, "What does it mean for the company to 'advance' money to the band? Why is this a debt? Who owes whom money? What is a 'royalty'? Who gets this money?" These ideas are important to creating sensible symbolic expressions, since students will have to keep track of constants (the advance and the deductions) and variables (the number of CDs sold), as well as which are positives (royalties and publishing rights) and which are negatives (the debt).

ⓐ $3,000,000 (that is, $15 × 200,000) is taken in from the sale of the CDs.

ⓑ It is not clear how much profit is made from the sales of the CDs. The profit is split between the record company and the retail store. The band doesn't make profit on the first 200,000 copies.

ⓒ You know that the more CDs sold, the greater the profit. If you had an algebraic model, you could use it to predict the profit or loss.

ⓓ A band needs to start somewhere. The band may hope that this CD will get it recognition and in turn a better contract on the next CD. It's also possible, though rare, for a debut disc to sell well enough to pay the debt completely.

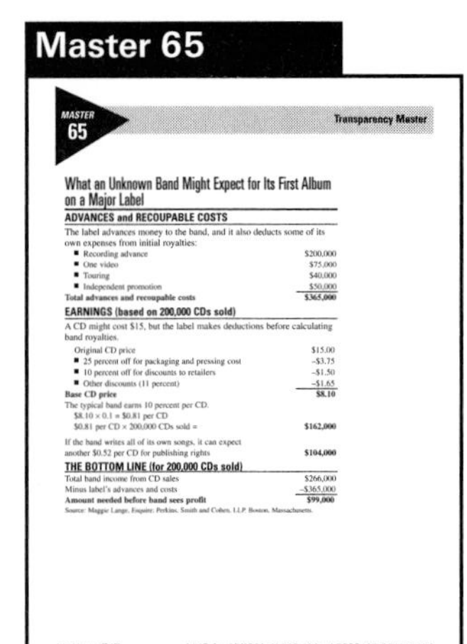

Master 65

MASTER 65 — Transparency Master

What an Unknown Band Might Expect for Its First Album on a Major Label

ADVANCES and RECOUPABLE COSTS

The label advances money to the band, and it also deducts some of its own expenses from initial royalties:

■ Recording advance	$200,000
■ One video	$75,000
■ Touring	$40,000
■ Independent promotion	$50,000
Total advances and recoupable costs	**$365,000**

EARNINGS (based on 200,000 CDs sold)

A CD might cost $15, but the label makes deductions before calculating band royalties.

Original CD price	$15.00
■ 25 percent off for packaging and pressing cost	–$3.75
■ 10 percent off for discounts to retailers	–$1.50
■ Other discounts (11 percent)	–$1.65
Base CD price	**$8.10**
The typical band earns 10 percent per CD.	
$8.10 × 0.1 = $0.81 per CD	
$0.81 per CD × 200,000 CDs sold =	**$162,000**
If the band writes all of its own songs, it can expect another $0.52 per CD for publishing rights	**$104,000**

THE BOTTOM LINE (for 200,000 CDs sold)

Total band income from CD sales	$266,000
Minus label's advances and costs	–$365,000
Amount needed before band sees profit	**$99,000**

Source: Maggie Lange, Esquire: Perkins, Smith and Cohen, LLP, Boston, Massachusetts.

Use with pages 187–188. UNIT 3 • SYMBOL SENSE AND ALGEBRAIC REASONING

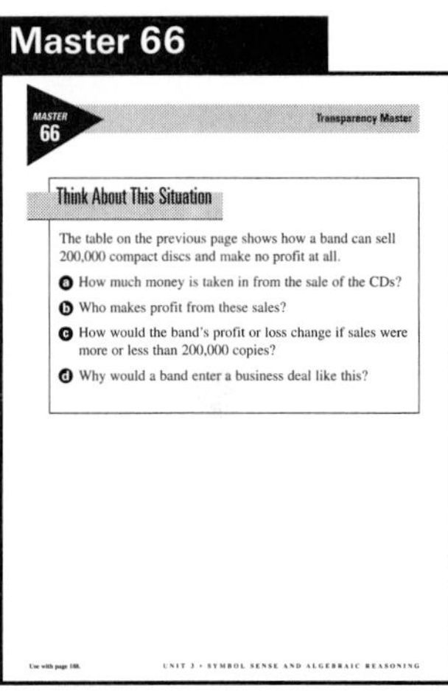

Master 66

MASTER 66 — Transparency Master

Think About This Situation

The table on the previous page shows how a band can sell 200,000 compact discs and make no profit at all.

ⓐ How much money is taken in from the sale of the CDs?

ⓑ Who makes profit from these sales?

ⓒ How would the band's profit or loss change if sales were more or less than 200,000 copies?

ⓓ Why would a band enter a business deal like this?

Use with page 188. UNIT 3 • SYMBOL SENSE AND ALGEBRAIC REASONING

EXPLORE small-group investigation

INVESTIGATION 1 How to Succeed in Business

In this investigation, students are asked to interpret and compare two equivalent functions and then to create two equivalent functions from contextual clues. They are asked for a "simpler" form, but the emphasis is on making sense of the expressions and on equivalence, rather than on following rules for "simplest" form. Students previously encountered the distributive property in Course 1. When they are adding like terms, they are applying this property. At this point in time, students may not use the distributive property formally, but rather they may apply contextual knowledge to make sense of rearrangements of symbols. In Investigation 2, the properties that permit the manipulation of symbolic expressions will be explored and formalized.

1. **a.** Yes, they both correctly express the relation between sales and profits. Profit is found by subtracting expenses from income. The total expenses are clearly \$365,000. The first profit equation gives the income from royalties and publishing rights separately to get total income. The second recognizes that both royalties and publishing rights apply to every CD sold; therefore, the band gets \$1.33 income for each CD, which makes total income \$1.33x.

   b. Responses may vary. Some students may like $P_2(x)$ better because it is simpler. On the other hand, $P_1(x)$ is more flexible because it can be easily altered to eliminate the \$0.52 profit in cases in which the band does not own the publishing rights to all the songs.

   c. If only 50,000 copies were sold, the band would lose \$298,500. If 500,000 copies were sold, the band would make \$300,000.

   d. If 274,436 copies of the CD were sold, the band would lose only 12 cents. If 274,437 copies are sold, the band would make \$1.21.

2. **a.** ■ $P_1(x) = 15x - 3.75x - 1.50x - 1.65x - 365{,}000$

   ■ $P_2(x) = 8.10x - 365{,}000$

   b. To see that the rules are the same, students can graph both and show that the graphs are the same, examine the tables for both rules to see that they are identical, or check the arithmetic to make sure that the first equation has been simplified correctly to get the second equation.

   c. The company would make \$40,000 if only 50,000 CDs were sold. If 100,000 copies of the CD were sold, the company would make \$445,000.

   d. For the record company to break even, 45,062 copies of the CD must be sold.

   e. The following functions do not include profit before the band has repaid the advance. Students may decide to include that profit, giving the total profit rather than additional profit. For these functions, x is the number of CDs sold after the band has repaid the advance.

   $$P_1(x) = 15x - 3.75x - 1.50x - 1.65x - 0.81x - 0.52x$$
   $$P_2(x) = 6.77x$$

   One way to demonstrate that the two functions are the same is to graph both functions on the same coordinate plane. Another way is to compare the tables for the two functions. A third way is to combine like terms in $P_1(x)$.

a. Do both function rules express the correct relation between sales and profits? How could you convince someone of your answer?

b. Which of the two rules do you believe expresses the band's profit function in the most useful way? Why?

c. What would the band's profit be if only 50,000 copies were sold? If 500,000 copies were sold?

d. How many CD copies must be sold for the band to break even?

2. Profit for the record company is also a function of sales. For the band in Activity 1, the label had the following production and distribution conditions to consider.

- Studio, video, touring, and promotion expenses of $365,000
- Pressing and packaging costs of $3.75 per CD
- Discounts to music stores of $1.50 per CD
- Other discounts of $1.65 per CD

Until the band's share of income repays the $365,000 for studio, video, touring, and promotion expenses, the band gets no share of the $15 per CD of sales income.

a. Use the information given above to write two equivalent expressions for the function that shows how the record company's profit depends on the number of CDs sold while the band is still repaying its advance. (The company would have other expenses, such as staff salaries and office expenses like electricity and rent. For this activity, though, you should ignore those expenses.)

- Write one rule that shows how each income and cost item enters the overall calculation of profit.
- Write another rule that will give profit for any number of CDs sold with the simplest possible calculation.

b. Explain how the two rules you wrote in Part a can be checked for equivalence using tables and graphs and by reasoning with the symbolic forms themselves.

c. What profit would the company make on sales of 50,000 CDs? On 100,000 copies?

d. How many copies of this CD must be sold for the record company to break even?

e. The company's profit function changes when the band has repaid its advance. Write two different expressions for profit as a function of CD sales beyond that point: one that shows each income and expense item, and another that is the simplest to use for actual calculation. Then explain in several ways how you know the two rules are equivalent.

Unit 3

LESSON 2 • ALGEBRAIC OPERATIONS: PART 1 189

As you have seen, bands don't often make much money on sales of their recordings. However, they do make money from concert tours and sales of T-shirts and other merchandise.

3. Suppose a band with a moderate following is preparing to go on a four-week tour. A market research survey gives the following information about prospects for a single show on the tour:

   - Ticket sales x and ticket price p are related by $p = -0.04x + 30$. The venue pays the band 10% of the income from ticket sales. Income from ticket sales is $I(x) = (-0.04x + 30)x$.
   - About 15% of ticket buyers will also buy a T-shirt, giving the band \$5 profit for each sale.
   - About 5% of ticket buyers will buy a poster, giving the band \$3.50 profit for each sale.
   - All the band's other expenses for each show will average about \$300.

   Because one of the band's main goals is to make a profit, the band manager might combine all the given information in a single relation showing profit as a function of the number of tickets sold at a show.

   a. One possibility is the following equation:

   $$P(x) = 0.10(-0.04x + 30)x + 5(0.15x) + 3.50(0.05x) - 300$$

   How does each part of this function rule relate to the given information?

   b. In what ways could you rewrite this rule for the profit function in a simpler yet equivalent form?

   c. How can you check to see that the simpler function rules you wrote in Part b are equivalent to the original?

   d. What is the maximum profit that the band could make from the show? How many ticket buyers will produce that maximum profit? What ticket price will produce that maximum profit?

Unit 3

190 UNIT 3 • SYMBOL SENSE AND ALGEBRAIC REASONING

EXPLORE *continued*

3. a.

$0.10(-0.04x + 30)x$	income from ticket sales
$5(0.15x)$	income from T-shirt sales
$3.50(0.05x)$	income from poster sales
300	operating expenses

   b. There are many possible ways, but the simplest form is the following:

$$P(x) = -0.004x^2 + 3.925x - 300$$

   c. You can graph them or compare table values. You can also check your arithmetic to see that the simplified forms are algebraically equivalent.

   d. The maximum profit of $662.85 comes when 491 people purchase tickets. The ticket price would need to be about $10.36 (that is, $-0.04 \cdot 491 + 30$).

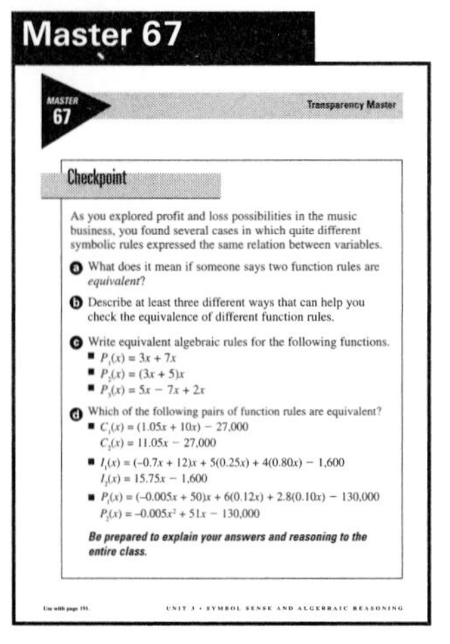

Master 67

MASTER 67 Transparency Master

Checkpoint

As you explored profit and loss possibilities in the music business, you found several cases in which quite different symbolic rules expressed the same relation between variables.

a What does it mean if someone says two function rules are *equivalent*?

b Describe at least three different ways that can help you check the equivalence of different function rules.

c Write equivalent algebraic rules for the following functions.
- $P_1(x) = 3x + 7x$
- $P_2(x) = (3x + 5)x$
- $P_3(x) = 5x - 7x + 2x$

d Which of the following pairs of function rules are equivalent?
- $C_1(x) = (1.05x + 10x) - 27{,}000$
  $C_2(x) = 11.05x - 27{,}000$
- $I_1(x) = (-0.7x + 12)x + 5(0.25x) + 4(0.80x) - 1{,}600$
  $I_2(x) = 15.75x - 1{,}600$
- $P_1(x) = (-0.005x + 50)x + 6(0.12x) + 2.8(0.10x) - 130{,}000$
  $P_2(x) = -0.005x^2 + 51x - 130{,}000$

Be prepared to explain your answers and reasoning to the entire class.

Use with page 191. UNIT 3 • SYMBOL SENSE AND ALGEBRAIC REASONING

SHARE AND SUMMARIZE full-class discussion

Checkpoint

See Teaching Master 67.

a They represent the same ordered pairs. Their graphs and tables will be the same.

b To check the equivalence of different function rules, you can graph the functions, look at the tables for the functions, or express the function rules in simplest form and compare them. You may wish to caution students about relying on only one method. It is possible to find windows in which two different functions will have graphs that look the same. Similarly, it is possible to find sets of table values that match but correspond to different functions.

c Responses may vary. The simplest expressions possible are given below.
- $P_1(x) = 10x$
- $P_2(x) = 3x^2 + 5x$
- $P_3(x) = 0$

d
- $C_1(x)$ and $C_2(x)$ are equivalent.
- $I_1(x)$ and $I_2(x)$ are not equivalent. The first simplifies to $I_1(x) = -0.7x^2 + 16.45x - 1{,}600$.
- $P_1(x)$ and $P_2(x)$ are equivalent.

Unit 3

Checkpoint

As you explored profit and loss possibilities in the music business, you found several cases in which quite different symbolic rules expressed the same relation between variables.

a What does it mean if someone says two function rules are *equivalent*?

b Describe at least three different ways that can help you check the equivalence of different function rules.

c Write equivalent algebraic rules for the following functions.

- $P_1(x) = 3x + 7x$
- $P_2(x) = (3x + 5)x$
- $P_3(x) = 5x - 7x + 2x$

d Which of the following pairs of function rules are equivalent?

- $C_1(x) = (1.05x + 10x) - 27{,}000$
  $C_2(x) = 11.05x - 27{,}000$
- $I_1(x) = (-0.7x + 12)x + 5(0.25x) + 4(0.80x) - 1{,}600$
  $I_2(x) = 15.75x - 1{,}600$
- $P_1(x) = (-0.005x + 50)x + 6(0.12x) + 2.8(0.10x) - 130{,}000$
  $P_2(x) = -0.005x^2 + 51x - 130{,}000$

Be prepared to explain your answers and reasoning to the entire class.

Unit 3

On Your Own

When a pair of athletic shoes costs \$70 in a retail store, that price is based on several factors.

- Average manufacturer's income is about \$20 per pair of shoes.
- Average wholesaler's income is about \$15.50 per pair of shoes.
- Average retailer's operating costs are about \$25.50 per pair of shoes sold.

Source: "Why It Costs \$70 for a Pair of Athletic Shoes," *Washington Post*, May 3, 1995.

LESSON 2 • ALGEBRAIC OPERATIONS: PART 1 191

a. One way to express retailer's profit as a function of the number of pairs of shoes sold is $P(x) = 70x - (20x + 15.50x + 25.50x)$. Write this function rule in several other equivalent forms, including one that you think is the simplest possible.

b. How much profit does the retail store make on each pair of shoes sold, and how is that shown in your simplest-form answer in Part a?

c. Suppose the athletic shoe store estimates that price p and monthly sales x of its most popular shoe model are related by $x = 500 - 4p$. Write a symbolic rule that will give income I from sales of that shoe model as a function of the price charged: $I(p) =$ _______.

d. Write the income function rule in Part c in other equivalent forms. Which form do you think is the simplest form? Why?

e. If that most popular shoe has cost factors that are the same as the averages described above, what function rule will give store profit on the most popular model alone?

f. Write the profit function from Part e in several equivalent forms, including one that you think is simplest for calculations.

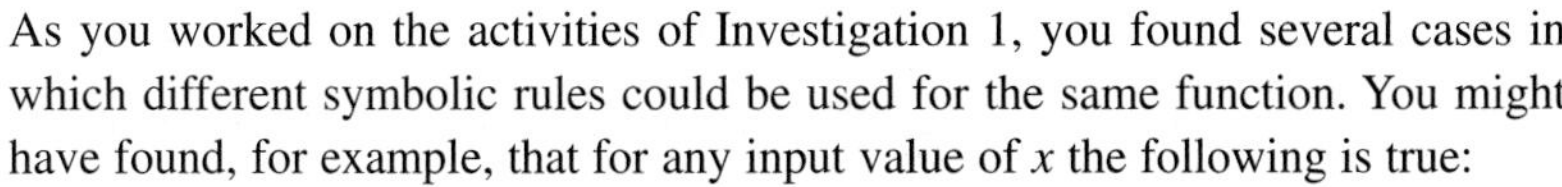

INVESTIGATION 2 Equivalent Expressions

As you worked on the activities of Investigation 1, you found several cases in which different symbolic rules could be used for the same function. You might have found, for example, that for any input value of x the following is true:

$$0.81x + 0.52x = 1.33x$$

You were told that the band in Activity 1 of Investigation 1 received \$0.81 in royalties on each CD sold and another \$0.52 per CD for publishing rights, so it makes sense that the total income was \$1.33 per CD. For any values of x, it seems quite reasonable that $0.81x + 0.52x = 1.33x$. The two profit function rules

$$P_1(x) = (0.81x + 0.52x) - 365{,}000$$

and

$$P_2(x) = 1.33x - 365{,}000$$

really are equivalent.

Sometimes you may have symbolic expressions without any details about a real-world situation being modeled. Still, it may be that simplifications and rearrangements can be made without changing the meaning of the functions involved. Look at the example above, and then consider the following question:

Does $ax + bx = (a + b)x$ for any value of x, regardless of the specific values of a and b?

192 UNIT 3 • SYMBOL SENSE AND ALGEBRAIC REASONING

APPLY individual task

On Your Own

a. The simplest form is $P(x) = 9x$. Nonsimplified forms will vary.

b. The retail store makes \$9 profit for each pair of shoes sold. This comes from taking the \$70 and subtracting all the various expenses. This is shown in Part a by the slope of 9.

c. $I(p) = (500 - 4p)p$

d. Equivalent forms may vary. The simplest form is either the factored form given above or $I(p) = 500p - 4p^2$.

e. Let $R(p)$ represent the profit and $C(p)$ represent the cost if the price in dollars is p. Note that the costs have been given in terms of number sold rather than price.

$$R(p) = I(p) - C(p)$$
$$= (500 - 4p)p - (20 + 15.50 + 25.50)(500 - 4p)$$
$$= (500 - 4p)p - 61(500 - 4p)$$

Another approach is to calculate profit by multiplying the number of pairs of shoes sold by the profit per pair of shoes. This results in the function $R(p) = (500 - 4p)(p - 61)$.

f. Equivalent forms may vary. Two equivalent forms are given below.

$$R(p) = 500p - 4p^2 - 30{,}500 + 244p$$
$$R(p) = -4p^2 + 744p - 30{,}500$$

MORE ASSIGNMENT *pp. 201–207*

Students can now begin Modeling Task 1 or 4 from the MORE assignment following Investigation 3.

Unit 3

EXPLORE small-group investigation

INVESTIGATION 2 Equivalent Expressions

In this investigation, students make sense of some of the rules that seem to be true when working with symbolic expressions. They have used the distributive property in Course 1, and they have examined operations with matrices in Course 2 to see if addition and multiplication of matrices are commutative and associative. This investigation provides a formalization of those properties.

When students are working on Activities 1 and 2, it is important that you give them a chance to make their own sense of why certain expressions are equivalent. You may wish to have students make their initial judgments about equivalence without the aid of a calculator so that you can assess how much knowledge they have already internalized about properties. The calculator can become an arbiter in any disagreements. Teaching Master 68 contains the 21 equations. Students can cut out the equations and group them for Activities 1 and 2, or they can rewrite them on separate pieces of paper. You may wish to have a full-class discussion of Activity 1 to be sure that all students are working with the same set of equivalent expressions when they move to Activity 2. Once students have discussed Activities 3 and 4 in their groups, you should facilitate a whole-class discussion sharing students ways of thinking about the properties.

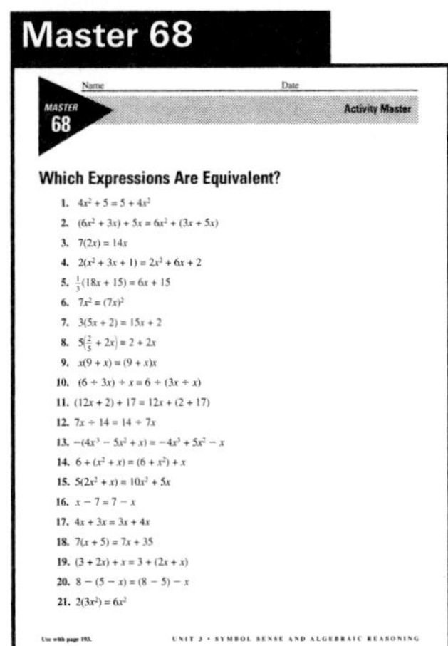

Master 68

Name ______ Date ______

MASTER 68 Activity Master

Which Expressions Are Equivalent?

1. $4x^2 + 5 = 5 + 4x^2$
2. $(6x^2 + 3x) + 5x = 6x^2 + (3x + 5x)$
3. $7(2x) = 14x$
4. $2(x^2 + 3x + 1) = 2x^2 + 6x + 2$
5. $\frac{1}{3}(18x + 15) = 6x + 15$
6. $7x^2 = (7x)^2$
7. $3(5x + 2) = 15x + 2$
8. $5\left(\frac{2}{5} + 2x\right) = 2 + 2x$
9. $x(9 + x) = (9 + x)x$
10. $(6 \div 3x) \div x = 6 \div (3x \div x)$
11. $(12x + 2) + 17 = 12x + (2 + 17)$
12. $7x \div 14 = 14 \div 7x$
13. $-(4x^3 - 5x^2 + x) = -4x^3 + 5x^2 - x$
14. $6 + (x^2 + x) = (6 + x^2) + x$
15. $5(2x^2 + x) = 10x^2 + 5x$
16. $x - 7 = 7 - x$
17. $4x + 3x = 3x + 4x$
18. $7(x + 5) = 7x + 35$
19. $(3 + 2x) + x = 3 + (2x + x)$
20. $8 - (5 - x) = (8 - 5) - x$
21. $2(3x^2) = 6x^2$

Use with page 193. UNIT 3 • SYMBOL SENSE AND ALGEBRAIC REASONING

EXPLORE *continued*

1. **See Teaching Master 68.**

   Activity 2 is the critical part of this investigation. The most important job the students are to do in Activity 1 is to determine which expressions are equivalent for all values of *x*.

   a. True for all values of x:

   $4x^2 + 5 = 5 + 4x^2$
   $7(2x) = 14x$
   $x(9 + x) = (9 + x)x$
   $-(4x^3 - 5x^2 + x) = -4x^3 + 5x^2 - x$
   $5(2x^2 + x) = 10x^2 + 5x$
   $7(x + 5) = 7x + 35$
   $2(3x^2) = 6x^2$
   $(6x^2 + 3x) + 5x = 6x^2 + (3x + 5x)$
   $2(x^2 + 3x + 1) = 2x^2 + 6x + 2$
   $(12x + 2) + 17 = 12x + (2 + 17)$
   $6 + (x^2 + x) = (6 + x^2) + x$
   $4x + 3x = 3x + 4x$
   $(3 + 2x) + x = 3 + (2x + x)$

   b. True for some values of x:

   $7x^2 = (7x)^2;\ x = 0$
   $(6 \div 3x) \div x = 6 \div (3x \div x);\ x = \pm 1$
   $x - 7 = 7 - x;\ x = 7$
   $5\left(\frac{2}{5} + 2x\right) = 2 + 2x;\ x = 0$
   $7x \div 14 = 14 \div 7x;\ x = \pm 2$
   $8 - (5 - x) = (8 - 5) - x;\ x = 0$

   c. Never true:

   $\frac{1}{3}(18x + 15) = 6x + 15$
   $3(5x + 2) = 15x + 2$

2. **a–b. As the groups are working on sorting the equations, be sure to circulate to make sure that they understand that it is okay for them to revise their piles or lists throughout the entire process. Summaries and examples may vary, but their categories should agree with the three below.**

   Associative

   $(6x^2 + 3x) + 5x = 6x^2 + (3x + 5x)$
   $7(2x) = 14x$
   $(12x + 2) + 17 = 12x + (2 + 17)$
   $6 + (x^2 + x) = (6 + x^2) + x$
   $(3 + 2x) + x = 3 + (2x + x)$
   $2(3x^2) = 6x^2$

   Commutative

   $4x^2 + 5 = 5 + 4x^2$
   $x(9 + x) = (9 + x)x$
   $4x + 3x = 3x + 4x$

   Distributive

   $2(x^2 + 3x + 1) = 2x^2 + 6x + 2$
   $-(4x^3 - 5x^2 + x) = -4x^3 + 5x^2 - x$
   $5(2x^2 + x) = 10x^2 + 5x$
   $7(x + 5) = 7x + 35$

In the following activities, you will explore this question and others that are similar. You will look for other ways that algebraic expressions can be rewritten without changing their meaning and for basic, general principles for rewriting algebraic expressions in equivalent forms.

1. Below are 21 equations. In some of those equations, the related expressions give identical outputs for all input values of x. In other equations, the related expressions give equal outputs for only a few specially chosen x values. In a few of the equations, the related expressions never give the same output from a given input.

Working with a partner, examine the equations and separate them as best you can into three groups:

a. Equations that are true for all values of x

b. Equations that are true for only some values of x

c. Equations that are true for no values of x

Share your ideas with the other members of your group. Resolve any differences, and then prepare convincing arguments in support of each agreed-upon conclusion.

Which Expressions Are Equivalent?

$4x^2 + 5 = 5 + 4x^2$	$(6x^2 + 3x) + 5x = 6x^2 + (3x + 5x)$
$7(2x) = 14x$	$2(x^2 + 3x + 1) = 2x^2 + 6x + 2$
$\frac{1}{3}(18x + 15) = 6x + 15$	$7x^2 = (7x)^2$
$3(5x + 2) = 15x + 2$	$5\left(\frac{2}{5} + 2x\right) = 2 + 2x$
$x(9 + x) = (9 + x)x$	$(6 \div 3x) \div x = 6 \div (3x \div x)$
$(12x + 2) + 17 = 12x + (2 + 17)$	$7x \div 14 = 14 \div 7x$
$-(4x^3 - 5x^2 + x) = -4x^3 + 5x^2 - x$	$6 + (x^2 + x) = (6 + x^2) + x$
$5(2x^2 + x) = 10x^2 + 5x$	$x - 7 = 7 - x$
$4x + 3x = 3x + 4x$	$7(x + 5) = 7x + 35$
$(3 + 2x) + x = 3 + (2x + x)$	$8 - (5 - x) = (8 - 5) - x$
$2(3x^2) = 6x^2$	

2. Now, working together as a group, sort the equations that are true for all values of the variable x into types that seem to involve similar patterns.

a. Write, in your own words, descriptions of the various patterns you found. For example, you might notice that several equations are similar in form to $4x + 3x = 3x + 4x$ and summarize this pattern by saying "You can switch the order of the terms being added."

Unit 3

LESSON 2 • ALGEBRAIC OPERATIONS: PART 1 193

b. For each pattern you agree on, make up another algebraic equation that shows its application. For example, the equation "$7 + 12x = 12x + 7$" illustrates the same pattern as "$4x + 3x = 3x + 4x$."

3. Compare your types of equations and pattern descriptions to those of other groups in class.

Mathematicians have spent a great deal of time studying arithmetic and algebraic operations to find basic principles that can guide work with symbolic expressions. They have generally agreed on the following basic properties of numbers and operations. You have already encountered most of these properties in your previous work with algebraic expressions.

Algebraic Properties

Commutative Property	
Of Addition:	For any numbers a and b, $a + b = b + a$
Of Multiplication:	For any numbers a and b, $a \times b = b \times a$
Associative Property	
Of Addition:	For any numbers a, b, and c, $a + (b + c) = (a + b) + c$
Of Multiplication:	For any numbers a, b, and c, $a \times (b \times c) = (a \times b) \times c$
Distributive Property	
Of Multiplication Over Addition:	For any numbers a, b, and c, $a \times (b + c) = a \times b + a \times c$
Of Multiplication Over Subtraction:	For any numbers a, b, and c, $a \times (b - c) = a \times b - a \times c$

4. Compare the patterns and descriptions that you identified in Activity 2 to the list of properties and names that are standard in mathematical usage. Then brainstorm with your group members about helpful ways to think about and remember the names of these properties.

5. Study each of the following arguments and identify the algebraic properties that justify each step. Then, try to reach the same conclusion using a different sequence of steps.

a. $5x + (3 + 7x)$ is equivalent to $5x + (7x + 3)$
is equivalent to $(5x + 7x) + 3$
is equivalent to $(5 + 7)x + 3$
is equivalent to $12x + 3$

b. $-5(x + 6) + 4x$ is equivalent to $(-5x + -30) + 4x$
is equivalent to $(-30 + -5x) + 4x$
is equivalent to $-30 + (-5x + 4x)$
is equivalent to $-30 + (-5 + 4)x$
is equivalent to $-30 + (-1x)$

194 UNIT 3 • SYMBOL SENSE AND ALGEBRAIC REASONING

EXPLORE *continued*

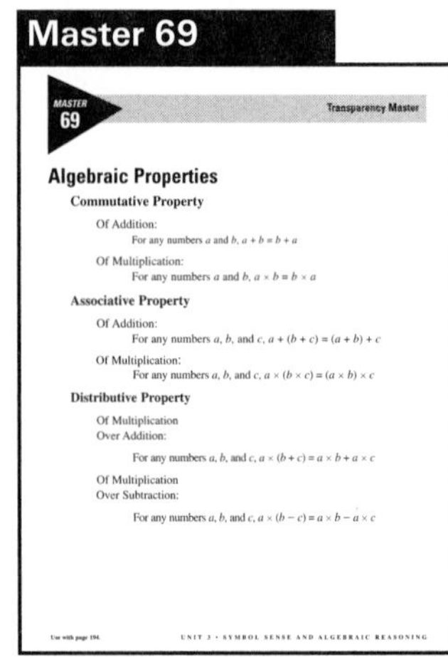
Master 69

MASTER 69 Transparency Master

Algebraic Properties

Commutative Property

Of Addition:
For any numbers a and b, $a + b = b + a$

Of Multiplication:
For any numbers a and b, $a \times b = b \times a$

Associative Property

Of Addition:
For any numbers a, b, and c, $a + (b + c) = (a + b) + c$

Of Multiplication:
For any numbers a, b, and c, $a \times (b \times c) = (a \times b) \times c$

Distributive Property

Of Multiplication Over Addition:
For any numbers a, b, and c, $a \times (b + c) = a \times b + a \times c$

Of Multiplication Over Subtraction:
For any numbers a, b, and c, $a \times (b - c) = a \times b - a \times c$

Use with page 194. UNIT 3 • SYMBOL SENSE AND ALGEBRAIC REASONING

3. After the groups have finished the sorting process, it is important for you to guide the class through a discussion to formalize the properties. Start the discussion by having one group write the equations on the board, separated by their categories, but without describing what those categories are. Have the class come to a final decision regarding what categories should be used. Each group should revise its own pile or list of equations to reflect the decision of the class. As this discussion develops, be sure to affirm good alternative categorizations. For example, some groups may have separated the commutative property for addition into a different pile or list from the commutative property for multiplication. It is best to let students decide if they want such specific categories.

   Finally, write the names of the properties (commutative, associative, and distributive) on the board. Have the groups share their descriptions, and then write each description under the correct name. Now, each group can read all the descriptions for each of the properties. Students should be able to connect each name to the proper list of examples. At this point, be sure to correct false statements through class discussion.

   After the class has discussed all their groupings, you may wish to have each of the small groups write a description of how each property allows students to transform an algebraic equation.

4. See Teaching Master 69.
   Students should recognize that their statements can be informal but still correct. For example, students may have written that for addition and multiplication, the order of the terms can be changed.

5. Your students may need some help getting started on this activity. Some students may think that checking that each step is a valid rearrangement is the point of the activity. It may seem foreign to them to focus on the property that justifies the step. Alternative sequences may vary.

   a. Step 1 Commutative property of addition
   Step 2 Associative property of addition
   Step 3 Distributive property
   Step 4 Arithmetic

   b. Step 1 Distributive property
   Step 2 Commutative property of addition
   Step 3 Associative property of addition
   Step 4 Distributive property
   Step 5 Arithmetic

Unit 3

6. Equivalent forms will vary. Some possible responses and explanations are provided below.

a.	$(3 + 5x) + 9$	Associative property of addition
	$(5x + 3) + 9$	Commutative property of addition
	$5x + (3 + 9)$	Associative property of addition
	$5x + 12$	Arithmetic
b.	$35x + 65x$	Distributive property
	$100x$	Distributive property and arithmetic
	$5(20x)$	Associative property of multiplication
c.	$(-5x^2 + 5x^2) + 35x$	Associative property of addition
	$0 + 35x$	Distributive property and arithmetic
	$-5x^2 + 5(x^2 + 7x)$	Distributive property
d.	$2x^2 + (10x^2 + 5x)$	Commutative property of addition
	$(2x^2 + 10x^2) + 5x$	Associative property of addition
	$12x^2 + 5x$	Distributive property and arithmetic
e.	$14x + 7x^2$	Commutative property of addition
	$7(2x + x^2)$	Distributive property
	$7x(2 + x)$	Distributive property

7. For each part, the original function was entered into Y_1 and the simplified version into Y_2. The graphs and tables of values for each pair are shown below.

a. $f(x) = 15x + 8$

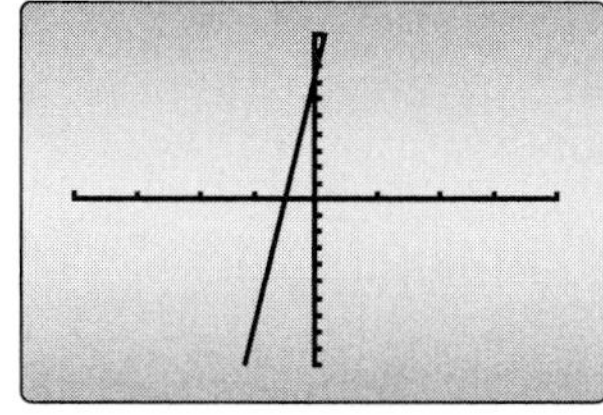

X	Y_1	Y_2
-4	-52	-52
-3	-37	-37
-2	-22	-22
-1	-7	-7
0	8	8
1	23	23
2	38	38

Y_1=7+12X+⁻4+7X+...

b. $g(x) = 20x - 25$

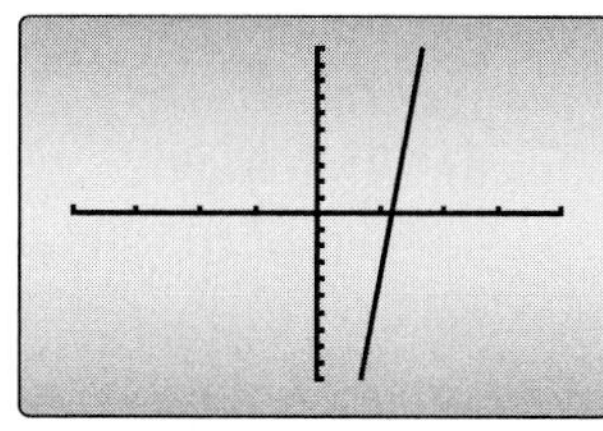

X	Y_1	Y_2
-4	-105	-105
-3	-85	-85
-2	-65	-65
-1	-45	-45
0	-25	-25
1	-5	-5
2	15	15

Y_1=5(X+4+3X+⁻9)

c. $h(t) = 65t^2 + 3t$

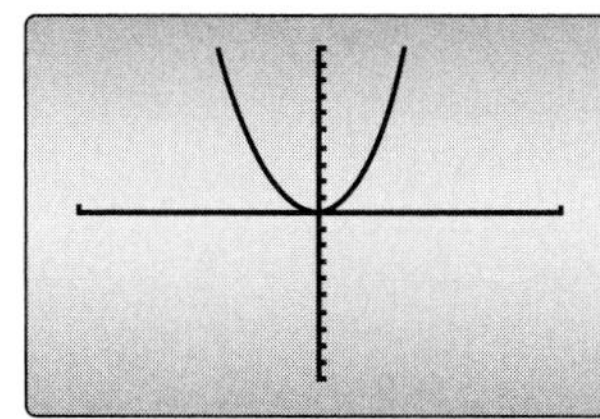

X	Y_1	Y_2
-4	1028	1028
-3	576	576
-2	254	254
-1	62	62
0	0	0
1	68	68
2	266	266

Y_1=X(-5X+40X+11...

d. $j(r) = 11r^2 + 2r + 36$

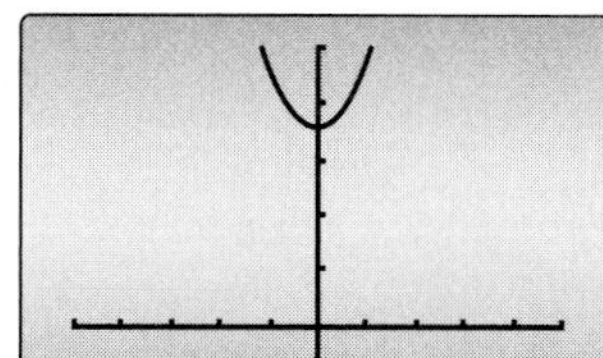

X	Y_1	Y_2
-4	204	204
-3	129	129
-2	76	76
-1	45	45
0	36	36
1	49	49
2	84	84

Y_1=7X²+9X+12+24...

e. $k(x) = 8x^3 + 8x^2 + 3.5x + 12$

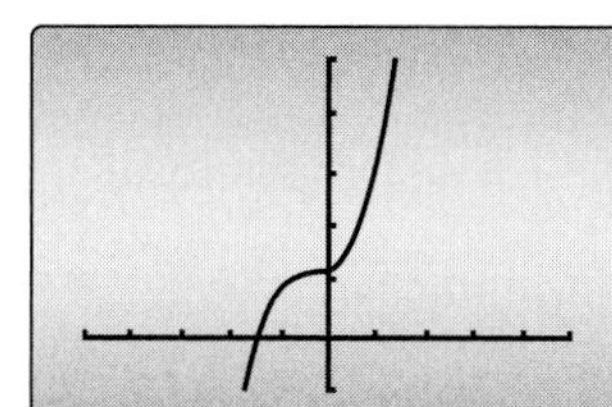

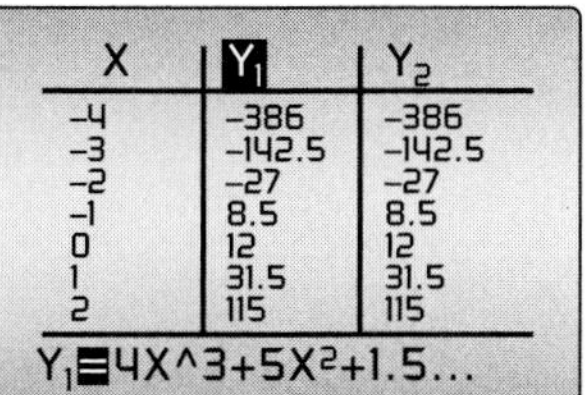

X	Y_1	Y_2
-4	-386	-386
-3	-142.5	-142.5
-2	-27	-27
-1	8.5	8.5
0	12	12
1	31.5	31.5
2	115	115

Y_1=4X^3+5X²+1.5...

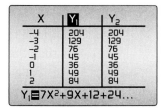

See additional Teaching Notes on page T257E.

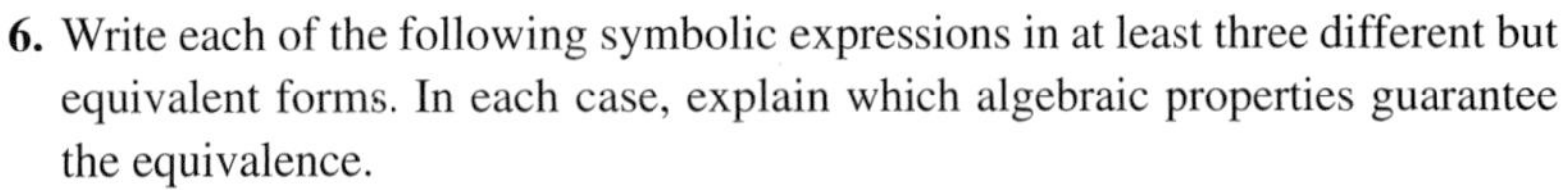

6. Write each of the following symbolic expressions in at least three different but equivalent forms. In each case, explain which algebraic properties guarantee the equivalence.

a. $3 + (5x + 9)$

b. $5(7x + 13x)$

c. $-5x^2 + (5x^2 + 35x)$

d. $2x^2 + (5x + 10x^2)$

e. $7x^2 + 14x$

The basic properties of numbers and operations seem to apply to expressions that involve at most three terms. But they can be applied to prove more general commutative, associative, and distributive properties that are quite useful.

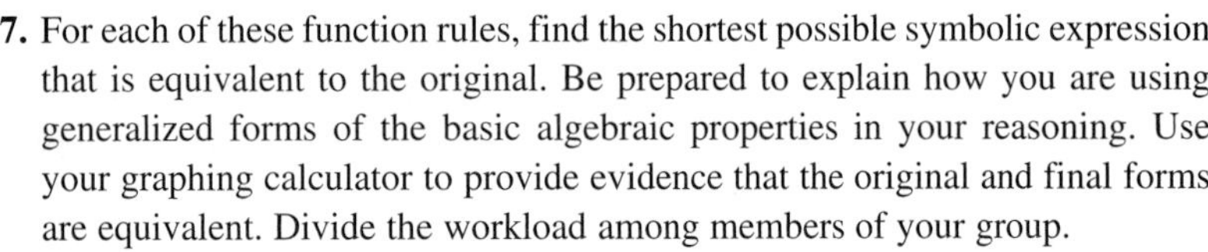

7. For each of these function rules, find the shortest possible symbolic expression that is equivalent to the original. Be prepared to explain how you are using generalized forms of the basic algebraic properties in your reasoning. Use your graphing calculator to provide evidence that the original and final forms are equivalent. Divide the workload among members of your group.

a. $f(x) = 7 + 12x + (-4) + 7x + (-4x) + 5$

b. $g(x) = 5[x + 4 + 3x + (-9)]$

c. $h(t) = t(-5t + 40t + 11) + 30t^2 + (-8t)$

d. $j(r) = (7r^2 + 9r + 12) + [24 + (-7r) + 4r^2]$

e. $k(x) = (4x^3 + 5x^2 + 1.5x + 12) + x(4x^2 + 3x + 2)$

When you analyze functions by operating with only their symbolic rules, it's easy to make mistakes. If you carefully apply the commutative, associative, or distributive properties, you'll always transform a given rule into an equivalent symbolic form. But there are some very tempting "shortcuts" that lead to trouble.

8. Check the following attempts to write algebraic expressions in equivalent forms. In some of these attempts, a common mistake has been made.

- For those that *are* correct, identify the algebraic properties that guarantee equivalence.
- For those that are *not* correct, see if you can explain the probable errors in thinking that led to the incorrect results. Then write a second expression that *is equivalent* to the first and identify the algebraic properties that guarantee equivalence.

a. Is $3x + 7x$ equivalent to $10x^2$?

b. Is $7(5x + 3)$ equivalent to $35x + 3$?

c. Is $-9x^2 + 4x^2$ equivalent to $-5x^2$?

d. Is $(-5t)(-8t)$ equivalent to $40t$?

e. Is $9x^3 + 5x^2$ equivalent to $14x^5$?

f. Is $9n^2 + 12n + 15$ equivalent to $3(n^2 + 4n + 15)$?

LESSON 2 • ALGEBRAIC OPERATIONS: PART 1 195

Unit 3

Checkpoint

The basic properties of numbers and operations can be used to write equivalent forms that simplify calculations.

a Which properties are used to write equivalent expressions in the following ways?

- By changing the grouping of terms
- By changing the order of terms to be added or multiplied
- By changing the order in which a combination of addition and multiplication operations is performed

b Which algebraic properties justify each step in the argument below? For any numbers a, b, and c and a variable x:

$a(x + b) + cx$ is equivalent to $(ax + ab) + cx$
is equivalent to $(ab + ax) + cx$
is equivalent to $ab + (ax + cx)$
is equivalent to $ab + (a + c)x$

c What basic algebraic properties guarantee the equivalence of each pair of expressions below?

$$(0.81x + 0.52x) - 365{,}000 = 1.33x - 365{,}000$$

$$(-0.04x + 30)x = -0.04x^2 + 30x$$

d Write your own examples to illustrate common mistakes in attempts to write equivalent algebraic expressions, and explain the error in each example.

Be prepared to share your use of and thinking about algebraic properties with the entire class.

The algebraic expressions and function rules that you've worked with in this investigation all involve symbolic forms that are called *polynomials*. A **polynomial** is a symbolic expression of the form $a_nx^n + \cdots + a_2x^2 + a_1x + a_0$. The **degree** of a polynomial is the largest integer n for which $a_n \neq 0$. A polynomial in which terms are written in order of decreasing (or increasing) powers is said to be **in standard form**.

Associated with any polynomial is a function $p(x) = a_nx^n + \cdots + a_1x + a_0$. You'll find that the algebraic rules for many functions can be written in equivalent standard polynomial form. For example, the standard form of the rule for $j(r) = (7r^2 + 9r + 12) + [24 + (-7r) + 4r^2]$ is $j(r) = 11r^2 + 2r + 36$.

196 UNIT 3 • SYMBOL SENSE AND ALGEBRAIC REASONING

SHARE AND SUMMARIZE full-class discussion

Checkpoint

See Teaching Masters 70a–70b.

a
- The associative property
- The commutative property
- The distributive property

b Step 1 Distributive property
Step 2 Commutative property of addition
Step 3 Associative property of addition
Step 4 Distributive property

c Distributive property and arithmetic
Distributive property

d Examples will vary. Students should give examples similar to the incorrect expressions in Activity 8.

CONSTRUCTING A MATH TOOLKIT: Students should record their own definitions of the algebraic properties from this unit and examples of each property. You may wish to have them describe what it means for a polynomial to be in standard form and how to determine the degree of a polynomial.

Masters 70a–70b

MASTER 70a Transparency Master

Checkpoint

The basic properties of numbers and operations can be used to write equivalent forms that simplify calculations.

a Which properties are used to write equivalent expressions in the following ways?
- By changing the grouping of terms
- By changing the order of terms to be added or multiplied
- By changing the order in which a combination of addition and multiplication operations is performed

b Which algebraic properties justify each step in the argument below?
For any numbers a, b, and c and a variable x:
$a(x + b) + cx$ is equivalent to $(ax + ab) + cx$
is equivalent to $(ab + ax) + cx$
is equivalent to $ab + (ax + cx)$
is equivalent to $ab + (a + c)x$

Use with page 196. UNIT 3 • SYMBOL SENSE AND ALGEBRAIC REASONING

NOTE: Students need to understand the paragraph following the Checkpoint before assigning the "On Your Own" task.

Unit 3

APPLY individual task

On Your Own

MORE ASSIGNMENT pp. 201–207

Students can now begin Organizing Task 1, 4, or 5; Reflecting Task 1; or Extending Task 2 from the MORE assignment following Investigation 3.

a. Responses will vary. Several equivalent forms for each expression are provided below.
   - $5x + (9x + 7)$ | $14x + 7$ | $5x + (5x + 4x + 7)$
   - $7x^2 + (3x + 2) + 2 + 4x(3x + 2)$ | $19x^2 + 11x + 4$ | $7x^2 + 3x + 4 + 12x^2 + 8x$

b.
   - Commutative property of addition
   - Distributive property

c. In the second step, the distributive property was not used properly. The second line should be $3(10 + 6) = 3(10) + 3(6)$.

d.
   - $7x^4 - 3x^2 + 5x + 3$
   - $-2x^2 + 10x + 8$

EXPLORE small-group investigation

INVESTIGATION 3 What a Difference Subtraction Makes

In this investigation, students find that subtraction is neither commutative nor associative and that the distributive property still applies but must be used with care. You may wish to have students make their first attempt at Activity 1 without a calculator; then have them check their decisions with a calculator. This will emphasize that what looks like an easy rearrangement should be handled with caution. A full-class discussion after Activity 1 will ensure that all students are using the same equivalent expressions from which to draw conclusions in Activity 2. During this discussion, you may wish to make a note on the board of any examples that seemed to cause confusion for many students. You can return to this list at the end of the investigation.

On Your Own

Use algebraic properties to reason about equivalent forms of the following algebraic expressions.

a. For each algebraic expression below, write at least three equivalent forms. Write one in standard polynomial form and one that has more terms than the given form.

- $5x + (7 + 9x)$
- $(7x^2 + 3x + 4) + 4x(3x + 2)$

b. Which properties justify the statements below?

- $3 + [5 + (-8)] = 3 + (-8 + 5)$
- $5(28) = 5(20) + 5(8)$

c. What is the error in the reasoning below?

$$\begin{aligned} 3(16) &= 3(10 + 6) \\ &= 3(10) + 6 \\ &= 30 + 6 \\ &= 36 \end{aligned}$$

d. Write these polynomials in standard form.

- $3 + 5x + 7x^4 - 3x^2$
- $x - 2x^2 + 8 + 9x$

Unit 3

INVESTIGATION 3 What a Difference Subtraction Makes

As you studied and applied the basic algebraic properties to write equivalent expressions for function rules, you might have wondered why those properties seem to involve only addition and multiplication. In the music business problems, you had to deal with subtraction in predicting profit. For example, the record company profit function could be derived by subtracting expenses from income to give the following rules.

Before the band advance is repaid:

$$P_1(x) = 15x - (1.65x + 1.50x + 3.75x + 365{,}000)$$

After the band advance is repaid:

$$P_2(x) = 15x - (1.65x + 1.50x + 3.75x + 0.81x + 0.52x)$$

Of course, there is a much simpler way to write this profit function. In this investigation, you will find some guidelines for writing simpler equivalent forms in cases like this, when subtraction or division appears in an expression.

LESSON 2 • ALGEBRAIC OPERATIONS: PART 1 197

1. Given below is another group of equations, this time involving subtraction in various ways. Working with a partner, examine the equations to find those that you think relate equivalent expressions. Share your ideas with your group and resolve any differences. Then prepare convincing arguments in support of each agreed-upon conclusion.

Which Expressions Are Equivalent?

$4x^2 - 5 = 5 - 4x^2$	$(6x^2 - 3x) - 5x = 6x^2 - (3x - 5x)$
$2(x^2 - 3x - 1) = 2x^2 - 6x - 2$	$3(5x - 2) = 15x - 6$
$\frac{1}{3}(18x - 15) = 6x - 5$	$10 - (7 + 2x) = (10 - 7) + 2x$
$6 - (x - 2) = (6 - x) - 2$	$3 - (9 - x) = (9 - x) - 3$
$7x - 14 = 14 - 7x$	$(x - 1) - 6 = 6 - (x - 1)$
$-(5x^3 - 6x^2 - x) = -5x^3 + 6x^2 + x$	$2 - (3 - x^2) = (2 - 3) - x^2$

2. Based on your analysis of these equations, summarize your conclusions about rewriting expressions involving subtraction.
   a. Is subtraction a commutative operation? That is, does $a - b = b - a$ for all numbers a and b? Explain your reasoning.
   b. Is subtraction an associative operation? That is, does $a - (b - c) = (a - b) - c$ for all numbers a, b, and c? Why or why not?
   c. Does $a(b - c) = ab - ac$ for all numbers a, b, and c? Explain your reasoning.

Your results from work on Activities 1 and 2 should make you cautious about rewriting algebraic expressions involving subtraction. One of the best ways to avoid the pitfalls of subtraction is to use the basic connection between subtraction and addition. For any numbers a and b: $a - b = a + (-b)$.

In words, the above definition of subtraction says that the difference "*a* minus *b*" is equal to the sum "*a* plus the opposite of *b*."

3. Test this definition of subtraction on these specific cases:
   a. Compare $15 - 8$ and $15 + (-8)$.
   b. Compare $15.8 - 23.5$ and $15.8 + (-23.5)$.
   c. Compare $\frac{2}{3} - \frac{1}{6}$ and $\frac{2}{3} + \left(-\frac{1}{6}\right)$.
   d. Compare $24 - (-6)$ and $24 + 6$.
   e. Compare $-18 - (-10)$ and $-18 + 10$.

Unit 3

198 UNIT 3 • SYMBOL SENSE AND ALGEBRAIC REASONING

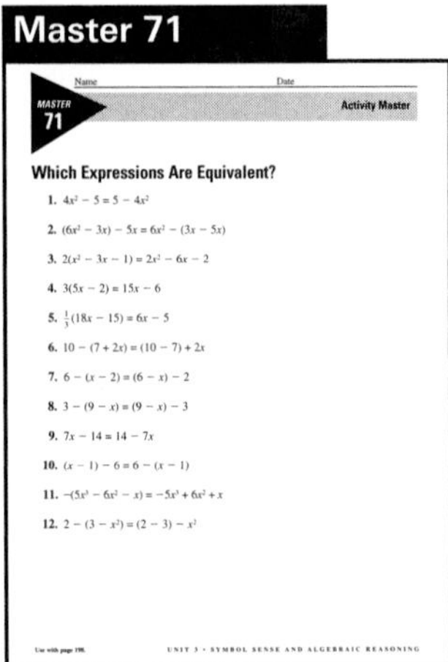
Master 71

Name Date

MASTER 71 Activity Master

Which Expressions Are Equivalent?

1. $4x^2 - 5 = 5 - 4x^2$
2. $(6x^2 - 3x) - 5x = 6x^2 - (3x - 5x)$
3. $2(x^2 - 3x - 1) = 2x^2 - 6x - 2$
4. $3(5x - 2) = 15x - 6$
5. $\frac{1}{3}(18x - 15) = 6x - 5$
6. $10 - (7 + 2x) = (10 - 7) + 2x$
7. $6 - (x - 2) = (6 - x) - 2$
8. $3 - (9 - x) = (9 - x) - 3$
9. $7x - 14 = 14 - 7x$
10. $(x - 1) - 6 = 6 - (x - 1)$
11. $-(5x^3 - 6x^2 - x) = -5x^3 + 6x^2 + x$
12. $2 - (3 - x^2) = (2 - 3) - x^2$

Use with page 198. UNIT 3 • SYMBOL SENSE AND ALGEBRAIC REASONING

1. **See Teaching Master 71.**
   Be sure that students can justify their conclusions. True statements can be shown to be true by looking at tables of values or graphs. False statements should be proven false by the use of a counterexample.
   $4x^2 - 5 = 5 - 4x^2$: not equivalent
   $(6x^2 - 3x) - 5x = 6x^2 - (3x - 5x)$: not equivalent
   $2(x^2 - 3x - 1) = 2x^2 - 6x - 2$: equivalent
   $3(5x - 2) = 15x - 6$: equivalent
   $\frac{1}{3}(18x - 15) = 6x - 5$: equivalent
   $10 - (7 + 2x) = (10 - 7) + 2x$: not equivalent
   $6 - (x - 2) = (6 - x) - 2$: not equivalent
   $3 - (9 - x) = (9 - x) - 3$: not equivalent
   $7x - 14 = 14 - 7x$: not equivalent
   $(x - 1) - 6 = 6 - (x - 1)$: not equivalent
   $-(5x^3 - 6x^2 - x) = -5x^3 + 6x^2 + x$: equivalent
   $2 - (3 - x^2) = (2 - 3) - x^2$: not equivalent
2. **a.** No, subtraction is not commutative. For example, $3 - 5 = -2$, but $5 - 3 = 2$.
   b. No, subtraction is not an associative operation. For example, $13 - (9 - 4) = 13 - 5 = 8$, but $(13 - 9) - 4 = 4 - 4 = 0$.
   c. Yes, the distributive property holds over subtraction. Some students' explanations may involve making sense of the symbolic notation. For example, multiplying the result of a subtraction problem by a value (a in this case) cannot be the same as $ab - c$ because the factor a also needs to have some effect on c since it is part of the difference.
   Students can refer to the examples in Activity 1, but you may want to point out that, while those examples support their conclusion, they do not show that the distributive property holds in all cases. After students have completed Activity 3, you may want them to come back to this activity and write a better explanation.
3. **a.** They are equivalent.
   b. They are equivalent.
   c. They are equivalent.
   d. They are equivalent.
   e. They are equivalent.

Unit 3

EXPLORE *continued*

4. a. $-(5 + 12) = [-5 + (-12)]$ b. $-(-5) = 5$
   c. $-(23 - 11) = (-23 + 11)$ d. $-(4 + 2x) = [-4 + (-2x)]$
   e. All three are equivalent.   f. $-(3x - 5) = (-3x + 5)$
   g. In general, $-(a + b) = -a + (-b)$, and $-(a - b) = -a - (-b) = -a + b = b - a$.
5. See Activity 4 Part g.
6. Responses will vary. Several equivalent expressions are given below.

	Expression	Justification
a.	$5x + (-7x)$	Definition of subtraction
	$-7x + 5x$	Commutative property of addition
	$(-7 + 5)x$	Distributive property
	$-2x$	Arithmetic
b.	$3 + -(5x + 9)$	Commutative property of addition
	$3 + (-5x + -9)$	Distributive property
	$3 + (-9 + -5x)$	Commutative property of addition
	$(3 + -9) + -5x$	Associative property of addition
	$-6 - 5x$	Arithmetic and defintion of subraction
c.	$-2x^2 - (-10x^2 + 5x)$	Commutative property of addition
	$-2x^2 + 10x^2 - 5x$	Distributive property
	$(-2x^2 + 10x^2) - 5x$	Associative property of addition
	$8x^2 - 5x$	Distributive property and arithmetic
d.	$-5x^2 - 5x^2 - 35x$	Distributive property
	$(-5 - 5)x^2 - 35x$	Distributive property
	$-10x^2 - 35x$	Arithmetic

7. For each part, the original function was entered in Y_1 and the simplified version into Y_2. The graphs and tables of values are shown below.

a. $f(x) = x + 8$

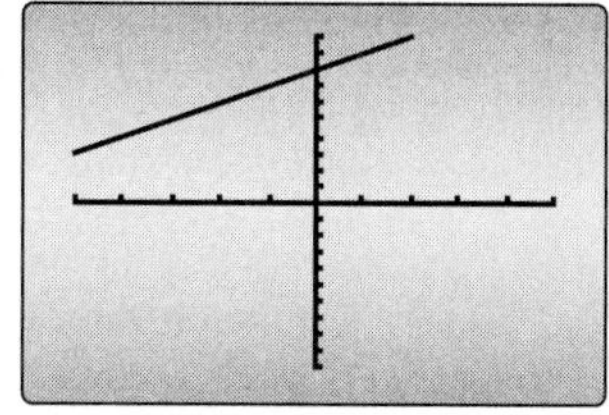

X	Y_1	Y_2
-4	4	4
-3	5	5
-2	6	6
-1	7	7
0	8	8
1	9	9
2	10	10

Y1=7+12X–4–7X–4...

b. $g(x) = -10x - 65$

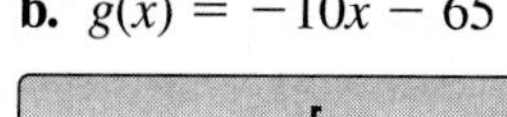

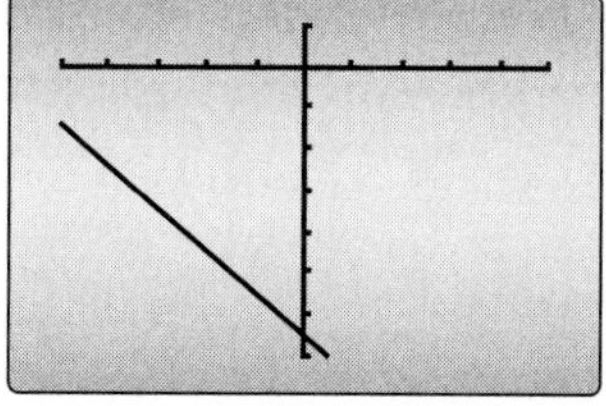

X	Y_1	Y_2
-4	-25	-25
-3	-35	-35
-2	-45	-45
-1	-55	-55
0	-65	-65
1	-75	-75
2	-85	-85

Y1=5(X–4–3X–9)

c. $h(t) = -75t^2 - 19t$

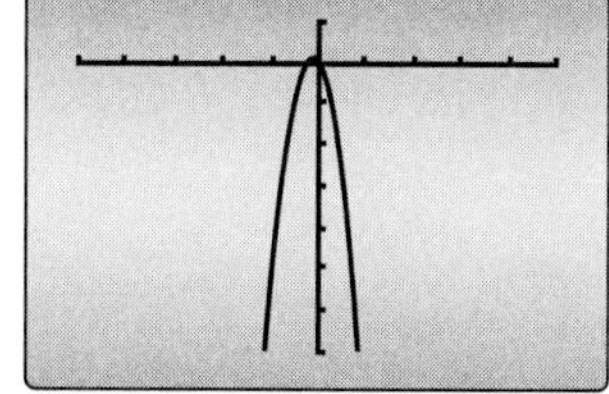

X	Y_1	Y_2
-4	-1124	-1124
-3	-618	-618
-2	-262	-262
-1	-56	-56
0	0	0
1	-94	-94
2	-338	-338

Y1=(–5X–40X–11...

d. $j(r) = 3r^2 - 16r + 12$

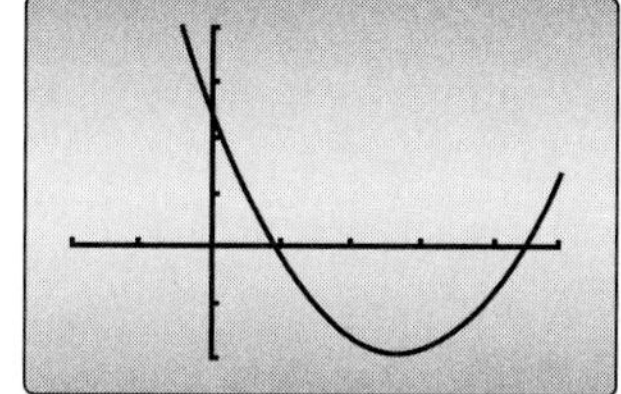

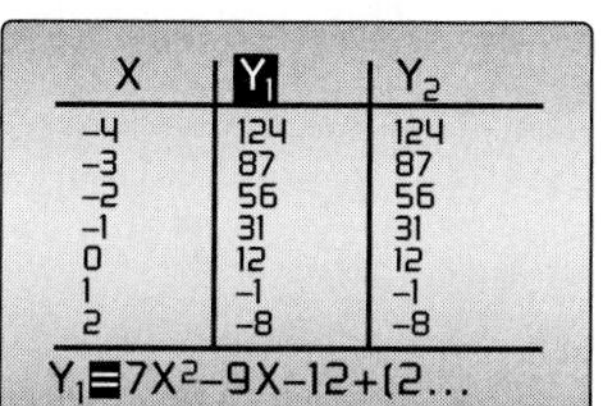

X	Y_1	Y_2
-4	124	124
-3	87	87
-2	56	56
-1	31	31
0	12	12
1	-1	-1
2	-8	-8

Y1=7X²–9X–12+(2...

e. $k(x) = -8x^2 + 0.5x + 12$

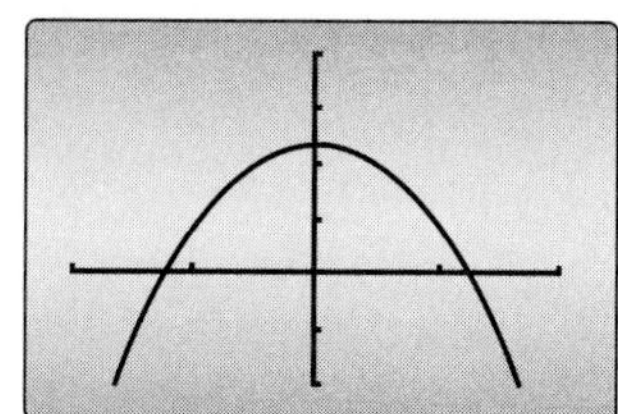

X	Y_1	Y_2
-4	-118	-118
-3	-61.5	-61.5
-2	-21	-21
-1	3.5	3.5
0	12	12
1	4.5	4.5
2	-1.9	-1.9

Y1=(4X^3–5X²–1....

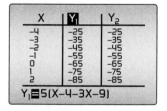

There is one other important caution about dealing with arithmetic and algebraic expressions that involve subtraction. It applies to expressions that include parentheses, such as the following:

$$(4 + 2x) - (7 + 5x)$$

Using the connection between subtraction and the opposite of a number, you can rewrite this expression:

$$(4 + 2x) + [-(7 + 5x)]$$

4. To discover a way to find the opposite of the sum (or difference) of two terms, experiment with some specific arithmetic and algebraic cases. Determine which of the following expressions are equivalent.

a. Compare $-(5 + 12)$, $(-5 + 12)$, and $[-5 + (-12)]$.

b. Compare -5, $-(-5)$, and 5.

c. Compare $-(23 - 11)$, $(-23 - 11)$, and $(-23 + 11)$.

d. Compare $-(4 + 2x)$, $(-4 + 2x)$, and $[-4 + (-2x)]$.

e. Compare $-(10 + 7)$, $(-1)(10 + 7)$, and $(-1)(10) + (-1)(7)$.

f. Compare $-(3x - 5)$, $(-3x + 5)$, and $(-3x - 5)$.

g. What general pattern do you see for dealing with expressions like $-(a + b)$? Like $-(a - b)$?

5. Using variables, write a summary of your findings in Activity 4. Compare your summary to those of other groups. Reach agreement on a property involving the "opposite of a sum." Write a similar property involving the "opposite of a difference."

6. Write each of the following symbolic expressions in at least three different but equivalent forms. In each case, explain which algebraic properties guarantee the equivalence.

a. $5x - 7x$

b. $-(5x + 9) + 3$

c. $-2x^2 - (5x - 10x^2)$

d. $-5x^2 - (5x^2 + 35x)$

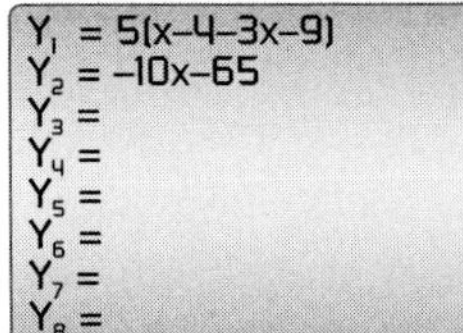

7. For each of the following function rules, find the shortest possible symbolic expression that is equivalent to the original. Be prepared to explain how you are using generalized forms of the basic algebraic properties in your reasoning. Use a graphing calculator or computer software to check that the original and final forms are equivalent.

a. $f(x) = 7 + 12x - 4 - 7x - 4x + 5$

b. $g(x) = 5(x - 4 - 3x - 9)$

c. $h(t) = t(-5t - 40t - 11) - 30t^2 - 8t$

d. $j(r) = (7r^2 - 9r - 12) + (24 - 7r - 4r^2)$

e. $k(x) = (4x^3 - 5x^2 - 1.5x + 12) - x(4x^2 + 3x - 2)$

Unit 3

LESSON 2 • ALGEBRAIC OPERATIONS: PART 1 199

8. Just as there are tempting but incorrect ways to rewrite algebraic expressions involving addition of terms, there are some common mistakes in working with expressions involving subtraction. Study the following pairs of expressions. In writing some of these pairs, common mistakes were made. For those that are not equivalent, see if you can explain the mistake that was made in trying to write an equivalent form of the first given expression. For those that are equivalent, explain which property was used correctly.

a. Is $-5(x + 2)$ equivalent to $-5x + 2$?

b. Is $(-3x - 12)$ equivalent to $-3(x - 4)$?

c. Is $-3x - 9$ equivalent to $9 - 3x$?

d. Is $(-5n)(-8n^2)$ equivalent to $-40n^2$?

e. Is $(24t^3 - 18t^2 - 3t)$ equivalent to $3t(8t^2 - 6t - 1)$?

Checkpoint

When subtraction appears in arithmetic or algebraic expressions, there are some cautions about evaluating and rewriting those expressions in equivalent forms.

a What properties are true for addition but not for subtraction?

b What properties are true for both addition and subtraction?

c How would you proceed in simplifying each of the following algebraic expressions?

- $5x - 7x + 8$
- $-(5x + 7)$
- $-5(7x + 12)$
- $-4x(6x - 7)$

d What seem to be the common mistakes in attempts to rewrite algebraic expressions involving subtraction and negative numbers in equivalent forms?

Be prepared to share your ideas with the rest of the class.

Unit 3

200 UNIT 3 • SYMBOL SENSE AND ALGEBRAIC REASONING

8. **a.** Incorrect, because −5 needs to be distributed over the 2. The correct expression is $-5x - 10$.
   b. Incorrect, because when the distributive property is used to separate out the factor −3, the term in the parentheses should be $x + 4$. The correct second expression is $-3(x + 4)$.
   c. Incorrect, because both terms should be negative. The correct second expression is $-9 - 3x$.
   d. Incorrect, because $(n)(n^2)$ is n^3 and the product of two negatives is a positive. The correct product is $40n^3$.
   e. Correct, because of the distributive property.

Master 72

MASTER 72 — Transparency Master

Checkpoint

When subtraction appears in arithmetic or algebraic expressions, there are some cautions about evaluating and rewriting those expressions in equivalent forms.

ⓐ What properties are true for addition but not for subtraction?

ⓑ What properties are true for both addition and subtraction?

ⓒ How would you proceed in simplifying each of the following algebraic expressions?

■ $5x - 7x + 8$ ■ $-(5x + 7)$
■ $-5(7x + 12)$ ■ $-4x(6x - 7)$

ⓓ What seem to be the common mistakes in attempts to rewrite algebraic expressions involving subtraction and negative numbers in equivalent forms?

Be prepared to share your ideas with the rest of the class.

Use with page 200. UNIT 3 • SYMBOL SENSE AND ALGEBRAIC REASONING

SHARE AND SUMMARIZE full-class discussion

Checkpoint

See Teaching Master 72.

ⓐ The commutative and associative properties are true for addition but not for subtraction.

ⓑ The distributive property is true for both addition and subtraction.

ⓒ Class discussion should center on explaining the procedures needed to simplify each expression.

■ $-2x + 8$ ■ $-5x - 7$
■ $-35x - 60$ ■ $-24x^2 + 28x$

ⓓ Common mistakes are incorrectly applying the distributive property, incorrectly subtracting expressions, and incorrectly rearranging the terms in an expression.

CONSTRUCTING A MATH TOOLKIT: Students should give an example for the commutative, associative, and distributive properties. Then they should explain how these properties can be used to rewrite symbolic expressions and how we know the commutative and associative properties do not hold for subtraction.

Unit 3

APPLY individual task

On Your Own

a. Responses will vary. The simplest form possible is given below.

- $-8x + 1$
- $-4x + 7$
- $-5x^2 - 11x - 4$

b.

- The distributive property and the commutative property of addition can be used to rewrite the left side so that the right side results.
- Arithmetic lets us rewrite 18 as $20 - 2$, and the application of the distributive property produces the expression on the right-hand side.

c.

$$
\begin{aligned}
-48 &= -3(16) \\
&= -3(20 - 4) \\
&= -3(20) - 3(4) && \text{This 4 should be } -4 \\
&= -60 - 12 && \text{which makes this } -60 + 12. \\
&= -48
\end{aligned}
$$

Unit 3

On Your Own

Use properties of subtraction to help you reason about equivalent forms of the following algebraic expressions.

a. For each algebraic expression below, write at least three equivalent forms. Make one as simple as possible, and write one that is actually longer than the given form.

- $7x - 12x + 8 - 3x - 7$
- $5x + (7 - 9x)$
- $(7x^2 - 3x - 4) - 4x(3x + 2)$

b. Without doing the indicated calculations, explain why properties of addition, subtraction, and multiplication guarantee that these statements are true.

- $3 - (5 - 8) = 3 + [8 + (-5)]$
- $5(18) = 5(20) - 5(2)$

c. Where are the errors in this reasoning?

$$\begin{aligned} -48 &= -3(16) \\ &= -3(20 - 4) \\ &= -3(20) - 3(4) \\ &= -60 - 12 \\ &= -48 \end{aligned}$$

MORE
Modeling • Organizing • Reflecting • Extending

Modeling

1. The operators of a high school all-star football game did some market research to help in setting prices to maximize operating profit. The following estimated relationships were found.

- Ticket price p and ticket sales x will be related by $p = -0.002x + 40$.
- Income from sales of food and drinks will average $1.50 per ticket sold.
- About 25% of the ticket buyers will park at the stadium, giving income of $5 per car.
- Expenses for the game will include operating expenses of about $100,000 and average food and drink costs of $0.50 per ticket sold.
- Past experience suggests that between 8,000 and 12,000 tickets will be sold.

LESSON 2 • ALGEBRAIC OPERATIONS: PART 1 201

a. Write algebraic rules for functions that give game *income* (i) from ticket sales, (ii) from food and drink concessions, and (iii) from parking. Write each rule as a function of the number of tickets sold.

b. Write an algebraic rule for the function giving game *profit* as a function of number of tickets sold. Write this profit function in two ways:

- One showing the separate contributions to profit from ticket sales, food and drink sales, and parking.
- One showing the shortest possible rule for calculating profit.

c. According to the information collected, what is the maximum profit possible? What ticket price will give the maximum profit?

d. Do the results of your work in Part c seem reasonable, or would you ask the market researchers to justify their conclusions? Explain your reasoning.

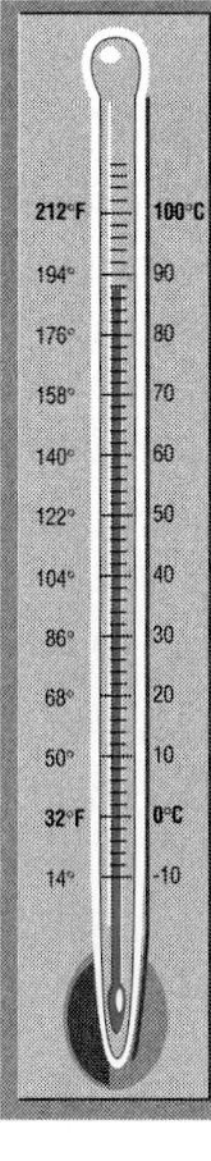

2. Temperature is measured on two common scales, Fahrenheit and Celsius. Those scales are related by the equation $F = 1.8C + 32$. Some people like to use the following rule, which they find easier to remember:

To convert Celsius to Fahrenheit, double and add 30.

a. Write this alternate rule as an equation: $F =$ ________________.

b. Is the rule in Part a equivalent to the original rule? Explain your reasoning.

c. Solve $F = 1.8C + 32$ for C in terms of F.

d. Similarly, there is another approximate rule for converting Fahrenheit to Celsius:

To convert Fahrenheit to Celsius, subtract 30 and divide by 2.

Write this rule as an equation: $C =$ _______. Explain whether the rule is equivalent to the one you derived in Part c.

e. Use tables or graphs to compare the two rules for converting from Celsius to Fahrenheit. Under what conditions do you think it's reasonable to use the easy-to-remember alternate?

202 UNIT 3 • SYMBOL SENSE AND ALGEBRAIC REASONING

MORE **independent assignment**

Modeling

1. a. i. $I(x) = x(-0.002x + 40)$
   ii. $F(x) = 1.5x$
   iii. $P(x) = (0.25x)(5)$
   b. ■ $P(x) = x(-0.002x + 40) + 1.5x + 1.25x - 100{,}000 - 0.50x$
   ■ $P(x) = -0.002x^2 + 42.25x - 100{,}000$
   c. The maximum profit is about \$123,133 with a ticket price of \$18.88. Remember that the input variable for profit is ticket sales, not price.
   d. Responses will vary. Some students may think that the price is high. Also, to get the maximum profit, 10,563 people must buy tickets. Some students may think this is too many people to expect to attend the game.
2. a. $F = 2C + 30$
   b. The two rules are not equivalent. A single counterexample is sufficient to prove this. For example, $1.8(0) + 32 = 32$ but $2(0) + 30 = 30$. Students may also point out that both rules are linear but have different slopes and y-intercepts. So, although the second rule is easier to remember, it only provides an approximate temperature.
   c. $C = \frac{F - 32}{1.8}$
   d. $C = \frac{F - 30}{2}$. Again, students need give only one counterexample.
   e. Responses will vary. The two functions intersect at (50, 50). The further from 50 x is, the larger the difference between the two. For temperatures ranging from $-15°$ to $35°$ Celsius ($5°$ to $95°$ Fahrenheit), the difference is at most $5°$. The rule is reasonable for quick estimations of outside temperatures, because accuracy within a few degrees is acceptable.

MORE
ASSIGNMENT *pp. 201–207*

Modeling: 3, 4, and choice of one*
Organizing: 3, 5, and choice of one*
Reflecting: 1 and 3
Extending: Choose one*

**When choice is indicated, it is important to leave the choice to the student.*
NOTE: *It is best if Organizing tasks are discussed as a whole class after they have been assigned as homework.*

3. a. ■ The formula finds the sum of the areas of the two triangles. This sum must equal the area of the trapezoid.

■ $A = \frac{1}{2}hb_1 + \frac{1}{2}hb_2$

$A = \frac{1}{2}(hb_1 + hb_2)$ Distributive property

$A = \frac{1}{2}(b_1 + b_2)h$ Distributive and commutative properties

b. ■ The trapezoid parts can be rearranged to form a triangle with base $b_2 - b_1$ and height h and a rectangle with base b_1.

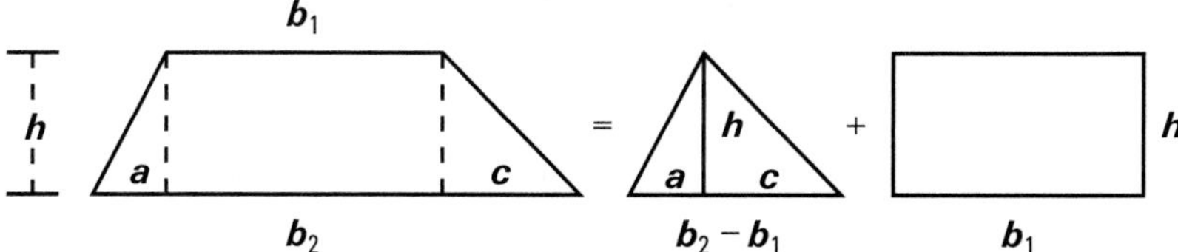

The area of the triangle is $\frac{1}{2}h(b_2 - b_1)$ and the area of the rectangle is b_1h. Thus, the formula for the area of the trapezoid is $\frac{1}{2}h(b_2 - b_1) + b_1h$.

■ Area of trapezoid

Area of trapezoid	$= \frac{1}{2}h(b_2 - b_1) + b_1h$	
	$= \frac{1}{2}hb_2 - \frac{1}{2}hb_1 + b_1h$	Distributive property
	$= \frac{1}{2}b_2h - \frac{1}{2}b_1h + b_1h$	Commutative property of multiplication
	$= \frac{1}{2}b_2h + \frac{1}{2}b_1h$	Combining like terms (Distributive property and arithmetic)
	$= \frac{1}{2}(b_1 + b_2)h$	Distributive property

4. a. $C = p + 0.15p$

Unit 3

3. One standard formula for calculating the area of a trapezoid is given by the equation $A = \frac{1}{2}(b_1 + b_2)h$, where the variables b_1, b_2, and h represent the lengths of the two bases and the height of the trapezoid, respectively.

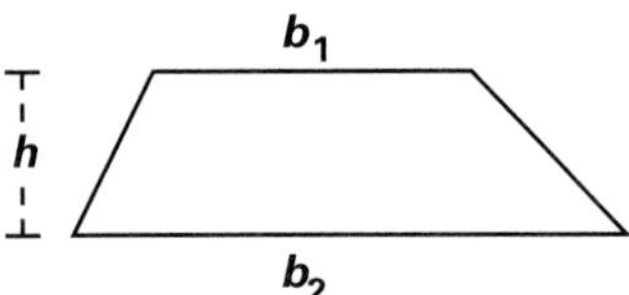

a. The sketch below shows a way of thinking about the area of a trapezoid that leads to a different formula: $A = \frac{1}{2}hb_1 + \frac{1}{2}hb_2$.

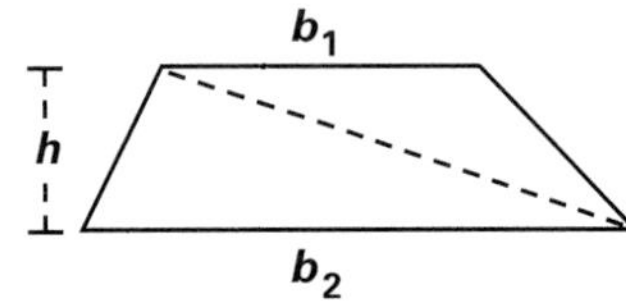

- Explain with a geometric argument why this other formula works.
- Use algebraic reasoning to show that this formula is equivalent to the standard form.

b. The sketch below shows yet another way of thinking about the area of some trapezoids, which leads to the formula $A = \frac{1}{2}h(b_2 - b_1) + b_1h$.

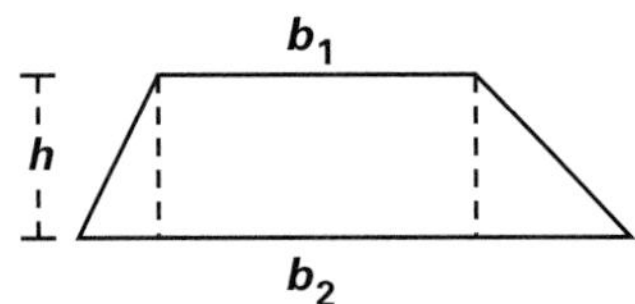

- Explain with a geometric argument why this formula gives the correct area.
- Use algebraic reasoning to show that this formula is equivalent to the standard formula.

4. The expense of dining out at a restaurant, other than fast-food restaurants, usually involves not only the price of the meal, but also tax and a tip. The standard tip for acceptable service is at least 15% of the price of the meal.

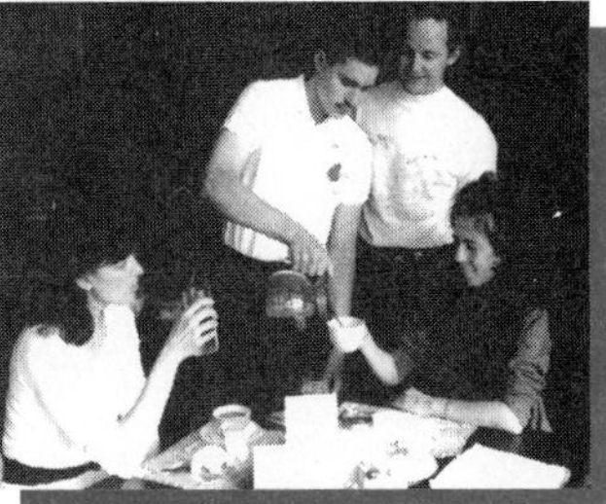

a. If p is the price of a meal, write a rule giving the cost C of the meal plus tip (*but not including tax*).

Unit 3

LESSON 2 • ALGEBRAIC OPERATIONS: PART 1 203

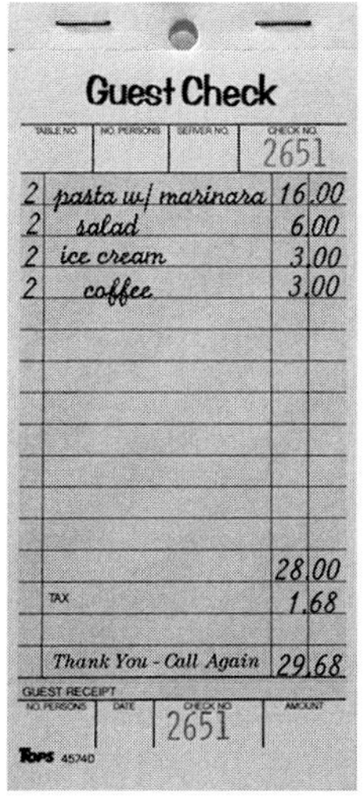
Guest Check

2	pasta w/ marinara	16.00
2	salad	6.00
2	ice cream	3.00
2	coffee	3.00
		28.00
	TAX	1.68
	Thank You - Call Again	29.68

Check No. 2651

b. Rewrite your rule in Part a in an equivalent form that is easier to calculate using a calculator.

c. Frequent diners often find it easier to calculate the tip mentally.

To calculate a 15% tip, find 10% of the meal price, and add $\frac{1}{2}$ of that result to it.

Try this mental method on a meal bill that totals \$28.00. Explain why this method works.

d. Now rewrite the rule in Part a to show this mental shortcut.

e. Suppose you are traveling through a state in which there is a 6% tax on restaurant meals. Modify your rule in Part a to show the total expense of the meal. Then rewrite this rule in the shortest form possible.

Organizing

1. Identify the algebraic properties that justify equivalence of these pairs of algebraic expressions. Some examples might involve a chain of operations in which several different properties are applied.

a. $-4(2x + 7) = -8x - 28$

b. $21 + 14x = 7(2x + 3)$

c. $5s + (9 + 12s) = 17s + 9$

d. $-36x^2 = (9x)(-4x)$

e. $5m + 12m + 3 = 3 + 17m$

f. $16t^2 - 160t = 16t(t - 10)$

2. Sketch graphs showing why the following pairs of algebraic expressions are *not* equivalent.

a. $x - 2$ is not equivalent to $2 - x$.

b. $-3x^2 + 5$ is not equivalent to $-5 + 3x^2$.

c. $5(2x + 3)$ is not equivalent to $10x + 3$.

d. $(2x)(3x)$ is not equivalent to $6x$.

e. $-3(x + 4)$ is not equivalent to $-3x + 12$.

3. Rewrite each of the following function rules in standard polynomial form, and record the number system properties that justify each step in the simplification process.

a. $f(x) = 5(9 + x)$

b. $g(x) = (2x - 11)(7x)$

c. $h(x) = 6(x - 3) - 5(x - 2)$

d. $i(x) = 12 - 5x^2 + 21x$

204 UNIT 3 • SYMBOL SENSE AND ALGEBRAIC REASONING

4. **b.** $C = 1.15p$

   c. 10% of the \$28.00 is \$2.80. Half of \$2.80 is \$1.40, so the tip should be \$4.20. This method works because 15% is 10% + 5% and 5% is one half of 10%.

   d. $C = p + 0.10p + 0.05p$

   e. You may get two different answers here. Some students may figure the tip before the tax is added, and others may include the tax when figuring the tip. If tip is figured before the tax, $T = p + 0.15p + 0.06p = 1.21p$. If tip is figured after the tax, $T = p + 0.06p + 0.15(p + 0.06p) = 1.219p$.

Organizing

1. **a.** Distributive property

   b. Distributive property and commutative property of addition

   c. Commutative and associative properties of addition, and distributive property

   d. Associative and commutative properties of multiplication

   e. Distributive property and commutative property of addition

   f. Distributive property

2. For each part, graphs of two equations associated with the given expressions are shown below. (For example, in Part a the graphs are of the expressions $y = x - 2$ and $y = 2 - x$.) Since the graphs are not identical, the expressions are not equivalent. Scales are not necessarily identical for all graphs.

   a.
   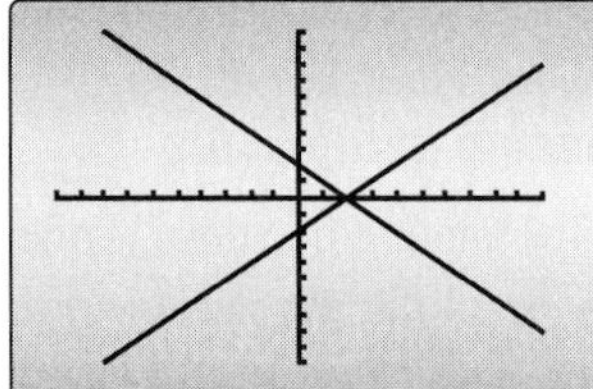

   b.
   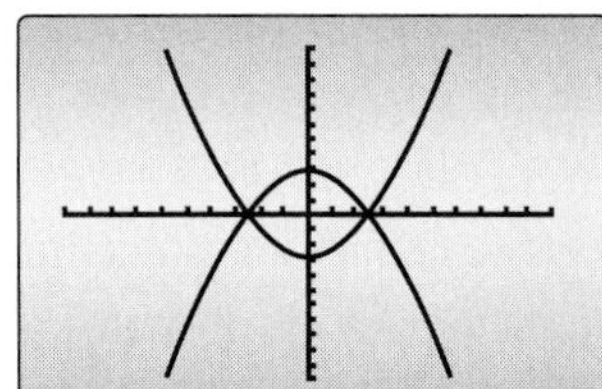

   c.
   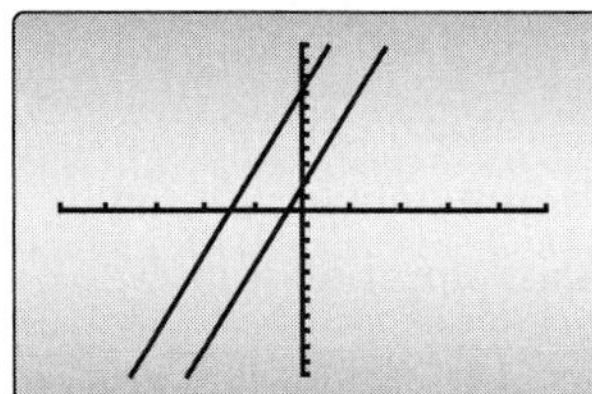

   d.
   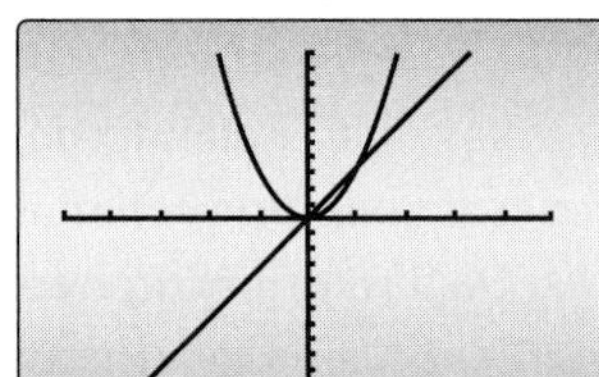

   e.
   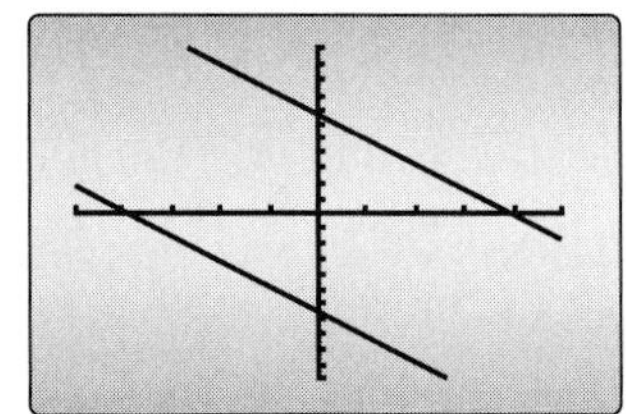

3. **a.** $f(x) = 5x + 45$, distributive property and commutative property of addition

   b. $g(x) = 14x^2 - 77x$, distributive property

   c. $h(x) = x - 8$, distributive property, and commutative and associative properties of addition

   d. $i(x) = -5x^2 + 21x + 12$, commutative property of addition

Unit 3

3. **e.** $j(x) = 50x^2 + 8x - 28$, distributive property, and commutative and associative properties of addition

   f. $k(x) = -3x^2 - 6x + 12$, distributive property, and commutative and associative properties of addition

   g. $m(x) = x^4 - 7x^3 + 4x^2 - 5x - 23$, distributive property, and commutative and associative properties of addition

   h. $n(x) = 8x^2 - 6x - 4$, distributive property and commutative property of addition

4. **a.** ■ 7 ■ 4.3 ■ 1,750

   b. $\frac{a + b}{2}$

   c. Yes, since $\frac{a+b}{2} = \frac{b+a}{2}$.

   d. No. Consider the following counterexample: From Part a, we know that $(500 \barwedge 1{,}500) \barwedge 2{,}500 = 1{,}750$. But $500 \barwedge (1{,}500 \barwedge 2{,}500) = 1{,}250$. So the operation $\barwedge$ is not associative.

   e. Yes. Students should provide some type of reasoning. One way is to show that $a(b \barwedge c) = ab \barwedge ac$.

   $a(b \barwedge c) = a\left(\frac{b + c}{2}\right) = \frac{ab + ac}{2}$ and $ab \barwedge ac = \frac{ab + ac}{2}$.

   So multiplication distributes over finding the average.

5. **a.** Answers will vary. A sample is given.

   $$\begin{bmatrix} 2 & 5 \\ -3 & 1 \end{bmatrix} + \begin{bmatrix} 5 & -2 \\ 4 & 0 \end{bmatrix} = \begin{bmatrix} 7 & 3 \\ 1 & 1 \end{bmatrix}$$

   $$\begin{bmatrix} 5 & -2 \\ 4 & 0 \end{bmatrix} + \begin{bmatrix} 2 & 5 \\ -3 & 1 \end{bmatrix} = \begin{bmatrix} 7 & 3 \\ 1 & 1 \end{bmatrix}$$

   b. It is reasonable that matrix addition should be commutative because (scalar) addition is commutative, and for matrix addition you are simply adding elements that are in the corresponding positions. The order is not going to matter.

   c. It is reasonable that matrix addition should be associative because addition is associative, and for matrix addition you are simply adding elements that are in the corresponding positions. The grouping is not going to matter.

   d. The commutative property of multiplication does not hold for multiplication of matrices. Students should justify this by providing specific matrices A and B for which $AB \neq BA$. The matrices in Part a will work as a counterexample.

Reflecting

1. Like terms are terms that have the same variables raised to the same powers. For example, $3x$ and $6x$ are like terms but $3x$ and $3x^2$ are not.

2. **a.** Remember to distribute a over all terms inside the parentheses. Drawing arrows may be helpful.

   b. Subtraction is not commutative. When you move a number, you must also move the sign.

   c. You must use the rules for exponents when multiplying the same variable. The number of times a variable appears as a factor should be equal to the power of that variable in the product.

   d. Some students find it helpful to think of the negative sign as -1. Remember to distribute -1 over all the terms inside the parentheses.

e. $j(x) = 8(x^2 + 4x - 5) - 6(-2 - 7x^2 + 4x)$

f. $k(x) = -(x^2 + 4x) - (-3x - 5) - (2x^2 + 5x - 7)$

g. $m(x) = (x^4 + 4x^2 - 11) - (7x^3 + 5x + 12)$

h. $n(x) = -\frac{2}{3}(9x - 12x^2 + 6)$

4. In many situations in everyday life, it makes sense to find the *average* or *arithmetic mean* of two given numbers. In the following questions, the notation "$a \barwedge b$" will be used to represent the operation "find the average of numbers a and b."

a. Evaluate:

■ $23 \barwedge -9$ ■ $5.4 \barwedge 3.2$ ■ $(500 \barwedge 1{,}500) \barwedge 2{,}500$

b. Give a rule for evaluating "$a \barwedge b$" for any two numbers a and b.

c. Is the operation $\barwedge$ commutative?

d. Is the operation $\barwedge$ associative?

e. Does the operation of multiplication distribute over the operation of finding the average?

5. In your previous work with matrices, you saw that they too have properties for addition like those summarized on page 194.

a. Give an example showing the commutativity of addition of 2×2 matrices.

b. Thinking about how you add matrices, explain why it is reasonable to expect that addition of matrices is commutative.

c. Thinking again about how you add matrices, explain why it is reasonable to expect that addition of matrices is associative.

d. Give an example of a property of multiplication of numbers that does *not* hold for multiplication of matrices.

Unit 3

Reflecting

1. In many of the tasks in this lesson, you performed an algebraic operation commonly referred to as *combining like terms*. You replaced algebraic expressions of several terms (like "$3x^2 - 7x^2$") with equivalent expressions of only one term ("$-4x^2$"). What do you think the phrase "like terms" means, and what examples would you give to show someone what you mean?

2. You've found that there are some common errors that occur when people operate on symbolic expressions in an effort to produce equivalent but more useful forms. What advice would you give to help someone understand why each of the following pairs of expressions is not equivalent?

a. $a(x + b)$ is not equivalent to $ax + b$.

b. $x - b$ is not equivalent to $b - x$.

c. $(ax)(bx)$ is not equivalent to abx.

d. $-(x - b)$ is not equivalent to $-x - b$.

LESSON 2 • ALGEBRAIC OPERATIONS: PART 1 205

3. What algebraic properties can be illustrated by the following sketches if you compare areas of the large rectangles to the areas of the smaller components?

a.

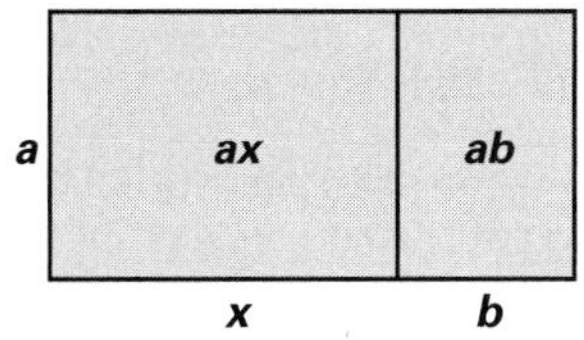

b.

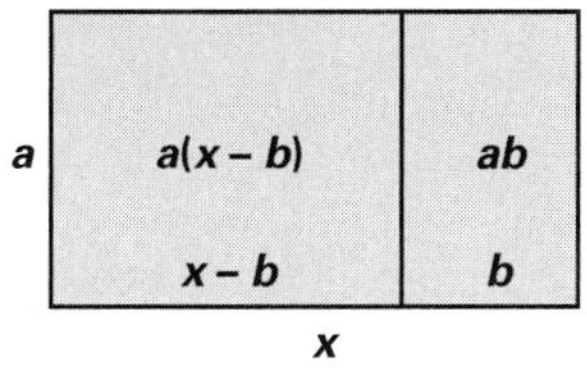

4. G. H. Hardy (1877–1947), a well-known mathematician who taught for many years at Cambridge University in England, wrote:

> "A mathematician, like a painter or a poet, is a maker of patterns. If his [or her] patterns are more permanent than theirs, it is because they are made with ideas."

What do you think about Hardy's statement? To what extent have you been a "maker of patterns" in your work in this unit?

Extending

1. Examine the step-by-step algebraic reasoning in simplifying the following expressions. State the property that justifies each step.

a. $(-x \cdot 9)\frac{1}{9} + 5x = -x\left(9 \cdot \frac{1}{9}\right) + 5x$
$= -x \cdot 1 + 5x$
$= -x + 5x$
$= x(-1 + 5)$
$= 4x$

b. $3(a + x) + (-3a) = 3a + 3x + (-3a)$
$= 3x + 3a + (-3a)$
$= 3x + 0$
$= 3x$

c. $-5(a - 4) + 7(a - 4) = (-5 + 7)(a - 4)$
$= 2(a - 4)$
$= 2a - 8$

206 UNIT 3 • SYMBOL SENSE AND ALGEBRAIC REASONING

3. **a.** The area of the large rectangle is $a(x + b)$, and the sum of the areas of the smaller rectangles is $ax + ab$. Since the sum of the two smaller rectangles is equal to the area of the large rectangle, $a(x + b) = ax + ab$. This illustrates the distributive property.

b. The area of the large rectangle is ax, and the sum of the areas of the smaller rectangles is $a(x - b) + ab$. Since the sum of the two smaller rectangles is equal to the area of the large rectangle, $ax = a(x - b) + ab$. To show algebraically that the right side is equivalent to the left side of this equation, the distributive and associative properties must be applied:

$$a(x - b) + ab = ax - ab + ab = ax + (-ab + ab) = ax + 0 = ax.$$

4. Responses will vary. Students have arrived at many of the mathematical "rules" in this unit by looking at examples for common patterns and then generalizing from these examples. Also, students have arrived at the commutative, associative, and distributive properties by looking for patterns.

Extending

1. **a.** Step 1 Associative property of multiplication
Step 2 Multiplication
Step 3 Multiplication
Step 4 Distributive property
Step 5 Addition and commutative property of multiplication

b. Step 1 Distributive property
Step 2 Commutative property of addition
Step 3 Addition of like terms
Step 4 Addition

c. Step 1 Distributive property
Step 2 Addition
Step 3 Distributive property

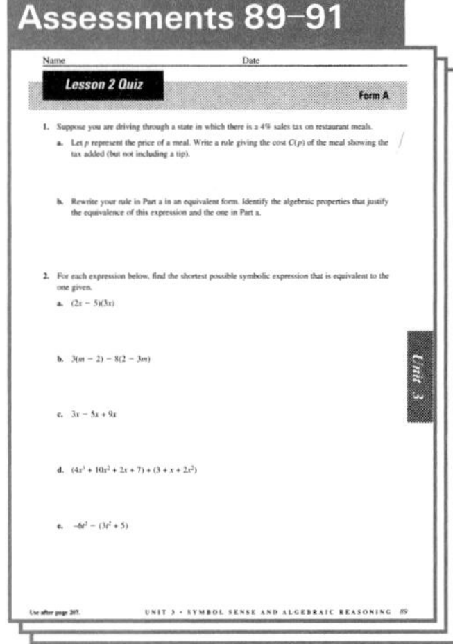

Assessments 89–91

Name ____ Date ____

Lesson 2 Quiz Form A

1. Suppose you are driving through a state in which there is a 4% sales tax on restaurant meals.
   a. Let p represent the price of a meal. Write a rule giving the cost $C(p)$ of the meal showing the tax added (but not including a tip).
   b. Rewrite your rule in Part a in an equivalent form. Identify the algebraic properties that justify the equivalence of this expression and the one in Part a.
2. For each expression below, find the shortest possible symbolic expression that is equivalent to the one given.
   a. $(2x - 5)(3x)$
   b. $3(m - 2) - 8(2 - 3m)$
   c. $3x - 5x + 9x$
   d. $(4x^3 + 10x^2 + 2x + 7) + (3 + x + 2x^2)$
   e. $-6t^2 - (3t^2 + 5)$

Unit 3

Use after page 207. UNIT 3 • SYMBOL SENSE AND ALGEBRAIC REASONING 89

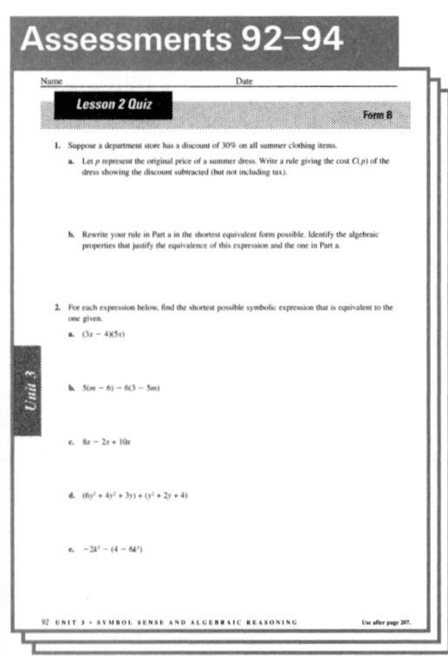

Assessments 92–94

Name ____ Date ____

Lesson 2 Quiz Form B

1. Suppose a department store has a discount of 30% on all summer clothing items.
   a. Let p represent the original price of a summer dress. Write a rule giving the cost $C(p)$ of the dress showing the discount subtracted (but not including tax).
   b. Rewrite your rule in Part a in the shortest equivalent form possible. Identify the algebraic properties that justify the equivalence of this expression and the one in Part a.
2. For each expression below, find the shortest possible symbolic expression that is equivalent to the one given.
   a. $(3x - 4)(5x)$
   b. $5(m - 6) - 6(3 - 5m)$
   c. $8x - 2x + 10x$
   d. $(6y^3 + 4y^2 + 3y) + (y^2 + 2y + 4)$
   e. $-2k^3 - (4 - 6k^3)$

Unit 3

92 UNIT 3 • SYMBOL SENSE AND ALGEBRAIC REASONING Use after page 207.

Unit 3

MORE *continued*

2. **a.** The graph of $g(x) = x^2 + 7x + 12$ crosses the x-axis two times.

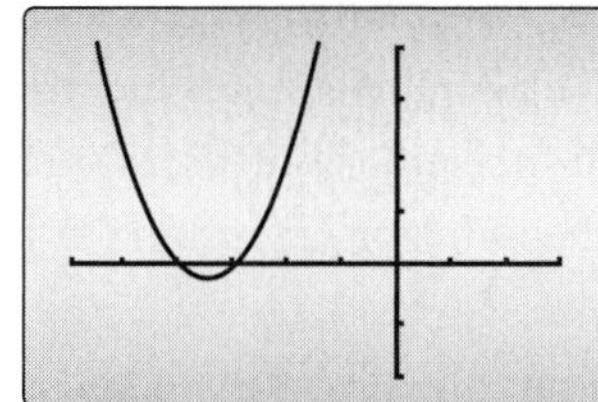

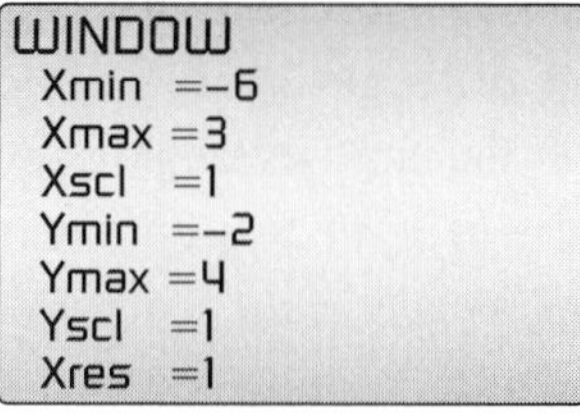

b. The graph of $h(x) = x^3 - 5x^2 - 4x + 20$ crosses the x-axis three times.

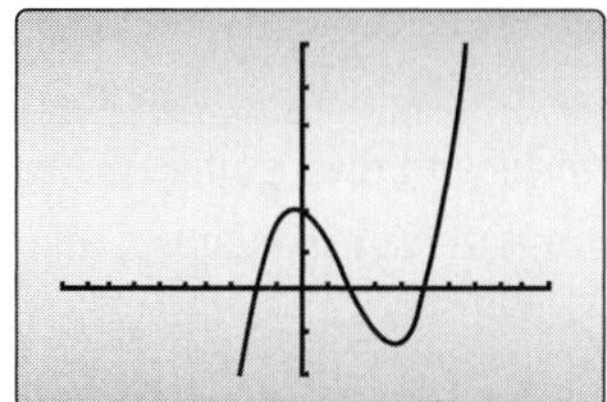

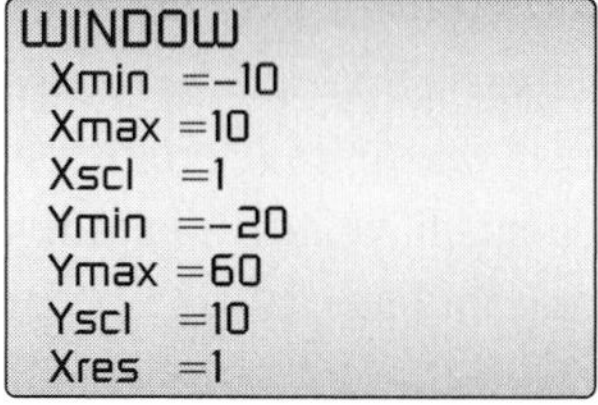

c. The graph of $f(x) = x^4 - 13x^2 + 36$ crosses the x-axis four times.

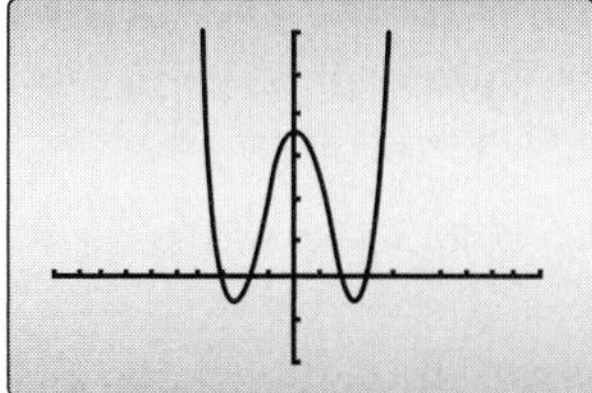

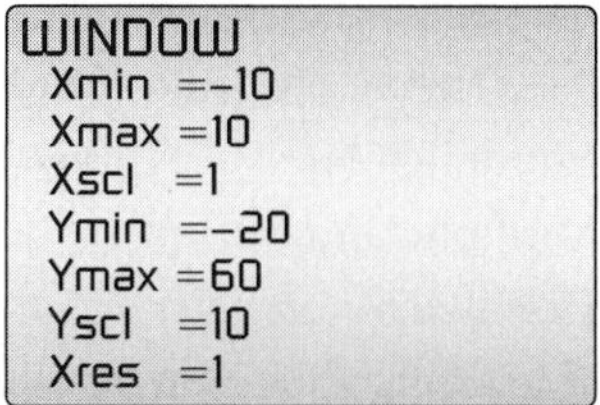

The degree of the polynomial gives the *maximum* number of times the graph will cross the x-axis. The maximum number of "turns" or changes between increasing and decreasing, as well as the maximum number of (local) extrema, is one less than the degree. (In all these cases, students might omit the word *maximum*. Ask them to consider functions like $y = x^2 + 1$, $y = x^3$, and $y = x^4 + 1$.) If the degree of the polynomial is even, both "tails" will go in the same direction (both up or both down). If the degree is odd, the "tails" will go in opposite directions (one up and one down).

3. **This problem is lengthy. It is best if students divide the workload so that no student has to do all these parts for homework.**

The degree of the sum or difference is equal to or less than the highest degree of the polynomials that are being added or subtracted. The degree will be less than the highest degree when the highest degree terms add or subtract to 0.

$f(x) + f(x) = (4x^3 + x^2 + 7x - 17) + (4x^3 + x^2 + 7x - 17) = 8x^3 + 2x^2 + 14x - 34$

$f(x) + g(x) = (4x^3 + x^2 + 7x - 17) + (3x^2 + 4x - 7) = 4x^3 + 4x^2 + 11x - 24$

$f(x) + h(x) = (4x^3 + x^2 + 7x - 17) + (5x + 2) = 4x^3 + x^2 + 12x - 15$

$f(x) + j(x) = (4x^3 + x^2 + 7x - 17) + (5x^4 + 3x^2) = 5x^4 + 4x^3 + 4x^2 + 7x - 17$

$g(x) + g(x) = (3x^2 + 4x - 7) + (3x^2 + 4x - 7) = 6x^2 + 8x - 14$

$g(x) + h(x) = (3x^2 + 4x - 7) + (5x + 2) = 3x^2 + 9x - 5$

$g(x) + j(x) = (3x^2 + 4x - 7) + (5x^4 + 3x^2) = 5x^4 + 6x^2 + 4x - 7$

$h(x) + h(x) = (5x + 2) + (5x + 2) = 10x + 4$

$h(x) + j(x) = (5x + 2) + (5x^4 + 3x^2) = 5x^4 + 3x^2 + 5x + 2$

$j(x) + j(x) = (5x^4 + 3x^2) + (5x^4 + 3x^2) = 10x^4 + 6x^2$

$f(x) - f(x) = (4x^3 + x^2 + 7x - 17) - (4x^3 + x^2 + 7x - 17) = 0$

$f(x) - g(x) = (4x^3 + x^2 + 7x - 17) - (3x^2 + 4x - 7) = 4x^3 - 2x^2 + 3x - 10$

$f(x) - h(x) = (4x^3 + x^2 + 7x - 17) - (5x + 2) = 4x^3 + x^2 + 2x - 19$

See additional Teaching Notes on page T257E.

2. Graph the following functions, and see if you can discover anything about the relationship between the degree of a polynomial function and the graph of the function. Explore other functions and their graphs to test your hypothesis.

a. $g(x) = x^2 + 7x + 12$

b. $h(x) = x^3 - 5x^2 - 4x + 20$

c. $f(x) = x^4 - 13x^2 + 36$

3. Suppose that a problem you are working on involves the following polynomial functions.

$f(x) = 4x^3 + x^2 + 7x - 17$

$g(x) = 3x^2 + 4x - 7$

$h(x) = 5x + 2$

$j(x) = 5x^4 + 3x^2$

With partners to share the workload, find all possible sums and differences of the four given polynomial functions. Study the results in search of a pattern describing how the degree of a sum or difference of polynomials is related to the degrees of the polynomials being added or subtracted.

4. Consider the following operation on geometric points of a plane: For any two given points A and B, $\boldsymbol{A}$ **tri** $\boldsymbol{B} = \boldsymbol{C}$ is the point located at the third vertex of an equilateral triangle ABC. The triangle is formed so that one moves counter-clockwise in going from A to B to C. For any single point A, $\boldsymbol{A}$ **tri** $\boldsymbol{A} = \boldsymbol{A}$.

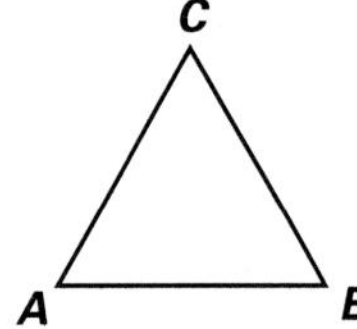

a. Is "tri" a commutative operation?

b. Is "tri" an associative operation?

c. Think back to the averaging operation "⊼" in Organizing Task 4, page 205. What numbers could be generated with this operation, starting from 0 and 1 and applying "⊼" repeatedly?

d. Suppose you start from two given points and apply the "tri" operation repeatedly to pairs chosen from the original points and points generated from those starting points. For example, after finding $C = A$ tri B, you can generate $D = A$ tri C and $J = D$ tri B, among others. What points of the plane can be generated in this way?

Unit 3

Lesson 3 Algebraic Operations: Part 2

In several earlier problem situations in this unit, you worked with quadratic functions that had rules of the form

$$f(x) = ax^2 + bx + c.$$

For example, if a gymnast bounces up off a trampoline, her height in feet above the trampoline at any time t seconds might be given by a quadratic function with rule

$$h(t) = -16t^2 + 24t.$$

Think About This Situation

Examine the graph below of the function $h(t) = -16t^2 + 24t$ giving a gymnast's height in feet above a trampoline at time t seconds. Following are three key questions that can be asked about this situation:

- When will the gymnast reach maximum height?
- What will that height be?
- When will she return to the trampoline surface?

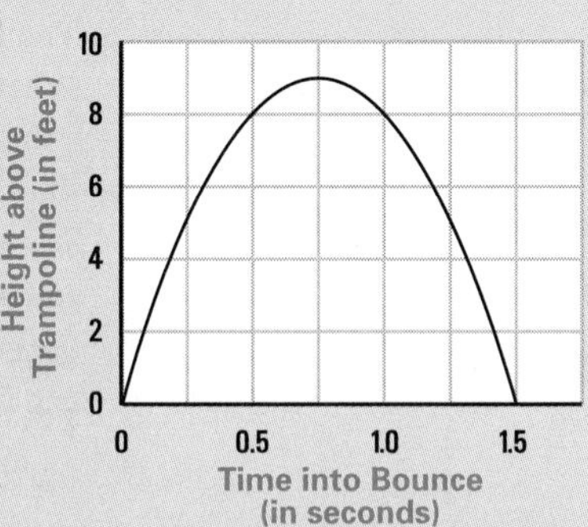

a How does the graph show estimates for answers to all three key questions above?

b How could information from the graph be used to derive the function rule itself?

208 UNIT 3 • SYMBOL SENSE AND ALGEBRAIC REASONING

Lesson 3 *Algebraic Operations: Part 2*

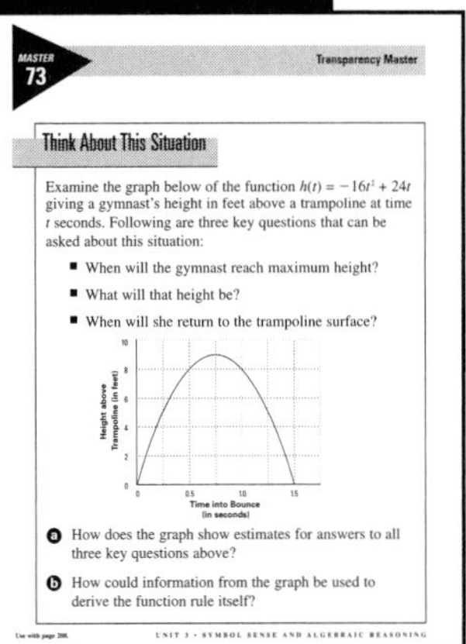

LESSON OVERVIEW Polynomials, factoring, and solving quadratic equations by factoring are studied in this lesson. Students are led through the development of factoring quadratic polynomials by first exploring the relationship between the factors of the polynomial and the roots of the equation. They also investigate the relationships among the axis of symmetry of the quadratic polynomial, the roots of the polynomial, and the minimum or maximum value of the quadratic polynomial.

Lesson Objectives

- To determine, by simplifying algebraic rules, by examining tables of values, and by graphing, that different forms of symbolic rules can express the same relation between variables
- To simplify algebraic fractions, multiply factors, and factor quadratic expressions
- To recognize the relationship between the factors and the zeroes of a polynomial function
- To recognize the relationship between the zeroes of a quadratic function and the line of symmetry of its graph and to use this relationship to determine the equation for the axis of symmetry and the extrema
- To write a function rule of a polynominal, given its zeroes

LAUNCH full-class discussion

Think About This Situation

See Teaching Master 73.

a
- The value of t for the highest point on the graph will give the gymnast's time when her maximum height is reached, 0.75 second in this example.
- The value of h for the highest point on the graph will give the gymnast's maximum height, 9 feet in this example.
- The time that corresponds to a height of zero after she has reached her maximum height will be the time that she returns to the trampoline surface. In this example, she returns to the trampoline after 1.5 seconds.

b Responses will vary. Some students might suggest taking three points, entering them into the calculator, and letting the calculator determine a quadratic regression model. Other students might suggest trial-and-error methods to find a, b, and c, since it is quadratic and therefore the general form of the function is $h(t) = at^2 + bt + c$. In either case, one would need to read points from the graph without an equation available, assuming that those points are accurate enough to fit the function rule. You should leave the discussion open for now.

Unit 3

EXPLORE small-group investigation

INVESTIGATION 1 Products and Factoring

In this investigation, students connect the zeroes of a function to the factored form of the function. For quadratic functions, they also go on to investigate connections among zeroes, maxima/minima, the factored form, and the expanded form of a function rule. By the end of the investigation, students will be familiar with factorization of quadratic expressions of the form $ax^2 + bx + c$.

1. **This activity includes all the logic necessary to analyze quadratic functions by factoring. Be sure that students explain their reasoning as carefully as possible. In particular, be aware that the logic behind Step 4 (the zero product property) may be elusive to many students. You may want to interrupt the exploration after Activity 1 to share explanations and to be sure that students get the idea. If they seem unconvinced, the following interaction may help. Ask, "I am thinking of two numbers whose product is 24. What are the numbers?" Of course, there are infinitely many answers: $3 \cdot 8$, $0.2 \cdot 120$, $(-48) \cdot -\frac{1}{2}$, *etc.* "That is a question for which you may never guess the right pair of numbers. What about if I say that the product of the two mystery numbers is zero?" Of course, this time one of the numbers has to be zero, maybe both. "So what would be the possible values of x if $x \cdot (x - 5) = 0$?"**

   (1) The distributive property was used to rewrite the function rule.

   (2) The function $h(t)$ gives the height, and the gymnast is back to the trampoline when $h(t) = 0$.

   (3) Zero was substituted for $h(t)$ in the factored form of $h(t)$ in Step 1.

   (4) The product will be 0 only when at least one of the factors is 0.

   (5) Multiplication and addition properties of equality were used to solve each equation for t.

   (6) It makes sense that it takes the same amount of time to go up as it does to come down. Also, we know that parabolas have an axis of symmetry that goes through the vertex. Thus, the maximum height occurs when t is equal to the average of the zeroes. In this case, $\frac{0 + 1.5}{2}$ or 0.75 would be the value for t when this parabola reaches the maximum height. Substituting 0.75 into the function rule gives 9 feet as the maximum height.

   (7) This is a translation into words of function notation used in Steps 5 and 6 within the context of this problem.

2. **a.** $f(0) = 0$ and $f(5) = 0$

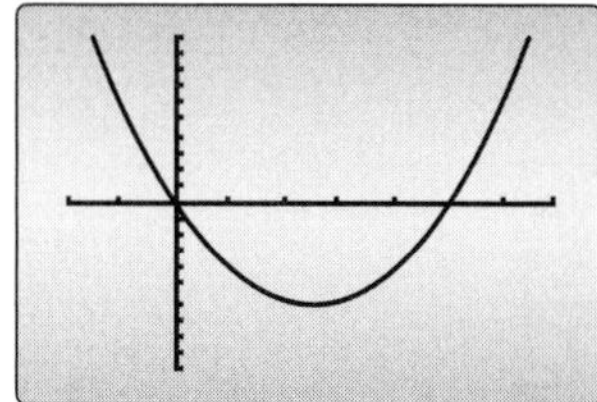

WINDOW
Xmin =-2
Xmax =7
Xscl =1
Ymin =-10
Ymax =10
Yscl =1
Xres =1

X	Y_1
-4	36
-3	24
-2	14
-1	6
0	0
1	-4
2	-6

Y_1=X(X-5)

X	Y_1
2	-6
3	-6
4	-4
5	0
6	6
7	14
8	24

Y_1=X(X-5)

See additional Teaching Notes on page T257F.

Unit 3

INVESTIGATION 1 ▸ Products and Factoring

The function rule $h(t) = -16t^2 + 24t$ can be used to produce a graph or a table of data describing the gymnast's bounce. But you can calculate values for the maximum height and landing time by using only algebraic reasoning with the rule.

1. Analyze the following way of answering the three key questions in the "Think About This Situation" on the previous page. Explain how properties of the function $h(t)$ and algebraic operations justify each step.

(1) The function rule $h(t) = -16t^2 + 24t$ can be rewritten as $h(t) = -8t(2t - 3)$.

(2) The gymnast returns to the trampoline surface when $h(t) = 0$.

(3) $h(t) = 0$ when $-8t(2t - 3) = 0$.

(4) $-8t(2t - 3) = 0$ when $-8t = 0$ or when $(2t - 3) = 0$.

(5) $-8t = 0$ when $t = 0$, and $(2t - 3) = 0$ when $t = 1.5$.

(6) The maximum value of $h(t)$ is $h(0.75)$ or 9.

(7) Therefore, the maximum height of 9 feet occurs 0.75 seconds after the gymnast bounces off the trampoline. She returns to the trampoline surface 1.5 seconds after she bounces upward.

The reasoning used in Activity 1 involved rewriting the given quadratic expression in an equivalent form from which it was easy to see when $h(t) = 0$. The idea was to write the given quadratic rule as a product of two *linear factors*. That technique is often called **factoring the quadratic**. The same idea can be used with a variety of other similar functions.

2. Below is a list of quadratic functions. For each function $f(x)$, do the following:

- Use symbolic reasoning to find all x for which $f(x) = 0$. These values are called the **zeroes** of the function.
- Use the zeroes of $f(x)$ and other things you know about quadratic functions to sketch a graph of the function.
- Check the results of your reasoning by producing appropriate calculator tables and graphs.

a. $f(x) = x(x - 5)$

b. $f(x) = -x(x + 3)$

c. $f(x) = (x + 3)(x - 5)$

d. $f(x) = (x - 6)(x - 1)$

e. $f(x) = -(x + 7)(x + 2)$

f. $f(x) = (x - 3)(x - 3)$

g. $f(x) = (5x + 12)(x - 3)$

h. $f(x) = (2x + 5)(3x + 1)$

i. $f(x) = -6(-7x + 11)(2 - x)$

Unit 3

LESSON 3 • ALGEBRAIC OPERATIONS: PART 2 209

3. Find all x for which $f(x) = 0$ in each of the following cases. Then use your calculator to produce graphs of the given functions and look for patterns relating the zeroes of the functions and the properties of their graphs.

a. $f(x) = x(x - 5)(x + 3)$

b. $f(x) = -x(x - 3)(x + 5)$

c. $f(x) = (x + 6)(2x - 1)(x - 4)$

d. $f(x) = x(3x - 3)(x - 1)(x + 2)$

e. $f(x) = (x^2 - 4)(3x + 5)$

4. Study your results from Activities 2 and 3 to find patterns relating rules, zeroes, and graphs of functions. Use your observations to write rules for functions that satisfy the following conditions.

a. $f(4) = 0$ and $f(1) = 0$

b. $g(5) = 0$ and $g(-3) = 0$

c. $h(7) = 0$, $h(0) = 0$, and $h(2) = 0$

d. $j(-1) = 0$ and $j(-5) = 0$

Look back over your work on Activities 2 through 4. You probably have some ideas about the way that a function rule, if written in *factored form*, can be quite useful in finding the zeroes and sketching graphs of polynomial functions, especially quadratics. If a function rule is expressed in the form of a product of linear factors, you can find the x-intercepts quickly. The next two activities will suggest some strategies you can use for functions that are not written in factored form, such as $f(x) = x^2 + 5x + 6$ or $g(x) = 4x^2 + 20x$.

5. Justify each step in the following reasoning sequences, which show connections between factored form and the more familiar forms of quadratic rules.

a. $f(x) = (x + 3)(x + 2)$
$= (x + 3)(x) + (x + 3)(2)$
$= (x^2 + 3x) + (2x + 6)$
$= x^2 + 5x + 6$

b. $g(x) = (x - 3)(x + 5)$
$= (x - 3)(x) + (x - 3)(5)$
$= (x^2 - 3x) + (5x - 15)$
$= x^2 + 2x - 15$

c. $h(t) = (5t + 2)(t - 4)$
$= (5t + 2)(t) - (5t + 2)(4)$
$= (5t^2 + 2t) - (20t + 8)$
$= 5t^2 - 18t - 8$

d. $j(x) = 7x(2x + 5)$
$= (7x)(2x) + (7x)(5)$
$= 14x^2 + 35x$

The examples in Activity 5 show how the factored form of a quadratic function rule can be transformed into a more familiar form. To reason in the other direction, that is, to find the factored form that matches a given standard form quadratic rule, it helps to find the common thread in all such problems.

Unit 3

210 UNIT 3 • SYMBOL SENSE AND ALGEBRAIC REASONING

3. **In this activity, students have to identify a zero for each of 3 or more factors. In Part d, two factors have the same zero, and in Part e, there are actually 2 zeroes for one factor, because $x^2 - 4$ will have a value of 0 if $x = 2$ or if $x = -2$. Students may miss these if they have slipped into thinking that the number of zeroes is the same as the number of factors. Ask how these factors are different from all the other factors. ($x^2 - 4$ is not a linear factor, and $3x - 3$ is equivalent to $3(x - 1)$.)**

   For each part, students should find that the zeroes of the functions correspond to the x-intercepts of the graphs.

   a. $f(0) = 0, f(5) = 0$, and $f(-3) = 0$

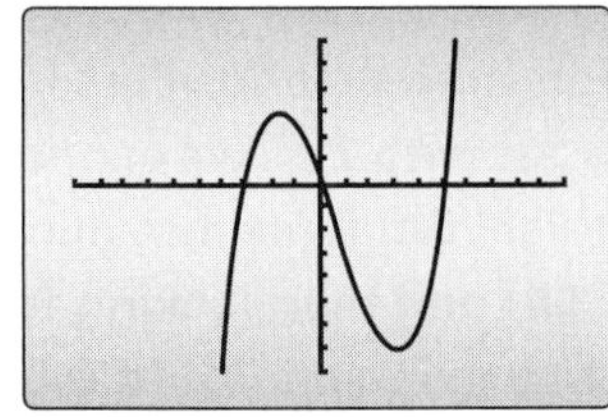

WINDOW
Xmin =-10
Xmax =10
Xscl =1
Ymin =-40
Ymax =30
Yscl =5
Xres =1

   b. $f(0) = 0, f(3) = 0$, and $f(-5) = 0$

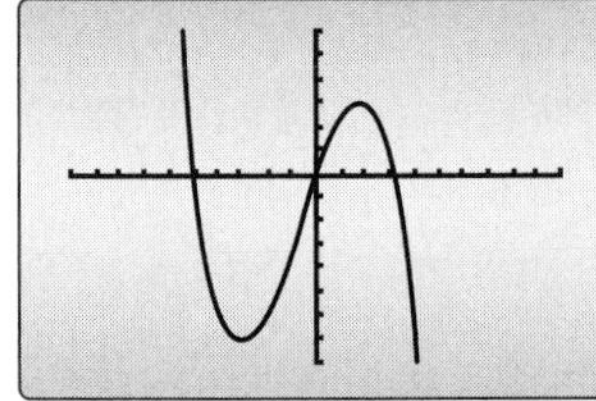

WINDOW
Xmin =-10
Xmax =10
Xscl =1
Ymin =-40
Ymax =30
Yscl =5
Xres =1

   c. $f(-6) = 0, f\left(\frac{1}{2}\right) = 0$, and $f(4) = 0$

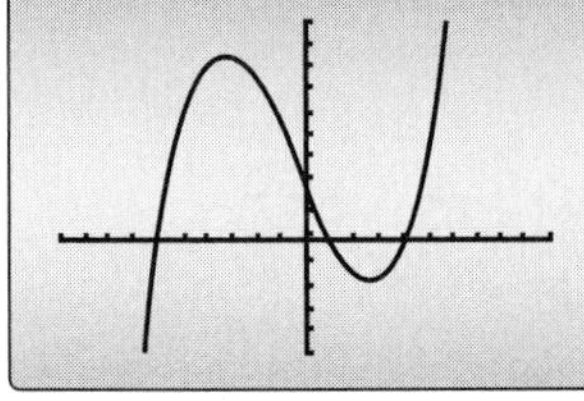

WINDOW
Xmin =-10
Xmax =10
Xscl =1
Ymin =-100
Ymax =200
Yscl =20
Xres =1

   d. $f(0) = 0, f(1) = 0$, and $f(-2) = 0$

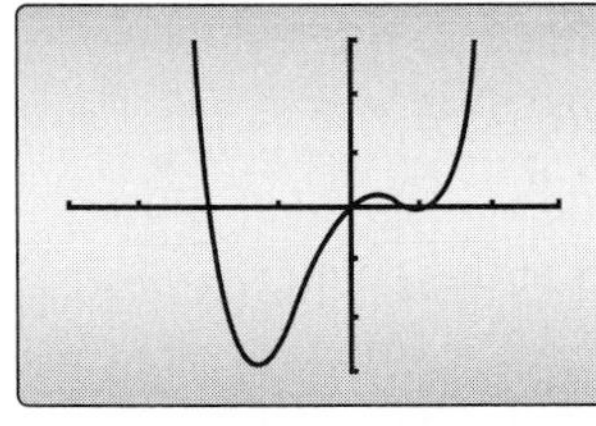

WINDOW
Xmin =-4
Xmax =3
Xscl =1
Ymin =-15
Ymax =15
Yscl =5
Xres =1

   e. $f(2) = 0, f(-2) = 0$, and $f\left(\frac{-5}{3}\right) = 0$

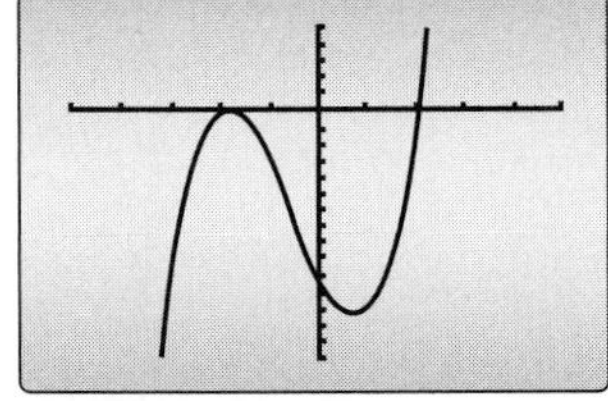

WINDOW
Xmin =-5
Xmax =5
Xscl =1
Ymin =-30
Ymax =10
Yscl =2
Xres =1

See additional Teaching Notes on page T257G.

Master 74

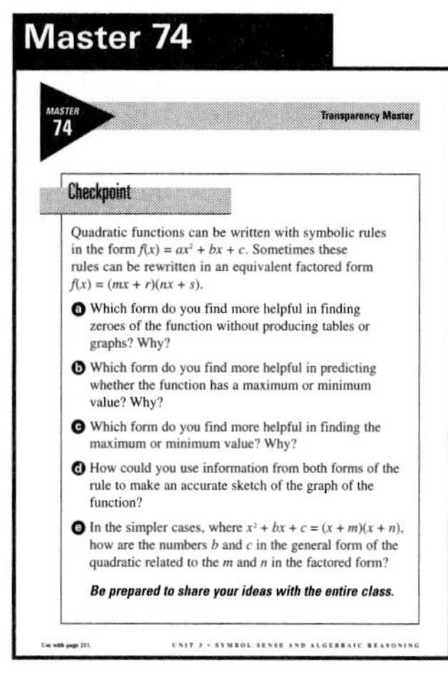

EXPLORE *continued*

6. $x^2 + (a + b)x + ab$

   If numbers can be found whose product is equal to the constant term and whose sum is the coefficient of the linear term, then the polynomial can be factored easily. This relationship is important. Make sure that students look at Activity 5 Parts a and b so they see that the sum and the product of a and b are the coefficient and the constant. You may also want to make up more problems of this type.

7. **In this activity, there are three examples in which the sum and product of the roots rule will not apply. These are worth some class discussion. Part j cannot be factored, and Parts g and l have leading coefficients other than 1. Make sure that students understand that we have a rule that makes it easy to move back and forth between expanded and factored form, but it applies only when the leading coefficient is 1. Ask students for strategies for Part l. "Part l actually does have factors. But since it does not start with $1x^2$, we cannot apply our rule. Can you think of any way to get around this?" Students may suggest writing the quadratic expression as $2(x^2 + 3.5x + 1.5)$ and then looking for two numbers whose sum is 3.5 and product is 1.5. The numbers 3 and 0.5 work, giving a factored form of $s(x) = 2(x + 3)(x + 0.5)$. This can then be rewritten as $s(x) = (x + 3)(2x + 1)$.**

   a. $f(x) = (x + 2)(x + 4)$
   b. $g(x) = (x + 3)(x + 4)$
   c. $h(x) = (x - 4)(x - 3)$
   d. $i(x) = (x - 4)(x + 3)$
   e. $j(x) = (x - 7)(x + 2)$
   f. $k(x) = (x - 4)(x - 2)$
   g. $m(x) = -(x - 4)(x - 2)$
   h. $n(x) = (x + 3)(x - 3)$
   i. $p(x) = (x + 3)(x + 3)$
   j. $q(x) = x^2 + 9$ cannot be factored
   k. $r(x) = (x + 7)(x - 1)$
   l. $s(x) = (2x + 1)(x + 3)$

8. The vertex of each parabola has an x-coordinate equal to the average of the zeroes of the polynomial. To find the y-coordinate, students can substitute x into the function rule and find the value of y.

   a. The zeroes are -2 and -4. The vertex is $(-3, -1)$.
   b. The zeroes are -3 and -4. The vertex is $(-3.5, -0.25)$.
   c. The zeroes are 4 and 3. The vertex is $(3.5, -0.25)$.
   d. The zeroes are 4 and -3. The vertex is $(0.5, -12.25)$.
   e. The zeroes are 7 and -2. The vertex is $(2.5, -20.25)$.
   f. The zeroes are 4 and 2. The vertex is $(3, -1)$.
   g. The zeroes are 4 and 2. The vertex is $(3, 1)$.
   h. The zeroes are -3 and 3. The vertex is $(0, -9)$.
   i. The zero is -3. The vertex is $(-3, 0)$.
   j. The vertex cannot be found symbolically at this point.
   k. The zeroes are -7 and 1. The vertex is $(-3, -16)$.
   l. The zeroes are $-\frac{1}{2}$ and -3. The vertex is $(-1.75, -3.125)$.

Unit 3

CONSTRUCTING A MATH TOOLKIT: Following the Checkpoint, students should describe the connections between the graph of a function, in both standard form and factored form. You may wish to have them also explain the steps they use to rewrite function rules in factored form.

See additional Teaching Notes on page T257H.

6. Consider the variety of functions with rules in the form $f(x) = (x + a)(x + b)$. Rules like these can always be rewritten in standard quadratic form. Complete this equation:

$$(x + a)(x + b) = x^2 + \_\_\_\_\_ x + \_\_\_\_\_$$

Study how the results in each part of this standard quadratic form are related to the numbers a and b in the factored form of the function rule. How can these relations help you factor quadratic expressions like $x^2 + 5x + 6$?

7. Now see if you can use the patterns relating factored and standard form for quadratic function rules to write factored forms for each of the following rules. Compare your factorizations to those of other groups.

a. $f(x) = x^2 + 6x + 8$

b. $g(x) = x^2 + 7x + 12$

c. $h(x) = x^2 - 7x + 12$

d. $i(x) = x^2 - x - 12$

e. $j(x) = x^2 - 5x - 14$

f. $k(x) = x^2 - 6x + 8$

g. $m(x) = -x^2 + 6x - 8$

h. $n(x) = x^2 - 9$

i. $p(x) = x^2 + 6x + 9$

j. $q(x) = x^2 + 9$

k. $r(x) = x^2 + 6x - 7$

l. $s(x) = 2x^2 + 7x + 3$

8. Use symbolic reasoning to find the vertex of each parabola described by the rules given in Activity 7. Divide the workload among members of your group, and then share and explain your findings.

Checkpoint

Quadratic functions can be written with symbolic rules in the form $f(x) = ax^2 + bx + c$. Sometimes these rules can be rewritten in an equivalent factored form $f(x) = (mx + r)(nx + s)$.

a Which form do you find more helpful in finding zeroes of the function without producing tables or graphs? Why?

b Which form do you find more helpful in predicting whether the function has a maximum or minimum value? Why?

c Which form do you find more helpful in finding the maximum or minimum value? Why?

d How could you use information from both forms of the rule to make an accurate sketch of the graph of the function?

e In the simpler cases, in which $x^2 + bx + c = (x + m)(x + n)$, how are the numbers b and c in the general form of the quadratic related to the m and n in the factored form?

Be prepared to share your ideas with the entire class.

Unit 3

LESSON 3 • ALGEBRAIC OPERATIONS: PART 2 211

On Your Own

Use what you have learned about factoring to help you complete the following tasks.

a. Rewrite each of the following function rules in an equivalent factored form (if possible).

- $f(x) = x^2 - 5x + 6$
- $g(x) = x^2 + 10x + 16$
- $h(x) = x^2 - 36$
- $j(x) = x^2 + 10$
- $k(t) = 7t^2 + 14t$

b. For each of the following functions, reason with the symbolic forms to find all x for which $f(x) = 0$. Then sketch a graph and find the minimum or maximum value of the function.

- $d(x) = (2x - 5)(x + 4)$
- $f(x) = x^2 + 5x - 6$
- $g(x) = x^2 - 12x$
- $h(x) = -x^2 + 7x + 18$

c. Write function rules (in factored and standard form) with these properties:

- $f(3) = 0$ and $f(5) = 0$
- $g(-2) = 0$ and $g(8) = 0$
- $h(-4) = 0$ and $h(0) = 0$
- $r(-5) = 0$, $r(2) = 0$, and $r(7) = 0$

d. For each function in Parts a through c, explain how you could use a graphing calculator to check your answer.

Unit 3

INVESTIGATION 2 Special Products and Factoring

Quadratic and higher-degree polynomials occur in many situations in both standard and factored forms. There are two special cases that have especially interesting and useful patterns.

1. Write each of the following indicated products in standard polynomial form. Then compare the factors and product in each case to look for a shortcut method for finding similar types of indicated products.

a. $(x + 4)(x - 4)$ **b.** $(t - 3)(t + 3)$ **c.** $(s + 1)(s - 1)$

2. Write each of these quadratic expressions in factored form. Compare your result in each case to the pattern observed in Activity 1 to look for a shortcut method of factoring this special type of quadratic polynomial.

a. $x^2 - 25$ **b.** $x^2 - 81$ **c.** $x^2 - 36$

3. Sketch graphs of each of the following quadratic functions. Use your understanding of symmetry and the connection between zeroes and factors to explain why the factored forms you found in Activity 2 make sense.

a. $f(x) = x^2 - 25$ **b.** $g(x) = x^2 - 81$ **c.** $h(x) = x^2 - 36$

212 UNIT 3 • SYMBOL SENSE AND ALGEBRAIC REASONING

APPLY individual task

On Your Own

a. ■ $f(x) = (x - 3)(x - 2)$ ■ $g(x) = (x + 8)(x + 2)$
■ $h(x) = (x - 6)(x + 6)$ ■ $j(x) = x^2 + 10$, cannot be factored
■ $k(t) = 7t(t + 2)$

b. ■ $d(x) = (2x - 5)(x + 4)$, so $d\left(\frac{5}{2}\right) = 0$ and $d(-4) = 0$. The minimum value is –21.125 when x equals $\frac{-3}{4}$.

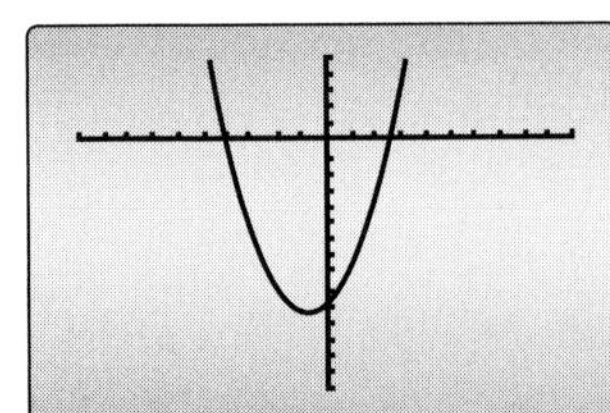

WINDOW
Xmin =–10
Xmax =10
Xscl =1
Ymin =–30
Ymax =10
Yscl =2
Xres =1

■ $f(x) = (x + 6)(x - 1)$, so $f(1) = 0$ and $f(-6) = 0$. The minimum value is $f(-2.5)$ or –12.25.

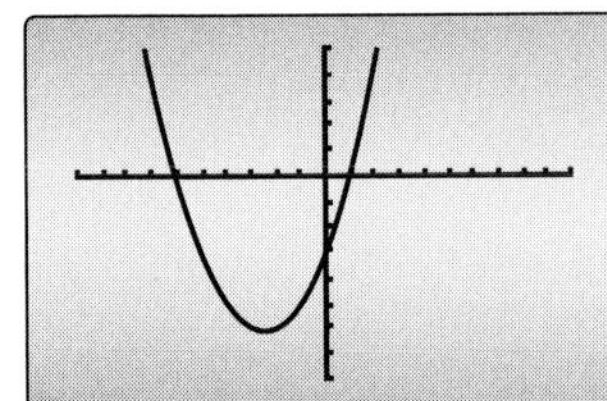

WINDOW
Xmin =–10
Xmax =10
Xscl =1
Ymin =–16
Ymax =10
Yscl =2
Xres =1

■ $g(x) = x(x - 12)$, so $g(0) = 0$ and $g(12) = 0$. The minimum value is $g(6)$ or –36.

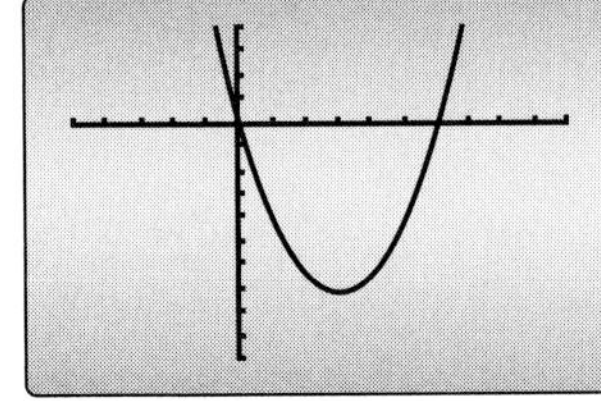

WINDOW
Xmin =–10
Xmax =20
Xscl =2
Ymin =–50
Ymax =20
Yscl =5
Xres =1

■ $h(x) = -(x - 9)(x + 2)$, so $h(9) = 0$ and $h(-2) = 0$. The maximum value is $h(3.5)$ or 30.25.

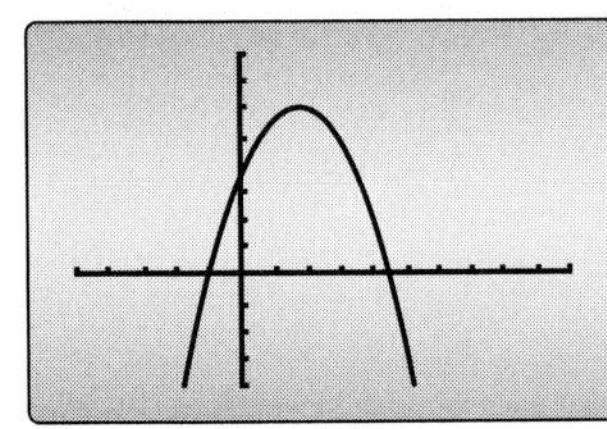

WINDOW
Xmin =–10
Xmax =20
Xscl =2
Ymin =–20
Ymax =40
Yscl =5
Xres =1

c. Note that answers may vary.
■ $f(x) = (x - 3)(x - 5)$; $f(x) = x^2 - 8x + 15$
■ $g(x) = (x + 2)(x - 8)$; $g(x) = x^2 - 6x - 16$
■ $h(x) = x(x + 4)$; $h(x) = x^2 + 4x$
■ $r(x) = (x + 5)(x - 2)(x - 7)$; $r(x) = x^3 - 4x^2 - 31x + 70$

See additional Teaching Notes on page T257I.

Unit 3

MORE ASSIGNMENT *pp. 218–224*

Students can now begin Modeling Task 1, Organizing Tasks 1 or 2, or Reflecting Task 2 from the MORE assignment following Investigation 3.

4. a. x^2
   b. The area of the white square is a^2.
      The area of the shaded region is $x^2 - a^2$.
   c. The height of the reassembled region is $x - a$. The length of the base of the reassembled region is $x + a$. Thus, the area of the region is $(x - a)(x + a)$ or $(x + a)(x - a)$.
   d. In Parts b and c, the expressions represent the area for the same shaded region. Therefore $(x + a)(x - a) = x^2 - a^2$.
5. a. $x^2 + 6x + 9$ b. $x^2 + 14x + 49$
   c. $x^2 + 2x + 1$ d. $x^2 - 10x + 25$
   e. $x^2 - 12x + 36$

   The general forms are $(x + a)^2 = x^2 + 2ax + a^2$ and $(x - a)^2 = x^2 - 2ax + a^2$. Using these patterns, you know that to determine the square of any binomial, you square both of the terms and add twice their product.
6. The area of the large square is equal to the edge length squared or $(x + a)^2$. The area of the square is also equal to the sum of the regions, which is $x^2 + ax + ax + a^2$ or $x^2 + 2ax + a^2$. Since these two expressions both represent the same area, they must be equal; therefore $(x + a)^2 = x^2 + 2ax + a^2$.

4. The expressions you have been investigating in Activities 1 through 3 involve the *difference of two squares*. Here is another way of thinking about factoring expressions like $x^2 - a^2$.

a. What is the area of the shaded square below on the left?

b. Refer to the figure on the right. What is the area of the white square? Of the shaded region?

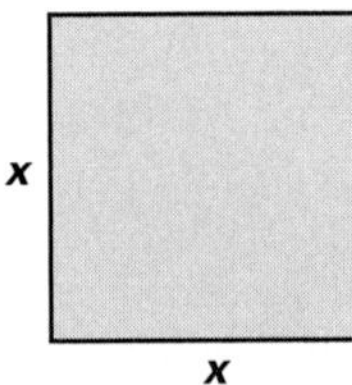

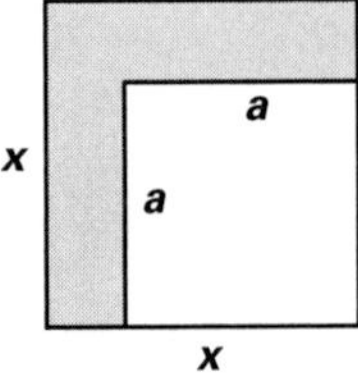

c. Suppose the shaded region above on the right is cut and reassembled as shown below. Write two expressions giving the area of the new shape.

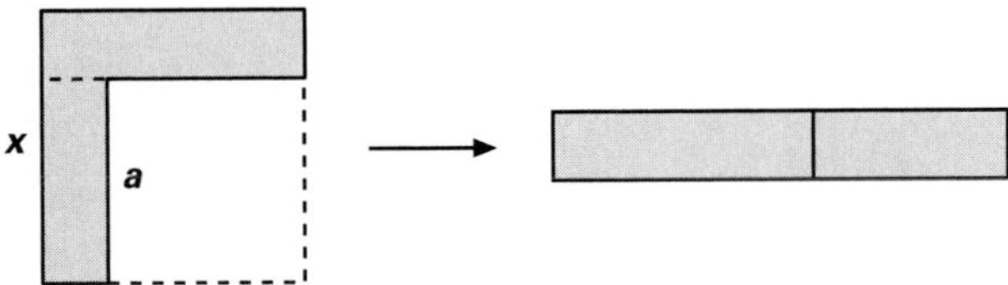

d. How does the sequence of sketches and algebraic expressions for areas in Parts a through c confirm the general pattern observed in factoring the difference of two squares in Activity 2?

The product and factoring pattern that you explored in Activities 1 through 4 involves the difference of squares of numbers. There is another simple pattern for expanding and factoring another special type of quadratic called a *perfect square*.

5. Use algebraic properties to expand each of the following expressions to standard polynomial form. Then look back over the results to see if you can find a general shortcut for expanding expressions in the form $(x + a)^2$ and $(x - a)^2$.

a. $(x + 3)^2$ **b.** $(x + 7)^2$

c. $(x + 1)^2$ **d.** $(x - 5)^2$

e. $(x - 6)^2$

6. Write expressions for areas of the regions in the diagram at the right. Then explain how the diagram illustrates a general pattern for expanding expressions in the form $(x + a)^2$ to standard polynomial form.

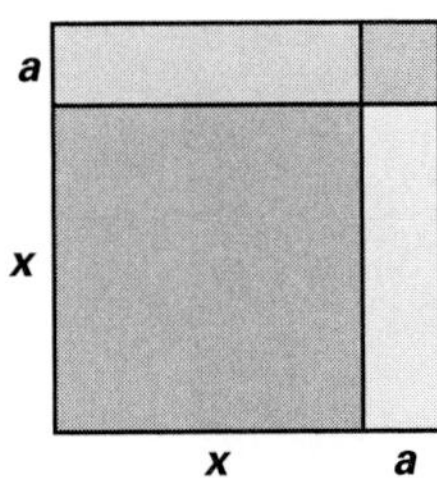

LESSON 3 • ALGEBRAIC OPERATIONS: PART 2 213

Unit 3

7. Use your discoveries in Activities 5 and 6 to write, if possible, each of these polynomials in factored form.

a. $x^2 + 8x + 16$ **b.** $x^2 + 10x + 25$

c. $x^2 - 6x + 9$ **d.** $x^2 - 2x + 1$

8. When beginning students are asked to expand expressions like $(x + a)^2$, one very common error is often made. What do you think that error is, and how could you help someone avoid making the error?

Checkpoint

Some quadratic functions have special connections between their standard polynomial and factored forms that allow some shortcuts in symbolic manipulation.

a What standard polynomial form is always equivalent to a product in the form $(x - a)(x + a)$?

b What standard polynomial form is always equivalent to an expression in the form $(x + a)^2$? In the form $(x - a)^2$?

c How could you use a sketch like the one in Activity 6 to convince someone that the expression $(x + 3)^2$ is *not* equivalent to $x^2 + 9$?

Be prepared to share your responses and thinking with the entire class.

On Your Own

Use what you have learned about special products and factoring to help you complete the following tasks.

a. Write each of these expressions in expanded standard polynomial form.

- $(x + 4)(x - 4)$
- $(x + 7)(x - 7)$
- $(x + 8)^2$
- $(x - 9)^2$
- $(x + 5)(x - 4)$

b. Write each of these polynomials in factored form (where possible).

- $r^2 - 36$
- $m^2 + 9$
- $m^2 + 6m + 9$
- $m^2 - 12m + 36$

Unit 3

214 UNIT 3 • SYMBOL SENSE AND ALGEBRAIC REASONING

7. **a.** $(x + 4)^2$ **b.** $(x + 5)^2$
   c. $(x - 3)^2$ **d.** $(x - 1)^2$
8. Students often forget the middle term and expand $(x + a)^2$ to $x^2 + a^2$. One way to help them avoid making the error is to suggest substituting numbers to see that it does not work. For example, $(3 + 5)^2 \neq 3^2 + 5^2$ because $64 \neq 9 + 25$. Students can also look at the graphs of $y = (x + a)^2$ and $y = x^2 + a^2$ to see that they are not identical. A third way is to think about what it means to square something and rewrite $(x + a)^2$ as $(x + a)(x + a)$; then use the distributive property to expand $(x + a)(x + a)$.

Master 75

MASTER 75 — Transparency Master

Checkpoint

Some quadratic functions have special connections between their standard polynomial and factored forms that allow some shortcuts in symbolic manipulation.

a What standard polynomial form is always equivalent to a product in the form $(x - a)(x + a)$?

b What standard polynomial form is always equivalent to an expression in the form $(x + a)^2$? In the form $(x - a)^2$?

c How could you use a sketch like the one in Activity 6 to convince someone that the expression $(x + 3)^2$ is *not* equivalent to $x^2 + 9$?

Be prepared to share your responses and thinking with the entire class.

SHARE AND SUMMARIZE full-class discussion

Checkpoint

See Teaching Master 75.

a $x^2 - a^2$

b $(x + a)^2 = x^2 + 2ax + a^2$
$(x - a)^2 = x^2 - 2ax + a^2$

c

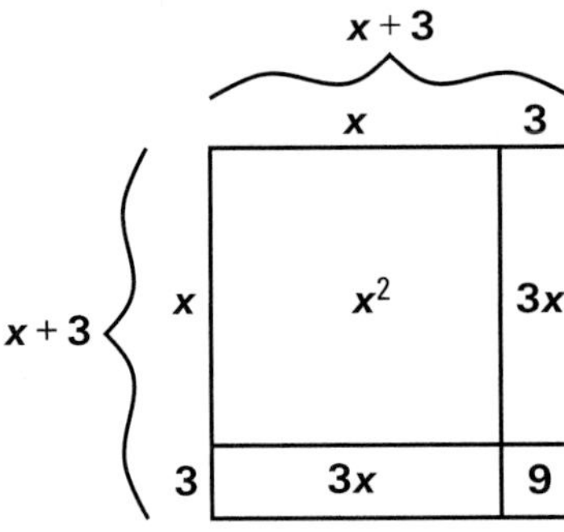

The area of the square is $(x + 3)^2$, which equals $x^2 + 3x + 3x + 9$ or $x^2 + 6x + 9$.

CONSTRUCTING A MATH TOOLKIT: Students should list in symbolic form the special product and factoring relationships that have been developed and studied in this investigation, along with explanations of these symbolic relationships.

APPLY individual task

On Your Own

a. ■ $x^2 - 16$ ■ $x^2 - 49$
■ $x^2 + 16x + 64$ ■ $x^2 - 18x + 81$
■ $x^2 + x - 20$

b. ■ $(r + 6)(r - 6)$ ■ cannot be factored
■ $(m + 3)^2$ ■ $(m - 6)^2$

MORE ASSIGNMENT *pp. 218–224*

Students can now begin Modeling Task 4 or Extending Task 1, 2, or 4 from the MORE assignment following Investigation 3.

Unit 3

EXPLORE small-group investigation

INVESTIGATION 3 Division and Fractions

This investigation allows students to connect what they already know about arithmetic fractions to algebraic fractions. They will rewrite rational expressions in equivalent forms, add fractions by creating a common denominator, and apply the distributive property to rewrite a fraction as a sum of two other fractions.

You might want to warm up with a discussion of some arithmetic fraction skills: "Why is $\frac{2}{7} + \frac{3}{7} = \frac{5}{7}$? Why is $\frac{2}{3} + \frac{3}{2} \neq \frac{5}{5}$? If the school has four fund-raisers to send five students to Washington and these raise \$400, \$120, \$80, and \$125, do you get the total amount each student gets by dividing the total (400 + 120 + 80 + 125) by 5, or by dividing each separate amount by 5 and then adding? What property justifies that $\frac{(400 + 120 + 80 + 125)}{5}$ is the same as $\frac{400}{5} + \frac{120}{5} + \frac{80}{5} + \frac{25}{5}$?"

Listen carefully to the explanations that students give about why expressions are equivalent. For example, in Activity 2, students may use their familiarity with tables to see the outputs of $s(t) = \frac{10t - 400}{4}$ in terms of taking the outputs of $p(t) = 10t - 400$ and dividing each by 4, or they may use the context to reason that $s(t) = 2.5t - 100$ is the result of each class making \$2.50 on a ticket and each class having to pay \$100 of the costs. They may see that $\frac{10t - 400}{4}$ is the same as $0.25(10t - 400)$ and apply the distributive property. Your students have rewritten linear relationships like $ax + by = c$ in the "$y = ...$" format, and many will have used the forms $y = \frac{c - ax}{b}$ and $y = \frac{c}{b} - \frac{ax}{b}$ interchangeably. You may wish to keep a list of all the ways that students make sense of the symbols so that all students can appreciate the diversity of strategies.

1. **a.** $P(t) = 10t - 400$

b. ■ $S_1(t) = \frac{10t - 400}{4}$, for each class

■ $S_2(t) = \frac{2(10t - 400)}{5}$ for the senior class because it receives $\frac{4}{10}$ or $\frac{2}{5}$ of the profits

c. $A(t) = \frac{10t - 400}{t}$

The graph below shows that as the number of tickets sold increases, the profit per ticket increases, quickly at first but then more slowly. In fact, there is a limit of \$10 for the average profit.

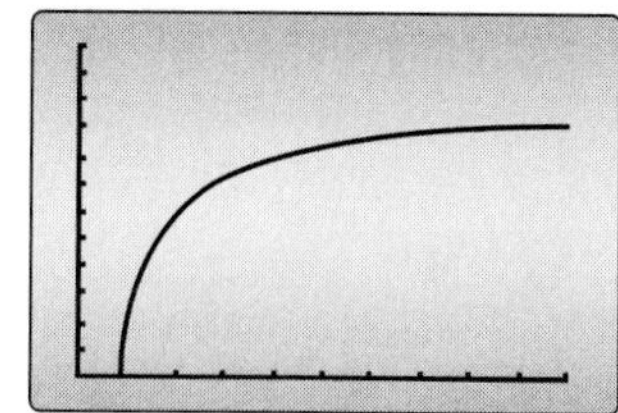

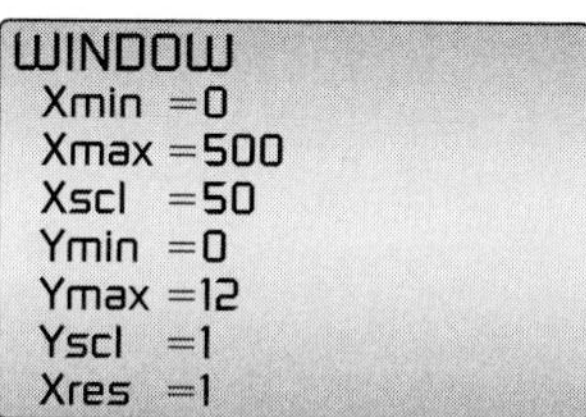

Unit 3

INVESTIGATION 3 Division and Fractions

In many important mathematical relationships, variables are multiplied to produce new information. For example:

- Distance, rate, and time are related by the formula $d = rt$.
- Savings account interest, principal, rate, and time are related by $i = prt$.
- Volume of a cylinder is related to radius and height by $V = \pi r^2 h$.

In solving problems that involve relationships like those, it is often helpful to express the relationships using division and fractions. For example:

- Time of a trip is related to distance and rate by $t = \frac{d}{r}$.
- Height of a cylinder is related to volume and radius by $h = \frac{V}{\pi r^2}$.

To work effectively with such relationships, it helps to be skillful in working with some basic types of algebraic fractions. Use what you already know about numerical fractions and division to investigate the following situations. As you complete the activities, try to formulate some general guidelines for operating with algebraic fractions.

1. When the Student Government Association (SGA) at River Hill High School planned an all-school formal dance, SGA members set ticket prices at $10. They hired a disc jockey for $300 and had to plan on a custodial fee of $100.

a. What algebraic expression gives the rule for calculating *total profit* from the dance as a function of the number of tickets sold?

b. There were various proposals for sharing profits from the dance. What function rule would describe the share for the senior class if profits were shared in the following way?

- Equally among the four classes in the school
- In a ratio 4:3:2:1 among the four classes in the school, with higher classes getting the greater shares

c. Write an equation giving average *profit per ticket* as a function of the number of tickets sold. Sketch a graph of that function (for 0 to 500 tickets), and explain what its shape tells about the relation between number of tickets sold and profit per ticket.

You now know that linear and quadratic function rules can be expressed in a variety of equivalent ways. Rules that involve fractions and inverse variation can also be written in different forms. Your choice among equivalent forms will often be influenced by the information you want from the function rules.

LESSON 3 • ALGEBRAIC OPERATIONS: PART 2 215

2. Consider the following questions about the profit and profit-per-ticket functions from planning for the River Hill High School dance.

   a. Under the plan to divide profits equally among the four classes in the school, the following three rules were proposed for senior class profit as a function of number of tickets sold.

   $s_1(t) = \frac{10t - 400}{4}$ $\quad s_2(t) = \frac{1}{4}(10t - 400)$ $\quad s_3(t) = 2.5t - 100$

   - Are these equivalent rules? If not, how do you know? If so, what reasoning about fractions supports your conclusion?
   - Which of the three rules seems to model the given situation in the most informative way? Why?
   - Which of the rules is probably most convenient for calculations? Why?

   b. Under the plan to split dance profits among classes in the ratio 4:3:2:1, the senior class share can be predicted by the function $s(t) = \frac{4}{10}(10t - 400)$.

   - Write at least two other equivalent rules for this function and explain how you know they are equivalent.
   - Identify the rule that you believe seems to model the situation in the most informative way. Which rule is most convenient for calculations?

   c. In studying the relation between ticket sales and profit per ticket for the dance, SGA members came up with two different rules:

   $f_1(t) = \frac{10t - 400}{t}$ $\quad f_2(t) = 10 - \frac{400}{t}$

   - Assuming $t \neq 0$, do you believe the two rules are equivalent? If not, how can you demonstrate the differences? If they are, what reasoning might have led to each form?
   - Which of the two given rules seems to model the situation in a more informative way? Which is more convenient for calculations?
   - Find yet another equivalent rule for profit per ticket.
   - Examine tables and graphs of the various profit-per-ticket functions as the number of tickets sold gets very large. Describe the way that average profit changes as number of tickets increases, and describe how that pattern of change could be predicted by analyzing the function rule itself.

In your analysis of the function rules for the River Hill High School dance profits, you probably used a variety of strategies for studying equivalence of different fractional forms. You probably also found that rearranging a given rule in a different equivalent form often reveals new information about the relationship among variables or makes calculations easier. There are two basic kinds of rearrangement that occur often: combining two fractions by multiplication or addition, and rewriting a given fraction as a product or sum of terms. The number system properties that you've used in studying polynomials and rules for operation with fractions can be used to guide those symbolic manipulations.

Unit 3

216 UNIT 3 • SYMBOL SENSE AND ALGEBRAIC REASONING

2. a. ■ All three rules are equivalent. Dividing an expression by 4 is the same thing as multiplying it by $\frac{1}{4}$. The third rule is equivalent since it can be obtained from the second by distributing the $\frac{1}{4}$.

■ The first rule will probably be selected by most students as representing the situation in the most informative way because it takes the total profit and splits (divides) it by 4. Some students might select the second rule for similar reasons, thinking that each class will get $\frac{1}{4}$ of the profit.

■ The third rule will be most convenient for calculations because it is in simplest algebraic form; therefore, fewer calculations will need to be made.

b. ■ Two possibilities are $s_1(t) = \frac{4(10t - 400)}{10}$ and $s_2(t) = 4t - 160$. The first expression is equivalent because multiplying by $\frac{4}{10}$ is the same as multiplying by 4 and then dividing by 10. The second expression is equivalent because it is the result obtained by distributing the 4 over the difference and then performing the division.

■ The first rule is more informative, but the second one would be more convenient to use for making calculations.

c. ■ Yes, the rules are equivalent. The first rule represents the situation very clearly; that is, the total profit divided by the number of tickets sold. The second rule is equivalent, but each term of the numerator has been written over the common denominator, t, and then simplified where that is possible.

■ The first rule is more informative, but the second is more convenient for calculations.

■ There are many possible rules. A common response might be $f(t) = \frac{1}{t}(10t - 400)$.

■ From the graph and tables, you can see that as the number of tickets sold increases, the average profit per ticket increases rapidly at first and then levels off, possibly approaching a single number. You can also see this easily (and more precisely) in the second form of the rule: As t becomes very large, the value for $\frac{400}{t}$ becomes very small and the expression $10 - \frac{400}{t}$ approaches 10.

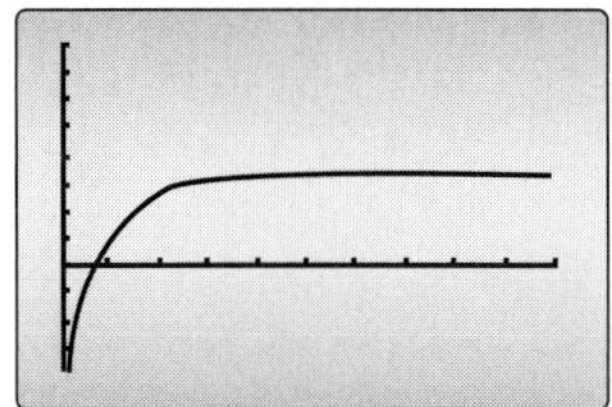

X	Y1
0	ERROR
100	6
200	8
300	8.6667
400	9
500	9.2
600	9.3333

X=0

X	Y1
700	9.4286
800	9.5
900	9.5556
1000	9.6
1100	9.6364
1200	9.6667
1300	9.6923

Y1=(10X−400)/X

X	Y1
1400	9.7143
1500	9.7333
1600	9.75
1700	9.7647
1800	9.7778
1900	9.7895
2000	9.8

Y1=(10X−400)/X

Master 76

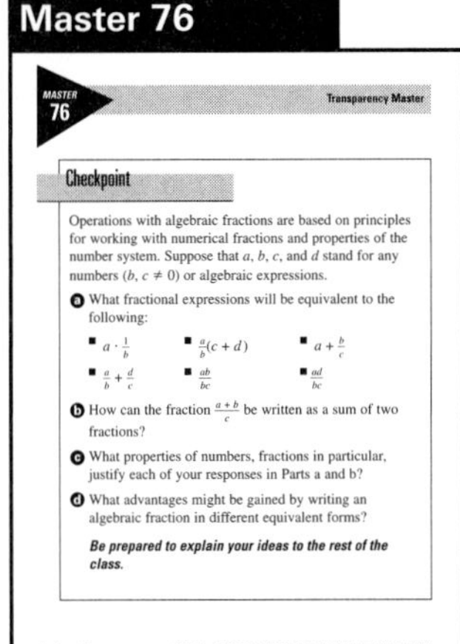
MASTER 76 Transparency Master

Checkpoint

Operations with algebraic fractions are based on principles for working with numerical fractions and properties of the number system. Suppose that a, b, c, and d stand for any numbers ($b, c \neq 0$) or algebraic expressions.

(a) What fractional expressions will be equivalent to the following:

- $a \cdot \frac{1}{b}$
- $\frac{a}{b}(c + d)$
- $a + \frac{b}{c}$
- $\frac{a}{b} + \frac{d}{c}$
- $\frac{ab}{bc}$
- $\frac{ad}{bc}$

(b) How can the fraction $\frac{a+b}{c}$ be written as a sum of two fractions?

(c) What properties of numbers, fractions in particular, justify each of your responses in Parts a and b?

(d) What advantages might be gained by writing an algebraic fraction in different equivalent forms?

Be prepared to explain your ideas to the rest of the class.

Use with page 217.

UNIT 3 • SYMBOL SENSE AND ALGEBRAIC REASONING

EXPLORE *continued*

3. **This activity might be difficult for students since they have had limited formal introduction to these properties. Responses will probably use less formal vocabulary, but where the thinking is correct, such responses should be accepted.**
   a. Step 1 Numerical factoring or definition of division
   Step 2 Distributive property
   Step 3 Definition of division
   b. Step 1 Multiplication
   Step 2 Simplification
   Step 3 Rules for dividing exponential expressions
   c. Step 1 Expressing two fractions with a common denominator
   Step 2 Distributive property or Subraction of fractions
   d. Step 1 Definition of division
   Step 2 Distributive property
   e. Step 1 Distributive property
   Step 2 Multiplication
   f. Step 1 Distributive property
   Step 2 Division and rules for dividing exponential expressions

4. **a.** When dividing by $3x$, each term in the numerator needs to be divided by the $3x$, not just the first term. The expression equivalent to the first is $5x + \frac{7}{3x}$.
   b. Each term in the numerator needs to be divided by all of the denominator.
   $\frac{4x^2 + 32x}{4x} = \frac{4x^2}{4x} + \frac{32x}{4x} = x + 8$
   c. Each term in the numerator needs to be divided by the entire denominator.
   $\frac{6x^2 + 12}{2x + 3} = \frac{6x^2}{2x + 3} + \frac{12}{2x + 3}$
   d. You can't separate the terms in the denominator. $\frac{6x^2}{2x + 3}$ can't be simplified at all.

SHARE AND SUMMARIZE full-class discussion

Checkpoint

See Teaching Master 76.

(a)
- $a \cdot \frac{1}{b} = \frac{a}{b}$
- $\frac{a}{b}(c + d) = \frac{a(c + d)}{b} = \frac{ac + ad}{b} = \frac{1}{b}(ac + ad)$
- $a + \frac{b}{c} = \frac{ac}{c} + \frac{b}{c} = \frac{ac + b}{c} = \frac{1}{c}(ac + b)$
- $\frac{a}{b} + \frac{d}{c} = \frac{ac}{bc} + \frac{bd}{bc} = \frac{ac + bd}{bc} = \frac{1}{bc}(ac + bd)$
- $\frac{ab}{bc} = \frac{ab}{cb} = \frac{a}{c} = \frac{1}{c}(a)$
- $\frac{ad}{bc} = (a)\frac{d}{bc} = (ad)\frac{1}{bc} = \frac{1}{b} \cdot \frac{ad}{c} = \frac{1}{bc} \cdot \frac{ad}{1} = \frac{1}{c} \cdot \frac{ad}{b} = \frac{a}{b} \cdot \frac{d}{c} = \frac{a}{c} \cdot \frac{d}{b}$

(b) Distribute the denominator to each term of the numerator:

$$\frac{a + b}{c} = \frac{1}{c}(a + b) = \frac{a}{c} + \frac{b}{c}$$

(c) Dividing by a number is the same as multiplying by its inverse.

A fraction with several terms in the numerator can be rewritten as a sum of fractions with one term each in the numerator. (This is because of the distributive property.)

To add fractions, you can rewrite the fractions with a common denominator, add the numerators, and put that sum over the common denominator. (Again, this is because of the distributive property.)

(d) Different forms of an algebraic fraction offer different advantages. For example, one form might give more information about an actual situation, another form might be easiest to calculate with, while yet another form might give insights into the shape of the graph or the limits of the function.

CONSTRUCTING A MATH TOOLKIT: Students should write a summary of how working with algebraic fractions is similar to and different from working with numerical fractions, including specific examples from Investigation 3.

Unit 3

3. Study each of the following procedures to write algebraic fractions in equivalent forms. In Parts b, c, and f, assume $x \neq 0$. Identify the algebraic properties and properties of fractions that justify each step.

a. $\frac{2}{3} + \frac{5x}{3} = 2\left(\frac{1}{3}\right) + 5x\left(\frac{1}{3}\right)$
$= (2 + 5x)\left(\frac{1}{3}\right)$
$= \frac{2 + 5x}{3}$

b. $\left(\frac{4x^2}{15}\right)\left(\frac{25}{x}\right) = \frac{100x^2}{15x}$
$= \frac{20x^2}{3x}$
$= \frac{20x}{3}$

c. $\frac{2}{3} - \frac{5}{x} = \frac{2x}{3x} - \frac{15}{3x}$
$= \frac{2x - 15}{3x}$

d. $\frac{3}{5}(7x^2 + 8x) = \frac{3(7x^2 + 8x)}{5}$
$= \frac{21x^2 + 24x}{5}$

e. $\frac{3}{5}(7x^2 + 8x) = \frac{3}{5}(7x^2) + \frac{3}{5}(8x)$
$= \frac{21x^2}{5} + \frac{24x}{5}$

f. $\frac{8x^2 + 32x}{4x} = \frac{8x^2}{4x} + \frac{32x}{4x}$
$= 2x + 8$

4. Just as there are some common errors in manipulation of linear and quadratic algebraic expressions, there are some common and tempting errors in work with algebraic fractions. Study the following examples and explain why each pair of expressions is not equivalent. In Parts a and b, assume $x \neq 0$. In Parts c and d, assume $x \neq -\frac{3}{2}$.

a. Why is $\frac{15x^2 + 7}{3x}$ *not* equivalent to $5x + 7$?

b. Why is $\frac{4x^2 + 32x}{4x}$ *not* equivalent to $x^2 + 32$?

c. Why is $\frac{6x^2 + 12}{2x + 3}$ *not* equivalent to $3x + 4$?

d. Why is $\frac{6x^2}{2x + 3}$ *not* equivalent to $3x + 2x^2$?

Checkpoint

Operations with algebraic fractions are based on principles for working with numerical fractions and properties of the number system. Suppose that a, b, c, and d stand for any numbers ($b, c \neq 0$) or algebraic expressions.

a What fractional expressions will be equivalent to the following:

- $a \cdot \frac{1}{b}$
- $\frac{a}{b}(c + d)$
- $a + \frac{b}{c}$
- $\frac{a}{b} + \frac{d}{c}$
- $\frac{ab}{bc}$
- $\frac{ad}{bc}$

b How can the fraction $\frac{a + b}{c}$ be written as a sum of two fractions?

c What properties of numbers, fractions in particular, justify each of your responses in Parts a and b?

d What advantages might be gained by writing an algebraic fraction in different equivalent forms?

Be prepared to explain your ideas to the rest of the class.

Unit 3

LESSON 3 • ALGEBRAIC OPERATIONS: PART 2 217

On Your Own

Use what you have learned about equivalent forms of algebraic fractions to complete the following tasks.

a. Write each of the following expressions in equivalent form as a single algebraic fraction. Assume $x \neq 0$ where necessary.

- $\frac{7}{9} + \frac{11}{x}$
- $\frac{3}{4}(5x + 7)$
- $\left(\frac{2x^2}{5}\right)\left(\frac{10}{7x}\right)$

b. Write each of these expressions in equivalent form as a sum of two or more algebraic fractions, each in simplest possible form:

- $\frac{125 + x}{5}$
- $\frac{6x^2 + 3x}{3x}\ (x \neq 0)$
- $\frac{27p^4 + 9p^2 + 3}{9p^2}\ (p \neq 0)$
- $\frac{36x + 72x^2}{36x}\ (x \neq 0)$

MORE

Modeling • Organizing • Reflecting • Extending

Modeling

1. When you have the rule for a function relating height and time of a moving object, you can use tables, graphs, and algebraic reasoning to deduce information about the motion. Explain each step in the following argument that uses given information to create a rule relating height and time for the flight of a softball hit into the air.

   a. The ball was hit from near ground level and returned to the ground 4 seconds later. In building a model for the (*time*, *height*) relationship, why does it make sense to start with $h(t) = t(t - 4)$?

   b. Why is the rule in Part a equivalent to $h(t) = t^2 - 4t$?

   c. To account for the effect of Earth's gravity, we need a factor of –16, so a better model might be $h(t) = -16(t^2 - 4t)$. Why is this revised model equivalent to $h(t) = -16t^2 + 64t$?

   d. Why does the model in Part c imply that the initial velocity of the ball must have been 64 feet per second? Why does it also suggest that the ball reached a maximum height of 64 feet?

Unit 3

218 UNIT 3 • SYMBOL SENSE AND ALGEBRAIC REASONING

APPLY individual task

On Your Own

At this point, students may not realize that they need to point out the domain restrictions in some of these cases. This issue is examined in Organizing Task 3, page 221.

a.
- $\frac{7x + 99}{9x}$ $(x \neq 0)$
- $\frac{15x + 21}{4}$
- $\frac{4x}{7}$ $(x \neq 0)$

b.
- $25 + \frac{x}{5}$
- $3p^2 + 1 + \frac{1}{3p^2}$ $(p \neq 0)$
- $2x + 1$ $(x \neq 0)$
- $1 + 2x$ $(x \neq 0)$

MORE independent assignment

Modeling

1. a. This equation makes sense because you know that the ball was on the ground to begin ($h(t) = 0$) and that it returned to the ground 4 seconds later.

b. If you apply the distributive property to the right-hand side of the equation from Part a, the result is $t^2 - 4t$.

c. Applying the distributive property results in the second equation.

d. In the model for projectile motion, the coefficient of the first-degree term is the initial velocity of the object. In this case, that means the initial velocity of the ball was 64 feet per second. The ball reached a maximum height at two seconds since it hit the ground after 4 seconds. By substituting 2 for t in the model in Part c, you find that the maximum height is 64 feet.

MORE ASSIGNMENT *pp. 218–224*

Modeling: 3 and choice of one*
Organizing: 1, 2, and 3
Reflecting: 2 and 4
Extending: Choose one*

**When choice is indicated, it is important to leave the choice to the student.*
NOTE: *It is best if Organizing tasks are discussed as a whole class after they have been assigned as homework.*

2. **a.** The total operating costs as a function of miles driven can be represented by $C(m) = 4{,}000 + 0.36m$.

   b. The cost per mile as a function of miles driven can be represented by:

   $$C(m) = \frac{4{,}000 + 0.36m}{m}$$

   or

   $$C(m) = \frac{4{,}000}{m} + 0.36$$

   c. The first equation above is more informative, and the second is more convenient for calculation.

   d. The cost per mile decreases at a decreasing rate, possibly approaching a lower bound or limit below which it cannot fall. This can be predicted from the rule itself since it is similar to an inverse variation function. From either equation $C(m) = \frac{4{,}000 + 0.36m}{m}$ or $C(m) = \frac{4{,}000}{m} + 0.36$, you can see that as m becomes very large, the value of the function approaches 0.36.

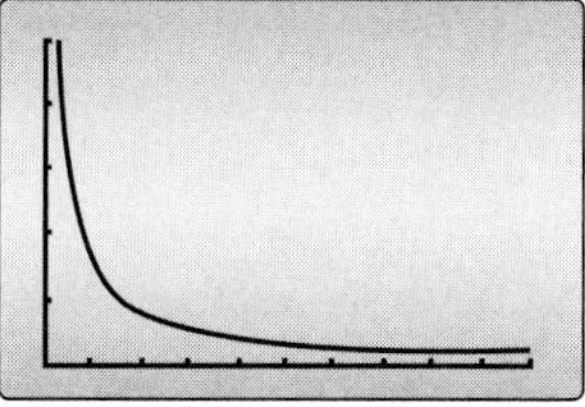

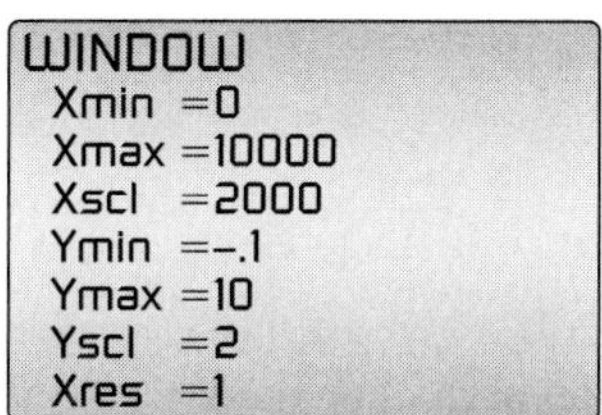

3. **a.** $2x^2 + 4hx = 1{,}000$

   b. $h = \frac{1{,}000 - 2x^2}{4x}$

   c. $h = \frac{1}{4x}(1{,}000 - 2x^2)$

   $h = \frac{250}{x} - \frac{x}{2}$

   d. Responses will vary, but $h = \frac{1{,}000 - 2x^2}{4x}$ is probably best since it shows the components that have led us to the relation.

   e. As the graph shows, the value of h decreases at a decreasing rate as the value of x increases. When x equals $\sqrt{500}$, the height will be zero.

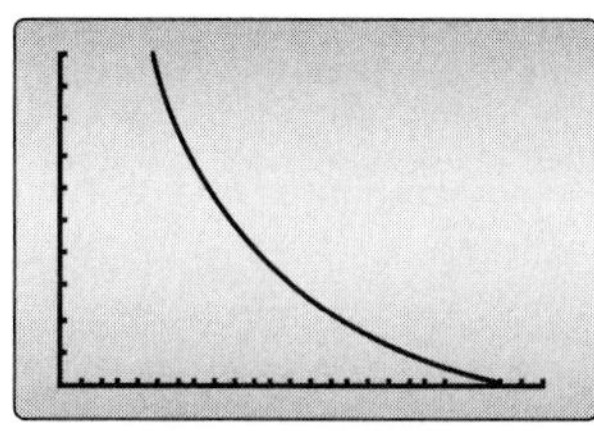

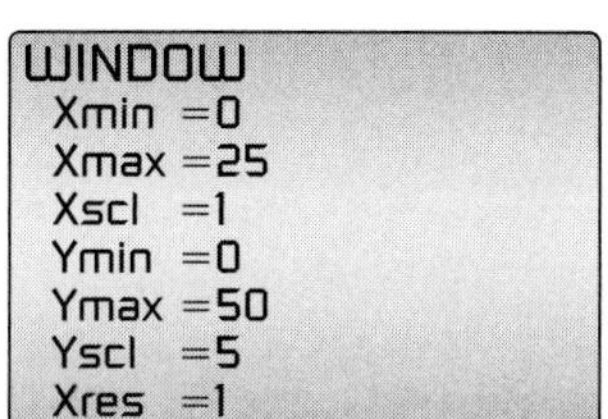

When you examine the equation $h = \frac{250}{x} - \frac{x}{2}$ as x gets very large, the value of h approaches $-\frac{x}{2}$. The graph approaches this line in the fourth quadrant, but this does not have much meaning for the physical model because for values of x greater than $\sqrt{500}$, there is not a box.

Unit 3

2. When a pizza restaurant leased a small truck for home deliveries, the lease cost \$4,000 for a year. Operation of the truck, including maintenance, averaged about \$0.36 per mile of operation. Thus, annual cost for the delivery truck depended on the number of miles it was driven.

   a. Write a function rule giving total operating costs as a function of the number of miles m that the truck was driven.

   b. Write a function rule giving cost per mile as a function of the number of miles m the truck was driven. Then write that rule in a different but equivalent form.

   c. Which of the two forms in Part b do you believe is more informative, and which is more convenient for calculation?

   d. Sketch a graph of the per-mile cost function for as many as 20,000 miles per year, and explain what the shape of that graph says about how cost per mile changes as the number of miles increases. Explain also how that pattern could be predicted by inspecting either of the rule forms themselves.

3. Suppose that in designing packaging for one of its products, the Miracle-Gro® fertilizer company wants a package to be made from 1,000 cm^2 of cardboard. The company also wants the box to have a square base as indicated by the sketch on the right.

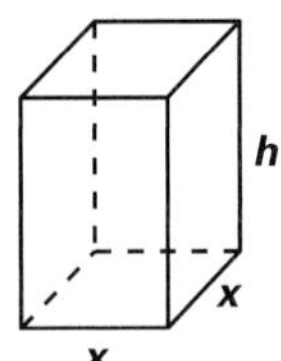

   a. Write an equation showing the relation between the surface area 1,000, the height h, and the base edge lengths x of the proposed container.

   b. Write another equation showing height h as a function of the base edge length x.

   c. Show how the expression for h in Part b can be written in several other equivalent forms.

   d. Which of the expressions for h in Parts b and c seems to best describe the relation between x and h?

   e. Use one of your expressions for height as a function of fixed area and base edge length to produce a graph that shows the way height changes as edge length changes. Explain how you can predict the pattern of that graph by analyzing the symbolic expressions for h.

LESSON 3 • ALGEBRAIC OPERATIONS: PART 2 219

4. In Investigation 2 of this lesson, you examined an area model for representing and factoring perfect square polynomials. The expression $x^3 + 15x^2 + 75x + 125$ can be represented by a volume model as shown at the right. This polynomial is an example of a *perfect cube polynomial*.

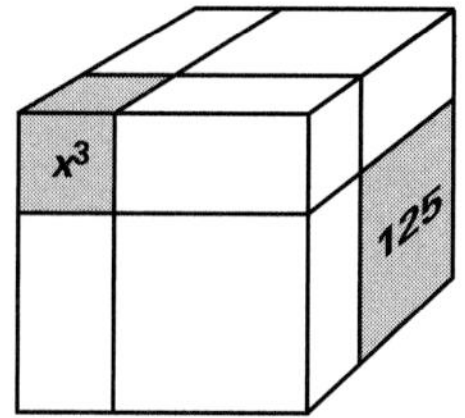

a. Explain why the volume of this cube can be represented by

$$x^3 + 15x^2 + 75x + 125.$$

b. Write a factored-form expression giving the volume of this cube.

c. Give an example of another perfect cube polynomial. Draw a sketch illustrating how you know it is a perfect cube.

Organizing

1. Write the following expressions in equivalent forms that meet the specified conditions.

a. Write these in standard polynomial form:

- $(x + 3)(x + 5)$
- $(2m - 4)(m + 8)$
- $(r - 7)(r + 7)$
- $(x + 12)^2$
- $(t - 8)^2$
- $(w + 5)(w - 3)$
- $(x - 4)(x - 1)$
- $(2v + 3)(4 - v)$
- $(3x + 2)(x^2 + 4x - 5)$

b. Write these in factored form:

- $x^2 - 121$
- $p^2 - 121p$
- $x^2 + 9x + 18$
- $r^2 + 6r + 9$
- $x^2 - 9x + 18$

Unit 3

220 UNIT 3 • SYMBOL SENSE AND ALGEBRAIC REASONING

MORE *continued*

4. **a.** The volume of each part of the cube is shown on the cube below. The unseen corner (bottom, back, and left-hand part) of the cube has volume $25x$.

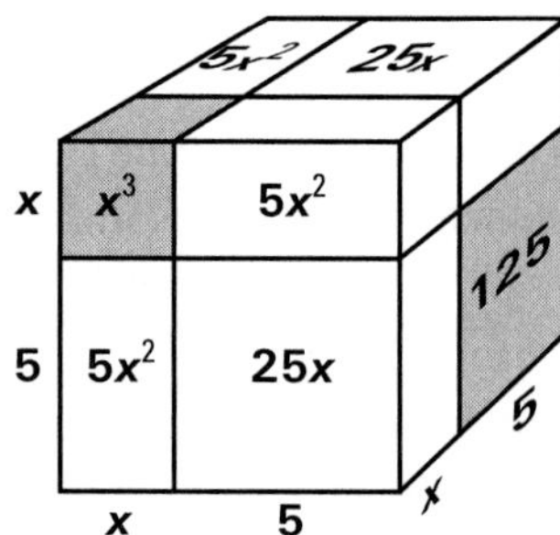

The sum of the parts is equal to the volume of the cube. Thus, the volume is $x^3 + 3(5x^2) + 3(25x) + 125$ or $x^3 + 15x^2 + 75x + 125$.

b. $V(x) = (x + 5)^3$

c. Responses will vary. Sketches should be similar to the diagram in Part a of this activity.

Organizing

1. **a.**
- $x^2 + 8x + 15$
- $2m^2 + 12m - 32$
- $r^2 - 49$
- $x^2 + 24x + 144$
- $t^2 - 16t + 64$
- $w^2 + 2w - 15$
- $x^2 - 5x + 4$
- $-2v^2 + 5v + 12$
- $3x^3 + 14x^2 - 7x - 10$

b.
- $(x + 11)(x - 11)$
- $p(p - 121)$
- $(x + 3)(x + 6)$
- $(r + 3)^2$
- $(x - 3)(x - 6)$

Unit 3

2. **a.** $x = 11, -11$

b. $x = -3, -6$

c. $x = -3, -5$

d. $x = 3, 6$

e. $x = 0, 121$

3. **a.** Consider $\frac{0}{4} = a$. This implies that $4a = 0$, which implies that $a = 0$. Thus, $\frac{0}{4} = 0$. Now consider the equation $\frac{4}{0} = b$. This implies that $b \cdot 0 = 4$. But it is impossible to multiply by 0 and get 4. Thus, $\frac{4}{0}$ is undefined.

b.
- $f(x)$ is never 0; $f(0)$ is undefined.
- $f(-2) = 0$; $f(0)$ is undefined.
- $f(7) = 0$; $f(-8)$ is undefined.
- $f(0) = 0$; $f(3)$ and $f\left(-\frac{1}{2}\right)$ are undefined.

4. One example of each rule follows.

a. $f(x) = (x - 13)(x - 10)$

b. $f(x) = \frac{x-1}{x+2}$

c. $f(x) = x(x - 12)$

d. $f(x) = (x + 3)^2$

e. $f(x) = (x + 15)(x - 15)$ or $f(x) = x^2 - 225$

5. **a.** The graph crosses the x-axis at 7 and –3. It is a parabola opening up with axis of symmetry $x = 2$. The minimum value of the function is –25.

b. As x approaches positive or negative infinity, $f(x)$ approaches 7. The graph of the function never crosses the x-axis because the value of the function never equals 0; in fact, the graph has a vertical asymptote at $x = 0$. Some students may say this will be the graph of $y = \frac{1}{x}$ stretched by 3 and shifted up 7.

c. The function is not defined and has a vertical asymptote for $x = -2$. The graph crosses the x-axis when $x = 5$.

d. The function is a parabola that opens upward and crosses the x-axis at 9 and –9. The vertex is at (0, –81), and the minimum value for the function is –81. Some students may say that this is the graph of $y = x^2$ shifted down 81, but they should include the fact that the x-intercepts are at 9 and –9.

2. Solve the following equations using symbolic reasoning alone.

a. $x^2 - 121 = 0$

b. $x^2 + 9x + 18 = 0$

c. $(x + 3)(x + 5) = 0$

d. $x^2 - 9x + 18 = 0$

e. $x^2 - 121x = 0$

3. From your study of fractions, you should recall that $\frac{0}{4} = 0$ and $\frac{4}{0}$ is undefined.

a. The connection between multiplication and division guarantees that for any nonzero numbers a and b, $\frac{a}{b} = c$ is equivalent to $a = bc$. Show that if this relation is to hold for any values of a and b, then $\frac{0}{4}$ must equal 0 and $\frac{4}{0}$ must be undefined. (**Hint:** If $0 = 4c$, what must be true of c? If $4 = 0c$, what must be true of c?)

b. Use the above idea to determine values of x for which the following function rules are equal to 0 and for which they are undefined. When a function rule is undefined for some values of the input variable, those input values must be excluded from the domain of the function.

- $f(x) = \frac{8}{x}$
- $f(x) = \frac{x + 2}{3x}$
- $f(x) = \frac{x - 7}{x + 8}$
- $f(x) = \frac{x}{(x - 3)(2x + 1)}$

4. Write polynomial or fractional function rules with the following properties.

a. $f(13) = 0$ and $f(10) = 0$.

b. $f(1) = 0$ and $f(-2)$ is undefined.

c. $f(0) = 0$ and $f(12) = 0$.

d. $f(x)$ is a quadratic function and $f(x) = 0$ only when $x = -3$.

e. $f(15) = 0$ and $f(-15) = 0$.

5. Using symbolic reasoning alone, what information can you determine about the graph of $f(x)$ in the following cases?

a. $f(x) = (x - 7)(x + 3)$

b. $f(x) = 7 + \frac{3}{x}$

c. $f(x) = \frac{x - 5}{x + 2}$

d. $f(x) = x^2 - 81$

LESSON 3 • ALGEBRAIC OPERATIONS: PART 2 221

Reflecting

1. What does it mean to say a quadratic expression is factorable? How could you convince a classmate that a particular quadratic expression is not factorable?

2. Suppose a function has a symbolic rule in the form $f(x) = (x - a)(x + b)$.

   a. How can you tell immediately the values of x for which $f(x) = 0$?

   b. What property of zero and multiplication is used in your answer to Part a?

   c. How do you find the corresponding zero if one of the factors of $f(x)$ is a linear expression like $(cx + d)$?

3. Compare the calculations involved in evaluating fractional expressions of these two types: $\frac{r+s}{t}$ and $m + \frac{n}{k}$.

   a. If you use a calculator to evaluate such expressions when specific values of the variables are given, what sequences of keystrokes would you use?

   b. Which form is easier to use for finding values of the variables that make the fractions 0? For finding values for which the fractions are undefined?

   c. What general operations are required to write fractions of the first type in the form of the second type and vice versa?

4. By now you've learned how to test equivalence of algebraic function rules by comparing calculator tables and graphs and by analyzing the symbolic expressions themselves.

   a. How do you decide which method (tables, graphs, or symbol manipulation) to use in a given situation?

   b. What can be learned from each method that is not clear from the others?

5. Study the algebraic reasoning used in the *Peanuts* cartoon below.

PEANUTS reprinted by permission of United Feature Syndicate, Inc.

   a. Is the building's factorization correct? If not, identify the error in its reasoning.

   b. What do you think was the key idea that enabled the building to get started on this problem? If possible, give an example of another higher-degree polynomial to which this idea could be applied.

Unit 3

222 UNIT 3 • SYMBOL SENSE AND ALGEBRAIC REASONING

Reflecting

1. A quadratic expression is factorable if it can be expressed as the product of two linear expressions. The easiest way to show that a quadratic is not factorable is to graph the related function and show that it does not cross the x-axis.
2. **a.** Set each factor equal to 0 and solve. If $f(x) = (x - a)(x + b)$, then $f(x) = 0$ when $x = a, -b$.
   b. The product of two numbers is 0 if and only if at least one of the numbers is 0.
   c. Set the factor equal to zero and solve: $cx + d = 0$, $cx = -d$, $x = -\frac{d}{c}$.
3. **a.** To evaluate $\frac{r+s}{t}$, press r [+] s, then [ENTER], then [÷] t; or press [(] r [+] s [)] [÷] t and then [ENTER].
   To evaluate $m + \frac{n}{k}$, press n [÷] k, then [ENTER], then [+] m; or press m [+] [(] n [÷] k [)] and then [ENTER].
   b. The first form is probably easier for finding values for which the expression is equal to 0. In that case, the numerator would be 0, which means that $r = -s$. For the second form, the expression is 0 when $m = -\frac{n}{k}$ or when $mk = -n$. For finding the values for which the expression is not defined, either form will do; just examine the denominators. In the first form, the expression is not defined when t is 0, and in the second form, the expression is not defined when k is 0.
   c. To change from the first type to the second, separate the expression into parts by taking the expressions in the numerator and writing them with the common denominator. To change from the second type to the first, write both expressions with a common denominator and then combine the numerators of the two fractions, putting that sum over the common denominator.
4. **a.** Responses will vary. Students need to be careful in deciding which method to use to test equivalency of algebraic function rules. If they are using graphs, do they have the complete graph, or are there missing parts that might lead to the wrong conclusion? For tables, they want to be sure that they examine enough parts so that the big picture is correct. If using rules, they need to put the equations in the same form so that they are not misled because the equations look different. The easiest way to do this is to put the rules in simplest form.
   b. The graphs will tell you right away if the equations are different; however, if they appear to be the same, you must be very careful to check all regions. The tables may indicate undefined points by showing error messages. If you have a line with a point missing, the table can be very helpful in pointing this out. The important thing is to make sure that you actually examine the relevant part of the table.
   The symbolic forms indicate which parts of the table need to be examined carefully, and the only way to *prove* that two algebraic function rules are the same is to do some careful algebraic manipulation with the symbolic forms. The rules should be written in the same form to be sure that they are the same.
5. **a.** Yes, the building's factorization is correct.
   b. The building was able to get started on the problem because it recognized the original expression as the difference of two squares. Examples will vary.

Extending

1. a. $x^2 + 2hx + h^2$

   b. ■ $(x + 5)^2$

   ■ Cannot be written in the required form

   ■ $(x - 5)^2$

   ■ $(x + 6)^2$

   ■ Cannot be written in the required form

2. a. $m^2x^2 + 2mhx + h^2$

   b. ■ $(3x + 2)^2$

   ■ $(2x - 1)^2$

   ■ $(7x + 3)^2$

3. a. This graph will be a parabola that passes through the origin. If *ab* is positive, the graph will open upward; and if the product is negative, the graph will open downward.

   The table will contain the point (0, 0). Other than 0, the function values will be either all positive or all negative, depending on whether the product *ab* is positive or negative. The table will show that the rate of change is not constant.

   b. The graph will be a parabola that crosses the *x*-axis at $-\frac{b}{a}$ and at $-\frac{d}{c}$. The parabola will have an axis of symmetry at $x = \left(\frac{-\frac{b}{a} - \frac{d}{c}}{2}\right)$. If *ac* is positive, the curve will open upward; if *ac* is negative, the curve will open downward.

   The table will contain the points $\left(-\frac{b}{a}, 0\right)$ and $\left(-\frac{d}{c}, 0\right)$. The table will also show that there is not a constant rate of change.

   c. The graph will be a line with slope $\frac{a}{b}$. The graph will look like it passes through the origin, but actually there is a hole in the graph at this point because the function is not defined when $x = 0$.

   The table shows a constant rate of change. The function is not defined for $x = 0$, so there is an error message on the calculator for this value of *x*.

   d. The graph will approximate a line with slope $\frac{a}{d}$ for very large (positive or negative) values of *x*. The graph is not defined and has a vertical asymptote for $x = -\frac{e}{d}$. As *x* gets very close to $-\frac{e}{d}$, the table of values changes very rapidly; but as *x* is further away from this value, the rate of change comes closer to a constant $\left(\frac{a}{d}\right)$.

Extending

1. Consider all quadratics of the type $(x + h)^2$, where x is the input variable and h is a fixed number.

a. Expand that expression into an equivalent expression in standard polynomial form.

b. Compare the following quadratic polynomials to the pattern in Part a to identify those that can be written easily as squares of linear binomials in the form $(x + h)^2$.

- $x^2 + 10x + 25$
- $x^2 + 6x + 16$
- $x^2 - 10x + 25$
- $x^2 + 12x + 36$
- $x^2 - 7x + 49$

2. Consider quadratics of the type $(mx + h)^2$, where x is the input variable and m and h are fixed numbers.

a. Expand the expression $(mx + h)^2$ into an equivalent expression in standard polynomial form.

b. Compare the following quadratic polynomials to the pattern in Part a to identify those that can be written as squares of linear binomials in the form $(mx + h)^2$.

- $9x^2 + 12x + 4$
- $4x^2 - 4x + 1$
- $49x^2 + 42x + 9$

3. What sorts of tables and graphs do you expect for the following general types of function rules? Test your ideas with a number of specific examples, and then summarize and explain your findings.

a. Products like $y = (ax)(bx)$

b. Products like $y = (ax + b)(cx + d)$

c. Quotients like $y = \frac{ax^2}{bx}$

d. Quotients like $y = \frac{ax^2 + bx + c}{dx + e}$

Unit 3

LESSON 3 • ALGEBRAIC OPERATIONS: PART 2 223

4. When the Hindu mathematician Bhaskara (1114–1185) first recorded a diagram similar to the one below, no explanation other than the word "behold" was offered. If you view the diagram through the combined "lenses" of geometry and algebra, what do you see?

BEHOLD!

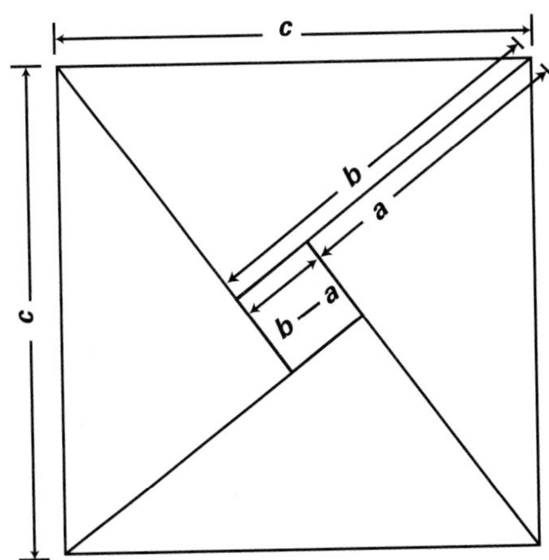

5. Justify each step in the following rewriting of a given quadratic $ax^2 + bx + c$ into a form that involves the square of a binomial and a constant term.

$$\begin{aligned} ax^2 + bx + c &= (ax^2 + bx) + c && (1) \\ &= a\left(x^2 + \frac{b}{a}x\right) + c && (2) \\ &= a\left(x^2 + \frac{b}{a}x + \frac{b^2}{4a^2}\right) + \left(c - \frac{b^2}{4a}\right) && (3) \\ &= a\left(x + \frac{b}{2a}\right)^2 + \left(c - \frac{b^2}{4a}\right) && (4) \\ &= a\left(x + \frac{b}{2a}\right)^2 + \left(\frac{4ac - b^2}{4a}\right) && (5) \end{aligned}$$

Unit 3

224 UNIT 3 • SYMBOL SENSE AND ALGEBRAIC REASONING

MORE *continued*

4. The outside figure is a square; assuming that the four triangles are congruent right triangles, we can write the following:

$$\begin{aligned} c^2 &= 4\left(\frac{1}{2}ab\right) + (b - a)^2 \\ &= 2ab + b^2 - 2ab + a^2 \\ &= b^2 + a^2 \end{aligned}$$

"BEHOLD!" We have another proof of the Pythagorean Theorem.

5. (1) Associative property of addition
   (2) Distributive property
   (3) The same expression has been both added and subtracted; commutative and associative properties were used.
   (4) The quadratic has been written as the square of a binomial.
   (5) Two expressions have been combined by writing them with a common denominator (distributive property). (You may want to ask students to explain what different forms of the equation tell about the graph of $y = ax^2 + bx + c$. Students will take this exercise to the next logical step, showing the derivation of the quadratic formula, in Lesson 5, page 242.)

See Assessment Resources pages 95–102.

Assessments 95–98

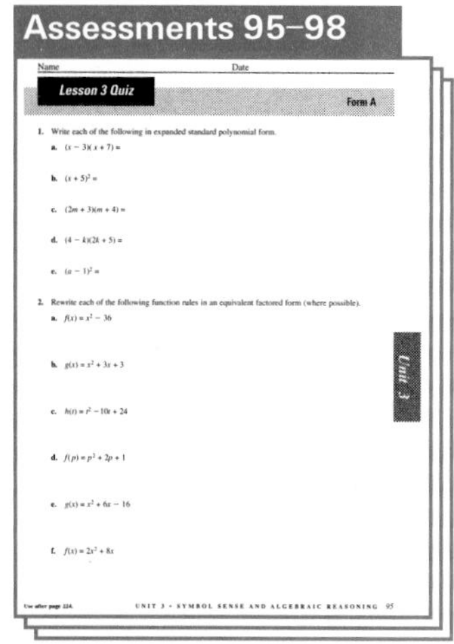
Name Date

Lesson 3 Quiz Form A

1. Write each of the following in expanded standard polynomial form.
   a. $(x - 3)(x + 7) =$
   b. $(x + 5)^2 =$
   c. $(2m + 3)(m + 4) =$
   d. $(4 - k)(2k + 5) =$
   e. $(a - 1)^2 =$
2. Rewrite each of the following function rules in an equivalent factored form (where possible).
   a. $f(x) = x^2 - 36$
   b. $g(x) = x^2 + 3x + 3$
   c. $h(t) = t^2 - 10t + 24$
   d. $f(p) = p^2 + 2p + 1$
   e. $g(x) = x^2 + 6x - 16$
   f. $f(x) = 2x^2 + 8x$

Unit 3

Use after page 224. UNIT 3 • SYMBOL SENSE AND ALGEBRAIC REASONING 95

Assessments 99–102

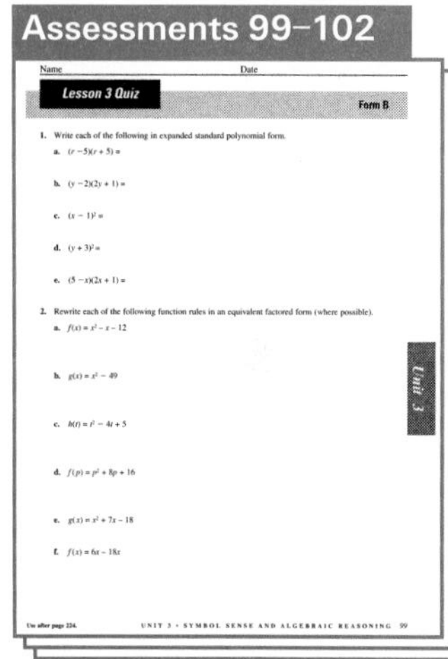
Name Date

Lesson 3 Quiz Form B

1. Write each of the following in expanded standard polynomial form.
   a. $(r - 5)(r + 5) =$
   b. $(y - 2)(2y + 1) =$
   c. $(x - 1)^2 =$
   d. $(y + 3)^2 =$
   e. $(5 - x)(2x + 1) =$
2. Rewrite each of the following function rules in an equivalent factored form (where possible).
   a. $f(x) = x^2 - x - 12$
   b. $g(x) = x^2 - 49$
   c. $h(t) = t^2 - 4t + 5$
   d. $f(p) = p^2 + 8p + 16$
   e. $g(x) = x^2 + 7x - 18$
   f. $f(x) = 6x - 18x$

Unit 3

Use after page 224. UNIT 3 • SYMBOL SENSE AND ALGEBRAIC REASONING 99

Unit 3

Master 77

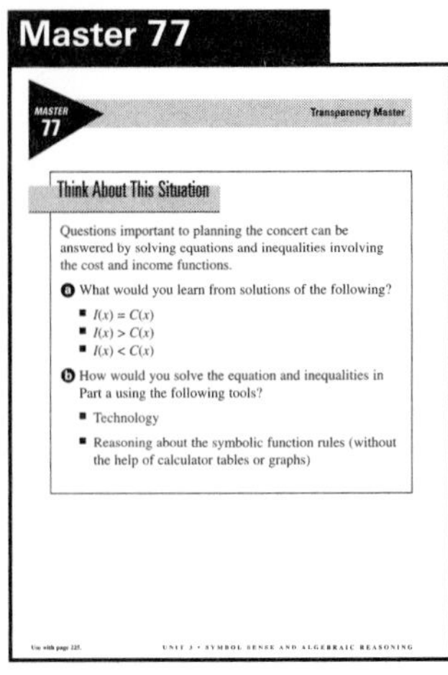

Lesson 4 *Reasoning to Solve Equations and Inequalities*

LESSON OVERVIEW **In this lesson, students develop symbolic methods for solving equations and inequalities by algebraic manipulation, including applying the quadratic formula. Students consider the appropriateness of answers about problems involving linear equations and inequalities. (Does the answer make sense, and does it seem reasonable?)**

In the second investigation of this lesson, students use the quadratic formula to solve quadratic equations that are not easily factored. The students discover that the equation of the axis of symmetry is $x = -\frac{b}{2a}$ and that the distance between the zeroes of a quadratic function is $2\left(\frac{\sqrt{b^2 - 4ac}}{2a}\right)$.

Lesson Objectives

- **To solve linear equations and inequalities using algebraic reasoning**
- **To identify whether a quadratic function has 0, 1, or 2 zeroes and to describe the graph of the function**
- **To solve quadratic equations and inequalities by using the quadratic formula**
- **To understand that for the quadratic function $f(x) = ax^2 + bx + c$ $(a \neq 0)$, $x = \frac{-b}{2a}$ is the equation for the axis of symmetry and the value $\frac{\sqrt{b^2 - 4ac}}{2a}$ is the distance between the zeroes of the function and the axis of symmetry**
- **To solve quadratic equations and inequalities by using the solve feature of a calculator or computer software**

LAUNCH **full-class discussion**

Think About This Situation

See Teaching Master 77.

a
- The solution of $I(x) = C(x)$ would be the ticket price for which the concert breaks even.
- The solution of $I(x) > C(x)$ identifies the ticket prices for which the concert will make a profit.
- The solution of $I(x) < C(x)$ identifies the ticket prices for which the concert will lose money.

See additional Teaching Notes on page T257J.

Unit 3

Lesson 4

Reasoning to Solve Equations and Inequalities

In earlier work in this unit, you modeled situations with several variables and equations. For example, suppose you were given business plans for a concert showing how operating cost and ticket sale income were expected to relate to ticket price x.

Cost: $C(x) = 22{,}500 - 100x$

Income: $I(x) = 2{,}500x - 50x^2$

A graph of those two functions looks like this:

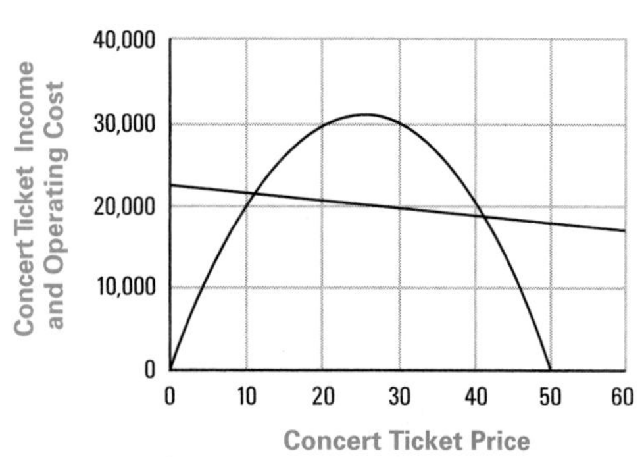

Think About This Situation

Questions important to planning the concert can be answered by solving equations and inequalities involving the cost and income functions.

a What would you learn from solutions of the following?

- $I(x) = C(x)$
- $I(x) > C(x)$
- $I(x) < C(x)$

b How would you solve the equation and inequalities in Part a using the following tools?

- Technology
- Reasoning about the symbolic function rules (without the help of calculator tables or graphs)

Unit 3

LESSON 4 • REASONING TO SOLVE EQUATIONS AND INEQUALITIES 225

INVESTIGATION 1 Reasoning about Linear Equations and Inequalities

Situations involving comparison of business plans often involve linear functions, leading to questions requiring the solution of linear equations and inequalities. For example, a pizza company considering lease options for a delivery truck might have choices like those shown below. In each case, the lease cost (in dollars) is a function of lease time (in weeks).

Plan A: $A(t) = 2{,}500 + 75t$

Plan B: $B(t) = 1{,}000 + 90t$

1. What do the numbers 2,500 and 1,000 tell about the conditions of each lease? What do the numbers 75 and 90 tell?

2. At the start, Plan A is more expensive than Plan B. To see when the lease costs might be equal, you could solve the equation $2{,}500 + 75t = 1{,}000 + 90t$. One way to solve that equation is to reason like this:

$$2{,}500 + 75t = 1{,}000 + 90t$$
$$1{,}500 + 75t = 90t$$
$$1{,}500 = 15t$$
$$100 = t$$

a. Justify each step in the solution process.

b. How can you check that $t = 100$ is the solution? What does $t = 100$ tell about the truck-lease plans?

c. How could you arrive at the same result with a different sequence of steps?

3. Now, consider the inequality $2{,}500 + 75t < 1{,}000 + 90t$.

a. What will a solution to this inequality tell about the truck-leasing situation?

b. Why does each step in the following reasoning make sense?

$$2{,}500 + 75t < 1{,}000 + 90t$$
$$2{,}500 < 1{,}000 + 15t$$
$$1{,}500 < 15t$$
$$100 < t$$

c. What does the solution $100 < t$ tell about the truck-leasing situation?

d. How can you check the solution?

e. Use similar reasoning to solve the inequality $2{,}500 + 75t > 1{,}000 + 90t$, and explain what the solution tells about the truck-leasing situation.

226 UNIT 3 • SYMBOL SENSE AND ALGEBRAIC REASONING

EXPLORE small-group investigation

INVESTIGATION 1 Reasoning about Linear Equations and Inequalities

In this investigation, students will revisit the properties of equality, which were developed in the "Multiple-Variable Models" unit, and use them to solve linear equations and inequalities. They are encouraged to see technological and symbolic solutions as complementary. In each case, students are asked to make sense of and check their solutions.

You might want to begin by revisiting equations solved in the "Multiple-Variable Models" unit. Ask, "Here are three equations or inequalities you have seen before: $ax + by = c$; $ax = by$; $2x + 3y < z$. How did we solve these for y? What logical reasoning justified the steps? Why might we want to solve these for y?" Since almost all of this investigation is a review of previous ideas, the atmosphere in the classroom will probably be one of confirmation and consolidation, rather than exploration.

1. 2,500 and 1,000 both represent the initial cost. 75 and 90 represent the weekly costs over the time periods of the leases.

2. **a.**

$1{,}500 + 75t = 90t$	Addition/subtraction property of equality
$1{,}500 = 15t$	Addition/subtraction property of equality
$100 = t$	Multiplication/division property of equality

b. Responses may vary. The simplest way is to substitute this value into the original equation. The solution means that the two plans will cost the same if the length of the lease plan is 100 weeks.

c. Responses will vary. It is important for students to realize that there is more than one path to the correct solution of equations.

3. **a.** The solution to this inequality will tell the lengths of the lease plans for which Plan B costs more than Plan A.

b.

$2{,}500 < 1{,}000 + 15t$	Addition/subtraction property of inequality
$1{,}500 < 15t$	Addition/subtraction property of inequality
$100 < t$	Multiplication/division property of inequality

c. Plan A costs less when the length of the lease plan exceeds 100 weeks.

d. Responses may vary. This solution can be checked by substitution, graphing, or looking at tables of values.

e. The solution is $t < 100$. This tells us that Plan B costs less for lease plans that are shorter than 100 weeks.

Unit 3

EXPLORE *continued*

4. **a.** $x = 30$ Addition/subtraction property of equality (twice)
   b. $14 = 7x$ Addition/subtraction property of equality (twice)
   $x = 2$ Multiplication/division property of equality
   c. $7x = 21$ Addition/subtraction property of equality
   $x = 3$ Multiplication/division property of equality
   d. $-25 = 10x$ Addition/subtraction property of equality (twice)
   $x = -2.5$ Multiplication/division property of equality
   e. $5x = -15$ Addition/subtraction property of equality (twice)
   $x = -3$ Multiplication/division property of equality
5. **a.** $3x < 4$ Addition/subtraction property of inequality
   $x < \frac{4}{3}$ Multiplication/division property of inequality
   b. $5x > 10$ Addition/subtraction property of inequality
   $x > 2$ Multiplication/division property of inequality
   c. $8x < 34$ Addition/subtraction property of inequality
   $x < \frac{17}{4}$ Multiplication/division property of inequality
   d. $6x > 120$ Addition/subtraction property of inequality
   $x > 20$ Multiplication/division property of inequality
6. **This property of inequalities was introduced in an Extending Task in Unit 1, "Multiple-Variable Models." It is formalized here and in the Checkpoint.**
   a–c. Students may show that each proposed solution is not correct in a variety of ways. They might look at the graphs or the tables of values, or they might substitute into the inequality a value that is in the identified solution set and show that it does not satisfy the inequality. The error in each part occurs when dividing by the negative coefficient of x in the last step of the solution. At that point, the inequality sign should be reversed.
7. **a.** $6 < 2x$ Addition/subtraction property of inequality (twice)
   $x > 3$ Multiplication/division property of inequality
   b. $36 > 12x$ Addition/subtraction property of inequality (twice)
   $x < 3$ Multiplication/division property of inequality
   c. $17x < 34$ Addition/subtraction property of inequality (twice)
   $x < 2$ Multiplication/division property of inequality
   d. $95 > 15x$ Addition/subtraction property of inequality (twice)
   $x < 6\frac{1}{3}$ Multiplication/division property of inequality

In solving the equations and inequalities that compare two truck-lease plans, it is helpful to keep in mind what the parts of each expression mean. Now try to use similar reasoning patterns to solve equations and inequalities without such clues.

4. Solve each of the following equations by symbolic reasoning alone. Record each step in your reasoning. Check your solutions.

a. $2x + 15 = 45 + x$

b. $10 - 4x = 3x - 4$

c. $7x - 11 = 10$

d. $-6x - 15 = 4x + 10$

e. $25 = 10 - 5x$

5. Solve each of the following inequalities by symbolic reasoning alone. Record each step in your reasoning. Check your answers.

a. $3x + 10 < 14$

b. $13 + 5x > 23$

c. $8x + 12 < 46$

d. $80 + 6x > 200$

6. Here are three solutions of inequalities that lead to incorrect results. In each case, show with function tables or graphs that the proposed solutions are not correct. Then find and correct the error in the reasoning process.

a. Solve:

$$5x + 20 < 3x$$
$$20 < -2x$$
$$-10 < x$$

b. Solve:

$$11x - 19 < 15x + 17$$
$$11x < 15x + 36$$
$$-4x < 36$$
$$x < -9$$

c. Solve:

$$10 + 9x < 3x - 8$$
$$18 + 9x < 3x$$
$$18 < -6x$$
$$-3 < x$$

7. Solve each of the following inequalities by symbolic reasoning alone. Show each step in your reasoning. Check your answers.

a. $3x + 10 < 5x + 4$

b. $23 - 5x > 7x - 13$

c. $8x + 12 < 46 - 9x$

d. $80 + 6x > 21x - 15$

Unit 3

LESSON 4 • REASONING TO SOLVE EQUATIONS AND INEQUALITIES 227

Two equations or inequalities are called **equivalent** if they have identical solutions. One strategy for solving linear equations and inequalities is to start with the given equation or inequality and construct a sequence of simpler forms, each equivalent to its predecessor, until you get an equation or inequality so simple that the solution is obvious. The challenge is to find ways of writing equivalent equations and inequalities that do become progressively simpler.

8. Which of the following pairs of equations and inequalities are equivalent? Explain your reasoning in each case.

a. $3x + 2 = 5$ and $3x = 3$

b. $7x - 8 = 12 + 3x$ and $4x = 20$

c. $\frac{1}{3}x + 9 = 6$ and $x + 9 = 18$

d. $10x + 15 = 35$ and $2x + 3 = 7$

e. $10x + 15 = 35$ and $10x = 20$

f. $3x + 2 < 5$ and $3x < 3$

g. $7x - 8 > 12 + 3x$ and $4x > 20$

h. $10x + 15 < 35$ and $2x + 3 < 7$

i. $10x + 15 > 35$ and $10x > 20$

9. Look back over the pairs of equations and inequalities in Activity 8 and your answers to the equivalence question. What operations on equations and inequalities seem likely to produce simpler equivalent forms?

Unit 3

Checkpoint

Many situations call for comparing two linear functions like the following:

$$f(x) = a + bx \qquad g(x) = c + dx$$

a What overall strategy and specific reasoning steps would you use to solve an equation of the form $a + bx = c + dx$? Explain how you could check the solution.

b What overall strategy and specific reasoning steps would you use to solve an inequality of the form $a + bx < c + dx$? How could you check the answer?

c How do the graphs of expressions like $y = a + bx$ and $y = c + dx$ illustrate solutions to the equations and inequalities described in Parts a and b? How would those solutions appear in tables of values for the two functions?

Be prepared to explain your strategies and reasoning to the entire class.

228 UNIT 3 • SYMBOL SENSE AND ALGEBRAIC REASONING

8. **a.** Equivalent: Subtracting 2 from each side of the first equation will result in the second equation.
   b. Equivalent: Adding 8 and $-3x$ to each side of the first equation will result in the second equation.
   c. Not equivalent: Multiplying the first equation by 3 will result in $x + 27 = 18$.
   d. Equivalent: Dividing the first equation by 5 will result in the second equation.
   e. Equivalent: Subtracting 15 from each side of the first equation will result in the second equation.
   f. Equivalent: Subtracting 2 from each side of the first inequality will produce the second inequality.
   g. Equivalent: Adding 8 and $-3x$ to each side of the first inequality will produce the second inequality.
   h. Equivalent: Dividing the first inequality by 5 will result in the second inequality.
   i. Equivalent: Subtracting 15 from each side of the first inequality will result in the second inequality.
9. Some of the operations that are likely to produce simpler equivalent forms are as follows:
   - Combining like terms and collecting the variables on one side of the equation or inequality
   - Multiplying or dividing both sides by the same number (reversing the inequality sign when multiplying or dividing by a negative number)
   - Adding or subtracting the same number or expression on both sides

Master 78

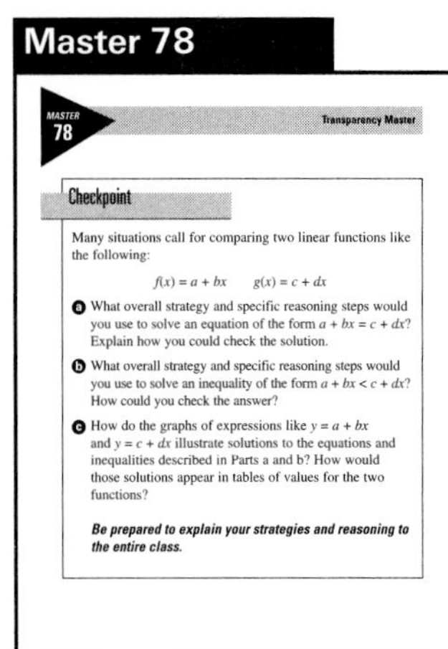
MASTER 78 Transparency Master

Checkpoint

Many situations call for comparing two linear functions like the following:

$f(x) = a + bx \qquad g(x) = c + dx$

ⓐ What overall strategy and specific reasoning steps would you use to solve an equation of the form $a + bx = c + dx$? Explain how you could check the solution.

ⓑ What overall strategy and specific reasoning steps would you use to solve an inequality of the form $a + bx < c + dx$? How could you check the answer?

ⓒ How do the graphs of expressions like $y = a + bx$ and $y = c + dx$ illustrate solutions to the equations and inequalities described in Parts a and b? How would those solutions appear in tables of values for the two functions?

Be prepared to explain your strategies and reasoning to the entire class.

Use with page 228. UNIT 3 • SYMBOL SENSE AND ALGEBRAIC REASONING

NOTE: Students will do more complex reasoning of this type when proving trigonometric identities in Unit 7 of Course 4.

SHARE AND SUMMARIZE full-class discussion

Checkpoint

See Teaching Master 78.

ⓐ Solve the equation by adding equal expressions to both sides, which results in putting the variables on one side of the equation and the constants on the other side, and then multiplying both sides of the equation by the reciprocal of the coefficient of the variable. Substitute the resulting value into the original equation to check.

ⓑ Solve the inequality by adding equal expressions to both sides, which results in putting the variables on one side of the inequality and the constants on the other side, and then multiplying both sides by the reciprocal of the coefficient of the variable (reversing the inequality sign if the coefficient is negative). Substitute a solution into the original inequality to check, or look at the graphs of $y = a + bx$ and $y = c + dx$.

ⓒ When you graph the two equations, you should see the lines intersect at the point at which the x value is your answer to Part a. In the table of values, the function values for that particular value of x are the same. For the inequality, you will see one line below the other for your solution to Part b. In the table, the one set of function values will always be less than the other for x values corresponding to your solution in Part b.

CONSTRUCTING A MATH TOOLKIT: Students should explain the strategy and reasoning steps for solving the equation and inequality in the Checkpoint. For most students, specific examples should be included and solved.

Unit 3

APPLY individual task

On Your Own

a. $35 + 0.30t < 25 + 0.50t$

$10 < 0.20t$

$50 < t$

$t > 50$

If someone plans to use the cellular phone more than 50 minutes a month, then Plan *B* would cost less.

b. $35 + 0.30t = 25 + 0.50t$

$10 = 0.20t$

$t = 50$

The two plans cost the same for 50 minutes of use per month.

c. $25 + 0.50t < 35 + 0.30t$

$0.20t < 10$

$t < 50$

Plan *C* costs less if someone plans to use the cellular phone for fewer than 50 minutes each month.

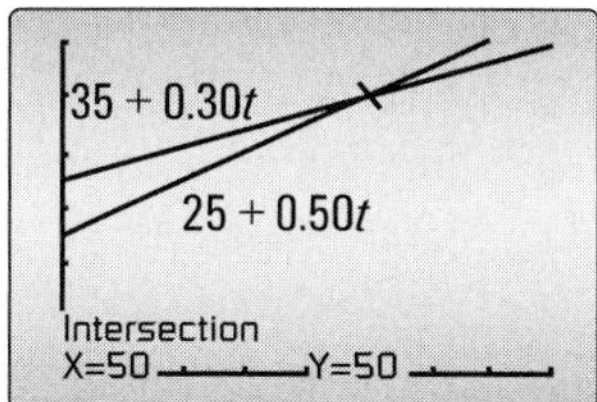

X	Y_1	Y_2
47	49.1	48.5
48	49.4	49
49	49.7	49.5
50	50	50
51	50.3	50.5
52	50.6	51
53	50.9	51.5

Y_1=35+.3X

MORE ASSIGNMENT *pp. 234–239*

Students can now begin Modeling Task 1 or 3 or Organizing Task 1, 2, or 3 from the MORE assignment following Investigation 2.

Unit 3

EXPLORE small-group investigation

INVESTIGATION 2 Reasoning about Quadratic Equations and Inequalities

This investigation revisits the logic used in Lesson 3 when students factored to find zeroes of a function; it also acknowledges that method's shortcomings. The quadratic formula is then introduced and its components are connected to the graph of a quadratic function. To set the stage, you might want to revisit an earlier problem and pose similar questions, such as: "What are the zeroes of $f(x) = x^2 + 7x + 12$? Can you get the exact value of the zeroes by factoring or with your calculator? What are the zeroes of $g(x) = x^2 + 7x + 14$? Of $k(x) = -50x^2 + 2{,}600x - 22{,}500$?" The factoring pattern that was used in Lesson 3 will only work for $f(x)$. The other examples will help motivate the need for the quadratic formula.

See additional Teaching Notes on page T257J.

On Your Own

Two cellular telephone service plans offer monthly costs (in dollars) that are functions of time used (in minutes) with the following rules:

$$B(t) = 35 + 0.30t$$

$$C(t) = 25 + 0.50t$$

Write and solve (without use of technology) equations and inequalities that help in answering these questions:

a. Under what conditions will Plan B cost less than Plan C?

b. Under what conditions will Plan B cost the same as Plan C?

c. Under what conditions will Plan C cost less than Plan B?

In each case, show how you can use a calculator to check your solutions.

INVESTIGATION 2 Reasoning about Quadratic Equations and Inequalities

Two key questions are often associated with quadratic function models of the form $f(x) = ax^2 + bx + c$:

- What is the maximum (minimum) value and where does it occur?
- For what values of the input variable x will $f(x) = 0$?

In the case of the concert-planning model described at the start of this lesson, the quadratic income function was $I(x) = 2{,}500x - 50x^2$. The two key questions can be stated in this way:

- What ticket price will lead to maximum projected income from ticket sales?
- What ticket prices will produce no projected ticket income at all?

You can answer both questions by scanning a table or graph of $(x, I(x))$ values. But you can also get the answers easily by using algebraic reasoning.

1. Justify each step in the following analysis of the concert-income situation.

   a. Solving the equation $2{,}500x - 50x^2 = 0$ will help.

   b. The equation in Part a is equivalent to $50x(50 - x) = 0$.

   c. $50x(50 - x) = 0$ when $x = 0$ or when $x = 50$.

   d. The maximum income will occur when $x = 25$.

   e. That income is $31,250.

Unit 3

LESSON 4 • REASONING TO SOLVE EQUATIONS AND INEQUALITIES 229

2. Unfortunately, many quadratic equations are not easy to solve using the type of factoring that worked so well in Activity 1. For example, consider the problem of finding projected break-even prices for the planned concert. Those are the prices for which income from ticket sales will equal expenses for operating costs. Since the cost equation for this situation was $C(x) = 22{,}500 - 100x$, this problem requires solving the equation $2{,}500x - 50x^2 = 22{,}500 - 100x$.

   a. You can start by writing an equivalent equation with a quadratic expression equal to 0:

   $$-50x^2 + 2{,}600x - 22{,}500 = 0$$

   Why is this equation equivalent to the original?

   b. Factor the left side of this equation to get $-50(x^2 - 52x + 450) = 0$. Why is this factored form equivalent to the equation in Part a?

The form of the equation given in Part b does not look easy to continue to solve by factoring!

There is another way you can solve quadratic equations, even when factoring seems impossible. You can use the **quadratic formula**. If $ax^2 + bx + c = 0$ (and $a \neq 0$), then the **roots** of the equation are

$$x = -\frac{b}{2a} \pm \frac{\sqrt{b^2 - 4ac}}{2a}$$

or, writing these separately,

$$x = -\frac{b}{2a} + \frac{\sqrt{b^2 - 4ac}}{2a} \text{ and } x = -\frac{b}{2a} - \frac{\sqrt{b^2 - 4ac}}{2a}$$

(You'll explore a derivation of this formula in Lesson 5.)

3. Solve the break-even equation $-50x^2 + 2{,}600x - 22{,}500 = 0$ using the quadratic formula.

   a. Give the values for a, b, and c.

   b. Evaluate $-\frac{b}{2a}$.

   c. Evaluate $\frac{\sqrt{b^2 - 4ac}}{2a}$.

   d. Now calculate $x = -\frac{b}{2a} + \frac{\sqrt{b^2 - 4ac}}{2a}$ and $x = -\frac{b}{2a} - \frac{\sqrt{b^2 - 4ac}}{2a}$.

   e. Describe at least three different ways to check your calculated roots in Part d. Check the roots in the original equation using one of those methods.

   f. Use the quadratic formula to solve the equation $x^2 - 52x + 450 = 0$. Compare the result to the answer in Part d and explain similarities or differences.

Unit 3

230 UNIT 3 • SYMBOL SENSE AND ALGEBRAIC REASONING

2. **a.** The addition property of equality was used to get all terms on the left-hand side of the equal sign. The commutative property of addition was used to rearrange the order of the terms.

   b. The distributive property allows us to factor –50 out of each term.

3. **a.** $a = -50, b = 2{,}600, c = -22{,}500$

   b. $-\frac{2{,}600}{2(-50)} = \frac{-2{,}600}{-100} = 26$

   c. $\frac{\sqrt{(2{,}600)^2 - 4(-50)(-22{,}500)}}{-100} \approx -15.03$

   d. $x \approx 26 + (-15.03) = 10.97$ and $x \approx 26 - (-15.03) = 41.03$

   e. Students can substitute the values back into the original equation, use a calculator to draw the graph and trace to x-intercepts, or use a table of values to verify that when $x = 10.97$ and when $x = 41.03$, the y value is (approximately) zero.

   f. $a = 1, b = -52, c = 450$

   $-\frac{b}{2a} = -\frac{-52}{2} = 26$

   $\frac{\sqrt{(-52)^2 - 4(1)(450)}}{2} \approx 15.03$

   $x \approx 26 \pm (15.03), x \approx 41.03, x \approx 10.97$

   The results are the same because the second equation is equivalent to the original equation. (Use the distributive property to factor out -50; then divide both sides by -50.)

Master 79

Master 80

Unit 3

EXPLORE *continued*

4. **See Teaching Masters 79 and 80. If it is the case with the calculators your class uses, be sure that students understand that each time they use the solve command, they will get only one root to the equation. This may be an opportunity to discuss why it is necessary to know more than how to use the calculator. In order for students to find all roots to a given equation, they must first know how many roots there are as well as an approximate value for each one.**

5. **a.** $a = 1, b = -6, c = 5$

   b. $-\frac{-6}{2} = 3$

   c. $\frac{\sqrt{36 - 4(1)(5)}}{2(1)} = \frac{\sqrt{16}}{2} = \frac{4}{2} = 2$

   d. $x = 5, 1$

   e. $x = -\frac{b}{2a}$ is the axis of symmetry. $\frac{\sqrt{b^2 - 4ac}}{2a}$ is the distance from the x-intercepts to the axis of symmetry. For this problem, the axis of symmetry is 3 and the roots are 2 units away. (If students don't see this connection yet, they have another chance in Activity 7.)

6. **a.** $x \approx 1.27, -2.77$; this polynomial does not have factors over the integers.

   b. $x = 1, -0.8$; in factored form, this equation is $(5x + 4)(x - 1) = 0$; thus, the roots are $x = -0.8$ and $x = 1$.

   c. There are no (real) roots to this equation. When students try to solve it using the quadratic formula, they will find that $b^2 - 4ac = -8$. At this point, $\sqrt{-8}$ is not defined, so the equation has no (real) roots. You also may want to discuss that a graph of $y = 3x^2 - 2x + 1$ would not have any x-intercepts. This is further explored in Activity 8, but you may wish to start students thinking about it here.

   d. There are no real roots to this equation.

   e. $x = -\frac{3}{2}$; in factored form, this equation is $(2x + 3)(2x + 3) = 0$. Solving gives $x = -\frac{3}{2}$.

4. Some computer software and some calculators have a "solve" feature that allows you to solve equations directly, if one side of the equation is equal to 0. The procedure for using these solving capabilities varies. You may need to consult your manual to learn how to use the feature.

EQUATION SOLVER
eqn : 0 = –50x²+2600
x – 22500

Use the solve feature on your calculator or computer software to check your solutions to Parts d and f of Activity 3.

5. Now consider the quadratic equation $x^2 - 6x + 5 = 0$. A graph of the function $f(x) = x^2 - 6x + 5$ is shown below.

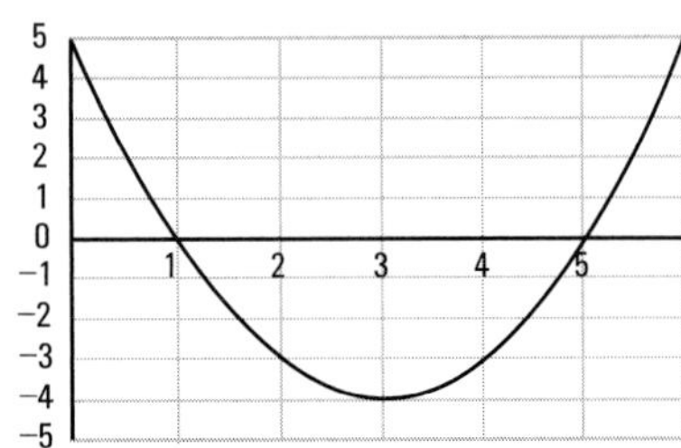

a. Give the values for a, b, and c that should be used to solve $x^2 - 6x + 5 = 0$ with the quadratic formula.

b. Evaluate $-\frac{b}{2a}$.

c. Evaluate $\frac{\sqrt{b^2 - 4ac}}{2a}$.

d. Now calculate $x = -\frac{b}{2a} + \frac{\sqrt{b^2 - 4ac}}{2a}$ and $x = -\frac{b}{2a} - \frac{\sqrt{b^2 - 4ac}}{2a}$.

e. Compare the quadratic formula calculations to the graph of $f(x) = x^2 - 6x + 5$. What information is provided by the expression $-\frac{b}{2a}$? By the expression $\frac{\sqrt{b^2 - 4ac}}{2a}$?

6. Use the quadratic formula to solve each of the following quadratic equations. Then try to solve the same equations by factoring. In each case, check your work by using the solve feature on your calculator or computer software or by substituting your proposed roots for x into the equation.

a. $-2x^2 - 3x + 7 = 0$

b. $5x^2 - x - 4 = 0$

c. $3x^2 - 2x + 1 = 0$

d. $-x^2 + 2x - 3 = 0$

e. $4x^2 + 12x + 9 = 0$

LESSON 4 • REASONING TO SOLVE EQUATIONS AND INEQUALITIES 231

7. Now look back at your work in Activity 6 and search for connections between the quadratic formula calculations and the graphs of the corresponding function rules.

- Explain the special significance of the equation $x = -\frac{b}{2a}$ for a quadratic function with rule in the form $f(x) = ax^2 + bx + c$.
- What information is provided by the expression $\frac{\sqrt{b^2 - 4ac}}{2a}$?

Test your ideas in each of the following cases by graphing the function and the vertical line $x = -\frac{b}{2a}$. (If you choose to use your calculator rather than sketching your graph, consult your manual as needed.)

a. $f(x) = 2x^2 + 4x - 9$

b. $f(x) = 3x^2 - 2x - 5$

c. $f(x) = x^2 + 6x - 10$

d. $f(x) = -x^2 + 2x - 9$

8. Think about the ways in which the graph of $f(x) = ax^2 + bx + c$ could intersect the x-axis. How many possible roots could the equation $ax^2 + bx + c = 0$ have?

a. Use the quadratic formula to solve each equation and identify the step that first shows the number of roots you can expect.

- $x^2 + 8x + 12 = 0$
- $x^2 + 8x + 16 = 0$
- $x^2 + 8x + 20 = 0$

b. Sketch graphs of the quadratic functions corresponding to the three equations above, and explain how those graphs show the number of roots in each case.

9. Suppose that $f(x)$, $g(x)$, $j(x)$, and $h(x)$ are quadratic functions with the zeroes indicated below. Find values of x for which each of these functions would have maximum or minimum values. Then write possible rules for the functions in factored form.

a. $f(6) = 0$ and $f(-2) = 0$

b. $g(-7) = 0$ and $g(3) = 0$

c. $j(-2) = 0$ and $j(-5) = 0$

d. $h(2) = 0$ and $h(4.5) = 0$

10. Explain how the quadratic formula can help you determine the minimum value of the function $f(x) = 4x^2 - 7x - 10$.

Unit 3

232 UNIT 3 • SYMBOL SENSE AND ALGEBRAIC REASONING

7. ■ $x = -\frac{b}{2a}$ is the axis of symmetry of the parabola $y = ax^2 + bx + c$.

■ The distance from the axis of symmetry to each zero is $\frac{\sqrt{b^2 - 4ac}}{2a}$.

a. $x = -\frac{b}{2a} = -\frac{4}{4} = -1$ is the axis of symmetry. The zeros are $-1 + \frac{\sqrt{88}}{4}$ and $-1 - \frac{\sqrt{88}}{4}$, or approximately 1.35 and -3.35.

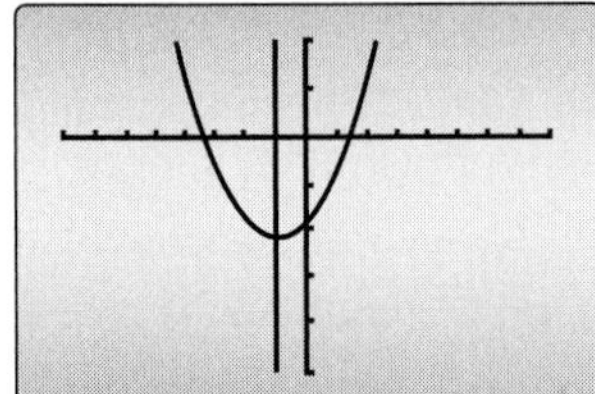

WINDOW
Xmin =-8
Xmax =8
Xscl =1
Ymin =-25
Ymax =10
Yscl =5
Xres =1

b. $x = -\frac{b}{2a} = -\frac{-2}{6} = \frac{1}{3}$ is the axis of symmetry. The zeros are $\frac{1}{3} + 1\frac{1}{3}$ and $\frac{1}{3} - 1\frac{1}{3}$, or $1\frac{2}{3}$ and -1.

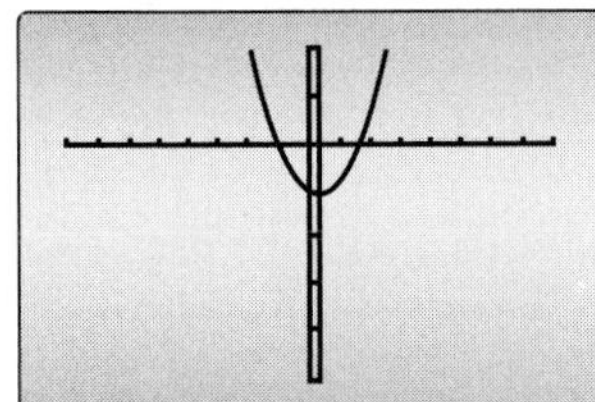

WINDOW
Xmin =-8
Xmax =8
Xscl =1
Ymin =-25
Ymax =10
Yscl =5
Xres =1

c. $x = -\frac{b}{2a} = -\frac{6}{2} = -3$ is the axis of symmetry. The zeros are $-3 + \frac{\sqrt{76}}{2}$ and $-3 - \frac{\sqrt{76}}{2}$, or approximately 1.36 and -7.36.

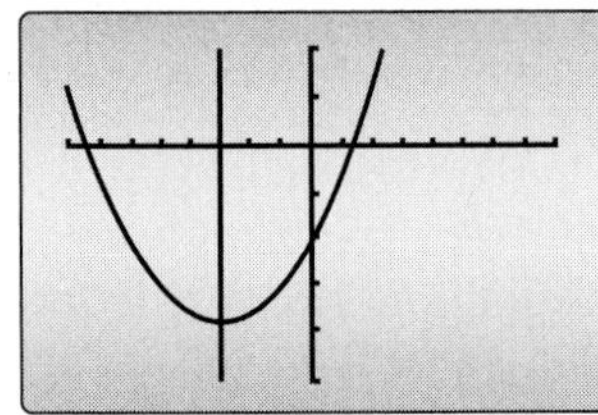

WINDOW
Xmin =-8
Xmax =8
Xscl =1
Ymin =-25
Ymax =10
Yscl =5
Xres =1

d. $x = -\frac{b}{2a} = -\frac{2}{-2} = 1$ is the axis of symmetry. There are no real roots, as shown by the graph and by the fact that the quadratic formula gives $\sqrt{-32}$ for $\sqrt{b^2 - 4ac}$.

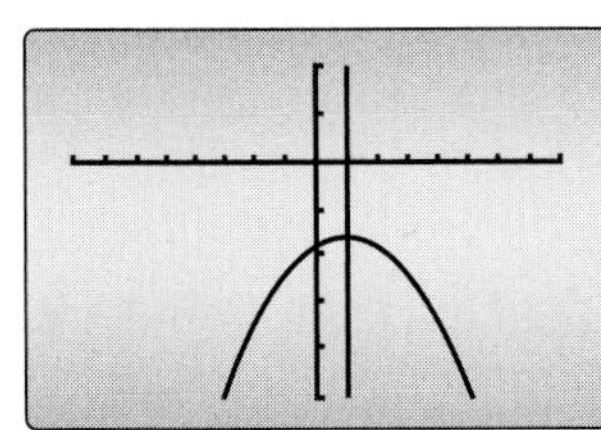

WINDOW
Xmin =-8
Xmax =8
Xscl =1
Ymin =-25
Ymax =10
Yscl =5
Xres =1

Unit 3

See additional Teaching Notes on page T257K.

Master 81

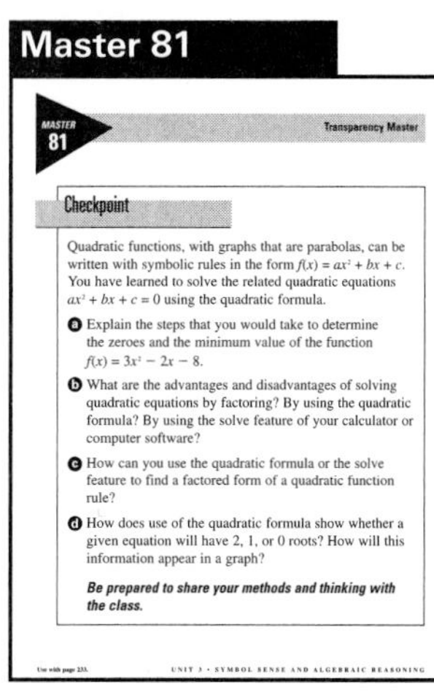

MASTER 81 — Transparency Master

Checkpoint

Quadratic functions, with graphs that are parabolas, can be written with symbolic rules in the form $f(x) = ax^2 + bx + c$. You have learned to solve the related quadratic equations $ax^2 + bx + c = 0$ using the quadratic formula.

a Explain the steps that you would take to determine the zeroes and the minimum value of the function $f(x) = 3x^2 - 2x - 8$.

b What are the advantages and disadvantages of solving quadratic equations by factoring? By using the quadratic formula? By using the solve feature of your calculator or computer software?

c How can you use the quadratic formula or the solve feature to find a factored form of a quadratic function rule?

d How does use of the quadratic formula show whether a given equation will have 2, 1, or 0 roots? How will this information appear in a graph?

Be prepared to share your methods and thinking with the class.

Use with page 233. UNIT 3 • SYMBOL SENSE AND ALGEBRAIC REASONING

EXPLORE *continued*

11. a. The number line graph indicates the values for which the inequality is true, $-1.5 < x < 4$, by darkening these values and using open circles to indicate that $x \neq -1.5$ or 4.

b. You can see from the graph that when x is between -1.5 and 4, the graph is below the x-axis, that is, the function is less than zero.

c.

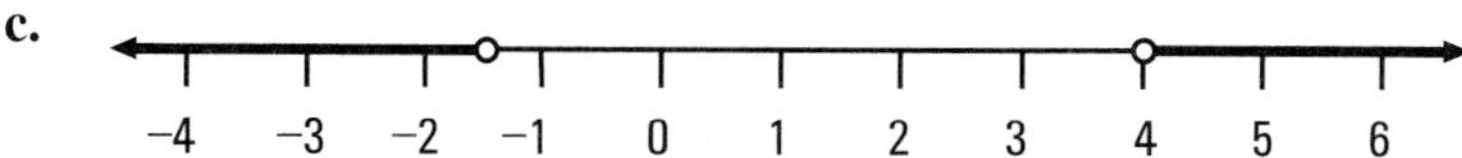

d. The open circles at -1.5 and 4 would be filled in indicating that -1.5 and 4 are also solutions. If students think of other useful ways to indicate inclusion of an endpoint, accept their answers, but then explain that the *convention* is to use filled circles.

12. a. $-2 < x < 3$

−3 −2 −1 0 1 2 3 4

b. $x < -2$ or $x > 3$

−3 −2 −1 0 1 2 3 4

c. $-1 < x < 6$

−1 0 1 2 3 4 5 6

d. $x < -2.5$ or $x > 1$

−4 −3 −2 −1 0 1 2 3

e. $x = 4$

0 1 2 3 4 5 6 7

f. $x \neq 4$

0 1 2 3 4 5 6 7

SHARE AND SUMMARIZE full-class discussion

Checkpoint

See Teaching Master 81.

a Responses may vary. Students might choose to use the quadratic formula or to use the solve feature or graphical root-calculating feature on their calculators to find the zeroes. The quadratic formula, $\frac{-b}{2a} \pm \frac{\sqrt{b^2 - 4ac}}{2a}$, where $a = 3$, $b = -2$, and $c = -8$, will give the zeroes of the function. One way to find the minimum value is to determine the value for $\frac{-b}{2a}$ and evaluate the function at that point. Another way to find the x-coordinate of the minimum point is to find the mean of the zeroes and then find the value of the function at that point. The minimum value occurs when $x = \frac{1}{3}$; therefore, the minimum value is $-\frac{25}{3}$.

b Some quadratics are not factorable. The quadratic formula always works, gives exact rather than approximate solutions, and is sometimes faster. In order to use the solve feature, you must know how many roots there are and also have reasonable guesses for them.

CONSTRUCTING A MATH TOOLKIT: Students should explain how to solve quadratic equations like $x^2 + 3x - 7 = 0$, which cannot be solved by factoring.

See additional Teaching Notes on page T257L.

Unit 3

11. The quadratic formula and other equation-solving methods can be used to solve quadratic inequalities as well. Examine the graph of the function $f(x) = 2x^2 - 5x - 12$ at the right. It has zeroes at $x = -1.5$ and $x = 4$.

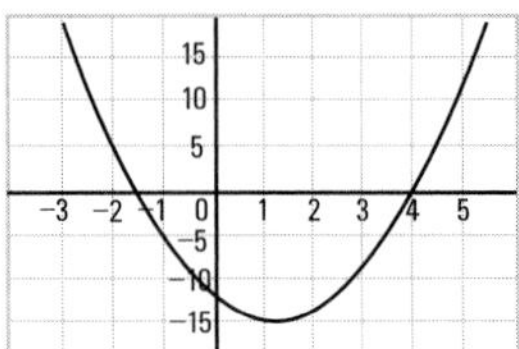

a. Explain how the number line graph below shows the solution of the quadratic inequality $2x^2 - 5x - 12 < 0$.

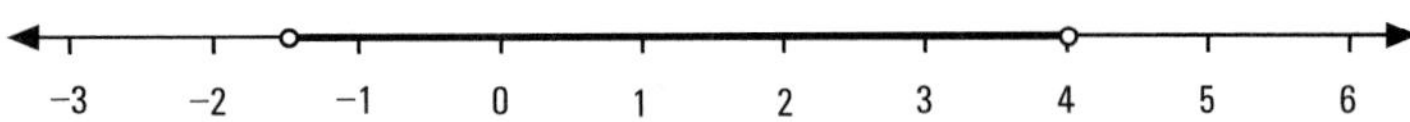

b. How does the number line graph in Part a relate to the graph of the function $f(x) = 2x^2 - 5x - 12$?

c. Make a number line graph showing the solution of the quadratic inequality $2x^2 - 5x - 12 > 0$.

d. How would you modify the number line graph in Part c to show the solution of the inequality $2x^2 - 5x - 12 \geq 0$?

12. Using Activity 11 as an example, if needed, solve the following quadratic inequalities.

a. $x^2 - x - 6 < 0$ **b.** $x^2 - x - 6 > 0$

c. $-x^2 + 5x + 6 > 0$ **d.** $-2x^2 - 3x + 5 < 0$

e. $x^2 - 8x + 16 \leq 0$ **f.** $x^2 - 8x + 16 > 0$

Checkpoint

Quadratic functions, with graphs that are parabolas, can be written with symbolic rules in the form $f(x) = ax^2 + bx + c$. You have learned to solve the related quadratic equations $ax^2 + bx + c = 0$ using the quadratic formula.

a Explain the steps that you would take to determine the zeroes and the minimum value of the function $f(x) = 3x^2 - 2x - 8$.

b What are the advantages and disadvantages of solving quadratic equations by factoring? By using the quadratic formula? By using the solve feature of your calculator or computer software?

c How can you use the quadratic formula or the solve feature to find a factored form of a quadratic function rule?

d How does use of the quadratic formula show whether a given equation will have 2, 1, or 0 roots? How will this information appear in a graph?

Be prepared to share your methods and thinking with the class.

Unit 3

LESSON 4 • REASONING TO SOLVE EQUATIONS AND INEQUALITIES 233

On Your Own

Use what you have learned about the quadratic formula to complete the following tasks.

a. Find the zeroes and the lines of symmetry for the graphs of the following functions.

- $f(x) = x^2 - 4x + 1$
- $g(x) = x^2 + 6x - 11$
- $h(x) = x^2 - 24$

b. For each of the following functions, find the minimum or maximum value of the function.

- $f(x) = x^2 - 3x + 9$
- $g(x) = -x^2 + 8x + 2$
- $h(x) = x^2 - 49$

c. Graph solutions for these quadratic inequalities:

- $x^2 - 3x - 4 > 0$
- $x^2 + x - 6 < 0$
- $-x^2 - 2x + 3 > 0$

Unit 3

MORE

Modeling • Organizing • Reflecting • Extending

Modeling

1. Owners of the Polar City Bears baseball team have two sources of operating profit: admission tickets and concession sales. Both depend on the number of fans who attend a game.

Experience suggests the following function rules for predicting profit from the number of people attending a game.

Profit from ticket sales:	$T(x) = 7.50x - 5{,}000$
Profit from concession sales:	$C(x) = 3.00x - 750$

234 UNIT 3 • SYMBOL SENSE AND ALGEBRAIC REASONING

APPLY individual task

On Your Own

a. ■ Zeroes: $x = \frac{4}{2} \pm \frac{\sqrt{12}}{2} = 2 \pm \sqrt{3} \approx 2 \pm 1.73$, or $x \approx 3.73$ and $x \approx 0.27$

Line of symmetry: $x = 2$

■ Zeroes: $x = \frac{-6}{2} \pm \frac{\sqrt{80}}{2} = -3 \pm 2\sqrt{5} \approx -3 \pm 4.47$, or $x \approx 1.47$ and $x \approx -7.47$

Line of symmetry: $x = -3$.

■ Zeroes: $x = -\frac{0}{2} \pm \frac{\sqrt{96}}{2} = \pm 2\sqrt{6} \approx \pm 4.90$

Line of symmetry: $x = 0$.

b. ■ The minimum occurs at $x = 1.5$; $f(1.5) = 6.75$.

■ The maximum occurs at $x = 4$; $f(4) = 18$.

■ The minimum occurs at $x = 0$; $f(0) = -49$.

c. ■ $x < -1$ or $x > 4$

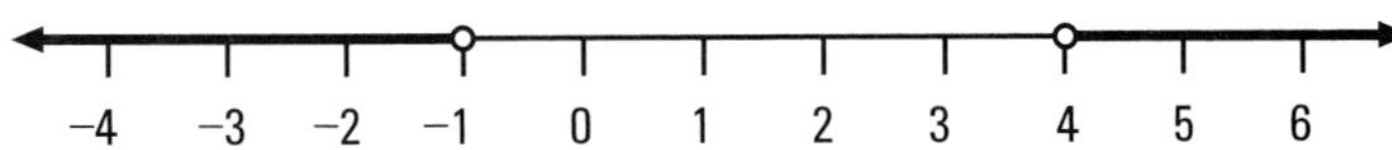

■ $-3 < x < 2$

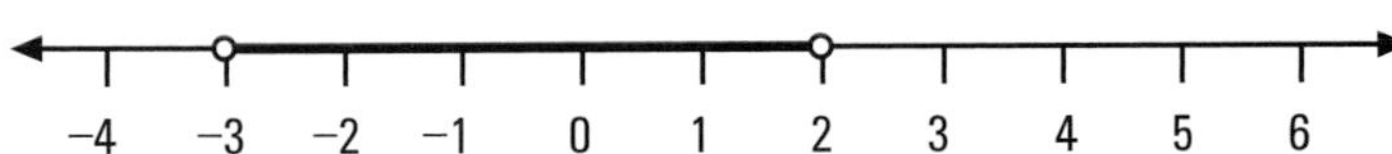

■ $-3 < x < 1$

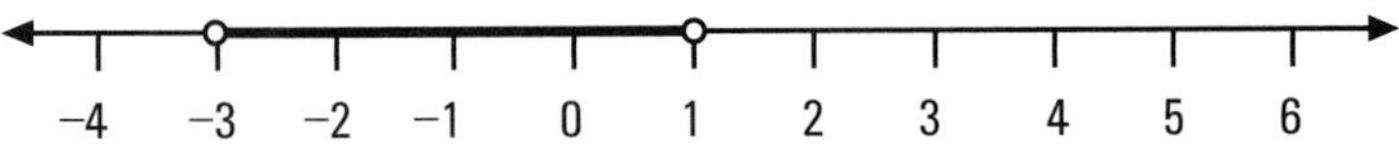

Unit 3

MORE
ASSIGNMENT pp. 234–239

Modeling: 3 and 4
Organizing: 1, 2, and 3 or 4*
Reflecting: 5
Extending: Choose one*

**When choice is indicated, it is important to leave the choice to the student.*
NOTE: *It is best if Organizing tasks are discussed as a whole class after they have been assigned as homework.*

Unit 3

MORE independent assignment

Modeling

1. a. The price of a ticket is \$7.50. The total fixed expenses for things such as team employees, equipment, and grounds maintenance are \$5,000. On the average, the concession stand makes a \$3 profit for each person buying a ticket. Fixed operating costs for the concession stand are \$750.
   b. $0 = 3.00x - 750$
   $x = 250$
   If 250 people attend the game, the concession operation will expect to break even.
   c. $0 = 7.50x - 5{,}000$
   $x \approx 666.67$
   If 667 tickets are sold, the team operation will break even.
   d. $3.00x - 750 > 7.50x - 5{,}000$
   $944\frac{4}{9} > x$
   If 944 or fewer people attend the game, the expected concession profit will be greater than the ticket sale profit.
   e. $3.00x - 750 < 7.50x - 5{,}000$
   $x > 944\frac{4}{9}$
   If 945 or more people attend the game, the expected concession profit will be less than the ticket sale profit.
   f. $3.00x - 750 = 7.50x - 5{,}000$
   $x \approx 944.44$
   There are no integers for which the expected profits are equal, but when $x = 944$ or $x = 945$, they are very close.
2. a. The equation $f(x)$ is a parabola with a maximum height of 75 yards at $x = 0$.
   b. Since the building is 250 yards long, the farthest point from the center of the building is 125 yards away. That point has the minimum height, which is $f(125)$ or 50 yards.
   c. $-0.0016x^2 + 75 \geq 60$
   $-0.0016x^2 \geq -15$
   $x^2 \leq 9{,}375$
   $-96.8 \leq x \leq 96.8$
   This means that the dome is at least 60 yards high for distances up to 96.8 yards from the center (in either direction).

a. How do you think the numbers 7.50, 3.00, 5,000, and 750 in the profit functions relate to the operation of the baseball team and its concession stands?

Write and solve (without calculator tables or graphs) equations and inequalities to help you answer the following questions. Record all steps in your reasoning.

b. For what number of tickets sold will the concession operation break even?

c. For what number of tickets sold will the team operation break even, without considering concessions?

d. For what number of tickets sold will concession profit be greater than ticket sale profit?

e. For what number of tickets sold will concession profit be less than ticket sale profit?

f. For what number of tickets sold will concession profit be equal to ticket sale profit?

2. The architect of a planned domed athletic stadium proposed the general shape shown in the following sketch. The peak of the roof was to be a parabolic curve with equation $f(x) = -0.0016x^2 + 75$, where x is distance in yards from the center of the building and $f(x)$ is the height of the dome in yards.

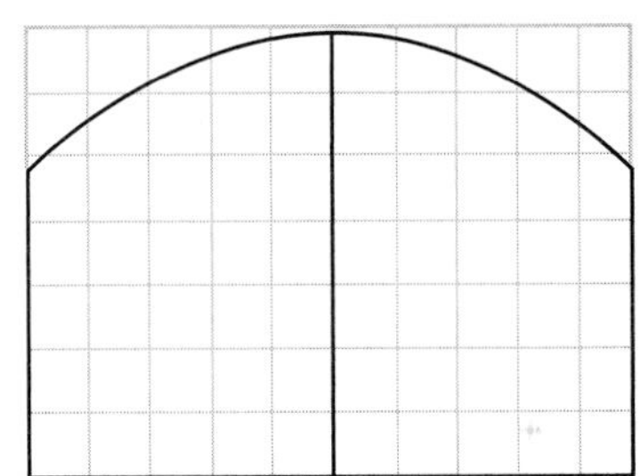

a. What is the maximum height of the dome?

b. If the total length of the building is 250 yards, what is the minimum height of the dome?

c. Solve the inequality $-0.0016x^2 + 75 \geq 60$ and explain what it tells about the dome design.

3. For staff members at the Grand Canyon Outfitters store in the Columbia Mall, pay depends in part on the dollar value of their sales. If they work a normal 40-hour week and sell x dollars of merchandise, they will earn $80 + 0.05x$ dollars. At the competing store, Rocky Mountain Trails, staff members earn pay on a different scale. For a similar 40-hour week with x dollars of sales, they will earn $120 + 0.03x$ dollars.

Unit 3

LESSON 4 • REASONING TO SOLVE EQUATIONS AND INEQUALITIES 235

a. What do the numbers 80, 0.05, 120, and 0.03 in the two rules tell about how pay is calculated?

Write and solve (without calculator tables or graphs) equations and inequalities to help you answer the following questions. Record all steps in your reasoning.

b. Under what conditions will pay at Grand Canyon Outfitters be equal to pay at Rocky Mountain Trails?

c. Under what conditions will pay at Grand Canyon Outfitters be greater than pay at Rocky Mountain Trails?

d. Under what conditions will pay at Grand Canyon Outfitters be less than pay at Rocky Mountain Trails?

e. What dollar value of sales will be required at Grand Canyon Outfitters for a sales staff person to earn more than $100?

f. If a sales staff person at Rocky Mountain Trails was paid $180 in one week, what was the dollar value of the merchandise that the person sold?

4. During the summer, James sells decorative wood-cuttings at two different locations. Since the two locations are very different, in the past he has had to consider two different weekly revenue functions, one for the store in the city and another for the store in the country. If x is the price (in dollars) for a cutting, the two revenue functions are:

City store: $R_1(x) = (150 - 4x)x$

Country store: $R_2(x) = (90 - 2x)x$

a. What price will give the maximum weekly revenue for the city store?

b. What price will give the maximum weekly revenue for the country store?

c. James wants to charge the same price at both stores. What price will maximize the combined revenue?

236 UNIT 3 • SYMBOL SENSE AND ALGEBRAIC REASONING

3. **a.** 80 and 120 are the base rates for 40 hours. They represent \$2 and \$3 per hour. The numbers 0.05 and 0.03 give the percentages of sales that will be given to the employee.

b. $80 + 0.05x = 120 + 0.03x$

$0.02x = 40$

$x = 2{,}000$

If a salesperson has sales of \$2,000 per week, he or she will earn the same amount of money at the two stores.

c. $80 + 0.05x > 120 + 0.03x$

$x > 2{,}000$

A person who has sales of more than \$2,000 per week will earn more at Grand Canyon Outfitters than at Rocky Mountain Trails.

d. $80 + 0.05x < 120 + 0.03x$

$x < 2{,}000$

A person who has sales of less than \$2,000 per week will earn more money at Rocky Mountain Trails than at Grand Canyon Outfitters.

e. $80 + 0.05x > 100$ if $x > 400$

A person working at Grand Canyon Outfitters needs to have weekly sales greater than \$400 in order to earn more than \$100 in one week.

f. $120 + 0.03x = 180$

$x = \$2{,}000$

The person had sales of \$2,000.

4. **a.** The zeroes of $R_1(x)$ are 0 and 37.50, so the maximum weekly revenue will be obtained when the woodcuttings are sold for $\frac{0 + 37.5}{2}$ or \$18.75. This price will result in weekly revenue of $[150 - 4(18.75)](18.75)$ or \$1,406.25.

b. The zeroes of $R_2(x)$ are 0 and 45. The maximum weekly revenue will be obtained when the woodcuttings are sold for $\frac{0 + 45}{2}$ or \$22.50. This price will give weekly revenue of $[90 - 2(22.50)](22.50)$ or \$1,012.50.

c. To find the price that maximizes the combined revenue, the maximum of $R_1(x) + R_2(x)$ must be found.

$$\begin{aligned} R_3(x) &= R_1(x) + R_2(x) \\ &= (150 - 4x)x + (90 - 2x)x \\ &= 150x - 4x^2 + 90x - 2x^2 \\ &= 240x - 6x^2 \end{aligned}$$

In factored form, this is $R_3(x) = (240 - 6x)x$ or $6x(40 - x)$. Thus, the price at which the maximum will be achieved is $\frac{0 + 40}{2}$ or \$20. (See Organizing Task 5 for an extension of this task.)

Unit 3

Organizing

1. **a.** $2x = -116$ Addition Property of Equality (twice)
   $x = -58$ Multiplication Property of Equality

   b. $7x < -11$ Addition Property of Inequality (twice)
   $x < -\frac{11}{7}$ Multiplication Property of Inequality

   c. $34.9 = 22.4x$ Addition Property of Equality (twice)
   $x = \frac{34.9}{22.4}$ Multiplication Property of Equality
   $x \approx 1.56$ Arithmetic

   d. $-22 < 2x$ Addition Property of Inequality (twice)
   $x > -11$ Multiplication Property of Inequality

   e. $25x > 100$ Addition/Subtraction Property of Inequality (twice)
   $x > 4$ Multiplication Property of Inequality

2. In each part, solutions can be checked by finding the x-intercepts.

   a. $x = \frac{-3}{2} \pm \frac{\sqrt{5}}{2}$
   $x \approx -1.5 \pm 1.12$
   $x \approx -0.38$ and $x \approx -2.62$

   b. $x = \frac{-7}{4} \pm \frac{\sqrt{-23}}{4}$
   No zeroes

   c. $x = \frac{10}{2} \pm \frac{\sqrt{0}}{2}$
   $x = 5$

   d. $x = -6$ and $x = -1.5$

   e. $x = -\frac{2}{3}$ and $x = 3$

3. One example of each case follows.
   One solution: $2x + 1 = 3x - 2$; $x = 3$

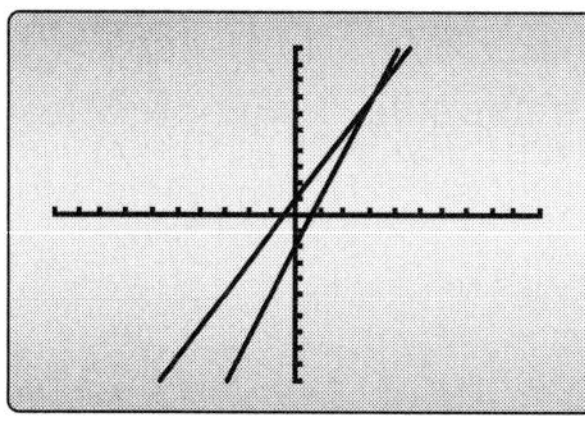

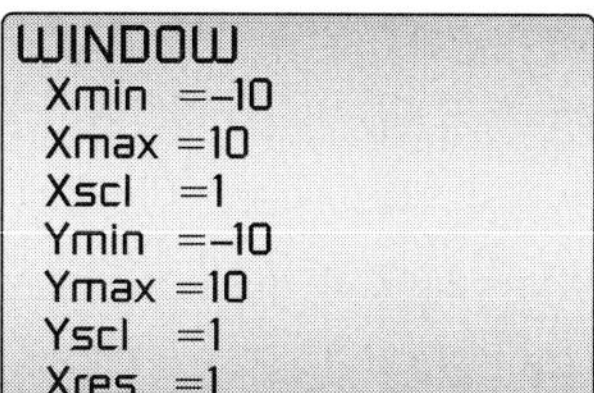

No solutions: $5x + 4 = 5x + 2$

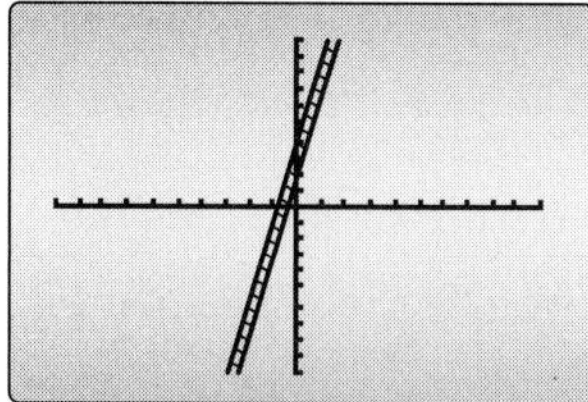

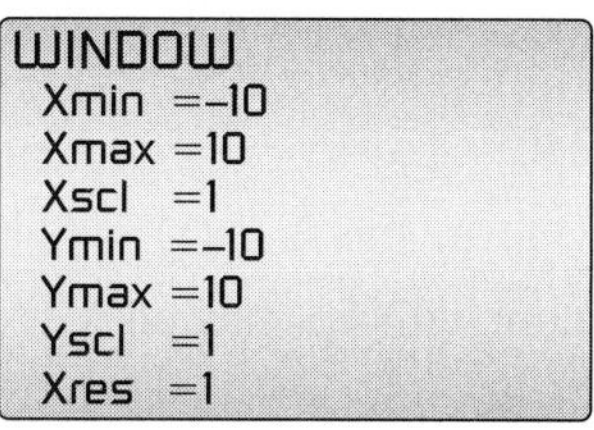

See additional Teaching Notes on page T257M.

Organizing

1. Solve each of the following linear equations or inequalities without using calculator tables or graphs. In each case, show and justify each step of your solution process. Then show how your answer can be checked.

a. $5x + 4 = 3x - 112$

b. $4x + 20 < 9 - 3x$

c. $-9x + 12.5 = 13.4x - 22.4$

d. $4x - 9 < 13 + 6x$

e. $18x + 7 > 107 - 7x$

2. Solve each of the following quadratic equations without using calculator tables or graphs. In each case, show and justify each step of your solution process. Then show how your answer can be checked using a graph of the related function.

a. $x^2 + 3x + 1 = 0$

b. $2x^2 + 7x + 9 = 0$

c. $x^2 - 10x + 25 = 0$

d. $2x^2 + 15x + 18 = 0$

e. $3x^2 - 7x - 6 = 0$

3. Consider linear equations of the form $ax + b = cx + d$. Give specific examples of such equations (and sketches of graphs for the functions involved) illustrating the cases in which the equation will have one solution, no solutions, and infinitely many solutions.

4. Consider quadratic equations of the form $ax^2 + bx + c = 0$. Give specific examples (other than those in previous problems you've solved) and sketches of graphs for the functions involved illustrating cases in which the equation will have exactly two roots, exactly one root, and no roots. In each case, show how use of the quadratic formula will lead to the conclusion illustrated in the function graphs.

5. Refer to Modeling Task 4 on page 236.

a. What is the average of the two prices that will maximize the weekly revenue when the stores are considered separately?

b. How does this compare to the price that will maximize revenue when the same price is charged at both stores? Explain why this is the case.

LESSON 4 • REASONING TO SOLVE EQUATIONS AND INEQUALITIES 237

Reflecting

1. What do you see as the advantages and disadvantages of using calculator-based methods (tables, graphs, a solve feature) versus reasoning with symbolic forms in solving the following?

   a. Linear equations

   b. Linear inequalities

   c. Quadratic equations

   d. Quadratic inequalities

2. Think about how you solved linear and quadratic equations by reasoning with the symbolic forms themselves.

   a. Describe the main ideas in solving a linear equation or inequality by formal reasoning for a student who hasn't learned that skill yet.

   b. Describe the main ideas in solving a quadratic equation by factoring for a student who has not learned that skill yet.

   c. Describe the main ideas in solving a quadratic equation by using the quadratic formula for a student who has not learned that skill yet.

3. Describe a type of problem that you have encountered in your science classes that requires algebraic thinking similar to the thinking you have done in this unit.

4. Quadratic functions have been used to model aspects of such structures as the St. Louis Gateway Arch, shown at the right. The height (in feet) of the St. Louis Arch, as a function of the distance (in feet) from one base, can be approximated by $h(x) = 4.2x - 0.007x^2$. (The curve is actually more complicated, but this quadratic model comes reasonably close.) Explain how you can use symbolic reasoning to figure out the width of the arch at the base and the maximum height of the arch.

5. Given a quadratic function $f(x) = ax^2 + bx + c$, how can you tell by examining the symbolic rule and thinking about its graph whether the function has a maximum or minimum value? Whether it has 0, 1, or 2 zeroes?

238 UNIT 3 • SYMBOL SENSE AND ALGEBRAIC REASONING

Reflecting

1. **a–b.** Responses will vary. Both linear equations and inequalities are fairly easy to solve using algebraic reasoning. However, using technology is also quick and easy.

   c–d. Responses will vary. Quadratic equations and inequalities may be more difficult to solve using algebraic reasoning, especially if the coefficients are not whole numbers. When the quadratic expression is not easily factored, it is often much easier to solve the quadratic equation or inequality using technology.

   In all cases, tables and graphs show how the specific solutions relate to all other values of the functions being analyzed.

2. **a.** Essentially, you want to isolate the term containing the variable on one side of the equation or inequality. Then you multiply both sides by the reciprocal of the coefficient of the variable, remembering to reverse the sign of the inequality if you multiply or divide by a negative number.

   b. To solve by factoring, factor the quadratic expression (rewrite it as a product of two linear factors), and then set each factor equal to zero and solve for the variable.

   c. To solve a quadratic equation using the quadratic formula, first put it in the form $ax^2 + bx + c = 0$. Then substitute the values for a, b, and c into the formula and evaluate it.

3. Responses will vary. There are many examples in both chemistry and physics.

4. The width of the arch at the base will be $|x_1 - x_2|$, where x_1 and x_2 are the zeroes of the function. The maximum height of the arch will be the value of $h(x)$ when it is evaluated at the average of x_1 and x_2. In this case, 0 is one of the zeroes, and 600 is the other one. So the width of the base is 600 feet. The height of the arch is $h(300)$ or 630 feet.

5. Students should recognize that for many rules they can determine the number of zeroes very quickly by examining only a and c. For example, when $b = 0$ the equation becomes a power model, translated vertically if $c \neq 0$. The minimum or maximum is the y-intercept c and examining a to determine whether its graph opens upward or downward gives a quick answer to the number of zeroes. When $b \neq 0$ and $c > 0$ and $a < 0$, the y-intercept is above the x-axis and the graph is open downward so there are two zeroes. Similar reasoning would determine that when $b \neq 0$ and $c < 0$ and $a > 0$, there are two zeroes.

   If $c > 0$ and $a > 0$, you need to examine more than a and c. You need to determine whether the minimum $f\left(\frac{-b}{2a}\right)$ is above the x-axis, implying no zeroes; on the x-axis, implying one zero; or below the x-axis, implying two zeroes. Similar reasoning would be applied if $c < 0$ and $a < 0$.

   If $c = 0$ and $b \neq 0$, you can conclude without determining the maximum or minimum that there will be two zeroes since the graph will cross the x-axis a second time whether it is open upward or downward. (Some students may correctly conclude that they can always determine $f\left(\frac{-b}{2a}\right)$ to assist their analysis of the number of zeroes. You may wish to ask them if that is always necessary.)

Assessments 103–105

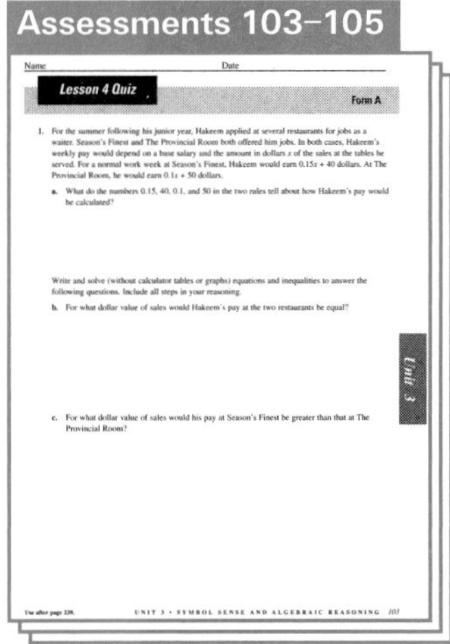
Name Date

Lesson 4 Quiz — Form A

1. For the summer following his junior year, Hakeem applied at several restaurants for jobs as a waiter. Season's Finest and The Provincial Room both offered him jobs. In both cases, Hakeem's weekly pay would depend on a base salary and the amount in dollars x of the sales at the tables he served. For a normal work week at Season's Finest, Hakeem would earn $0.15x + 40$ dollars. At The Provincial Room, he would earn $0.1x + 50$ dollars.
   a. What do the numbers 0.15, 40, 0.1, and 50 in the two rules tell about how Hakeem's pay would be calculated?

   Write and solve (without calculator tables or graphs) equations and inequalities to answer the following questions. Include all steps in your reasoning.

   b. For what dollar value of sales would Hakeem's pay at the two restaurants be equal?
   c. For what dollar value of sales would his pay at Season's Finest be greater than that at The Provincial Room?

Unit 3

Use after page 239. UNIT 3 • SYMBOL SENSE AND ALGEBRAIC REASONING 103

Assessments 106–108

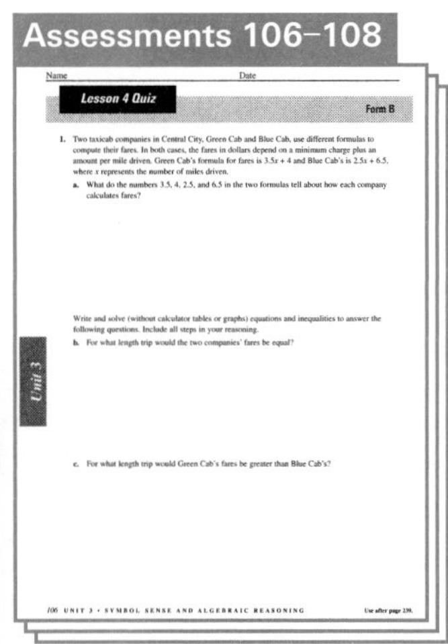
Name Date

Lesson 4 Quiz — Form B

1. Two taxicab companies in Central City, Green Cab and Blue Cab, use different formulas to compute their fares. In both cases, the fares in dollars depend on a minimum charge plus an amount per mile driven. Green Cab's formula for fares is $3.5x + 4$ and Blue Cab's is $2.5x + 6.5$, where x represents the number of miles driven.
   a. What do the numbers 3.5, 4, 2.5, and 6.5 in the two formulas tell about how each company calculates fares?

   Write and solve (without calculator tables or graphs) equations and inequalities to answer the following questions. Include all steps in your reasoning.

   b. For what length trip would the two companies' fares be equal?
   c. For what length trip would Green Cab's fares be greater than Blue Cab's?

Unit 3

106 UNIT 3 • SYMBOL SENSE AND ALGEBRAIC REASONING Use after page 239.

Extending

1. a. Responses may be multiples of the given functions.
   $f(x) = (x + 1)(x - 5) = x^2 - 4x - 5$
   The minimum value for this function is -9 when $x = 2$.
   b. $g(x) = 2(x + 1)(x - 5) = 2x^2 - 8x - 10$
   $h(x) = -3(x + 1)(x - 5) = -3x^2 + 12x + 15$
   c. There will be an infinite number because any function in the form $f(x) = k(x + 1)(x - 5)$ will have zeroes at $x = -1$ and $x = 5$. The factor k can be any real number.
2. First factor the quadratic to determine when it is equal to zero. Since $(2x + 3)(x - 5) = 0$ when $x = -1.5$ and when $x = 5$, mark these points on a number line. Then test each region to determine whether the quadratic inequality is true in that region. It is easiest to test $x = 0$ here. Since $(3)(-5) < 0$, the answer is $-1.5 < x < 5$.

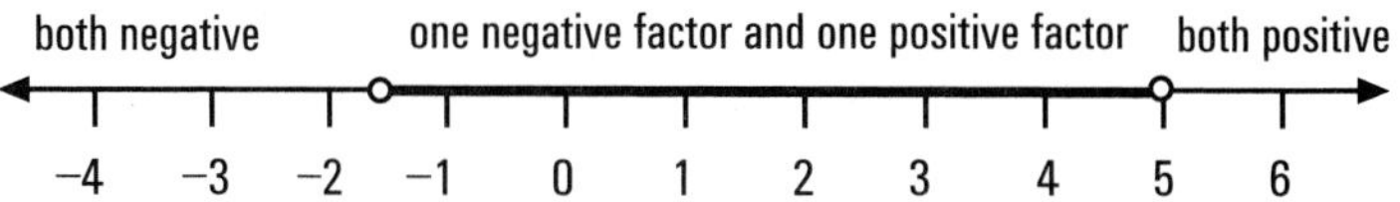

3. $-0.004x^2 + 61.1x - 125{,}000 \geq 80{,}000$
   To use the quadratic formula, move the 80,000 to the left-hand side. This equation is $-0.004x^2 + 61.1x - 205{,}000 = 0$.
   So, $a = -0.004$, $b = 61.1$, $c = -205{,}000$.
   $$x = \frac{-61.1}{-0.008} \pm \frac{\sqrt{61.1^2 - 4(-0.004)(-205{,}000)}}{-0.008}$$
   $$\approx 7{,}637.5 \pm (-2{,}661.09)$$
   $$\approx 4{,}976.41 \text{ and } 10{,}298.59$$
   Since $a < 0$, the quadratic has a maximum value, so x values between these two will have a greater $P(x)$ value. Therefore, if the number of tickets sold is at least 4,977 and no more than 10,298, the profit will be at least $80,000.
   Graphs and tables show the same solution.

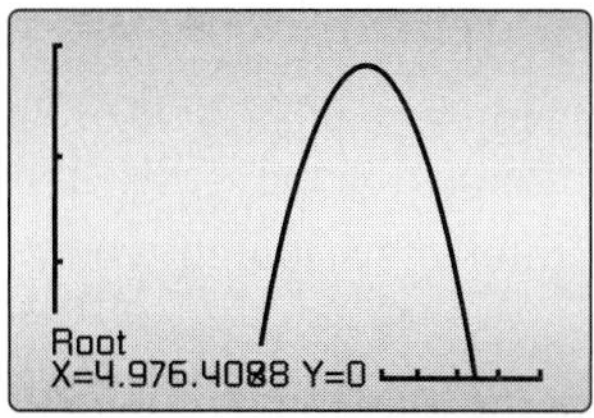

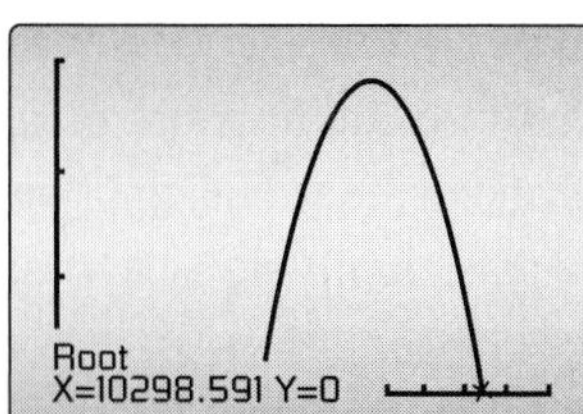

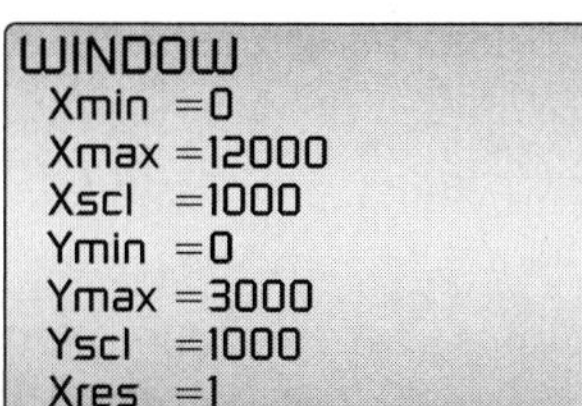

X	Y_1
4972	-93.94
4973	-72.62
4974	-51.3
4975	-30
4976	-8.704
4977	12.584
4978	33.864

Y_1=-.004X²+61.1...

X	Y_1
10297	33.864
10298	12.584
10299	-8.704
10300	-30
10301	-51.3
10302	-72.62
10303	-93.94

Y_1=-.004X²+61.1...

See additional Teaching Notes on page T257N.

Unit 3

Extending

1. Parabolas, the graphs of quadratic functions, come in many different specific shapes.

a. Find a rule for a quadratic function that has zeroes at $x = -1$ and $x = 5$. Find the maximum or minimum value of your function and the value of x at which that maximum or minimum value occurs.

b. Use your results from Part a to find rules for two other quadratic functions $g(x)$ and $h(x)$ with the following properties:

- $g(-1) = 0$, $g(5) = 0$, and $g(x)$ has a minimum value of –18.
- $h(-1) = 0$, $h(5) = 0$, and $h(x)$ has a maximum value of 27.

c. How many different quadratic functions will have their zeroes at $x = -1$ and $x = 5$? Prepare an argument supporting your answer.

2. Explain how to solve a quadratic inequality, without use of a calculator table or graph, by working through the specific example $2x^2 - 7x - 15 < 0$. Show all of your reasoning steps.

3. Consider the profit function $P(x) = -0.004x^2 + 61.1x - 125{,}000$, which gives the profit for a rock band concert as a function of the number of tickets sold. Write and solve an inequality representing the question, "How many tickets must be sold to get a profit of at least \$80,000?" Explain how the quadratic formula can be used to find that solution and how the solution can be found using calculator tables and graphs of a suitable function.

4. Solve each quadratic equation below without use of technology. Then check your results.

a. $2x^2 - 7x - 15 = 10 - 4x$

b. $2x^2 - 7x - 15 = -x^2 + 5x + 10$

5. Explore a variety of specific cases to find answers to the following questions.

a. In general, how many solutions could occur in an equation of the form $ax^2 + bx + c = dx + e$? How would those possibilities be shown by a function graph?

b. In general, how many solutions could occur in an equation of the form $ax^2 + bx + c = dx^2 + ex + f$? How would those possibilities be shown by a function graph?

Unit 3

LESSON 4 • REASONING TO SOLVE EQUATIONS AND INEQUALITIES 239

Lesson 5

Proof through Algebraic Reasoning

Algebraic reasoning—that is, rewriting symbolic expressions, equations, and inequalities in equivalent forms—can be very helpful in convincing yourself and others that observed patterns are *always true*. Algebraic reasoning also helps in understanding the patterns themselves. For example, study the following number "trick" that an Alaskan teacher often uses to amaze her students. She directs each student in the class to think of a number between 0 and 10 and perform the indicated calculations.

At this point, she asks various students to tell her their final results, and she quickly identifies the numbers that each started with. For example, when a student reported his final result as 19, she immediately guessed his original number to be 9; when another reported 13, the teacher correctly guessed that she had started with 6.

Think About This Situation

The students were suspicious that their teacher had simply memorized all the possible results from the indicated calculations, so they asked her to stretch the rules to allow starting numbers from 0 to 20 and then from 0 to 50. She still guessed their starting numbers correctly every time.

a What do you think the starting number is when the final calculation results in a 9? When it results in a 17?

b Can you think of a way to use algebraic reasoning to uncover and prove the teacher's number-guessing strategy?

Unit 3

240 UNIT 3 • SYMBOL SENSE AND ALGEBRAIC REASONING

Lesson 5 *Proof through Algebraic Reasoning*

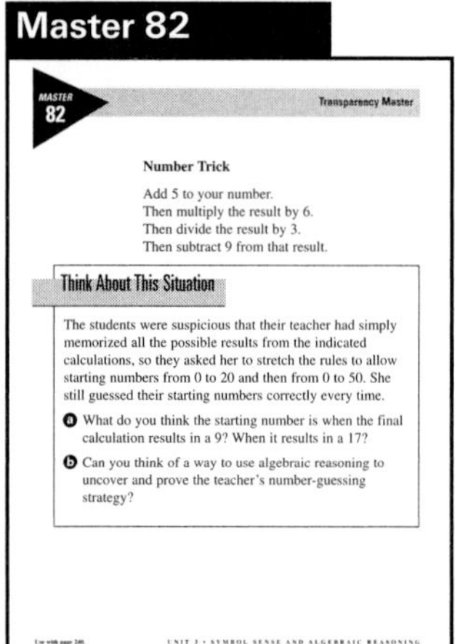
Master 82

MASTER 82 Transparency Master

Number Trick

Add 5 to your number.
Then multiply the result by 6.
Then divide the result by 3.
Then subtract 9 from that result.

Think About This Situation

The students were suspicious that their teacher had simply memorized all the possible results from the indicated calculations, so they asked her to stretch the rules to allow starting numbers from 0 to 20 and then from 0 to 50. She still guessed their starting numbers correctly every time.

ⓐ What do you think the starting number is when the final calculation results in a 9? When it results in a 17?

ⓑ Can you think of a way to use algebraic reasoning to uncover and prove the teacher's number-guessing strategy?

Use with page 240. UNIT 3 • SYMBOL SENSE AND ALGEBRAIC REASONING

LESSON OVERVIEW In this lesson, students prove important mathematical patterns by writing algebraic expressions, equations, and inequalities in equivalent forms and by applying algebraic reasoning. In the first investigation, students use various properties of numbers, operations, and algebra to analyze number tricks and, in the process, develop some general rules and strategies for analyzing algebraic expressions.

Algebraic proofs involving coordinate geometry and statistical topics that the students have previously studied are covered in Investigation 2. Students take geometric definitions and express those relationships algebraically to prove various relationships. Students will also prove the Law of Cosines and the Pythagorean Theorem.

Lesson Objectives

- To prove mathematical patterns by using a variety of algebraic properties, operations, and reasoning strategies
- To write expressions, equations, and inequalities in equivalent symbolic forms to prove relationships
- To prove the Pythagorean Theorem
- To prove the Law of Cosines

LAUNCH full-class discussion

Think About This Situation

See Teaching Master 82.

ⓐ When the final calculation is 9, the starting number is 4. When the final calculation is 17, the starting number is 8.

ⓑ At this point, some students may realize that they need to generalize the steps by expressing the situation in general terms. Activity 1 helps students think about this question, so you may want to cut off this discussion before it is fully analyzed by a few students and let the class work on this activity.

Unit 3

EXPLORE small-group investigation

INVESTIGATION 1 Proving It Always Works

The focus of this investigation is on introducing students to using symbolic logic to prove general results with respect to various mathematical topics. In the past, students have advanced their ability to reason with symbols for specific purposes: to find the zeroes of a particular function, to solve for *y* prior to graphing, to graph constraints, *etc*. The logic of the process, rather than the specifically useful result, is now emphasized.

Students will need time to write the symbol version of the instructions in Activities 1 and 2. If they are not completely successful, you can lead a full-class discussion to clear any confusion. Then give students time to make up their own tricks. Groups can try their tricks on one another.

1. **a.** $n + 5$
$6(n + 5)$
$2(n + 5)$
$2(n + 5) - 9 = 2n + 10 - 9 = 2n + 1$

b. $2n + 1$

c. The teacher subtracts 1 and then divides the result by 2.

d. With this modification, the final expression is $3(n + 5) - 9$ or $3n + 6$. The teacher would need to subtract 6 and then divide the result by 3 to get the starting number.

e. Many methods are possible. You may wish to spend some time allowing each group to share their method with the class.

2. **a.** Step 1: x
Step 2: $x + 76$
Step 3: $x + 76 - 100 + 1 = x - 23$
Step 4: $x - (x - 23)$
The number on the slip of paper is 23.
When discussing Activity 2 with the class, make sure that students understand why we know to subtract 100 and add 1 (as opposed to 200 and 2) to the expression in Step 3. If $50 \leq x \leq 100$, $125 \leq x + 75 \leq 175$, so the result of Step 2 must have a 1 in the hundreds place.

b. Responses will vary. One similar trick is provided below.

Step 1: Pick a number between 150 and 200.	x
Step 2: Add 83 to that number.	$x + 83$
Step 3: Cross out the digit in the hundreds place and add that number to the remaining two-digit number.	$x + 83 - 200 + 2 = x - 115$
Step 4: Subtract Step 3's result from the original number.	$x - (x - 115)$

The number on the slip of paper is 115.

Unit 3

INVESTIGATION 1 Proving It Always Works

You can use algebraic reasoning to prove that some patterns will always hold, to reveal some patterns that start well but break down when all cases are considered, and to develop some useful general rules of your own.

1. Think again about the number-guessing trick on the previous page.

a. Using the letter n to represent the starting number, write a single expression that shows how all calculations combine to produce the result reported to the teacher.

b. Write an expression that is equivalent to the one you wrote for Part a but in simplest form possible.

c. See if you can figure out the easy mental arithmetic the teacher uses to deduce starting numbers from the final results that are reported to her.

d. Modify the third direction of the number trick to read: Then divide the result by 2. What strategy would the teacher use to guess the starting number for this revised trick?

e. Revise the original number trick so that no matter what number you start with, the result at the end of the trick is always the starting number.

2. Here's another mathematics teacher's amazing number trick.

a. See if you can figure out how and why it works by testing some specific start numbers and then writing the operations in algebraic form.

Step 1: Think of a number between 50 and 100.

Step 2: Add 76 to the number.

Step 3: Cross out the digit in the hundreds place and add that number to the remaining two-digit number.

Step 4: Subtract the result in Step 3 from the original number.

The teacher then pulls a sealed envelope from her desk and gives it to a student to open. Inside is a slip of paper with the result of Step 4 already on it.

b. Now see if you can vary the trick to make one of your own. Test your trick with students in another group.

3. Sometimes number patterns lead to conjectures that aren't true. For example, one student looked at the following pattern of squares and cubes for whole numbers:

x^2	0	1	4	9	16	25	36	49	64	81
x^3	0	1	8	27	64	125	216	343	512	729

The student concluded that $x^3 \geq x^2$ for all nonnegative numbers.

Unit 3

LESSON 5 • PROOF THROUGH ALGEBRAIC REASONING 241

a. Why is the inequality $x^3 \geq x^2$ equivalent to $x^3 - x^2 \geq 0$?

b. Why is the inequality $x^3 - x^2 \geq 0$ equivalent to $x^2(x - 1) \geq 0$?

c. For what values of x is the inequality $x^2(x - 1) \geq 0$ true?

4. In linear programming problems and applications of algebra to geometry, you used linear equations written in the form $ax + by = c$. The values of a, b, and c were determined by problem conditions.

a. Identify the slope and coordinates of the x- and y-intercepts of each line below.

- $3x + 2y = 5$
- $-2x + 5y = 10$
- $x - 4y = 9$

b. Based on your results from Part a, formulate general rules for calculating the slope and intercepts of any line with an equation given in the form $px + qy = r$, where $q \neq 0$.

c. Use algebraic reasoning with equivalent expressions and equations to prove that your rules in Part b will always work.

5. Some of you may have completed Extending Task 5, page 224, in Lesson 3. In that task, you were asked to justify that the quadratic expression $ax^2 + bx + c$ is equivalent to $a\left(x + \frac{b}{2a}\right)^2 + \frac{4ac - b^2}{4a}$.

Use that fact and algebraic reasoning to justify each remaining step in the following derivation of the quadratic formula.

$ax^2 + bx + c = 0$ is equivalent to $a\left(x + \frac{b}{2a}\right)^2 + \left(\frac{4ac - b^2}{4a}\right) = 0$,

which is equivalent to $a\left(x + \frac{b}{2a}\right)^2 = \left(\frac{b^2 - 4ac}{4a}\right)$,

which is equivalent to $\left(x + \frac{b}{2a}\right)^2 = \frac{b^2 - 4ac}{4a^2}$,

which is equivalent to $x + \frac{b}{2a} = \pm\sqrt{\frac{b^2 - 4ac}{4a^2}}$ provided $b^2 - 4ac \geq 0$,

which is equivalent to $x = -\frac{b}{2a} \pm\sqrt{\frac{b^2 - 4ac}{4a^2}}$,

which is equivalent to $x = -\frac{b}{2a} \pm \frac{\sqrt{b^2 - 4ac}}{2a}$.

242 UNIT 3 • SYMBOL SENSE AND ALGEBRAIC REASONING

Unit 3

EXPLORE *continued*

3\. **a.** $x^3 \geq x^2$

$x^3 - x^2 \geq x^2 - x^2$ Subtraction property of inequality

$x^3 - x^2 \geq 0$ Any number subtracted from itself is 0

b. $x^3 - x^2 \geq 0$

$x^2(x - 1) \geq 0$ Distributive property

c. $x^2(x - 1) \geq 0$ is true when $x - 1 \geq 0$ and when $x = 0$. This happens when $x \geq 1$ or $x = 0$. Ask students to provide a number for which $x^3 < x^2$. You may also wish to have students graph $y = x^3 - x^2$ and investigate when $y \geq 0$. ($y \geq 0$ when $x = 0$ and when $x \geq 1$.)

4\. **a.**
- slope: $-\frac{3}{2}$ or -1.5; x-intercept: $\left(\frac{5}{3}, 0\right)$; y-intercept: $\left(0, \frac{5}{2}\right)$
- slope: $\frac{2}{5}$ or 0.4; x-intercept: $(-5, 0)$; y-intercept: $(0, 2)$
- slope: $\frac{1}{4}$ or 0.25; x-intercept: $(9, 0)$; y-intercept: $\left(0, -\frac{9}{4}\right)$ or $(0, -2.25)$

b–c. For $px + qy = r$, $q \neq 0$:

$qy = r - px$ Subtraction property of equality

$y = \frac{r - px}{q}$ Division property of equality

$y = \frac{r}{q} - \frac{p}{q}x$ Distributive property or equivalent fractions

slope: $-\frac{p}{q}$ From the slope-intercept form of the line

y-intercept: $\left(0, \frac{r}{q}\right)$ From the slope-intercept form of the line

To find x-intercept,

solve $px = r$ for x, Substituting $y = 0$ in $px + qy = r$

$x = \frac{r}{p}$ Division property of equality

x-intercept: $\left(\frac{r}{p}, 0\right)$

5\. $ax^2 + bx + c = 0$

$a\left(x + \frac{b}{2a}\right)^2 + \left(\frac{4ac - b^2}{4a}\right) = 0$ Given fact

$a\left(x + \frac{b}{2a}\right)^2 = \frac{b^2 - 4ac}{4a}$ Subtraction property of equality

$\left(x + \frac{b}{2a}\right)^2 = \frac{b^2 - 4ac}{4a^2}$ Division property of equality

$x + \frac{b}{2a} = \pm\sqrt{\frac{b^2 - 4ac}{4a^2}}$ Square root property of equality (provided $b^2 - 4ac \geq 0$)

You may need to discuss why the "±" is necessary. The property states that if $p = q$ and $p, q \geq 0$, $\sqrt{p} = \sqrt{q}$. Here, we don't know if $x + \frac{b}{2a}$ is positive, so we include both possibilities with the "±" symbol.

$x = -\frac{b}{2a} \pm \frac{\sqrt{b^2 - 4ac}}{4a^2}$ Subtraction property of equality

$x = -\frac{b}{2a} \pm \frac{\sqrt{b^2 - 4ac}}{2a}$ Inverse of squaring property

Again, you may need to discuss this property, which says that $\sqrt{p^2} = p$ if $p \geq 0$. If $p < 0$, $\sqrt{p^2} = -p$. In this case, we don't know if a is positive or negative, but both possibilities are included by the "±" symbol.

Master 83

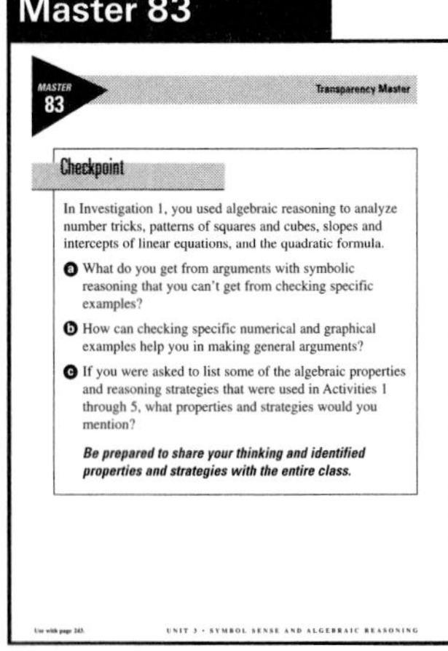

MASTER 83 Transparency Master

Checkpoint

In Investigation 1, you used algebraic reasoning to analyze number tricks, patterns of squares and cubes, slopes and intercepts of linear equations, and the quadratic formula.

(a) What do you get from arguments with symbolic reasoning that you can't get from checking specific examples?

(b) How can checking specific numerical and graphical examples help you in making general arguments?

(c) If you were asked to list some of the algebraic properties and reasoning strategies that were used in Activities 1 through 5, what properties and strategies would you mention?

Be prepared to share your thinking and identified properties and strategies with the entire class.

Use with page 243. UNIT 3 • SYMBOL SENSE AND ALGEBRAIC REASONING

SHARE AND SUMMARIZE full-class discussion

Checkpoint

See Teaching Master 83.

After the class has discussed the Checkpoint, you may want to revisit Activity 3. Ask, "Can we solve $x^3 \geq x^2$ graphically? Why is this the same as solving $x^3 - x^2 \geq 0$ graphically? What are the advantages and disadvantages of reasoning purely symbolically? Of relying solely on a graph?"

(a) Algebra and symbolic reasoning allow us to use a variable to represent any number; we can, therefore, prove statements for all (or a subset of) real numbers, not just for certain cases.

(b) Checking specific examples helps you see general patterns. It can also help you develop a strategy with which you can prove the general case.

(c) Responses may vary. Common properties are listed below.
Distributive property
Addition property of equality
Subtraction property of equality
Multiplication property of equality
Division property of equality
Equivalent fractions
Square roots

APPLY individual task

On Your Own

a. Let the chosen number be x.
$2x + 7$
$5(2x + 7) - 25 = 10x + 35 - 25 = 10x + 10$
$\frac{10x + 10}{10} = x + 1$

b.

$ax + b = cx + d$	
$ax - cx = d - b$	Subtraction property of equality (twice)
$x(a - c) = d - b$	Distributive property
$x = \frac{d - b}{a - c}$	Division property of equality

Note that x is not defined when $a = c$, so those cases would not be satisfied by any value of x, unless $b = d$ also. In the latter case, all values of x are solutions.

c.

$x^2 \geq x$	
$x^2 - x \geq 0$	Subtraction property of inequality
$x(x - 1) \geq 0$	Distributive property

This product will be positive when x and $x - 1$ are either both positive or both negative. Only for $0 < x < 1$ do these two expressions have opposite signs. (The product will be zero when $x = 0$ or $x = 1$.)

MORE ASSIGNMENT pp. 247–252

Students can now begin Modeling Task 1 or Organizing Task 1 or 4 from the MORE assignment following Investigation 2.

Unit 3

Checkpoint

In Investigation 1, you used algebraic reasoning to analyze number tricks, patterns of squares and cubes, slopes and intercepts of linear equations, and the quadratic formula.

a What do you get from arguments with symbolic reasoning that you can't get from checking specific examples?

b How can checking specific numerical and graphical examples help you in making general arguments?

c If you were asked to list some of the algebraic properties and reasoning strategies that were used in Activities 1 through 5, what properties and strategies would you mention?

Be prepared to share your thinking and identified properties and strategies with the entire class.

On Your Own

Use algebraic reasoning to complete the following tasks involving expressions, equations, and inequalities.

a. Prove that whatever the starting number, the following instructions always will bring you back to that number plus 1:

Think of a number.

Double that number and add 7.

Multiply the result by 5 and subtract 25.

Divide the result by 10.

b. Find a formula that gives the solution of $ax + b = cx + d$ for x in terms of a, b, c, and d. Show why the formula works and how it reveals cases in which the equation is not satisfied by *any* value of x.

c. Use an argument like the one you developed in Activity 3 to prove that $x^2 \geq x$ except when $0 < x < 1$.

Unit 3

INVESTIGATION 2 Algebraic Reasoning in Geometry and Statistics

So far, you have used reasoning strategies for writing expressions, equations, and inequalities in equivalent symbolic forms primarily for studying questions about quantitative variables related by functions. But those same strategies are often helpful in proving relationships in geometry, trigonometry, and statistics as well.

LESSON 5 • PROOF THROUGH ALGEBRAIC REASONING 243

For example, in earlier work you've seen that when a geometric shape is modeled in a coordinate plane with number pairs for points and equations for lines, many questions can be answered using simple calculations. If you have a question about a general parallelogram, you can represent the figure in a coordinate plane like this:

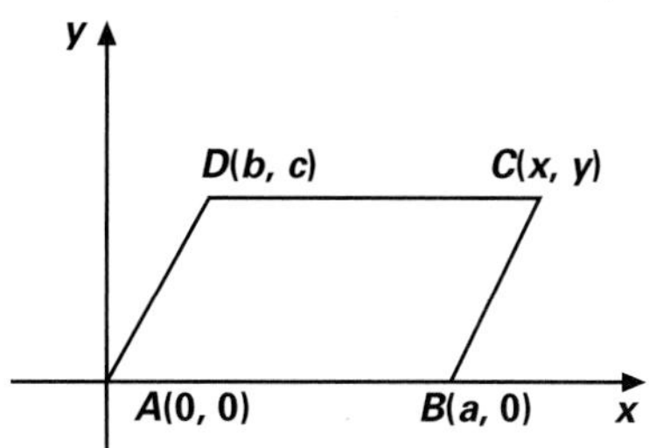

1. Use algebraic reasoning and what you know about slopes of lines and distances to complete the following tasks involving the quadrilateral *ABCD*, above.

   a. Prove that if quadrilateral *ABCD* is to be a parallelogram, then
      - $y = c$ and
      - $x = a + b$

   b. Prove that opposite sides of parallelogram *ABCD* are the same length.

   c. Find expressions for the midpoints of the two diagonals $\overline{AC}$ and $\overline{DB}$, and show that they are identical. What general property of parallelograms have you proved?

One of the most famous and useful theorems in geometry is the Pythagorean Theorem. In Course 1, you discovered this theorem by constructing squares on the sides of various right triangles, calculating their areas, and looking for a pattern relating the areas. You found that in any right triangle with legs a and b and hypotenuse c, $c^2 = a^2 + b^2$. You now can establish this theorem in general using a combination of algebraic and geometric reasoning.

2. Consider the relation between the large square below and the regions into which it has been divided: a smaller square and four right triangles.

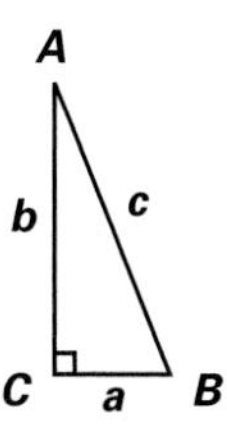

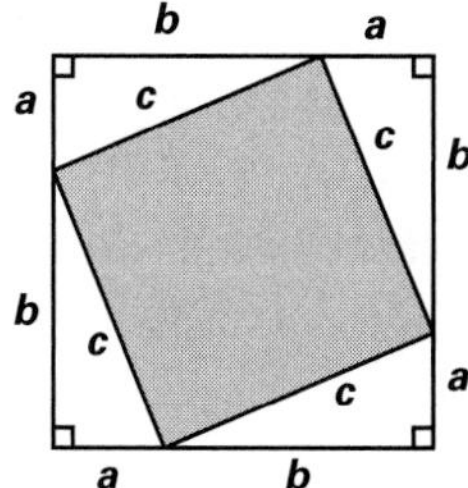

   a. How can you be sure that the shaded region is a square?

244 UNIT 3 • SYMBOL SENSE AND ALGEBRAIC REASONING

Unit 3

EXPLORE small-group investigation

INVESTIGATION 2 Algebraic Reasoning in Geometry and Statistics

In this investigation, students apply the particular skills and ideas they learned in Lessons 3 and 4 (factoring, expanding, and the quadratic formula) to prove some geometric and statistical results that they have used in the past.

A good way to introduce this investigation might be to ask students to recall the properties of a parallelogram, the Pythagorean Theorem, the Law of Sines, and the Law of Cosines. List student answers on the board and ask, "Why do you believe these results? Which of them have you proved?"

As you circulate among groups, be sure to urge students to be logical and to not make assumptions without accompanying explanations. When two groups have similar or different approaches, ask them to share their ideas. When a group has a convincing proof, you might ask those students to write it on a large sheet of paper to be posted in the classroom. This should make the Checkpoint and summarizing discussion more complete.

1. **Some students may wonder if we indeed have the most general case here, which is an excellent question. Of course, we can define our axes as we choose so that one vertex is at the origin and one side lies along the *x*-axis. You may want to ask such a student if any of our calculations need alteration for variables that are negative.**

   a. ■ The y-coordinates of D and C must be the same because opposite sides of a parallelogram are parallel. Since $\overline{AB}$ is horizontal, $\overline{DC}$ must also be. Thus, the y-coordinate of C must be the same as the y-coordinate of D. So $y = c$.

   ■ Sides $\overline{AD}$ and $\overline{BC}$ will be parallel if and only if they have the same slope. This implies that $\frac{c-0}{b-0} = \frac{c-0}{x-a}$. This will be true only when $b - 0 = x - a$ or when $x = b + a$.

   b. $AB = \sqrt{(a-0)^2 + 0^2} = \sqrt{a^2} = a$
   $DC = \sqrt{(a+b-b)^2 + (c-c)^2} = \sqrt{a^2} = a$
   So $AB = DC$.
   $AD = \sqrt{(b-0)^2 + (c-0)^2} = \sqrt{b^2 + c^2}$
   $CB = \sqrt{(a+b-a)^2 + (c-0)^2} = \sqrt{b^2 + c^2}$
   So $AD = CB$.

   c. The midpoint of $\overline{AC}$ is $\left(\frac{a+b}{2}, \frac{c}{2}\right)$. The midpoint of $\overline{DB}$ is $\left(\frac{a+b}{2}, \frac{c}{2}\right)$. The midpoints have the same coordinates, so they are the same point. This proves that the diagonals of a parallelogram bisect each other.

2. **a.** In right triangle ABC, the sum of the measures of $\angle A$ and $\angle B$ is 90° because the sum of the measures of the angles of a triangle is 180° and $\angle C$ has measure 90°. At each point on the side of the large square where the shaded square touches the side of the large square, there are three angles whose sum is 180°, because this is a straight angle. Two of the angles are $\angle A$ and $\angle B$. Since these two angles have a sum of 90°, you know that each corner angle of the shaded region must measure 90°. Additionally, each side has length c, so the shaded region is a square.

Unit 3

EXPLORE *continued*

2. **b.** Area of the large square $= (a + b)^2 = a^2 + 2ab + b^2$
Area of the large square $= c^2 + 4\left(\frac{1}{2}ab\right) = c^2 + 2ab$

c. $a^2 + 2ab + b^2 = c^2 + 2ab$
$a^2 + b^2 = c^2$ — Subtraction property of equality

3. **a.** $h^2 = b^2 - x^2$
$h^2 = c^2 - (a - x)^2$

b. $b^2 - x^2 = c^2 - (a - x)^2$ — Both expressions are equal to h^2
$c^2 = b^2 - x^2 + (a - x)^2$ — Addition property of equality
$c^2 = b^2 - x^2 + (a^2 - 2ax + x^2)$ — Square of a binomial
$c^2 = b^2 + a^2 - 2ax$ — Associative and commutative properties; any number subtracted from itself is zero

c. $\cos C = \frac{x}{b}$ — Definition of cosine
$x = b \cos C$ — Multiplication property of equality
$c^2 = b^2 + a^2 - 2ab \cos C$ — Substitution into the result of Part b

Unit 3

b. Express the area of the large square in two different ways, one using only a and b and the other using all three lengths a, b, and c.

c. Equate the two expressions from Part b and show how algebraic reasoning can lead from that equation to the Pythagorean Theorem as a conclusion.

There are three important relationships in trigonometry that are closely connected to the Pythagorean Theorem. In the "Multiple-Variable Models" unit, you examined a derivation of the Law of Sines, relating sides and angles of any triangle. The Law of Sines guarantees that if ABC is a triangle with angles A, B, and C and opposite sides a, b, and c, then

$$\frac{\sin A}{a} = \frac{\sin B}{b} = \frac{\sin C}{c}$$

or equivalently

$$\frac{a}{\sin A} = \frac{b}{\sin B} = \frac{c}{\sin C}.$$

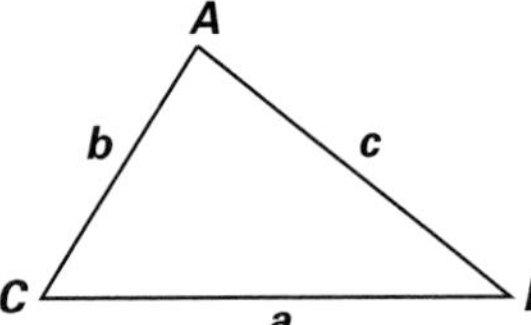

Another important relationship is the Law of Cosines, which was stated and used without proof or derivation in the same unit. It guarantees that in any triangle ABC as described above,

$$c^2 = a^2 + b^2 - 2ab \cos C.$$

With the algebraic reasoning principles that you've studied in this unit, it's now possible to prove this important relationship.

3. To prove the Law of Cosines, consider the diagram at the right, where h is the altitude of ΔABC from vertex A, dividing side CB into segments of lengths x and $a - x$.

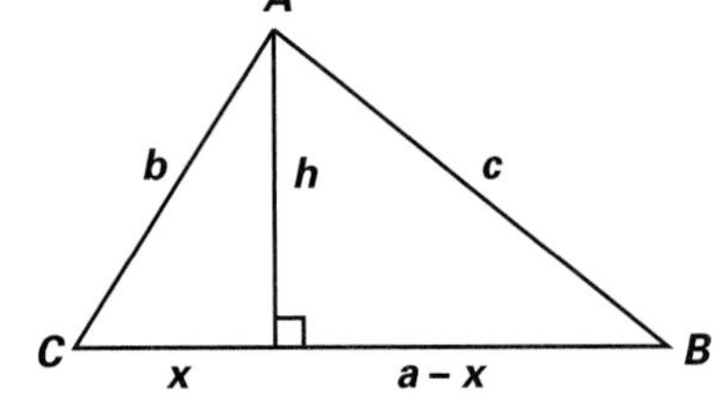

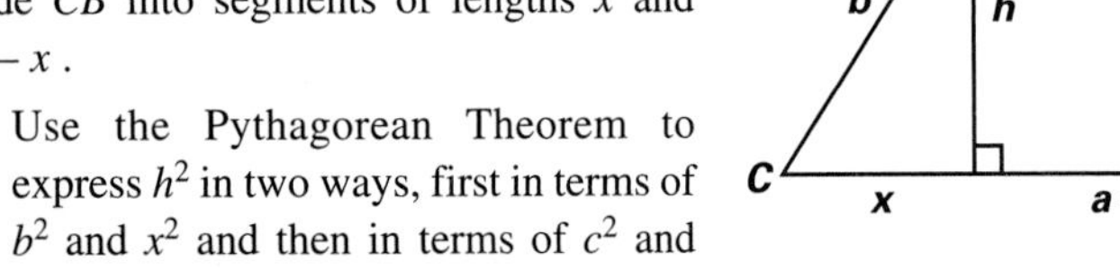

a. Use the Pythagorean Theorem to express h^2 in two ways, first in terms of b^2 and x^2 and then in terms of c^2 and $(a - x)^2$.

b. Use the two expressions for h^2 from Part a to write an equation expressing c^2 in terms of $(a - x)^2$, b^2, and x^2. Then expand $(a - x)^2$ and simplify the resulting expression for c^2 as much as possible.

c. Express x in terms of b and $\cos C$, and substitute that expression for x in the relation you got in Part b. Your result should be the Law of Cosines!

Note: You should be suspicious of the way the proof is guided by particular relations in the diagram. Your proof is valid only if $\angle C$ is acute or right. There is another possible picture, with an obtuse angle at C. You can finish the proof by examining that case in Extending Task 2 on page 251.

Unit 3

LESSON 5 • PROOF THROUGH ALGEBRAIC REASONING 245

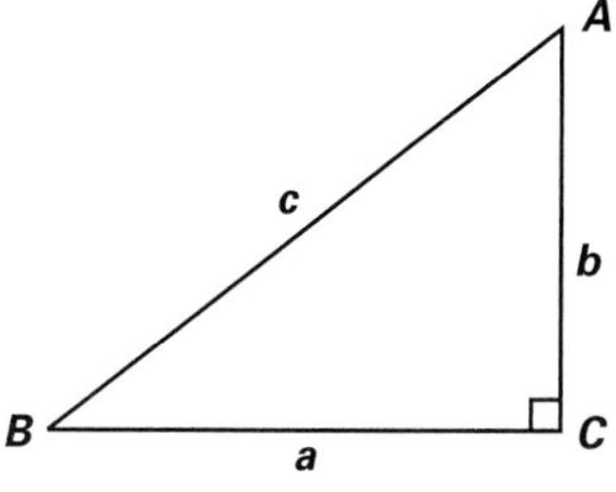

4. Now consider the third very important trigonometric relation with close connections to the Pythagorean Theorem. You can use your skill in algebraic reasoning to prove that for any angle B in a right triangle, $(\sin B)^2 + (\cos B)^2 = 1$. Consider the situation pictured in the diagram at the left.

   a. Express $\sin B$ and $\cos B$ in terms of the sides of the given right triangle.

   b. Express the Pythagorean relation among a^2, b^2, and c^2.

   c. Find a way to combine the relationships of Parts a and b to get the equation $(\sin B)^2 + (\cos B)^2 = 1$.

   d. Investigate whether this relation holds for angles whose measures are greater than or equal to 90°. Make a conjecture.

In previous courses, you have investigated the effects of data transformations on measures of center and variability. You can use variables and a combination of algebraic and statistical reasoning to prove these properties.

5. Suppose a data set consists of five values: x_1, x_2, x_3, x_4, x_5.

   a. Write an algebraic expression for the mean, $\bar{x}$, of this set.

   b. Now multiply each data value by a constant c and write an expression for the mean $\bar{x}_T$ of this transformed set.

   c. Use algebraic properties to prove that $\bar{x}_T = c\bar{x}$.

   d. Explain how similar reasoning could be used to show $\bar{x}_T = c\bar{x}$, if there were n data values.

   e. Prove that if a constant c is added to each of the original five data values, then the mean $\bar{x}_T$ of the transformed set is given by $\bar{x}_T = \bar{x} + c$.

Checkpoint

The activities of Investigation 2 have demonstrated ways that algebraic reasoning can be used to prove important general properties of geometric figures, trigonometric relations, and descriptive statistics.

a What general strategies and specific techniques for working with algebraic expressions did you find useful in the various activities?

b How would you describe in words what is proven by the arguments in each of Activities 2 through 4?

c How would you describe in words what is proven by the arguments in Activity 5?

d How is a *proof* different from reasoning that gives several examples of an interesting pattern?

Be prepared to explain your strategies and descriptions to the entire class.

Unit 3

246 UNIT 3 • SYMBOL SENSE AND ALGEBRAIC REASONING

EXPLORE *continued*

4. **a.** $\sin B = \frac{b}{c}$ Definition of sine

$\cos B = \frac{a}{c}$ Definition of cosine

b. $c^2 = a^2 + b^2$ Pythagorean Theorem

c. Substitute $b = c\sin B$ and $a = c\cos B$ into the statement of the Pythagorean Theorem and simplify:

$c^2 = c^2 (\cos B)^2 + c^2 (\sin B)^2$ Substitution

$1 = (\cos B)^2 + (\sin B)^2$ Division property of equality

d. The relation holds for all angle measures although we have proved it only for angles less than 90°. Students might choose to use tables of values or graphs of the function $y(B) = (\cos B)^2 + (\sin B)^2$ to help them investigate this relationship.

5. **a.** 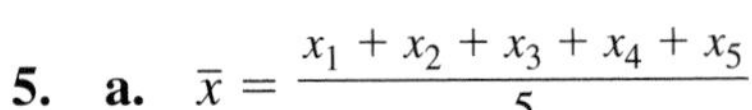

$\bar{x} = \frac{x_1 + x_2 + x_3 + x_4 + x_5}{5}$

b. $\bar{x}_T = \frac{cx_1 + cx_2 + cx_3 + cx_4 + cx_5}{5}$

c. $\bar{x}_T = c\left(\frac{x_1 + x_2 + x_3 + x_4 + x_5}{5}\right)$ Distributive property

$\bar{x}_T = c\bar{x}$ Substitution

d. $\bar{x} = \frac{x_1 + x_2 + x_3 + \ldots + x_n}{n}$ Definition of mean

$\bar{x}_T = \frac{cx_1 + cx_2 + cx_3 + \ldots + cx_n}{n}$ Definition of the transformation

$\bar{x}_T = c\left(\frac{x_1 + x_2 + x_3 + \ldots + x_n}{n}\right)$ Distributive property

$\bar{x}_T = c\bar{x}$ Substitution

e. $\bar{x} = \frac{x_1 + x_2 + x_3 + x_4 + x_5}{5}$ Definition of mean

$\bar{x}_T = \frac{(x_1 + c) + (x_2 + c) + (x_3 + c) + (x_4 + c) + (x_5 + c)}{5}$ Add c to each data value

$\bar{x}_T = \frac{x_1 + x_2 + x_3 + x_4 + x_5 + 5c}{5}$ Associative property and addition

$\bar{x}_T = \frac{x_1 + x_2 + x_3 + x_4 + x_5}{5} + \frac{5c}{5}$ Distributive property

$\bar{x}_T = \frac{x_1 + x_2 + x_3 + x_4 + x_5}{5} + c$ Division

$\bar{x}_T = \bar{x} + c$ Substitution

Master 84

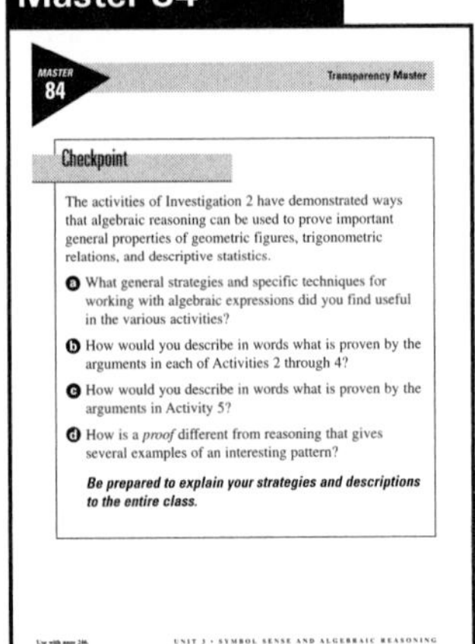

MASTER 84 Transparency Master

Checkpoint

The activities of Investigation 2 have demonstrated ways that algebraic reasoning can be used to prove important general properties of geometric figures, trigonometric relations, and descriptive statistics.

a What general strategies and specific techniques for working with algebraic expressions did you find useful in the various activities?

b How would you describe in words what is proven by the arguments in each of Activities 2 through 4?

c How would you describe in words what is proven by the arguments in Activity 5?

d How is a *proof* different from reasoning that gives several examples of an interesting pattern?

Be prepared to explain your strategies and descriptions to the entire class.

JOURNAL ENTRY: Explain why proofs are an important part of mathematics and why algebra is often fundamental to the process of proof.

Unit 3

See additional Teaching Notes on page T257O.

APPLY individual task

On Your Own

a. ■ (p, q)

■ Using the distance formula to find the lengths of the diagonals, we can see that they are equal in length:

$$AC = \sqrt{(p - 0)^2 + (q - 0)^2} = \sqrt{p^2 + q^2}$$

$$BD = \sqrt{(0 - p)^2 + (q - 0)^2} = \sqrt{p^2 + q^2}$$

b. ■ If a constant c is added to each data value, the range will not change. Let a be the smallest data value in the set and let b be the largest data value in the set. Then $b - a$ is the range of the original data. The new range is $(b + c) - (a + c)$, which is $b - a$. So the new range is equal to the original range.

■ If each data value is multiplied by c, the range will be multiplied by c. Let a and b be the smallest and largest data values in the original set. Then the range is $b - a$. The new range will be $bc - ac$, which is $c(b - a)$. This proves that the new range is the old range multiplied by c.

On Your Own

Use algebraic reasoning to answer the following general questions and to provide proofs about relations in geometry and statistics.

a. When a rectangle is modeled with coordinate methods, the situation can be pictured like this:

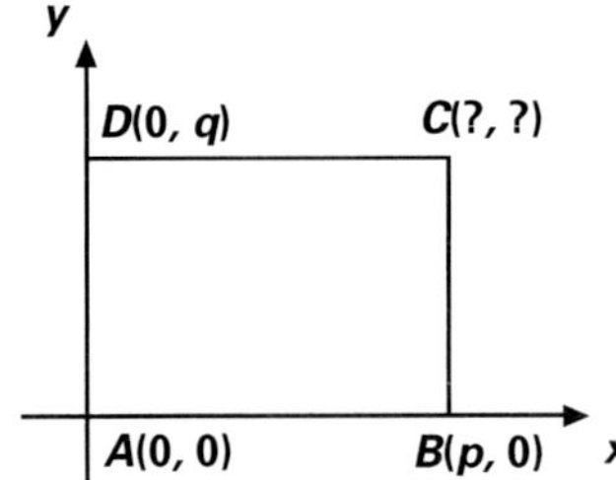

- What must the coordinates of point *C* be?
- Use the above result to prove that the diagonals of any rectangle are equal in length.

b. The range of a numerical data set is the difference between the largest and smallest values. How, if at all, will the range change in the following cases? Prove your answer in each case.

- Each data value is increased by adding the same fixed amount *c*.
- Each data value is multiplied by the same positive constant *c*.

MORE Modeling • Organizing • Reflecting • Extending

Modeling

1. Shown below are calculator programs for solving any equations of the following types.

Type I: $ax + b = c$

Type II: $ax^2 + b = c$

```
PROGRAM: I
: Input "A = ",A
: Input "B = ",B
: Input "C = ",C
: (C−B)/A→X
: Disp "THE SOLUTION IS ",
  X
```

```
PROGRAM: II
: Input "A = ",A
: Input "B = ",B
: Input "C = ",C
: √((C−B)/A)→X
: Disp "THE SOLUTIONS
  ARE ",X
: Disp −X
```


LESSON 5 • PROOF THROUGH ALGEBRAIC REASONING 247

a. Use algebraic reasoning to prove that the formula used in line 4 of the first program is correct.

b. For what input values of a, b, and c will the equation $ax + b = c$ have a solution?

c. Use algebraic reasoning to prove that the formula used in line 4 of the second program is correct. Why are both values of x and $-x$ displayed?

d. For what input values of a, b, and c will the equation $ax^2 + b = c$ have solutions?

2. In any square, there is a relation between the lengths of the sides s and the diagonals d. Use the Pythagorean Theorem and algebraic reasoning to derive an expression showing how d is a function of s.

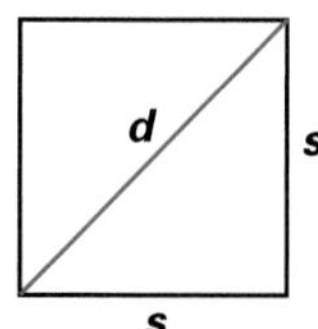

3. A circle is the set of all points in a plane that are a given distance from a given point in the plane (called the center).

a. Shown below on the left is a circle with radius 3 and center at the origin.

- Prove that the point with coordinates $(2, \sqrt{5})$ is on the circle.
- State the coordinates of seven other points on the circle.

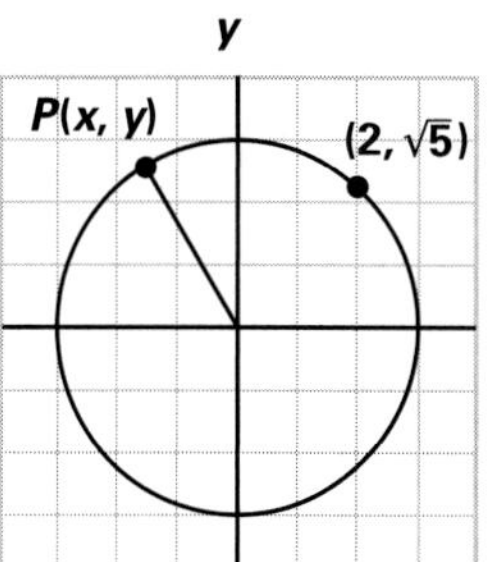

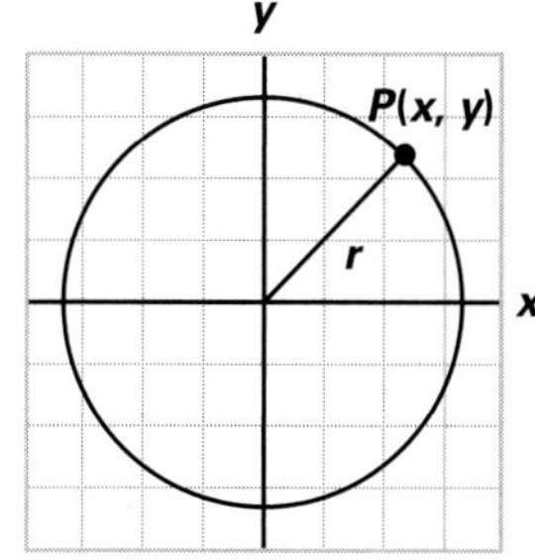

b. Prove that the equation of the circle on the left above is $x^2 + y^2 = 9$.

c. Is the relation $x^2 + y^2 = 9$ a function? Why or why not?

d. Prove that the equation of any circle with center at the origin and radius r is $x^2 + y^2 = r^2$.

e. Use algebraic reasoning to find a way to graph $x^2 + y^2 = 9$ using a graphing calculator or computer software.

Unit 3

248 UNIT 3 • SYMBOL SENSE AND ALGEBRAIC REASONING

MORE independent assignment

Modeling

1. a. $ax + b = c$

$ax = c - b$ Subtraction property of equality

$x = \frac{c - b}{a}$ Division property of equality

b. The equation $ax + b = c$ will have a solution if $a \neq 0$. If $a = 0$, there are no solutions if $b \neq c$ and infinitely many solutions if $b = c$.

c. $ax^2 + b = c$

$ax^2 = c - b$ Subtraction property of equality

$x^2 = \frac{c - b}{a}$ Division property of equality

$x = \pm\sqrt{\frac{c - b}{a}}$ Square root

The square root function gives only the positive square root. However, the negative square root is also a solution.

d. Unless $b = c$, the equation does not have a real solution when a is 0. Also, there is no real solution when $\frac{c - b}{a}$ is negative. For all other values of a, b, c, there are solutions.

2. By the Pythagorean Theorem $d^2 = s^2 + s^2 = 2s^2$. Therefore, by taking the square root of both sides, $d = \sqrt{2s^2} = s\sqrt{2}$. Note that in this case you are considering only the positive root because in this physical situation, it is not possible for s to be negative.

3. a. ■ To show that the point $(2, \sqrt{5})$ is on the circle, we need to show that the distance from the point $(2, \sqrt{5})$ to the origin (the center of the circle) is 3.

$$d = \sqrt{(2 - 0)^2 + (\sqrt{5} - 0)^2}$$
$$= \sqrt{4 + 5}$$
$$= \sqrt{9}$$
$$= 3$$

So $(2, \sqrt{5})$ is on the circle.

■ Responses may vary. Any point at a distance of 3 units from the origin is on the circle. Obvious choices are $(-2, \sqrt{5})$, $(-2, -\sqrt{5})$, $(2, -\sqrt{5})$, $(0, 3)$, $(3, 0)$, $(-3, 0)$, and $(0, -3)$.

b. Since the distance from any point (x, y) to the origin must be 3, we have the following:

$$\sqrt{(x - 0)^2 + (y - 0)^2} = 3$$
$$\sqrt{x^2 + y^2} = 3$$
$$x^2 + y^2 = 9$$

c. No, it is not a function since there are many x values that have more than one possible y value. For example, (0, 3) and (0, –3) both satisfy the equation.

d. The equation of a circle with center at the origin and radius r is $r = \sqrt{(x - 0)^2 + (y - 0)^2}$. Squaring both sides of this equation produces $r^2 = x^2 + y^2$.

e. $x^2 + y^2 = 9$

$y^2 = 9 - x^2$

$y = \pm\sqrt{9 - x^2}$

To graph the circle, graph two functions: $y = \sqrt{9 - x^2}$ and $y = -\sqrt{9 - x^2}$.

MORE

ASSIGNMENT pp. 247–252

Modeling: 1 and 3
Organizing: 1 and 4
Reflecting: 3 and 4
Extending: Choose one*

**When choice is indicated, it is important to leave the choice to the student.*
NOTE: *It is best if Organizing tasks are discussed as a whole class after they have been assigned as homework.*

Unit 3

4. a. $\dfrac{x_1 + x_n}{2}$

b. The midrange will increase by c if a constant c is added to each member of the data set. The new midrange will be as follows:

$$\frac{(x_1 + c) + (x_n + c)}{2} = \frac{x_1 + x_n + 2c}{2} = \frac{x_1 + x_n}{2} + c$$

c. If each member of a data set is multiplied by a positive constant c, the midrange will be multiplied by c. The new midrange will be

$$\frac{cx_1 + cx_n}{2} = \frac{c(x_1 + x_n)}{2} = c\left(\frac{x_1 + x_n}{2}\right)$$

d. No, the midrange is not resistant to outliers. If either the smallest or largest value is an outlier, it will "pull" the midrange toward it since it is involved in the formula.

Organizing

1. From the graph, you can see that if $-1 < x < 1$, then $x^2 > x^4$.

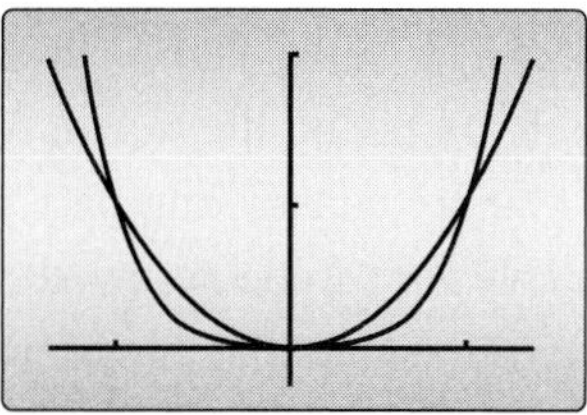

X	Y_1	Y_2
0	0	0
.25	.0625	.00391
.5	.25	.0625
.75	.5625	.31641
1	1	1
1.25	1.5625	2.4414
1.5	2.25	5.0625

$Y_1 = X^2$

To determine when $x^2 > x^4$, consider the following:

$x^2 - x^2 > x^4 - x^2$	Subtraction property of inequality
$0 > x^4 - x^2$	Any number subtracted from itself is 0
$0 > x^2(x^2 - 1)$	Distributive property
$0 > x^2(x - 1)(x + 1)$	Factors for the difference of two perfect squares

The quantity on the right-hand side of the inequality will be equal to zero when $x = 0$, 1, or -1. The product will be negative when one of the factors, $(x - 1)$ and $(x + 1)$, is positive and the other is negative. This occurs when $-1 < x < 1$.

2. a. Combining like terms, distributive property, commutative and associative properties, applying basic definitions.

b. Substitution, theorems, multiplying or dividing both sides by the same number (for inequalities, reversing the sign of the inequality if the number is negative), adding or subtracting the same number to both sides, and all of the properties mentioned in Part a.

3. The quadratic formula states that for $ax^2 + bx + c = 0$, $x = -\dfrac{b}{2a} \pm \dfrac{\sqrt{b^2 - 4ac}}{2a}$.

a. In order to have only one root, $\dfrac{\sqrt{b^2 - 4ac}}{2a}$ must be equal to zero.

$\dfrac{\sqrt{b^2 - 4ac}}{2a} = 0$

$\sqrt{b^2 - 4ac} = 0$	Multiplication property of equality
$b^2 - 4ac = 0$	Squaring both sides
$b^2 = 4ac$	Addition property of equality

b. $\dfrac{\sqrt{b^2 - 4ac}}{2a}$ must be undefined. This will happen when $b^2 - 4ac < 0$. An explanation would resemble the one in Part a.

See additional Teaching Notes on page T257O.

4. Another measure of the center of a set of data is the **midrange**, the number that is halfway between the largest and smallest data values. (The midrange, like the mean, may or may not be a member of the data set.) Suppose a data set consists of n values $x_1, x_2, \ldots, x_n$ ordered from smallest to largest.

   a. Write a formula for the midrange MR.

   b. How, if at all, will the midrange change if a constant c is added to each member of the data set? Prove your answer.

   c. How, if at all, will the midrange change if each member of the data set is multiplied by a positive constant c? Prove your answer.

   d. Recall that unlike the mean, the median is resistant to outliers. Is the midrange resistant to outliers? Explain your reasoning.

Organizing

1. If you use a calculator to graph $y = x^2$ and $y = x^4$, it may look as if $x^2 \leq x^4$ for all values of x. Use the zoom feature on a graphing calculator and inspection of tables for each relation to test that conjecture. Then use algebraic reasoning to prove your conclusion.

2. In constructing a proof with algebraic reasoning, what principles are available to help you with the following tasks?

   a. Show that two expressions are equivalent to each other.

   b. Show that two equations or inequalities are equivalent to each other.

3. Inspect the quadratic formula and explain how you can use it to discover whether a quadratic equation has

   a. only one root.

   b. no roots.

4. Use algebraic reasoning to prove each of the following rules for working with polynomial expressions.

   a. For all a, b, c, and d: $(ax + b) + (cx + d) = (a + c)x + (b + d)$ for all x.

   b. For all a and b: $(x + a)(x + b) = x^2 + (a + b)x + ab$ for all x.

   c. For all a: $(x + a)^2 = x^2 + 2ax + a^2$ for all x.

Reflecting

1. In what ways should an algebraic proof increase a person's confidence in some pattern involving numbers, geometric shapes, trigonometric relations, or statistics?

2. How do the goals and methods of proof in mathematics compare to those that you'd expect in fields like science, politics, or law?

LESSON 5 • PROOF THROUGH ALGEBRAIC REASONING 249

3. Suppose the following vertex-edge graph represents six businesses that are protected by the Allied Security Service and the typical time (in minutes) it takes for a night inspector to travel from place to place.

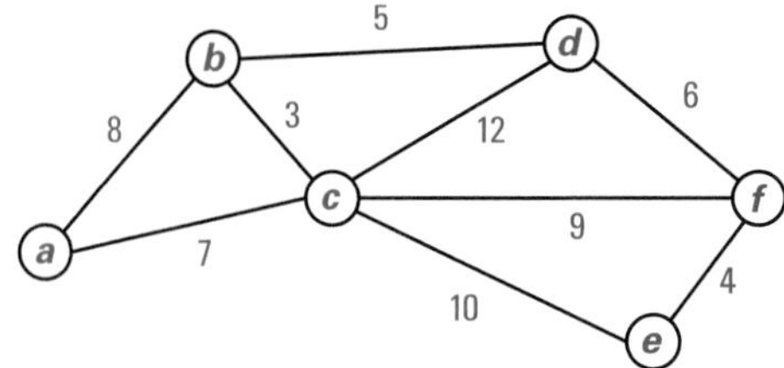

a. How would you find the most efficient route for the nightly check of each of the businesses?

b. How would you prove that a particular route is the most efficient?

c. How does the proof in Part b differ from proof strategies using reasoning with symbolic algebra?

4. Here is a visual "proof" that $(x + p)(x + q) = x^2 + (p + q)x + pq$, for any p and q.

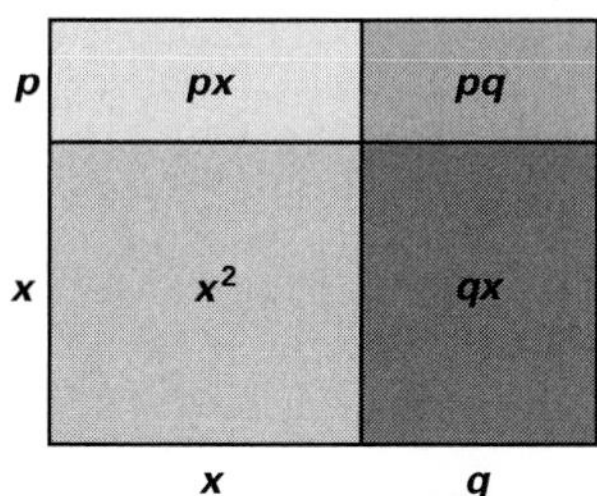

$$(x + p)(x + q) = x^2 + px + qx + pq$$
$$= x^2 + (p + q)x + pq$$

How does this compare to an algebraic proof based on the distributive property? Which do you find more convincing? Which is easier to remember?

Extending

1. The following number trick has puzzled both students and researchers in number theory. Think of a positive integer and then follow these instructions:

Step 1: Write the number.

Step 2: If the number is 1, stop.

Step 3: If the number is even, divide it by 2 and then return to Step 1; follow through the sequence of steps with this new number.

Step 4: If the number is odd, multiply it by 3, add 1, and then return to Step 1 and follow the sequence of steps with the new number.

250 UNIT 3 • SYMBOL SENSE AND ALGEBRAIC REASONING

Unit 3

3. **a.** Students should realize that you need to make a chart or run a computer program to test every single possiblity in order to determine which route would take the inspector from one business to each of the other businesses in the least time. Every starting vertex should be analyzed. (There are many algorithms for finding similar routes. This question is similar to the Traveling Salesperson problem but does not require a circuit.)

   b. The simplest way to prove that a particular route is most efficient would be to show that it is faster than every other possibility. (In Course 2, Unit 5, "Network Optimization," students learned that there is no known efficient algorithm for solving the Traveling Salesperson problem. All possible circuits would need to be checked.)

   c. This proof differs from algebraic strategies because there is a finite number of possible routes. This is not true for many algebra statements. In most cases, there is an infinite number of possibilities; therefore, you cannot show that a statement is true for every single possible variable value.

4. The visual proof and the algebraic proof using the distributive property both express the general patterns found in squaring a binomial. Students' proof preferences may vary. For some students, the visual sketch helps them remember the various parts of the algebraic expansion. For other students, using the distributive property is simple and direct.

Extending

1. **a.** Students may choose any starting number.
Starting with 7 gives the sequence

7, 22, 11, 34, 17, 52, 26, 13, 40, 20, 10, 5, 16, 8, 4, 2, 1

Starting with 24 gives the sequence 24, 12, 6, 3, 10, 5, 16, 8, 4, 2, 1
Starting with 32 gives the sequence 32, 16, 8, 4, 2, 1
It appears that the sequence will always reach 1.

b. A computer or calculator program could test only a finite (though large) number of the possible sequences to be generated. If any sequence does not end in 1, the conjecture could be disproved; but if it does not terminate in 1, the test would never be finished, so even a computer would not have time to test all possible sequences.

c. If n is a power of 2, then $n = 2^k$ for some k. n is also even, since 2^k is divisible by 2. Hence the trick tells us to divide by 2.

$$\frac{n}{2} = \frac{2^k}{2} = 2^{k-1}$$

But 2^{k-1} is also even, so we continue to divide by 2 and see that we will always end with 1 because any power of 2 divided by 2 is still even.

$$2^k, 2^{k-1}, 2^{k-2}, 2^{k-3}, \ldots, 2^2, 2^1, 1$$

d. Student responses will vary. One family is numbers in the form $\frac{2^k - 1}{3}$.

2.

$h^2 = b^2 - x^2$	Pythagorean Theorem
$h^2 = c^2 - (x + a)^2$	Pythagorean Theorem
$b^2 - x^2 = c^2 - (x + a)^2$	Both expressions are equal to h^2
$c^2 = b^2 - x^2 + (x + a)^2$	Addition property of equality
$c^2 = b^2 - x^2 + (x^2 + 2ax + a^2)$	Square of a binomial
$c^2 = b^2 + a^2 + 2ax$	Associative and commutative properties; any number subtracted from itself is zero
$\cos C = -\frac{x}{b}$	Definition of cosine (modified since $90° \leq C \leq 180°$)
$x = -b \cos C$	Multiplication property of equality
$c^2 = b^2 + a^2 - 2ab \cos C$	Substitution

3. **a.** The derivation is given in the student text on page 29.

b.

$\sin A = \frac{h}{b}$	Definition of sine for $90° \leq A \leq 180°$
$\sin B = \frac{h}{a}$	Definition of sine
$h = b \sin A$ and $h = a \sin B$	Multiplication property of equality
$b \sin A = a \sin B$	Both equal to h
$\frac{\sin A}{a} = \frac{\sin B}{b}$	Divide both sides of previous equation by ab

a. Test this trick with several numbers, and then make a conjecture about the output of the sequence of steps.

b. Could a computer or calculator program be used to prove your conjecture? If so, how? If not, why not?

c. Your conjecture should be true for any positive integer that is a power of 2. Prove that it is.

d. For what other sets of positive integers can you prove your conjecture?

2. The diagram at the right shows a triangle in which the angle at vertex C is obtuse and an altitude from A lies outside the triangle. Revise the proof given in Investigation 2, Activity 3 (page 245) to establish the Law of Cosines in this case.

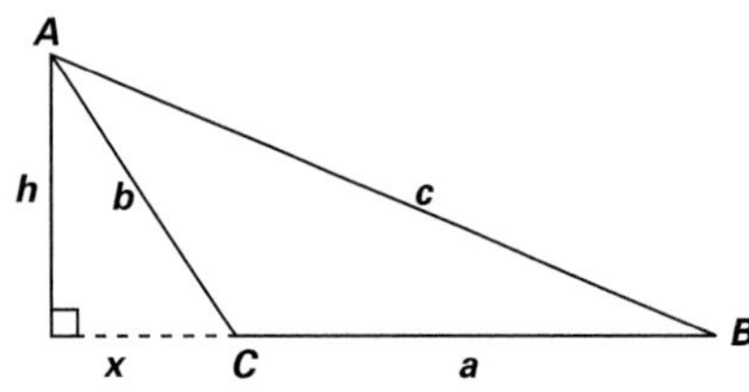

3. In the "Multiple-Variable Models" unit, you used a diagram like the one below to examine a derivation of the Law of Sines.

$$\frac{\sin A}{a} = \frac{\sin B}{b}$$

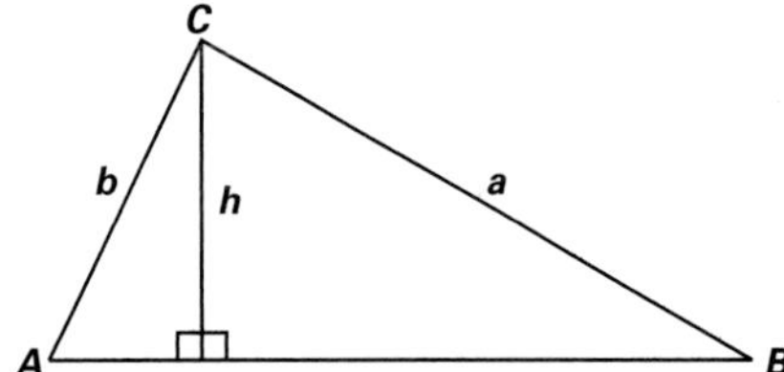

a. The key to the derivation was to write two expressions for h, one in terms of $\sin A$ and b and the other in terms of $\sin B$ and a. See if you can reconstruct the derivation on your own. If you have difficulty, see page 29.

b. Modify the argument in Part a to cover the case in which the altitude lies outside $\triangle ABC$ as in the diagram below.

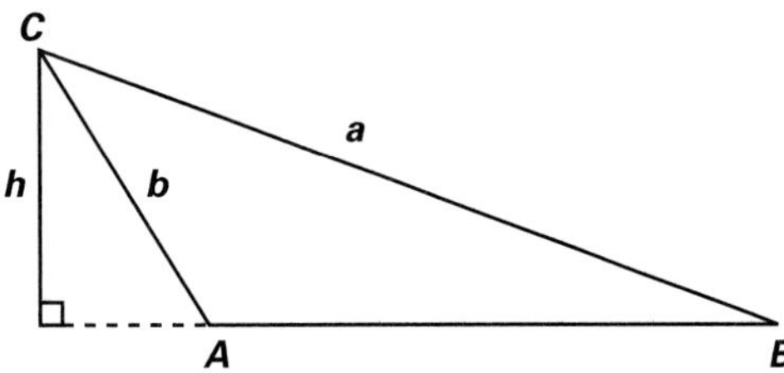

Unit 3

LESSON 5 • PROOF THROUGH ALGEBRAIC REASONING 251

4. In Modeling Task 3, page 248, you developed a coordinate model for a circle with radius r and center at the origin. Similar reasoning can be used to develop an equation for any circle given its center and radius.

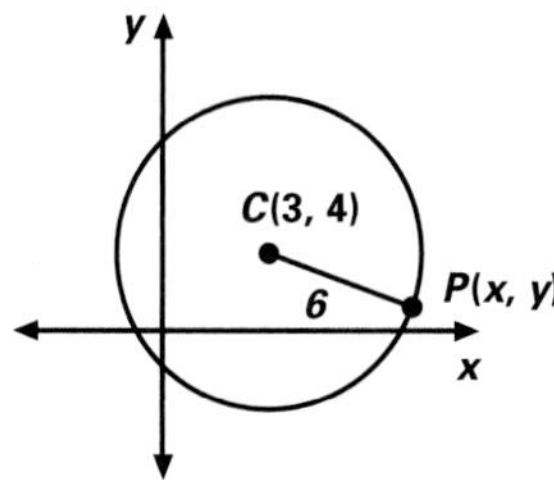

a. Shown above is a circle with center $C(3, 4)$ and radius 6. Write an equation for this circle.

b. Write your equation from Part a in expanded form: $x^2 + y^2 + ax + by = c$.

c. Prove that the equation of a circle with center $C(h, k)$ and radius r is $(x - h)^2 + (y - k)^2 = r^2$.

d. In a calculus text, the following equation was given as an equation of a circle:

$$x^2 + y^2 + 6x - 4y = 12$$

Rebecca believed she could reason as follows to determine the center and radius of the circle and then easily sketch it.

$x^2 + y^2 + 6x - 4y = 12$ is equivalent to $(x^2 + 6x) + (y^2 - 4y) = 12$,
which is equivalent to $(x^2 + 6x + 9) + (y^2 - 4y + 4) = 12 + 9 + 4$,
which is equivalent to $(x + 3)^2 + (y - 2)^2 = 25$.

Explain Rebecca's strategy and how it is related to your earlier work with recognizing the form of perfect square quadratics. Sketch the circle in a coordinate plane.

e. Use algebraic reasoning to identify the center and radius of each circle below, and then sketch the circle in a coordinate plane.

- $x^2 + y^2 + 12x - 2y = -21$
- $x^2 + y^2 + 8y = 9$

Unit 3

252 UNIT 3 • SYMBOL SENSE AND ALGEBRAIC REASONING

MORE *continued*

4. **a.** Using the distance formula, $\sqrt{(x - 3)^2 + (y - 4)^2} = 6$. Squaring both sides of the equation, we get $(x - 3)^2 + (y - 4)^2 = 6^2$.

   b. $x^2 - 6x + 9 + y^2 - 8y + 16 = 36$
   $x^2 + y^2 - 6x - 8y = 11$

   c. The point (x, y) is on a circle with center (h, k) and radius r if the distance from (x, y) to (h, k) is r. The distance formula says $\sqrt{(x - h)^2 + (y - k)^2} = r$. Now squaring both sides of the equation, we get $(x - h)^2 + (y - k)^2 = r^2$. Every point (x, y) satisfying this equation lies on the circle with center (h, k) and radius r. Thus, this is the equation of the circle.

   d. Rebecca's reasoning can be justified as follows:

$x^2 + y^2 + 6x - 4y = 12$	
$(x^2 + 6x \qquad) + (y^2 - 4y \qquad) = 12$	Commutative property of addition
$(x^2 + 6x + \mathbf{9}) + (y^2 - 4y + \mathbf{4}) = 12 + \mathbf{9} + \mathbf{4}$	Adding equal quantities to both sides of equation
$(x + 3)^2 + (y - 2)^2 = 25$	Writing a perfect square trinomial as the square of a binomial

   This is the equation of a circle with center at $(-3, 2)$ and radius 5. See the first graph below.

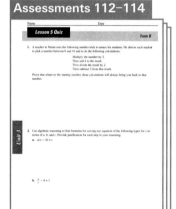

   e. ■ $x^2 + y^2 + 12x - 2y = -21$
   $(x^2 + 12x \qquad) + (y^2 - 2y \qquad) = -21$
   $(x^2 + 12x + \mathbf{36}) + (y^2 - 2y + \mathbf{1}) = -21 + \mathbf{36} + \mathbf{1}$
   $(x + 6)^2 + (y - 1)^2 = 16$
   This is the equation of a circle with center at $(-6, 1)$ and radius 4. (See the second graph below.)

   ■ $x^2 + y^2 + 8y = 9$
   $x^2 + (y^2 + 8y \qquad) = 9$
   $x^2 + (y^2 + 8y + \mathbf{16}) = 9 + \mathbf{16}$
   $x^2 + (y + 4)^2 = 25$
   This is the equation of a circle with center at $(0, -4)$ and radius 5. (See the third graph below.)

   Graph for 4d.

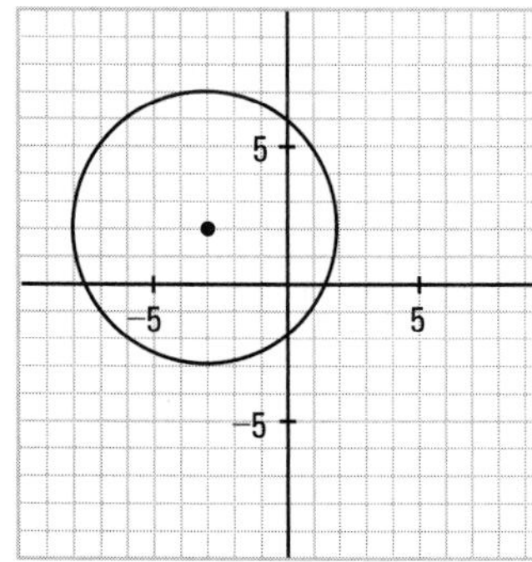

   Graphs for 4e.

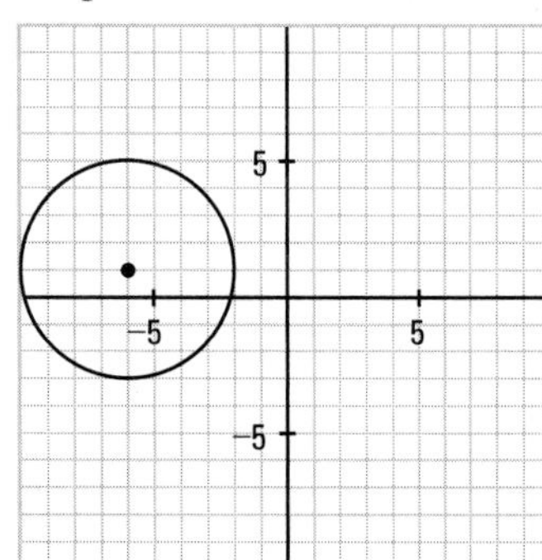

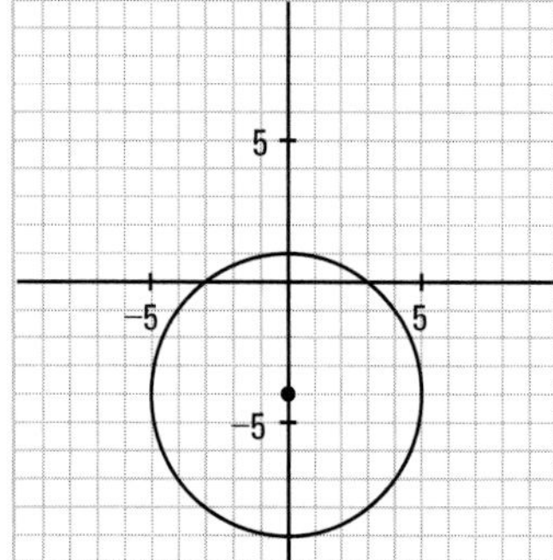

See Assessment Resources pages 109–114.

Assessments 109–111

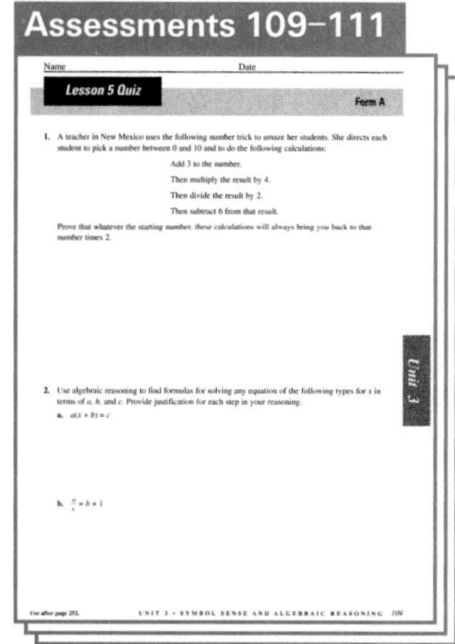

Name Date

Lesson 5 Quiz

Form A

1. A teacher in New Mexico uses the following number trick to amaze her students. She directs each student to pick a number between 0 and 10 and to do the following calculations:

   Add 3 to the number.

   Then multiply the result by 4.

   Then divide the result by 2.

   Then subtract 6 from that result.

   Prove that whatever the starting number, these calculations will always bring you back to that number times 2.

2. Use algebraic reasoning to find formulas for solving any equation of the following types for x in terms of a, b, and c. Provide justification for each step in your reasoning.

   a. $a(x + b) = c$

   b. $\frac{a}{x} = b + 1$

Unit 3

Use after page 252. UNIT 3 • SYMBOL SENSE AND ALGEBRAIC REASONING 109

Assessments 112–114

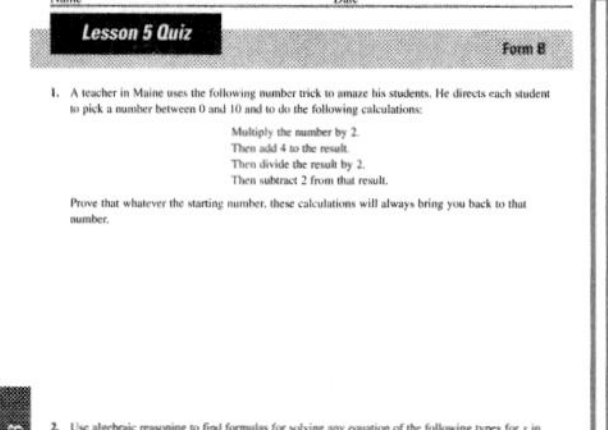

Name Date

Lesson 5 Quiz

Form B

1. A teacher in Maine uses the following number trick to amaze his students. He directs each student to pick a number between 0 and 10 and to do the following calculations:

   Multiply the number by 2.
   Then add 4 to the result.
   Then divide the result by 2.
   Then subtract 2 from that result.

   Prove that whatever the starting number, these calculations will always bring you back to that number.

2. Use algebraic reasoning to find formulas for solving any equation of the following types for x in terms of a, b, and c. Provide justification for each step in your reasoning.

   a. $a(x - b) = c$

   b. $\frac{a}{x} - b = 1$

Unit 3

112 UNIT 3 • SYMBOL SENSE AND ALGEBRAIC REASONING Use after page 252.

Unit 3

Lesson 6 *Looking Back*

SYNTHESIZE UNIT IDEAS small-group activity

1. **a.** $I(x) = -30x^2 + 5{,}000x + 300x = -30x^2 + 5{,}300x$
   $C(x) = 200x + 40{,}000$

   b.

$r(50) = 175{,}000$	The rental cost for 50,000 square feet is \$175,000.
$s(50) = 15{,}000$	The monthly surcharge paid to the mall when a total area of 50,000 square feet is rented is \$15,000.
$m(50) = 10{,}000$	The maintenance and security costs when a total area of 50,000 square feet is rented are \$10,000.
$t(50) = 40{,}000$	The taxes and other indirect costs when a total area of 50,000 square feet is rented are \$40,000.
$I(50) = 190{,}000$	The income for the mall when a total area of 50,000 square feet is rented is \$190,000.
$C(50) = 50{,}000$	The total cost to the mall for renting an area of 50,000 square feet is \$50,000.

Lesson 6

Looking Back

In this unit, you have studied functions and used symbolic notation to express and reason about relations among variables modeled by those functions. You've discovered a variety of principles and strategies for manipulating symbolic expressions into equivalent forms and applied them to reveal important properties of relationships, to solve equations and inequalities, and to prove the generality of patterns in algebra, geometry, trigonometry, and statistics. The tasks in this section will help you review these important topics.

1. The Blackstone Plaza shopping mall has a total of 100,000 square feet of floor space for stores to rent. The mall rents in units of 1,000 square feet, and monthly income and operating costs (in dollars) depend on the number of floor space units x that are rented. The models below approximate the indicated quantities when the mall has 40% to 85% of its space occupied.

Sources of Income:	Basic rent payments	$r(x) = -30x^2 + 5{,}000x$
	Monthly surcharge for improvements	$s(x) = 300x$
Operating Costs:	Maintenance and security	$m(x) = 200x$
	Property taxes, utilities for common areas, and promotion	$t(x) = 40{,}000$

a. Write algebraic rules for two functions $I(x)$ and $C(x)$ showing how monthly *income* and operating *costs* of the mall depend on the amount of floor space rented.

b. Evaluate $r(50)$, $s(50)$, $m(50)$, $t(50)$, $I(50)$, and $C(50)$, and explain what each tells about the Blackstone Plaza.

Unit 3

LESSON 6 • LOOKING BACK 253

c. Explore tables and graphs of the income and cost functions, and then describe both the practical and the theoretical domains and ranges for those functions.

d. Write two algebraic rules for the function $P(x)$ showing how Blackstone Plaza's monthly operating *profit* depends on floor space rented. Give one rule in standard polynomial form and the other in an informative equivalent form. Explain how algebraic properties guarantee equivalence of the two rules.

e. Evaluate $P(40)$ and explain what the result tells about profits for the mall.

f. Explain how you can test the equivalence of the two profit rules in Part d with function tables and graphs.

g. Explore tables and graphs of $P(x)$, and then describe both practical and theoretical domains and ranges for the profit function.

2. Write and solve, by symbolic reasoning methods of this unit, equations and inequalities so that you can answer the following questions about Blackstone Plaza business prospects.

a. If the mall reports operating costs of \$56,000, how much floor space must have been rented to stores?

b. How many units of store floor space must be rented for the mall to produce an income of \$210,000?

c. At what floor space rental levels will mall operating costs exceed \$51,000?

d. At what rental levels will mall income equal operating costs?

3. In studying the Blackstone Plaza profit situation, you will find that $P(x) = 0$ at $x \approx 8$ and $x \approx 162$. How does this information help you locate the rental level that will produce maximum profit for the mall? Can the mall profit be maximum when some space is still unrented?

4. To compare the profitability of Blackstone Plaza to similar properties, the owners believed it would make sense to calculate their profit per 1,000 square feet of store floor space.

a. What is the profit per 1,000 square feet of floor space when $x = 40$, $x = 60$, and $x = 80$?

b. Write several equivalent algebraic expressions for a function $A(x)$ showing how profit per square foot of rented floor space changes as x increases. Include one that you believe involves the simplest calculations and another that best shows the contribution of each income and cost component. Be prepared to explain how you know the various expressions are equivalent.

Unit 3

254 UNIT 3 • SYMBOL SENSE AND ALGEBRAIC REASONING

1. c. 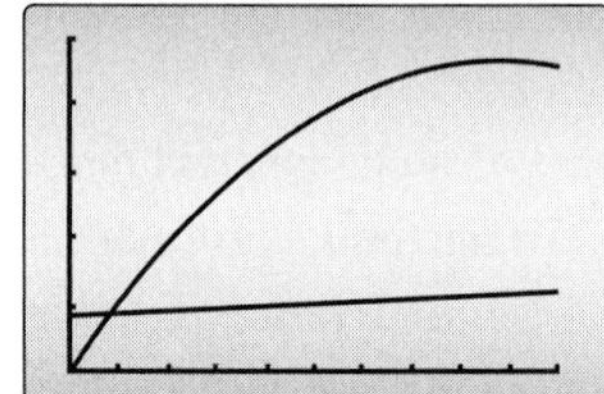

WINDOW
Xmin =0
Xmax =100
Xscl =10
Ymin =0
Ymax =250000
Yscl =50000
Xres =1

X	Y_1	Y_2
40	164000	48000
50	190000	50000
60	210000	52000
70	224000	54000
80	232000	56000
90	234000	58000
100	230000	60000

X=40

Since the functions given are reliable for only 40% to 85% occupancy, the maximum income we can estimate is \$233,750 and the maximum costs are \$57,000.

The practical domain for the income function is $40 \le x \le 85$, where x is an integer, and the practical range is $164{,}000 \le I(x) \le 233{,}750$. The theoretical domain is the set of all real numbers, and the theoretical range is $I(x) \le 234{,}083.33$.

The practical domain for the cost function is $40 \le x \le 85$. The practical range is $48{,}000 \le C(x) \le 57{,}000$. Both the theoretical domain and the theoretical range of the cost function are all real numbers.

d. $P(x) = -30x^2 + 5{,}300x - 200x - 40{,}000$

$P(x) = -30x^2 + 5{,}100x - 40{,}000$

e. $P(40) = 116{,}000$ means that if a total area of 40,000 square feet is rented, the profit will be \$116,000.

f. Enter both rules into the calculator and compare the graphs and the tables to see that they are the same.

g. The practical domain of the profit function is $40 \le x \le 85$, and the range is $116{,}000 \le P(x) \le 176{,}750$.

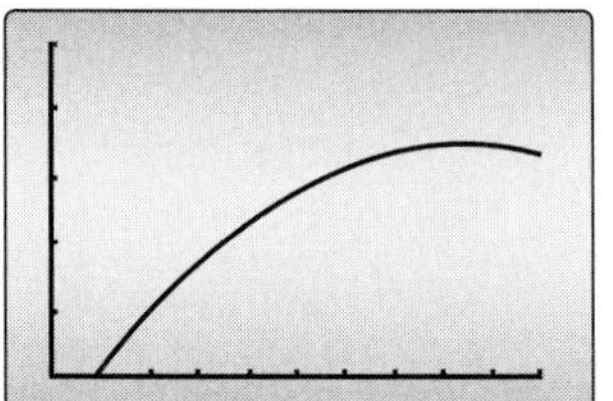

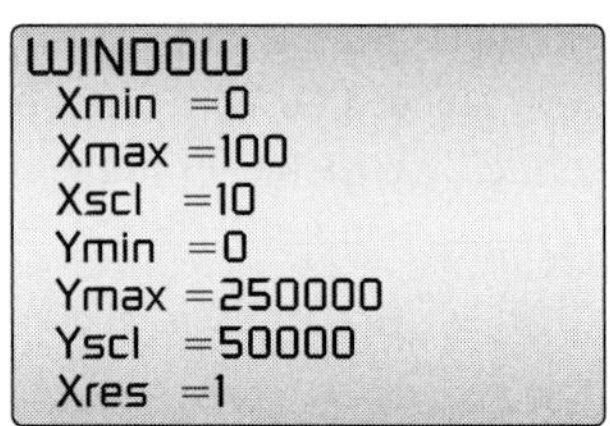

X	Y_3
40	116000
50	140000
60	158000
70	170000
80	176000
90	176000
100	170000

X=40

2. a. $200x + 40{,}000 = 56{,}000$

$200x = 16{,}000$

$x = 80$

This means that 80,000 square feet must have been rented.

b. $-30x^2 + 5{,}300x = 210{,}000$

$-30x^2 + 5{,}300x - 210{,}000 = 0$

$$x = \frac{-5{,}300}{-60} \pm \frac{\sqrt{5{,}300^2 - 4(-30)(-210{,}000)}}{-60}$$

$x = 60$ and $x \approx 116.67$, but since 116.67 is not in the practical domain, the solution of 60 means that 60 units must be rented to produce an income of \$210,000.

c. $200x + 40{,}000 > \$51{,}000$

$200x > 11{,}000$

$x > 55$

d. $-30x^2 + 5{,}300x = 200x + 40{,}000$

$-30x^2 + 5{,}100x - 40{,}000 = 0$

$$x = \frac{-5{,}100}{-60} \pm \frac{\sqrt{5{,}100^2 - 4(-30)(-40{,}000)}}{-60}$$

$x \approx 8.24$ and 161.76. Both these values are outside our practical domain; the mall doesn't have 161 units, and we cannot rely on our equation for $x < 40$.

See additional Teaching Notes on page T257P.

Unit 3

5. **a.** Responses will vary. Reasonable monthly rates per square foot are probably \$1.00 to \$5.00.

   b. The graph shows that the company will lose money if it charges less than \$1.00 per square foot. Its profits will gradually increase up to a maximum profit of \$32,000 per month when it charges \$3 per square foot. Its profits will decrease if it charges more than \$3 per square foot. If the rent is greater than \$5 per square foot, the company will lose money.

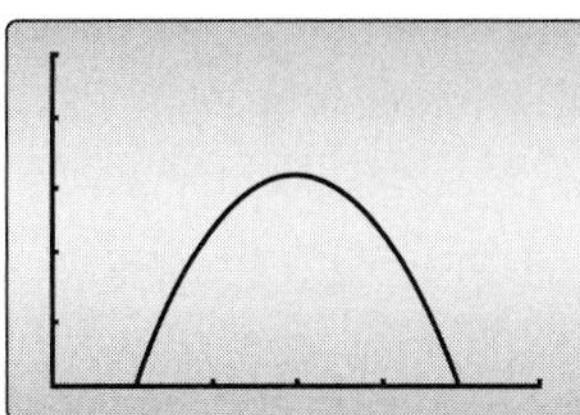

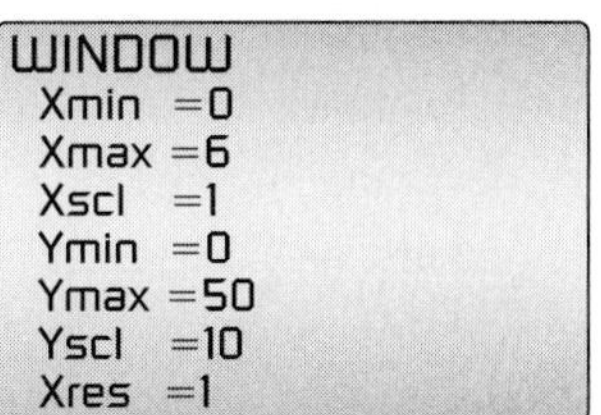

   c. The solution is $r = 1$ or $r = 5$. This means that the company will break even on this building if it charges \$1 or \$5 per square foot.

   d. The solution is $1 < r < 5$. So the company will make a profit if the rent is between \$1 and \$5.

   e. The solution is $r \approx 1.54$ or $r \approx 4.46$. So the company will make a monthly profit of \$15,000 if it sets the rent at \$1.54 or \$4.46 per square foot.

   f. The solution is $1.54 < r < 4.46$. So if the rent is set between \$1.54 and \$4.46 per square foot, the profit will be greater than \$15,000.

   g. The solution is $r < 1.34$ or $r > 4.66$. So if the rent is less than \$1.34 per square foot or greater than \$4.66 per square foot, the profit will be less than \$10,000.

6. **a.** $f(x) = -4x^3 + 5x^2 - 9x + 12$

   b. $g(x) = 77x - 28x^2 + 3x - 9$
   $= -28x^2 + 80x - 9$

   c. $h(x) = (x + 4)2x + (x + 4)(-3) + 7$
   $= 2x^2 + 8x - 3x - 12 + 7$
   $= 2x^2 + 5x - 5$

   d. $j(x) = 4(x^2 + 6x + 9) - 7x + 56$
   $= 4x^2 + 24x + 36 - 7x + 56$
   $= 4x^2 + 17x + 92$

7. **a.** The zeroes of the function are equal to the values that make each factor equal to 0. If r_1 and r_2 are zeroes, then $(x - r_1)$ and $(x - r_2)$ are factors.

   b. If a and b are the zeroes of a quadratic function, then the line of symmetry of the function has equation $x = \frac{a + b}{2}$.

8. **a.** $f(x) + g(x) = 2x^2 + 4x + 1$

   b. $f(x) - g(x) = 2x^2 - 2x + 3$

   c. $f(x) \times g(x) = 6x^3 + x^2 + 5x - 2$

   d. $5[f(x)] - 3[g(x)] = (10x^2 + 5x + 10) - (9x - 3) = 10x^2 - 4x + 13$

5. The owners of Blackstone Plaza decided that by constructing an office building attached to their mall, they could increase traffic in the stores, making the mall more desirable for stores and thus increasing their own profit. They collected various kinds of information about construction and operating costs and the relation between rent charged and amount of space that would be rented. They determined that the relation between monthly rent charged r (in dollars per square foot) and monthly profit $P(r)$ (in thousands of dollars) from the new building would be approximated well by the following rule:

$$P(r) = -8r^2 + 48r - 40$$

   a. What values of r (the rent per square foot per month) seem reasonable to consider as the practical domain of this function and what values seem unreasonable? (**Hint:** Look at advertisements for apartment and house rentals in a local newspaper, and think about the relation between the area of a house or apartment and typical monthly rent for such space. Then remember that commercial space is generally a bit more expensive.)

   b. Sketch a graph of the function over what seems to be a practical domain, and explain what the shape of that graph tells about the relation between rent charged and profit prospects for the new building.

   Solve each of the following quadratic equations and inequalities, using factoring or the quadratic formula, and explain what each answer tells about the relation between monthly rent charges and profit for the planned building.

   c. $-8r^2 + 48r - 40 = 0$
   d. $-8r^2 + 48r - 40 > 0$
   e. $-8r^2 + 48r - 40 = 15$
   f. $-8r^2 + 48r - 40 > 15$
   g. $-8r^2 + 48r - 40 < 10$

6. Use algebraic properties to write each of the following expressions for polynomial function rules in equivalent standard form.

   a. $f(x) = 5x^2 - 4x^3 + 12 - 9x$
   b. $g(x) = 7x(11 - 4x) + 3x - 9$
   c. $h(x) = (x + 4)(2x - 3) + 7$
   d. $j(x) = 4(x + 3)^2 - 7(x - 8)$

7. Think about the relationships between symbolic and graphical representations of quadratic functions.

   a. What is the relationship between the factors of a quadratic expression and the zeroes of the function defined by that expression?

   b. What is the relationship between the zeroes of a quadratic function and the line of symmetry of its graph?

8. Given $f(x) = 2x^2 + x + 2$ and $g(x) = 3x - 1$, write standard polynomial rules for each of the following combinations of those functions. Be prepared to use algebraic properties to justify each step in your reasoning.

   a. $f(x) + g(x)$
   b. $f(x) - g(x)$
   c. $f(x) \times g(x)$
   d. $5[f(x)] - 3[g(x)]$

Unit 3

LESSON 6 • LOOKING BACK 255

9. Solve these equations and inequalities by reasoning with the symbolic expressions alone. Then draw graphs illustrating each solution.

   a. $2(x - 3) + 5(x + 2) = 0$ **b.** $5x - 7 < 15 + 3x$

   c. $0 \leq 2x^2 + 3x + 1$ **d.** $x^2 + 5x + 6 = 1 - x$

10. Describe four different methods for solving the equation $x^2 + 2x - 15 = 0$. Use one of the methods to solve the equation and show how that solution can be checked without use of a calculator.

11. For each of the following quadratic functions, decide whether it has 0, 1, or 2 zeroes. Then explain how the graph of the function illustrates the number of solutions.

   a. $g(x) = 2x^2 + 5x + 3$ **b.** $h(x) = -x^2 - 7x - 1$

   c. $j(x) = 6x^2 - 2x + 1$ **d.** $p(x) = x^2 + 2x - 1$

12. Explain the relationship between the graph of $f(x) = ax^2 + bx + c$, $x = \frac{-b}{2a}$, and the value $\frac{\sqrt{b^2 - 4ac}}{2a}$.

13. Write each of the following algebraic expressions in standard polynomial form. Be prepared to explain the properties of algebraic operations that justify each answer.

   a. $(x + 7)(x - 7)$ **b.** $(x + 7)^2$

   c. $(x - 3)(x + 8)$ **d.** $(2x + 5)(x - 4)$

14. Write each of the following polynomials as a product of linear factors.

   a. $x^2 + 7x + 12$ **b.** $x^2 + 6x + 9$

   c. $x^2 - 25$ **d.** $x^2 - 7x - 8$

   e. $3x^2 - 7x + 2$

15. The quadratic formula gives the roots of $ax^2 + bx + c = 0$ where $a \neq 0$. Using algebraic reasoning with the formula also reveals interesting relationships between the roots.

   a. Prove that the sum of the roots of $ax^2 + bx + c = 0$ is $-\frac{b}{a}$.

   b. Prove that the product of the roots of $ax^2 + bx + c = 0$ is $\frac{c}{a}$.

   c. Suppose the quadratic equation $ax^2 + bx + c = 0$ were rewritten in the equivalent form $x^2 + mx + n = 0$. Write expressions for m and n in terms of a, b, and c. What does Part a above show about m, the coefficient of x? What does Part b show about n, the constant term?

256 UNIT 3 • SYMBOL SENSE AND ALGEBRAIC REASONING

SYNTHESIZE *continued*

9. a. $2(x - 3) + 5(x + 2) = 0$
$2x - 6 + 5x + 10 = 0$
$7x + 4 = 0$
$x = -\frac{4}{7}$

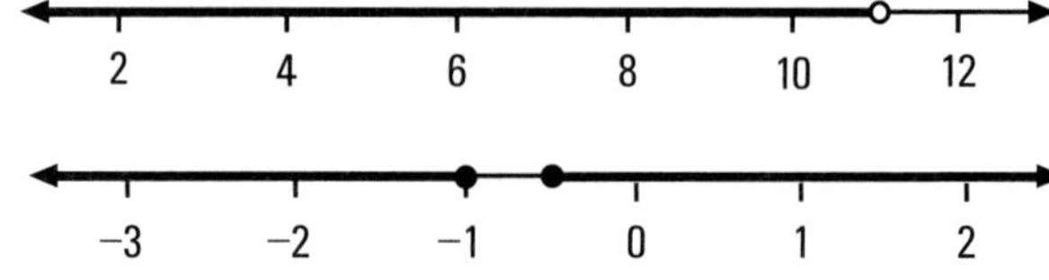

b. $5x - 7 < 15 + 3x$
$2x < 22$
$x < 11$

c. $0 \leq (2x + 1)(x + 1)$
$x \leq -1$ or $x \geq -\frac{1}{2}$

d. $x^2 + 5x + 6 = 1 - x$
$x^2 + 6x + 5 = 0$
$(x + 5)(x + 1) = 0$
$x = -5$ or $x = -1$

10. Methods that could be used to solve this equation include the following:

- Draw the graph of $y = x^2 + 2x - 15$ and trace to find the x-intercepts.
- Examine a table of values for $y = x^2 + 2x - 15$ to find x values for which the y value is zero.
- Factor the quadratic expression and then set each factor equal to zero.
- Use the solve feature of the calculator or use the quadratic formula.

The solutions to the equation are $x = -5$ or $x = 3$. To check, use another method or substitute each value into the equation.

11. a. The function has two zeroes.
The graph has two x-intercepts.

b. The function has two zeroes.
The graph has two x-intercepts.

c. The function has no real zeroes.
The graph opens up and has a minimum above the x-axis, so it has no x-intercepts.

d. The function has two zeroes.
The graph has two x-intercepts.

12. The axis of symmetry for $f(x) = ax^2 + bx + c$ is $x = \frac{-b}{2a}$, and the value $\frac{\sqrt{b^2 - 4ac}}{2a}$ is the distance from the axis of symmetry to the roots of the function.

13. a. $x^2 - 49$ **b.** $x^2 + 14x + 49$

c. $x^2 + 5x - 24$ **d.** $2x^2 - 3x - 20$

14. a. $(x + 4)(x + 3)$ **b.** $(x + 3)^2$

c. $(x - 5)(x + 5)$ **d.** $(x - 8)(x + 1)$

e. $(3x - 1)(x - 2)$

Unit 3

See additional Teaching Notes on page T257P.

Masters 85a–85b

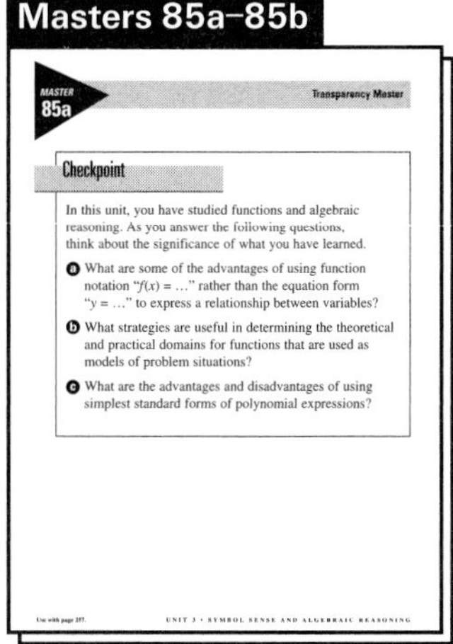
MASTER 85a

Transparency Master

Checkpoint

In this unit, you have studied functions and algebraic reasoning. As you answer the following questions, think about the significance of what you have learned.

(a) What are some of the advantages of using function notation "$f(x)$ = ..." rather than the equation form "y = ..." to express a relationship between variables?

(b) What strategies are useful in determining the theoretical and practical domains for functions that are used as models of problem situations?

(c) What are the advantages and disadvantages of using simplest standard forms of polynomial expressions?

Use with page 257. UNIT 3 • SYMBOL SENSE AND ALGEBRAIC REASONING

Unit 3 Summary

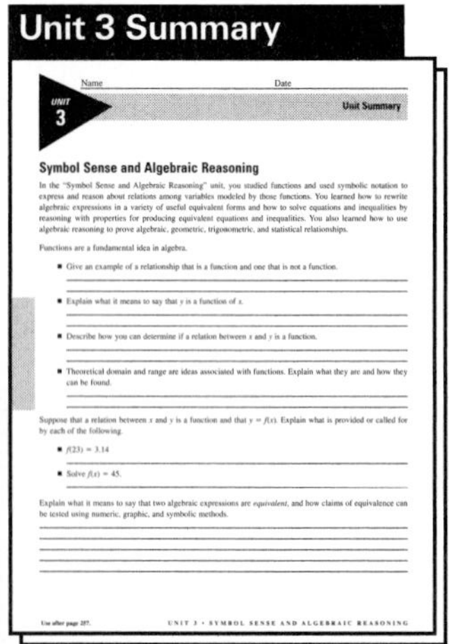
Name Date

UNIT 3 Unit Summary

Symbol Sense and Algebraic Reasoning

In the "Symbol Sense and Algebraic Reasoning" unit, you studied functions and used symbolic notation to express and reason about relations among variables modeled by those functions. You learned how to rewrite algebraic expressions in a variety of useful equivalent forms and how to solve equations and inequalities by reasoning with properties for producing equivalent equations and inequalities. You also learned how to use algebraic reasoning to prove algebraic, geometric, trigonometric, and statistical relationships.

Functions are a fundamental idea in algebra.

- Give an example of a relationship that is a function and one that is not a function.
- Explain what it means to say that y is a function of x.
- Describe how you can determine if a relation between x and y is a function.
- Theoretical domain and range are ideas associated with functions. Explain what they are and how they can be found.

Suppose that a relation between x and y is a function and that $y = f(x)$. Explain what is provided or called for by each of the following.

- $f(23) = 3.14$
- Solve $f(x) = 45$.

Explain what it means to say that two algebraic expressions are *equivalent*, and how claims of equivalence can be tested using numeric, graphic, and symbolic methods.

Use after page 257. UNIT 3 • SYMBOL SENSE AND ALGEBRAIC REASONING

Assessments 115–157

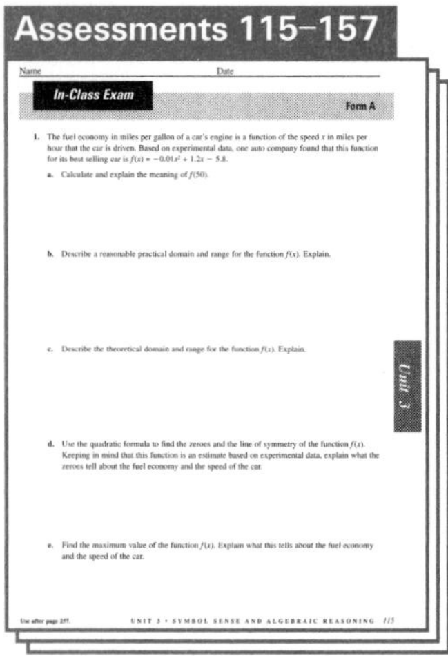
Name Date

In-Class Exam Form A

1. The fuel economy in miles per gallon of a car's engine is a function of the speed x in miles per hour that the car is driven. Based on experimental data, one auto company found that this function for its best selling car is $f(x) = -0.01x^2 + 1.2x - 5.8$.
   a. Calculate and explain the meaning of $f(50)$.
   b. Describe a reasonable practical domain and range for the function $f(x)$. Explain.
   c. Describe the theoretical domain and range for the function $f(x)$. Explain.
   d. Use the quadratic formula to find the zeroes and the line of symmetry of the function $f(x)$. Keeping in mind that this function is an estimate based on experimental data, explain what the zeroes tell about the fuel economy and the speed of the car.
   e. Find the maximum value of the function $f(x)$. Explain what this tells about the fuel economy and the speed of the car.

Unit 3

Use after page 257. UNIT 3 • SYMBOL SENSE AND ALGEBRAIC REASONING 115

Unit 3

SHARE AND SUMMARIZE full-class discussion

Checkpoint

See Teaching Masters 85a–85b.

(a) When you are graphing several functions at the same time, you can distinguish between them by using $g(x)$, $f(x)$, or $k(x)$ instead of just y. You can also use names that have some connection to your problem. For example, $I(x)$ can refer to an interest function and $H(t)$ can refer to a height function. When you refer to the value of the function for a particular value of x, it is easier to denote this using function notation.

(b) The most important strategy in determining the practical domain is to read the problem carefully to determine the real-world constraints of the particular model. In determining the theoretical domain for a function, you want to look for restrictions on the domain caused by a variable expression in a denominator or other constraints that will limit the domain.

(c) Responses may vary. One advantage is that it is easy to tell if two expressions are equivalent. However, at times, some other form will be more enlightening. For example, when trying to find the zeroes of a quadratic expression, the factored form, if it exists, provides an easy way to find the zeroes.

(d) The associative, commutative, and distributive properties are used to simplify polynomial expressions. There are several ways to check that two given expressions are actually equivalent. If two expressions are equivalent, their related tables and graphs should be identical. You can also use algebraic properties to simplify both expressions. When put into simplest standard form, they should be identical.

(e) In general, combining two fractions $\left(\text{such as } \frac{4x}{3} + \frac{7}{x}\right)$ involves multiplying each fraction by some form of 1 so that they have a common denominator and then combining the numerators and placing that expression over the common denominator. In some cases, the distributive property might be used, depending upon the complexity of the expressions in the two fractions.

When you are simplifying an expression similar to $\frac{6x^2 + 8x}{2x}$, the distributive property is often used. Reducing a fraction by dividing the numerator and the denominator by common factors is often helpful as well.

(f) You can solve linear equations or inequalities by (1) putting the variables on one side of the equation, (2) putting the constants on the other side of the equation, and then (3) multiplying both sides by the reciprocal of the coefficient of the variable. (If the value you multiply by is a negative number, you must reverse the inequality sign.)

Although some quadratic equations can be solved by factoring and then finding the zeroes of each factor, all quadratic equations can be solved using the quadratic formula. The equation must first be set equal to 0, and then the appropriate values for a, b, and c can be substituted into the quadratic formula to get the solutions, if there are any. For an inequality, you also need to check the intervals between and on each side of the zeroes.

(g) When you use algebraic proof, you are proving something for the general case, not just showing that something is true for specific examples.

See additional Teaching Notes on page T257P.

Checkpoint

In this unit, you have studied functions and algebraic reasoning. As you answer the following questions, think about the significance of what you have learned.

a What are some of the advantages of using function notation "$f(x) = ...$" rather than the equation form "$y = ...$" to express a relationship between variables?

b What strategies are useful in determining the theoretical and practical domains for functions that are used as models of problem situations?

c What are the advantages and disadvantages of using simplest standard forms of polynomial expressions?

d What algebraic properties are used in simplifying polynomial expressions like $5(x^2 + 4x) - x(3 + 4x) + 7(x + 9)$, and how can you check that two given expressions are actually equivalent?

e What properties of numbers and operations guide combination and separation of fractional algebraic expressions like $\frac{4x}{3} + \frac{7}{x}$ and $\frac{6x^2 + 8x}{2x}$ (where $x \neq 0$)?

f What general strategies are involved in the use of symbolic reasoning to solve linear equations and inequalities? To solve quadratic equations and inequalities?

g How can algebraic reasoning provide proof that patterns you find will hold, even in cases you've not checked?

Be prepared to share your descriptions and thinking with the entire class.

Unit 3

On Your Own

Write, in outline form, a summary of the important mathematical concepts and methods developed in this unit. Organize your summary so that it can be used as a quick reference in future units and courses.

LESSON 6 • LOOKING BACK 257

Looking Back, Looking Ahead

Reflecting on Mathematical Content

Algebra plays a fundamental role in representing and reasoning about relationships among quantitative variables. The *Contemporary Mathematics in Context* curriculum is committed to helping students become adept at representing and reasoning about quantitative relationships. By taking advantage of the numerical, graphic, symbolic, and statistical tools now available on graphing calculators, we've been able to develop student understanding and widely applicable problem-solving skills without a long apprenticeship in formal symbol manipulation.

The key mathematical idea in our approach to algebraic representation and reasoning is the concept of function and the use of various families of functions to model problem situations. Students have studied algebra units focusing on patterns of change, linear models, exponential models, power models, and multivariable models. They have learned to recognize important patterns of variation in quantitative variables, to use statistical tools to construct symbolic models of those patterns, and to use technology-based numeric and graphic strategies for solving the equations and inequalities that can be used to answer important questions about the modeled situations. Along the way, they have acquired some of the traditional symbol manipulation skills of algebra, and, in this unit, they have focused on formal reasoning.

In addition to the mathematical emphasis on the concept of function, this approach to algebra and symbol manipulation has two other important features. First, the use of functions together with multiple-representation, problem-solving tools gives students early access to authentic and interesting problem material that reflects the kind of mathematical work they are apt to do in future study in other disciplines and in many occupations. Second, by building a strong intuitive foundation, for use of symbolic expressions, students prepare for a more successful study of formal reasoning.

It also is very important that students develop a certain level of skill in formal symbolic representation and reasoning. No calculator-generated table or graph can establish validity of a pattern "for all x," and even the most powerful computer symbol manipulation program will not help the user decide on the most appropriate form to use or help the user interpret the results of that manipulation. Thus, this unit was designed to start from firm algebraic intuition and to begin developing student ability to use personal symbol manipulation as a powerful tool in general reasoning about many quantitative situations, including applications in geometry and statistics.

Even a fairly extensive unit on symbolic reasoning will not provide students with the skill and level of confidence that they might find useful in future mathematical study and applications. Thus, the algebra strand of *Contemporary Mathematics in Context* will continue in Course 3 with one additional core unit, along with connections to several units in which the focus is on a different strand. The fourth year will include further development of symbolic skills for college-bound students. In Unit 6 of Course 3, students explore families of functions. They learn how to adapt basic function models to more complex situations by use of symbolic expressions corresponding to reflection, translation, and stretching of basic function graph types. They learn how to adapt basic function models to more complex situations by use of symbolic expressions corresponding to reflection, translation, and stretching of basic function graph types.

In Course 4, Unit 1, students develop an understanding of average and instantaneous rate of change of functions and the fundamental concepts underlying calculus and its applications. Course 4, Unit 3, "Logarithmic Functions and Data Models" develops symbolic manipulation of exponential and logarithmic expressions. Unit 6, "Polynomial and Rational Functions," includes symbolic manipulation principles that are part of the classical theory of equations. Unit 7, "Functions and Symbolic Reasoning," pulls together broad principles for reasoning with symbolic expressions including the study of complex numbers. The algebra and functions strand units are connected to and enhanced by the symbolic manipulation content in Course 3, Unit 7, "Discrete Models of Change" and all Course 4 units.

The development of student ability to use formal symbolic reasoning in algebra and other applications of algebra will continue to get serious attention from this point on in *Contemporary Mathematics in Context*. At the same time, we continue to build the function/modeling point of view that is so fruitful in helping students make sense of symbolic operations and in solving important, realistic problems.

Unit 3 Assessment

	Assessment Resources
Lesson Quizzes	
Lesson 1 *Algebra and Functions*	pp. 83–88
Lesson 2 *Algebraic Operations: Part 1*	pp. 89–94
Lesson 3 *Algebraic Operations: Part 2*	pp. 95–102
Lesson 4 *Reasoning to Solve Equations and Inequalities*	pp. 103–108
Lesson 5 *Proof through Algebraic Reasoning*	pp. 109–114
In-Class Exams	
Form A	pp. 115–120
Form B	pp. 121–126
Take-Home Assessments	pp. 127–129
Unit 3 Projects	
Algebra II and You	pp. 130–131
Multiple Algebraic Methods	pp. 132–133
Midterm and Cumulative Assessments Units 1–3	
Exam Tasks	pp. 134–152
Project: *Looking Back Over Course 3*	pp. 153–155
Project: *Algebra and the Calculator*	pp. 156–157

Unit 3

Teaching Notes continued

Notes continued from page T178

b ■ Linear graphs, with the algebraic model $f(x) = a + bx$, are straight lines with slope b and y-intercept a.

Exponential models are curves that cross the y-axis; as x increases, the curve rises (or falls) at an increasing (or decreasing) rate, depending on whether the positive base is greater than one or less than one.

Power models for direct variation pass through the origin and then vary in shape, depending on whether the function is even or odd. For even powers, opposite input values, such as $x = 3$ or $x = -3$, will create identical output values so that the curves will have reflection symmetry over the y-axis. This means that the curve will "begin and end" with positive y values or "begin and end" with negative y values. For odd powers, opposite input values create opposite output values. This means that if the curve "begins" in the third quadrant, it will "end" in the first (and vice versa). For inverse variation power models, the x- and y-axes are asymptotes.

Quadratic models open upward (if the coefficient of the x^2 term is positive) or downward (if the coefficient of the x^2 term is negative), and they are symmetric about a line that is parallel to the y-axis. They have a maximum or minimum value, which falls on the line of symmetry.

Trigonometric models are periodic in nature. There is a definite cyclical, repetitive pattern.

■ Linear models have table values that indicate constant change.

Exponential models have tables that indicate an increasing or decreasing rate of change.

Power models for direct variation have (0, 0) in their table. For inverse variation power models, x and y can never be equal to zero in the table of values.

Quadratic models have tables that indicate symmetry, as well as a maximum or minimum value. The rate of change in the table is not constant.

Trigonometric models show repetitive values in the table that are cyclical in nature.

■ Linear models: $y = a + bx$

Exponential models: $y = a(b)^x$ $(b \neq 0)$

Power models for direct variation: $y = ax^b$ $(b > 0)$

Power models for inverse variation: $y = \frac{a}{x^b}$ $(b > 0)$

Quadratic models: $y = ax^2 + bx + c$

Trigonometric models: $y = a \sin (bx) + d$ or $y = a \cos (bx) + d$. The most general form of a trigonometric model, $y = a \sin [b(x - c)] + d$, will be introduced later in the curriculum.

Page T178 Teaching Notes continued on next page.

Teaching Notes *continued*

Notes continued from page T178

C Linear models theoretically have a domain and range of all real numbers. Practical constraints often limit the range and domain to positive numbers or integers.

Exponential models for $a > 0$ theoretically have a domain equal to all real numbers and a range of $y > 0$. Practical constraints may limit the domain to positive numbers or positive integers.

Power models of $y = x^b$ have several kinds of possible domains and ranges, depending on the value of the power b.

- If b is a positive integer, the domain is all values of x. If b is even, the range is all positive y; if b is odd, the range is all values of y.
- If b is a negative integer, the domain is all nonzero x. If b is even, the range is all positive y; if b is odd, the range is all nonzero values of y.
- The main cases we've considered in which b is not an integer are the square root and cube root functions. The square root has domain nonnegative values of x and range all nonnegative values of y. The cube root has domain and range all real numbers.

In variations of the basic power models by introduction of a multiplicative constant $y = a(x^b)$, the sign of a changes the range in some cases.

Quadratic models have a domain of all real numbers. The range will be equal to or less than the maximum value of the function or equal to and greater than the minimum value of the function. Practical situations often make only positive values realistic.

Trigonometric models have a domain of all real numbers, and the range depends on the actual function. For the simplest form of the sine and cosine functions, the range is $-1 \le y \le 1$. Practical situations may change the domain to only positive real numbers and the range to such values as those in the Ferris wheel problem where $5 \le y \le 65$.

Notes continued from page T195

8. **a.** Incorrect, because an x term plus an x term equals an x term, not an x^2 term. $3x + 7x = 10x$ by the distributive property.
   b. Incorrect, because 7 was not distributed to each term in the sum. $7(5x + 3) = 35x + 21$ by the distributive property.
   c. Correct, distributive property and arithmetic.
   d. Incorrect, because $t \times t$ equals t^2. $(-5t)(-8t) = 40t^2$ by rules for multiplying variables with exponents, along with the commutative and associative properties.
   e. Incorrect, because you can add terms only when the variable portions are the same. $9x^3 + 5x^2$ is already in simplest form. An equivalent form would be $x^2(9x + 5)$ by the distributive property.
   f. Incorrect, because when you rewrite this expression using the distributive property to separate out a factor of 3, the n^2 term must have a coefficient of 3, and the constant term must be 5. $9n^2 + 12n + 15 = 3(3n^2 + 4n + 5)$ by the distributive property.

Notes continued from page T207

3. $f(x) - j(x) = (4x^3 + x^2 + 7x - 17) - (5x^4 + 3x^2) = -5x^4 + 4x^3 - 2x^2 + 7x - 17$
   $g(x) - f(x) = (3x^2 + 4x - 7) - (4x^3 + x^2 + 7x - 17) = -4x^3 + 2x^2 - 3x + 10$
   $g(x) - g(x) = (3x^2 + 4x - 7) - (3x^2 + 4x - 7) = 0$
   $g(x) - h(x) = (3x^2 + 4x - 7) - (5x + 2) = 3x^2 - x - 9$
   $g(x) - j(x) = (3x^2 + 4x - 7) - (5x^4 + 3x^2) = -5x^4 + 4x - 7$
   $h(x) - f(x) = (5x + 2) - (4x^3 + x^2 + 7x - 17) = -4x^3 - x^2 - 2x + 19$
   $h(x) - g(x) = (5x + 2) - (3x^2 + 4x - 7) = -3x^2 + x + 9$
   $h(x) - h(x) = (5x + 2) - (5x + 2) = 0$
   $h(x) - j(x) = (5x + 2) - (5x^4 + 3x^2) = -5x^4 - 3x^2 + 5x + 2$
   $j(x) - f(x) = (5x^4 + 3x^2) - (4x^3 + x^2 + 7x - 17) = 5x^4 - 4x^3 + 2x^2 - 7x + 17$
   $j(x) - g(x) = (5x^4 + 3x^2) - (3x^2 + 4x - 7) = 5x^4 - 4x + 7$
   $j(x) - h(x) = (5x^4 + 3x^2) - (5x + 2) = 5x^4 + 3x^2 - 5x - 2$
   $j(x) - j(x) = (5x^4 + 3x^2) - (5x^4 + 3x^2) = 0$
4. **a.** No. For example, in the given diagram, A tri $B = C$, but B tri $A \neq C$. B tri A is the reflection of point C over $\overline{AB}$.
   b. No. For example, (A tri B) tri $C = C$ tri $C = C$, but A tri (B tri C) $= A$ tri $A = A$.
   c. The numbers generated will be greater than zero and less than one, and they will have some positive power of two for the denominator. All numbers of the form $\frac{a}{2^n}$, where $n \geq 1$ and $a < 2^n$, can be generated.
   d. This pattern will generate an infinite set of points. If you consider the first pair of points A and B, A tri B generates C, where triangle ABC is equilateral. If you tessellate triangle ABC over the entire plane, the vertices will be the set of points generated from A, B by the "tri" operation.

See Assessment Resources pages 89–94.

Teaching Notes *continued*

Notes continued from page T209

2. **b.** $f(0) = 0$ and $f(-3) = 0$

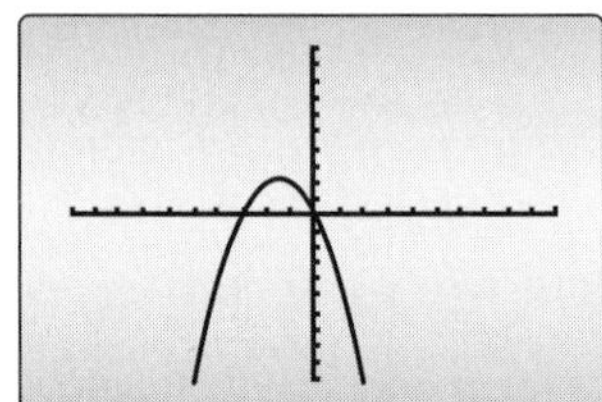

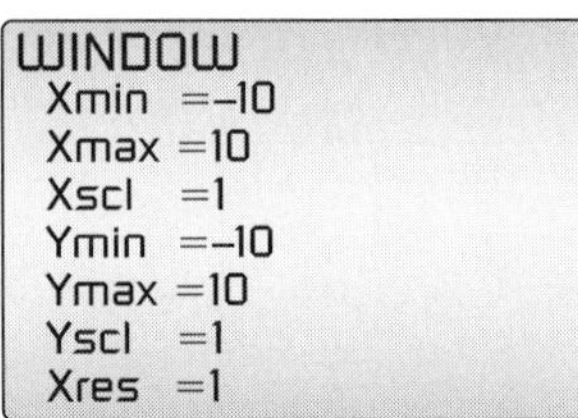

WINDOW
Xmin =−10
Xmax =10
Xscl =1
Ymin =−10
Ymax =10
Yscl =1
Xres =1

X	Y_1
−6	−18
−5	−10
−4	−4
−3	0
−2	2
−1	2
0	0

Y_1=−X(X+3)

X	Y_1
0	0
1	−4
2	−10
3	−18
4	−28
5	−40
6	−54

Y_1=−X(X+3)

c. $f(-3) = 0$ and $f(5) = 0$

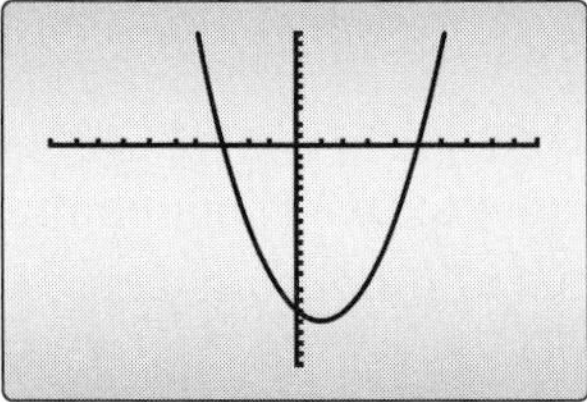

WINDOW
Xmin =−10
Xmax =10
Xscl =1
Ymin =−20
Ymax =10
Yscl =1
Xres =1

X	Y_1
−5	20
−4	9
−3	0
−2	−7
−1	−12
0	−15
1	−16

Y_1=(X+3)(X−5)

X	Y_1
1	−16
2	−15
3	−12
4	−7
5	0
6	9
7	20

Y_1=(X+3)(X−5)

d. $f(6) = 0$ and $f(1) = 0$

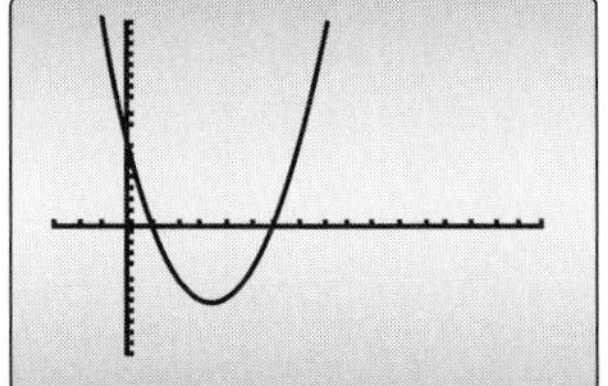

WINDOW
Xmin =−3
Xmax =10
Xscl =1
Ymin =−7
Ymax =10
Yscl =1
Xres =1

X	Y_1
−2	24
−1	14
0	6
1	0
2	−4
3	−6
4	−6

Y_1=(X−6)(X−1)

X	Y_1
4	−6
5	−4
6	0
7	6
8	14
9	24
10	36

Y_1=(X−6)(X−1)

e. $f(-7) = 0$ and $f(-2) = 0$

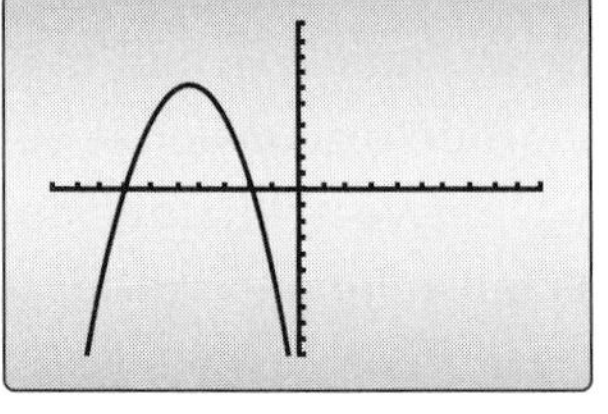

WINDOW
Xmin =−10
Xmax =10
Xscl =1
Ymin =−10
Ymax =10
Yscl =1
Xres =1

X	Y_1
−11	−36
−10	−24
−9	−14
−8	−6
−7	0
−6	4
−5	6

Y_1=−(X+7)(X+2)

X	Y_1
−5	6
−4	6
−3	4
−2	0
−1	−6
0	−14
1	−24

Y_1=−(X+7)(X+2)

f. $f(3) = 0$

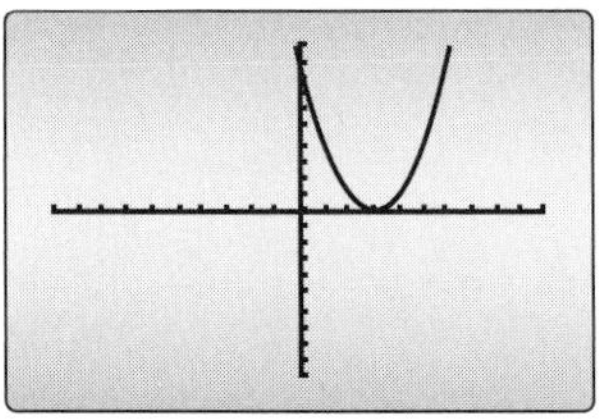

WINDOW
Xmin =−10
Xmax =10
Xscl =1
Ymin =−10
Ymax =10
Yscl =1
Xres =1

X	Y_1
−3	36
−2	25
−1	16
0	9
1	4
2	1
3	0

Y_1=(X−3)(X−3)

X	Y_1
3	0
4	1
5	4
6	9
7	16
8	25
9	36

Y_1=(X−3)(X−3)

g. $f\left(\frac{-12}{5}\right) = 0$ and $f(3) = 0$

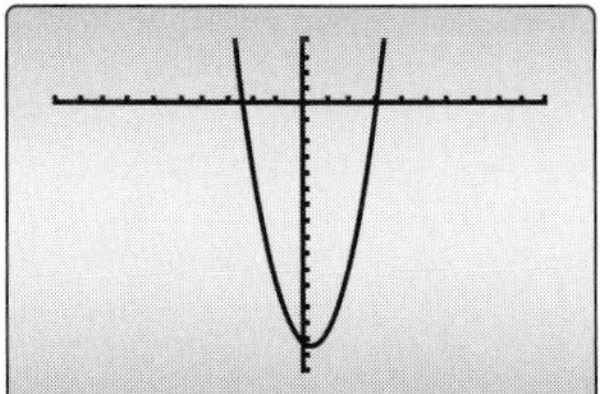

WINDOW
Xmin =−10
Xmax =10
Xscl =1
Ymin =−40
Ymax =10
Yscl =5
Xres =1

X	Y_1
−3	18
−2.8	11.6
−2.6	5.6
−2.4	0
−2.2	−5.2
−2	−10
−1.8	−14.4

Y_1=(5X+12)(X−3)

X	Y_1
0	−36
1	−34
2	−22
3	0
4	32
5	74
6	126

Y_1=(5X+12)(X−3)

Page T209 Teaching Notes continued on next page.

Teaching Notes *continued*

Notes continued from page T209

h. $f\left(-\frac{5}{2}\right) = 0$ and $f\left(-\frac{1}{3}\right) = 0$

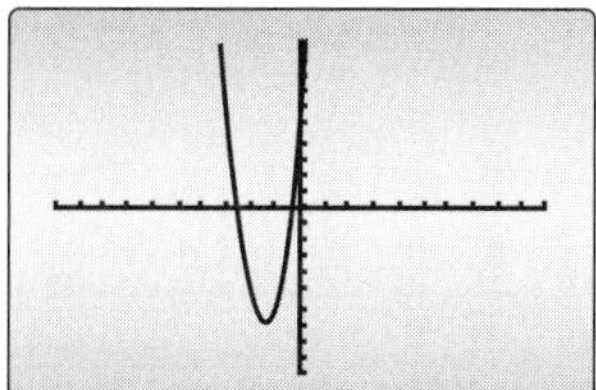

WINDOW
Xmin =−10
Xmax =10
Xscl =1
Ymin =−10
Ymax =10
Yscl =1
Xres =1

X	Y1
-3	8
-2.5	0
-2	-5
-1.5	-7
-1	-6
-.5	-2
0	5

Y1=(2X+5)(3X+1)

X	Y1
-1	-6
-.6667	-3.667
-.3333	0
0	5
.33333	11.333
.66667	19
1	28

Y1=(2X+5)(3X+1)

i. **In this part, there is a constant factor. Some students will see 3 factors and write 3 zeroes. Ask them what the factors are. "So each of these factors could be 0, right? So 6 could be 0? Or $(-7x + 11)$ could be 0? Or $(2 - x)$ could be zero? So what value of *x* would make 6 equal to 0?" The idea that a factor must involve a variable to have the potential of producing a zero is an important one.**

$f\left(\frac{11}{7}\right) = 0$ and $f(2) = 0$

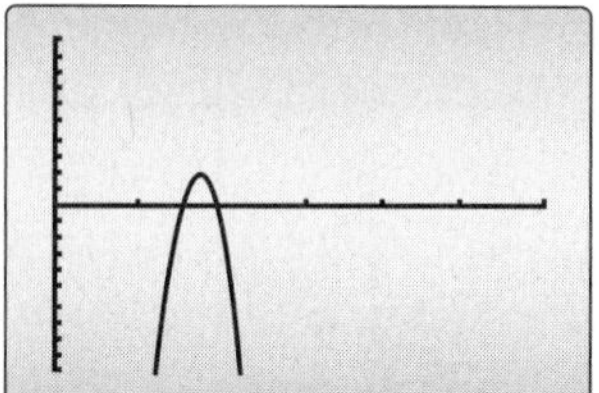

WINDOW
Xmin =0
Xmax =6
Xscl =1
Ymin =−10
Ymax =10
Yscl =1
Xres =1

X	Y1
1	-24
1.1429	-15.43
1.2857	-8.571
1.4286	-3.429
1.5714	0
1.7143	1.7143
1.8571	1.7143

Y1=−6(−7X+11)(2−X)

X	Y1
1.7	1.62
1.8	1.92
1.9	1.38
2	0
2.1	-2.22
2.2	-5.28
2.3	-9.18

Y1=−6(−7X+11)(2−X)

Notes continued from page T210

4. **As you circulate among groups, ask students to explain how they are sure that their factors are correct. You may wish to have a large group discussion if you observe that students have not made the connection between factors and zeroes of a polynomial function. Pairs of students can challenge each other to write function rules for specified zeroes.**

Responses may vary; factors may be multiples of the ones given below, and factors may be repeated.

a. $f(x) = (x - 4)(x - 1)$

b. $g(x) = (x - 5)(x + 3)$

c. $h(x) = x(x - 7)(x - 2)$

d. $j(x) = (x + 1)(x + 5)$

5. **a.** Step 1 Distributive Property
Step 2 Distributive Property
Step 3 Associative and Distributive Properties

b. Step 1 Distributive Property
Step 2 Distributive Property
Step 3 Associative and Distributive Properties

c. Step 1 Distributive Property
Step 2 Distributive Property
Step 3 Associative and Distributive Properties

d. Step 1 Distributive Property
Step 2 Multiplication and Commutativity

SHARE AND SUMMARIZE full-class discussion

Notes continued from page T211

Checkpoint

See Teaching Master 74.

a The factored form is easier to use when finding the zeroes of the function. When you have the factored form, all that needs to be done to find the zeroes is to find the values that make each factor zero. This can often be done by inspection.

b The standard form, $f(x) = ax^2 + bx + c$, is slightly easier to use when determining whether the function has a minimum or a maximum. Using this form, all you have to do is look at the value of a. If a is positive, the function has a minimum. If a is negative, the function has a maximum.

c Responses may vary, but at this point, most students will agree that the factored form is easier to use when trying to find the maximum or minimum value. From the factored form, the zeroes of the function can be easily found. Then the average of the two zeroes will be the x value corresponding to the maximum or minimum value of the function. That x value is then substituted into the function rule to find the maximum or minimum value. It is also often easier to evaluate the function rule using the factored form.

d The graph has x-intercepts that are equal to the zeroes of the function. The y-intercept is equal to the constant when the rule is in standard form. The maximum or minimum point can be found. Also it is easy to determine whether the graph opens up or down by looking at a. Students can plot the known points and then connect them using a curve.

e $m \cdot n = c$ and $m + n = b$

NOTE: We have purposefully avoided discussion of the set of numbers over which a quadratic polynomial is factored. In most cases, what is intended is factorization over integers. Some students might well reason that any quadratic whose graph has x-intercepts can be factored (over the real numbers).

JOURNAL ENTRY: Find an equation for a quadratic function that fits each description below, and then explain how you can tell, without graphing, that the graph would have the indicated properties.

- The function opens up and has two zeroes.
- The function has a maximum and a positive y-intercept.

Notes continued from page T212

d. To verify that two forms of a function rule are equivalent, students can either graph the two functions or look at the tables of values. If the forms are equivalent, the graphs and tables of values should be identical.

To find the zeroes and the maximum or minimum value, students can graph the function and then trace it to find the values, or they can zoom-in on the table of values. There may be other options, such as using the CALC menu on the TI-83.

To check if a function rule has the given zeroes, students can graph the function and find the x-intercepts or look at the table of values for that function rule.

EXPLORE small-group investigation

INVESTIGATION 2 Special Products and Factoring

In this investigation, students explore patterns for two special types of quadratic expressions: the difference of two squares and perfect trinomial squares.

1. **a.** $x^2 - 16$ **b.** $t^2 - 9$ **c.** $s^2 - 1$

For the general pattern $(x + a)(x - a)$, the product will be $x^2 - a^2$.

2. **a.** $(x + 5)(x - 5)$ **b.** $(x + 9)(x - 9)$ **c.** $(x + 6)(x - 6)$

The factors for the general form $x^2 - a^2$ are $(x + a)(x - a)$.

3. **a.** $f(x) = x^2 - 25$ **b.** $g(x) = x^2 - 81$ **c.** $h(x) = x^2 - 36$

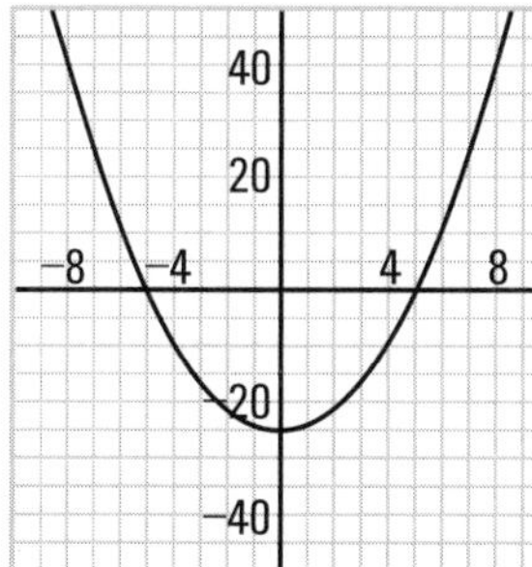

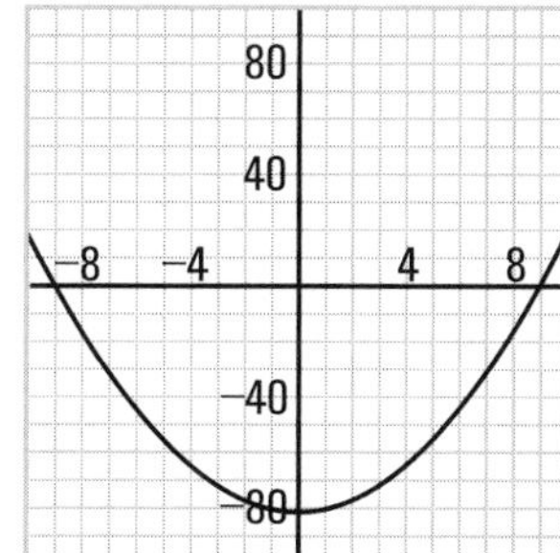

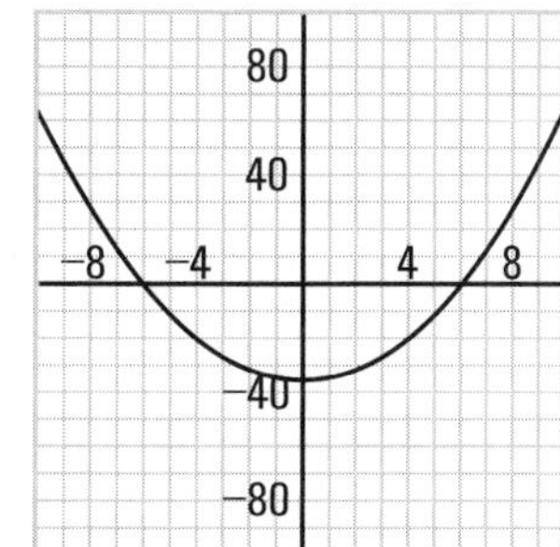

The graph of $f(x) = x^2 - a^2$ is a parabola with vertex on the x-axis. Thus, because parabolas are symmetric, the x-intercepts or zeroes must be equidistant from the x-axis. Also, since the zeroes are a and $-a$, the factors must be $(x - a)$ and $(x + a)$.

Notes continued from page T225

b ■ Responses may vary. Students might suggest looking in the tables to determine when the values are the same (break-even point), when $I(x)$ is greater than $C(x)$ (operating with a profit), and when $I(x)$ is less than $C(x)$ (operating at a loss). Using graphs, you can determine the point at which the curves cross (break-even point), where the $I(x)$ curve is above the $C(x)$ curve (operating with a profit), and where the $I(x)$ curve is below the $C(x)$ curve (operating at a loss).

■ Determining when the difference is 0 (break-even point), when the difference is positive (operating with a profit), and when the difference is negative (operating at a loss) will provide the necessary solutions. At this point, your students may not know how to proceed with manipulations of the symbols. However, it is important to acknowledge and assess what they do know from previous experiences.

For example, you might give them the equation:

$$22{,}500 - 100x = 2{,}500x - 50x^2$$

Ask, "What have we done before in trying to solve for x?"

One possible strategy is to add the same quantity, $100x$, to each side. (This is one of the properties of equality.) This results in $22{,}500 = 2{,}600x - 50x^2$. But then we still have an x and an x^2 term. Another possible strategy is to rearrange the equation as a quadratic and search for zeroes by factoring $-50x^2 + 2{,}600x - 22{,}500 = 0$. Effectively, we are trying to find the zeroes of $g(x) = -50x^2 + 2{,}600x - 22{,}500$.

Students have not had much experience solving quadratics that start with ax^2. They may think of, or you may suggest, avoiding this problem by writing the equation as $-50(x^2 - 52x + 450) = 0$. Then you can ask students about the difficulties in completing this strategy.

It is important to urge students as far as they can go along lines of reasoning open to them. Some will feel that this is all rather pointless since they can get an accurate solution by using a graphing calculator. But some will be curious and will want to see how far their logic will take them.

Notes continued from page T229

Groups of students should be able to work through Activities 1 and 2, at which point you may want to interrupt to summarize the problem and introduce the quadratic formula as a remedy. Or you may choose to do Activities 1 and 2 and the introduction to the quadratic formula as a large group. In either case, students will need help evaluating $\frac{\sqrt{b^2 - 4ac}}{2a}$ for the first time. They will want to use their calculators, but even then they may need some help to avoid pitfalls. For example, if $a = 1.5$, $b = -4$, and $c = 2$, then parentheses must be used carefully.

1. a. The solutions to this equation will be the ticket prices that would produce no ticket income at all. Solving the equation will also allow you to determine where the axis of symmetry is located because the axis is midway between the zeroes of the function. The maximum income is the y value at the point of intersection of the parabola and the axis of symmetry.

b. Distributive property

c. Multiplication property of zero

d. Parabolas are symmetric, and 25 is halfway between 0 and 50. (See Part a.)

e. Substitution: $2{,}500(25) - 50(25)^2 = 31{,}250$

Teaching Notes continued

Notes continued from page T232

After Activity 7, students have connected enough ideas that you may want to insert a full-class summary. You can do this effectively by having different groups of students present their solutions for Activities 5 and 6. This presentation lets all students see the quadratic formula in action, connect $-\frac{b}{2a}$ to the graph, and assess the relative usefulness of factoring as a strategy. They should also discuss any common pitfalls in the evaluation process. Be sure to probe to see if students connect roots for the equation $ax^2 + bx + c = 0$ to the zeroes of the function $f(x) = ax^2 + bx + c$.

The graphical meaning of $\frac{\sqrt{b^2 - 4ac}}{2a}$ is the next logical step, and students should have made this connection in Activity 7.

8. The equation $ax^2 + bx + c = 0$ could have 0, 1, or 2 roots.

a. In each case, it is the value of $\sqrt{b^2 - 4ac}$ that first indicates the number of roots that the equation has. In the first equation, $\sqrt{b^2 - 4ac} = \sqrt{64 - 48} = 4$, so there are two roots. (Adding and subtracting 4 will give two distinct values.) In the second equation, $\sqrt{b^2 - 4ac} = \sqrt{64 - 64} = 0$, so there is one root. (Adding 0 gives the same value as subtracting 0.) In the third equation, $\sqrt{b^2 - 4ac} = \sqrt{64 - 80} = \sqrt{-16}$, so there are no real roots.

b.

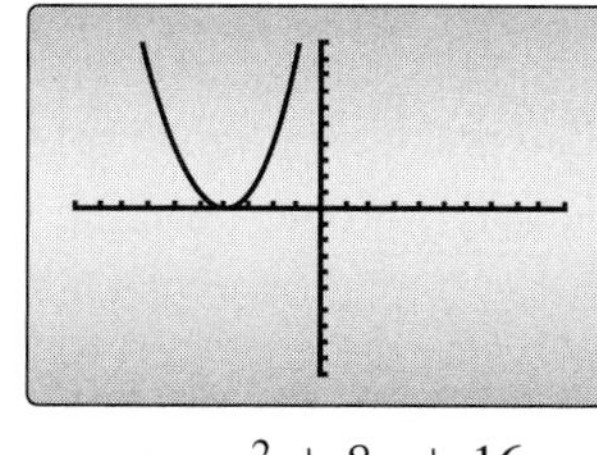

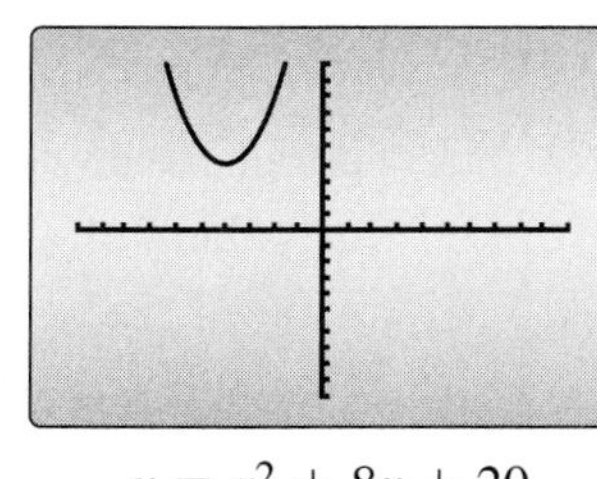

$y = x^2 + 8x + 12$ $\quad$ $y = x^2 + 8x + 16$ $\quad$ $y = x^2 + 8x + 20$

The number of roots to the equation $ax^2 + bx + c = 0$ is the same as the number of x-intercepts of the graph of $y = ax^2 + bx + c$.

9. There is an infinite number of functions with the indicated zeroes. Students probably will write a function rule so that the graph has a minimum rather than a maximum value. As you facilitate group work, watch for examples other than those below. During the Checkpoint discussion, you might ask students for their examples.

a. minimum or maximum at $x = 2$ $\quad$ $f(x) = (x - 6)(x + 2)$

b. minimum or maximum at $x = -2$ $\quad$ $g(x) = (x + 7)(x - 3)$

c. minimum or maximum at $x = -3.5$ $\quad$ $j(x) = (x + 2)(x + 5)$

d. minimum or maximum at $x = 3.25$ $\quad$ $h(x) = (x - 2)(x - 4.5)$

10. $x = \frac{-b}{2a}$ gives the line of symmetry, or $x = \frac{7}{8}$ in this case. The minimum value must occur on the axis of symmetry. When $x = \frac{7}{8}$, the function has a minimum value of -13.0625.

Notes continued from page T233

c For $f(x) = ax^2 + bx + c$, find the roots r_1 and r_2, then $f(x) = a(x - r_1)(x - r_2)$ will be the function rule in factored form. You may wish to discuss how to rewrite the factors in the cases for which one of the roots is not an integer. For example, in factoring $3x^2 - 2x - 8$, students would get $(3x + 4)(x - 2)$. Finding the roots and then writing factors would give $3\left(x + \frac{4}{3}\right)(x - 2)$. Students should understand and be able to show that these are equivalent.

d If $b^2 - 4ac > 0$, then there are two real roots.
If $b^2 - 4ac = 0$, then there is one real root.
If $b^2 - 4ac < 0$, then there are no real roots.

In a graph, the number of x-intercepts of the quadratic function will be the number of solutions of the related quadratic equation.

Teaching Notes *continued*

Notes continued from page T237

3. Infinitely many solutions: $\frac{1}{2}x + 5 = \frac{4}{8}x + \frac{40}{8}$; all real numbers

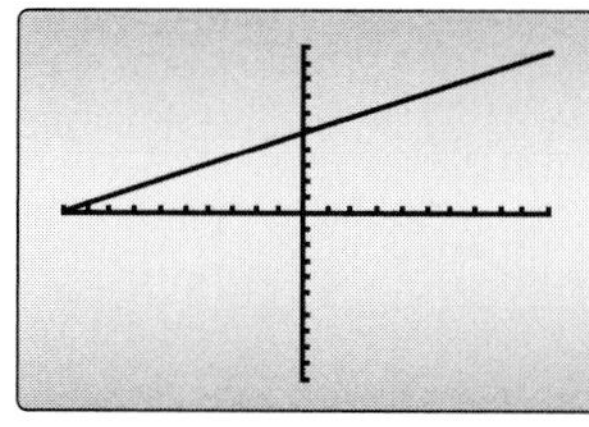

WINDOW
Xmin =-10
Xmax =10
Xscl =1
Ymin =-10
Ymax =10
Yscl =1
Xres =1

4. Exactly two roots: $2x^2 - 8x - 10 = 0$; $x = 5$ and $x = -1$

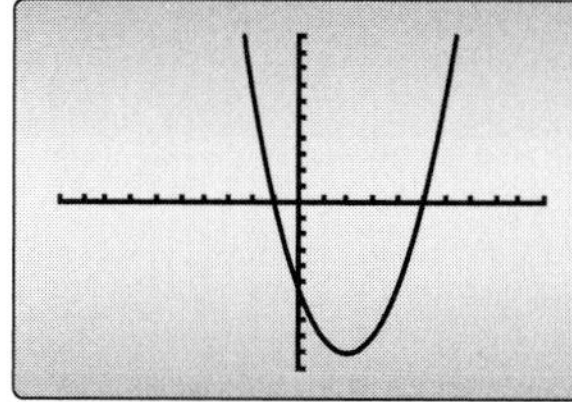

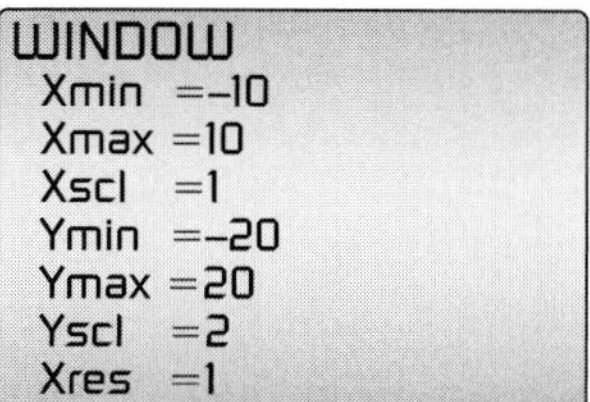

Evaluating $b^2 - 4ac$, we get $64 - 4(2)(-10) = 64 + 80 = 144$. Since this is greater than zero, we know the equation has two roots.
Exactly one root: $6x^2 - 24x + 24 = 0$; $x = 2$

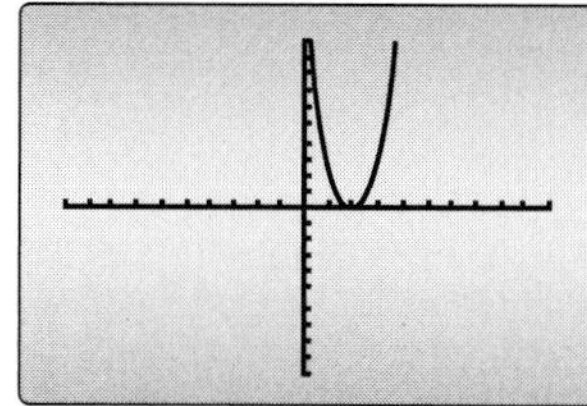

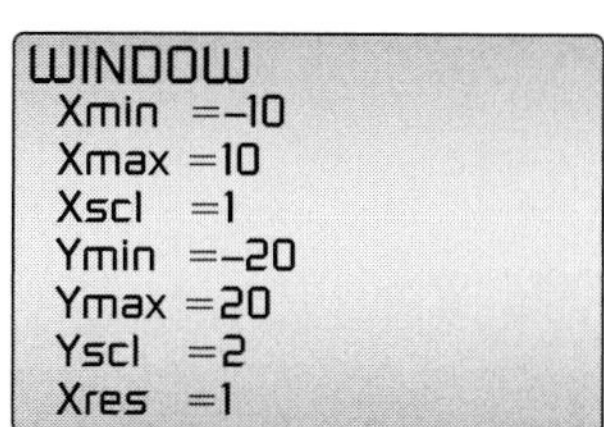

Evaluating $b^2 - 4ac$, we get $(-24)^2 - 4(6)(24) = 0$. Since this equals zero, the equation has only one root.
No roots: $3x^2 + 2x + 1 = 0$

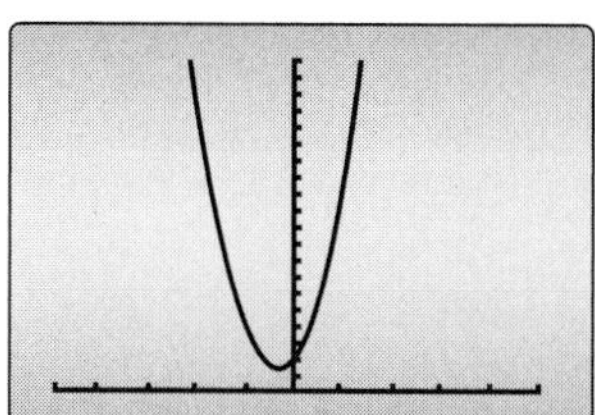

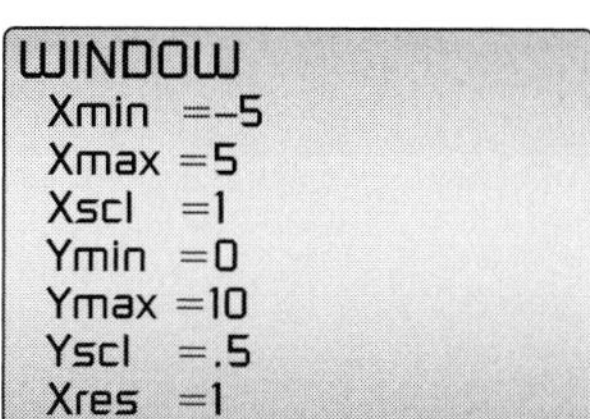

Evaluating $b^2 - 4ac$ results in $4 - 4(3)(1) = -8$. Since this is less than zero, we know there are no roots.

5. **a.** The price that maximizes revenue at the city store is \$18.75 and at the country store is \$22.50. The average of these two is $\frac{18.75 + 22.50}{2}$ or 20.625.

b. This average is not equal to the price that will produce maximum revenue when the same price is charged at both stores. It is 0.625 higher. This is the case because, at the individual prices that maximize revenue, there are more wood cuttings sold in the city than in the country.

Teaching Notes *continued*

Notes continued from page T239

4. a. $2x^2 - 3x - 25 = 0$

$a = 2, b = -3, c = -25$

$x = \frac{3}{4} \pm \frac{\sqrt{(-3)^2 - 4(2)(-25)}}{4}$

$x \approx 0.75 \pm 3.61$

$x \approx 4.36$ and -2.86

Check:

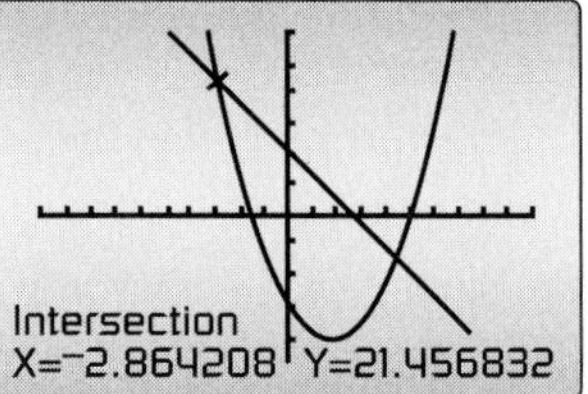

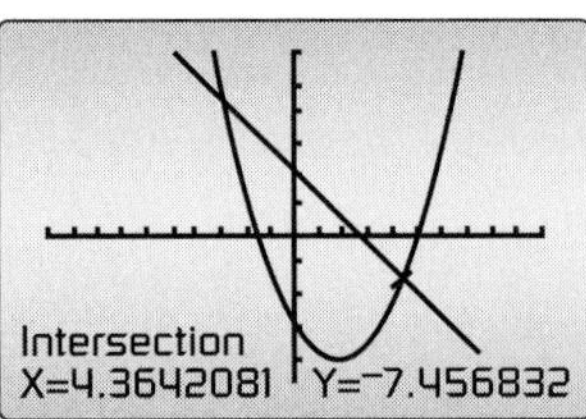

WINDOW
Xmin =-10
Xmax =10
Xscl =1
Ymin =-25
Ymax =30
Yscl =5
Xres =1

b. $3x^2 - 12x - 25 = 0$

$a = 3, b = -12, c = -25$

$x = \frac{12}{6} \pm \frac{\sqrt{(-12)^2 - 4(3)(-25)}}{6}$

$x \approx 2 \pm 3.51$

$x \approx 5.51$ and -1.51

Check:

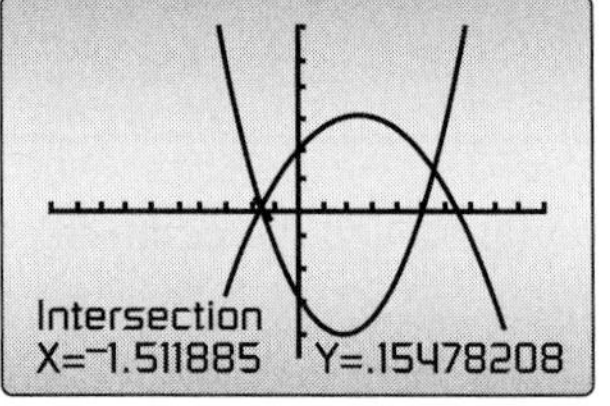

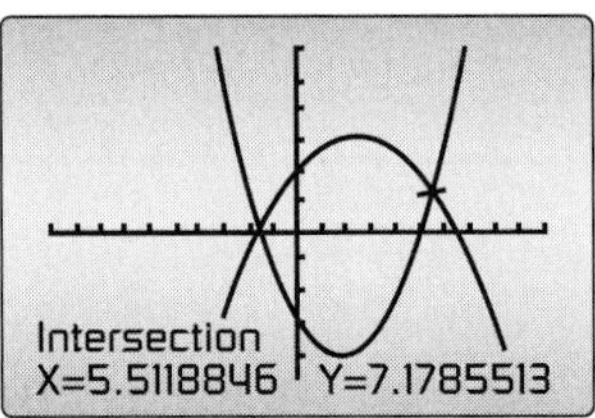

WINDOW
Xmin =-10
Xmax =10
Xscl =1
Ymin =-25
Ymax =30
Yscl =5
Xres =1

5. a. 2, 1, or 0. The line could intersect the parabola as in Activity 4 Part a, the line could be tangent to the parabola, or it might not intersect at all.

b. 2, 1, or 0. The two parabolas could intersect as in Activity 5 Part b, they could be tangent to each other, or they might not intersect at all.

See Assessment Resources pages 103–108.

Teaching Notes *continued*

Notes continued from page T246

SHARE AND SUMMARIZE full-class discussion

Checkpoint

See Teaching Master 84.

ⓐ Useful general strategies and specific techniques that were used in this investigation include the following:

- Expressing the same quantity in two different forms and then equating the two expressions
- Applying definitions to express relationships
- Using substitution
- Applying many of the basic properties, such as the distributive property and the addition, subtraction, multiplication, and division properties of equality

ⓑ Activity 2 (Pythagorean Theorem): In any right triangle, the square of the length of the hypotenuse is equal to the sum of the squares of the other two sides.

Activity 3 (Law of Cosines): In any triangle *ABC*, the square of one side, *c*, is equal to the sum of the squares of the other two sides minus twice the product of the lengths of the other two sides and the cosine of the angle opposite the side of length *c*.

Activity 4 (Trigonometric Pythagorean Identity): The sum of the squares of the sine of an angle and the cosine of the same angle equals one.

ⓒ For any given set of data with mean of $\bar{x}$, if you multiply each data value by *c*, then the new mean is $c\bar{x}$. If you add *c* to each data value, then the new mean is $\bar{x} + c$.

ⓓ A proof uses general variables and shows something to be true for all values of the variables involved. Several examples of a pattern show that the pattern is true only for specific cases, not all cases.

Notes continued from page T249

4. **a.** $(ax + b) + (cx + d) = (ax + cx) + (b + d)$ — Commutative and Associative Properties
$= x(a + c) + (b + d)$ — Distributive Property
$= (a + c)x + (b + d)$ — Commutative Property

b. $(x + a)(x + b) = x(x + b) + a(x + b)$ — Distributive Property
$= x^2 + xb + ax + ab$ — Distributive Property
$= x^2 + x(b + a) + ab$ — Distributive and Commutative Properties
$= x^2 + (a + b)x + ab$ — Commutative Properties

c. $(x + a)^2 = (x + a)(x + a)$ — Definition of squaring a quantity
$= x(x + a) + a(x + a)$ — Distributive Property
$= x^2 + xa + ax + a^2$ — Distributive Property
$= x^2 + 2ax + a^2$ — Commutative Property and combining like terms

Reflecting

1. An algebraic proof allows you to show that something is true for all values of a variable, not just for certain cases. If you prove algebraically that something is true for the general case, then it will always be true.
2. You would expect that the basic process, making assumptions or accepting certain things to be true and then building on that foundation with logic, would be true in other fields as well as mathematics. However, in politics and law, things are not as clear and well defined as they are in science and mathematics. In science, we often have to "prove" things empirically through a lot of experiments.

Teaching Notes continued

Notes continued from page T254

3. Since $P(x) = 0$ at $x \approx 8$ and $x \approx 162$ and the profit function is quadratic, the maximum profit will occur when $x \approx \frac{8 + 162}{2} = 85$. The fact that maximum profit occurs when some space is not rented is understandable based on the fact that basic rent is a quadratic function. The income does not always increase as more space is rented because in order to rent more space, the rent has to be lowered. However, our functions are reliable only up to $x = 85$, so we cannot say if the profit will be higher when more space is rented. Unless the mall charges less for the last 15 units than the addition to its operating costs when those units are included, the profit should not go down.

4. **a.** $A(x) = \frac{P(x)}{x} = \frac{-30x^2 + 5{,}100x - 40{,}000}{x}$

$A(40) = \$2{,}900$

$A(60) \approx \$2{,}633.33$

$A(80) \approx \$2{,}200$

b. $A(x) = \frac{P(x)}{x} = \frac{(-30x^2 + 5{,}300x) - (200x + 40{,}000)}{x}$

$A(x) = \frac{P(x)}{x} = \frac{-30x^2 + 5{,}100x - 40{,}000}{x}$

$A(x) = \frac{1}{x}(-30x^2 + 5{,}100x - 40{,}000)$

$A(x) = -30x + 5{,}100 - \frac{40{,}000}{x}$

The first model listed best shows the contributions of income and cost, and the last is easiest to use for calculation. By plotting these functions and examining their tables of values, you can see that the models are equivalent.

Notes continued from page T256

15. The roots of $ax^2 + bx + c = 0$ are $\frac{-b}{2a} + \frac{\sqrt{b^2 - 4ac}}{2a}$ and $\frac{-b}{2a} - \frac{\sqrt{b^2 - 4ac}}{2a}$.

a. The sum S of the roots is

$$S = \left(\frac{-b}{2a} + \frac{\sqrt{b^2 - 4ac}}{2a}\right) + \left(\frac{-b}{2a} - \frac{\sqrt{b^2 - 4ac}}{2a}\right)$$
$$= \left(\frac{-b}{2a} + \frac{-b}{2a}\right) + \frac{\sqrt{b^2 - 4ac}}{2a} - \frac{\sqrt{b^2 - 4ac}}{2a}$$
$$= \frac{-2b}{2a}$$
$$= \frac{-b}{a}$$

b. The product P of the roots is

$$P = \left(\frac{-b}{2a} + \frac{\sqrt{b^2 - 4ac}}{2a}\right)\left(\frac{-b}{2a} - \frac{\sqrt{b^2 - 4ac}}{2a}\right)$$
$$= \left(\frac{-b}{2a}\right)^2 - \left(\frac{\sqrt{b^2 - 4ac}}{2a}\right)^2$$
$$= \frac{b^2}{4a^2} - \frac{b^2 - 4ac}{4a^2}$$
$$= \frac{b^2}{4a^2} - \frac{b^2}{4a^2} + \frac{4ac}{4a^2}$$
$$= \frac{c}{a}$$

c. $m = \frac{b}{c}$; $n = \frac{a}{c}$. The coefficient of x (that is, m) is the sum of the roots; the constant term n is the product of the roots.

APPLY individual task

Notes continued from page T257

On Your Own

See Unit 3 Summary Masters.

Responses will vary. Above all, preparation of this unit summary should be something that is useful to the individual student. You may wish to have students use the unit sumary masters for "Symbol Sense and Algebraic Reasoning" to help them organize the information.

See Assessment Resources, pages 115–157 for Unit 3 and Midterm assessments.

Unit 3

Unit 4

Shapes and Geometric Reasoning

UNIT OVERVIEW In this unit, students begin to develop an understanding of formal reasoning in geometric contexts. Students consider arguments presented in differing forms. They are asked to judge these arguments on the basis of how well the arguments convince them that the proposition made is true. From these experiences, they are asked to identify characteristics of arguments that make them convincing and logically correct.

Once some beginning understanding of the desirable characteristics of an argument in mathematics is developed, students are asked to apply the construction of an argument to familiar geometric situations involving lines and angles. It is here that the need for certain assumptions is introduced. The assumption about linear pairs involves the special position of pairs of angles. The assumption about parallel lines and transversals involves the congruence of corresponding angles. (This is functionally equivalent to assuming the parallel postulate of Euclid. See Activity 8 Part b, page 287.) These two assumptions are used to prove familiar relations involving angles when parallel lines are cut by a transversal.

The Law of Cosines is an especially powerful tool for use in reasoning about geometric situations involving triangles. This power is demonstrated in Lesson 2, where all the triangle similarity theorems are discovered by examining the expressions resulting from the Law of Cosines or the Law of Sines. Congruence theorems for triangles are easily and efficiently proved by applying the similarity theorems when the scale factor is one. Thus, congruent triangles are similar triangles with scale factor one.

Finally, in Lesson 3, students reason about quadrilaterals. Parallelograms are examined and their properties established, using synthetic or coordinate proofs as appropriate. Comparisons of synthetic and coordinate proofs underscore the connectedness of mathematics and encourage flexibility in approach. Necessary and sufficient conditions for a shape to be a parallelogram are introduced. The unit ends with students considering properties of special kinds of parallelograms, such as the rhombus, square, and rectangle. You may need to help students recall that in Course 1, Unit 5, a trapezoid was defined as a quadrilateral with exactly one pair of parallel sides. (Some texts may define a trapezoid as having at least one pair of parallel sides.)

Overall, this unit helps students extend their understanding of proof in geometric settings while also broadening student understanding of important geometric relationships. It includes development of important geometric ideas in an efficient manner, and it illustrates the "oneness" of mathematics by making use of algebraic notation to reason in geometric settings.

Shapes and Geometric Reasoning

Unit 4

260 • **Lesson 1**
Reasoned Arguments

297 • **Lesson 2**
Reasoning about Similar and Congruent Triangles

325 • **Lesson 3**
Parallelograms: Necessary and Sufficient Conditions

340 • **Lesson 4**
Looking Back

259

Unit 4

Masters 86a–86d

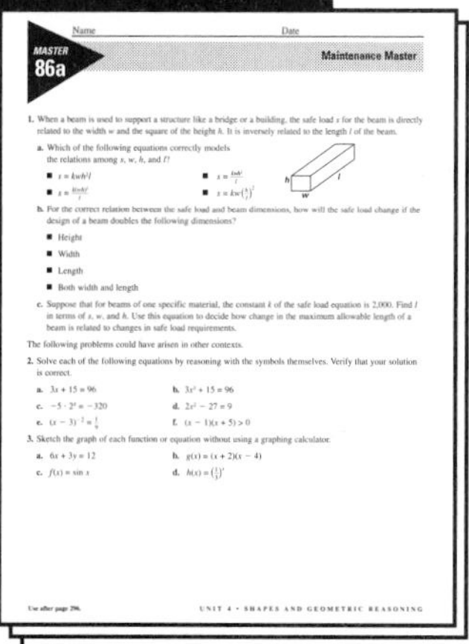

Name Date

MASTER 86a

Maintenance Master

1. When a beam is used to support a structure like a bridge or a building, the safe load s for the beam is directly related to the width w and the square of the height h. It is inversely related to the length l of the beam.

   a. Which of the following equations correctly models the relations among s, w, h, and l?
      - $s = kwh^2l$
      - $s = \frac{kwh^2}{l}$
      - $s = \frac{k(wh)^2}{l}$
      - $s = kw\left(\frac{h}{l}\right)^2$

   b. For the correct relation between the safe load and beam dimensions, how will the safe load change if the design of a beam doubles the following dimensions?
      - Height
      - Width
      - Length
      - Both width and length

   c. Suppose that for beams of one specific material, the constant k of the safe load equation is 2,000. Find l in terms of s, w, and h. Use this equation to decide how change in the maximum allowable length of a beam is related to changes in safe load requirements.

The following problems could have arisen in other contexts.

2. Solve each of the following equations by reasoning with the symbols themselves. Verify that your solution is correct.

   a. $3x + 15 = 96$ b. $3x^2 + 15 = 96$
   c. $-5 \cdot 2^x = -320$ d. $2x^2 - 27 = 9$
   e. $(x - 3)^{-2} = \frac{1}{9}$ f. $(x - 1)(x + 5) > 0$

3. Sketch the graph of each function or equation without using a graphing calculator.

   a. $6x + 3y = 12$ b. $g(x) = (x + 2)(x - 4)$
   c. $f(x) = \sin x$ d. $h(x) = \left(\frac{1}{3}\right)^x$

Use after page 296. UNIT 4 • SHAPES AND GEOMETRIC REASONING

Unit 4 Objectives

- To recognize the differences between, as well as the complementary nature of, inductive and deductive reasoning
- To develop some facility in producing deductive arguments in geometric situations
- To know and be able to use the relations among the angles formed when two lines intersect
- To know and be able to use the necessary and sufficient conditions for two lines to be parallel
- To know and be able to use triangle similarity and congruence theorems
- To know and be able to use the necessary and sufficient conditions for quadrilaterals to be (special) parallelograms
- To use a variety of conditions relating to triangles, lines, and quadrilaterals to prove the correctness of related geometric statements or provide counterexamples

See Teaching Masters 86a–86d for Maintenance tasks that students can work after Lesson 1.

Unit 4

Unit 4 Planning Guide

Lesson Objectives	MORE Assignments	Suggested Pacing	Materials
Lesson 1 *Reasoned Arguments* • To recognize the role of inductive reasoning in making conjectures • To recognize the need for proof and to be able to create a simple deductive argument to prove a conjecture is true • To be able to create a counterexample to prove a conjecture false • To know and be able to use the angle relationship theorems that result from the intersection of two lines • To know and be able to use the angle relationship theorems that result from two parallel lines being cut by a transversal and their converses • To know and be able to use the angle-sum theorem for triangles	**after page 265** Students can begin Mod. Task 1 or 2, Ref. Task 4, or Ext. Task 3 from p. 272. **after page 269** Students can begin Org. Task 1 or 2 or Ref. Task 1 or 5 from p. 272. **page 272** **Modeling:** 1 or 2, and 4* **Organizing:** 1 and 2 **Reflecting:** Choose one* **Extending:** 1 or 2* **after page 282** Students can begin Ref. Task 4 or Ext. Task 1 or 4 from p. 288. **after page 284** Students can begin Mod. Task 2 or Ref. Task 2 from p. 288. **after page 286** Students can begin Mod. Task 1 or 3 or Org. Task 3 or 6 from p. 288. **page 288** **Modeling:** 1 or 2, and 3* **Organizing:** 3 and 6 **Reflecting:** 2 and 4 **Extending:** 1 and 4	5 days	• Teaching Resources 87–95 • Assessment Resources 158–163 • *Optional*: RAP Book Exercise Set 11
Lesson 2 *Reasoning about Similar and Congruent Triangles* • To know and be able to use the three theorems used to prove triangles are similar (SSS, SAS, AA) • To know and be able to use the four theorems used to prove triangles are congruent (SSS, SAS, AAS, ASA) • To be able to create a valid argument for a given conjecture using previously proven theorems	**after page 304** Students can begin Mod. Task 4 or Ref. Task 1 or 4 from p. 310. **after page 308** Students can begin Modeling Task 1 or Reflecting Task 5 from p. 310. **page 310** **Modeling:** 1, 4, and choice of one* **Organizing:** 3 and 4 **Reflecting:** 3 and 5 **Extending:** 3 **page 319** **Modeling:** 1 or 2, and choice of one* **Organizing:** 1 and 5 **Reflecting:** 2 and 5 **Extending:** 1 and 3	5 days	• Teaching Resources 86a–86d, 96–105 • Assessment Resources 164–169 • *Optional*: RAP Book Exercise Set 12
Lesson 3 *Parallelograms: Necessary and Sufficient Conditions* • To know and be able to use both necessary and sufficient conditions for parallelograms • To know and be able to use properties unique to special parallelograms • To know and be able to use the Midpoint Connector Theorems for Triangles and Quadrilaterals	**after page 329** Students can begin Reflecting Task 1, 2, or 4 from p. 333. **after page 330** Students can begin Modeling Task 1 or Organizing Task 1 from p. 333. **page 333** **Modeling:** 1 and choice of one* **Organizing:** 1 or 2, and 3* **Reflecting:** Choose one* **Extending:** 1	8 days	• Teaching Resources 106–109 • Assessment Resources 170–175 • *Optional*: RAP Book Exercise Set 13
Lesson 4 *Looking Back* • To review the major objectives of the unit		2-3 days (includes testing)	• Teaching Resources 110–112 • Unit Summary Master • Assessment Resources 176–192 • *Optional*: RAP Book Practice Set 6

**When choice is indicated, it is important to leave the choice to the student.*
Note: *It is best if Organizing tasks are discussed as a whole class after they have been assigned as homework.*

Unit 4

Lesson 1 Reasoned Arguments

Careful reasoning, whether it is concerned with mathematics, science, history, or daily affairs, is important if you want to have faith in the conclusions reached. Often, reasoning about daily affairs, such as in politics, government, business, or the legal system, is flawed because meanings of basic terms, as well as assumptions and relations involving the terms, are in dispute. For example, when President Bush announced his 2002 budget, he stated that the Department of Education was getting $44.5 billion in appropriations, an 11.5% increase over the 2001 funding level. The Democrats disagreed and claimed that it was only a 4.2% increase. The discrepancy was the result of either including or excluding the advance appropriation that had been granted to the Department of Education during 2001, and adjusting or not adjusting for inflation.

There are many claims made in daily affairs that you should carefully analyze to be sure that what you are being told follows logically from information and facts that you know are correct. Consider the following two advertisements.

I wished a thousand times for a brighter smile. One tube of Dentacleen gave it to me. The guys with the great smiles always had dates. With Dentacleen my smiles are bright too.

A brain harassed by a pen that runs dry loses its brilliance, power, and expression. Hence, our pens have 102% more ink capacity.

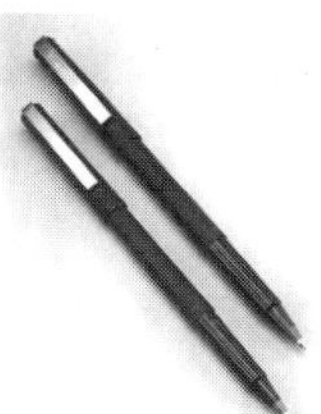

Think About This Situation

The toothpaste and ballpoint pen ads are each intended to persuade you to purchase a particular product. Analyze each of the claims. For each example, answer the following:

a What facts are to be assumed by the reader? Do these assumptions seem reasonable?

b What conclusion would you make? Explain your reasoning.

c What similar claims have you recently seen in the media?

Unit 4

260 UNIT 4 • SHAPES AND GEOMETRIC REASONING

Lesson 1 *Reasoned Arguments*

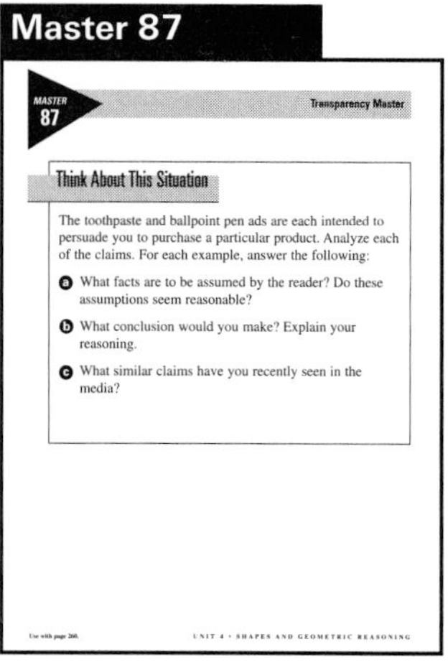
Master 87

MASTER 87 — Transparency Master

Think About This Situation

The toothpaste and ballpoint pen ads are each intended to persuade you to purchase a particular product. Analyze each of the claims. For each example, answer the following:

a. What facts are to be assumed by the reader? Do these assumptions seem reasonable?

b. What conclusion would you make? Explain your reasoning.

c. What similar claims have you recently seen in the media?

Use with page 260. UNIT 4 • SHAPES AND GEOMETRIC REASONING

LESSON OVERVIEW The four investigations in this lesson help students appreciate the need for proof in a mathematical setting and provide opportunities for students to analyze and construct deductive arguments. The first investigation introduces students to a variety of forms of deductive arguments: pictorial, paragraph, chain of if-then statements, and flow diagram. The goals are for students to understand the role of assumptions in proof and to begin to identify features of a good deductive argument, such as (a) uses valid assumptions and accepted mathematical information, (b) is complete, (c) follows appropriate logical principles, and (d) uses generalities rather than illustrative examples.

The second investigation contrasts deductive and inductive reasoning patterns. It introduces students to basic ideas about true and false if-then statements and discusses why one counterexample can disprove a conjecture while no number of examples can prove a conjecture. Students should understand the complementary nature of inductive and deductive reasoning. Inductive reasoning often leads to a conjecture, which may or may not always be true. Deductive reasoning provides a way to establish that a conjecture is always true.

The third and fourth investigations begin student development of constructing proofs in geometric settings, in particular, reasoning about angles formed by intersecting lines and necessary and sufficient conditions related to parallel lines cut by a transversal.

Most students will need to move through these investigations fairly slowly. Assure them from the start that it takes time and practice to become comfortable writing valid arguments and that they will have lots of opportunities to work on developing their proof-writing abilities. You may also consider spending a bit more time than usual on the MORE tasks. They offer a good opportunity for students to practice creating proofs and thereby gain some confidence in this area.

Lesson Objectives

- To recognize the role of inductive reasoning in making conjectures
- To recognize the need for proof and to be able to create a simple deductive argument to prove a conjecture is true
- To be able to create a counterexample to prove a conjecture false
- To know and be able to use the angle relationship theorems that result from the intersection of two lines
- To know and be able to use the angle relationship theorems that result from two parallel lines being cut by a transversal and their converses
- To know and be able to use the angle-sum theorem for triangles

See additional Teaching Notes on page T344C.

Unit 4

EXPLORE small-group investigation

INVESTIGATION 1 Analyzing Arguments

This investigation opens with two activities to help students learn about the role of assumptions in proof, followed by three activities that illustrate good and not-so-good arguments presented in a variety of forms. Activities 4 and 5 revisit a task found in Unit 3, "Symbol Sense and Algebraic Reasoning." A variety of arguments are proposed, and students are asked to analyze them, evaluate them, identify the assumptions made, and begin to pick out features of an argument that are necessary.

This investigation will take students quite a bit of time to complete. In order to develop an understanding of deductive and inductive reasoning, students need to carefully address the issues, working first in their groups and then reaching a consensus with the whole class. Be sure to note the Checkpoint Part b and Math Toolkit suggestions.

1. The focus in this activity is developing a conceptual understanding of what constitutes an assumption and building an awareness of the variety of assumptions that may be behind any argument.

- **a.** Assumed; probably true in many cases
- **b.** Assumed; probably true
- **c.** Assumed; false
- **d.** Assumed; probably false
- **e.** Assumed; probably false
- **f.** Not assumed
- **g.** Not assumed
- **h.** Not assumed, but the advertiser may want the reader to make this assumption
- **i.** Assumed (implicitly); not necessarily true

Unit 4

In this unit, you will expand your ability to make reasoned arguments or **proofs** in the context of geometric situations. As in algebraic reasoning, the goal is to reach conclusions by applying correct logical principles to combinations of previously proven or assumed facts and relations.

INVESTIGATION 1 Analyzing Arguments

In mathematics, in other academic fields, and in daily affairs, it is important to be able to analyze and understand arguments provided by other people. As you may have noted in your discussion of the "Think About This Situation" on the previous page, assumptions have an important influence on such arguments. In the next two activities, you are asked to identify and think about assumptions that are being made.

1. Examine the claim below, from a newspaper advertisement for The Men's Wearhouse.

> We sell men's clothing for less than our competitors do, because our store is not in the high rent district.

Decide whether each of the following statements was taken for granted (assumed) in the above advertisement. If the statement was assumed, indicate whether you think it is probably true or probably false. Explain your thinking.

a. The competitors charge more than The Men's Wearhouse for men's clothing.

b. It is necessary for a store to charge more for clothing as rent increases.

c. Rent is the only factor that influences the price of clothing.

d. The Men's Wearhouse charges less for every piece of men's clothing.

e. All of The Men's Wearhouse competitors are in the high rent district.

f. A store that accepts only cash (no credit cards) can charge less for clothing.

g. A high volume of sales at The Men's Wearhouse permits it to sell clothing for less than its competitors.

h. The Men's Wearhouse always sells its clothing at the lowest possible prices.

i. The quality of clothing at The Men's Wearhouse is similar to the quality of clothing at competing stores.

Unit 4

LESSON 1 • REASONED ARGUMENTS 261

2. At the beginning of a new school year, Rosa and her college roommate Wendy bought 180 square feet of carpeting for their dorm room. Later in the semester, while on a shopping excursion, they found a wallpaper border pattern that they loved. They decided to purchase enough paper to run a strip around their dorm room. Rosa suggested buying 56 feet from the 60-yard roll. Wendy thought they would need 58 feet of the border strip.

a. What assumptions might each have made that led them to their conclusions about the amount of paper to buy?

b. If Rosa and Wendy had a third roommate, is it possible that independently she might have suggested yet a third length of paper for the room? Explain her possible assumptions.

c. In your group, discuss what length of wallpaper border strip you might have purchased. What assumptions would you make? Explain your rationale.

Now consider the role that assumptions play in mathematical arguments.

3. You have probably noticed that when you add two odd integers, the sum always seems to be an even integer. In Maria and Toby's mathematics class, it is commonplace for observations of patterns like this to lead to conjectures and then to attempted proofs. Maria and Toby's conjecture was the following:

If a and b are odd integers, then $a + b$ (the sum) is an even integer.

Both students tried to prove the conjecture independently. Maria's proof went as follows:

If a and b are odd integers, then a and b can be written $a = 2m + 1$ and $b = 2n + 1$, where m and n are other integers.

If $a = 2m + 1$ and $b = 2n + 1$, then $a + b = 2m + 1 + 2n + 1$.

If $a + b = 2m + 1 + 2n + 1$, then $a + b = 2m + 2n + 2$.

If $a + b = 2m + 2n + 2$, then $a + b = 2(m + n + 1)$.

If $a + b = 2(m + n + 1)$, then $a + b$ is an even integer.

Toby took some square counters and reasoned, "I can use these to prove the sum of any two odd numbers is even. For example, if I take the numbers 5 and 11 and organize the counters as shown, you can see the pattern."

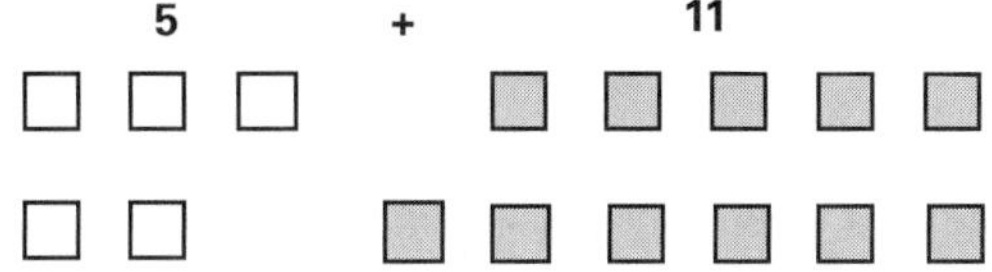

262 UNIT 4 • SHAPES AND GEOMETRIC REASONING

2. This activity provides examples of the dependence of outcomes on assumptions. It also provides some reinforcement of the differences between area and perimeter.
   - **a.** Rosa may have been assuming that the room was 18 feet by 10 feet. The perimeter would then be 56 feet. Wendy may have assumed the room was 9 feet by 20 feet which gives a perimeter of 58 feet.
   - **b.** If the room is assumed to be rectangular, she might suggest a length based on different dimensions, such as 12 feet by 15 feet for a perimeter of 54 feet.
   - **c.** Responses may vary. Students may assume other dimensions, account for doors or windows, or discuss using extra paper for other decorating purposes.
3. **The key point here is that an example proves nothing. It makes a conjecture more plausible, but it can never constitute a proof of the truth of a statement for all cases. Student groups should be able to work through this activity on their own, but be sure that the key idea surfaces in a full-class discussion, either at the end of the class period or at the Checkpoint.**

3. **a.** Maria assumes that you can always write an odd integer in the form $2k + 1$, where k is some other integer. Within the argument, she used the algebraic properties of real numbers. She also used the fact that if a number has a factor of 2, it is an even number.
   b. Toby assumed that since the sum of 5 and 11 is even, the sum of any two odd integers will be even.
   c. Yes, it proves the conjecture. It is a sequence of true statements that logically follow each other. Also, it uses accepted and well understood mathematics.
   d. Toby's argument does not prove the conjecture. His argument only shows that the conjecture is true for two specific odd integers.
   e. Toby's model for odd numbers may help students visualize why odd numbers can be written in the form $2m + 1$. In his model for 11, when $11 = 2m + 1$, then m is shown as 5, $2m$ as a 2×5 rectangle, and $2m + 1$ as a 2×5 rectangle with one extra block.
4. **Because of the difficulty of analyzing the arguments in terms of their adequacy as logical arguments, we recommend that Activity 4 be done using coordinated combinations of small-group and full-class thought and discussion. Ask the groups to look at each argument and to identify and describe the features of the argument that are positive. Then, discuss these ideas as a full class using the parts of Activity 4. Ask students what they can add to make each argument even clearer.**

"You can see that when you put the sets together (add the numbers), the two extra blocks will form a pair and the answer is always even."

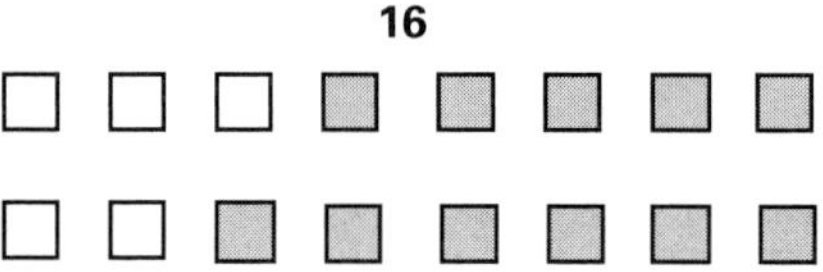

a. Look at Maria's first statement. What does she assume? What additional assumptions, facts, or algebraic properties did she use within her argument?

b. Next look at Toby's argument. What did he assume?

c. Does Maria's argument prove the conjecture? Describe the features of her argument that support your position.

d. Does Toby's argument prove the conjecture? Describe the features of his argument that support your position.

e. How can Toby's model of odd numbers help you understand Maria's proof?

4. Below is a restatement of Modeling Task 3 Part b from Lesson 2 of the "Symbol Sense and Algebraic Reasoning" unit (page 203).

Given: b_1 and b_2 are the lengths of the bases of the trapezoid shown, with height h.

Prove: The area of the trapezoid is $A = \frac{1}{2}h(b_2 - b_1) + b_1h$.

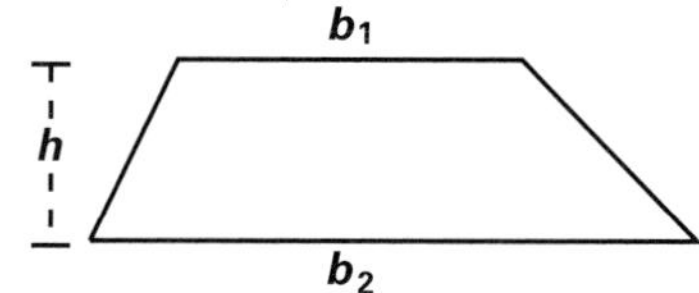

Study each of the three sample student arguments that follow.

Barbara's argument:

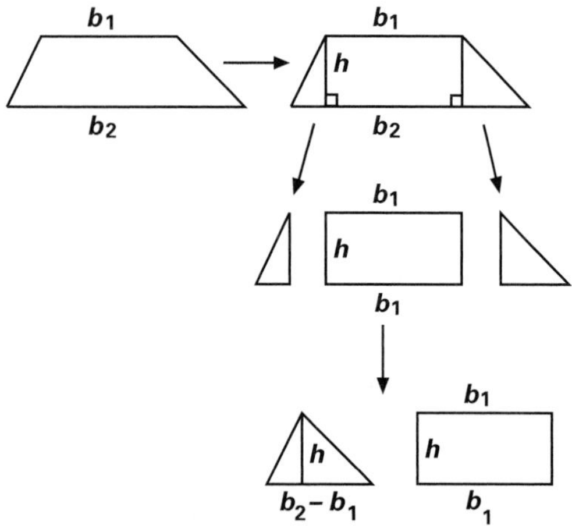

So the area of the trapezoid is $\frac{1}{2}h(b_2 - b_1) + b_1h$.

Unit 4

LESSON 1 • REASONED ARGUMENTS 263

Hsui's argument: The area of a trapezoid with bases b_1 and b_2 and altitude h is $\frac{1}{2}h(b_2 - b_1) + b_1h$ because the trapezoid can be cut up into a b_1-by-h rectangle with area b_1h and two triangles with altitude h, which together make a triangle with area $\frac{1}{2}h(b_2 - b_1)$.

Jorge's argument: The area of the trapezoid is $\frac{1}{2}h(b_2 - b_1) + b_1h$ because you can cut up the shape and find the areas of the individual pieces.

Each of these student arguments was offered as a justification of the area formula for a trapezoid: $A = \frac{1}{2}h(b_2 - b_1) + b_1h$.

a. Look back at Barbara's, Hsui's, and Jorge's arguments. What assumptions did each make at the beginning of his or her argument? What assumptions and facts did each student use within his or her argument?

b. As a group, decide which of these arguments do a good job of justifying the formula and which do not.

c. Describe the features of an argument that your group thought was good. What could you *add* to that argument to improve it?

d. Choose an argument your group thought was not good. Describe why your group decided it was not good.

e. Of the good arguments, which one do you prefer? Explain your preference.

5. A standard formula for calculating the area A of a trapezoid is $A = \frac{1}{2}h(b_2 + b_1)$. Kenya thought that she could use algebraic reasoning to show that the formula in Activity 4 is equivalent to the standard formula for the area of a trapezoid. Study Kenya's proof shown below.

$$\begin{aligned} \tfrac{1}{2}h(b_2 - b_1) + b_1h &= \tfrac{1}{2}hb_2 - \tfrac{1}{2}hb_1 + b_1h && (1) \\ &= \tfrac{1}{2}hb_2 + \tfrac{1}{2}hb_1 && (2) \\ &= \tfrac{1}{2}h(b_2 + b_1) && (3) \end{aligned}$$

a. What mathematical facts and relationships did Kenya assume were true at the beginning of her argument?

b. What mathematical facts and properties support each step in her argument?

c. Compare the set of assumptions, facts, and properties used by Kenya to those used in the student arguments in Activity 4.

6. Now look back at the student attempts to prove the mathematical statements in Activities 3 through 5.

a. Examine these arguments, both good and not so good, and then identify and describe the features of an argument that make it a *valid argument*.

b. Examine these arguments, both good and not so good, and then describe the different forms in which the arguments were presented. Are there examples that could be described as pictorial, flow diagram, chain of if-then statements, or paragraph form? Characterize each example you find.

c. Investigate and then make a conjecture about the sum of any two even integers. What would you do to prove your conjecture?

264 UNIT 4 • SHAPES AND GEOMETRIC REASONING

4. **a.** Each student uses the same basic assumptions. At the beginning of their arguments, they assumed that the figure was a trapezoid with parallel bases of lengths b_1 and b_2 and that the distance between the two bases was constant.

Within the argument, they assumed that the areas of parts of a figure add to the area of the entire figure and that when a length of b_1 is taken from a length of b_2, the remaining portions together have length $b_2 - b_1$.

b. The arguments presented by Barbara and Hsui do a reasonably good job justifying the formula, even though each can be improved upon. Jorge's argument is too vague and incomplete. It doesn't do a good job of justifying the formula.

c. Students should choose to look at either Barbara's or Hsui's argument. The good features might include that the argument is logically organized and uses accepted mathematical ideas (such as the area of a shape is the sum of the areas of its pieces and the area of a shape is not changed when it is moved in the plane).

To improve Barbara's argument, you might add some notes explaining the dissection and why the parts together have the same area as the whole. Also, a verbal explanation of where $b_2 - b_1$ came from and why it is the measure of the base of the final triangle would make the argument clearer.

The most obvious thing that could be added to Hsui's argument would be some diagrams illustrating his reasoning.

d. Jorge's argument is not carefully explained to the reader. Jorge does not identify the pieces into which the trapezoid is to be cut, nor does he indicate how the areas combine to produce the formula for the area of a trapezoid.

e. Responses will vary. Reasons for choosing one argument over another might include the visual nature of the argument or the succinctness of the symbolic argument.

5. **This activity should be done in groups and completed by all students. It might be useful to have a full-class discussion following this activity. Make sure that students see that different assumptions lead to different arguments, all or some of which may be correct. A key idea here is that acceptance of an argument implicitly accepts the assumptions on which the argument is based. If those assumptions are faulty, then so is the conclusion. You may wish to revisit the advertisements discussed in the "Think About This Situation" on page 260.**

a. She assumed that $\frac{1}{2}h(b_2 - b_1) + b_1h$ gave the area of a trapezoid. Within her argument, she assumed h, b_1, and b_2 were real numbers and used the properties of those numbers.

b. She used the distributive property in each step plus the commutative property and arithmetic in Step 2.

c. Kenya began with the desired formula and showed it was equivalent to an accepted formula. Her reasoning depended on algebraic properties, primarily the distributive property. The other students did not start with an algebraic formula; rather, they started with the shape and used its geometric properties and measures.

6. **Students need to wrestle with these ideas in small groups first, but make sure a full-class discussion at the Checkpoint brings out these ideas.**

a. To be valid, an argument must be completely general, be built on correct beginning assumptions, use only correct mathematics, have a logical flow with each new conclusion logically following from previous ones, and contain no gaps or holes.

b. Barbara's proof is pictorial and is also a flow diagram. Maria's proof is a chain of if-then statements. Hsui's proof is a paragraph.

c. The sum of any two even integers is an even integer. Students may choose different ways to prove this. You may wish to have groups share their proofs with the class.

Master 88

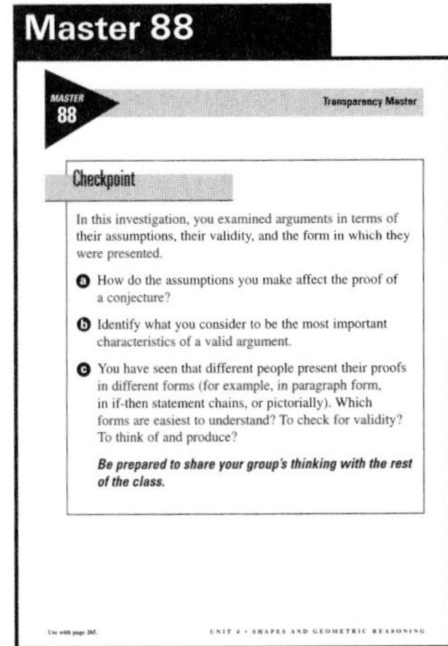

MASTER 88 Transparency Master

Checkpoint

In this investigation, you examined arguments in terms of their assumptions, their validity, and the form in which they were presented.

a. How do the assumptions you make affect the proof of a conjecture?

b. Identify what you consider to be the most important characteristics of a valid argument.

c. You have seen that different people present their proofs in different forms (for example, in paragraph form, in if-then statement chains, or pictorially). Which forms are easiest to understand? To check for validity? To think of and produce?

Be prepared to share your group's thinking with the rest of the class.

Use with page 265. UNIT 4 • SHAPES AND GEOMETRIC REASONING

SHARE AND SUMMARIZE full-class discussion

Checkpoint

See Teaching Master 88.

Full-class discussions that have punctuated this investigation can be summarized along with this Checkpoint. You may wish to reread the comments included with Activities 1–6 preceding this Checkpoint.

a. The assumptions you make form the basis of the argument. If the assumptions made at the beginning of an argument are not valid, then any conclusions that are made as a result of the argument will not be valid either.

b. In general a valid argument must be logical; use correct mathematical facts, operations, or relations; be general in nature; and communicate well.

It may be helpful to begin a class poster with a list of the characteristics that students note should be found in a valid proof. The list can be expanded and improved as students see more examples of good proofs. The list may also be referred to as students begin to create their own proofs. They should ask, "Does my proof meet all of the conditions we listed as part of a valid argument?"

c. Responses will vary. The form that is easiest for one student may be the hardest for another. Also, the type of problem or setting may make one form more accessible than another.

CONSTRUCTING A MATH TOOLKIT: Students should create a list of the characteristics of a valid argument which they can expand in Investigations 3 and 4. This unit also includes a tremendous amount of new mathematics vocabulary. It will be very helpful for students to begin a vocabulary list that can be added to as the unit progresses. Encourage students to illustrate the vocabulary as needed.

APPLY individual task

On Your Own

a. Karen assumed each of the statements in the ad. They formed the first three lines of the argument. In addition, she assumed that facing life like a queen means she will have an easy life.

b. No. Although the statements follow in a logical sequence and the argument is complete, the argument depends on false assumptions, and so it is not a valid argument.

c. A chain of if-then statements

MORE ASSIGNMENT *pp. 272–278*

Students can now begin Modeling Task 1 or 2, Reflecting Task 4, or Extending Task 3 from the MORE assignment following Investigation 2.

Unit 4

Checkpoint

In this investigation, you examined arguments in terms of their assumptions, their validity, and the form in which they were presented.

a How do the assumptions you make affect the proof of a conjecture?

b Identify what you consider to be the most important characteristics of a valid argument.

c You have seen that different people present their proofs in different forms (for example, in paragraph form, in if-then statement chains, or pictorially). Which forms are easiest to understand? To check for validity? To think of and produce?

Be prepared to share your group's thinking with the rest of the class.

On Your Own

Fresh Makeup

Give your skin a treat with Fresh Makeup, the clean, fresh, look that lets your skin breathe. That keeps your skin glowing. That lets you face the world like a queen.

After reading the above advertisement, Karen showed it to her mother, saying, "Mom, look. This ad says I can drop out of school and have an easy life. All I need to do is use Fresh Makeup." You can imagine her mother's response!

Here is the argument Karen constructed.

If I use Fresh Makeup, then my skin can breathe.

If my skin breathes, then it will glow.

If my skin glows, then I'll face life like I'm a queen.

If I can face life like a queen, then I'll have an easy life.

a. What assumptions does this argument make?

b. Is this a valid argument? Describe the characteristics of the argument that led you to conclude that it was or was not valid.

c. Describe the form of Karen's proof.

Unit 4

LESSON 1 • REASONED ARGUMENTS 265

INVESTIGATION 2 Reasoning *to* and *from* If-Then Statements

Maria's argument in Activity 3 of the previous investigation (page 262) involved reasoning with a chain of if-then statements. That kind of reasoning is based on a fundamental principle of logic:

If you have a known fact	(an if-then statement that is always true)
and you also know	the "if" part is true in a particular case,
you can conclude	the "then" part is true in that case.

For example, consider how this principle supports the reasoning in the last statement of Maria's proof.

Known fact: If $p = 2n$, where n is an integer, then p is an even integer.

Given: $a + b = 2(m + n + 1)$, where m and n are integers.

Conclusion: $a + b$ is an even integer.

1. In your group, decide what can be concluded from each of the following sets of statements.

a. *Known fact:* If $f(x) = ax^2 + bx + c$ is a quadratic function with $a < 0$, then $f(x)$ has a maximum value.

Given: $g(x) = -8x^2 + 5x - 2$

Conclusion: ?

b. *Known fact:* If A and B are two independent events, then the probability $P(A \text{ and } B) = P(A) \cdot P(B)$.

Given: Josh and Jeanette are playing a game in which they each draw a card from separate standard decks of playing cards. They are curious about the probability that both will draw a red card.

Conclusion: ?

c. *Known fact:* If a connected vertex-edge graph has vertices all of even degree, then the graph has an Euler circuit.

Given: The degrees of the vertices of a connected graph G are 2, 4, 2, 4, 2, 4, 2, 4, 2, 4.

Conclusion: ?

d. *Known fact:* If a data set with mean $\bar{x}$ and mean absolute deviation (MAD) d is transformed by adding a constant c to each value, then the mean of the transformed data set is $\bar{x} + c$ and the MAD is d.

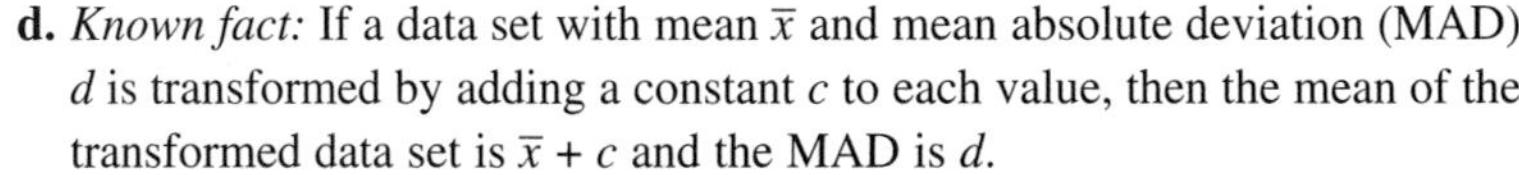

Given: The Oak Park hockey team has a mean height of 5 feet 9 inches and a MAD of $2\frac{1}{2}$ inches. Ice skates add approximately $1\frac{3}{4}$ inches to the height of a skater.

Conclusion: ?

266 UNIT 4 • SHAPES AND GEOMETRIC REASONING

EXPLORE small-group investigation

INVESTIGATION 2 Reasoning *to* and *from* If-Then Statements

This investigation has two main goals. The first is to help students understand the need for careful analysis of mathematical statements to ensure their truth. The second is to make clear the nature of true if-then statements and to help students as they begin thinking about constructing proofs.

The investigation is made up of eleven activities that naturally fall into three groups: conditional statements, inductive reasoning, and deductive reasoning. In Activity 1, students are asked to draw conclusions from general known facts and specific examples. Students are not expected to prove or disprove, but rather to consider each statement, check their mathematical knowledge, and decide what can be concluded. Note that several of these statements deal with nongeometric content.

Activity 2 contains formal symbols and vocabulary that students may find difficult. You may choose to do this activity as a large group or to immediately follow the small-group attempts with a full-class discussion.

Activities 3–7 help students develop an understanding of using inductive reasoning to provide conjectures and the role of the counterexamples and careful if-then reasoning for proving or disproving a statement.

Activities 8–11 introduce students to deductive reasoning and ask them to create their own valid arguments. Note that Activity 3 in Investigation 1 included a proof that is similar to the proof needed for Activity 10. Students who need help should be encouraged to use the given proof as a model to write their own. In general, for many students who are just learning to create valid arguments, it will be helpful for them to collect and record in a journal sample proofs that they can use as models for their own proofs. Ideas such as how to write an expression for an even number, or using substitution and the properties of equality, may not occur to some students. However, once students see these ideas used in proofs, either in the textbook or from other student work, they should be encouraged to remember and then use these ideas in their own work. Encourage students to use the valid proofs they write and read to build a repertoire of strategies to be used in proofs.

Students should note that proofs, like so many other problems in mathematics, can be completed correctly in many different ways. It is reasonable to expect that initial proofs may be incomplete, but all students should be urged to use complete, reasonably sequenced if-then statements with easily identifiable clauses. Rigor and skill will follow. Notice also that no particular form for a proof is required. You and your class should develop an acceptable format for presenting proofs. It may be paragraph, a string of connected conditionals, or some other format. The curriculum developers recommend not requiring the two-column format. The logical argument is the important emphasis, not an arbitrarily predetermined, inflexible format. Students should be encouraged to think in if-then format: IF I know such-and-such, THEN I also know this-and-that. This kind of thinking is the key to deduction!

1. **a.** Function $g(x)$ has a maximum value.

b. The probability that both of them will draw a red card is $\frac{1}{2} \cdot \frac{1}{2}$ or $\frac{1}{4}$.

c. Graph G has an Euler circuit.

d. With skates on, the mean height of the Oak Park hockey team is 5 feet $10\frac{3}{4}$ inches and the MAD is $2\frac{1}{2}$ inches.

EXPLORE *continued*

1. e. The area of hexagon $P'Q'R'S'T'U'$ is $9 \cdot 32$ or 288 cm^2.

2. Another version of the symbolic form for this type of reasoning that may be helpful for some students looks like this:

$$p \Rightarrow q$$
$$p \text{ is true.}$$
$$\therefore q \text{ is true.}$$

   a. If-then statement: If $f(x) = ax^2 + bx + c$ is a quadratic function with $a < 0$, then $f(x)$ has a maximum value.
      Hypothesis: $g(x) = -8x^2 + 5x - 2$
      Conclusion: $g(x)$ has a maximum value.

   b. p: A size transformation with center at the origin and magnitude 3 is applied to a hexagon $PQRSTU$ with area 32 cm^2.
      q: The area of the image of the hexagon is $9 \cdot 32$ cm^2.
      $p \Rightarrow q$: Under a size transformation with center at the origin and magnitude k, the area of the image of a figure is $k^2 \cdot$ *area of the pre-image*.

   c. If a student at Calvin High School is a sophomore, then the student takes physical education. The hypothesis is "a student at Calvin High School is a sophomore." The conclusion is "the student takes physical education."
      - Tommy takes physical education.
      - Nothing can be concluded from the fact that Rosa is taking a physical education class at Calvin, since we cannot assume that only sophomores take physical education. This may be difficult for some students to understand; they will consider this question again later.

3. Responses will vary. One possible experiment or case study for each statement is provided here.

   a. You could use the calculator to graph many equations of the form $f(x) = ax^2 + bx + c$ with $a < 0$ and notice that they all have a maximum value.

   b. You could set up probability situations and find the experimental probability $P(A \text{ and } B)$.

   c. You could draw many vertex-edge graphs in which all the vertices have even degree. You could then see that each of them has an Euler circuit.

   d. You could make up a data set and find the mean and MAD of that data set. Then you could add different constants c to each element in the data set and recalculate the mean and MAD. You should see that the mean increases by c and the MAD does not change.

   e. Using various rectangles, you could find the area of many pre-image and image figures using different scale factors. You should notice that with magnitude k, the area of the image is k^2 times the area of the pre-image.

4. a. You might conclude that you are allergic to cats. This is an example of inductive reasoning because we are generalizing from four known cases.

   b. Responses will vary. Inductive reasoning is used often in everyday life. You might choose to shop one place rather than another because the prices or selection have been better in the past. You might dress warmly when visiting a certain person because in the past you have been cold at his or her residence.

e. *Known fact:* Under a size transformation with center at the origin and magnitude k, the area of the image of a figure is $k^2 \cdot$ area of the pre-image.

Given: Hexagon $P'Q'R'S'T'U'$ is the image under a size transformation with center at the origin and magnitude 3 of hexagon $PQRSTU$ whose area is 32 cm^2.

Conclusion: ?

2. If-then statements and reasoning patterns can be represented symbolically. For example, the reasoning pattern you used in Activity 1 can be represented as follows:

	Words	Symbolic form
Known fact:	"If p then q" is always true,	$p \Rightarrow q$
Given:	**and** p is true in a particular case,	p
Conclusion:	**thus** q is true in that case.	q

The clause corresponding to p (following "if") is called the **hypothesis**. The clause corresponding to q (following "then") is called the **conclusion**.

a. In Activity 1 Part a, identify the if-then statement, the hypothesis, and the conclusion.

b. For the known fact in Part e of Activity 1, identify p, q, and $p \Rightarrow q$.

c. Write, in if-then form, the statement "All sophomores at Calvin High School take physical education." What is the hypothesis? The conclusion?

- If Tommy is a sophomore at Calvin, what can you conclude?
- If Rosa is taking a physical education class at Calvin, what can you conclude? Explain your reasoning.

The "known facts" you used in Activity 1 were relationships you probably discovered and, as a class, agreed upon in previous mathematics courses. Your discoveries were probably based on studying cases or experimenting, collecting data, and searching for patterns.

3. In your group, discuss some possible case explorations or experiments that might have suggested the statements given as known facts in Activity 1.

4. Reasoning from patterns based on analysis of specific cases is called **inductive reasoning**. You use this kind of reasoning often in mathematics and in everyday life.

a. Suppose during the last month you visited four friends, each of whom has a cat. In each case, you noticed that your eyes began to itch and water after a while. What might you conclude? How is this an example of inductive reasoning?

b. Record, from each group member, at least one example of how he or she has used inductive reasoning outside of mathematics class.

Unit 4

LESSON 1 • REASONED ARGUMENTS 267

Now consider some examples of inductive reasoning in mathematics.

5. Recall that the *degree* of a vertex in a vertex-edge graph without loops is the number of edges meeting at the vertex. Use inductive reasoning and Parts a through c below to develop a conjecture about the *sum* of the degrees of the vertices of a vertex-edge graph with no loops.

   a. For each of the graphs shown, determine the number of edges, the degree of each vertex, and the sum of the degrees of the vertices. Organize your results in a table. Leave room to extend your table.

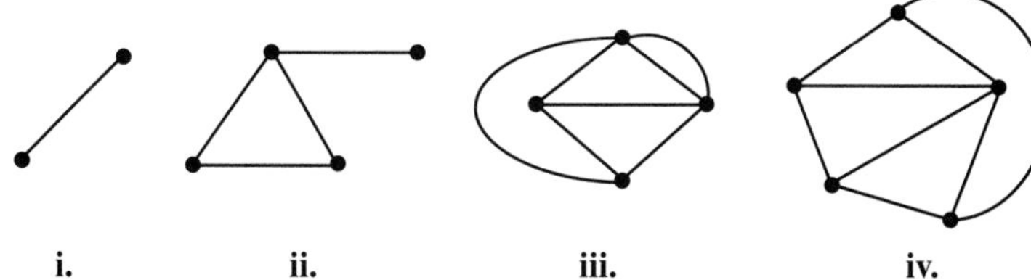

i. **ii.** **iii.** **iv.**

   b. Draw four additional vertex-edge graphs. Find the number of edges and the sum of the degrees of the vertices for each graph. Record your findings in your table.

   c. If you have a vertex-edge graph with 10 edges, what do you think is the sum of the degrees of the vertices? Check your prediction with a drawing.

   d. Write a conjecture relating the number of edges E and the sum of the degrees of the vertices S.

   e. State your conjecture in if-then form.

   f. Are you absolutely positive that your conjecture is true for all possible vertex-edge graphs? Explain.

In Activity 5, you developed a conjecture by looking for patterns in specific cases. In the next activity, you will examine two conjectures already formulated. The first conjecture involves prime numbers.

6. Recall that a **prime number** is an integer greater than 1 that has exactly two positive factors, 1 and the number itself. The first 10 primes are 2, 3, 5, 7, 11, 13, 17, 19, 23, and 29. Study Benjamin's conjecture below, which proposes a way to produce prime numbers using a quadratic expression:

   If n is a positive integer, then $n^2 - n + 41$ is a prime number.

   a. Test Benjamin's conjecture by examining some specific cases. Choose several positive values for n and see if the formula gives a prime number. Share the work in your group.

   b. Based on your calculations, does the conjecture seem correct? Can you conclude for sure that it is always true? Explain your reasoning.

   c. Now test $n^2 - n + 41$ for $n = 41$. Is the result a prime number? Why or why not?

   d. What would you say to Benjamin about the correctness of his conjecture?

Unit 4

268 UNIT 4 • SHAPES AND GEOMETRIC REASONING

5. a.

Graph	Edges	Degrees	Sum of Degrees
i	1	1, 1	2
ii	4	3, 1, 2, 2	8
iii	7	4, 3, 4, 3	14
iv	8	3, 3, 4, 3, 3	16

b. Responses will vary, but the sum of the degrees of the vertices in each graph will be twice the number of edges in the graph.

c. The sum of the degrees will be 2×10 or 20.

d. The sum S of the degrees of the vertices of a graph with E edges will be $2 \times E$. This relationship can be represented by the equation $S = 2E$.

e. If a vertex-edge graph has E edges, then the sum of the degrees of the vertices is $2E$.

f. Most students will say yes because they have seen many cases. You may wish to challenge them here by asking how they know the conjecture is true for *all* graphs. Better reasoning is that each edge contributes exactly 2 endpoints to the sum of the degrees of the vertices of a graph. See Activity 9 page 270 for a thorough proof.

Since the conclusion is that the sum of the degrees is always 2*E*, this implies that there can never be a graph with an odd sum of degrees. Since we know that particular vertices can have odd degree, this also implies that we cannot have a graph with an odd number of odd vertices. Without telling your students these facts, you might want to challenge them to draw the following:

- **A graph with one odd vertex**
- **A graph with two odd vertices**
- **A graph with three odd vertices**
- **A graph with four odd vertices**

After a few days have gone by, ask if anyone was successful. Since no one will have a graph with an odd number of odd vertices, students might conjecture that such a graph is not possible. Ask them if the fact that no one was able to draw a graph with an odd number of odd vertices constitutes a proof that doing so is not possible. (This will give you a fair assessment of how sophisticated their understanding of "proof" is at this point.) Then ask them if they can reason from the conclusion they drew in Activity 5, using if-then form. (If a graph has *E* edges, then it has a degree sum of 2*E*. If a graph has degree sum 2*E*, then the degree sum is even. If the degree sum is even, then it is made by adding all even vertices, or adding pairs of odds, or some combination of even vertices and pairs of odd vertices. Therefore, for any graph with *E* edges, there will be either all even vertices or pairs of odd vertices possibly with even vertices.)

NOTE: In Activities 6 and 7, students consider situations in which it is impossible to test all of the possibilities.

6. This example motivates the need for deductive reasoning.

a. The equation will work for most values of n. An efficient method for testing several values of the function is to put the equation into the functions list on a calculator and then look at a table of values. You can also put specific values for n into a data list and enter the function into another, using the first list for the variable. Students may need some guidance on how to determine if a number is prime.

b. From the work done in Part a, it seems as though the conjecture is probably correct. However, you cannot conclude it will be true for all values of n just because a few values do work. See Part c.

c. The result is not a prime number.
$41^2 - 41 + 41 = 41^2 = 1{,}681$, and 41 is a factor of 1,681.

d. This counterexample ($n = 41$) shows that the statement is not correct because it is not true for all values of n.

Unit 4

Master 89

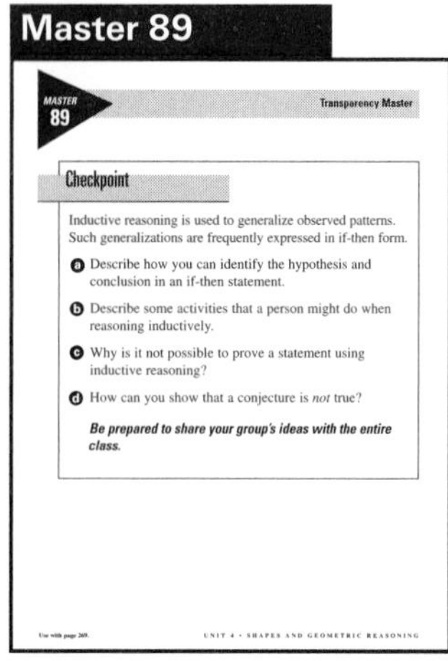

EXPLORE *continued*

7. Terry's conjecture is not correct. If x is any positive number less than 1, then $\sqrt{x} \geq x$. Students may provide a specific counterexample.

SHARE AND SUMMARIZE full-class discussion

Checkpoint

See Teaching Master 89.

a. The hypothesis is generally the clause following "if," and the conclusion is generally the clause following "then." If there is no "if" and "then" in the statement, the conclusion is usually the predicate (see Activity 2 Part c, page 267) or the main sentence (see Activity 1 Part e, page 267).

b. Responses may vary. Some people might look at several examples and try to identify patterns. Others might do an experiment or simulation.

c. It is not possible because you would need to test an unlimited number of possibilities. (In the rare instance that there is a finite number of cases, the statement can be proved by confirming it for each case.)

d. To show that a conjecture is *not* true, you need find only one counterexample.

MORE ASSIGNMENT *pp. 272–278*

Students can now begin Organizing Task 1 or 2 or Reflecting Task 1 or 5 from the MORE assignment following Investigation 2.

APPLY individual task

On Your Own

Conjectures may vary slightly; however, adding the middle two and subtracting the smallest gives the largest. Students will probably arrive at this conjecture after considering a few examples.

EXPLORE small-group investigation

8. a. If you have four consecutive positive integers, add the middle two, and then subtract the smallest, then the result will be equal to the largest of the integers.
   b. The other three integers would be $n + 1$, $n + 2$, and $n + 3$.
   c. The sum of the middle two integers is $(n + 1) + (n + 2)$ or $2n + 3$. Subtracting the smallest integer results in $2n + 3 - n$ or $n + 3$, which is equal to the largest integer.

Unit 4

7. Now examine Teri's conjecture about a property of square roots:

If x is a positive real number, then $\sqrt{x} \le x$.

Write a response to Teri about the correctness of her conjecture.

Checkpoint

Inductive reasoning is used to generalize observed patterns. Such generalizations are frequently expressed in if-then form.

a. Describe how you can identify the hypothesis and conclusion in an if-then statement.

b. Describe some activities that a person might do when reasoning inductively.

c. Why is it not possible to prove a statement using inductive reasoning?

d. How can you show that a conjecture is *not* true?

Be prepared to share your group's ideas with the entire class.

On Your Own

Make a conjecture about what happens when you choose any four consecutive positive integers, add the middle two, and then subtract the smallest of the four from that sum. Describe the procedure you used to generate your conjecture.

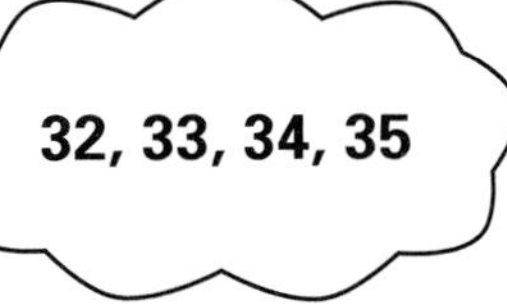

Sherlock Holmes, Master of Deduction

Inductive reasoning may lead to an if-then statement that is plausible. However, the statement may or may not always be true. Another type of reasoning, **deductive reasoning**, involves reasoning *from* facts, definitions, and accepted properties *to* new statements using principles of logic. Under correct deductive reasoning, the conclusions reached are certain, not just plausible.

8. Compare the conjectures members of your group made in the above "On Your Own" task.

   a. Choose one conjecture that all of you believe is probably always true. Write the conjecture in if-then form.

   b. If n represents the smallest of four consecutive integers, how would you represent the other three numbers?

   c. Using your representations in Part b, prove your conjecture in Part a.

Unit 4

LESSON 1 • REASONED ARGUMENTS 269

The algebraic reasoning you used in Activity 8 and in the previous unit to prove general statements about number patterns and relationships in geometry, trigonometry, and statistics is a form of deductive reasoning. In the next activity, you will examine how deductive reasoning is used to establish a relationship in discrete mathematics.

9. In Activity 5, your group may have arrived at the following conjecture:

If G is a vertex-edge graph with E edges, none of which are loops, then the sum of the degrees of the vertices S is equal to $2E$.

Here is an argument that is claimed to be a proof of this conjecture. Study it carefully.

If G is a vertex-edge graph with E edges, none of which are loops, then each of the E edges joins two vertices.

If each of the E edges joins two vertices, then each of the E edges contributes 2 to the sum of the degrees of the vertices S.

If each of the E edges contributes 2 to the sum of the degrees of the vertices S, then $S = 2E$.

Therefore, if G is a vertex-edge graph with E edges, none of which are loops, then the sum of the degrees of the vertices S is $2E$.

a. Does this argument convince you that the conjecture is correct? Why or why not?

b. Is the argument based on information that is known to be correct? Look critically at each of the first three if-then statements. Are they correct? Explain why or why not.

c. What do the first two statements in the proof have in common? How are the common parts used differently? Is the same true for the second and third statements?

d. How is the final if-then statement derived from the first three if-then statements in the proof?

e. Rewrite this proof in a different form that you find easy to understand and to write.

10. In Investigation 1, you examined conjectures about the sum of two odd integers.

a. Now, suppose a is an odd integer and b is an even integer. What can you conclude about their sum?

b. Write your conjecture as an if-then statement.

c. Write a deductive argument that you could use to convince the most skeptical person that your conjecture is, in fact, correct.

d. What known mathematical facts did you use in your argument?

e. Share and compare your argument with others in class. How do they differ in form and in assumptions?

Unit 4

270 UNIT 4 • SHAPES AND GEOMETRIC REASONING

9. a. Responses may vary, but most students will correctly believe that this argument proves the conjecture.

b. Each statement is known to be correct. (At this point, you might want to discuss why the words "none of which are loops" are needed. Would the first statement be true if there were loops? However, even in a graph with loops, the sum of the degrees is $2E$.)

c. The conclusion ("then" clause) of the first statement is the hypothesis ("if" clause) of the second statement. The same is true for the second and third statements. The conclusion of the second statement is the hypothesis for the third statement.

d. The final if-then statement has the hypothesis of the first statement and the conclusion of the last. It illustrates the chain rule of logic.

e. Responses will vary. Students may give a paragraph proof or some other form. You might ask some students to put their proofs on an overhead transparency for sharing with and critique by the entire class. Be sure that students' proofs are general.

10. Students may have trouble with this activity, which requires them to show that the sum of an even and an odd number is an odd number. If they do have difficulty, consider having them brainstorm what they know about even and odd numbers. It is hoped that someone will realize or remember that even numbers can be expressed as a multiple of 2, or 2*m*, where *m* is an integer, and that an odd number is an even number plus 1, or 2*n* + 1, where *n* is an integer. Alternatively, you may wish to refer students back to Maria's proof in Investigation 1. It may be helpful for the groups to reproduce their proofs on transparencies to share with the entire class.

a. The sum of an odd and an even integer will always be odd.

b. If an odd and an even integer are added together, then the sum will be odd.

c. Here is one possible proof.
If a is an odd integer, then $a = 2m + 1$ for some integer value of m.
If b is an even integer, then $b = 2n$ for some integer value of n.
If a and b are added together, then $a + b = 2m + 1 + 2n$.
If $a + b = 2m + 1 + 2n$, then $a + b = 2(m + n) + 1$.
If a is an odd integer and b is an even integer, then $a + b = 2(m + n) + 1$, which is an odd integer.

d. In the argument above, writing an odd integer as an even integer ($2n$) plus 1 is taken as a mathematical fact, as is writing an even integer as $2m$. The commutative and distributive properties were also used.

e. Students should compare and critique their proofs.

Unit 4

Master 90

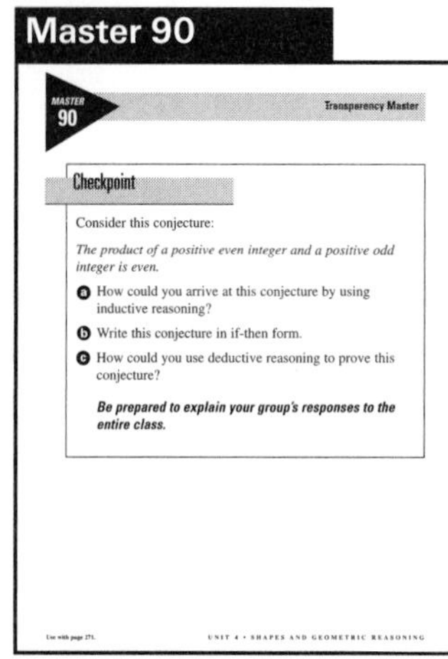

MASTER 90 Transparency Master

Checkpoint

Consider this conjecture:

The product of a positive even integer and a positive odd integer is even.

a How could you arrive at this conjecture by using inductive reasoning?

b Write this conjecture in if-then form.

c How could you use deductive reasoning to prove this conjecture?

Be prepared to explain your group's responses to the entire class.

Use with page 271. UNIT 4 • SHAPES AND GEOMETRIC REASONING

11. a. Numbers will vary. Some possible examples are 1 and 3, 5 and 7, and 9 and 11. These number pairs are consecutive odd integers since they follow each other on a number line that has only odd numbers.

b. In the example set above, $\frac{1+3}{4} = 1$, $\frac{5+7}{4} = 3$, and $\frac{9+11}{4} = 5$. Such patterns might suggest further conjectures to the students.

c. A possible proof might use the representation of odd integers suggested in Maria's argument in the previous investigation, the fact that consecutive odd integers differ by two, and the distributive property:

If $2m + 1$ is one odd integer, then $2m + 1 + 2$ is the next consecutive odd integer. So the sum can be represented as

$$\begin{aligned}(2m + 1) + (2m + 1 + 2) &= 4m + 4 \\ &= 4(m + 1)\end{aligned}$$

which is divisible by 4: $\frac{4(m+1)}{4} = m + 1$ which is an integer.

SHARE AND SUMMARIZE full-class discussion

Checkpoint

JOURNAL ENTRY: Ask students to discuss the danger of quick generalizations inherent in inductive reasoning. Also, ask them to discuss deductive arguments: What characteristics do they notice? How do such arguments begin? How do they end? Students can keep watch for arguments in newspapers or magazines they read that they believe are deductive arguments.

NOTE: You may wish to ask students to identify previous instances in their mathematics classes when they used both inductive and deductive reasoning.

See Teaching Master 90.

a Inductive reasoning could be used to arrive at this conjecture by repeatedly picking a positive even integer and a positive odd integer and multiplying them. Each time this is done, the product is an even integer, so we could propose the given conjecture, which may or may not be true.

b If a is a positive even integer and b is a positive odd integer, then $a \cdot b$ is an even integer.

c Responses may vary. An algebraic proof is provided here.

If a is an even integer, then $a = 2m$ for some positive integer m.

If b is an odd integer, then $b = 2n + 1$ for some positive integer n.

The product of a and b is $(2m)(2n + 1)$ or $4mn + 2m$, which is $2(2mn + m)$. This product is even because it has a factor of 2.

APPLY individual task

On Your Own

a. The only correct statement is Statement i.

b. Counterexamples will vary. Examples are given.

ii. If $a = 2$, then $a + b + c = 2 + 3 + 4 = 9$ and 9 is not divisible by 6.

iii. If $x = -3$, then $-x = -(-3)$, which is not less than -3. In fact, the given statement is false for any $x \leq 0$.

iv. If $x = 0.5$, then x is not greater than $\frac{1}{x}$, since 0.5 is not greater than $\frac{1}{0.5}$ or 2. The given statement is false whenever $x \leq -1$ or $0 < x \leq 1$.

c. If a, b, and c are consecutive integers, then $b = a + 1$ and $c = a + 2$.

If three consecutive integers a, b, and c are added together, then the sum is

$a + b + c = a + a + 1 + a + 2 = 3a + 3 = 3(a + 1)$.

If an integer can be written as $3(a + 1)$, then it is divisible by 3: $\frac{3(a+1)}{3} = a + 1$ which is an integer.

Unit 4

11. Tonja made the following conjecture about odd integers:

If a and b are consecutive odd integers, then their sum is divisible by 4.

a. Give three examples of pairs of consecutive odd integers. Why are they "consecutive"?

b. Test Tonja's conjecture for the pairs of integers in Part a.

c. Give either a counterexample or a deductive proof of Tonja's conjecture.

Checkpoint

Consider this conjecture:

The product of a positive even integer and a positive odd integer is even.

a How could you arrive at this conjecture by using inductive reasoning?

b Write this conjecture in if-then form.

c How could you use deductive reasoning to prove this conjecture?

Be prepared to explain your group's responses to the entire class.

Inductive reasoning and deductive reasoning are important and often complementary aspects of mathematical thinking. Inductive reasoning often leads to conjectures of new relationships or properties. These conjectures may or may not always be true. Deductive reasoning provides a way to establish, using principles of logic, that a conjecture is always true.

On Your Own

Examine the following if-then statements about properties of numbers.

i. If a, b, and c are consecutive positive integers, then $a + b + c$ is divisible by 3.

ii. If a, b, and c are consecutive positive integers, then $a + b + c$ is divisible by 6.

iii. If x is a real number, then $-x < x$.

iv. If x is a nonzero real number, then $x > \frac{1}{x}$.

a. Use inductive reasoning to help you decide which statements might be correct and which are incorrect.

b. For each statement that is incorrect, give a counterexample.

c. Write a proof that could convince a skeptic that the correct statements are true.

Unit 4

LESSON 1 • REASONED ARGUMENTS 271

MORE
Modeling • Organizing • Reflecting • Extending

Modeling

1. The United States Supreme Court has ruled that each state has power over all schools in the state and it is the responsibility of the state to require the following:
   - "That all children of proper age attend some school."
   - "That teachers shall be of good moral character and patriotic disposition."

   a. What words and phrases need to be defined clearly in order that a state may discharge its duty?

   b. Write a defining statement for "school" and "teacher."

   c. Do your definitions in Part b permit a parent to educate a child at home? Explain.

   d. What is meant by "good moral character"? How could a state certify that a teacher has good moral character?

2. In the early 1980s, a constitutional amendment requiring a balanced budget for the federal government was proposed. In the late 1990s, the question of such an amendment was still being discussed. Part of the discussion included when the amendment could take effect. One writer reasoned that since the 18th Amendment was ratified in 13 months, the 19th in 15 months, the 20th in 11 months, and the 21st in 9.5 months, once a balanced-budget amendment has been submitted to the people, the ratification time will be about a year.

   a. What conjecture is the writer making? Write it in if-then form.

   b. What argument is given to support the conjecture?

   c. Does the argument establish the conjecture? Explain.

3. Underlying the beliefs of an individual are numerous assumptions. Anyone who accepts a conclusion regarding an issue at the same time accepts certain assumptions on which that conclusion might depend, even though the particular assumptions are not explicit. (Note, however, that two people might base the same conclusion on entirely different assumptions.) The facts and assumptions on which logical arguments are built must be correct for the argument to be valid, so it's important to consider them carefully.

Unit 4

272 UNIT 4 • SHAPES AND GEOMETRIC REASONING

MORE **independent assignment**

Modeling

1. **a.** The words and phrases that need to be clearly defined are proper age, some school, teacher, good moral character, and patriotic disposition
   b. One sample response is given here.
   School: A school is a location in which students study a prescribed curriculum.
   Teacher: A teacher is a person or device that guides the learning of a student.
   c. Responses will vary. Some students' definitions may include the home as a school and the parent as a teacher. The example given in Part b allows a parent to educate his or her child at home.
   d. Most students and teachers will find it difficult to define "good moral character." Without being dictatorial, a state will have a hard time certifying good moral character. Usually a person (teacher) is assumed to be of good moral character until he or she does something that society considers the act of one without good moral character. Then the counterexample demonstrates that the assumption was in error.
2. **a.** If an amendment to the Constitution is passed by Congress and signed by the President, then it will be ratified in about one year.
   b. The argument given is the observation of four specific examples.
   c. No, the argument does not establish the conjecture. Examples do not prove the correctness of an if-then statement.

MORE
ASSIGNMENT *pp. 272–278*

Modeling: 1 or 2, and 4*
Organizing: 1 and 2
Reflecting: Choose one*
Extending: 1 or 2*

**When choice is indicated, it is important to leave the choice to the student.*
NOTE: *It is best if Organizing tasks are discussed as a whole class after they have been assigned as homework.*

Unit 4

3. **Responses will vary. Your students may have very strong opinions on many or all of these topics. Be sure that students clearly state their position and analyze the facts and assumptions on which it is based. In assessing students' written work, be sure to focus on how the facts and their assumptions support or fail to support their opinions. If students from your class give clear, thoughtful arguments for opposite beliefs, you may wish to have the students present their arguments to the class. However, be aware that students' feelings about an issue may interfere with a discussion about differing opinions. Focusing students on the assumptions and validity of facts used in the argument should facilitate the discussion.**

4. **a.** The specific numbers that students choose to test will vary, but all of the pairs should support Bishiva's claim.

   b. Proofs may vary. One proof is provided here.

   If a and b are odd integers, then they can be represented as $a = 2m + 1$ and $b = 2n + 1$ for some integers m and n.

   If $a = 2m + 1$ and $b = 2n + 1$, then the product ab is equal to $(2m + 1)(2n + 1)$ or $4mn + 2m + 2n + 1$.

   If $ab = 4mn + 2m + 2n + 1$, then $ab = 2(2mn + m + n) + 1$.

   If $ab = 2(2mn + m + n) + 1$, then the product of a and b is odd (2 times some integer, plus 1).

Organizing

1. **a–j.** Responses will vary. You may wish to have students share their examples as a means of confirming correctness and reviewing some key ideas from previous units.

Unit 4

Choose one of the following topics. Clearly state your position regarding the topic. (The descriptions given do not present every possible position; if you have a different opinion, express it!) Then try to state all of the facts and assumptions on which your position depends.

a. *Balanced Federal Budget* Some people believe that spending should be cut or taxes should be raised (or both) so that federal income and spending each year are equal. Some people believe that deficit spending is acceptable.

b. *School Uniforms* Many public schools have considered requiring a particular uniform that all students must wear. Some people believe this allows students to ignore differences in economic status. Some people believe this suppresses individual expression.

c. *School Awards* Some high school students think that there should be a set of fixed criteria for honors and awards and that once these criteria are attained, the honor or award should be granted. Some students think that a set of fixed criteria is not flexible enough to meet various situations or circumstances.

d. *College Affirmative Action* Some people believe that affirmative action programs for college admissions should be maintained so some individuals who belong to certain groups will have a better opportunity to attend college. Some people believe that college admissions should be granted on a standard of merit and accomplishment that is fixed for all people.

4. Bishiva claims that the product of any two positive odd integers is also an odd integer.

a. Test Bishiva's claim for five different pairs of odd integers. What seems to be true?

b. Provide an argument that Bishiva is correct or produce a counterexample to establish that he is not correct.

Organizing

1. Most statements in mathematics are written in if-then form or can be expressed in that form. Think about the mathematics you have studied this year and in previous courses. Write one correct if-then statement related to each of the topics listed below.

a. Vertex-edge graphs
b. Linear equations
c. Parallelograms
d. A data distribution
e. Exponential functions
f. Translations
g. Correlation coefficients
h. Similar shapes
i. Matrices
j. Trigonometric functions

Unit 4

2. Activity 2 of Investigation 2 (page 267) illustrated a symbolic model for reasoning with an if-then statement. You can also think of if-then statements geometrically using **Venn diagrams**.

a. Examine these if-then statements and the corresponding Venn diagrams.

$p \Rightarrow q$
If a creature is a butterfly, then it is an insect.

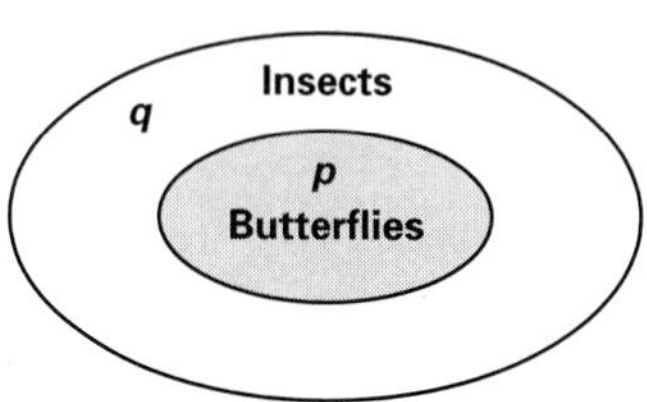

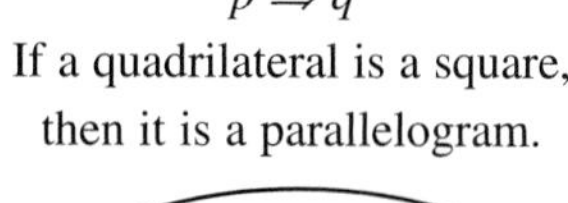

$p \Rightarrow q$
If a quadrilateral is a square,
then it is a parallelogram.

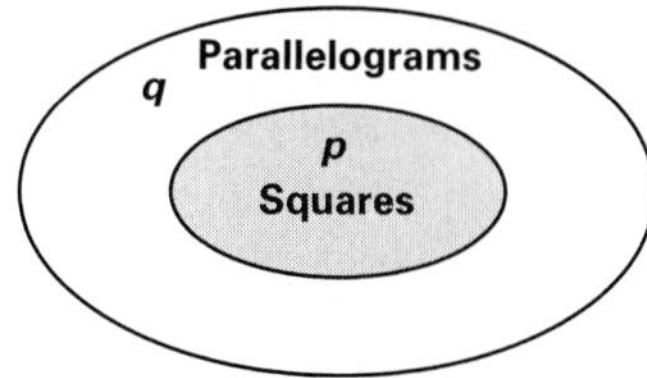

- If you know that a monarch is a butterfly, what can you conclude?
- If you know that quadrilateral *WXYZ* is a square, what can you conclude?

b. Refer to Investigation 2, Activity 2 Part c (page 267). Represent your if-then statement geometrically with a Venn diagram. How can you use the Venn diagram in reasoning about Tommy's situation in that activity?

c. A common error in deductive reasoning is to assume that because an if-then statement $p \Rightarrow q$ is always true, the *converse* statement $q \Rightarrow p$ is also always true.

- Write the converse of each statement in Part a.
- How do the Venn diagrams in Part a show that the converse of a statement is not always true? How is this analysis related to your reasoning about the case of Rosa in Activity 2 Part c of Investigation 2 (page 267)?

3. Among the algebraic properties you used in the "Symbol Sense and Algebraic Reasoning" unit were the commutative and associative properties for addition.

a. Write these properties in if-then form.

b. When Karl finds himself in a situation in which he needs to add three numbers such as 27 + 19 + 43, he thinks "27 plus 43 is 70, plus 19 equals 89." He says he uses the "Switch Property for Addition":

If a, b, and c are real numbers, then $(a + b) + c = (a + c) + b$.

Show how you can use the commutative and associative properties and a chain of if-then reasoning to prove Karl's Switch Property.

Unit 4

274 UNIT 4 • SHAPES AND GEOMETRIC REASONING

2. **Since assuming that the converse of a statement is true is such a common error, it is crucial that this task receive a full-class discussion.**
   a. ■ You can conclude that a monarch is an insect.
      ■ You can conclude that quadrilateral *WXYZ* is a parallelogram.
   b.

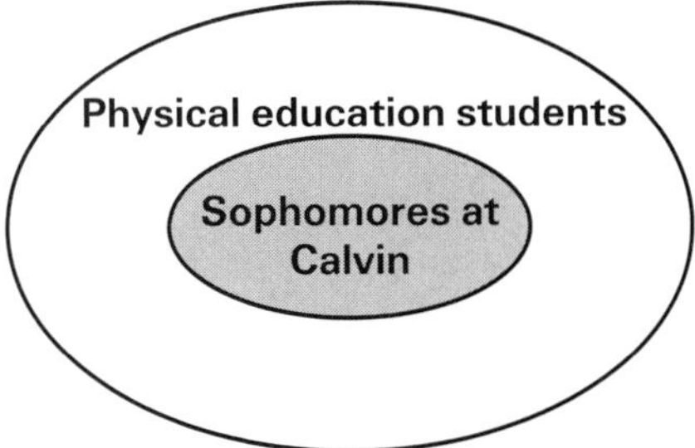

Since Tommy is a sophomore at Calvin High School, he would be placed inside the inner region. Since this region is entirely inside the physical education students region, Tommy must be a physical education student.

   c. ■ If a creature is an insect, then it is a butterfly. If a quadrilateral is a parallelogram, then it is a square.
      ■ The Venn diagrams in Part a show that one can be in the insect region without being in the butterfly region and that one can be in the parallelogram region without being in the square region. The case of Rosa asks us to consider the converse of the statement given in Part c of Activity 2. Since we don't know whether or not the converse is true, we cannot make any conclusions about Rosa.

3. a. Commutative property for addition: If a and b are real numbers, then $a + b = b + a$.
   Associative property for addition: If a, b, and c are real numbers, then $(a + b) + c = a + (b + c)$.
   b. If a, b, and c are real numbers, then $(a + b) + c = a + (b + c)$.
   If $(a + b) + c = a + (b + c)$, then $(a + b) + c = a + (c + b)$.
   If $(a + b) + c = a + (c + b)$, then $(a + b) + c = (a + c) + b$.

NOTE: You may wish to have students write about the error of assuming the converse of a true statement in their Math Toolkits.

Unit 4

4. **a.** Test cases and proofs may vary. A sample proof follows.

If a, b, and c are integers where a is a factor of b and a is a factor of c, then $b = an$ and $c = am$, where n and m are integers.

If $b = an$ and $c = am$, then $b + c = an + am$.

If $b + c = an + am$, then $b + c = a(n + m)$.

If $b + c = a(n + m)$, then a is a factor of $b + c$.

Therefore, if a, b, and c are integers where a is a factor of b and a is a factor of c, then a is a factor of $b + c$.

b. If a, b, and c are integers where a is a factor of b and a is a factor of c, then a is a factor of $bm + cn$ for all integers m and n.

- Students might pick some sample values for a, b, and c that satisfy the hypothesis. Then, since the conclusion must be true for all integers m and n, they can choose m and n and see if a is a factor of $bm + cn$. This type of exploration should lead them to think that the if-then statement is true. Some students may be able to see that the additional factors on each term will not change the reasoning they followed in Part a.
- If a, b, and c are integers where a is a factor of b and a is a factor of c, then $b = ax$ and $c = ay$.

  If $b = ax$ and $c = ay$, then $bm + cn = axm + ayn$.

  If $bm + cn = axm + ayn$, then $bm + cn = a(xm + yn)$.

  If $bm + cn = a(xm + yn)$, then a is a factor of $bm + cn$.

  Therefore, if a, b, and c are integers where a is a factor of b and a is a factor of c, then a is a factor of $bm + cn$ for all integers m and n.

Reflecting

1. Student examples will vary. Examples are given.

a. An automobile driver might use inductive reasoning by observing that since most of the cars are not speeding on a certain section of the highway, it is a well-patrolled section and exceeding the speed limit there may be more likely than usual to lead to a ticket.

b. A golfer who plays the same course many times may notice that on a particular green the putt always rolls right. He or she might reason inductively that this time the ball will also roll right, so he or she must adjust the putt accordingly.

c. A medical researcher might use inductive reasoning to help form conjectures that will be further explored. For example, if many people with common symptoms had all recently visited the same foreign country, the researcher might reason that it was something in that country that made all of the people sick.

2. Inductive reasoning begins with examples, looks for a pattern or relationship, and then conjectures that the relationship holds for all similar situations. Deductive reasoning begins with known information and logically concludes the truth of some statement.

Inductive reasoning leads to plausibility (or refutation), while deductive reasoning leads to certainty.

3. Responses may vary. Law, all academic disciplines, and medicine are fields in which deductive reasoning is used extensively.

4. *Number theory* is a branch of mathematics that has flourished since ancient times and continues to be an important field of mathematical activity, particularly in the applied area of *coding* (encrypting messages so only the intended recipients can read them). One of the first definitions appearing in the theory of numbers is a definition for *factor* or *divisor*. An integer b is a factor (divisor) of an integer a provided there is an integer c such that $a = bc$.

   a. One of the first theorems in number theory is the following:

   If a, b, and c are integers where a is a factor of b and a is a factor of c, then a is a factor of b + c.

   Test this theorem for some specific cases to develop an understanding for what it is saying. Then write a deductive argument showing that the theorem is always true.

   b. Form a new if-then statement as follows: Use the hypothesis of the theorem in Part a and replace the conclusion with "a is a factor of $bm + cn$ for all integers m and n."

   - Do you think this new if-then statement is always true? Explain your reasoning.
   - If you think the statement is true, write a proof of it. If not, give a counterexample.

Reflecting

1. If you think about it, inductive reasoning is a common form of reasoning in the world around you. Give an example of how inductive reasoning might be used by the following people:

   a. An automobile driver

   b. A golfer

   c. A medical researcher

2. Explain how inductive and deductive reasoning differ. In doing mathematics, how does one form of reasoning support the other?

3. Identify two or three occupations or professions in which you think deductive reasoning is used extensively. Explain how you think such reasoning is used.

LESSON 1 • REASONED ARGUMENTS 275

4. Examine the following cartoon. Is the child's argument a valid argument? What would you say to the child if you were his parent?

THE BORN LOSER reprinted by permission of Newspaper Enterprise Association, Inc.

5. The reasoning pattern illustrated in Activity 2 of Investigation 2 (page 267) is sometimes called "affirming the hypothesis," "the law of detachment," or "*modus ponens*." Why do you think these labels are used for that reasoning pattern? Which label makes most sense to you?

Extending

1. Consider the following if-then statement:

If two lines are parallel to a third line, then they are parallel to each other.

This statement is of the form $p \Rightarrow q$, where p is the clause "two lines are parallel to a third line" and q is the clause "they are parallel to each other." Use these clauses in completing Parts a through e.

a. Write in words the statement $q \Rightarrow p$.

b. If the *negation* of a simple statement r is "not r," write the negations of the given statements p and q.

c. Write in words the statement not $q \Rightarrow$ not p.

d. Write in words the statement not $p \Rightarrow$ not q.

Unit 4

276 UNIT 4 • SHAPES AND GEOMETRIC REASONING

4. The child's argument is not valid. To convince the child that the reasoning is not valid, you might try providing another example using the same reasoning. For example: Cardinals are red and cardinals fly. By the child's reasoning, we would get "Red things fly." However, this is clearly not true.
5. "Affirming the hypothesis" might be used for this reasoning pattern if one wishes to emphasize that the conclusion is automatic once you know the hypothesis is true. "Law of detachment" is used for this reasoning pattern because you "detach" the conclusion from the if-then statement. When the hypothesis is true, the conclusion is known to be true and may be used as a true statement when evaluating the truth of hypotheses in other if-then statements. (Again note that the conclusion is true only because other things are true. It is not just true forever and ever.) "*Modus ponens*" (method of affirming) is the act of reasoning from a true hypothesis.

Extending

1. **a.** If two lines are parallel to each other, then they are parallel to a third line.
   b. Not p: Two lines are not parallel to a third line.
   Not q: The two lines are not parallel to each other.
   c. If two lines are not parallel to each other, then they are not parallel to a third line.
   d. If two lines are not parallel to a third line, then they are not parallel to each other.

MORE *continued*

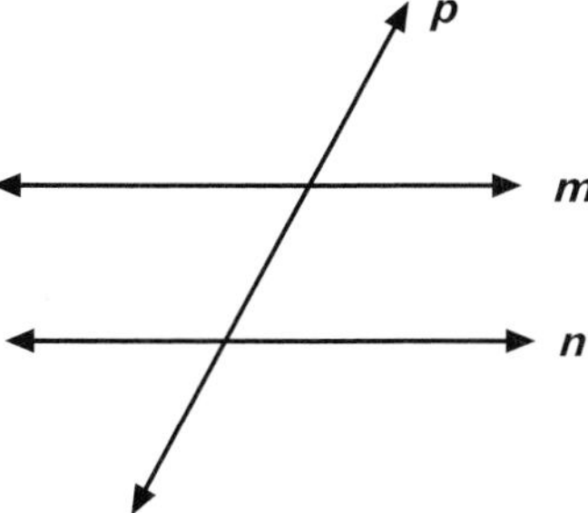

1. **e.** Part a: $q \Rightarrow p$ is not correct. In the diagram at the right, $m \parallel n$, but they are not parallel to the third line p.

   Part c: Not $q \Rightarrow$ not p is true.

   Part d: Not $p \Rightarrow$ not q is not a true statement. In the diagram at the right, neither m nor n is parallel to the third line p, but they are parallel to each other.

   f. Students may need to use a large dictionary in the library to find a definition for *contrapositive*. Their definitions should allow them to identify the converse as $q \Rightarrow p$, the contrapositive as not $q \Rightarrow$ not p, and the inverse as not $p \Rightarrow$ not q. For a true statement, only its contrapositive is guaranteed to be true as well.

2. **a.** If the engine runs but the mower does not, you should check for a slipping belt or a faulty clutch.

Unit 4

e. It can be proven that $p \Rightarrow q$ is a correct statement. Are the "related" statements in Parts a, c, and d correct or incorrect? For each incorrect statement, draw a sketch showing a counterexample.

f. Look up in a dictionary the words *converse*, *contrapositive*, and *inverse*. How do these terms apply to Parts a through e?

2. Many people, such as auto technicians, make a living out of repairing things. Often repairs can be done at home if you have the right tools and can reason deductively. The first step in making a repair is identifying the problem. Examine the troubleshooting chart below for diagnosing problems that often occur with small engines, such as the one on a lawn mower.

a. What are the first things you should check if the engine runs but the mower does not?

Four-cycle engine with horizontal crankshaft

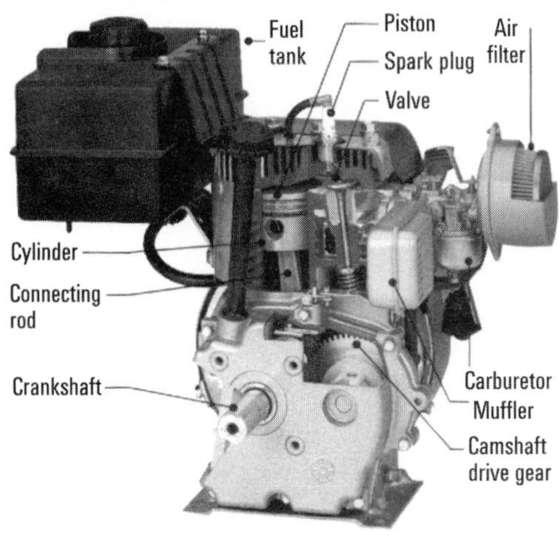

PROBLEM

Starter doesn't turn engine	Engine turns, will not start	Engine starts, then stalls	Runs unevenly, lacks power	Engine stalls at idle speed	Engine dies during use	Engine runs too fast	Engine runs, device doesn't	Engine vibrates excessively	Engine smokes profusely	Engine overheats	Engine backfires	Engine is extra-noisy	POSSIBLE CAUSE
●													Starter rope jammed or broken (p.366)
●													Recoil starter spring weak or broken (p.366)
●													Electric starter battery low, connections loose or corroded, or power cord damaged (p.366)
		●	●	●	●				●				Clogged air filter (p.367)
	●	●			●								Fuel tank empty; add fuel
	●	●	●	●	●								Contaminated fuel (p.367)
		●	●		●								Fuel cap breather holes blocked (p.367)
	●	●	●		●								Clogged fuel filter (p.367)
	●	●			●								Obstructed or damaged fuel line (p.367)
	●	●	●	●					●				Sticky choke; clean with solvent (you may have to disassemble the carburetor; see pages 360–361)
		●		●									Idle speed incorrect; see owner's manual to adjust
			●		●	●							Governor linkage out of adjustment (p.361)
	●	●	●	●	●	●			●	●	●		Carburetor fouled or poorly adjusted (pp.360–361)
	●	●	●		●				●	●			On two-cycle engine, incorrect fuel mixture (p.368)
	●		●	●							●		On two-cycle engine, faulty reed valve (p.365)
	●	●	●	●	●								Fouled spark plug or damaged cable (p.363)
					●					●		●	Insufficient oil in crankcase; add oil to oil tank
			●		●								Overheated; allow engine to cool, then restart
			●								●	●	Valves sticking, burned, or need adjusting (p.364)
	●	●	●		●					●	●		Breaker points dirty or improperly set (p.362)
	●	●	●	●	●				●				Low compression (p.365)
		●	●	●	●					●		●	Clogged muffler or exhaust port (p.367)
							●						Slipping belt (see pages on specific machinery)
							●	●					Faulty clutch (pp.370 and 379)
										●			Cooling fins dirty; clean fins
	●	●	●	●	●			●			●		Flywheel key bent, broken, or worn (p.363)
								●				●	Flywheel loose or fins damaged; tighten or replace (p.363)
	●	●						●					Crankshaft bent; have engine replaced

Unit 4

LESSON 1 • REASONED ARGUMENTS 277

b. What should you check if the engine starts and then stalls?

c. Some of the "possible causes" listed in the Troubleshooting chart often suggest a next course of action. Explain how if-then reasoning is used in these cases.

3. Suppose p and q represent two statements. Describe under what conditions for p and q you think each of the following *compound statements* is true.

a. p and q

b. p or q

c. p if and only if q

d. not (p and q)

e. not (p or q)

4. Recall that the basic if-then reasoning pattern can be represented symbolically as shown at the right. In the symbolic form, everything above the horizontal line is accepted as correct or true. What is written below the line is supposed to follow logically from the accepted information. Shown below are several other possible reasoning patterns. Which patterns show valid reasoning, and which show invalid reasoning? Justify your conclusions.

$$\begin{array}{l} p \Rightarrow q \\ p \\ \hline q \end{array}$$

a.
$$\begin{array}{l} p \Rightarrow q \\ q \Rightarrow r \\ \hline p \Rightarrow r \end{array}$$

b.
$$\begin{array}{l} p \Rightarrow q \\ q \\ \hline p \end{array}$$

c.
$$\begin{array}{l} p \Rightarrow q \\ \text{not } q \\ \hline \text{not } p \end{array}$$

d.
$$\begin{array}{l} p \Rightarrow q \\ \text{not } p \\ \hline \text{not } q \end{array}$$

e.
$$\begin{array}{l} p \Rightarrow \text{not } q \\ p \\ \hline \text{not } q \end{array}$$

f.
$$\begin{array}{l} p \Rightarrow q \\ q \Rightarrow r \\ r \Rightarrow s \\ \hline p \Rightarrow s \\ p \\ \hline s \end{array}$$

g.
$$\begin{array}{l} p \Rightarrow q \\ p \\ \hline q \\ q \Rightarrow r \\ \hline r \\ r \Rightarrow s \\ \hline s \end{array}$$

278 UNIT 4 • SHAPES AND GEOMETRIC REASONING

2. **b.** If the engine starts and then stalls, you should check to see if the air filter is clogged; the fuel tank is empty; the fuel is contaminated; the fuel cap breather holes are blocked; the fuel filter is clogged; the fuel line is obstructed or damaged; the choke is sticking; the idle speed is incorrect; the carburetor is fouled or needs adjusting; the fuel mixture is incorrect; the spark plugs are fouled or there are damaged cables; the breaker points are dirty or improperly set; there is low compression; the muffler or exhaust port is clogged; the flywheel key is bent, broke, or worn; or the crankshaft is bent.

c. The possible cause corresponds to the if part of the statement and the next course of action corresponds to the then part. For example: If the fuel tank is empty, then add fuel.

3. **a.** p and q: true when both are true

b. p or q: true when either or both are true

c. p if and only if q: true when $p \Rightarrow q$ and $q \Rightarrow p$ are true

d. Not (p and q): true when either p or q (or both) are false

e. Not (p or q): true when both p and q are false

4. **You may wish to assign Reflecting Task 5 and Extending Task 1 before students do this task.**

a. Valid: This is the law of detachment and is the form of most proofs.

b. Invalid: This is the most commonly used erroneous reasoning pattern. It is reasoning from the converse, which is not valid.

c. Valid: This is reasoning from the contrapositive.

d. Invalid: This assumes the inverse is logically equivalent to the given statement, which is not correct.

e. Valid: This is the law of detachment.

f. Valid: This combines three uses of the law of detachment.

g. Valid: This also combines three uses of the law of detachment in a sequence.

EXPLORE small-group investigation

INVESTIGATION 3 Reasoning about Intersecting Lines and Angles

In this investigation, students will begin to develop the skills needed to create a valid deductive argument in the context of exploring and trying to understand the angle relationships created when two lines intersect. The approach used is to have students look at a given context, in this case two intersecting lines, and to make some conjectures about that context (inductive reasoning). The next step is for students to learn to prove (deductive reasoning) or disprove (counterexample) their own conjectures. This approach is used throughout this unit on geometric reasoning: explore, conjecture, and then prove or disprove. Using this process with confidence is important for students, because it is not only relevant in the study of mathematics, but also generally applicable to all areas of knowledge acquisition.

You may want to launch this investigation by quickly reviewing the big ideas from the previous investigation and then letting students know that their mathematical attention will be pushed in two directions in the next two investigations. First, explain that they will be asked to explore the angle relationships that occur when two lines intersect. Second, they will focus on learning to create a valid argument to prove that the conjectures they made in their explorations are true. It will help them if they understand that proof is a skill that they will develop over time and that during each investigation in this unit they will have an opportunity to work on this skill.

As students create these initial proofs, expect that the language used may be somewhat wordy, imprecise, or invented, because the geometric vocabulary has not been presented yet. You may choose to offer students the terminology as it becomes relevant to the activity they are working on or wait until it is presented in the student material near the end of the investigation. For example, vertical, supplementary, and adjacent angles are used frequently in this investigation. Also, students may name specific angles or line segments rather than the general terms in their proofs. This is fine for now. Initially, the focus should be on looking for clear "if-then" language that is given in an appropriate sequence.

It may be helpful to stop the small-group work periodically throughout this investigation in order to let groups share, compare, and revise their work. The class list of characteristics of a valid argument may help students evaluate their work. (See the Checkpoint following Investigation 1, page 265.) You might ask students to summarize what they have learned about the angle relationships they investigated and about creating valid proofs. As students see more proofs, the class may decide to add or reword elements on the list of valid argument characteristics.

Students will also have an opportunity to expand their list of techniques for creating a valid argument (substitution, properties of equality). Activities 3 and 4 provide opportunities for students to use theorems they have proven earlier in this lesson. Make sure that students appreciate the power they gain by recognizing that once they have proven a theorem, it can be used in many varied ways to prove new theorems.

See additional Teaching Notes on page T344D.

INVESTIGATION 3 Reasoning about Intersecting Lines and Angles

Skill in reasoning, like skill in sculpting, playing a musical instrument, or playing a sport, comes from practicing that skill and reflecting on the process. In the previous unit, you reasoned in algebraic settings. Using certain assumptions about the operations on and relations among real numbers, you were able to rewrite symbolic expressions in equivalent simpler forms. In this investigation, and in the remainder of the unit, you will sharpen your reasoning skills in geometric settings. As you progress through the unit, pay particular attention to the assumptions you make to support your reasoning, as well as to the validity of the reasoning.

The photo at the right illustrates two of the simplest and most common shapes in a plane: lines and angles. When two lines intersect at a single point, several angles are formed. By varying the size of the base angle, the truck bed can be raised or lowered. Consider how changing the size of this base angle seems to affect the sizes of the angles formed by the two lines. In Activity 1, you will use a geometric model of this situation to gather evidence that may further support your thinking.

1. In the diagram below, lines k and n intersect at point A, forming the numbered angles shown.

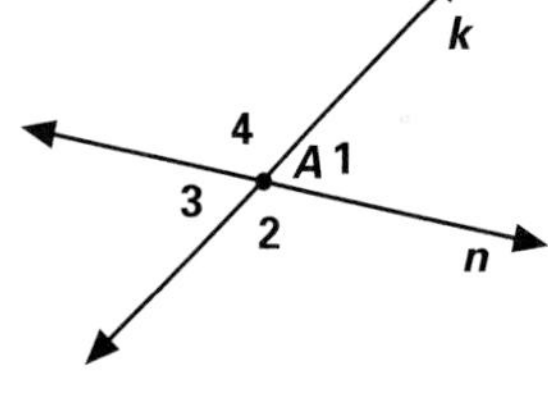

a. If $m\angle 1 = 72^\circ$, what can you say about $m\angle 2$? About $m\angle 3$? About $m\angle 4$?

b. If $m\angle 2 = 130^\circ$, what can you say about $m\angle 1$? About $m\angle 3$? About $m\angle 4$?

c. In general, what relationships among the angles do you think are true? Make a list of them.

d. Will the general relationships you listed for Part c hold for any pair of intersecting lines? Test your conjectures using specific examples.

e. Pairs of angles like $\angle 1$ and $\angle 4$ are called *linear pairs* of angles. Name other pairs of angles in the diagram that form a linear pair.

f. Pairs of angles like $\angle 2$ and $\angle 4$ are called *vertical angles*. Name another pair of vertical angles.

g. Write an if-then statement about vertical angles that you think is *always* correct. You may want to begin as follows: If two lines intersect, then … .

h. Compare your conjecture to those of other groups.

Unit 4

LESSON 1 • REASONED ARGUMENTS 279

In the remainder of this lesson, you will continue to use inductive reasoning to discover possible relations among lines and angles, but you will also attempt to use deductive reasoning to prove your conjectures are always true. To reason deductively, you must first have some known facts to reason from. For the remainder of this unit, you are to assume as a known fact the following property of linear pairs of angles.

Linear Pair Property

If two angles are a linear pair, then the sum of their measures is 180°.

2. Study the following attempt by one group of students to prove the conjecture they made in Part g of Activity 1. Based on the labeling of the diagram below, they set out to prove the following:

If lines n and k intersect at point A, then $m\angle 1 = m\angle 3$.

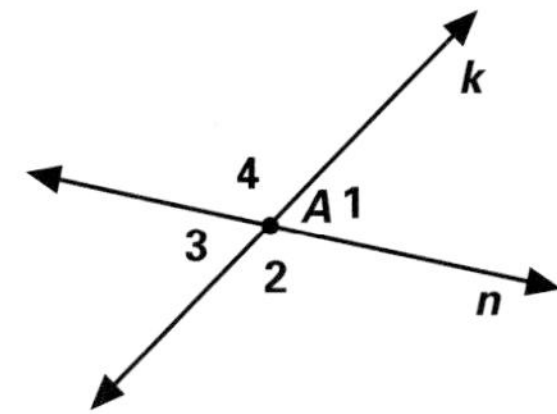

They reasoned as follows:

(1) If lines n and k intersect at A, then $m\angle 1 + m\angle 2 = 180°$.

(2) If lines n and k intersect at A, then $m\angle 2 + m\angle 3 = 180°$.

(3) If $m\angle 1 + m\angle 2 = 180°$ and $m\angle 2 + m\angle 3 = 180°$, then $m\angle 1 + m\angle 2 = m\angle 2 + m\angle 3$.

(4) If $m\angle 1 + m\angle 2 = m\angle 2 + m\angle 3$, then $m\angle 1 = m\angle 3$.

a. Explain why each of the statements above is or is not correct.

b. Now, in your group, write an argument to show the following: If lines n and k intersect at point A, then $m\angle 2 = m\angle 4$.

c. What features of a valid argument are illustrated by the given proof and by the one you constructed?

In mathematics, a statement that has been proved using deductive reasoning with accepted facts and relations is called a **theorem**. The statement proved in Activity 2 is sometimes referred to as the **Vertical Angles Theorem**. (Not all theorems are given names.) After a theorem has been proved, it may be used to prove other conjectures. As the unit progresses, you will want to know which theorems have been proved. Thus, you should prepare a geometry toolkit by listing assumptions, such as the Linear Pair Property, and proven theorems. Add each new theorem to your toolkit as it is proved.

Unit 4

280 UNIT 4 • SHAPES AND GEOMETRIC REASONING

2. **a.** (1) This is correct, since $\angle 1$ and $\angle 2$ form a linear pair and so by the Linear Pair Property the sum of their measures is $180°$.

(2) This is correct, since $\angle 2$ and $\angle 3$ are a linear pair.

(3) This is correct, since if both $m\angle 1 + m\angle 2$ and $m\angle 2 + m\angle 3$ equal $180°$, then the two sums must be equal to each other.

(4) This is correct, because the subtraction property of equality allows us to subtract $m\angle 2$ from each side of the equation.

b. Proofs may vary. One possible proof is provided below.

If lines n and k intersect at point A, then the Linear Pair Property allows us to conclude that $m\angle 2 + m\angle 3 = 180°$.

Similarly, $m\angle 3 + m\angle 4 = 180°$.

If $m\angle 2 + m\angle 3 = 180°$ and $m\angle 3 + m\angle 4 = 180°$, then $m\angle 2 + m\angle 3 = m\angle 3 + m\angle 4$.

If $m\angle 2 + m\angle 3 = m\angle 3 + m\angle 4$, then $m\angle 2 = m\angle 4$.

c. Both proofs use only valid mathematical theorems and properties, have statements that follow logically from previous statements, and are general arguments rather than specific examples.

NOTE: A general proof that vertical angles are congruent occurs in Organizing Task 5 on page 294.

Unit 4

Master 91

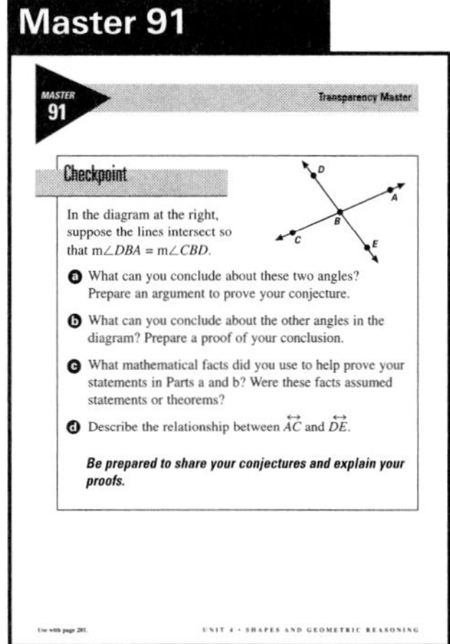
MASTER 91 Transparency Master

Checkpoint

In the diagram at the right, suppose the lines intersect so that m∠DBA = m∠CBD.

a. What can you conclude about these two angles? Prepare an argument to prove your conjecture.

b. What can you conclude about the other angles in the diagram? Prepare a proof of your conclusion.

c. What mathematical facts did you use to help prove your statements in Parts a and b? Were these facts assumed statements or theorems?

d. Describe the relationship between $\overleftrightarrow{AC}$ and $\overleftrightarrow{DE}$.

Be prepared to share your conjectures and explain your proofs.

EXPLORE ***continued***

3. **a.** $m\angle DBA = 102°$, $m\angle ABE = 78°$

   b. Since $m\angle CBE = m\angle ABD$, $m\angle CBE = 72°$. Thus, $m\angle DBC = 108°$.

   c. Because $\angle CBE$ and $\angle DBC$ are supplementary, we can write

$$\begin{aligned}(2n + 5) + (3n + 10) &= 180° \\ 5n + 15 &= 180° \\ 5n &= 165° \\ n &= 33°\end{aligned}$$

   Substitute n into the original equations to get the angle measures.

$$\begin{aligned} m\angle CBE &= 2n + 5 & m\angle DBC &= 3n + 10 \\ &= 2(33) + 5 & &= 3(33) + 10 \\ &= 66 + 5 & &= 99 + 10 \\ m\angle CBE &= 71° & m\angle DBC &= 109° \end{aligned}$$

4. **a.** Each pair of lines intersects at point B (and thus forms linear pairs of angles).

   b. $m\angle DBC = 90°$

   c. $m\angle FBA = 90° - 27° = 63°$
   $m\angle FBD = 90° + 27° = 117°$
   $m\angle EBG = 180° - 27° = 153°$

   d. $m\angle ABG = 180° - 51° = 129°$
   $m\angle FBE = 90° - 51° = 39°$

   e. $m\angle FBA = 90° - p°$
   $m\angle FBD = 90° + p°$
   $m\angle EBG = 180° - p°$

CONSTRUCTING A MATH TOOLKIT: Ask students to begin keeping a list of the theorems that they have proven. Most students will find it helpful to include a sketch with each of their theorems. They should rewrite the theorems from this investigation using their new vocabulary of vertical, adjacent, and supplementary angles. Again, consider having students organize their theorems around the shape relations and shapes as they are explored in this unit. These organizers include intersecting lines, parallel lines cut by a transversal, triangles, and quadrilaterals (parallelograms, rhombuses, and rectangles).

SHARE AND SUMMARIZE full-class discussion

Checkpoint

See Teaching Master 91.

a Both $\angle DBA$ and $\angle CBD$ have measure 90°.

Proof: If $\overleftrightarrow{AC}$ and $\overleftrightarrow{DE}$ intersect at point B, then the Linear Pair Property tells us that $m\angle DBA + m\angle CBD = 180°$.
If $m\angle DBA = m\angle CBD$, then $m\angle DBA + m\angle DBA = 180°$.
If $m\angle DBA + m\angle DBA = 180°$, then $2m\angle DBA = 180°$.
If $2m\angle DBA = 180°$, then $m\angle DBA = 90°$.
If $m\angle DBA = 90°$ and $m\angle DBA = m\angle CBD$, then $m\angle CBD = 90°$.
Hence if $\overleftrightarrow{AC}$ and $\overleftrightarrow{DE}$ intersect at point B and $m\angle DBA = m\angle CBD$, then $\angle DBA$ and $\angle CBD$ each have measure 90°.

b We can conclude that $\angle CBE$ and $\angle ABE$ also have measure 90°.

Proof: If $m\angle DBA = 90°$, then by the Vertical Angles Theorem $m\angle CBE = 90°$.
If $m\angle DBC = 90°$, then by the Vertical Angles Theorem $m\angle ABE = 90°$.
Hence if $\overleftrightarrow{AC}$ and $\overleftrightarrow{DE}$ intersect at point B and $m\angle DBA = m\angle CBD$, then $\angle CBE$ and $\angle ABE$ each have measure 90°.

See additional Teaching Notes on page T344D.

3. Referring to the labeled diagram at the right, determine the angle measures in the following situations.

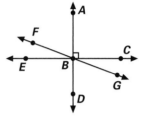

   a. Suppose m∠*CBE* = 102°. Find m∠*DBA*. Find m∠*ABE*.

   b. Suppose m∠*CBE* + m∠*ABD* = 144°. Find m∠*DBC*.

   c. Suppose m∠*CBE* = $2n + 5$ and m∠*DBC* = $3n + 10$, where n is a positive integer. Find the measures of ∠*CBE* and ∠*DBC*.

4. In the diagram at the right, the three lines intersect at point *B*. Line *AD* is perpendicular to line *EC* (written $\overleftrightarrow{AD} \perp \overleftrightarrow{EC}$).

   a. If *any* three lines intersect at *B*, what is true about each pair of these lines?

   b. What is m∠*DBC*?

   c. Suppose m∠*FBE* = 27°. Find m∠*FBA* and m∠*FBD*. Find m∠*EBG*.

   d. Suppose m∠*FBA* = 51°. Find m∠*ABG* and m∠*FBE*.

   e. How would your answers to Part c change if m∠*FBE* = p, $0° < p < 90°$?

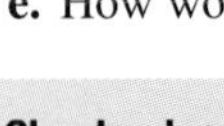

Checkpoint

In the diagram at the right, suppose the lines intersect so that m∠*DBA* = m∠*CBD*.

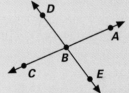

a What can you conclude about these two angles? Prepare an argument to prove your conjecture.

b What can you conclude about the other angles in the diagram? Prepare a proof of your conclusion.

c What mathematical facts did you use to help prove your statements in Parts a and b? Were these facts assumed statements or theorems?

d Describe the relationship between $\overleftrightarrow{AC}$ and $\overleftrightarrow{DE}$.

Be prepared to share your conjectures and explain your proofs.

In geometry, some pairs of angles have special names. In Investigation 3, you worked with vertical angles, linear pairs, and supplementary angles. **Vertical angles** share only a vertex. (They are across from each other.) The angles in a **linear pair** share a vertex and one side (they are *adjacent* to each other), *and* their noncommon sides form a straight angle. **Supplementary angles** are two angles that have measures that add to 180°. They need not be a linear pair.

LESSON 1 • REASONED ARGUMENTS 281

On Your Own

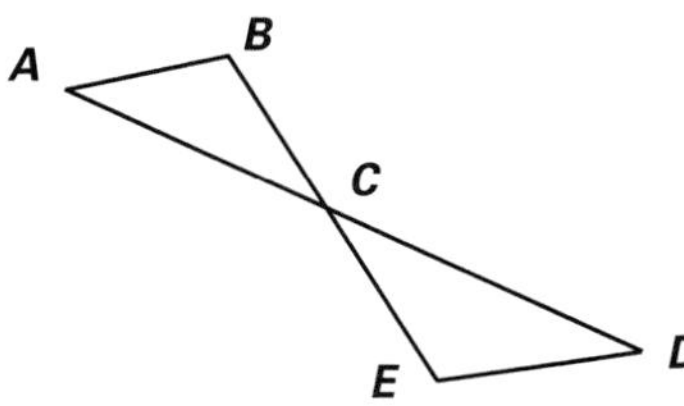

In the diagram at the right, segments AD and BE (denoted $\overline{AD}$ and $\overline{BE}$) intersect at point C and $m\angle ECD = m\angle CDE$. Write a proof or give a counterexample for each of the following conjectures.

a. If the given conditions hold, then $m\angle ACB = m\angle CDE$.

b. If the given conditions hold, then $m\angle CAB = m\angle CDE$.

INVESTIGATION 4 Parallel Lines, Transversals, and Angles

When a line intersects another line, four angles are formed; some of the pairs have equal measures, and some pairs are supplementary angles. When a line intersects *two* lines, many more relationships are possible. Perhaps the most interesting case is when the two lines are parallel, as with the various pairs of support beams on the sides of the John Hancock Building in Chicago, shown at the right.

Lines in a plane that do not intersect are called **parallel lines**. In the diagram below, line m is parallel to line n (written $m \parallel n$). Line p, which intersects the two lines, is called a **transversal**. Find some examples of transversals in the photo of the John Hancock Building.

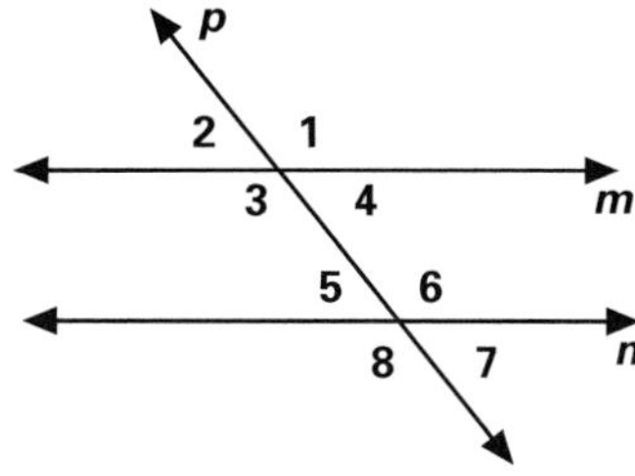

1. In the diagram above, the angles at each point of intersection are numbered so that they can be easily identified.

a. What pairs of angles, if any, appear to be equal in measure? List them.

b. What angle pairs appear to be supplementary angles? List them.

282 UNIT 4 • SHAPES AND GEOMETRIC REASONING

APPLY individual task

On Your Own

a. This conjecture is true.

Proof: If $\overleftrightarrow{AD}$ and $\overleftrightarrow{BE}$ intersect at point C, then $m\angle ECD = m\angle ACB$ (vertical angles). If $m\angle ECD = m\angle CDE$ and $m\angle ECD = m\angle ACB$, then $m\angle CDE = m\angle ACB$. Hence if $\overleftrightarrow{AD}$ and $\overleftrightarrow{BE}$ intersect at point C and $m\angle ECD = m\angle CDE$, then $m\angle CDE = m\angle ACB$.

b. The second conjecture will not always be true. As a counterexample, let $m\angle ECD = m\angle CDE = 35°$, then $m\angle ACB$ must also be 35°. But $m\angle CAB$ does not have to equal 35°; it could be any measure $x°$, where $0° < x < 145°$. Therefore $m\angle CAB$ is not always equal to $m\angle CDE$. Students may be able to see this better if they redraw the figure in the text so that $\overline{AB}$ is not parallel to $\overline{ED}$ as shown below.

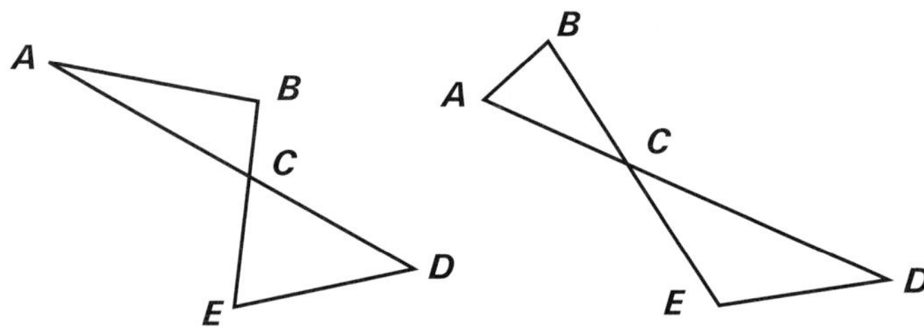

MORE ASSIGNMENT *pp. 288–296*

Students can now begin Reflecting Task 4 or Extending Task 1 or 4 from the MORE assignment following Investigation 4.

EXPLORE small-group investigation

INVESTIGATION 4 Parallel Lines, Transversals, and Angles

In this investigation, students will continue working to develop the skills needed to create valid deductive arguments. The context used is the angle relationships created when two parallel lines are cut by a transversal. The approach is the same as the one in the previous investigation; that is, students explore a given context, in this case two parallel lines cut by a transversal, make some conjectures about that context, and then prove or disprove their own conjectures.

You might want to launch this investigation with a brief discussion of how the theorems in the previous unit were developed. Students should note that, initially, they explored and discussed ideas about how the angles formed by the intersecting lines might be related; then they made formal conjectures using previous knowledge and intuition. Finally, they confirmed the validity of their conjectures by proving (or disproving) that they were indeed true (or false). Once they had proven a theorem, it could be utilized in the proof of another conjecture. This process resulted in a list of conditional statements, called theorems, that students knew for sure were true. Keep reinforcing the idea that this process of exploration, conjecture, and validation is the foundation for human growth and development. It is critical that every student understand this process and become as skilled in its use as possible.

See additional Teaching Notes on page T344E.

Unit 4

EXPLORE *continued*

1. **c.** Yes, the same pairs of angles in the new diagram should appear equal and supplementary.

2. **This activity sets the stage for assuming the congruence of corresponding angles when parallel lines are cut by a transversal. As you circulate among the groups, focus their thinking on this assumption. To help students identify corresponding angles, language such as "the northeast (or upper right) corner of the intersection" may help students locate the angles in question.**

   a. Other corresponding angles in the diagram are angles 4 and 7 and angles 2 and 5. The corresponding angles were among the pairs that appeared equal. They were not among the angles that appeared supplementary.

   b. From Investigation 3, students should be able to find the measures of angles 2, 3, and 4.

   $m\angle 2 = 57°$
   $m\angle 3 = 123°$
   $m\angle 4 = 57°$

   If students further assume the congruence of corresponding angles they will find the following. Be sure that students know that this congruence is just an assumption.

   $m\angle 5 = 57°$
   $m\angle 6 = 123°$
   $m\angle 7 = 57°$
   $m\angle 8 = 123°$

3. **a.**
   - Interior angles on the same side of the transversal are between the parallel lines and on the same side of the transversal: $\angle 3$ and $\angle 5$.
   - Exterior angles on same side of transversal are not between the parallel lines and are on the same side of the transversal: $\angle 1$ and $\angle 7$.
   - Alternate interior angles are between the two parallel lines and on opposite sides of the transversal: $\angle 4$ and $\angle 5$.
   - Alternate exterior angles are not between the two parallel lines and are on opposite sides of the transversal: $\angle 2$ and $\angle 7$.

   b. If two parallel lines are intersected by a transversal, then
   - interior angles on the same side of the transversal are supplementary.
   - exterior angles on the same side of the transversal are supplementary.
   - alternate interior angles are congruent.
   - alternate exterior angles are congruent.

4. **At this point, students should be making an effort to have complete, properly sequenced arguments with well-written if-then statements, and they should be supplying reasons why each if-then statement is correct. You will need to decide if you want students to write proofs for both pairs of the identified angles. If you decide to have them do only one, be sure you discuss with the class why this is really only half of the proof.**

Unit 4

See additional Teaching Notes on page T344E.

c. Draw another pair of parallel lines and a transversal. Number the angles as in the figure on the previous page. Do the same pairs of angles appear equal in measure? Supplementary?

Angles that are in the same relative position with respect to each parallel line and the transversal are called **corresponding angles**. In the diagram on the previous page, angles 1 and 6 are corresponding angles; similarly, angles 3 and 8 are corresponding.

2. Examine the diagram you drew for Part c of Activity 1.

a. Name two pairs of corresponding angles, other than angles 1 and 6 or angles 3 and 8. Were the corresponding angles among the pairs of angles that you thought had equal measure? Were they supplementary angles?

b. Suppose $m\angle 1 = 123°$. Find the measures of as many angles as you can.

3. Now consider the labeled diagram below. In this diagram, $m \parallel n$ and p is the transversal intersecting m and n.

a. Descriptive names are also given to pairs of angles other than the corresponding angles, when the angles are formed by a transversal and two parallel lines. For each name and angle pair given, describe how such angles can be identified in a diagram, and give one more example of such a pair.

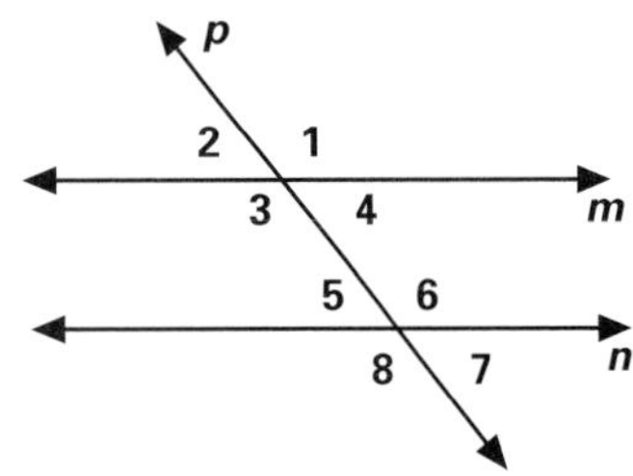

- **Interior angles on the same side of the transversal:** $\angle 4$ and $\angle 6$
- **Exterior angles on the same side of the transversal:** $\angle 2$ and $\angle 8$
- **Alternate interior angles:** $\angle 3$ and $\angle 6$
- **Alternate exterior angles:** $\angle 8$ and $\angle 1$

b. Using your work in Activities 1 and 2, identify a relationship that seems to exist for each kind of angle pair named in Part a. Write your observations in if-then form, beginning as follows: If two parallel lines are intersected by a transversal, then … .

4. For this activity, *assume* the following as a known fact:

If two parallel lines are cut by a transversal, then corresponding angles have equal measure.

a. Using this assumption, construct arguments to prove that each of your conjectures in Part b of Activity 3 is correct. Share the workload among your group members.

b. Discuss each argument within your group. Correct any errors in reasoning. Make sure each member can prove each statement.

Unit 4

LESSON 1 • REASONED ARGUMENTS 283

Checkpoint

In the diagram at the right below, p and m are parallel lines.

a Give the name for each pair of angles below.

- $\angle 2$ and $\angle 8$
- $\angle 4$ and $\angle 5$
- $\angle 1$ and $\angle 3$
- $\angle 3$ and $\angle 5$
- $\angle 6$ and $\angle 2$

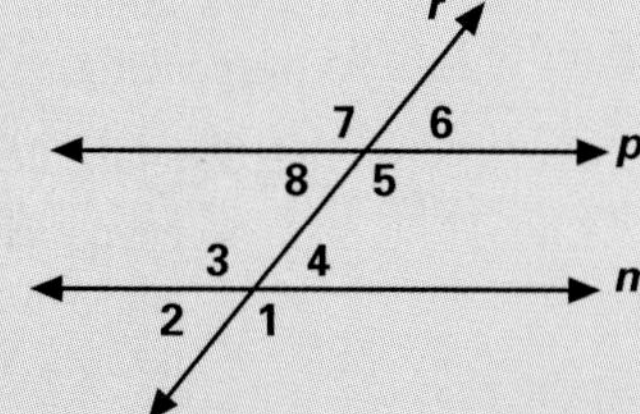

b Using the relation in Activity 4 about corresponding angles, explain how the measures of each pair of angles in Part a are related.

Be prepared to share and compare your group's list of angle names and relations with those of other groups.

On Your Own

In the diagram below, $\overleftrightarrow{AD}$ and $\overleftrightarrow{EH}$ are parallel. Name the second angle in the pair identified, and use the relation about corresponding angles in Activity 4 to show how the measures of the angles in the pair are related.

a. $\angle ABC$, corresponding angles

b. $\angle ABC$, alternate exterior angles

c. $\angle ABC$, exterior angles on the same side of the transversal

d. $\angle DBF$, alternate interior angles

e. $\angle DBF$, interior angles on the same side of the transversal

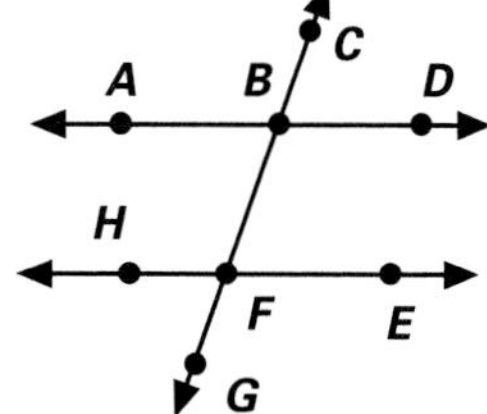

Now refer back to the assumption in Activity 4. With that assumption, you can conclude that if two parallel lines are cut by a transversal, then certain relations among the angles will always be true. The following related question is also important:

What relations among the angles formed when two lines are cut by a third line allow you to conclude that the lines are parallel?

Unit 4

284 UNIT 4 • SHAPES AND GEOMETRIC REASONING

SHARE AND SUMMARIZE full-class discussion

Checkpoint

See Teaching Master 92.

a
- Corresponding angles
- Interior angles on the same side of the transversal
- Vertical angles
- Alternate interior angles
- Alternate exterior angles

b
- $m\angle 2 = m\angle 8$
- $m\angle 4 + m\angle 5 = 180^\circ$
- $m\angle 1 = m\angle 3$
- $m\angle 3 = m\angle 5$
- $m\angle 6 = m\angle 2$

Master 92

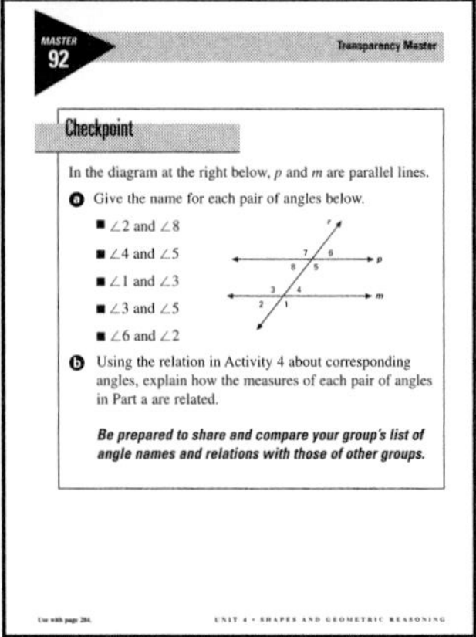

APPLY individual task

On Your Own

a. $\angle HFB$; corresponding angles have equal measure.
b. $\angle GFE$; alternate exterior angles have equal measure.
c. $\angle HFG$; exterior angles on the same side of the transversal are supplementary.
d. $\angle HFB$; alternate interior angles have equal measure.
e. $\angle EFB$; interior angles on the same side of the transversal are supplementary.

MORE
ASSIGNMENT *pp. 288–296*

Students can now begin Modeling Task 2 or Reflecting Task 2 from the MORE assignment following Investigation 4.

Unit 4

EXPLORE small-group investigation

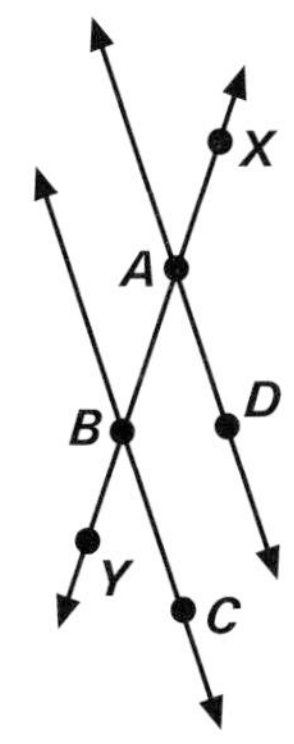

5. **a.** Lines *BC* and *AD* appear to be parallel.
   b. Again $\overleftrightarrow{BC}$ and $\overleftrightarrow{AD}$ appear to be parallel.
   c. If two lines are cut by a transversal so that a pair of corresponding angles have equal measure, then the lines are parallel.

When Euclid began building his rules of geometry, he started with five assumptions. The assumption in the text, that corresponding angles are congruent if and only if the lines cut by the transversal are parallel, is functionally equivalent to Euclid's parallel postulate: Given a line and a point not on the line, there is exactly one line parallel to the original line that passes through the point. It seemed to many mathematicians that this should be provable from the other four assumptions, but it was, in fact, a necessary assumption. Assuming otherwise will lead to other geometries: spherical (there are no lines through the point that are parallel, also called Riemannian geometry) and hyperbolic (there are an infinite number of lines through the point that are parallel, also called elliptic or Lobachevskian geometry). The assumption in the text is equivalent to the parallel postulate because given either assumption, the other can be proved. (See Activity 8 in this investigation.) Hence, by making this assumption, the students are studying Euclidean (plane) geometry.

Until this investigation, students have either been given information (such as vertical angles are congruent) or been asked to prove a particular statement. Having them accept an assumption, then, may seem odd to them. If a student seems particularly interested in why this property is being handled differently, you may want to ask if they would be interested in doing some research on the origins of spherical or hyperbolic geometry.

To begin the next portion of this investigation, it would help if you facilitate a full-class discussion about the converse of a statement and connect it to the Parallel Lines Property and the notion that students will be assuming both the statement and its converse. In the discussion, be sure students understand the "if and only if" statement. If your students have completed Organizing Task 2 of the MORE set following Investigation 2, ask them what a Venn diagram for an "if and only if" statement would look like. This conversation would be valuable at the end of a class period, even if not all groups have completed Activity 5. The groups that have not completed Activity 5 could complete it as homework.

Examples of converses that are not necessarily true might help students see that if-then statements cannot always be reversed. Nongeometric settings can be helpful. For example: If you have a driver's license, then you must be at least 16 years old; if you are at least 16 years old, then you must have a driver's license.

6. **a.** All of the relations given in Activity 3 Part b, page T283, guarantee the lines are parallel. See Part b below.
   b.
   - If two lines are cut by a transversal so that a pair of alternate interior angles have equal measure, then the lines are parallel.
   - If two lines are cut by a transversal so that a pair of alternate exterior angles have equal measure, then the lines are parallel.
   - If two lines are cut by a transversal so that a pair of interior angles on the same side of the transversal are supplementary, then the lines are parallel.
   - If two lines are cut by a transversal so that a pair of exterior angles on the same side of the transversal are supplementary, then the lines are parallel.

5. Conduct the following experiment:

   a. Draw a line XY on your paper. Choose two different points on the line and label them A and B as shown here. Draw a line BC through B so that $m\angle YBC = 38^\circ$. Draw a line AD through A so that $m\angle YAD = 38^\circ$ and D and C are on the same side of $\overleftrightarrow{XY}$. Examine $\overleftrightarrow{BC}$ and $\overleftrightarrow{AD}$. What appears to be true about these two lines?

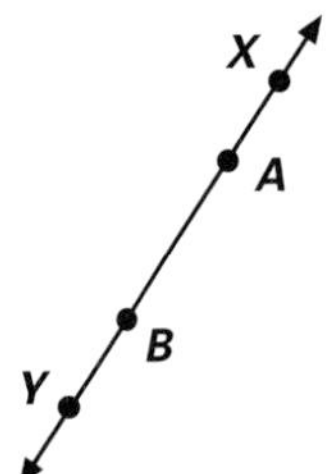

   b. Repeat the experiment in Part a, but this time use $m\angle YBC = m\angle YAD = 111^\circ$. What do you observe about $\overleftrightarrow{BC}$ and $\overleftrightarrow{AD}$ this time?

   c. Write a conjecture in if-then form that generalizes the observations you made in the experiments.

In order to reason deductively about parallel lines and figures formed by parallel lines, you need to begin with some information about when two lines are parallel. The conjecture you made in Activity 5 should be basically the same as the statement below:

If two lines are cut by a transversal so that corresponding angles have equal measure, then the lines are parallel.

This is the **converse** of the assumption made in Activity 4. There you assumed that if two parallel lines are cut by a transversal, then corresponding angles have equal measure. The converse is formed by interchanging the hypothesis with the conclusion. The converse of a true if-then statement is not necessarily true. In symbols, the converse of "If p, then q" is "If q, then p." The truth of "If p, then q" does not assure the truth of "If q, then p."

For the remainder of this unit, you can assume that both the statement in Activity 4 and its converse are true. These statements are combined in the *Parallel Lines Property*.

Parallel Lines Property

In a plane, two lines cut by a transversal are parallel if and only if corresponding angles have the same measure.

6. It is reasonable to ask if there are other relations between two angles formed by a line intersecting two other lines that would allow you to conclude that the two lines are parallel.

   a. Consider the relations between the pairs of angles named in Part a of Activity 3 (page 283). If the angles in the pair have equal measure (or are supplementary), does that ensure that the lines are parallel? Working as a group, make a list of those relations that appear to guarantee that the lines are parallel.

   b. Write each of your conjectures in Part a in if-then form.

LESSON 1 • REASONED ARGUMENTS 285

c. Each group member should choose a different if-then statement and then try to prove it.

d. Share and discuss the reasoning in your proof with the rest of your group. Correct any reasoning errors found.

e. As a group, choose one of your statements and its proof to share and discuss with the entire class.

Checkpoint

The Parallel Lines Property implies more than the relation between parallel lines and corresponding angles.

a What other conditions on angles will be true when two parallel lines are cut by a transversal?

b What other conditions on angles formed by two lines and a transversal will ensure that the lines are parallel?

Be prepared to share and compare your group's list of conditions with those of other groups.

On Your Own

Using the angles and lines identified in the diagram below, decide whether each of the following conditions ensures that $q \parallel r$. Explain your reasoning in each case.

a. $m\angle 2 = m\angle 7$

b. $m\angle 8 = m\angle 4$

c. $m\angle 4 + m\angle 5 = 180°$

d. $m\angle 1 = m\angle 3$

e. $m\angle 3 = m\angle 5$

f. $m\angle 3 + m\angle 4 = 180°$

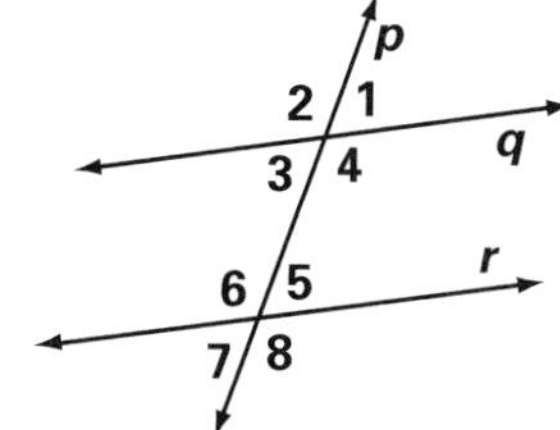

7. In the diagram shown at the right, $GUSH$ is a quadrilateral with diagonal GS; $m\angle 1 + m\angle 2 = 90°$; $m\angle 2 + m\angle 3 = 90°$. Is it correct to conclude that $\overleftrightarrow{GU}$ and $\overleftrightarrow{SH}$ are parallel? If so, prove it. If not, give a counterexample.

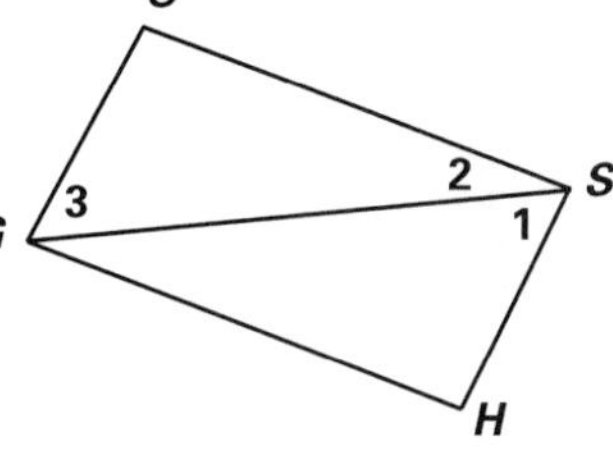

Unit 4

6. c. See the diagram in the margin.

Alternate interior angles:

Proof: If two lines intersect, then m∠1 = m∠3 (Vertical Angles Theorem).
If m∠1 = m∠3 and m∠3 = m∠5 (since alternate interior angles have equal measures), then m∠1 = m∠5.
If m∠1 = m∠5, then by the Parallel Lines Property the lines are parallel.
Hence, if two lines are cut by a transversal so that a pair of alternate interior angles are equal, then the lines are parallel.

Alternate exterior angles:

Alter the second statement in the proof for alternate interior angles to use the given fact that alternate exterior angles, ∠7 and ∠1, have equal measures.

Interior angles on same side:

Proof: If two lines intersect, then m∠1 + m∠4 = 180° (Linear Pair Property).
If m∠1 + m∠4 = 180 and m∠4 + m∠5 = 180° (since interior angles on the same side of the transversal are supplementary), then m∠1 = m∠5. Thus, by the Parallel Lines Property the lines are parallel.
Hence, if two lines are cut by a transversal so that a pair of interior angles on the same side of the transversal are supplementary, the lines are parallel.

Exterior angles on same side:

The argument will be similar to the proof for interior angles on the same side of the transversal.

d. It is important for students to consider other students' proofs carefully. This type of critical reading and discussion will improve everybody's reasoning skills.

e. As a whole class, discuss proofs for each of the statements in Part b.

SHARE AND SUMMARIZE full-class discussion

Checkpoint

See Teaching Master 93.

ⓐ Using the Parallel Lines Property, we can conclude that interior angles on the same side of the transversal will be supplementary, exterior angles on the same side of the transversal will be supplementary, alternate interior angles will have equal measures, and alternate exterior angles will have equal measures.

ⓑ Two lines will be parallel if one of the following conditions holds:
A pair of interior angles on the same side of the transversal are supplementary.
A pair of exterior angles on the same side of the transversal are supplementary.
A pair of alternate interior angles have equal measure.
A pair of alternate exterior angles have equal measure.

APPLY individual task

On Your Own

a. Not necessarily parallel. Exterior angles on the same side must be supplementary to ensure parallelism.

See additional Teaching Notes on page T344F.

Master 93

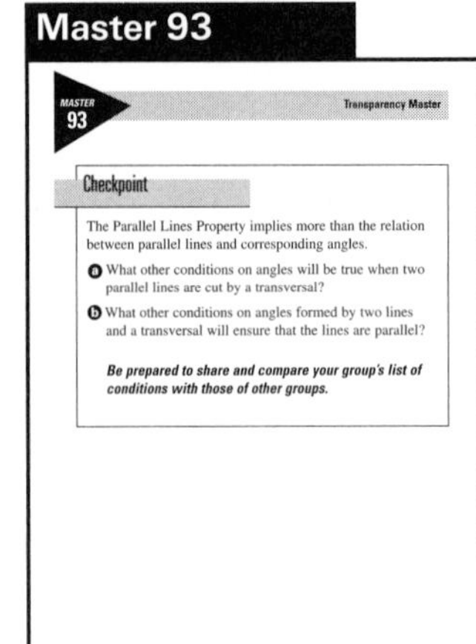

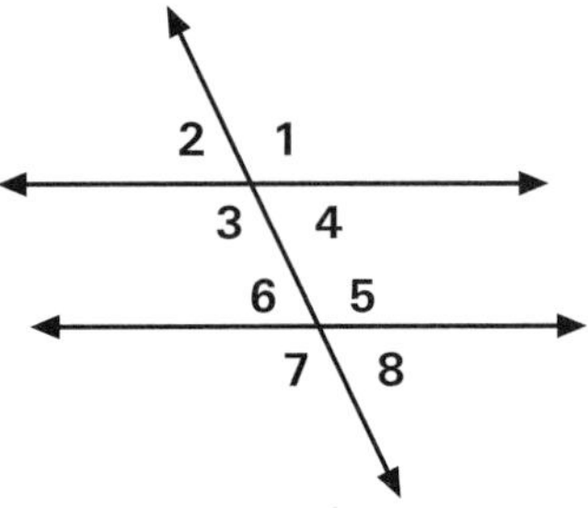

Unit 4

MORE ASSIGNMENT *pp. 288–296*

Students can now begin Modeling Task 1 or 3 or Organizing Task 3 or 6 from the MORE assignment following Investigation 4.

Master 94

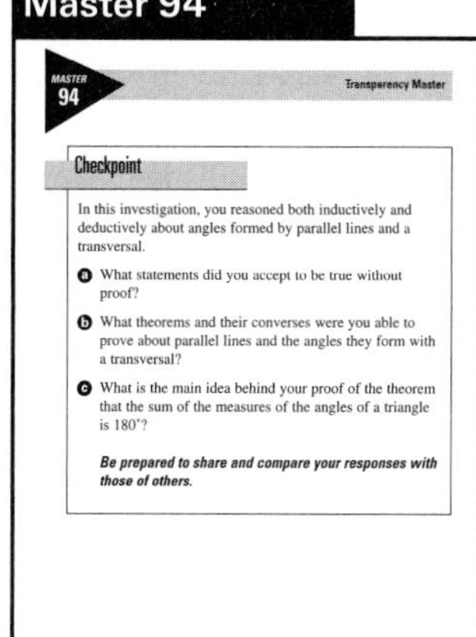
MASTER 94 — Transparency Master

Checkpoint

In this investigation, you reasoned both inductively and deductively about angles formed by parallel lines and a transversal.

ⓐ What statements did you accept to be true without proof?

ⓑ What theorems and their converses were you able to prove about parallel lines and the angles they form with a transversal?

ⓒ What is the main idea behind your proof of the theorem that the sum of the measures of the angles of a triangle is 180°?

Be prepared to share and compare your responses with those of others.

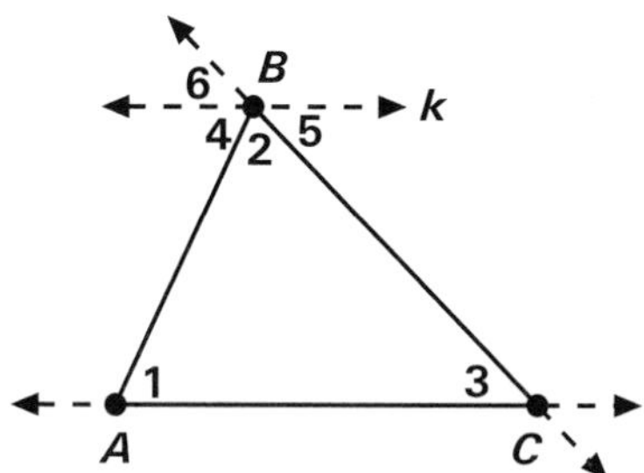

EXPLORE *continued*

8. Since the vertices of the triangle determine a plane, students should be thinking about this problem in two dimensions.

a. When the three angles are placed next to each other at a point, a straight angle is formed. (Be sure to ask students if this tearing off and repositioning of the corners constitutes a proof.)

b. ■ Through a point not on a line, only one line can be drawn parallel to the given line. This fact is a consequence of the Parallel Lines Property. Students are not expected to be able to prove this fact, but such a proof is given here.

See the diagram in the margin. It is clear that it is possible to draw at least one line through point B that is parallel to $\overleftrightarrow{AC}$. The Parallel Lines Property tells us that in order for line k to be parallel to $\overleftrightarrow{AC}$, $\angle 3$ and $\angle 6$ must have equal measure. But this then fixes line k and so there is exactly one line through point B that is parallel to $\overleftrightarrow{AC}$.

■ *Proof:* If $k \parallel \overleftrightarrow{AC}$ with transversal $\overleftrightarrow{AB}$, then $m\angle 1 = m\angle 4$ (alternate interior angles).

If $k \parallel \overleftrightarrow{AC}$ with transversal $\overleftrightarrow{BC}$, then $m\angle 3 = m\angle 5$ (alternate interior angles).

If $m\angle 4 + m\angle 2 + m\angle 5 = 180°$ (a straight angle measures 180°, that is, the Linear Pairs Property) and $m\angle 1 = m\angle 4$ and $m\angle 3 = m\angle 5$, then $m\angle 1 + m\angle 2 + m\angle 3 = 180°$.

SHARE AND SUMMARIZE full-class discussion

Checkpoint

See Teaching Master 94.

ⓐ In this investigation, two assumptions were accepted without proof:

- Parallel lines cut by a transversal form congruent corresponding angles.
- If corresponding angles are congruent, then the lines cut by the transversal are parallel.

ⓑ If two parallel lines are cut by a transversal, then alternate interior angles have equal measure.

If two parallel lines are cut by a transversal, then alternate exterior angles have equal measure.

If two parallel lines are cut by a transversal, then interior angles on the same side of the transversal are supplementary.

If two parallel lines are cut by a transversal, then exterior angles on the same side of the transversal are supplementary.

If two lines are cut by a transversal so that alternate interior angles have equal measure, then the lines are parallel.

If two lines are cut by a transversal so that alternate exterior angles have equal measure, then the lines are parallel.

Unit 4

CONSTRUCTING A MATH TOOLKIT: Ask students to review and sort the theorems they have proven in this investigation, writing statements and their converses in "if and only if" form. New vocabulary words should also be added to their lists.

See additional Teaching Notes on page T344F.

8. In previous courses, you have used the fact that the sum of the measures of the angles of a triangle is 180°.

a. Test the plausibility of this fact by conducting the following experiment. Have each group member cut out a paper model of a different-shaped triangle. Label the angles with 1, 2, and 3. Tear off the angles and place them next to each other at a point. What kind of angle appears to have been formed?

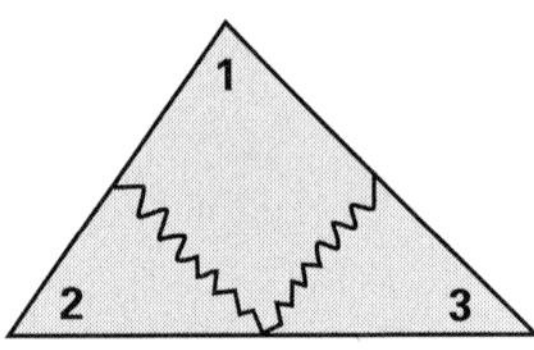

b. The diagram at the right shows $\triangle ABC$ and line k drawn parallel to line AC through point B.

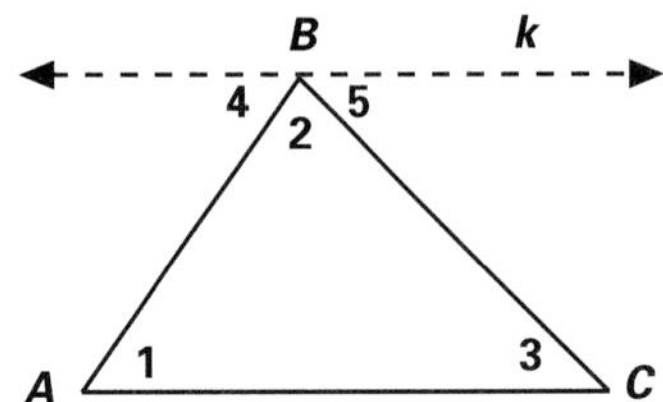

- If you draw a line l through point B and parallel to $\overleftrightarrow{AC}$, how must it be related to line k?
- Write a deductive argument to show that $m\angle 1 + m\angle 2 + m\angle 3 = 180°$.

Checkpoint

In this investigation, you reasoned both inductively and deductively about angles formed by parallel lines and a transversal.

a What statements did you accept to be true without proof?

b What theorems and their converses were you able to prove about parallel lines and the angles they form with a transversal?

c What is the main idea behind your proof of the theorem that the sum of the measures of the angles of a triangle is 180°?

Be prepared to share and compare your responses with those of others.

On Your Own

In the diagram at the right, $\overleftrightarrow{AD}$ and $\overleftrightarrow{HE}$ are cut by transversal $\overleftrightarrow{GC}$. Angles 1 and 2 are supplementary. Can you conclude $\overleftrightarrow{AD} \parallel \overleftrightarrow{HE}$? If so, prove it; if not, find a counterexample.

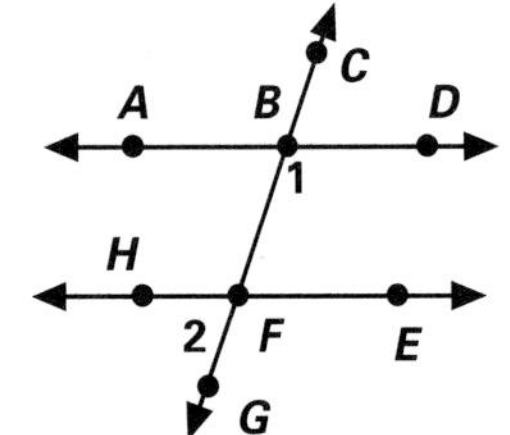

Unit 4

LESSON 1 • REASONED ARGUMENTS 287

MORE Modeling • Organizing • Reflecting • Extending

Modeling

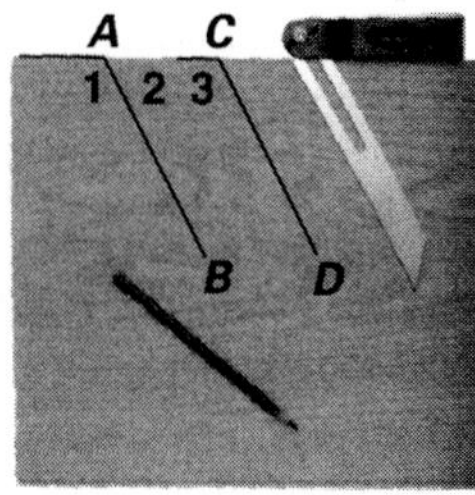

1. The photo at the right shows a carpenter's bevel, which is used to draw parallel lines.
   a. Where is the transversal?
   b. How are angles 1 and 3 related? How do you know?
   c. Is $\overleftrightarrow{AB} \parallel \overleftrightarrow{CD}$? How do you know?
   d. How are angles 2 and 3 related? How do you know?

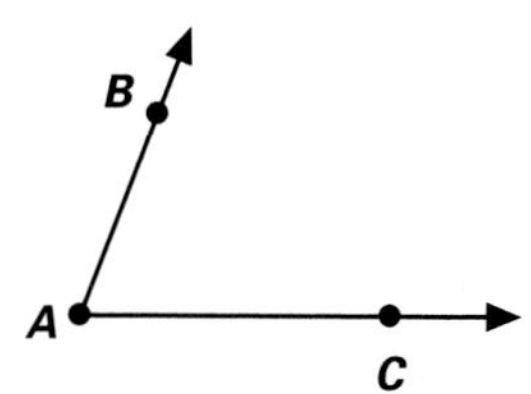

2. Draw an angle *BAC*, like the one at the right, on your paper. Now draw another angle *XYZ* so that the sides *BA* and *XY* are parallel and the sides *CA* and *ZY* are parallel.
   a. Draw several different angles for *XYZ*, some with the sides pointing in the same directions as those of $\angle BAC$ and some with the sides pointing in the opposite directions. What relation, if any, exists between $\angle BAC$ and $\angle XYZ$?
   b. In the diagram at the right, the sides of the two angles point in the same directions. How are $\angle XYZ$ and $\angle BAC$ related? Write a proof of your claim.

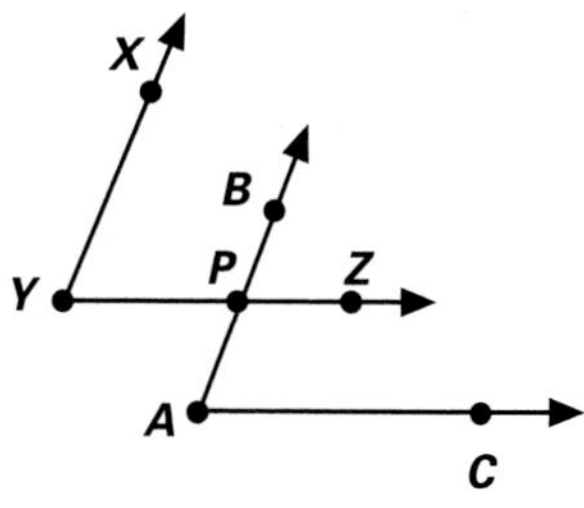

   c. In this diagram, side *YX* points in the direction opposite to side *AB*, while the other sides point in the same direction. How are $\angle XYZ$ and $\angle BAC$ related? Prove your claim.

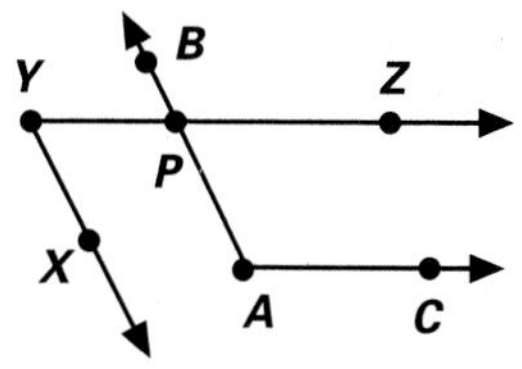

   d. Write one if-then statement summarizing the results in Parts a through c. It could begin like this:

      If the sides of two angles are parallel in pairs, then … .

Unit 4

288 UNIT 4 • SHAPES AND GEOMETRIC REASONING

MORE independent assignment

Modeling

1. **a.** The transversal is the top edge of the board. It is labeled $\overleftrightarrow{AC}$.
   b. Angles 1 and 3 are corresponding angles. They are formed by drawing lines without changing the angle on the carpenter's bevel, and so they have equal measure.
   c. $\overleftrightarrow{AB} \parallel \overleftrightarrow{CD}$, because $m\angle 1 = m\angle 3$ the angles are corresponding angles.
   d. They are supplementary. We know that $\overleftrightarrow{AB} \parallel \overleftrightarrow{CD}$ and $\overleftrightarrow{AC}$ is a transversal. Since $\angle 2$ and $\angle 3$ are interior angles on the same side of the transversal, they are supplementary.
2. **a.** Angles *BAC* and *XYZ* are either congruent or supplementary as illustrated in the diagrams in Parts b and c of the student text.
   b. $m\angle XYZ = m\angle BAC$
   If $\overleftrightarrow{XY} \parallel \overleftrightarrow{AB}$, then $m\angle Y = m\angle BPZ$ (corresponding angles). If $\overleftrightarrow{YZ} \parallel \overleftrightarrow{AC}$, then $m\angle A = m\angle BPZ$ (corresponding angles). If $m\angle Y = m\angle BPZ$ and $m\angle A = m\angle BPZ$, then $m\angle Y = m\angle A$. Thus, if $\overleftrightarrow{YZ} \parallel \overleftrightarrow{AB}$ and $\overleftrightarrow{YZ} \parallel \overleftrightarrow{AC}$, then $m\angle Y = m\angle A$.
   c. Angles *XYZ* and *BAC* are supplementary.
   If $\overleftrightarrow{XY} \parallel \overleftrightarrow{AB}$, then $\angle Y$ and $\angle YPA$ are supplementary since they are interior angles on the same side of the transversal. If $\overleftrightarrow{YZ} \parallel \overleftrightarrow{AC}$, then $m\angle A = m\angle YPA$ since they are alternate interior angles. If $\angle Y$ and $\angle YPA$ are supplementary, then $m\angle Y + m\angle YPA = 180°$ and $m\angle A = m\angle YPA$. Thus, $m\angle Y + m\angle A = 180°$. If $m\angle Y + m\angle A = 180°$, then $\angle Y$ and $\angle A$ are supplementary.
   d. If the sides of two angles are parallel in pairs, then the two angles are either supplementary or equal in measure.

MORE

ASSIGNMENT *pp. 288–296*

Modeling: 1 or 2, and 3*
Organizing: 3 and 6
Reflecting: 2 and 4
Extending: 1 and 4

**When choice is indicated, it is important to leave the choice to the student.*
NOTE: *It is best if Organizing tasks are discussed as a whole class after they have been assigned as homework.*

NOTE: You may wish to have students include this theorem and others proved in the MORE set in their geometry toolkit.

Unit 4

3. **a.** The string makes a 90° angle with the wall baseboard.

   b. Make a vertical edge of the picture frame coincide with the plumb line. Since the picture frame has right angles in it, fixing the vertical edges makes the horizontal edges perpendicular to the plumb line. Thus, corresponding angles are equal, and so the horizontal edge of the picture is parallel to the floor.

   c. In order to guarantee that the shelves are parallel to the floor, you need to make sure the shelves are perpendicular to the plumb line.

4. **a.** This proof makes extensive use of algebraic reasoning. To help students get started, you may wish to suggest that they write down as many correct equations involving the measures of the angles in the diagram as they can.

   In order for the exiting light rays to be parallel, we must have $m\angle 2 + m\angle 5 = 180°$. Also $m\angle 1 + m\angle 2 + m\angle 3 = 180°$ and $m\angle 4 + m\angle 5 + m\angle 6 = 180°$. Combining these two equations we get $m\angle 1 + m\angle 2 + m\angle 3 + m\angle 4 + m\angle 5 + m\angle 6 = 360°$. But if $m\angle 2 + m\angle 5 = 180°$, then this equation becomes $m\angle 1 + m\angle 3 + m\angle 4 + m\angle 6 = 180°$. If $m\angle 1 = m\angle 3$ and $m\angle 4 = m\angle 6$, then we get $2m\angle 3 + 2m\angle 4 = 180°$. We can then divide both sides of this equation by 2 to get $m\angle 3 + m\angle 4 = 90°$. But in $\triangle XYQ$, we know that $m\angle 3 + m\angle 4 + m\angle Q = 180°$, so $m\angle Q = 90°$.

   b. To use inductive reasoning, you could keep drawing diagrams and measuring angles until you got a diagram for which the entering and exiting light rays were parallel.

   c. It is very time-consuming to keep drawing diagrams and also very difficult to draw the diagrams accurately. But deductive reasoning leads us directly to the correct angle.

   d. The simplifying assumption that was made in this situation is that the light ray would not be refracted upon entering or leaving the diamond.

3. A plumb line (weight hanging by a string) is attached to a wall near the ceiling, as shown at the right.
   a. What angle does the string make with the wall baseboard?
   b. How could the plumb line be used to straighten a picture in a rectangular frame? What mathematics justifies your response?
   c. How could the plumb line be used to place shelving on the wall so the shelves were parallel to the floor? Explain.

4. The sparkle of a diamond results from light being reflected from facet to facet of the jewel and then directly to the eye of the observer. When a light ray strikes a smooth surface, such as a facet of a jewel, the angle at which the ray strikes the surface is congruent to the angle at which the ray leaves the surface. A diamond can be cut in such a way that a light ray entering the top will be parallel to the same ray as it exits the top.

   Examine the cross sections of the two diamonds shown below. The diamond at the left has been cut too deeply. The entering and exiting light rays are not parallel. The diamond on the right appears to be cut correctly.

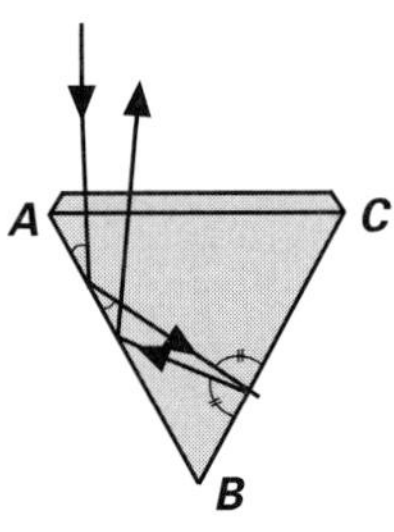

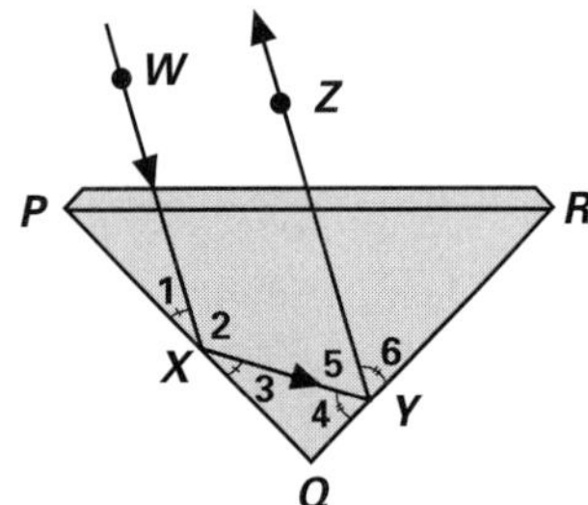

   a. Use deductive reasoning to determine the measure of $\angle Q$ at the base of the diamond to ensure that the entering and exiting light rays will be parallel.
   b. Explain how you could use inductive reasoning to conjecture what the measure of $\angle Q$ should be to ensure that the entering and exiting light rays will be parallel.
   c. What are the advantages of deductive reasoning in this case?
   d. As you have seen before, when modeling a situation, it often helps to make simplifying assumptions. Consult with a science teacher about reflection and refraction of light and the modeling of the diamond cut. What simplifying assumptions were made in this situation?

Unit 4

LESSON 1 • REASONED ARGUMENTS 289

Organizing

1. In Activity 8 of Investigation 4, page 287, you proved that the sum of the measures of the angles of a triangle is 180°. Decide whether each of the following statements is correct. If correct, prove the statement. Otherwise, give a counterexample. (Note that an **acute angle** is an angle whose measure is less than 90°.)

a. If the measures of two angles of one triangle are equal to the measures of two angles of another triangle, then the measures of the third angles are equal.

b. The sum of the measures of the acute angles of a right triangle is 90°.

c. If two angles of a triangle are acute, then the third angle is not acute.

d. If a triangle is equiangular (all angles have the same measure), then each angle has measure 60°.

2. In the diagram at the right, lines l and m are parallel, and lines m and n are parallel. Line p intersects each of these lines.

a. Are angles 1 and 2 equal in measure or supplementary? Explain.

b. How are the measures of angles 1 and 4 related? Explain your reasoning.

c. Using your deductions in Parts a and b, prove that lines l and n are parallel.

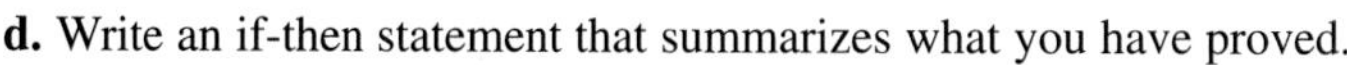

d. Write an if-then statement that summarizes what you have proved.

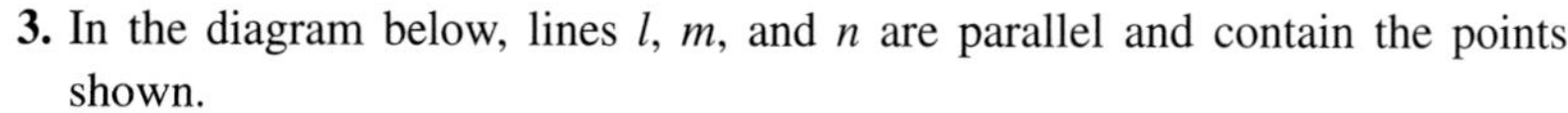

3. In the diagram below, lines l, m, and n are parallel and contain the points shown.

a. Write an equation for each line.

b. On a copy of this diagram, draw lines perpendicular to each line through its y-intercept.

c. How are the lines you drew in Part b related to each other?

d. Prove your conclusion in Part c using ideas from Investigation 4.

e. Prove your conclusion in Part c using the equations of the lines and algebraic reasoning.

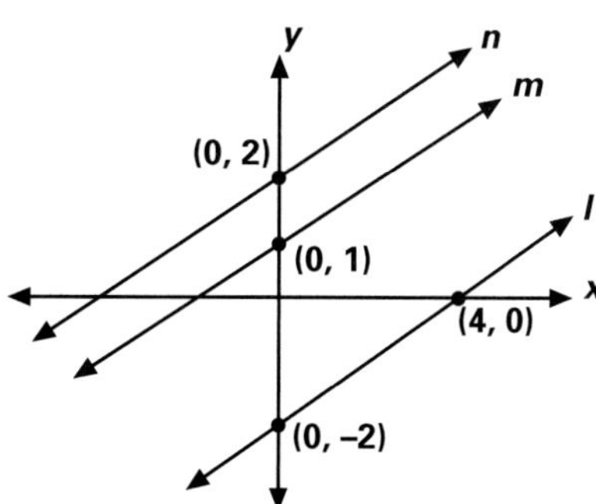

290 UNIT 4 • SHAPES AND GEOMETRIC REASONING

Organizing

1. **a.** Suppose $\triangle ABC$ and $\triangle XYZ$ are such that $m\angle A = m\angle X$ and $m\angle B = m\angle Y$. In $\triangle ABC$ we know that $m\angle A + m\angle B + m\angle C = 180°$, and in $\triangle XYZ$ we know that $m\angle X + m\angle Y + m\angle Z = 180°$. Thus, $m\angle A + m\angle B + m\angle C = m\angle X + m\angle Y + m\angle Z$. If $m\angle A = m\angle X$ and $m\angle B = m\angle Y$, then by the subtraction property of equality, $m\angle C = m\angle Z$.
   b. If $\triangle ABC$ is a right triangle with acute angles A and B and right angle C, then $m\angle A + m\angle B + m\angle C = 180°$. If $m\angle C = 90°$ and $m\angle A + m\angle B + m\angle C = 180°$, then $m\angle A + m\angle B = 90°$.
   c. This statement is not correct. Consider a triangle with angles of 50°, 60°, and 70°. All three angles are acute, which is a counterexample to the proposition.
   d. If $\triangle ABC$ is equiangular, then $3m\angle A = 180°$. Thus, $m\angle A = 60°$, and since all the angles have equal measure, they all have measure 60°.
2. **a.** $m\angle 1 = m\angle 2$. If two parallel lines are cut by a transversal, then the alternate exterior angles are congruent.
   b. $\angle 1$ and $\angle 4$ are supplementary. If $m\angle 1 = m\angle 2$ (from Part a) and $m\angle 2 = m\angle 3$ (alternate interior angles), then $m\angle 1 = m\angle 3$. If $\angle 3$ and $\angle 4$ are supplementary (Linear Pair Property), then $m\angle 3 + m\angle 4 = 180°$. Since $m\angle 1 = m\angle 3$, $m\angle 1 + m\angle 4 = 180°$ and $\angle 1$ and $\angle 4$ are supplementary.
   c. In Part b, we reasoned that $m\angle 1 = m\angle 3$. Therefore, $l \parallel n$ because corresponding angles ($\angle 1$ and $\angle 3$) are equal.
   d. If two lines are each parallel to a third line, then they are parallel to each other.

NOTE: You may wish to have students write this conclusion in if-then form to include in their toolkit of theorems to use.

3. **a.** Line l has slope $\frac{0+2}{4-0}$ or $\frac{1}{2}$. Therefore, because the lines are parallel, each line has slope $\frac{1}{2}$.
   l: $y = \frac{1}{2}x - 2$
   m: $y = \frac{1}{2}x + 1$
   n: $y = \frac{1}{2}x + 2$
   b.

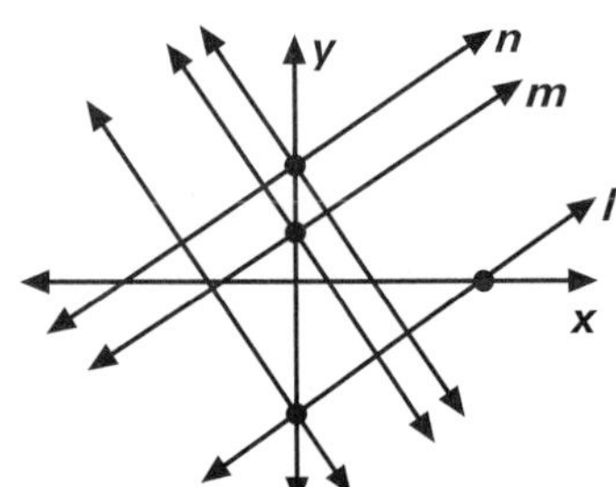

   c. The lines are parallel.
   d. Each new line is perpendicular to each of the given lines, and therefore the three new lines are parallel since corresponding angles are equal.
   e. The slope of each of the new lines is -2 since each is perpendicular to a line with slope $\frac{1}{2}$. Thus, since all three of the new lines have the same slope, they must all be parallel to each other.

Unit 4

MORE *continued*

4. a. $$m\angle 1 + m\angle 2 = 180^\circ$$
$$26^\circ + 5x + 34^\circ + x = 180^\circ$$
$$60^\circ + 6x = 180^\circ$$
$$6x = 120^\circ$$
$$x = 20^\circ$$

$m\angle 1 = 126^\circ$

$m\angle 2 = 54^\circ$

b. $$m\angle A + m\angle B = 90^\circ$$
$$5x + 3^\circ + 2x + 3^\circ = 90^\circ$$
$$7x + 6^\circ = 90^\circ$$
$$7x = 84^\circ$$
$$x = 12^\circ$$

$m\angle A = 63^\circ$

$m\angle B = 27^\circ$

5. a. Since $\overleftrightarrow{AT} \parallel \overleftrightarrow{CS}$, both pairs of angles are supplementary because they are interior angles on the same side of the transversal.

b. If *CATS* is a trapezoid with $\overleftrightarrow{AT} \parallel \overleftrightarrow{CS}$, then $\angle C$ and $\angle A$ are supplementary.

Proof If $\overleftrightarrow{AT} \parallel \overleftrightarrow{CS}$, then $\angle C$ and $\angle A$ are interior angles on the same side of the transversal *CA*. If $\angle C$ and $\angle A$ are interior angles on the same side of the transversal and $\overleftrightarrow{AT} \parallel \overleftrightarrow{CS}$, then $\angle C$ and $\angle A$ are supplementary.

c. $m\angle A = m\angle T$

Proof: If $\overleftrightarrow{AT} \parallel \overleftrightarrow{CS}$, then $m\angle A + m\angle C = 180^\circ$ and $m\angle T + m\angle S = 180^\circ$.

If $m\angle A + m\angle C = 180^\circ$ and $m\angle T + m\angle S = 180^\circ$, then $m\angle A + m\angle C = m\angle T + m\angle S$.

If $m\angle A + m\angle C = m\angle T + m\angle S$ and $m\angle C = m\angle S$, then $m\angle A = m\angle T$.

Hence, if *CATS* is a trapezoid with $\overleftrightarrow{AT} \parallel \overleftrightarrow{CS}$ and $m\angle C = m\angle S$, then $m\angle A = m\angle T$.

Unit 4

4. Refer to the diagrams below.

a. Lines l and m are parallel. $m\angle 1 = 26 + 5x$ and $m\angle 2 = 34 + x$. Find the values of x, $m\angle 1$, and $m\angle 2$.

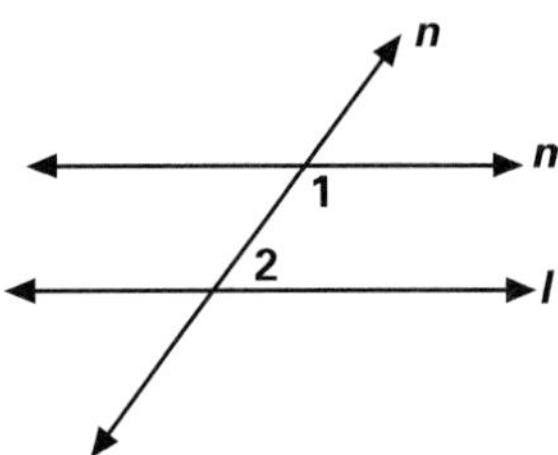

b. Triangle ABC is a right triangle. $m\angle A = 5x + 3$ and $m\angle B = 2x + 3$. Find the value of x, $m\angle A$, and $m\angle B$.

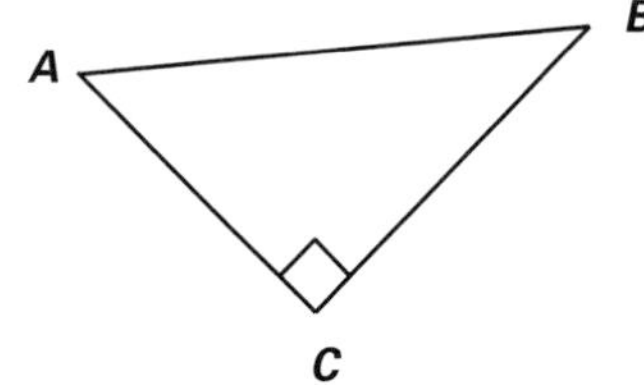

5. The figure *CATS* is a trapezoid with $\overline{AT} \parallel \overline{CS}$.

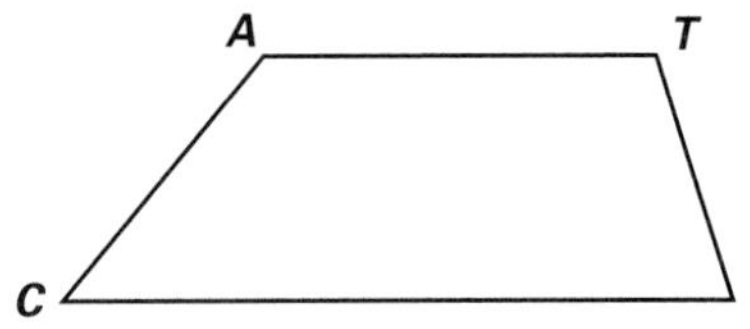

a. What can you conclude about $\angle C$ and $\angle A$? About $\angle T$ and $\angle S$?

b. Write an if-then statement summarizing one of your observations in Part a and prove it is correct.

c. Suppose $m\angle C = m\angle S$. What can you conclude about $\angle A$ and $\angle T$? Write a proof.

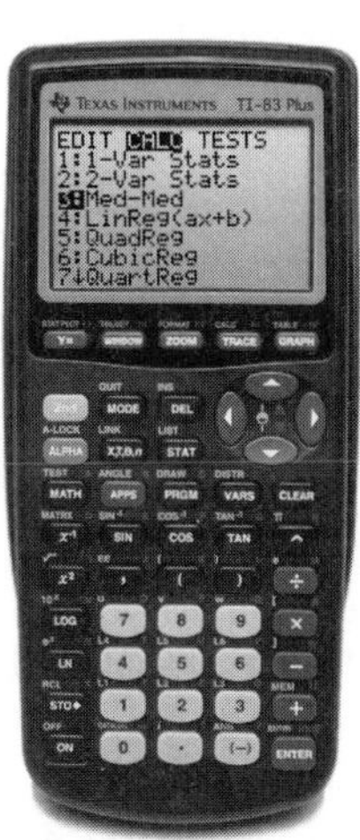

6. A recurring topic in your study of mathematics has been fitting models to data patterns. If a scatterplot reveals a linear pattern, you have produced linear models in two ways: estimating the model by eye and finding the least squares regression line. As you saw in Course 2, the calculations to determine the slope and y-intercept of the least squares regression line involve every point. If the data set has outliers, this line may be influenced a great deal. In contrast, the **median-median line** is highly resistant to the effects of outliers. The *median-fit* procedure outlined on the next page uses ideas from both statistics and geometry.

Unit 4

LESSON 1 • REASONED ARGUMENTS 291

a. Examine the following data from a study of the amount of exposure in nine Oregon counties to radioactive waste from a nuclear reactor in Hanford, Washington, and the rate of deaths due to cancer in these counties.

Radioactive Waste Exposure

County	Index of Exposure	Cancer Deaths (per 100,000 residents)
Sherman	1.3	114
Wasco	1.6	138
Umatilla	2.5	147
Morrow	2.6	130
Gilliam	3.4	130
Hood River	3.8	162
Columbia	6.4	178
Clatsop	8.3	210
Portland	11.6	208

Source: *Journal of Environmental Health*, National Environmental Health Association, May–June 1965.

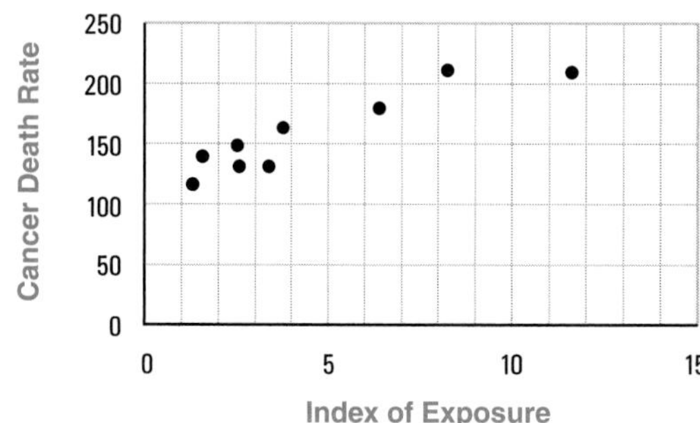

On a copy of this scatterplot, find the median-median line as follows:

- Draw two vertical lines to divide the scatterplot into three sets of equal size, if possible. (If this is not possible, the outer sets should contain the same number of points.)
- Next, find the median point for each set; that is, find the point whose x-coordinate is the median of the x values of all points in that set and whose y-coordinate is the median of the y values. Plot these points and mark each. You will locate three points, one for each set.
- Place a clear ruler on the median points of the two outer sets. This determines the general direction of the linear model. To account for the median point of the middle set, move the ruler one-third the distance to that point. Be sure to keep the ruler parallel to its original position. Draw the line. This is the median-median line.

Unit 4

292 UNIT 4 • SHAPES AND GEOMETRIC REASONING

6. See Teaching Master 95.

a. Median points are marked with a cross.

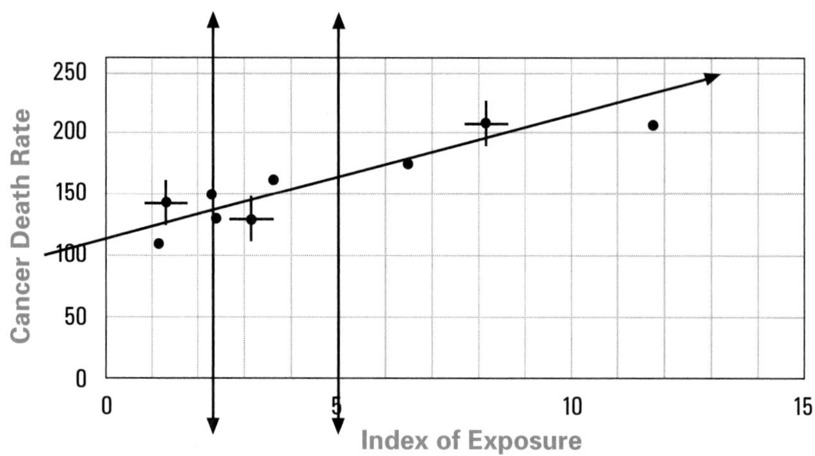

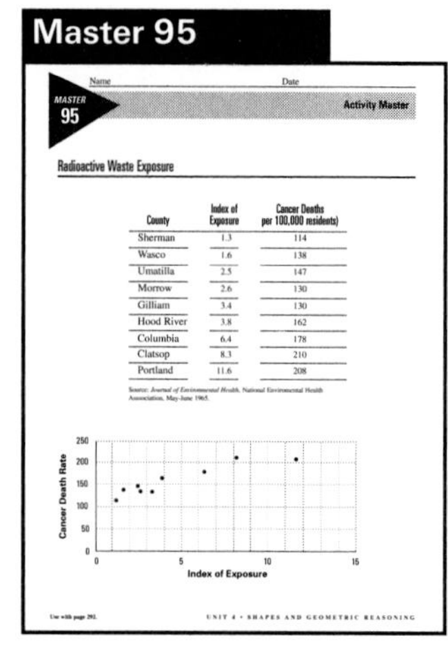

Master 95

Name Date

MASTER 95 Activity Master

Radioactive Waste Exposure

County	Index of Exposure	Cancer Deaths per 100,000 residents)
Sherman	1.3	114
Wasco	1.6	138
Umatilla	2.5	147
Morrow	2.6	130
Gilliam	3.4	130
Hood River	3.8	162
Columbia	6.4	178
Clatsop	8.3	210
Portland	11.6	208

UNIT 4 • SHAPES AND GEOMETRIC REASONING

Unit 4

6. **b.** A consequence of the Parallel Lines Property is that there is only one line through a point parallel to a given line. (See page T287, Activity 8, Part b.) The median-median fit procedure uses this idea when drawing a line parallel to the first drawn line, through the point $\frac{1}{3}$ of the distance to the middle median point.

   c. The equation of the median-median line is $y = 10.45x + 112.3$. The line drawn in Part a should be nearly the same as the graph of this equation.

   d. Since there are no real outliers in this data set, the linear regression line and the median-median line should be very close to the same line. The equation of the linear regression line is $y = 115 + 9.27x$.

   e. ■ The equation of the median-median line is $y = x$. The one outlying point (6, 30) does not influence this line at all.

   ■ The line will be moved up some and will be steeper because of the point (6, 30).

   ■ The equation of the least squares regression line is $y = 0.67 + 1.4x$.

Reflecting

1. Responses will vary. Many students may say they don't see what to do next. You might suggest students consider something they know as an hypothesis and then complete the statement by supplying a conclusion. This would help them think in the manner of "If I know p, then I also know q." This thinking is needed in proofmaking.

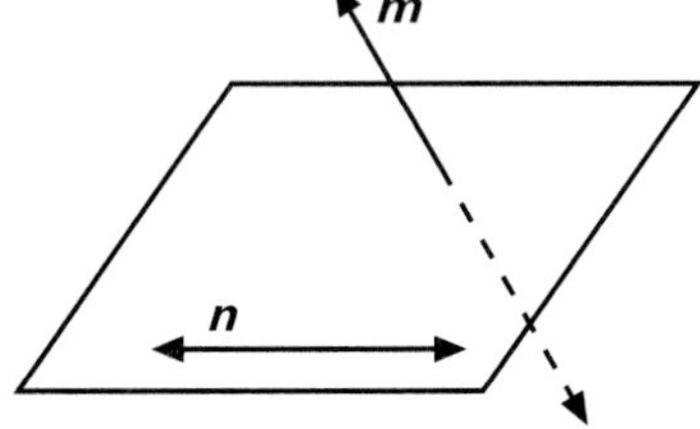

2. It is possible for two lines in three-dimensional space to be neither parallel nor intersecting. Lines with this relationship are called **skew lines**. See lines m and n at the left.

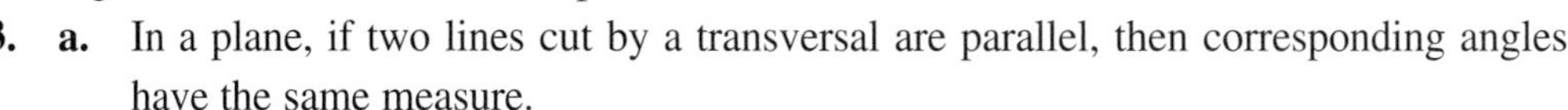

3. **a.** In a plane, if two lines cut by a transversal are parallel, then corresponding angles have the same measure.

   In a plane, if two lines are cut by a transversal and corresponding angles have the same measure, then the lines are parallel.

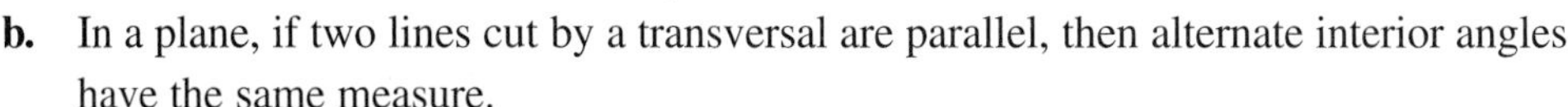

   b. In a plane, if two lines cut by a transversal are parallel, then alternate interior angles have the same measure.

   In a plane, if two lines are cut by a transversal and alternate interior angles have the same measure, then the lines are parallel.

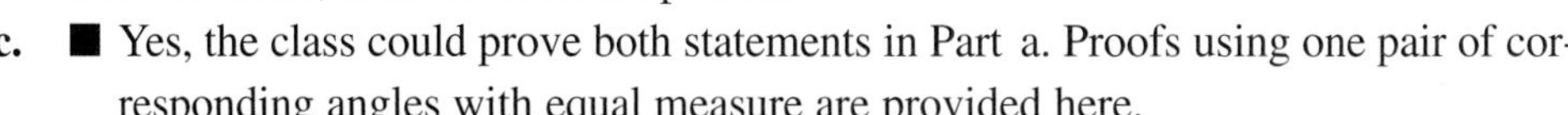

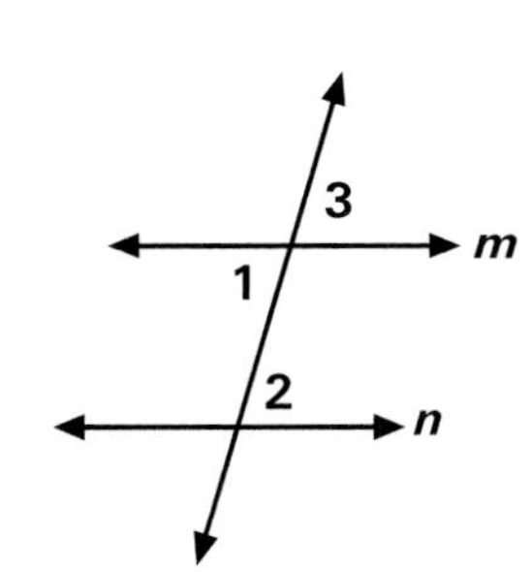

   c. ■ Yes, the class could prove both statements in Part a. Proofs using one pair of corresponding angles with equal measure are provided here.

   To show that parallel lines imply corresponding angles have equal measure:

   If $m \parallel n$, then $m\angle 1 = m\angle 2$, since they are alternate interior angles. Also, $m\angle 1 = m\angle 3$ since they are vertical angles. If $m\angle 1 = m\angle 2$ and $m\angle 1 = m\angle 3$, then $m\angle 2 = m\angle 3$. Hence, if two lines cut by a transversal are parallel, then corresponding angles have the same measure.

   To show that corresponding angles having equal measure implies that the lines are parallel:

   Since $\angle 2$ and $\angle 3$ are corresponding angles, $m\angle 2 = m\angle 3$. Also, $m\angle 3 = m\angle 1$ since they are vertical angles. If $m\angle 2 = m\angle 3$ and $m\angle 3 = m\angle 1$, then $m\angle 2 = m\angle 1$. Since $\angle 2$ and $\angle 1$ are alternate interior angles and have equal measure, m is parallel to n. Hence, if two lines are cut by a transversal and corresponding angles have equal measures, then the lines are parallel.

   ■ Yes; once the relationship using corresponding angles has been established in the previous item, the argument in Investigation 4, Activity 4 (page 283) can be used.

   d. The path that geometric reasoning follows is dependent upon the assumptions made.

b. What property of parallel lines is used in drawing the median-median line? Is only one such median-median line possible?

c. Calculate the median-median (med-med) line using your calculator, if it has such an option. Is it nearly the same as the line you drew? If not, why do you think it is different?

d. How do you think the least squares regression line for these data will be related to the median-median line? Check your conjecture.

e. Examine the data in the table below.

x	1	2	3	4	5	6	7	8	9
y	1	2	3	4	5	30	7	8	9

- Predict the equation of the median-median line.
- Predict how the least squares line will be influenced by the point (6, 30).
- Check your predictions.

Reflecting

1. In this lesson, you were introduced to proving mathematical statements in geometric settings. What did you find to be most difficult about constructing a proof? What is it that makes this so difficult? How are you trying to overcome the difficulty?

2. Parallel lines were defined to be lines in a plane that do not intersect. Is it possible for two lines in three-dimensional space neither to be parallel nor to intersect? Illustrate your reasoning.

3. In Investigation 4, you saw that if you *assume* the Parallel Lines Property, then it is possible to prove other conditions on angles that result when parallel lines are cut by a transversal. It is also possible to prove other conditions on angles that ensure two lines are parallel.

a. Rewrite the Parallel Lines Property as two if-then statements.

b. Replace each occurrence of the phrase "corresponding angles" with "alternate interior angles" in your statements in Part a.

c. Suppose next year's math class *assumes* your statements in Part b as its Parallel Lines Property.

- Could the class then *prove* the statements in Part a? Explain your reasoning.
- Could the class prove the relationships between parallelism of lines and angles on the same side of the transversal? Explain.

d. What, if anything, can you conclude about geometric reasoning from your work in Parts a through c?

LESSON 1 • REASONED ARGUMENTS 293

4. In the book *Through the Looking Glass, and What Alice Found There*, Humpty-Dumpty asserts, "When I use a word, it means just what I choose it to mean—neither more nor less." However, as you know in everyday life, words often have several different meanings. To reason logically, the meanings of key words must be strictly defined as they will be used in the arguments. Formulating descriptions or definitions of terms is an important part of doing mathematical research.

a. In the diagram below, point B is *between* points A and C. Devise a way to describe what this means. Could numbers help you in some way?

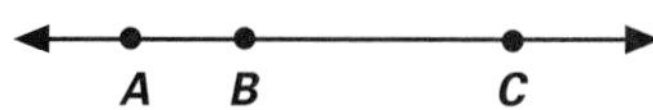

b. In the diagram below, ray PB (denoted $\overrightarrow{PB}$) is between rays PA and PC. Devise a way to describe what this means. Could you use numbers in some way?

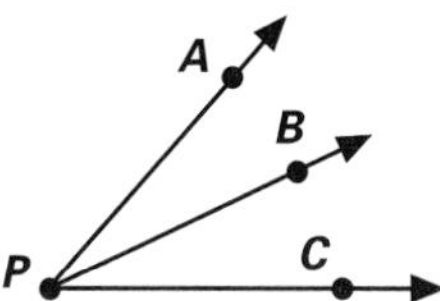

5. In the diagram below, lines m and n intersect at point A in such a way that $m\angle 1 = x^\circ$. Analyze the argument following the diagram.

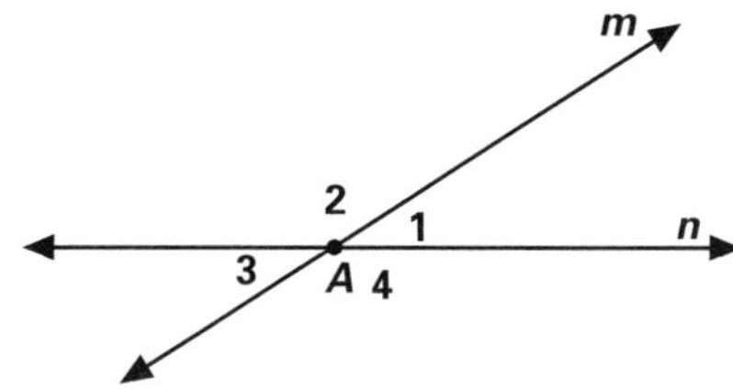

Since $m\angle 1 = x^\circ$ and $m\angle 1 + m\angle 2 = 180^\circ$, $m\angle 2 = 180^\circ - x^\circ$.

Since $m\angle 2 = 180^\circ - x^\circ$ and $m\angle 3 + m\angle 2 = 180^\circ$, $m\angle 3 = 180^\circ - (180^\circ - x^\circ)$.

Since $m\angle 3 = 180^\circ - (180^\circ - x^\circ)$, then $m\angle 3 = x^\circ$.

a. Is this a valid proof? On what mathematical relationships is it based?

b. Should this proof be classified as geometric reasoning, algebraic reasoning, or something else? Explain your rationale.

c. State the theorem proved here.

294 UNIT 4 • SHAPES AND GEOMETRIC REASONING

4. **a.** Responses may vary. For B to be between A and C, A, B, and C must be collinear and $AB + BC$ must equal AC. Another way is to impose a coordinate system on the line, then B is between A and C whenever B's coordinates satisfy the equation for the line AC.

   b. Responses may vary. The sum of $m\angle APB$ and $m\angle BPC$ must be equal to $m\angle APC$. Alternatively, you could impose a coordinate system with P at the origin. Then ray PB is between rays PA and PC if point B is in the smaller region bounded by ray PA and ray PC (if there is one).

5. This task provides a general proof that vertical angles have equal measures.

   a. The proof is valid. It uses the fact that an angle is the sum of its parts and the Linear Pair Property. Number properties are also used, namely, the definition of subtraction and substitution.

   b. It is difficult to classify this proof. The proof uses algebraic reasoning, but that reasoning is founded in the geometric setting.

   c. If two lines intersect at a point, then vertical angles are equal in measure.

Extending

NOTE: Students should include the definition of an exterior angle and the results from this task in their Math Toolkits.

1. **a.** The exterior angles at vertex C are vertical angles and equal in measure.
   b. Angles ACD and ACB form a linear pair and thus are supplementary.
   c. $m\angle A + m\angle B + m\angle ACB = 180°$ and $m\angle ACB + m\angle ACD = 180°$, so $m\angle A + m\angle B + m\angle ACB = m\angle ACB + m\angle ACD$. Thus, $m\angle A + m\angle B = m\angle ACD$.
   d. $m\angle 1 + m\angle 2 + m\angle 3 = 360°$
   e. The sum of the measures of the exterior angles of any triangle, one exterior angle at each vertex, is 360°. Using the diagram in Part d we have the following:
   $$m\angle 1 = m\angle BAC + m\angle ABC$$
   $$m\angle 2 = m\angle BAC + m\angle ACB$$
   $$m\angle 3 = m\angle ABC + m\angle ACB$$
   Thus, $m\angle 1 + m\angle 2 + m\angle 3 = 2(m\angle BAC + m\angle ABC + m\angle ACB)$
   $= 2 \times 180° = 360°$
2. **a.**
   - The pentagon can be dissected into 3 nonoverlapping triangles. Thus, the sum of the measures of the angles is $3 \times 180° = 540°$.
   - The sum of the measures of its exterior angles, one at each vertex, is 360°. Each exterior angle is the supplement of one of the interior angles of the pentagon. Since there are 5 such supplementary pairs, their sum is $5 \times 180°$. Subtracting the sum of the interior angles, we find that the sum of the exterior angles is therefore $(5 \times 180°) - (3 \times 180°)$ or 360°.

   b. A convex n-gon can be divided into $n - 2$ nonoverlapping triangles. Since the sum of the measures of each triangle is 180°, the sum of the measures of the interior angles of the convex n-gon is $(n - 2)(180°)$.
   c. The sum of the measures of the exterior angles of a convex n-gon, one angle at each vertex, is $n(180°) - (n - 2)(180°)$ or 360°.
3. **a.** If two lines are perpendicular to the same line at distinct points, then the lines are parallel to each other.
   b. *Proof:* If $\overleftrightarrow{AC} \perp \overleftrightarrow{AB}$ and $\overleftrightarrow{DB} \perp \overleftrightarrow{AB}$, then $m\angle CAB + m\angle DBA = 90° + 90° = 180°$. Thus, $\overleftrightarrow{AC} \parallel \overleftrightarrow{BD}$ (interior angles on the same side of the transversal are supplementary).

Extending

1. An **exterior angle** of a triangle is formed when one side is extended. The sides of the angle are the extension and a side of the triangle.

a. Draw $\triangle ABC$ on your paper. Extend sides BC and AC to show the two exterior angles at vertex C. How are these angles related?

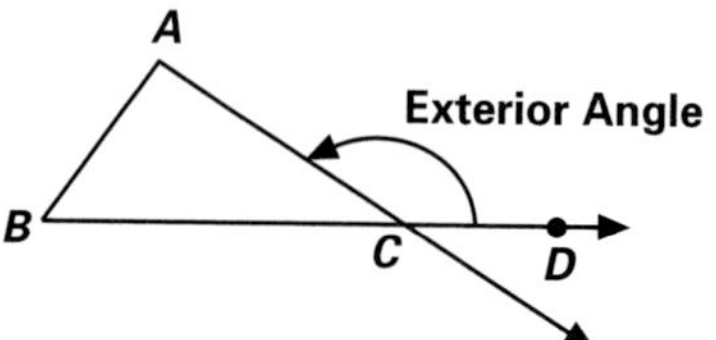

b. How is exterior angle ACD related to $\angle ACB$?

c. How is exterior angle ACD related to $\angle B$ and $\angle A$?

d. Now consider the diagram at the right showing exterior angles 1, 2, and 3 of $\triangle ABC$. What is the sum of their measures?

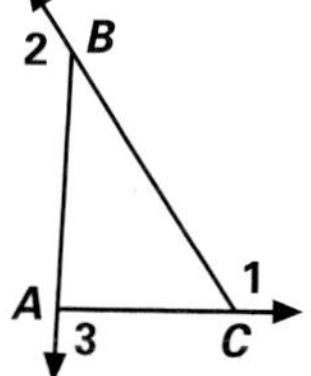

e. State and prove a conjecture about the sum of the measures of the exterior angles of any triangle, one exterior angle at each vertex.

2. Exterior angles of any polygon can be formed as was done for the triangles in Extending Task 1.

a. Draw a pentagon. Without using a protractor, do the following:

- Find the sum of the measures of its angles.
- Find the sum of the measures of its exterior angles, one angle at each vertex.

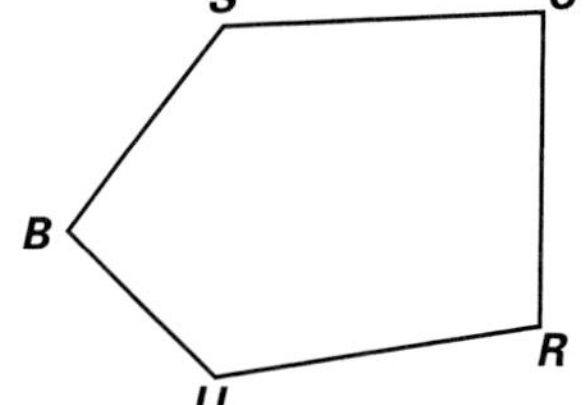

b. In your previous coursework, you may have discovered that the sum of the measures of the interior angles of a convex n-gon is $(n - 2)180°$. Explain why this formula makes sense.

c. Experiment or use deductive reasoning to find a formula for the sum of the measures of the exterior angles of a convex n-gon, one angle at each vertex.

3. Draw a line l and locate two points on it. At each point, draw a line perpendicular to line l.

a. Make a conjecture about the relation between the two lines perpendicular to line l. Write it in if-then form.

b. Prove your conjecture or produce a counterexample.

LESSON 1 • REASONED ARGUMENTS 295

4. Use a compass or computer drawing software to draw a circle with center C and radius 2 inches. Choose a length, n, between 0.5 and 3.5 inches.

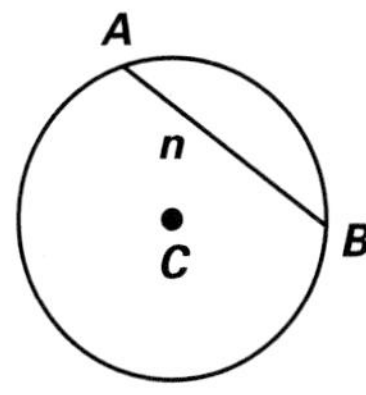

a. Draw four different chords of length n in your circle. (A **chord** is a segment with its endpoints on a circle. See chord AB at the right.)

b. Carefully, draw and measure the angle formed by joining the endpoints of your chords to the center C. (Such angles are called **central angles** because the vertex is the center of the circle.)

c. What do you observe about the angle measures found in Part b? Do you think this will be true for each central angle formed by a chord of length n?

d. What happens to the central angle as the length n increases? As the length n decreases?

5. Use a compass or computer drawing software to draw a circle with center C. Then draw a chord AB in the circle.

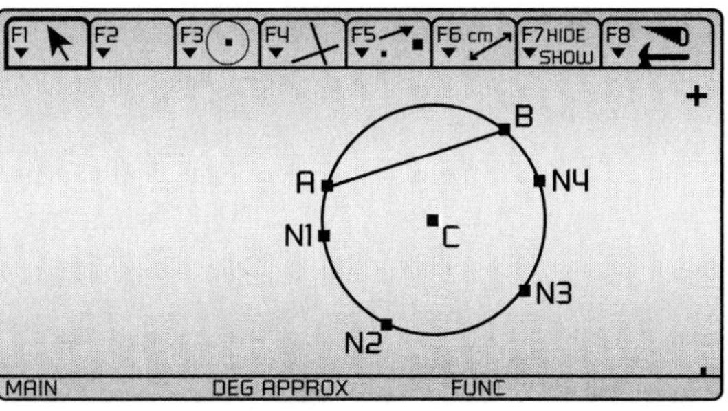

a. Choose four points, N_i ($i = 1, 2, 3, 4$) on the circle and on the same side of the line containing chord AB. Carefully draw and measure the angles, $\angle AN_iB$. (These angles are called *inscribed angles.*)

b. What do you observe about the measures of these angles?

c. Is there any relationship between the measure of an inscribed angle, $\angle AN_iB$, and the central angle, $\angle ACB$? If so, describe it.

d. Suppose the four points, N_i, were all on the other side of the line containing chord AB. How are the angles, $\angle AN_iB$, related to each other? To the angles you drew in Part a?

Unit 4

296 UNIT 4 • SHAPES AND GEOMETRIC REASONING

MORE *continued*

4. **a.** See student drawings.
   b. See student drawings. There should be four angles, one for each chord.
   c. The measures of all four angles should be the same. Yes, all central angles formed by a chord of length n will have this same measure.
   d. As n increases, the measure of the central angle increases until $n = 4$ (the diameter) and the angle measures 180°. As n decreases, the size of the central angle also decreases.
5. **a.** See student drawings.
   b. The angles all have equal measure.
   c. The measure of the inscribed angle is half the measure of the central angle.
   d. The angles $\angle AN_iB$ all have the same measure. These angles are supplementary to the angles drawn in Part a.

See Assessment Resources, pages 158–163.

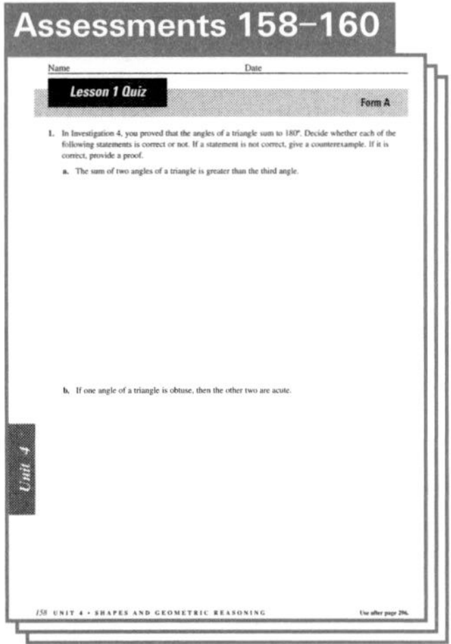
Assessments 158–160

Name Date

Lesson 1 Quiz — Form A

1. In Investigation 4, you proved that the angles of a triangle sum to 180°. Decide whether each of the following statements is correct or not. If a statement is not correct, give a counterexample. If it is correct, provide a proof.
   a. The sum of two angles of a triangle is greater than the third angle.
   b. If one angle of a triangle is obtuse, then the other two are acute.

Unit 4

158 UNIT 4 • SHAPES AND GEOMETRIC REASONING — Use after page 296.

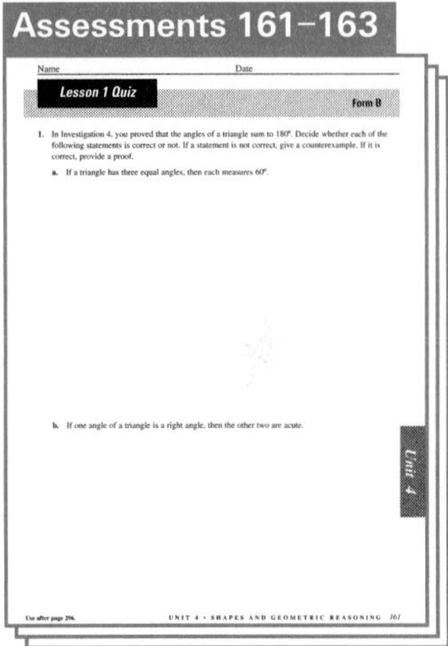
Assessments 161–163

Name Date

Lesson 1 Quiz — Form B

1. In Investigation 4, you proved that the angles of a triangle sum to 180°. Decide whether each of the following statements is correct or not. If a statement is not correct, give a counterexample. If it is correct, provide a proof.
   a. If a triangle has three equal angles, then each measures 60°.
   b. If one angle of a triangle is a right angle, then the other two are acute.

Unit 4

Use after page 296. — UNIT 4 • SHAPES AND GEOMETRIC REASONING 161

Unit 4

Master 96

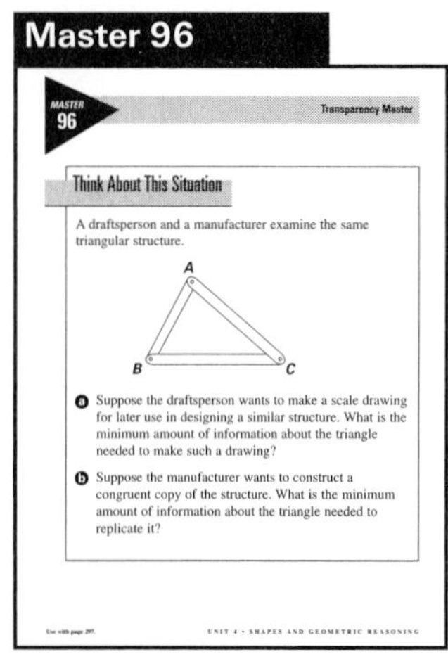
MASTER 96

Transparency Master

Think About This Situation

A draftsperson and a manufacturer examine the same triangular structure.

(a) Suppose the draftsperson wants to make a scale drawing for later use in designing a similar structure. What is the minimum amount of information about the triangle needed to make such a drawing?

(b) Suppose the manufacturer wants to construct a congruent copy of the structure. What is the minimum amount of information about the triangle needed to replicate it?

Use with page 297.   UNIT 4 • SHAPES AND GEOMETRIC REASONING

Lesson 2 *Reasoning about Similar and Congruent Triangles*

LESSON OVERVIEW Like Lesson 1, Lesson 2 is designed to help students develop mathematical power simultaneously in two areas, reasoning skills and geometric content. Therefore, formal reasoning or proof continues to be developed and emphasized using the same process employed in the first lesson: explore, conjecture, and then verify. The context is now triangular shapes and the search for congruence and similarity relations among triangle pairs.

Emphasis is placed on the conditions for triangles that ensure they are similar or congruent. First, Investigation 1 guides students through the development of the theorems used to prove two triangles are similar. Conditions necessary to guarantee two triangles are congruent are explored and identified in Investigation 2, and in Investigation 3, students are asked to prove increasingly sophisticated conjectures that require a working knowledge of the full set of theorems they have proven in this unit.

Two characteristics of this lesson should be noted here. The Laws of Cosines and Sines are used to deduce the triangle similarity theorems. The tactic is to demonstrate that a set of conditions on a triangle, such as knowing the lengths of two sides and the measure of the included angle, uniquely determines the triangle. Once this has been demonstrated, then two sets of conditions uniquely determine each triangle and thus their similarity. The key concept is the use of the solvability of the Law of Cosines or Sines to uniquely determine an angle or a side.

A second characteristic of this development is that similarity is done first and congruence is considered a special case of similarity: congruence is similarity with a scale factor of 1. This approach allows the congruence theorems to be deduced easily.

Lesson Objectives

- To know and be able to use the three theorems used to prove triangles are similar (SSS, SAS, AA)
- To know and be able to use the four theorems used to prove triangles are congruent (SSS, SAS, AAS, ASA)
- To be able to create a valid argument for a given conjecture using previously proven theorems

Unit 4

See additional Teaching Notes on page T344G.

Lesson 2

Reasoning about Similar and Congruent Triangles

A triangle is the only rigid polygon. Since it is rigid, it is fundamental to the design of many structures, both large and small. Some bridges and large construction cranes, as well as the supports for roofs, use triangles to maintain rigidity. When a roof sags, it is often the result of a breakdown in the material of the supporting triangles.

Architects and draftspeople often need to make scale drawings of triangles and shapes based on triangles that are *similar* to the real things that they are designing. Manufacturers of the components of shapes based on triangles need to know the measurements that must be made to ensure that triangular components are *congruent*. Even so, there will be small variations in the parts, and these variations must be monitored by quality control procedures.

Think About This Situation

A draftsperson and a manufacturer examine the same triangular structure.

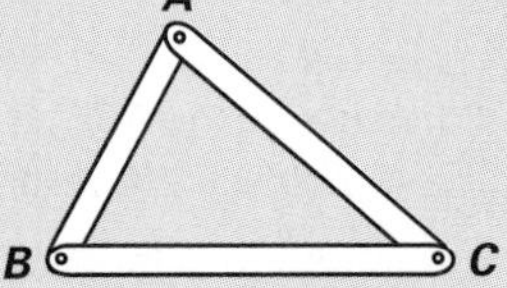

a Suppose the draftsperson wants to make a scale drawing for later use in designing a similar structure. What is the minimum amount of information about the triangle needed to make such a drawing?

b Suppose the manufacturer wants to construct a congruent copy of the structure. What is the minimum amount of information about the triangle needed to replicate it?

Unit 4

INVESTIGATION 1 When Are Two Triangles Similar?

If two plane shapes are **similar**, such as the two pentagons shown below, then corresponding angles have the same measure and the lengths of corresponding sides are constant multiples of each other. The constant multiplier is called the *scale factor*.

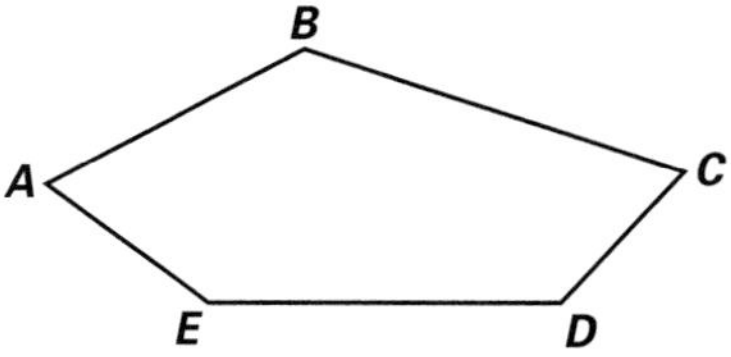

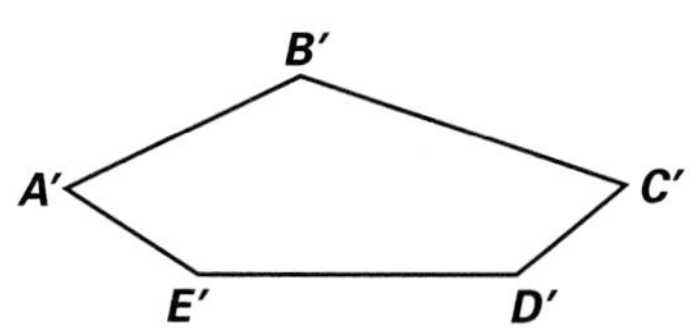

In the diagram above, $ABCDE \sim A'B'C'D'E'$. The symbol ~ means "is similar to." It follows that $m\angle A = m\angle A'$, $m\angle B = m\angle B'$, and so on. If the scale factor is k, you can also conclude that $B'C' = k \cdot BC$, $A'E' = k \cdot AE$, $DC = \frac{1}{k} \cdot D'C'$, and so on.

1. Suppose $\triangle ABC \sim \triangle PQR$ and the scale factor relating $\triangle ABC$ to $\triangle PQR$ is 5. In your group, write as many mathematical statements as you can about pairs of corresponding angles and about pairs of corresponding sides.

Knowing that two triangles are similar allows you to conclude that the three pairs of corresponding angles are congruent and the three pairs of corresponding sides are related by the same scale factor. Conversely, if you know that the three pairs of corresponding angles are congruent and the three pairs of corresponding sides are related by the same scale factor, you can conclude that the triangles are similar. In this investigation, you will explore whether fewer than all six conditions will ensure that two triangles are similar. In conducting this investigation, you will use the Law of Sines and the Law of Cosines. The Law of Sines was derived in Unit 1, "Multiple-Variable Models." The Law of Cosines was proved in Unit 3, "Symbol Sense and Algebraic Reasoning." These two laws are reproduced below.

Law of Sines

In any triangle ABC, if a, b, and c are the lengths of the sides opposite $\angle A$, $\angle B$, and $\angle C$ respectively, then:

$$\frac{a}{\sin A} = \frac{b}{\sin B} = \frac{c}{\sin C}$$

Law of Cosines

In any triangle ABC, if a, b, and c are the lengths of the sides opposite $\angle A$, $\angle B$, and $\angle C$ respectively, then:

$$a^2 = b^2 + c^2 - 2bc \cos A$$
$$b^2 = a^2 + c^2 - 2ac \cos B$$
$$c^2 = a^2 + b^2 - 2ab \cos C$$

Unit 4

298 UNIT 4 • SHAPES AND GEOMETRIC REASONING

EXPLORE small-group investigation

INVESTIGATION 1 When Are Two Triangles Similar?

In Lesson 2 of Unit 1, "Multiple-Variable Models," students learned how useful the Laws of Sines and Cosines are in solving practical problems that involve finding missing parts of triangles. In this investigation, students will discover further evidence of the power and importance of these laws as they use them to verify each of the similarity and congruence theorems for triangles. Investigation 1 opens by asking students to reconsider the "Think About This Situation" question about similarity, this time using the Law of Cosines to help determine how much information about the pairs of angles and sides is needed to conclude that the triangles are similar. Most of the reasoning in this lesson is algebraic, and the emphasis will be on learning the three similarity theorems (SAS, SSS, and AA). Later, in the third investigation, the emphasis shifts back to geometric reasoning once students have developed the repertoire of relevant theorems.

This is a long and fairly complex investigation, involving a lot of algebraic work. It is reasonable to ask all student groups to work on Activities 1 and 2 and then to share and summarize their results. This discussion provides the opportunity to make sure students see the need for three characteristics of a triangle and how to solve for a side or for the cosine of an angle.

Be sure to point out to students that the definition of *similar* is given before the first activity. They may want to write this definition in their Math Toolkits, if it is not already there. Likewise, after student groups have attempted Activities 1 and 2, everyone can record the Law of Cosines in its original format (you might ask if it is necessary to note all three variations), in the format $a = \sqrt{(\ldots\ldots\ldots\ldots)}$, and perhaps $\cos B = \frac{b^2 - a^2 - c^2}{-2ac}$, if this format was discussed in the large-group sharing of Activity 2.

1. Since the triangles are similar, corresponding angles have the same measure and corresponding sides are proportional. The mathematical statements are as follows:

   $m\angle A = m\angle P$, $m\angle B = m\angle Q$, $m\angle C = m\angle R$

   $5 \cdot AB = PQ$, $5 \cdot BC = QR$, $5 \cdot AC = PR$

Unit 4

2. a. There are four variables in each form of the Law of Cosines. The lowercase letters represent the lengths of the sides of a triangle, and the uppercase letter represents the angle across from the side with the same letter.
   b. Knowing the value of only b, you cannot determine the value of a because the Law of Cosines requires values for three of the four variables before you can use it to solve for the fourth. Using the same reasoning, you will not be able to solve for $m\angle A$ or c either.
   c. No, again you cannot solve for any variables knowing values for only two of the other variables.
   d. Yes, knowing a, b, and $m\angle A$, you can use the Law of Cosines to determine the value of c. You will have only one unknown value, so you can solve for it. Similarly, knowing a, b, and c, you can use the Law of Cosines to find $m\angle A$.
   e. Using $a^2 = b^2 + c^2 - 2bc \cos A$, solve for a: $a = \sqrt{b^2 + c^2 - 2bc \cos A}$.
   f. $b^2 = a^2 + c^2 - 2ac \cos B$ can be used to solve for $\cos B$.
   $c^2 = a^2 + b^2 - 2ab \cos C$ can be used to solve for $\cos C$.

Activities 3 and 4 help students develop the approach used to deduce the similarity theorems. It would be helpful if you discuss both the reasoning and the conclusions as a class after groups have completed Activities 3 and 4.

3. **It might help your students if you have 2 straws, cut to lengths 15 cm and 11 cm, and a pipecleaner to connect the straws into an angle of approximately 43°. After students have reached their own conclusions about the possibility of finding the missing sides and angles and about the uniqueness of the results, probably by reasoning solely with the symbols, it will confirm their reasoning if someone demonstrates that the shape made by the two known sides and included angle is rigid, defining what the third side and other angles must be.**
   a. Most people would find a first using $a = \sqrt{b^2 + c^2 - 2bc \cos A}$ because this equation already has a isolated on the left side of the equation.
   $a = \sqrt{15^2 + 11^2 - 2 \times 15 \times 11 \times \cos 43°} \approx \sqrt{104.65} \approx 10.23$
   b. Next, you could find the measure of either of the two remaining angles. (The Law of Sines also could be used here, but you must keep in mind that there are two angles less than 180° possible when using sines.)
   $\cos B = \dfrac{a^2 + c^2 - b^2}{2ac} \Rightarrow \cos B = 0.0029 \Rightarrow m\angle B \approx 89.83°$
   $\cos C = \dfrac{a^2 + b^2 - c^2}{2ab} \Rightarrow \cos C = 0.6798 \Rightarrow m\angle C \approx 47.17°$
   c. It is not possible to find more than one value for a, $m\angle B$, or $m\angle C$. If students consider the illustration, they may visualize that by fixing the lengths of two sides and the included angle, the length of the third side is fixed, as are the other two angles. Students may also consider the problem using the Law of Cosines; here too they will realize that if the Law of Cosines is used to find a, it will give you only one possible value for a. Then using the measures of the three sides and the appropriate form of the Law of Cosines, you will get unique values for the other angles.
   d. Yes, given two sides, b and c, and the included angle A, the remaining values can be found using the Law of Cosines. Each of a, $m\angle B$, and $m\angle C$ will have only one value.
   e. In a triangle, if the lengths of two sides and the measure of the angle included between those sides are known, then the measures of the remaining angles and the length of the third side can be found. (In Activity 4 Part a, we will begin to say these measures are "uniquely determined.")

2. Begin by reexamining the Law of Cosines to see what it tells you about the characteristics of a particular triangle *ABC*.

a. The first form of the Law of Cosines says $a^2 = b^2 + c^2 - 2bc\cos A$. How many variables are in this equation? What are they? What do they represent?

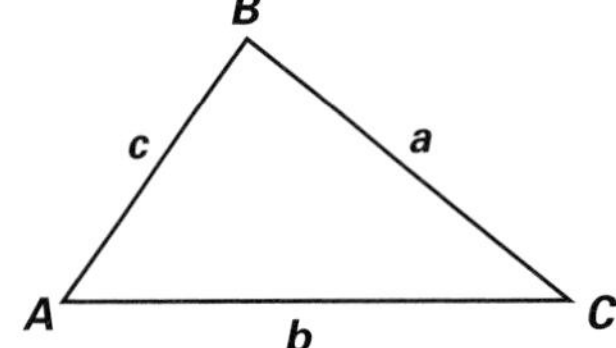

b. If you know only that *b* is 5, can you determine the value of *a*? Explain.

- Can you determine m∠*A*? Explain.
- Can *c* be determined? Why or why not?

c. If you know the values of *a* and *c*, can you determine either *b* or m∠*A*? Both *b* and m∠*A*? Explain your reasoning.

d. If you know the values of *a*, *b*, and m∠*A*, can you determine the value of *c*? Explain. If you know values for *a*, *b*, and *c*, can you find m∠*A*? Why or why not?

e. Suppose you know *b*, *c*, and m∠*A*. Write an equation ($a = \ldots$) that expresses the relation between *a* and these variables.

f. What equation can you solve to find $\cos B$? To find $\cos C$?

3. Suppose in △*ABC*, m∠*A*, *b*, and *c* are given as follows:
m∠*A* = 43°, *b* = 15 cm, and *c* = 11 cm.

a. In finding values for *a*, m∠*B*, and m∠*C*, which measure would you find first? Why? Find the value of that measure.

b. Which measure would you find second? Why? Determine the remaining two values.

c. Is it possible to find more than one value for *a*, m∠*B*, or m∠*C*? Explain your reasoning.

d. In general, if you know m∠*A*, *b*, and *c*, can values for *a*, m∠*B*, and m∠*C* be found? Could any of *a*, m∠*B*, or m∠*C* have two or more values when m∠*A*, *b*, and *c* are given? Explain.

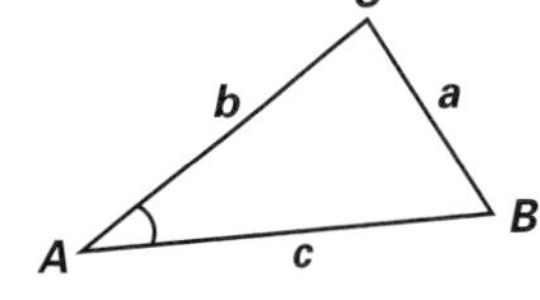

e. Summarize your work in Parts a through d in an if-then statement that begins as follows:

In a triangle, if the lengths of two sides and the measure of the angle included between those sides are known, then … .

Unit 4

LESSON 2 • REASONING ABOUT SIMILAR AND CONGRUENT TRIANGLES 299

4. Examine ΔABC and ΔXYZ shown below. In both cases, you have information given about two sides and an included angle. (In ΔXYZ, k is a constant.)

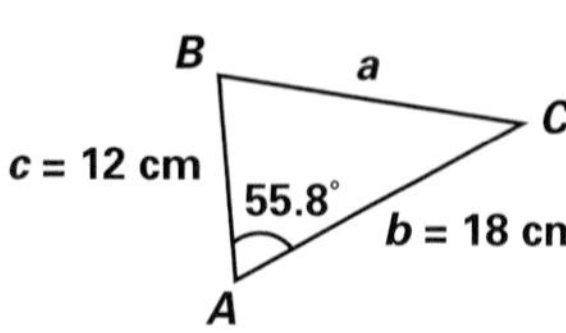

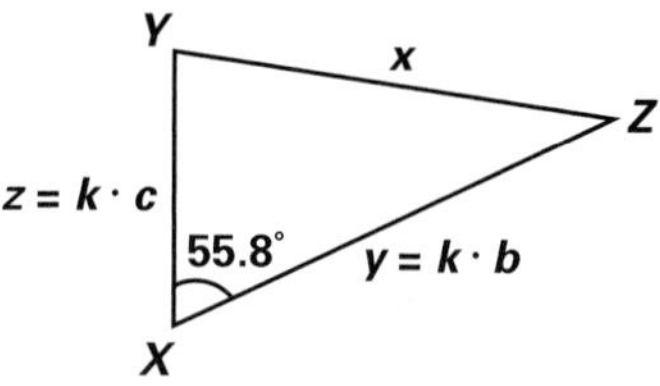

a. In ΔABC, $m\angle A = 55.8°$, $b = 18$ cm, and $c = 12$ cm. Are a, $m\angle B$, and $m\angle C$ *uniquely determined*? That is, is there exactly one value possible for each? Find a.

b. In ΔXYZ, $m\angle X = m\angle A = 55.8°$, $z = k \cdot c = 12k$ cm, and $y = k \cdot b = 18k$ cm, where k is a constant. Explain why x, $m\angle Y$, and $m\angle Z$ are uniquely determined.

c. Use the Law of Cosines to find x. Are x and a related in the same way as y and b or as z and c? Explain your reasoning.

d. Find $m\angle B$ and $m\angle Y$. How are they related?

e. Find $m\angle C$ and $m\angle Z$. How are they related?

f. Considering all the information in Parts a through e, what can you conclude about ΔABC and ΔXYZ?

g. Suppose you know that in ΔABC and ΔXYZ, $m\angle C = m\angle Z$, $x = ka$, and $y = kb$. Could you prove that $\Delta ABC \sim \Delta XYZ$? If so, explain how. If not, explain why not.

h. Summarize your work in Parts a through g by completing the following statement:

If an angle of one triangle has the same measure as an angle of a second triangle, and if the lengths of the corresponding sides including these angles are related by a scale factor k, then … .

Compare your statement to those of other groups. Resolve any differences.

Your conclusion in Part h of Activity 4 gives at least a partial answer to the question of finding minimal conditions that will ensure two triangles are similar. In the next several activities, you will explore other sets of minimal conditions.

5. Refer to ΔABC shown at the right.

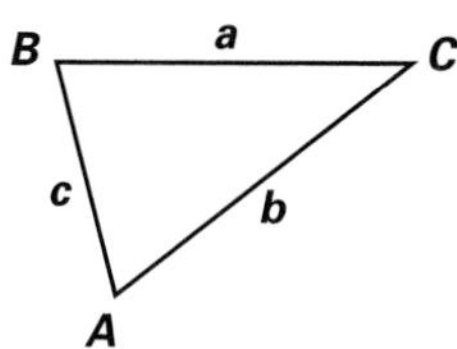

a. Suppose $a = 10$ cm, $b = 18$ cm, and $c = 12$ cm. Is it possible to calculate the measures of angles A, B, and C? If so, do so. If not, explain why not.

Unit 4

300 UNIT 4 • SHAPES AND GEOMETRIC REASONING

4. a. Yes, a, $m\angle B$, and $m\angle C$ are uniquely determined, because two sides and an included angle are known.

$a = \sqrt{18^2 + 12^2 - 2(18)(12)(\cos 55.8^\circ)} \approx \sqrt{225.18} \approx 15$ cm

b. x is uniquely determined because two sides and an included angle (y, z, and $\angle X$) are known. Similarly, $\angle Y$ and $\angle Z$ are determined when x, y, and z are known.

NOTE: Be sure that students are not *assuming* that the triangles are similar for Parts c–e.

---

c. $x^2 = y^2 + z^2 - 2yz \cos X$

$= (18k)^2 + (12k)^2 - 2(18k)(12k)(\cos 55.8^\circ)$

$\approx 225.18k^2$

$x^2 \approx 225.18k^2$

$x \approx 15k$

Since $a \approx 15$, $x = a \cdot k$ and so x and a are related in the same way as y and b and as z and c are.

d. $\cos B = \dfrac{a^2 + c^2 - b^2}{2ac} = \dfrac{15^2 + 12^2 - 18^2}{2(15)(12)} = 0.125$

$m\angle B \approx 82.8^\circ$

$\cos Y = \dfrac{x^2 + z^2 - y^2}{2xz} = \dfrac{(15k)^2 + (12k)^2 - (18k)^2}{2(15k)(12k)} = \dfrac{45k^2}{360k^2} = 0.125$

$m\angle Y \approx 82.8^\circ$

$m\angle B = m\angle Y$

e. Both $m\angle C$ and $m\angle Z$ could be found using the Law of Cosines or the fact that the sum of the angle measures in a triangle is 180°.

$m\angle C = 180^\circ - m\angle A - m\angle B = 180^\circ - 55.8^\circ - 82.8^\circ = 41.4^\circ$

$m\angle Z = 180^\circ - m\angle X - m\angle Y = 180^\circ - 55.8^\circ - 82.8^\circ = 41.4^\circ$

$m\angle C = m\angle Z$

f. $\triangle ABC \sim \triangle XYZ$

g. Yes, you could prove that the two triangles are similar. It would be done by repeating Parts a–e of this activity using the appropriate angle measures and side lengths. Students should understand that the steps given in those parts could be completed for any values of $m\angle A$ and lengths of sides b and c. (Some students may note that this might be considered an inductive argument rather than a general proof. Many students could follow the example to create a more complete deductive argument, but it is time-consuming and not particularly instructive. However, it could be an extra credit task for interested students to complete outside of class.)

h. If the lengths of two sides of one triangle are related by a scale factor k to two sides of a second triangle and the included angles have equal measure, then the two triangles are similar.

Activities 5–7 should be assigned for group investigation, and a check of the statements of the generalizations of Activity 5 Part b and Activity 6 should be done before groups continue to Activity 8.

5. a. Yes, the measures of angles A, B, and C can be computed.

$\cos A = \dfrac{b^2 + c^2 - a^2}{2bc} \Rightarrow \cos A \approx 0.852 \Rightarrow m\angle A \approx 31.6^\circ$

$\cos B = \dfrac{a^2 + c^2 - b^2}{2ac} \Rightarrow \cos B \approx -0.333 \Rightarrow m\angle B \approx 109.5^\circ$

$\cos C = \dfrac{a^2 + b^2 - c^2}{2ab} \Rightarrow \cos C \approx 0.778 \Rightarrow m\angle C \approx 38.9^\circ$

5. **b.** Yes, given the measures of three sides of a triangle, it is possible to determine the measures of the three angles of the triangle. There is only one possible measure for each angle. Students may note that once the lengths of the sides are fixed, the triangle becomes rigid and the angles cannot be altered. Hence, they are uniquely determined. Students may also note that the Law of Cosines will allow them to calculate these angles given three sides and that they will get only one answer for each angle.

6. **Your students may have trouble with the logic needed for this activity, or they may get lost in the algebraic manipulations. If so you may find it helpful to direct them to write formulas for cos *A* and for cos *X*. You may have to help them simplify the fraction they get for cos *X*. Then you can ask, "If cos *X* and cos *A* have the same value, will the angles be the same size?"**

   a. $\cos A = \dfrac{b^2 + c^2 - a^2}{2bc}$

   $\cos X = \dfrac{y^2 + z^2 - x^2}{2yz} = \dfrac{(bk)^2 + (ck)^2 - (ak)^2}{2(bk)(ck)} = \dfrac{k^2(b^2 + c^2 - a^2)}{k^2(2bc)} = \dfrac{b^2 + c^2 - a^2}{2bc}$

   Since cos A and cos X are equal to the same expression (and $m\angle A < 180°$ and $m\angle X < 180°$), it follows that $m\angle A = m\angle X$.

   b. $\cos B = \dfrac{a^2 + c^2 - b^2}{2ac}$

   $\cos Y = \dfrac{x^2 + z^2 - y^2}{2xz} = \dfrac{(ak)^2 + (ck)^2 - (bk)^2}{2(ak)(ck)} = \dfrac{k^2(a^2 + c^2 - b^2)}{k^2(2ac)} = \dfrac{a^2 + c^2 - b^2}{2ac}$

   Since cos B and cos Y are equal to the same expression (and $m\angle B < 180°$ and $m\angle Y < 180°$), it follows that $m\angle B = m\angle Y$.

   c. Students may use the same method used in Parts a and b, or they may note that for the given triangles, since they have shown that two pairs of corresponding angles are congruent, the third pairs must also be congruent using the following proof.

   Since the sum of the angles of all triangles is 180°, we can say that

   $$m\angle A + m\angle B + m\angle C = m\angle X + m\angle Y + m\angle Z.$$

   Subtracting equal angle pairs ($m\angle A = m\angle X$ and $m\angle B = m\angle Y$) from both sides, we get $m\angle C = m\angle Z$.

7. **a.** The name of the SAS Similarity Theorem should remind students that if they know that two triangles have one pair of equal angles and two pairs of corresponding sides related by a scale factor k, with the angles included between the sides, then they can conclude that the triangles are similar.

   b. SSS Similarity Theorem: If the lengths of the three sides of one triangle are related by a scale factor k to the lengths of the three sides of another triangle, then the triangles are similar.

Just before students move to the following set of activities, briefly revisit the list generated during the "Think About This Situation" Part b, to see if there are any minimum information sets suggested by students but not yet verified. If needed, ask for additional conjectures that have not been considered. Raise the question: Could the Law of Sines help us to verify the remaining conjectures? Again ask students to work in small groups to complete Activities 8 and 9 and the Checkpoint.

8. **a.** The equation uses four variables; a and b are sides with opposite angles A and B, respectively.

See additional Teaching Notes on page T344H.

b. In general, suppose for any ΔABC you know a, b, and c. Can the measures of the three angles be determined? If so, can you find more than one possible measure for each of the angles? Explain your reasoning.

6. Suppose now you know that in ΔABC and ΔXYZ, $x = ka$, $y = kb$, and $z = kc$.

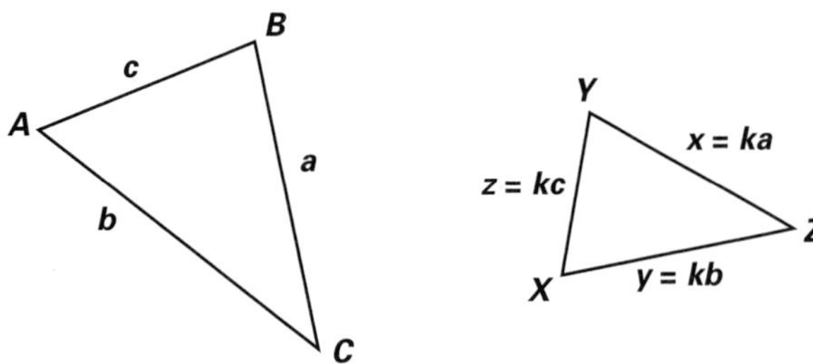

To prove $\Delta ABC \sim \Delta XYZ$, you need to deduce that corresponding angles have the same measure. Sharing the workload among your group, write deductive arguments for each of the following equalities.

a. $m\angle A = m\angle X$

b. $m\angle B = m\angle Y$

c. $m\angle C = m\angle Z$

7. The generalization you stated and proved in Activity 4 is called the **Side-Angle-Side Similarity Theorem**, or just SAS Similarity Theorem, for short.

a. How can you use the name of the theorem to help you remember your generalization?

b. The results of your work in Activity 6 establish a **Side-Side-Side Similarity Theorem**. Write this SSS Similarity Theorem in if-then form.

So far, you have used only the Law of Cosines to deduce conditions that ensure pairs of triangles are similar. In the next two activities, you will use the Law of Sines to explore other conditions that might ensure similarity of two triangles.

8. Begin by reexamining the first part of the Law of Sines for ΔABC: $\frac{a}{\sin A} = \frac{b}{\sin B}$.

a. How many variables are there in this equation? What does each represent?

b. Solve the equation above for a. For b. For $\sin A$. For $\sin B$.

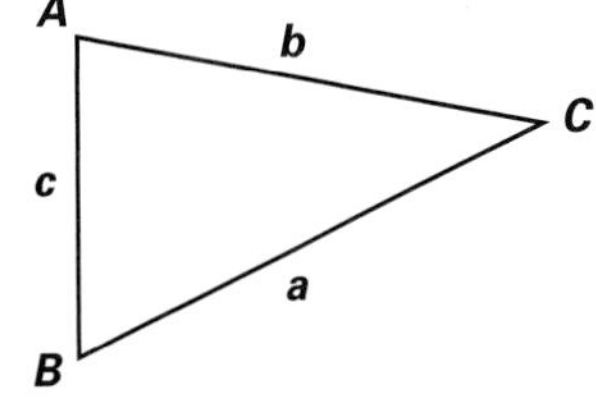

c. If $b = 5$, $m\angle A = 40°$, and $m\angle B = 58°$, what other measures can you deduce? Find the measures.

d. What information do you need to know in order to determine a? To determine b? To determine $\sin A$? To determine $m\angle B$?

e. If you know $m\angle A$, $m\angle B$, and a, can you determine $m\angle C$, b, and c? Explain how. Are their values unique? Why or why not?

Unit 4

LESSON 2 • REASONING ABOUT SIMILAR AND CONGRUENT TRIANGLES 301

f. Summarize your work in Parts a through e by completing the following statement:

In a triangle, if the measures of two angles and the length of a side opposite one of them are known, then … .

9. In Activities 4 and 6, you needed to know three corresponding measures of the pair of triangles involved to determine that the triangles were similar. In this activity, you will examine a situation in which only two corresponding measures of two triangles are known.

a. Suppose you are given ΔABC and ΔXYZ in which $m\angle X = m\angle A$ and $m\angle Y = m\angle B$. Do you think these triangles are similar? Why or why not?

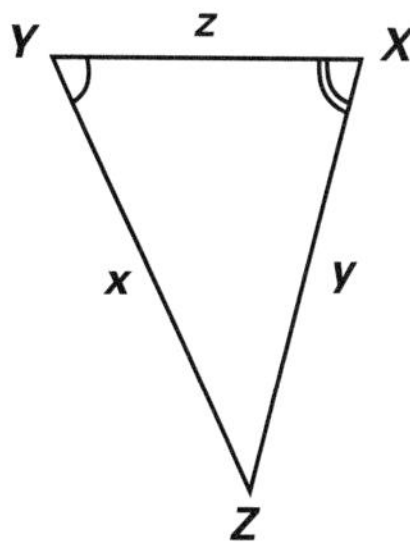

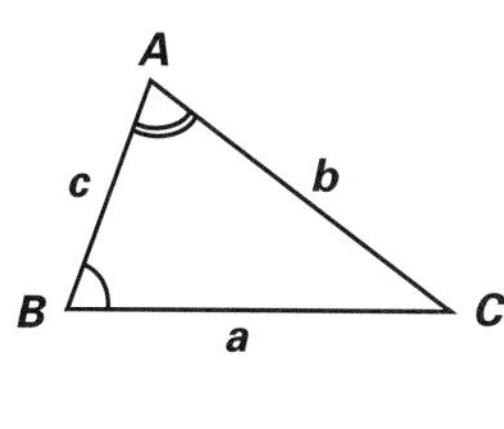

b. Examine the proposed proof by one group of students, shown below and on the next page. Discuss each part of their argument within your group; then answer the questions following the proof.

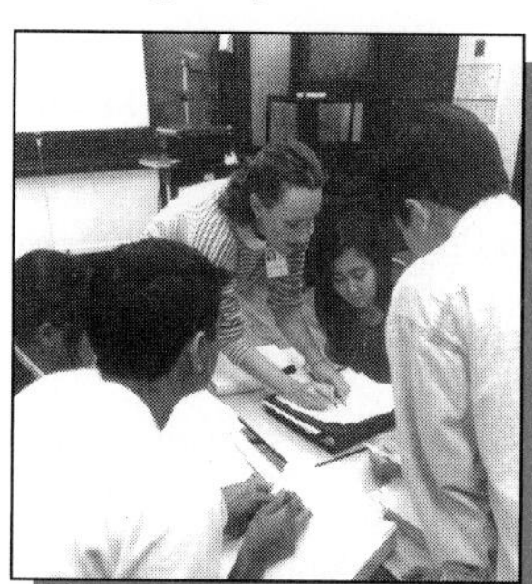

Proof:
We first looked at the ratio of the lengths of a pair of corresponding sides. Let $k = \frac{x}{a}$. Then $x = ka$.

For ΔABC, we know that $\frac{a}{\sin A} = \frac{b}{\sin B}$.
So, $b = \frac{a \sin B}{\sin A}$.

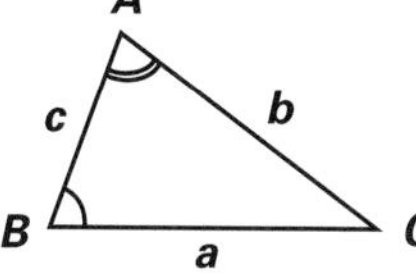

Unit 4

302 UNIT 4 • SHAPES AND GEOMETRIC REASONING

8. **f.** In a triangle, if the measures of two angles and the length of a side opposite one of them are known, then you can find the lengths of the other two sides and the measure of the third angle. (The triangle is uniquely determined.)

9. **a.** You may wish to encourage students to draw some triangles, measure the sides, and use inductive reasoning to conjecture that the triangles are similar.

Master 97

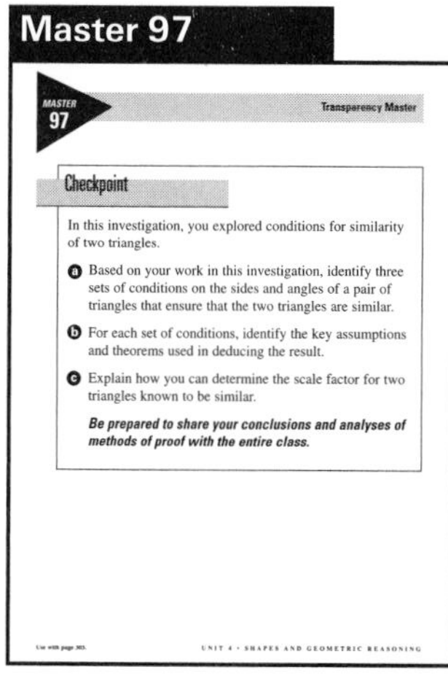
MASTER 97 Transparency Master

Checkpoint

In this investigation, you explored conditions for similarity of two triangles.

ⓐ Based on your work in this investigation, identify three sets of conditions on the sides and angles of a pair of triangles that ensure that the two triangles are similar.

ⓑ For each set of conditions, identify the key assumptions and theorems used in deducing the result.

ⓒ Explain how you can determine the scale factor for two triangles known to be similar.

Be prepared to share your conclusions and analyses of methods of proof with the entire class.

Use with page 303. UNIT 4 • SHAPES AND GEOMETRIC REASONING

EXPLORE *continued*

9. b.
- The proof is correct.
- $y = \dfrac{ka \sin Y}{\sin X}$ because $x = ka$.
- $y = \dfrac{ka \sin B}{\sin A}$ because $m\angle Y = m\angle B$ and $m\angle X = m\angle A$, so $\sin Y = \sin B$ and $\sin X = \sin A$.
- Since the sum of the angles of all triangles is 180°, we can say that $m\angle A + m\angle B + m\angle C = m\angle X + m\angle Y + m\angle Z$. Subtracting equal angle pairs ($m\angle A = m\angle X$ and $m\angle B = m\angle Y$) from both sides, we get $m\angle C = m\angle Z$.
- The argument should be convincing to most students.
- Students should note that because we proved the SAS Similarity Theorem in Activity 4, it can now be used in proofs.
- Students may notice the group could have repeated the first four steps of the proof using $\dfrac{b}{\sin B} = \dfrac{c}{\sin C}$ and $\dfrac{y}{\sin Y} = \dfrac{z}{\sin Z}$, concluding $z = kc$.

  Therefore, the triangles are similar using the SSS Similarity Theorem from Activity 6.

c. If two angles of one triangle are congruent to two angles of another triangle, then the two triangles are similar. This is called the AA (Angle-Angle) Similarity Theorem.

SHARE AND SUMMARIZE full-class discussion

Checkpoint

See Teaching Master 97.

Students can sometimes give the impression that they are fluent with these theorems, while really they are skimming over the meaning. As part of this Checkpoint, you may want to provide some examples that challenge students to think about what they are saying. Such challenges might be drawings on the board or overhead showing pairs of triangles that are not conveniently oriented, including reflections, and deliberately not drawn accurately, so that simple visual clues will not suffice. Providing insufficient or disorganized information, such as two sides and a nonincluded angle, only two sides, two angles in one triangle (say 36° and 49°) and a different pair in another triangle (36° and 95°), or a special case with a right triangle and only two sides given, will give students an opportunity to explain what they are looking for and will give you a chance to assess their true understanding.

ⓐ SAS: If the lengths of two sides of one triangle are related by a scale factor k to the lengths of two sides of a second triangle and the included angles have equal measures, then the triangles are similar.

SSS: If the lengths of three sides of one triangle are related by a scale factor k to the lengths of three sides of a second triangle, then the triangles are similar.

AA: If the measures of two angles of one triangle are equal to the measures of two angles of a second triangle, then the triangles are similar.

NOTE: See the Math Toolkit prompt on page T344H.

See additional Teaching Notes on page T344H.

Unit 4

Similarly for ΔXYZ, $\frac{x}{\sin X} = \frac{y}{\sin Y}$. So, $y = \frac{x \sin Y}{\sin X}$.

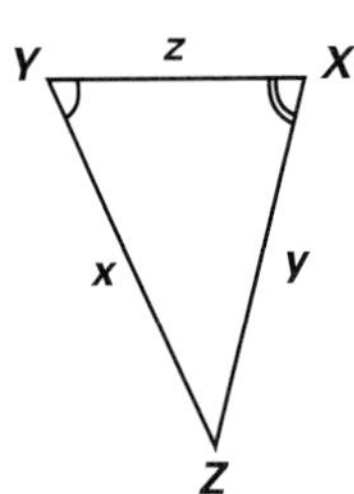

It follows that $y = \frac{ka \sin Y}{\sin X}$.

Since $m\angle Y = m\angle B$ and $m\angle X = m\angle A$, $y = ka \frac{\sin B}{\sin A}$.

Since $b = \frac{a \sin B}{\sin A}$, it follows that $y = kb$.

Since $m\angle X = m\angle A$ and $m\angle Y = m\angle B$, then $m\angle Z = m\angle C$.

We've shown $x = ka$, $y = kb$, and $m\angle Z = m\angle C$, so $\Delta ABC \sim \Delta XYZ$ by the SAS Similarity Theorem.

- Are there any errors? If so, can you correct them?
- Why can the students conclude that $y = \frac{ka \sin Y}{\sin X}$?
- Why can they conclude that $y = \frac{ka \sin B}{\sin A}$?
- Why can they conclude that $m\angle Z = m\angle C$?
- Does their argument convince you that the triangles are similar?
- Why can the SAS Similarity Theorem be used in the last step of the argument?
- Could the group of students have reasoned differently at the end? How?

c. Write an if-then statement of the theorem proved in this activity. What name would you give the theorem?

Checkpoint

In this investigation, you explored conditions for similarity of two triangles.

a Based on your work in this investigation, identify three sets of conditions on the sides and angles of a pair of triangles that ensure that the two triangles are similar.

b For each set of conditions, identify the key assumptions and theorems used in deducing the result.

c Explain how you can determine the scale factor for two triangles known to be similar.

Be prepared to share your conclusions and analyses of methods of proof with the entire class.

The three triangle similarity conditions—SAS, SSS, and AA—developed and used in this investigation are the only minimal conditions that, when satisfied, allow you to conclude that a pair of triangles are similar.

LESSON 2 • REASONING ABOUT SIMILAR AND CONGRUENT TRIANGLES 303

On Your Own

For each Part a through e, suppose a pair of triangular braces have the given characteristics. For the parts in which $\Delta ABC \sim \Delta PQR$, explain how you know that the triangles are similar and give the scale factor. For cases in which ΔABC is not similar to ΔPQR, give a reason for your conclusion.

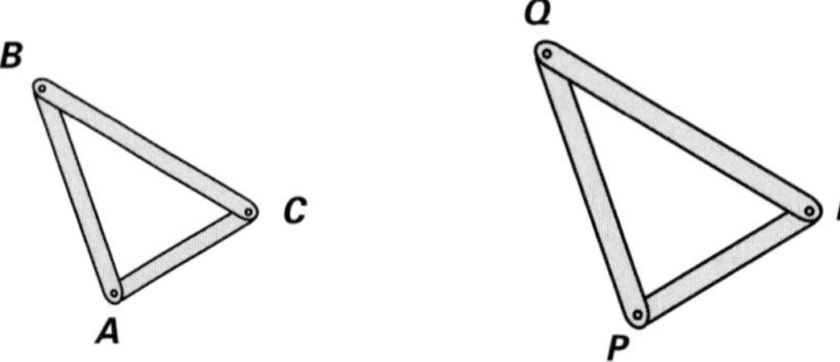

a. $m\angle A = 57°$, $m\angle B = 38°$, $m\angle P = 57°$, $m\angle R = 95°$

b. $AB = 8$, $BC = 12$, $m\angle B = 35°$, $PQ = 20$, $QR = 30$, $m\angle Q = 35°$

c. $AB = BC$, $m\angle B = m\angle Q$, $PQ = QR$

d. $AC = 4$, $BC = 16$, $BA = 18$, $PR = 10$, $QR = 40$, $PQ = 48$

e. $AB = 12$, $m\angle A = 63°$, $m\angle C = 83°$, $m\angle P = 63°$, $m\angle Q = 34°$, $PQ = 12$

f. Create your own set of side lengths for ΔABC and ΔPQR that satisfy SSS with a scale factor of 3.

INVESTIGATION 2 When Are Two Triangles Congruent?

Shown at the right is another view of the John Hancock Building in Chicago. In Investigation 4 of Lesson 1, page 282, you observed patterns and relationships involving parallel lines and transversals on the sides of the building. If you look closer, you will also note interesting patterns of *similar* and *congruent* triangles.

1. In your group, examine the patterns of triangles on the exterior of the Hancock Center.

Unit 4

304 UNIT 4 • SHAPES AND GEOMETRIC REASONING

APPLY individual task

On Your Own

a. Not similar: From m∠A and m∠B, you can conclude m∠C = 85°. From m∠P = 57° and m∠R = 95°, you know m∠Q = 28°. There are not two pairs of equal angles.

b. Similar: The ratios $\frac{PQ}{AB}$ and $\frac{QR}{BC}$ are both equal to $\frac{5}{2}$ and the included angles (B and Q) are congruent. By SAS, the triangles are similar. The scale factor is $\frac{5}{2}$.

c. Similar: The ratios of sides PQ to AB and QR to BC will be equal and the included angles (B and Q) are congruent. By SAS, the triangles are similar. The scale factor cannot be determined numerically, but symbolically it is $\frac{PQ}{AB}$.

d. Not similar: The ratios of all three pairs of sides are not equal.

e. Similar: From m∠A and m∠C, you can conclude m∠B = 34°; then use the AA Similarity Theorem since m∠A = m∠P and m∠B = m∠Q. Scale factor is 1 since $\frac{PQ}{AB} = 1$.

f. Answers will vary. However, the sum of any two sides should be greater than the third, and all ratios between corresponding sides should be 3 (or $\frac{1}{3}$ depending on which triangle is used for the numerator).

MORE

ASSIGNMENT *pp. 310–315*

Students can now begin Modeling Task 4 or Reflecting Task 1 or 4 from the MORE assignment following Investigation 2.

EXPLORE small-group investigation

INVESTIGATION 2 When Are Two Triangles Congruent?

In Investigation 2, students move on to congruence theorems for triangles. The first half should need very little setup; simply let students know that they will be working to verify the conditions needed to guarantee that two triangles are congruent using what they learned about similarity.

One major departure from familiar terrain comes when students find that the information encapsulated by the abbreviation SSA does *not* result in a pair of similar or congruent triangles. This is a significant moment, not so much because of the particular result as because the example returns to the point of the lesson: We need to be careful about the combinations of measurements that we can use, and uniqueness of the shape is important. You may want to return to the power of if-then statements in proofs. These statements are the building blocks of arguments because whenever the hypothesis of the statement is true, the conclusion can be relied upon to be true.

The second half of this investigation asks students to complete their first proofs using the new congruence and similarity theorems. Consider working through Activity 6 Part a either as a full-class activity or as an activity for pairs of students with a full-class follow-up. The whole class can then discuss marking the figures with the various critical aspects of a complete, succinct proof, such as the given information, the final conditional statement, and the careful statements of the theorems. Once students have a model proof or two to work from, they can continue with the rest of Activity 6 and the Checkpoint.

See additional Teaching Notes on page T344I.

EXPLORE *continued*

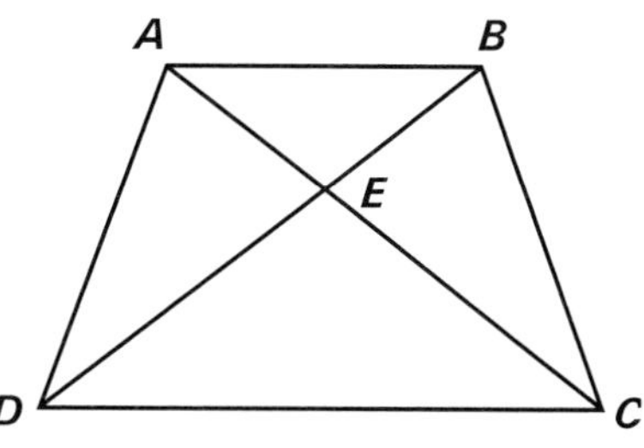

1. **a.** Responses will vary. Consider a section of the building that looks like the diagram at the right. $\triangle ABE \sim \triangle CDE$ by the AA Similarity Theorem. (Assuming $\overline{AB} \parallel \overline{DC}$, $\angle ABE$ and $\angle CDE$ are alternate interior angles, and therefore congruent, as are $\angle BAE$ and $\angle DCE$.)

   b. Referring to the diagram above, it would appear that $\triangle AED \cong \triangle BEC$ and $\triangle ABD \cong \triangle BAC$.

   Student explanations will vary and may not be well formulated. Students may find it helpful to list the assumptions they are making, such as the horizontal lines (floors) are parallel ($\overleftrightarrow{AB}$ is parallel to $\overleftrightarrow{DC}$) or that the almost vertical edges of the buildings are not parallel ($\overleftrightarrow{AD}$ is not parallel to $\overleftrightarrow{BC}$).

2. **a.** Using the ordered naming of the triangles to identify correspondences, we have the following:

   $\angle A \cong \angle P$, $\angle B \cong \angle Q$, $\angle C \cong \angle R$, $\overline{AB} \cong \overline{PQ}$, $\overline{BC} \cong \overline{QR}$, $\overline{AC} \cong \overline{PR}$

   b. $m\angle P = 73^\circ$ and $AB = 7$ cm

   c. Proof of first statement:

   If two triangles are congruent, then all the corresponding angles are congruent.

   If two or more angles of one triangle are congruent to the corresponding angles of a second triangle, then the triangles are similar.

   Therefore, if two triangles are congruent, then the triangles are similar.

   The second statement is not correct. Any counterexample will disprove this statement. You can also argue deductively as follows:

   If two triangles are similar, then the ratios of their corresponding sides are equal.

   If the ratio of corresponding sides for two similar triangles is anything other than 1, then the corresponding sides are not equal and the two triangles are not congruent.

   d. To correct the second statement, add the condition that the scale factor must be 1. If two triangles are similar and their scale factor is 1, then the triangles are congruent. (You may wish to have students think again about if-and-only-if statements for cases in which a statement and its converse are both true.)

a. Identify a pair of similar triangles in the photo and explain why you know they are similar.

b. Identify a pair of triangles that you think are congruent. Explain why you think they are congruent.

In the previous investigation, you determined three sets of conditions that could be used to ensure that two triangular structures are similar. Mass production of interchangeable parts is based on the congruence of the parts, within very small tolerances. You will begin your study of congruence by considering the minimal conditions that ensure two triangles are congruent.

2. When two triangles are **congruent**, corresponding angles have the same measure and corresponding sides have the same length. Angles with the same measure are called *congruent angles*. Segments with the same length are called *congruent segments*.

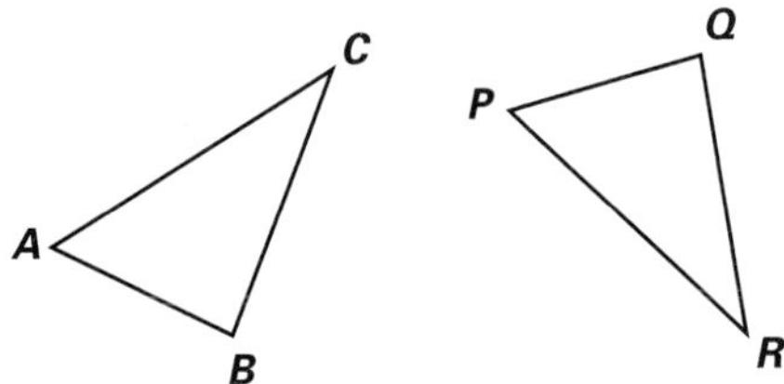

a. Suppose $\triangle ABC$ and $\triangle PQR$ shown above are congruent; this is denoted $\triangle ABC \cong \triangle PQR$. The symbol $\cong$ means "is congruent to." The orders *A-B-C* and *P-Q-R* indicate a particular correspondence between the vertices: *A* corresponds to *P*, *B* corresponds to *Q*, and *C* corresponds to *R*. Write six statements of congruence relating the angles and sides of these triangles.

b. If $m\angle A = 73°$ and $PQ = 7$ cm, what other measures do you know?

c. Consider the following two if-then statements, which are converses of each other.

If two triangles are congruent, then they are similar.

If two triangles are similar, then they are congruent.

Prove that one of these statements is correct and the other is not.

d. What additional information about scale factors could you add to the false statement so that it, too, would be correct?

The results of Parts c and d of Activity 2 suggest the following definition of **congruent triangles**:

Two triangles are congruent if and only if they are similar with a scale factor of 1.

This definition of congruence implies that congruence is just a special kind of similarity.

Unit 4

LESSON 2 • REASONING ABOUT SIMILAR AND CONGRUENT TRIANGLES 305

3. Now investigate how you might modify the conditions that ensure similarity so that they could also be used to ensure congruence of two triangles.

a. What does the SSS Similarity Theorem say?

- How can you modify the hypothesis of the theorem so that the conclusion involves congruence of triangles?
- Write a statement of an SSS Congruence Theorem.

b. What does the SAS Similarity Theorem say?

- Explain how the theorem can be modified so that the triangles are congruent.
- Write a statement of an SAS Congruence Theorem.

c. The third similarity theorem is the AA Similarity Theorem. How does this theorem differ from the SSS and SAS Similarity Theorems?

- What needs to be added to the AA Similarity Theorem to make it into a correct statement about conditions that ensure congruence of the triangles? There are two possible different additions, each of which gives a correct congruence theorem. Find them both.
- Write complete statements of each of these new congruence theorems. Give them appropriate short names.

4. In Activity 8 of Investigation 1 (page 301), you used the Law of Sines to show that when the measures of two angles and the length of a side opposite one of them are known, the remaining angle measure and side lengths are uniquely determined. Investigate whether the measures of the angles of a triangle are uniquely determined when you know the lengths of two sides and the measure of an angle opposite one of them.

a. First examine a special case. Let $m\angle A = 40°$ and $AB = 6$ cm. Draw $\angle A$ and segment AB as shown.

B
6 cm
40°
A
D

b. Now find point(s) C on the ray AD so that $BC = 4.5$ cm. Draw segment(s) BC.

c. What can you conclude about the triangle(s) drawn?

d. Use the Law of Sines to find $\sin C$.

e. Is there a unique $\angle C$ whose sine has the value calculated in Part d? Why does this occur when sines are calculated?

5. Do you think it is possible to derive a SSA Congruence Theorem or a SSA Similarity Theorem? Explain your reasoning.

Unit 4

306 UNIT 4 • SHAPES AND GEOMETRIC REASONING

3. **a.** SSS Similarity Theorem: If the lengths of three sides of one triangle are related by a scale factor k to the lengths of three sides of a second triangle, then the triangles are similar.

- Add that the scale factor must be 1 or that corresponding sides must be congruent.
- SSS Congruence Theorem: If three sides of one triangle are congruent to three sides of a second triangle, then the triangles are congruent.

b. SAS Similarity Theorem: If the lengths of two sides of one triangle are related by a scale factor k to the lengths of two sides of a second triangle and the included angles are congruent, then the triangles are similar.

- Add that the scale factor must be 1 or that the sides must be congruent.
- SAS Congruence Theorem: If two sides and the included angle of one triangle are congruent to the corresponding sides and included angle of a second triangle, then the triangles are congruent.

c. The AA Similarity Theorem does not directly require that we know anything about the sides of the triangles. It also requires only two pieces of information, rather than three.

- You must know that the sides included between the congruent angles are congruent or that one of the other pairs of corresponding sides are congruent.
- ASA Congruence Theorem: If two angles and the included side of one triangle are congruent to corresponding angles and included side of a second triangle, then the triangles are congruent.

  AAS Congruence Theorem: If two angles and a nonincluded side of one triangle are congruent to corresponding two angles and side of a second triangle, then the triangles are congruent.

4. **a–b.** There are two possible locations for C, indicated in the diagram at the right as C_1 and C_2.

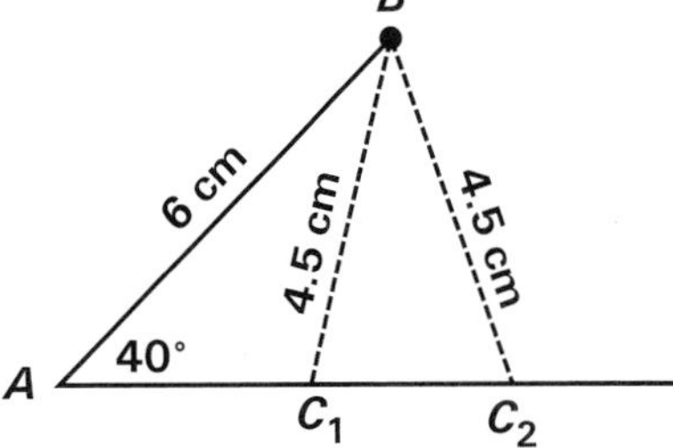

c. There are two possible triangles that can be drawn. They are not uniquely determined.

d. If you apply the Law of Sines, you get $\frac{4.5}{\sin 40^\circ} = \frac{6}{\sin C}$ or $\sin C = \frac{6 \sin 40^\circ}{4.5} \approx 0.857$.

e. Since the sine function is line symmetric across the vertical line at $x = 90^\circ$, $\sin(90^\circ + x) = \sin(90^\circ - x)$ and $m\angle C$ can be either of these two values, which will result in one obtuse and one acute triangle. In this case, $m\angle C$ can be either 58.99° or 121.01°. Note that when $m\angle BCA = 90^\circ$, then the triangle is uniquely determined. It is also uniquely determined when $BC \geq AB$, because then angle BCA must be an acute angle. Students are not expected to realize this at this point.

5. It is not possible to derive a general SSA Congruence or Similarity Theorem. The example in Activity 4 shows that there may be two possible triangles that can be drawn given two sides and a nonincluded angle.

Master 98

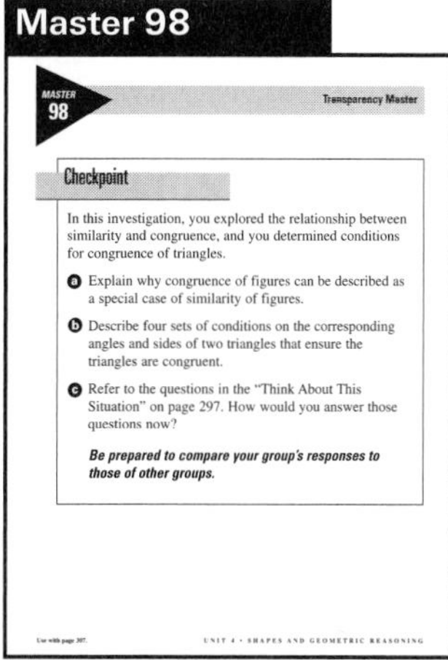
MASTER 98 — Transparency Master

Checkpoint

In this investigation, you explored the relationship between similarity and congruence, and you determined conditions for congruence of triangles.

ⓐ Explain why congruence of figures can be described as a special case of similarity of figures.

ⓑ Describe four sets of conditions on the corresponding angles and sides of two triangles that ensure the triangles are congruent.

ⓒ Refer to the questions in the "Think About This Situation" on page 297. How would you answer those questions now?

Be prepared to compare your group's responses to those of other groups.

Use with page 307. UNIT 4 • SHAPES AND GEOMETRIC REASONING

EXPLORE *continued*

6. **a.** They are not necessarily congruent.
b. Yes, they are congruent by the AAS Congruence Theorem.
c. Yes, they are congruent by the SAS Congruence Theorem.
d. They are not necessarily congruent.
e. Yes, they are congruent by the SSS Congruence Theorem.
f. Yes, they are congruent by the ASA Congruence Theorem.

SHARE AND SUMMARIZE **full-class discussion**

Checkpoint

See Teaching Master 98.

ⓐ Congruence of figures can be described as a special case of similarity of figures because all congruent figures are also similar. Students may also note that the conditions that define congruence are a special case of those that define similarity.

ⓑ SSS Congruence Theorem: If three sides of one triangle are congruent to the corresponding sides of a second triangle, then the triangles are congruent.

SAS Congruence Theorem: If two sides and the included angle of one triangle are congruent to the corresponding two sides and the included angle of another triangle, then the triangles are congruent.

ASA Congruence Theorem: If two angles and the included side of one triangle are congruent to corresponding two angles and included side of another triangle, then the triangles are congruent.

AAS Congruence Theorem: If two angles and a nonincluded side of one triangle are congruent to corresponding two angles and nonincluded side of another triangle, then the triangles are congruent.

ⓒ The minimum amount of information needed to make a scale drawing is the measure of two of the angles of the triangular structure. A congruent shape could be made if we knew any three measures for the triangle, except for two sides and a nonincluded angle or three angle measures.

6. Examine each of the following pairs of triangles and the markings showing congruence of corresponding angles and sides. In each case, decide whether the information given by the markings ensures that the triangles are congruent. If the triangles are congruent, cite an appropriate theorem to support your conclusion.

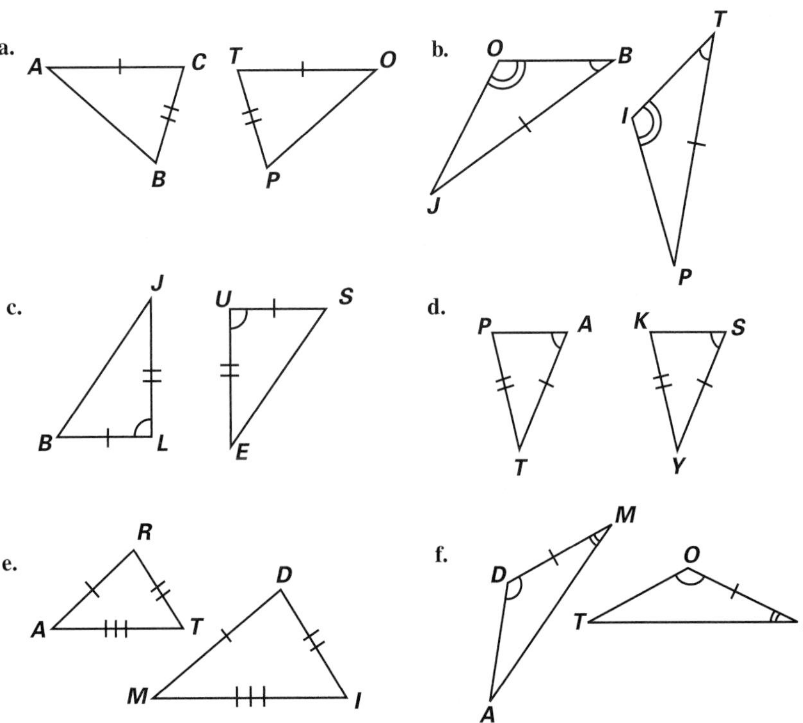

Checkpoint

In this investigation, you explored the relationship between similarity and congruence, and you determined conditions for congruence of triangles.

a Explain why congruence of figures can be described as a special case of similarity of figures.

b Describe four sets of conditions on the corresponding angles and sides of two triangles that ensure the triangles are congruent.

c Refer to the questions in the "Think About This Situation" on page 297. How would you answer those questions now?

Be prepared to compare your group's responses to those of other groups.

LESSON 2 • REASONING ABOUT SIMILAR AND CONGRUENT TRIANGLES 307

On Your Own

Following are possible sets of conditions on the angles and sides of $\triangle DEF$ and $\triangle XYZ$. Decide whether the given conditions ensure congruence, similarity, or neither, and justify each decision by citing an appropriate theorem.

a. $DE = XY$, $EF = 8$ cm, $YZ = 8$ cm, $\angle E \cong \angle Y$

b. $\angle D \cong \angle X$, $m\angle Z = 40^\circ$, $m\angle F = 40^\circ$, $DE = 10$ cm, $XY = 10$ cm

c. $m\angle D = 73^\circ$, $m\angle E = 47^\circ$, $m\angle X = 47^\circ$, $m\angle Z = 60^\circ$, $EF = YZ$

d. $\angle D \cong \angle X$, $\overline{DE} \cong \overline{XY}$, $\overline{EF} \cong \overline{YZ}$

e. $DE = 10 \text{ cm} = XY$, $\overline{EF} \cong \overline{YZ}$, $\overline{DF} \cong \overline{XZ}$

f. $m\angle D = 83^\circ$, $m\angle Z = 83^\circ$, $m\angle F = 57^\circ$, $m\angle Y = 40^\circ$

g. $\overline{DE} \cong \overline{EF}$, $\overline{XY} \cong \overline{YZ}$, $\overline{DF} \cong \overline{XZ}$

You now know minimal sets of information about a triangle that would permit you to make a similar or congruent copy of it. Sometimes you may be working in a situation or provided with a shape that is comprised of triangles, as in Activities 7, 8, and 9 below. Typically, you know some information about the situation or the shape and need to determine whether you have enough information to conclude that the triangles involved are congruent or similar. In such situations, it usually helps to first mark corresponding parts of the triangles to show congruences, as illustrated in Activity 6. The same marking indicates the same size or a congruence.

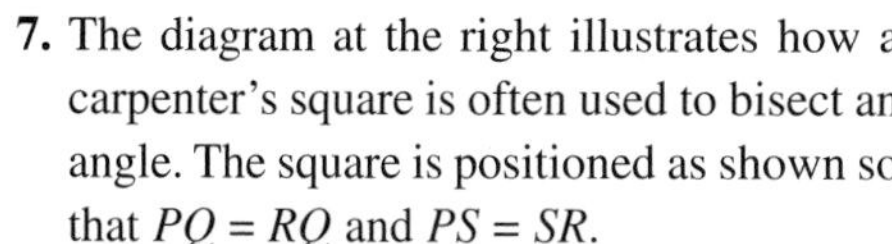

7. The diagram at the right illustrates how a carpenter's square is often used to bisect an angle. The square is positioned as shown so that $PQ = RQ$ and $PS = SR$.

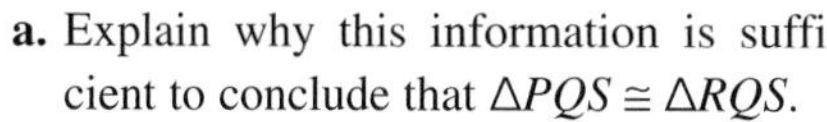

a. Explain why this information is sufficient to conclude that $\triangle PQS \cong \triangle RQS$.

b. Why does $\overrightarrow{QS}$ bisect $\angle PQR$?

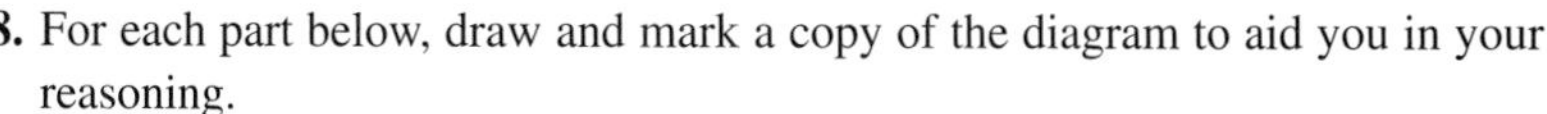

8. For each part below, draw and mark a copy of the diagram to aid you in your reasoning.

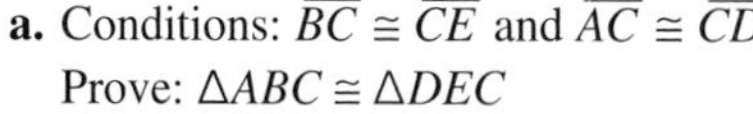

a. Conditions: $\overline{BC} \cong \overline{CE}$ and $\overline{AC} \cong \overline{CD}$
Prove: $\triangle ABC \cong \triangle DEC$

b. Conditions: $\angle B \cong \angle E$ and $\overline{BC} \cong \overline{CE}$
Prove: $\triangle ABC \cong \triangle DEC$

c. Conditions: $\overleftrightarrow{BA} \parallel \overleftrightarrow{DE}$ and C is the midpoint of $\overline{AD}$
Prove: $\triangle ABC \cong \triangle DEC$

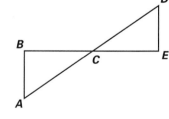

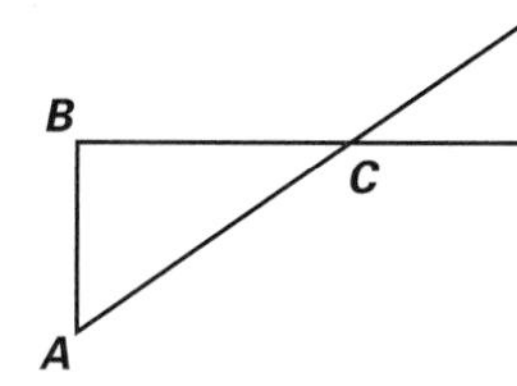

Unit 4

308 UNIT 4 • SHAPES AND GEOMETRIC REASONING

APPLY individual task

On Your Own

a. The triangles are congruent by the SAS Congruence Theorem.
b. The triangles are congruent by the AAS Congruence Theorem.
c. The triangles are similar by the AA Similarity Theorem. We are not guaranteed congruence, however, because congruent sides are not corresponding.
d. The conditions are not sufficient to ensure that the triangles are similar or congruent.
e. The triangles are congruent by the SSS Congruence Theorem.
f. The triangles are similar by the AA Similarity Theorem.
g. The conditions do not ensure congruence or similarity.

MORE ASSIGNMENT *pp. 310–315*

Students can now begin Modeling Task 1 or Reflecting Task 5 from the MORE assignment following Investigation 2.

EXPLORE small-group investigation

Consider having students do each of the tasks in Activities 7 and 8 individually, then sharing answers with a partner as they complete each part so that students can get some individual practice and students who may be struggling can get immediate feedback.

7. **a.** When you position the carpenter's square so that $PQ = RQ$ and $PS = SR$, you also have $QS = QS$. Thus, we have $\triangle PQS \cong \triangle RQS$ by the SSS Congruence Theorem.

b. Since $\triangle PQS \cong \triangle RQS$, corresponding angles, $\angle PQS$ and $\angle RQS$, are congruent.

8. **a.** We know that $\overline{BC} \cong \overline{CE}$ and $\overline{AC} \cong \overline{CD}$ in $\triangle ABC$ and $\triangle DEC$. Vertical angles, $\angle BCA$ and $\angle DCE$, are congruent. Since $\overline{BC} \cong \overline{CE}$, $\overline{AC} \cong \overline{CD}$, and $\angle BCA \cong \angle DCE$, we know $\triangle ABC \cong \triangle DEC$ by the SAS Congruence Theorem.

b. We know that $\angle B \cong \angle E$ and $\overline{BC} \cong \overline{CE}$ in $\triangle ABC$ and $\triangle DEC$. Vertical angles $\angle ACB$ and $\angle DCE$, are congruent. Since $\overline{BC} \cong \overline{CE}$, $\angle B \cong \angle E$, and $\angle ACB \cong \angle DCE$, we know $\triangle ABC \cong \triangle DEC$ by the ASA Congruence Theorem.

c. We know that $\overleftrightarrow{BA}$ is parallel to $\overleftrightarrow{DE}$ and C is the midpoint of $\overline{AD}$. If C is the midpoint of $\overline{AD}$, then $\overline{AC} \cong \overline{CD}$ because a midpoint divides a line segment into two segments of equal length. If two parallel lines $\overleftrightarrow{AB}$ and $\overleftrightarrow{DE}$ are cut by a transversal, then the alternate interior angles, $\angle ABC$ and $\angle DEC$, are congruent. If two lines intersect to form vertical angles, $\angle ACB$ and $\angle DCE$, then $\angle ACB \cong \angle DCE$. If in $\triangle ABC$ and $\triangle DEC$ we know $\overline{AC} \cong \overline{CD}$, $\angle ABC \cong \angle DEC$, and $\angle ACB \cong \angle DCE$, then $\triangle ABC \cong \triangle DEC$ by the AAS Congruence Theorem.

Master 99

MASTER 99 — Transparency Master

Checkpoint

Think about some of the strategies you use and the decisions you make when reasoning about the congruence or similarity of two triangles.

ⓐ What information do you need in order to conclude that two triangles are congruent?

ⓑ How are the conditions ensuring congruence of two triangles different from the conditions ensuring similarity?

ⓒ How does marking a diagram to show congruent parts help you decide congruence or similarity of triangles?

Be prepared to explain your ideas to the entire class.

Use with page 309 — UNIT 4 • SHAPES AND GEOMETRIC REASONING

EXPLORE *continued*

9. a. We know that in $\triangle ABC$ and $\triangle DBE$, $AB = 2DB$ and $BC = 2EB$. If $AB = 2DB$ and $BC = 2EB$, then AB is a multiple of DB and BC is the same multiple of EB. $\angle ABC \cong \angle DBE$ because they are the same angle. If in $\triangle ABC$ and $\triangle DBE$, AB is a multiple of DB, BC is the same multiple of EB, and $\angle ABC \cong \angle DBE$, then the triangles are similar by the SAS Similarity Theorem.

b. We know that $\overleftrightarrow{DE}$ is parallel to $\overleftrightarrow{AC}$. $\angle ABC \cong \angle DBE$ because they are the same angle. If two parallel lines $\overleftrightarrow{DE}$ and $\overleftrightarrow{AC}$ are cut by a transversal $\overleftrightarrow{AB}$, then corresponding angles $\angle BAC$ and $\angle BDE$ are congruent. If in $\triangle ABC$ and $\triangle DBE$ we know $\angle ABC \cong \angle DBE$ and $\angle BAC \cong \angle BDE$, then $\triangle ABC \sim \triangle DBE$ by the AA Similarity Theorem.

c. We know that $\angle BED \cong \angle C$. $\angle ABC \cong \angle DBE$ because they are the same angle. If in $\triangle ABC$ and $\triangle DBE$ we know $\angle BED \cong \angle C$ and $\angle ABC \cong \angle DBE$, then $\triangle ABC \sim \triangle DBE$ by the AA Similarity Theorem.

SHARE AND SUMMARIZE full-class discussion

Checkpoint

See Teaching Master 99.

ⓐ You need to know that the corresponding parts of the triangles satisfy one of the triangle congruence theorems: SSS, SAS, ASA, or AAS.

ⓑ The conditions ensuring congruence require that the sides be congruent rather than related by a scale factor.

ⓒ Student responses may vary. It is hoped that students will notice that marking a figure for a proof allows them to visualize the relative orientation of several given sides and angles simultaneously, helping them select an appropriate theorem. For example, by marking a triangle, you can easily see if a given side is between two given angles.

CONSTRUCTING A MATH TOOLKIT: Students should include the four theorems for proving triangles congruent in their list of theorems. These theorems can be included under the heading "Minimal Conditions to Ensure Congruence of Triangles." Again, if students are going to use the abbreviations for the theorems, such as SAS, caution them to make sure they understand what the abbreviations mean. Most students will find it helpful to include a sketch with each of their theorems.

JOURNAL ENTRY: A second important concept in this lesson is the distinction between similarity and congruence. Write a brief paragraph comparing and contrasting the two relationships. Give examples of nontriangular objects from the world around you that are similar and examples of objects that are congruent.

APPLY individual task

On Your Own

a. $\triangle ABC \cong \triangle DEF$ by the AAS Congruence Theorem.

b. $\angle BAD \cong \angle EDF$ since they are corresponding angles when $\overleftrightarrow{AB}$ and $\overleftrightarrow{DE}$ are cut by transversal $\overleftrightarrow{AF}$. Similarly, $\angle ACB \cong \angle DFE$. $\triangle ABC \sim \triangle DEF$ by the AA Similarity Theorem.

c. Since $\overline{AD} \cong \overline{FC}$ and $\overline{DC} \cong \overline{CD}$, $\overline{AC} \cong \overline{DF}$ Corresponding angles, $\angle BCA$ and $\angle EFD$, are congruent. $\triangle ABC \cong \triangle DEF$ by the AAS Congruence Theorem.

d. The triangles are not necessarily congruent or similar.

e. $\triangle ABC \cong \triangle DEF$ by the SSS Congruence Theorem.

9. For each part below, draw and mark a diagram to aid you in preparing a proof.

a. Conditions: $AB = 2DB$ and $BC = 2EB$
Prove: $\triangle DBE \sim \triangle ABC$

b. Conditions: $\overleftrightarrow{DE} \parallel \overleftrightarrow{AC}$
Prove: $\triangle ABC \sim \triangle DBE$

c. Conditions: $\angle BED \cong \angle C$
Prove: $\triangle ABC \sim \triangle DBE$

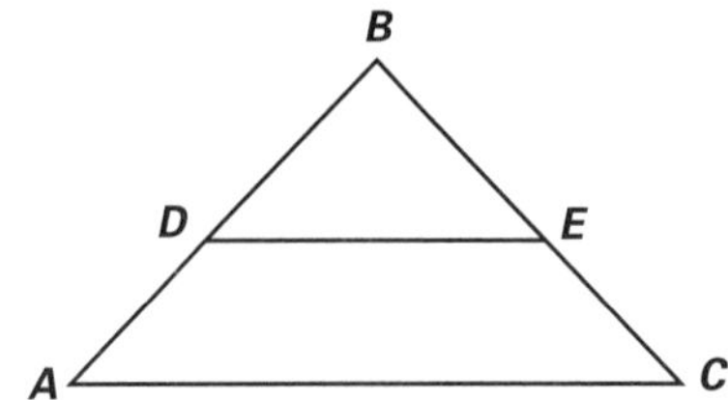

Checkpoint

Think about some of the strategies you use and the decisions you make when reasoning about the congruence or similarity of two triangles.

a What information do you need in order to conclude that two triangles are congruent?

b How are the conditions ensuring congruence of two triangles different from the conditions ensuring similarity?

c How does marking a diagram to show congruent parts help you decide congruence or similarity of triangles?

Be prepared to explain your ideas to the entire class.

The four triangle congruence conditions developed and used in this investigation — SAS, SSS, ASA, and AAS—are the only minimal conditions that, when satisfied, imply that a pair of triangles are congruent.

On Your Own

For each set of information given below, draw and mark a copy of the diagram. Then decide if $\triangle ABC \cong \triangle DEF$ or $\triangle ABC \sim \triangle DEF$. Explain your reasoning.

a. $\angle B \cong \angle E$, $\angle A \cong \angle EDF$, and $\overline{AC} \cong \overline{FD}$

b. $\overleftrightarrow{AB} \parallel \overleftrightarrow{DE}$ and $\overleftrightarrow{BC} \parallel \overleftrightarrow{EF}$

c. $\overline{AD} \cong \overline{FC}$, $\overline{BC} \parallel \overline{EF}$, and $\angle B \cong \angle E$

d. $\overline{BC} \cong \overline{ED}$, $\overline{AB} \cong \overline{FE}$, and $\angle A \cong \angle F$

e. $\overline{AD} \cong \overline{FC}$, $\overline{BC} \cong \overline{EF}$, and $\overline{AB} \cong \overline{DE}$

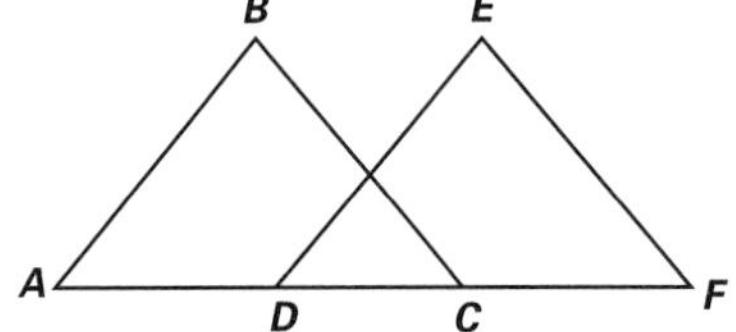

Unit 4

LESSON 2 • REASONING ABOUT SIMILAR AND CONGRUENT TRIANGLES 309

MORE
Modeling • Organizing • Reflecting • Extending

Modeling

1. Examine each pair of triangles. Determine, using the information given, whether the triangles are congruent, the triangles are similar, or the information is inconclusive. Explain your reasoning.

a.

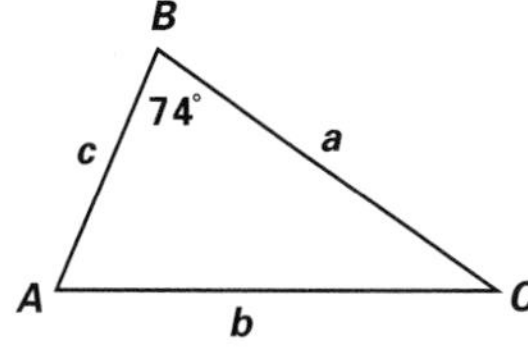

Q
$\frac{1}{3}c$
74°
$\frac{1}{3}a$
P
R

b.

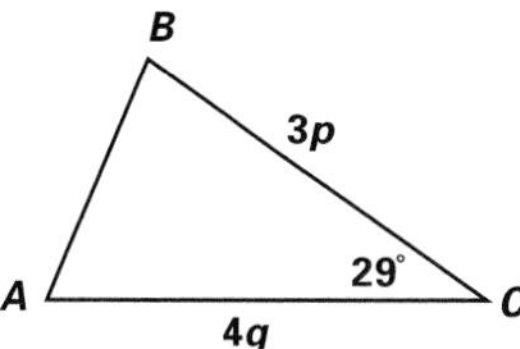

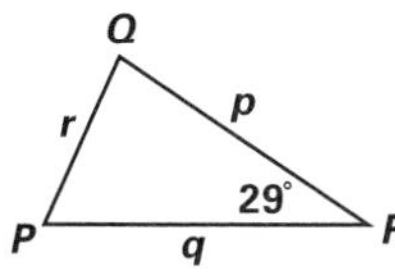

c.

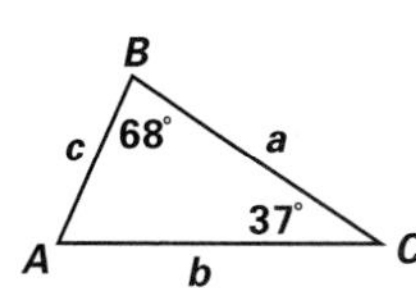

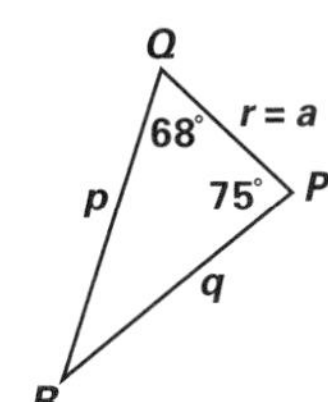

d.

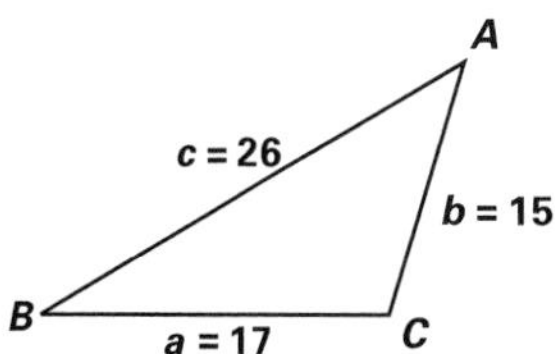

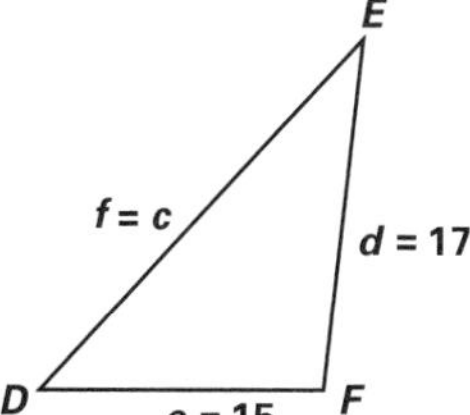

e.

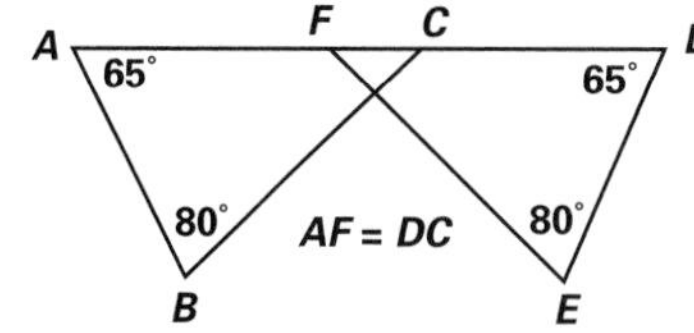

Unit 4

310 UNIT 4 • SHAPES AND GEOMETRIC REASONING

MORE **independent assignment**

Modeling

1. **a.** Similar by SAS Similarity Theorem.
   b. Neither congruent nor similar because the multipliers of p and of q are not equal.
   c. Similar by AA Similarity Theorem (but not congruent because congruent segments are not corresponding).
   d. Congruent by SSS Congruence Theorem.
   e. Congruent by AAS Congruence Theorem. (Since $AF=DC$ and $FC=CF$, $AC = DF$.)

MORE
ASSIGNMENT *pp. 310–315*

Modeling: 1, 4, and choice of one*
Organizing: 3 and 4
Reflecting: 3 and 5
Extending: 3

**When choice is indicated, it is important to leave the choice to the student.*
NOTE: *It is best if Organizing tasks are discussed as a whole class after they have been assigned as homework.*

Unit 4

2. **a.** If point C is the midpoint of $\overline{BD}$, then $\overline{DC} \cong \overline{CB}$. If $\overline{AE}$ and $\overline{BD}$ intersect at point C, then vertical angles, $\angle ACB$ and $\angle ECD$, are congruent. If $\angle B \cong \angle D$, $\overline{DC} \cong \overline{CB}$, and $\angle ACB \cong \angle ECD$, then $\triangle ABC \cong \triangle EDC$ by the ASA Congruence Theorem.

b. If $\overline{AE}$ and $\overline{BD}$ intersect at point C, then vertical angles, $\angle ACB$ and $\angle ECD$, are congruent. If point C is the midpoint of $\overline{AE}$ and $\overline{BD}$, then $AC = CE$ and $BC = CD$. If $AC = CE$, $\angle ACB \cong \angle ECD$, and $BC = CD$, then $\triangle ABC \cong \triangle EDC$ by the SAS Congruence Theorem.

c. If $\angle A \cong \angle E$ and $\angle B \cong \angle D$, then $\triangle ABC \sim \triangle EDC$ by the AA Similarity Theorem.

d. If $\overleftrightarrow{AB} \parallel \overleftrightarrow{DE}$, then $m\angle A = m\angle E$ and $m\angle B = m\angle D$ since they are alternate interior angles. If $m\angle A = m\angle E$ and $m\angle B = m\angle D$, then $\triangle ABC \sim \triangle EDC$ by the AA Similarity Theorem. The fact that $AB = 2 \cdot DE$ is not needed, except to specify the scale factor.

3. **a.** If $DC = BC$, $m\angle DCA = m\angle BCA$, and $AC = AC$, then $\triangle DCA \cong \triangle BCA$ by the SAS Congruence Theorem.

b. Dmitri is correct since the procedure produced two congruent triangles, $\triangle ABC$ and $\triangle ADC$, and all the corresponding parts are congruent.

c. $AB^2 = AC^2 + BC^2 - 2(AC)(BC)(\cos 100^\circ)$

$= 5^2 + 2^2 - 2(5)(2)(\cos 100^\circ) \approx 32.47$

$AB \approx 5.7$ km

4. **a.** The triangle and its image are similar. Since $\frac{10}{4} = 2.5$, 2.5 is the scale factor. The other sides measure 2.5×3 or 7.5 cm and 2.5×5 or 12.5 cm.

b. The scale factor is $\frac{7.5}{5}$ or 1.5. The other sides are 1.5×3 or 4.5 cm and 1.5×4 or 6 cm.

c. The scale factor is 3, so the distance from the light to the wall should be 3 times the distance from the light to the triangle. The distance from the light to the wall is 24 cm, so the triangle should be 8 cm from the light source.

2. Prove, if it is possible, that $\triangle ABC \cong \triangle EDC$ or $\triangle ABC \sim \triangle EDC$ under each of the following conditions. If it is not possible, explain why not.

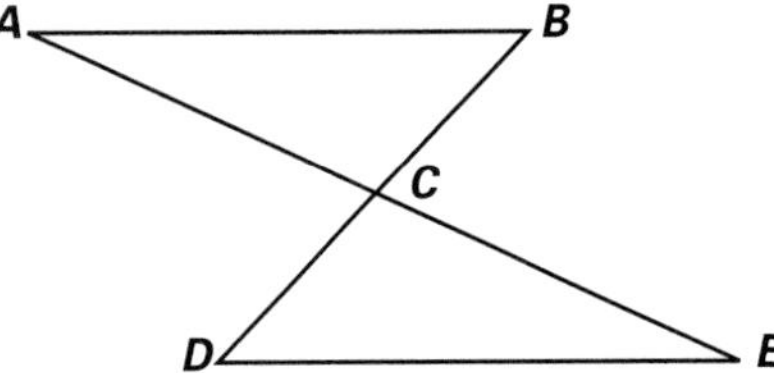

   a. C is the midpoint of $\overline{BD}$ and $m\angle B = m\angle D$.

   b. C is the midpoint of both $\overline{AE}$ and $\overline{BD}$.

   c. $\angle A \cong \angle E$ and $\angle B \cong \angle D$.

   d. $\overleftrightarrow{AB} \parallel \overleftrightarrow{DE}$ and $AB = 2 \cdot DE$.

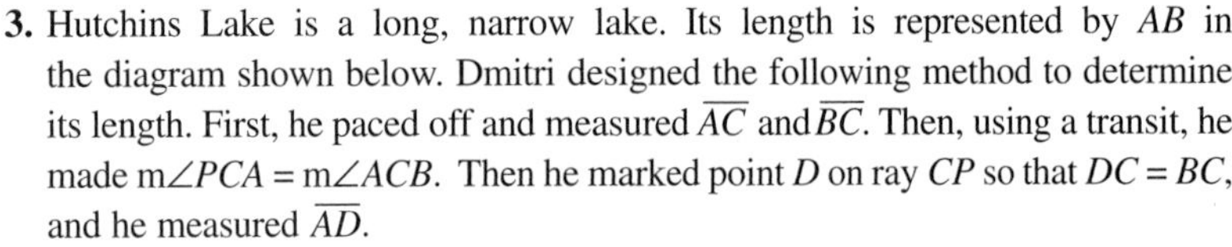

3. Hutchins Lake is a long, narrow lake. Its length is represented by AB in the diagram shown below. Dmitri designed the following method to determine its length. First, he paced off and measured $\overline{AC}$ and $\overline{BC}$. Then, using a transit, he made $m\angle PCA = m\angle ACB$. Then he marked point D on ray CP so that $DC = BC$, and he measured $\overline{AD}$.

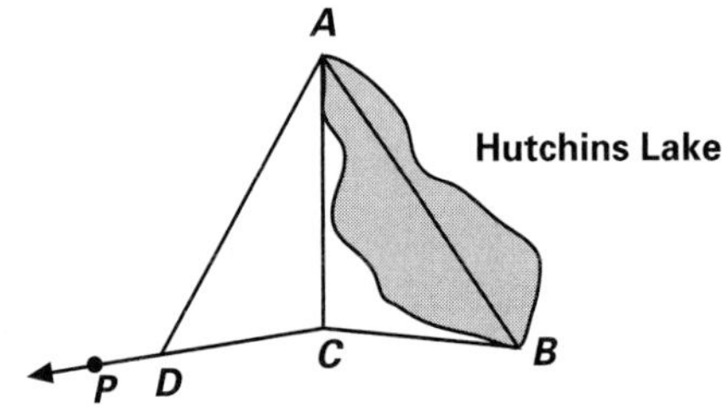

   a. Prove, if you can, that $\triangle ABC \cong \triangle ADC$.

   b. Dmitri claimed $AB = AD$. Is he correct? Justify your answer.

   c. Andrea claimed she could find the length AB of the lake without sighting $\triangle ADC$. Suppose $AC = 5$ km, $BC = 2$ km, and $m\angle ACB = 100°$. What is the length of Hutchins Lake?

4. A flashlight is directed perpendicularly at a vertical wall 24 cm away. A cardboard triangle with sides of lengths 3, 4, and 5 cm is positioned directly between the light and the wall, parallel to the wall.

   a. Suppose the shadow of the 4 cm side is 10 cm. Find the lengths of the shadows of the other two sides.

   b. Suppose the shadow of the 5 cm side is 7.5 cm. Find the lengths of the other two sides of the shadow.

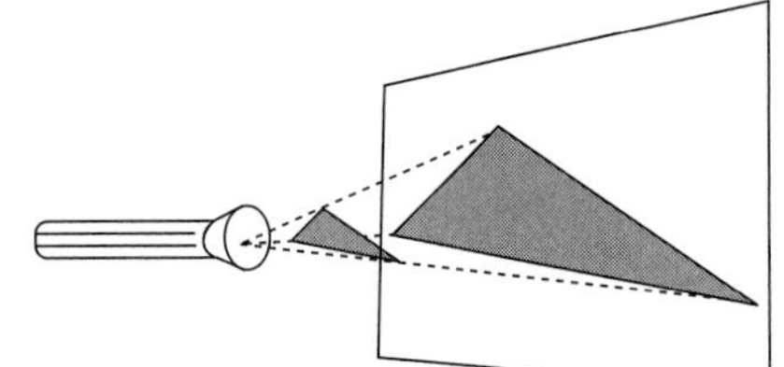

   c. How far from the light source should you place the cardboard triangle so that the 4 cm side has a 12 cm shadow?

Unit 4

LESSON 2 • REASONING ABOUT SIMILAR AND CONGRUENT TRIANGLES 311

Organizing

1. Prove, if possible, that $\Delta TOS \cong \Delta TOP$ under each set of conditions below.

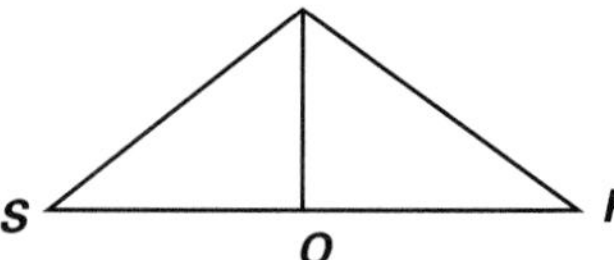

   a. $\overline{ST} \cong \overline{TP}$ and $\angle STO \cong \angle PTO$.

   b. $\overline{TO}$ is the perpendicular bisector of $\overline{SP}$.

   c. $\overline{TO} \perp \overline{SP}$ and $m\angle S = m\angle P$.

   d. $ST = TP$ and O is the midpoint of $\overline{SP}$.

2. Refer to the diagram of quadrilateral *ABCD*.

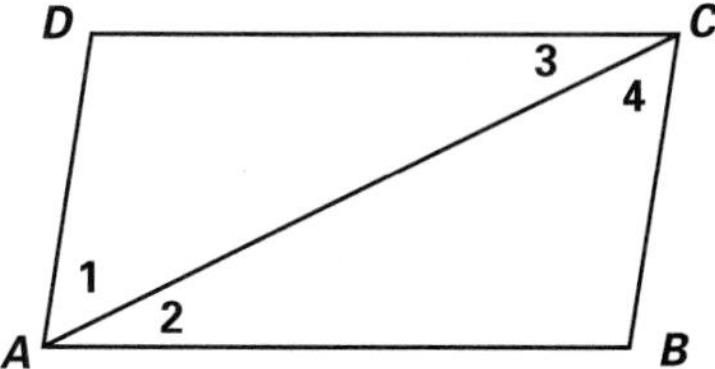

   a. Suppose that $m\angle 2 = m\angle 3$ and $m\angle B = m\angle D$. Can you conclude $AB = CD$? Write a justification.

   b. Suppose you know $AB = CD$ and $m\angle 2 = m\angle 3$. Can you conclude $\overleftrightarrow{AD} \parallel \overleftrightarrow{BC}$. Write a justification.

   c. Can you conclude $\overline{AD}$ is perpendicular to $\overline{DC}$ if you know $AD = CB$ and $m\angle 1 = m\angle 4$? Justify your position.

   d. Can you conclude $AB = CD$ if you know $m\angle 1 = m\angle 4$, $\overline{AD} \perp \overline{CD}$, and $\overline{AB} \perp \overline{BC}$? Justify your position.

3. Right triangles are special triangles in that one of the angles is known to measure 90°. Investigate which of the following conditions ensure the congruence of a pair of *right* triangles. Write a proof of each condition that you believe is correct. Provide a counterexample for each incorrect statement.

   a. If the legs in one right triangle are congruent to the corresponding legs in another right triangle, then the triangles are congruent.

   b. If a leg and an acute angle in one right triangle are congruent to a corresponding leg and acute angle in another right triangle, then the triangles are congruent.

   c. If the hypotenuse and an acute angle in one right triangle are congruent to the corresponding hypotenuse and acute angle in another right triangle, then the triangles are congruent.

   d. If an acute angle in one right triangle is congruent to the corresponding acute angle in another right triangle, then the triangles are congruent.

4. The arguments or proofs you have been writing in this unit are sometimes called *synthetic proofs*. Your proofs involved reasoning from a combination of assumed or established statements which were independent of a coordinate system. In this task, you will write and compare two different proofs of the following theorem:

   If a line segment joins the midpoints of two sides of a triangle, then it is parallel to the third side.

312 UNIT 4 • SHAPES AND GEOMETRIC REASONING

Organizing

1. a. $\overline{ST} \cong \overline{TP}$, $\angle STO \cong \angle PTO$, and $TO = TO$, so $\triangle TOS \cong \triangle TOP$ by the SAS Congruence Theorem.
   b. If $\overline{TO} \perp \overline{SP}$, then $\angle SOT \cong \angle POT$. If $\overline{TO}$ bisects $\overline{SP}$, then $SO = OP$. Of course, $TO = TO$. So $\triangle TOS \cong \triangle TOP$ by the SAS Congruence Theorem.
   c. If $\overline{TO} \perp \overline{SP}$, then $\angle SOT \cong \angle POT$. We also know that $TO = TO$ and $m\angle S = m\angle P$. So $\triangle TOS \cong \triangle TOP$ by the AAS Congruence Theorem.
   d. If O is the midpoint of $\overline{SP}$, then $SO = OP$. We also know that $TO = TO$ and $ST = TP$. So $\triangle TOS \cong \triangle TOP$ by the SSS Congruence Theorem.
2. a. Yes, $AB = CD$. If $m\angle 2 = m\angle 3$, $m\angle B = m\angle D$, and $AC = AC$, then $\triangle ADC \cong \triangle CBA$ by the AAS Congruence Theorem. If $\triangle ADC \cong \triangle CBA$, then $AB = CD$ because the segments are corresponding parts of congruent triangles.
   b. Yes, $\overleftrightarrow{AD} \parallel \overleftrightarrow{BC}$. If $AB = CD$, $m\angle 2 = m\angle 3$, and $AC = AC$, then $\triangle ADC \cong \triangle CBA$ by the SAS Congruence Theorem. If $\triangle ADC \cong \triangle CBA$, then $\angle 1 \cong \angle 4$. If $\angle 1 \cong \angle 4$, then $\overleftrightarrow{AD} \parallel \overleftrightarrow{BC}$ (alternate interior angles).
   c. No, you can show that $\triangle ADC \cong \triangle CBA$ and $m\angle 2 = m\angle 3$. Thus, $m\angle 1 + m\angle 2 = m\angle 3 + m\angle 4$, but there is no information about the actual measures. A counter-example would be a parallelogram with no right angles.
   d. Yes, $AB = CD$. If $AC = AC$, $m\angle 1 = m\angle 4$, and $m\angle D = m\angle B = 90°$, then $\triangle ADC \cong \triangle CBA$ by the AAS Congruence Theorem. If $\triangle ADC \cong \triangle CBA$, then $AB = CD$ because the segments are corresponding parts of congruent triangles.
3. a. Correct: Use SAS because the legs include the right angles.
   b. Correct: Use ASA.
   c. Correct: Use AAS.
   d. Incorrect: The triangles are similar, but not necessarily with scale factor of 1.

NOTE: Students should include the theorems from Task 3, Parts a–c in their Math Toolkits.

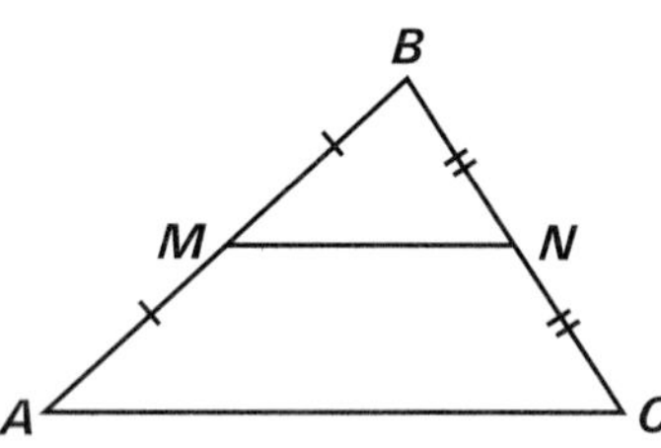

4. **a.** See the diagram to the left.
If point M is the midpoint of $\overline{AB}$, then $AB = 2MB$. If point N is the midpoint of $\overline{BC}$, then $BC = 2BN$. Since $AB = 2MB$, $BC = 2BN$, and $\angle B \cong \angle B$, we can use the SAS Similarity Theorem to conclude that $\triangle ABC \sim \triangle MBN$. If $\triangle ABC \sim \triangle MBN$, then $m\angle BMN = m\angle BAC$ since corresponding angles of similar triangles have equal measure. If $m\angle BMN = m\angle BAC$, then $\overleftrightarrow{MN} \parallel \overleftrightarrow{AC}$ by the Parallel Lines Property.

b. To use coordinates to show that two lines are parallel, we need to show that the lines have equal slopes. The coordinates of point M are $\left(\frac{b}{2}, \frac{c}{2}\right)$ and the coordinates of point N are $\left(\frac{a+b}{2}, \frac{c}{2}\right)$. The slope of $\overleftrightarrow{MN}$ is $\dfrac{\frac{c}{2} - \frac{c}{2}}{\frac{a+b}{2} - \frac{b}{2}} = \dfrac{0}{\frac{a}{2}} = 0$. The slope of $\overleftrightarrow{AC}$ is $\dfrac{0-0}{a-0} = 0$. Since the slopes of the two lines are equal, $\overleftrightarrow{MN} \parallel \overleftrightarrow{AC}$.

c. Responses will vary.

- Encourage students to discuss why one proof was easier for them. Their choices may depend on how well they understand how to use the similarity congruence theorems versus how comfortable they are with finding midpoints and slopes.
- Again, encourage students to explain their choices. In this case, their choice may depend on the person to whom they are explaining the proof.

d. Responses will vary. Possible conclusions are $\triangle MBN \sim \triangle ABC$, $2MN = AC$, Area $(\triangle MBN) = \frac{1}{4}$Area $(\triangle BAC)$.

NOTE: Again, students should record the theorems they prove so that they are available to use in later proofs.

Reflecting

1. Two angles are congruent if they are
- Vertical angles
- Right angles
- Angles with equal measures
- Supplements of equal angles
- Corresponding, alternate interior, or alternate exterior angles formed by parallel lines cut by a transversal
- Corresponding angles in similar or congruent triangles

2. **a.** The two sides of the triangle form the angle. Thus, the angle is "included" because it is the angle "determined by" the sides.

b. The side is "included" in that it is common to and determined by the two angles.

3. *Definitions* state precisely the conditions or characteristics which identify a particular object. A definition tells you what something is. It is always an if-and-only-if statement. A *theorem* states a conclusion you can draw whenever you have a given collection of conditions. It may be an if-and-only-if statement, or the converse may not be true. A *conjecture* is a statement of a relationship that the conjecturer thinks is true but has not yet been proved. Conjectures become theorems when proved. A *property* is a characteristic of a shape or other mathematical object. Properties often include theorems and definitions.

4. The triangles are similar, but there is no condition that insures that the scale factor is one.

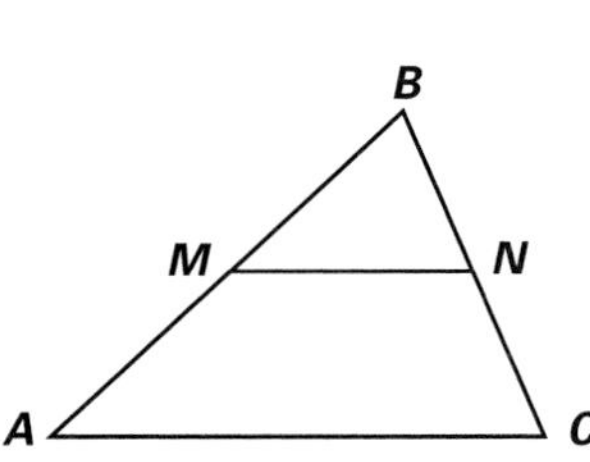

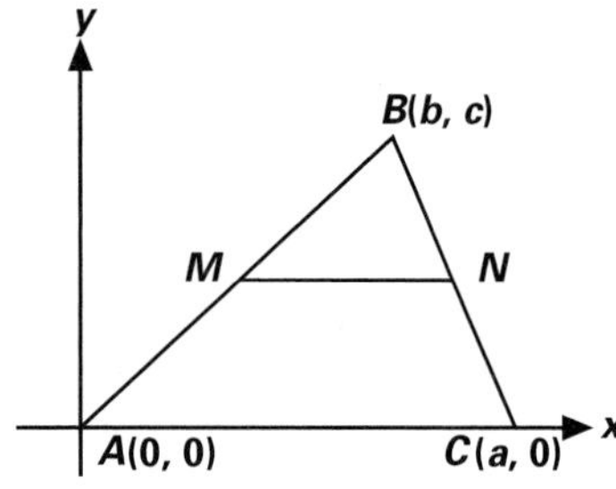

a. Make and mark a copy of the diagram on the left above. Write a synthetic proof that $\overleftrightarrow{MN} \parallel \overleftrightarrow{AC}$.

b. Use the labeled diagram on the right above to help you write a proof, using coordinates, that $\overleftrightarrow{MN} \parallel \overleftrightarrow{AC}$.

c. Compare your two proofs.

- Which proof was easier for you to construct? Why?
- Which proof would be easier for you to explain to someone else? Why?

d. Write another conclusion that you think follows from the hypothesis that $\overline{MN}$ joins the midpoints of two sides of a triangle. Write a proof of your conjecture. Did you use synthetic or coordinate methods?

Reflecting

1. Given two angles, there is a variety of conditions that would allow you to conclude without measuring that the angles are congruent. For example, if you know the angles are vertical angles, then you know they are congruent. What other conditions will allow you to conclude two angles are congruent? List as many as you can.

2. Think about the information conveyed by the abbreviations of the names of the various triangle similarity and congruence theorems.

a. SAS is often thought of as "two sides and the included angle." In what sense is the angle included?

b. ASA is often thought of as "two angles and the included side." In what sense is the side included?

3. Throughout this unit, you have been using several kinds of mathematical statements: definitions, conjectures, properties, and theorems. What are the differences among these kinds of statements?

4. Knowing that two pairs of corresponding angles in two triangles are congruent ensures that the triangles are similar, but it does *not* ensure that they are congruent. Why?

LESSON 2 • REASONING ABOUT SIMILAR AND CONGRUENT TRIANGLES 313

5. In your previous mathematics courses, you investigated representations, properties, and applications of three sets of geometric transformations: rigid transformations, size transformations, and similarity transformations.
   a. Draw a Venn diagram (see page 274) illustrating the relationship between these three sets of transformations.
   b. Explain how these transformations are related to the ideas of similarity and congruence.

Extending

1. The Law of Cosines can be derived using the distance formula, but you need to use trigonometric expressions for the coordinates of the vertex of the triangle that is not on the x-axis. Examine the coordinate representation of ΔABC below.

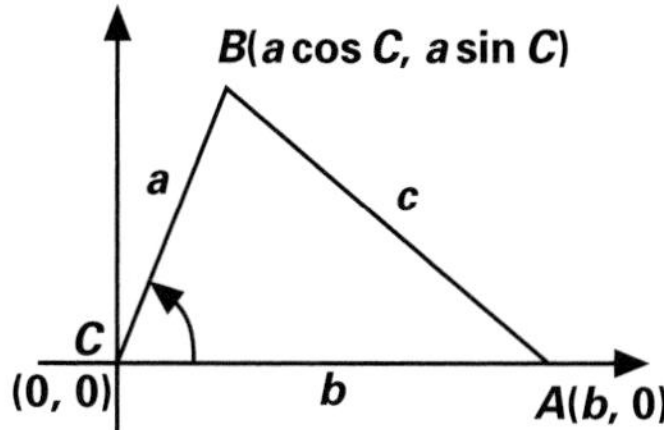

   a. Explain why the coordinates of point B are $(a \cos C, a \sin C)$.
   b. Find c^2 using the distance formula and the coordinates of points A and B.
   c. Simplify your expression in Part b to give the Law of Cosines for c^2. You will need to use a proven result from Investigation 2 of Lesson 5 in the "Symbol Sense and Algebraic Reasoning" unit (pages 243 to 246).

2. *Dissection* of shapes into several congruent shapes is a source for commercial games and an interesting class of geometric problems. The triangle below is dissected into four congruent shapes, each similar to the large triangle.

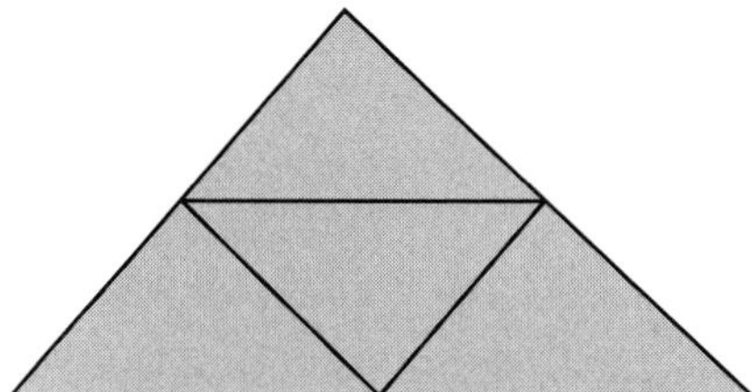

314 UNIT 4 • SHAPES AND GEOMETRIC REASONING

5. a.

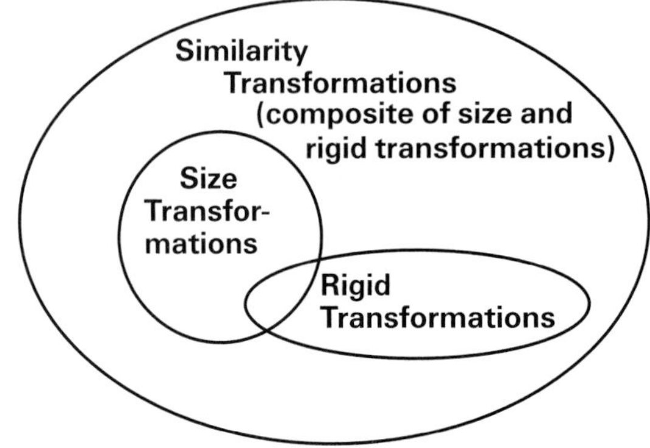

b. A similarity transformation (size change, reflection, rotation, translation, or any composite of these) will always result in an image similar to the pre-image. Rigid transformations will always result in an image congruent to the pre-image. The intersection of size transformations and rigid transformations is the identity transformation.

Extending

1. a. Add a point D on $\overline{AC}$ to form a right triangle CBD with hypotenuse CB. Let $CD = x$. Then $\cos C = \frac{x}{a}$. Thus $x = a \cos C$. Similarly, $\sin C = \frac{y}{a}$ and so $y = a \sin C$. Thus, $B(x, y) = B(a \cos C, a \sin C)$.

b. $c^2 = (a \cos C - b)^2 + (a \sin C - 0)^2$
$= a^2 \cos^2 C - 2ab \cos C + b^2 + a^2 \sin^2 C$
$= a^2(\cos^2 C + \sin^2 C) + b^2 - 2ab \cos C$

c. $c^2 = a^2 + b^2 - 2ab \cos C$ since $\cos^2 C + \sin^2 C = 1$

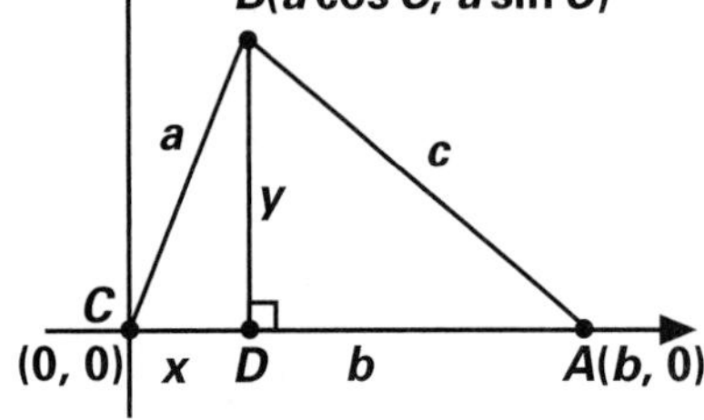

Unit 4

MORE *continued*

2. a.

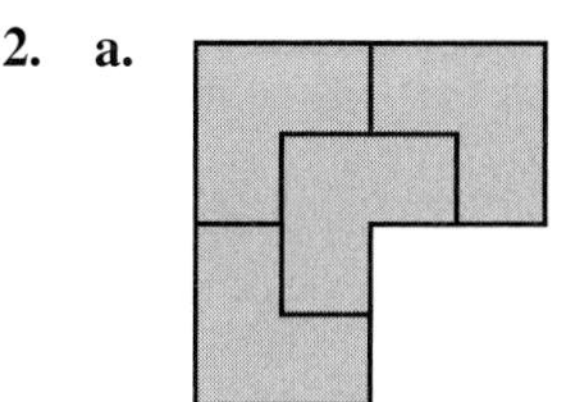

b.

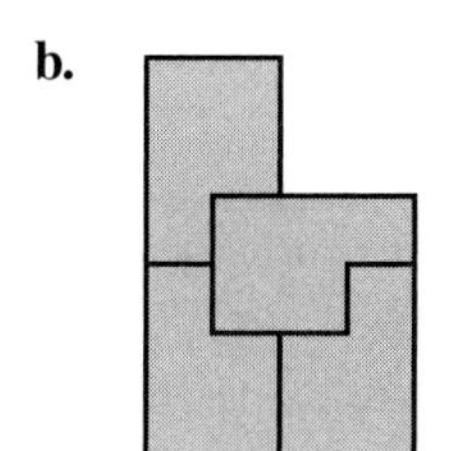

c.

d.

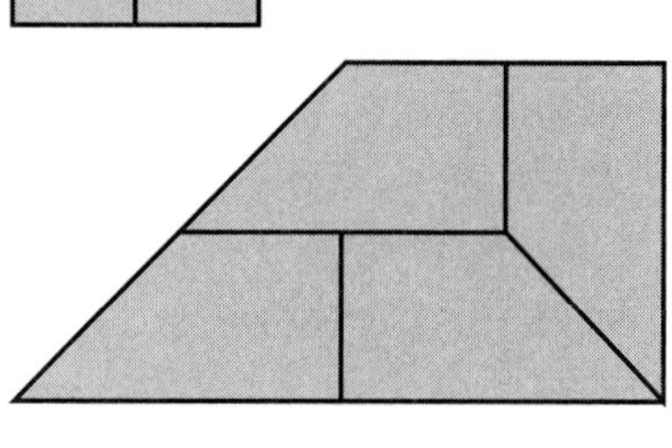

e.

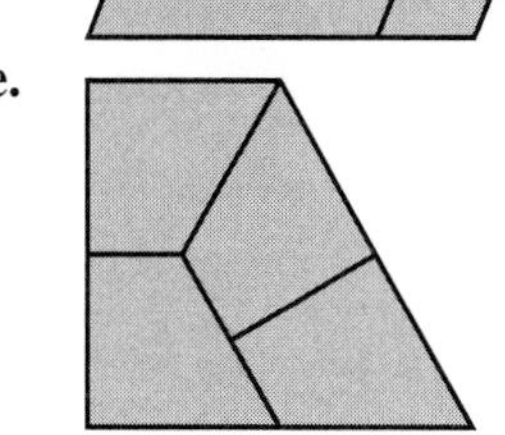

f.

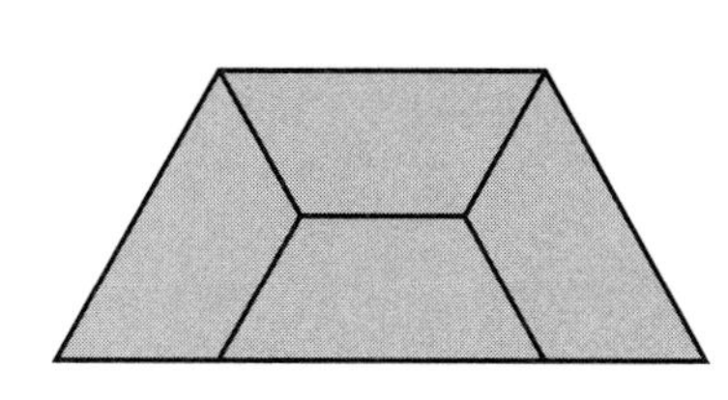

NOTE: This theorem should be recorded for later use.

3. Since the Pythagorean Theorem is known, the hypotenuse and leg of a right triangle uniquely determine the other leg. Thus, the two triangles are congruent by either SSS or SAS. Another argument is that the cosine of the angle included between the hypotenuse and leg is unique. Thus, these corresponding angles are congruent and so the two triangles are congruent by either SAS or ASA.

4. **a.** If $\overleftrightarrow{XY} \parallel \overleftrightarrow{SO}$, then $\angle SOP \cong \angle XYP$ (corresponding angles). $\angle P \cong \angle P$. If $\angle SOP \cong \angle XYP$ and $\angle P \cong \angle P$, then $\triangle XYP \sim \triangle SOP$.

   b. Since quadrilateral *STOP* is a rectangle, $\overleftrightarrow{TO} \parallel \overleftrightarrow{SP}$, $m\angle P = 90°$, and $m\angle T = 90°$. So $\angle TOS \cong \angle OSP$ since they are alternate interior angles formed by the parallel lines $\overleftrightarrow{TO}$ and $\overleftrightarrow{SP}$. Also $\angle P \cong \angle T$ and $\overline{SO} \cong \overline{SO}$. Thus, $\triangle OST \cong \triangle SOP$ by the AAS Congruence Theorem. In Part a, we showed that $\triangle XYP \sim \triangle SOP$. Since $\triangle SOP \cong \triangle OST$, we can conclude that $\triangle XYP \sim \triangle OST$.

   c. By Part a, $\triangle XYP \sim \triangle SOP$. Thus, the corresponding sides are related by the scale factor k. Since Y is the midpoint of $\overline{OP}$, $PY = YO$ and $PO = 2PY$. Thus, $k = \frac{PO}{PY} = \frac{2PY}{PY} = 2$.

   - Since $\overline{XP}$ and $\overline{SP}$ are corresponding parts of similar triangles with scale factor 2, $SP = 2XP$. But $SP = SX + XP = 2XP$, so $SX = XP$. If $SX = XP$, then X is the midpoint of $\overline{SP}$ (since X is on $\overline{SP}$).
   - Since $\overline{XY}$ and $\overline{SO}$ are corresponding parts of the similar triangles and $k = 2$, $SO = 2XY$.

Unit 4

Dissect each of the following shapes into four shapes similar to the given shape but congruent to each other.

a. 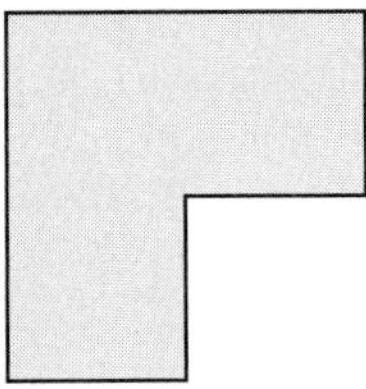

b. 

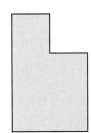

c. 

d. 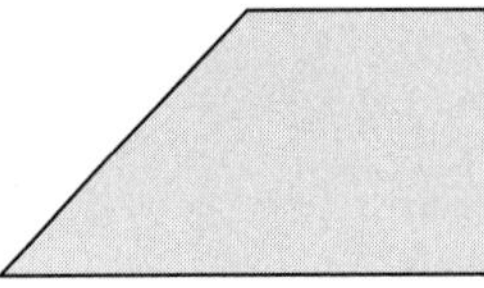

e. 

f. 

3. Two right triangles can be proved to be congruent when the hypotenuse and leg of one are congruent respectively to the hypotenuse and leg of another. Construct a convincing argument that this is correct.

4. In the diagram here, quadrilateral *STOP* is a rectangle and $\overline{SO}$ is a diagonal.

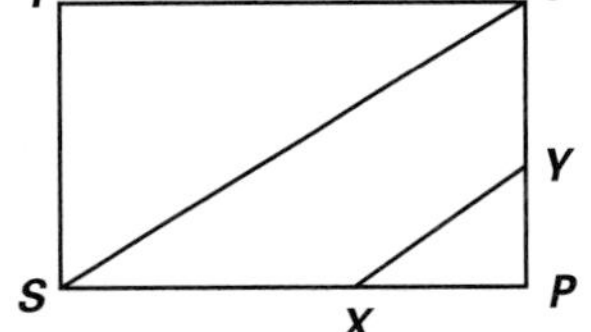

a. Assuming $\overleftrightarrow{XY} \parallel \overleftrightarrow{SO}$, prove that $\triangle XYP \sim \triangle SOP$.

b. Assuming $\overleftrightarrow{XY} \parallel \overleftrightarrow{SO}$, prove that $\triangle XYP \sim \triangle OST$.

c. Assuming $\overleftrightarrow{XY} \parallel \overleftrightarrow{SO}$, and *Y* is the midpoint of $\overline{OP}$, prove the following:

- *X* is the midpoint of $\overline{SP}$.
- $SO = 2 \cdot XY$.

Unit 4

LESSON 2 • REASONING ABOUT SIMILAR AND CONGRUENT TRIANGLES 315

INVESTIGATION 3 Reasoning with Congruence and Similarity Conditions

Reproduced below is a lithograph by M. C. Escher called *Ascending and Descending*. The stairway is a vivid reminder that you cannot always believe your eyes.

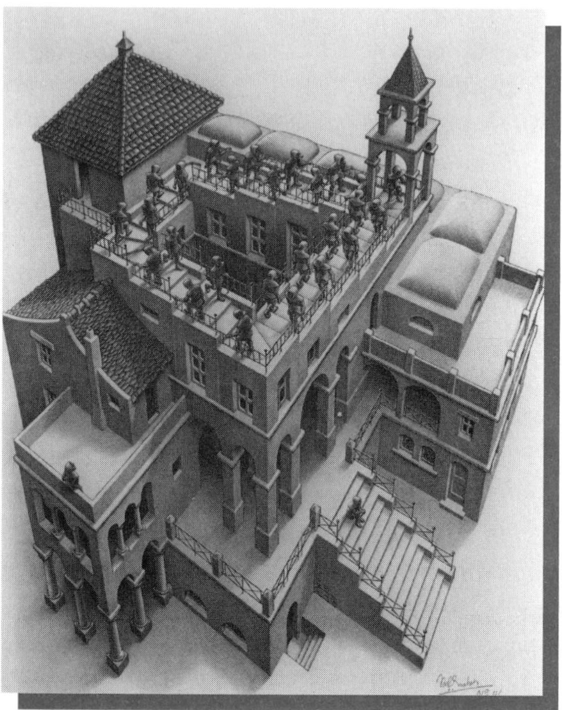

"Ascending and Descending" by M.C. Escher.

1. Provide an argument why what appears to be true about the stairway cannot possibly be true in the real world.

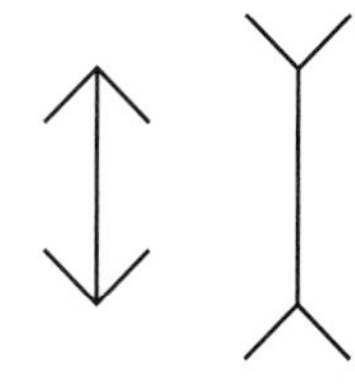

Even simple figures such as the ones at the right can be deceiving to the eye. Which segment connecting the V shapes is longer? Direct measurement is one way to settle a claim about segment lengths or angle measures. If the segments or angles are parts of triangles, the four triangle congruence theorems (SSS, SAS, ASA, and AAS) and the three triangle similarity theorems (SSS, SAS, and AA) are important and often-used tools to settle geometric claims and conjectures. If you can prove it, your eyes are not deceiving you. If you cannot prove it, look for a counterexample.

316 UNIT 4 • SHAPES AND GEOMETRIC REASONING

EXPLORE small-group investigation

INVESTIGATION 3 Reasoning with Congruence and Similarity Conditions

Masters 100–104

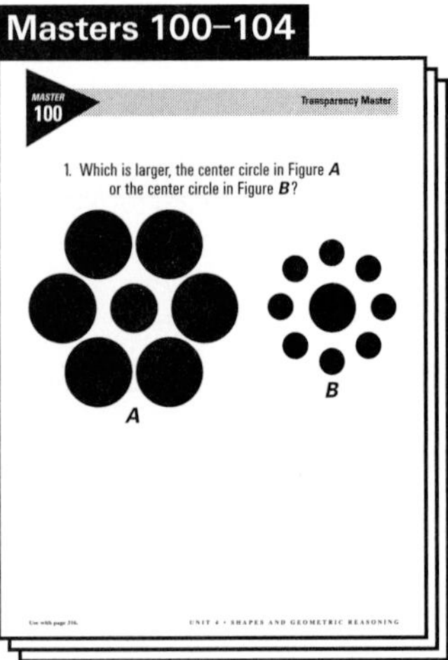

This investigation continues to extend students' work with congruence and similarity using triangles. Students use all of the congruence and similarity theorems they have proven in the last two investigations. They will encounter overlapping triangles, triangles with dissimilar orientations, and the need to draw additional line segments, and they will go beyond proving one pair of triangles similar or congruent to conclude that corresponding parts of congruent triangles are congruent (CPCTC) and that sides are proportional for similar triangles. (This result was foreshadowed in the previous MORE set in Modeling Task 3, Organizing Tasks 2 and 4, and Extending Task 4.) Also in this investigation, students will need to draw on many of the angle equality theorems they have previously proved for intersecting, perpendicular, and parallel lines. It is appropriate to expect that, gradually, the language in students' proofs will become more succinct and that their ability to draw upon a large collection of theorems will improve.

One way to motivate the need for formal argument is to help students understand that lines and figures can create optical illusions, so our eyes cannot be relied upon to identify congruence and similarity. After reading the introduction to this investigation with the class, ask students to reflect on and discuss optical illusions that they may have encountered. Possible examples include the fact that vertical line patterns in clothing tend to make a person appear thinner while horizontal line patterns definitely do not; the heights of telephone poles appear to decrease as you look at poles that are farther and farther away; stripes on television (such as in a newscaster's clothes) appear to vibrate; and a room that is lit with fluorescent light will appear differently when lit by incandescent lamps. See Teaching Masters 100–104 for additional examples of optical illusions. Other optical illusions can be found on commercially available posters and may help promote group discussion.

Before students begin small-group work on these activities, let them know that these proofs may seem a bit more challenging because students will be expected to use the four congruence and similarity theorems developed previously, as well as the many other types of theorems they have proven in this unit. They will want to approach these proofs with their lists of theorems and properties ready for quick reference.

This is a long set of activities, and students will vary widely in how capable they are at constructing logical proofs. In Activity 1, students are encouraged to write individually and then share. Alternating group and individual work should be monitored to ensure each student has to verbalize proofs. It makes sense for the initial steps to be taken with pairs of students working together. In order to assist each student in developing his or her abilities, you may want to model how to share the lead role of a pair. With one other student as your partner, start by saying (about Activity 4 for example), "The question asks me to prove the triangles congruent. I know 4 ways to prove triangles congruent. In this diagram, I can mark right angles

Unit 4

See additional Teaching Notes on page T344I.

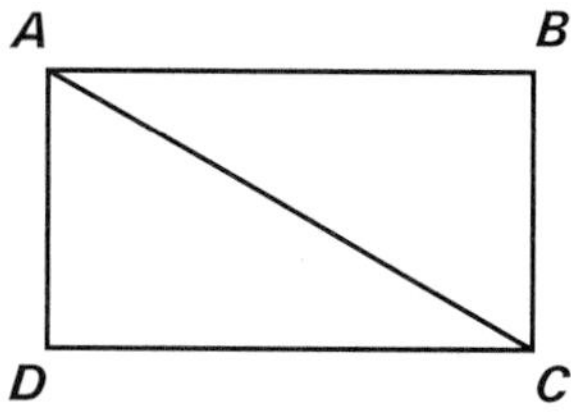

2. a. Student drawings will vary (see margin). Students should agree that the conjecture is correct.
 b. If diagonal $\overline{AC}$ is drawn in rectangle *ABCD*, then $\triangle ABC \cong \triangle CDA$.
 c. Important characteristics include opposite sides of a rectangle are parallel ($\overline{AB} \parallel \overline{CD}$ and $\overline{AD} \parallel \overline{BC}$), opposite sides of a rectangle are congruent ($AB = CD$ and $AD = BC$), and a rectangle has four right angles. Students may mention that since *B* and *D* are right angles, $\triangle ABC$ and $\triangle CDA$ are right triangles. All of these can be used in a proof.
 d. If students completed Extending Task 4 in the previous MORE set, page 315, then they may use the hypotenuses and corresponding legs of right triangles. Other options include SSS, SAS, ASA, or AAS.
 e. **Many proofs are possible. Students should state the figure is a rectangle; the last statement should contain the needed conclusion (see Part b); and all the characteristics needed for the selected congruence theorem should be properly included in the body of the argument. Below is a possible proof using the SAS Congruence Theorem. It is important, in this case, that students name the correct pair of alternate interior angles for the parallel lines they select. For example, students working with $\overline{AB} \parallel \overline{CD}$ may be tempted to call $\angle ACB$ and $\angle CAD$ congruent alternate interior angles, because they may forget to disregard the vertical segments $\overline{AD}$ and $\overline{BC}$.**
 Rectangle *ABCD* has diagonal $\overline{AC}$. If *ABCD* is a rectangle, then $\overline{CD} \parallel \overline{AB}$ and $CD = AB$ because opposite sides of a rectangle are parallel and congruent. If $\overline{CD}$ and $\overline{AB}$ are cut by transversal $\overline{AC}$, then $\angle BAC \cong \angle DCA$ because they are alternate interior angles. $\overline{AC}$ is congruent to itself. If for $\triangle ABC$ and $\triangle CDA$ we know $\overline{AB} \cong \overline{DC}$, $\angle BAC \cong \angle DCA$, and $\overline{AC} \cong \overline{AC}$, then the triangles are congruent by the SAS Congruence Theorem.
 f. The new conjecture is also true. The proof given in Part e used only the properties of rectangles that are shared by parallelograms. To prove the new conjecture, replace the word "rectangle" with the word "parallelogram" in the proof in Part e.

NOTE: The familiar "corresponding parts of congruent triangles are congruent" is introduced in the paragraph after Activity 5. You may wish to have a short discussion here and introduce the "CPCTC" shorthand for use in proofs.

3. We are given that $\overline{ST} \cong \overline{SP}$ and $\overline{TO} \cong \overline{PO}$. $\overline{SO}$ is congruent to itself. If for $\triangle STO$ and $\triangle SPO$ we know $\overline{ST} \cong \overline{SP}$, $\overline{TO} \cong \overline{PO}$, and $\overline{SO} \cong \overline{SO}$, then the triangles are congruent by the SSS Congruence Theorem.
4. a. We are given that $\overline{BD}$ is perpendicular to $\overline{AE}$. If $\overline{BD}$ is perpendicular to $\overline{AE}$, then $\angle ACB$ and $\angle ECD$ are right angles, because perpendicular lines meet to form right angles. If *C* is the midpoint of $\overline{AE}$, then $\overline{AC} \cong \overline{CE}$. If *C* is the midpoint of $\overline{BD}$, then $\overline{BC} \cong \overline{CD}$. If for $\triangle ABC$ and $\triangle EDC$ we know $\overline{BC} \cong \overline{CD}$, $\angle ACB \cong \angle ECD$, and $\overline{AC} \cong \overline{CE}$, then the triangles are congruent by the SAS Congruence Theorem.
 b. ■ $\overline{AB} \cong \overline{DE}$ because they are corresponding sides of congruent triangles.
 ■ $\angle ABC \cong \angle EDC$ because they are corresponding angles of congruent triangles.
 ■ $\overleftrightarrow{AB} \parallel \overleftrightarrow{DE}$ because $\angle ABC$ and $\angle EDC$ are alternate interior angles and are congruent, so the lines are parallel.
 c. No. $\overline{BD}$ is not congruent to $\overline{AE}$ because they are not sides of the congruent triangles. A diagram such as the one at the right is a convincing counterexample.

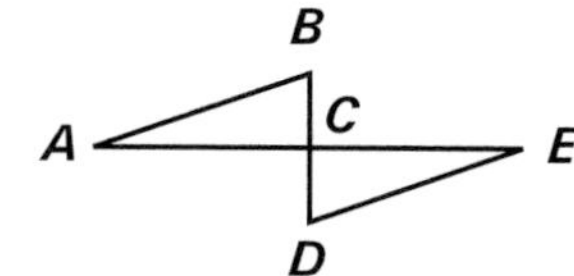

5. a. We are given that $\overleftrightarrow{AB} \parallel \overleftrightarrow{DE}$ and *C* is the midpoint of $\overline{BD}$. If $\overleftrightarrow{AB}$ and $\overleftrightarrow{DE}$ are cut by transversal $\overleftrightarrow{BD}$, then alternate interior angles, $\angle ABC$ and $\angle EDC$, are congruent. If *C* is the midpoint of $\overline{DB}$, then $\overline{CB} \cong \overline{DC}$ because a midpoint divides a segment into two congruent segments. Vertical angles, $\angle ACB$ and $\angle ECD$, are congruent. If for $\triangle ABC$ and $\triangle EDC$ we know $\angle ABC \cong \angle EDC$, $\overline{CB} \cong \overline{CD}$, and $\angle ACB \cong \angle ECD$, then the triangles are congruent using the ASA Congruence Theorem.
 b. You can conclude that *C* is the midpoint of $\overline{AE}$ because $\overline{AC}$ and $\overline{CE}$ are corresponding parts of the congruent triangles and so are congruent.

2. Consider this conjecture:

A diagonal of a rectangle forms two congruent triangles.

a. Draw and label a diagram that illustrates the conjecture. Does it seem to be correct?

b. Write the conjecture in if-then form, in terms of your labeled diagram.

c. List some characteristics of rectangles. Could any of these be used to help you prove the conjecture?

d. Which congruent triangle theorem might you use in your proof? Explain your choice.

e. Individually, write a proof of this conjecture. Compare your proof to those of others in your group.

f. Replace the word "rectangle" in the conjecture with "parallelogram." Is this new conjecture correct? Explain your reasoning.

Often, information about a specific figure is given, and a conjecture (what you or someone else saw) is proposed. Your task is to confirm the conjecture with a proof or show it is wrong with a counterexample.

3. Suppose you are given the following information about the figure shown at the right.

$\overline{ST} \cong \overline{SP}$ and $\overline{TO} \cong \overline{PO}$

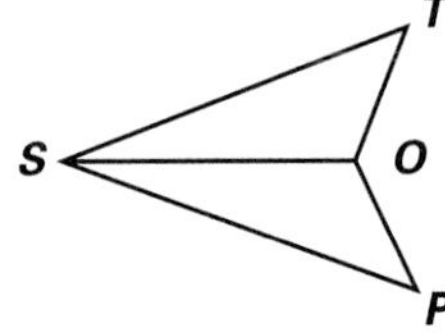

Can you conclude that $\triangle STO \cong \triangle SPO$? Write a proof or give a counterexample.

4. In the diagram below, $\overline{BD}$ is perpendicular to $\overline{AE}$ and C is the midpoint of both $\overline{BD}$ and $\overline{AE}$.

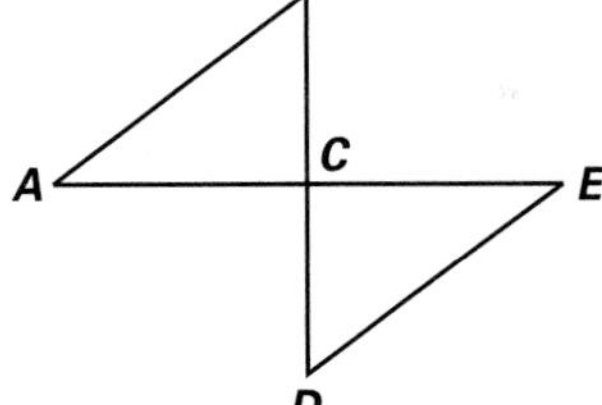

a. Prove that $\triangle ABC \cong \triangle EDC$.

b. Use the given information and your proof that $\triangle ABC \cong \triangle EDC$ to explain why you can also conclude each of the following:

- $\overline{AB} \cong \overline{DE}$
- $\angle ABC \cong \angle EDC$
- $\overleftrightarrow{AB} \parallel \overleftrightarrow{DE}$

c. Can you also conclude that $\overline{BD} \cong \overline{AE}$? Why or why not?

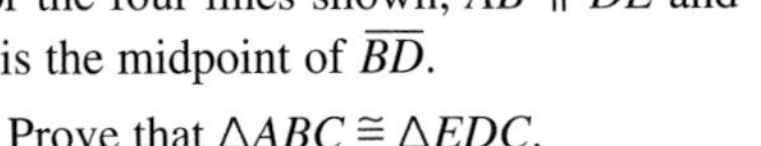

5. For the four lines shown, $\overleftrightarrow{AB} \parallel \overleftrightarrow{DE}$ and C is the midpoint of $\overline{BD}$.

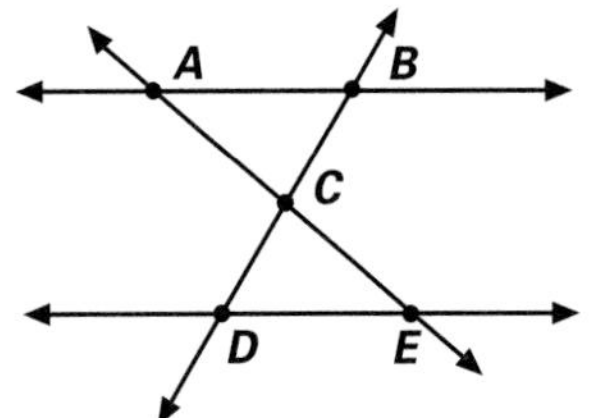

a. Prove that $\triangle ABC \cong \triangle EDC$.

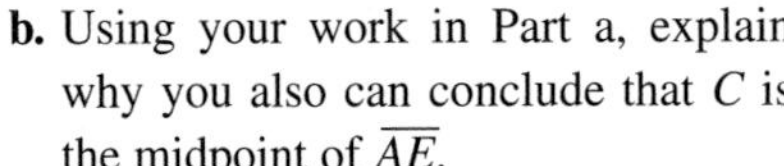

b. Using your work in Part a, explain why you also can conclude that C is the midpoint of $\overline{AE}$.

Unit 4

LESSON 2 • REASONING ABOUT SIMILAR AND CONGRUENT TRIANGLES 317

In the last two activities, you were asked to deduce further conclusions after you had proved two triangles congruent. The conclusions were based on the congruence of the triangles: once triangles are known to be congruent, then all the corresponding angles and sides are also known to be congruent. This is summarized by saying "corresponding parts of congruent triangles are congruent."

Similarity, as well as congruence, is often suggested visually. Again, "looking similar" is not good enough, particularly for an architect or an engineer. They must "know" two shapes are similar. So again, reasoning about the geometry is used to ensure the correctness of the visual impression.

6. Examine the diagram at the right. Does $\triangle ABC$ appear to be similar to $\triangle EDC$? For each condition below, determine if that condition will *guarantee* $\triangle ABC \sim \triangle EDC$. Justify your conclusion.

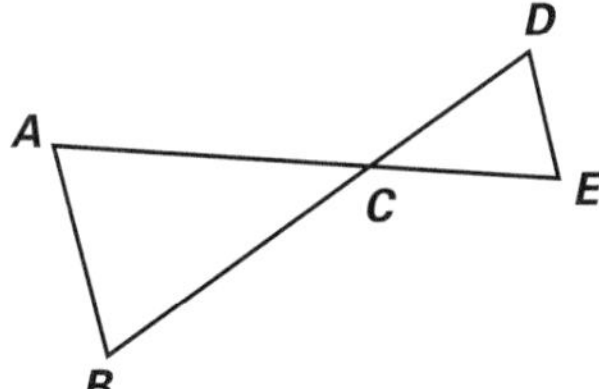

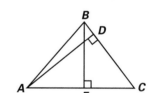

a. $\overleftrightarrow{AB} \parallel \overleftrightarrow{DE}$

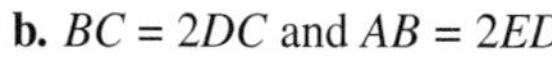

b. $BC = 2DC$ and $AB = 2ED$

c. $\frac{AB}{ED} = \frac{BC}{CD} = \frac{AC}{CE}$

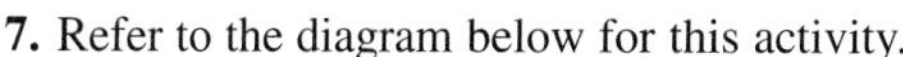

7. Refer to the diagram below for this activity.

a. Prove that if $\overleftrightarrow{DE} \parallel \overleftrightarrow{BC}$, then $\frac{AC}{AE} = \frac{AB}{AD}$.

b. Prove that if $\triangle ABC \sim \triangle ADE$, then $\overleftrightarrow{ED} \parallel \overleftrightarrow{CB}$.

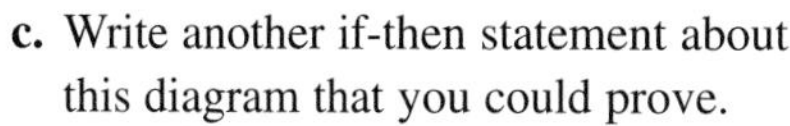

c. Write another if-then statement about this diagram that you could prove.

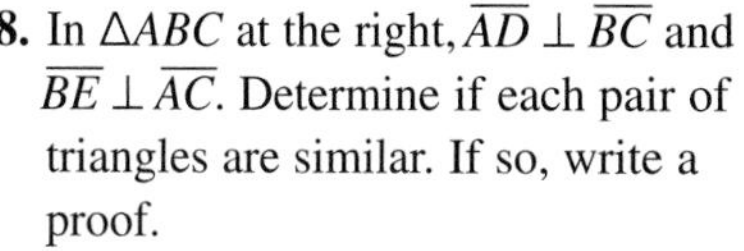

8. In $\triangle ABC$ at the right, $\overline{AD} \perp \overline{BC}$ and $\overline{BE} \perp \overline{AC}$. Determine if each pair of triangles are similar. If so, write a proof.

a. $\triangle ADC \sim \triangle BEC$

b. $\triangle ADB \sim \triangle BEA$

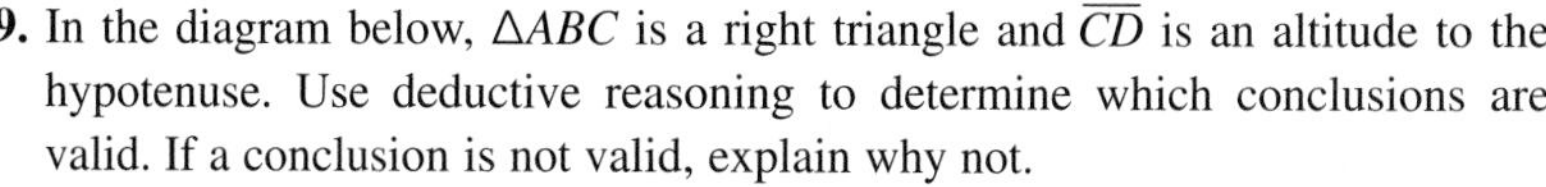

9. In the diagram below, $\triangle ABC$ is a right triangle and $\overline{CD}$ is an altitude to the hypotenuse. Use deductive reasoning to determine which conclusions are valid. If a conclusion is not valid, explain why not.

a. $\triangle ADC \sim \triangle ACB$

b. $\triangle CDB \sim \triangle ACB$

c. $\triangle ADC \sim \triangle CDB$

d. $CD^2 = AD \cdot BD$

e. $CA^2 = BA \cdot DA$

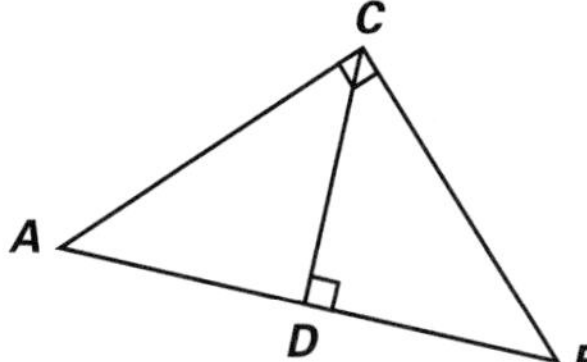

Unit 4

318 UNIT 4 • SHAPES AND GEOMETRIC REASONING

6. **a.** Yes, $\overleftrightarrow{AB} \parallel \overleftrightarrow{DE}$ allows us to conclude that $\triangle ABC \sim \triangle EDC$. We can conclude that $\angle A \cong \angle E$ and $\angle B \cong \angle D$ (alternate interior angles), therefore the triangles are similar using the AA Similarity Theorem.

b. No, we can't conclude the triangles are similar. The vertical angles, $\angle ACB$ and $\angle ECD$, are not included between the given two pairs of sides that are known to be proportional.

c. Yes, we can conclude that $\triangle ABC \sim \triangle EDC$. The ratios of all three sets of corresponding sides are equal, therefore the triangles are similar using the SSS Similarity Theorem.

7. **a.** Since $\overleftrightarrow{DE} \parallel \overleftrightarrow{BC}$, corresponding angles, $\angle AED$ and $\angle ACB$, are congruent. $\angle A$ is congruent to itself. If for $\triangle ABC$ and $\triangle ADE$ we know $\angle AED \cong \angle ACB$ and $\angle A \cong \angle A$, then the triangles are similar using the AA Similarity Theorem. If $\triangle ABC \sim \triangle ADE$, $\frac{AC}{AE} = \frac{AB}{AD}$ because the ratios of corresponding sides of similar triangles are equal.

b. If $\triangle ABC \sim \triangle ADE$, then $\angle ADE \cong \angle ABC$. If $\angle ADE \cong \angle ABC$, then $\overleftrightarrow{ED} \parallel \overleftrightarrow{CB}$ by the Parallel Lines Property.

c. You may wish to have each student write an if-then statement and then have the groups discuss how they could prove (or disprove) each statement.

8. **a.** Given $\overline{AD} \perp \overline{BC}$ and $\overline{BE} \perp \overline{AC}$, we know $\angle ADC \cong \angle BEC$ because perpendicular lines meet to form right angles and all right angles are congruent. $\angle C$ is congruent to itself. If for $\triangle ADC$ and $\triangle BEC$ we know $\angle ADC \cong \angle BEC$ and $\angle C$ is congruent to itself, then the triangles are similar using the AA Similarity Theorem.

b. You cannot prove that $\triangle ADB \sim \triangle BEA$ because you cannot determine congruence for either of the acute angle pairs. (Students may note that the triangles share a common side, but that fact is not sufficient to prove similarity.)

9. Proofs may vary. Examples are given.

a. $\angle A$ is congruent to itself. $\angle ADC \cong \angle ACB$ since they both are right angles. If $\angle A \cong \angle A$ and $\angle ADC \cong \angle ACB$, then $\triangle ADC \sim \triangle ACB$ by the AA Similarity Theorem.

b. $\angle ACB$ and $\angle CDB$ are right angles and are congruent because all right angles are congruent. $\angle B$ is congruent to itself. If $\angle ACB \cong \angle CDB$ and $\angle B$ is congruent to itself, then the triangles are similar using the AA Similarity Theorem.

c. By Parts a and b, $\triangle ADC \sim \triangle ACB$ and $\triangle CDB \sim \triangle ACB$. Since both are similar to the same triangle, $\triangle ADC \sim \triangle CDB$.

d. $\frac{CD}{BD} = \frac{AD}{CD}$ because $\triangle ADC \sim \triangle CDB$ (Part c). If $\frac{CD}{BD} = \frac{AD}{CD}$, then $CD^2 = AD \cdot BD$.

e. If $\triangle ACB \sim \triangle ADC$ (by Part a), then $\frac{CA}{BA} = \frac{DA}{CA}$ because the ratio of corresponding parts of similar triangles are equal. If $\frac{CA}{BA} = \frac{DA}{CA}$, then $CA^2 = BA \cdot DA$.

Master 105

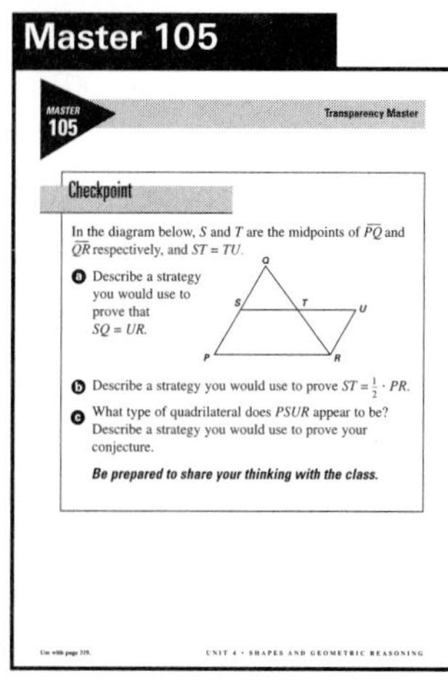

MASTER 105 — Transparency Master

Checkpoint

In the diagram below, S and T are the midpoints of $\overline{PQ}$ and $\overline{QR}$ respectively, and $ST = TU$.

a Describe a strategy you would use to prove that $SQ = UR$.

b Describe a strategy you would use to prove $ST = \frac{1}{2} \cdot PR$.

c What type of quadrilateral does $PSUR$ appear to be? Describe a strategy you would use to prove your conjecture.

Be prepared to share your thinking with the class.

Use with page 319. UNIT 4 • SHAPES AND GEOMETRIC REASONING

SHARE AND SUMMARIZE full-class discussion

Checkpoint

See Teaching Master 105.

a Show that $\triangle QTS \cong \triangle RTU$ by using the SAS Congruence Theorem. Then the corresponding parts $\overline{SQ}$ and $\overline{UR}$ must also be congruent.

b Use the SAS Similarity Theorem to show that $\triangle QST \sim \triangle QPR$ with a scale factor of 2. Thus, $\frac{PR}{ST} = 2$ and $ST = \frac{1}{2}PR$.

c Quadrilateral $PSUR$ appears to be a parallelogram. Prove $\triangle QST \sim \triangle QPR$, so $\angle QST \cong \angle QPR$ and thus, by the Parallel Lines Property, $\overleftrightarrow{ST} \parallel \overleftrightarrow{PR}$. Then show $\triangle QST \cong \triangle RUT$, so $\angle SQT \cong \angle URT$ and thus, by the Parallel Lines Property, $\overleftrightarrow{SQ} \parallel \overleftrightarrow{UR}$. If $\overleftrightarrow{SQ} \parallel \overleftrightarrow{UR}$ and $\overleftrightarrow{ST} \parallel \overleftrightarrow{PR}$, then quadrilateral $PSUR$ is a parallelogram.

NOTE: You may wish to use the journal entry below as an assignment and follow with a full-class discussion of the students' responses.

JOURNAL ENTRY: Review the several proofs that you completed in this investigation and consider the various "tricks" you used. ("Tricks" include identifying vertical angles, angles that appear in both triangles, or corresponding or alternate interior angles from given parallel lines.) Using this list, comment on which proof was difficult to see and which you found easily. With which are you comfortable, and with which do you feel you still need to practice?

APPLY individual task

On Your Own

a.
- $\triangle PAD \sim \triangle PCD$ by the AA Similarity Theorem.
- $\triangle PAD \cong \triangle PCD$ by the ASA Congruence Theorem.
- Since $\triangle PAD \cong \triangle PCD$, the corresponding sides $\overline{PA}$ and $\overline{PC}$ will have the same length.
- $\triangle PAB \cong \triangle PCB$ by the SAS Congruence Theorem.

b. Students should choose one of the statements to prove. All are proven below.
- We are given that $m\angle 1 = m\angle 2$. If $\overline{PB} \perp \overline{AC}$, then $\angle ADP \cong \angle CDP$ because perpendicular lines meet to form right angles and all right angles are congruent. So $\triangle PAD \sim \triangle PCD$ by the AA Similarity Theorem.
- As above, $m\angle 1 = m\angle 2$ and $\angle ADP \cong \angle CDP$. Also, $\overline{PD} \cong \overline{PD}$. Thus, $\triangle PAD \cong \triangle PCD$ by the ASA Congruence Theorem.
- If $\triangle PAD \cong \triangle PCD$ (see above), then $PA = PC$ because corresponding parts of congruent triangles are congruent.
- $\overline{PB}$ is congruent to itself. If for $\triangle PAB$ and $\triangle PCB$ we know $PA = PC$, $\overline{PB} \cong \overline{PB}$, and $m\angle 1 = m\angle 2$ (see above), then the triangles are congruent using the SAS Congruence Theorem.

Unit 4

Checkpoint

In the diagram below, S and T are the midpoints of $\overline{PQ}$ and $\overline{QR}$ respectively, and $ST = TU$.

a Describe a strategy you would use to prove that $SQ = UR$.

b Describe a strategy you would use to prove $ST = \frac{1}{2} \cdot PR$.

c What type of quadrilateral does $PSUR$ appear to be? Describe a strategy you would use to prove your conjecture.

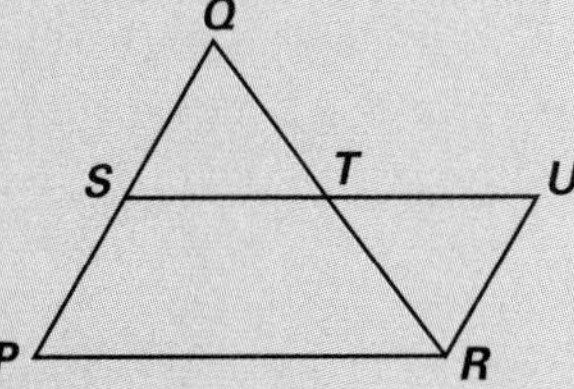

Be prepared to share your thinking with the class.

On Your Own

In the diagram below, $m\angle 1 = m\angle 2$ and $\overline{PB} \perp \overline{AC}$.

a. Which of the following conclusions can you deduce?

- $\triangle PAD \sim \triangle PCD$
- $\triangle PAD \cong \triangle PCD$
- $PA = PC$
- $\triangle PAB \cong \triangle PCB$

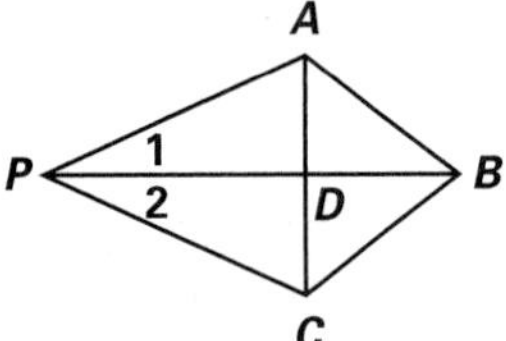

b. Choose one conclusion you can deduce and write an argument proving it.

MORE

Modeling • Organizing • Reflecting • Extending

Modeling

1. Drafters and people involved in industrial design use a variety of tools in their work. Depending on the nature of the task, these tools vary from sophisticated CAD (computer-assisted design) software to *compasses* (instruments for drawing circles and arcs) and *straightedges* (devices for drawing lines that have no marks for measuring).

Unit 4

LESSON 2 • REASONING ABOUT SIMILAR AND CONGRUENT TRIANGLES 319

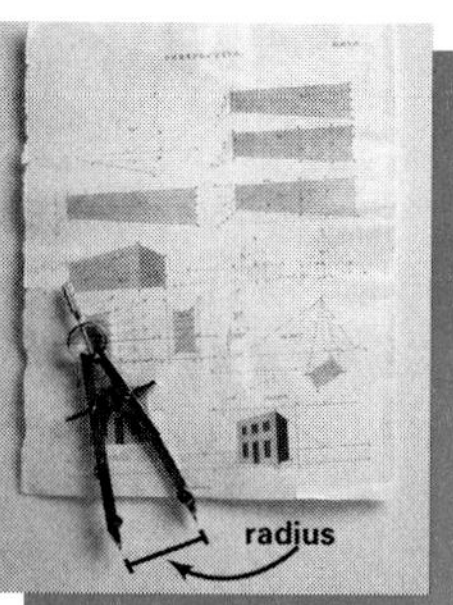

a. Draw an acute angle, $\angle ABC$. Using a compass, a straightedge, and the algorithm below, construct the bisector of $\angle ABC$. A **bisector of an angle** is a ray that begins at the vertex of the angle and divides the angle into two angles of equal measure.

Angle Bisector Algorithm: To bisect $\angle ABC$, do the following.

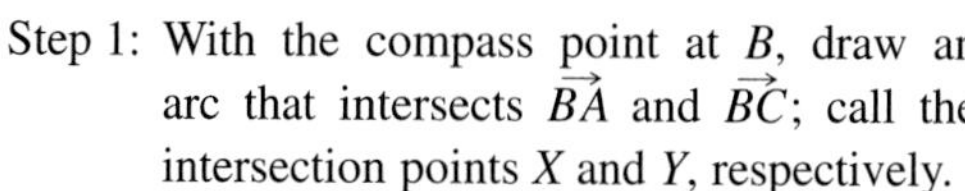

Step 1: With the compass point at B, draw an arc that intersects $\overrightarrow{BA}$ and $\overrightarrow{BC}$; call the intersection points X and Y, respectively.

Step 2: With the compass point at point X (and then at point Y) and using a radius greater than $\frac{1}{2}XY$, draw two arcs that intersect in the interior of $\angle ABC$. Label the point of intersection D.

Step 3: Draw the ray BD. Ray BD bisects $\angle ABC$.

b. Prove that this algorithm produces the bisector of an angle. That is, prove that $\overrightarrow{BD}$ bisects $\angle ABC$.

c. Can this algorithm be used to construct the bisector of an obtuse angle? Explain your reasoning.

2. In this task, you will examine an algorithm for duplicating an angle using a straightedge and a compass or using a computer-based drawing program.

a. Carefully draw an angle, $\angle ABC$. Then use the following algorithm to construct an angle congruent to $\angle ABC$.

Angle Construction Algorithm: To construct an angle PQR congruent to the given angle, $\angle ABC$, do the following.

Step 1: Use a straightedge to draw $\overrightarrow{QR}$.

Step 2: With B as the center, construct an arc that intersects sides $\overrightarrow{BA}$ and $\overrightarrow{BC}$ of $\angle ABC$; label the intersections points D and E respectively.

Step 3: With point Q as the center and radius BD, construct an arc which intersects $\overrightarrow{QR}$; label the intersection point S.

Step 4: With center point S and radius DE, construct an arc which intersects the arc in Step 3. Label the intersection point P.

Step 5: Draw $\overrightarrow{QP}$. Then $\angle PQR \cong \angle ABC$.

b. Prove that the two angles in Step 5 are congruent.

c. Carefully draw a triangle, $\triangle XYZ$. Design and test an algorithm for using a compass and a straightedge to construct $\triangle ABC$ so that $\triangle ABC \cong \triangle XYZ$. Prove that your algorithm will always work.

Unit 4

320 UNIT 4 • SHAPES AND GEOMETRIC REASONING

MORE independent assignment

Modeling

1. a. See student constructions of the angle bisector $\overrightarrow{BD}$.

   b.

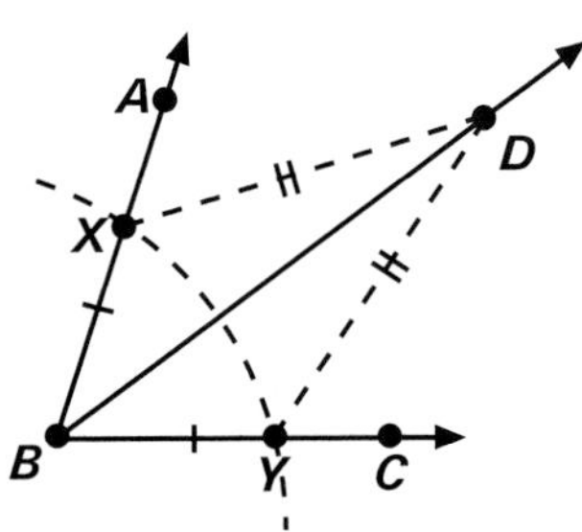

Step 1 of the algorithm assures that $BX = BY$. Step 2 of the algorithm assures that $XD = YD$. Of course, $BD = BD$. So by the SSS Congruence Theorem, $\triangle BXD \cong \triangle BYD$. Thus, $m\angle ABD = m\angle CBD$, and so $\overrightarrow{BD}$ bisects $\angle ABC$.

   c. Yes, there is nothing about the algorithm that limits its use to acute angles.

2. a. See student constructions.

   b.

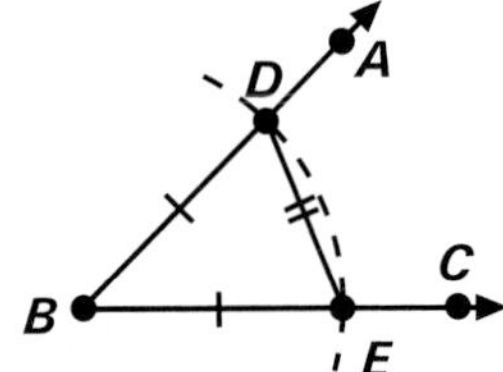

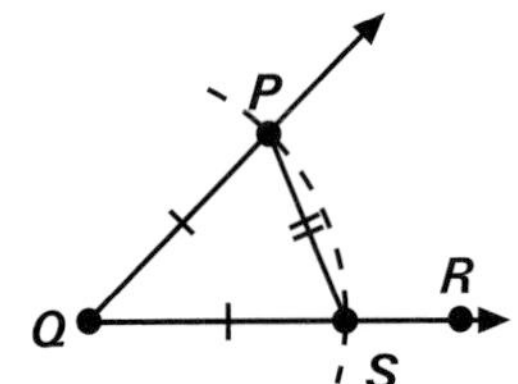

Step 3 makes $BE = QS$. Step 4 makes $DE = PS$. Since P is on the arc with radius BD, $BD = QP$. Thus, by the SSS Congruence Theorem, $\triangle BDE \cong \triangle QPS$. Thus, $\angle ABC \cong \angle PQR$.

   c. Responses will vary. The algorithms should be based on one of the triangle congruence theorems. You may wish to have students discuss their algorithms with each other in order to see that more than one algorithm is possible. One way to construct the triangle would be to duplicate one angle as in Part b, then use the compass to mark corresponding congruent sides that include the duplicated angle. For example, after duplicating $\angle XYZ$ to match $\angle B$, make $\overline{AB} \cong \overline{XY}$ and $\overline{BC} \cong \overline{YZ}$.

MORE

ASSIGNMENT *pp. 319–324*

Modeling: 1 or 2, and choice of one*

Organizing: 1 and 5

Reflecting: 2 and 5

Extending: 1 and 3

**When choice is indicated, it is important to leave the choice to the student.*

NOTE: *It is best if Organizing tasks are discussed as a whole class after they have been assigned as homework.*

Unit 4

MORE *continued*

3. a. Yes: If $AE = k \cdot AC$, $m\angle A = m\angle A$, and $AD = k \cdot AB$, then $\triangle AED \sim \triangle ACB$ by the SAS Similarity Theorem. If $\triangle AED \sim \triangle ACB$, then $m\angle AED = m\angle ACB$.
   b. No, you cannot prove that $\overleftrightarrow{BC} \parallel \overleftrightarrow{ED}$ because you have no congruence relation for $\angle CBA$ and $\angle DEA$ or for $\angle BCA$ and $\angle EDA$.
   c. Since $\triangle AED \sim \triangle ACB$ (see Part a), $\frac{AE}{AC} = \frac{ED}{CB}$.

NOTE: Since students will prove in Modeling Task 4 that the length of the angle bisectors drawn to the opposite sides, the altitudes, and the medians of similar triangles are proportional, these theorem statements could be entered in students' Math Toolkits.

4. **These three items in Activity 4 are important because they show that the scale factor associated with two similar triangles is also the scale factor for corresponding angle bisectors, medians, and altitudes in the two triangles. This fact is needed, for example, to confirm the k^2 relationship between the areas of two similar polygonal figures. Once these relationships are proved they can be placed in Math Toolkits.**
   a. If $\triangle ABC \sim \triangle XYZ$, then $\angle ABC \cong \angle XYZ$ and $\angle A \cong \angle X$. If $\angle ABC \cong \angle XYZ$, $\overrightarrow{BD}$ bisects $\angle ABC$, and $\overrightarrow{YW}$ bisects $\angle XYZ$, then $\angle ABD \cong \angle XYW$. If $\angle A \cong \angle X$ and $\angle ABD \cong \angle XYW$, then $\triangle ABD \sim \triangle XYW$. Since $XY = k \cdot AB$, the scale factor for $\triangle ABD$ and $\triangle XYW$ is k. If $\triangle ABD \sim \triangle XYW$ with scale factor k, then $YW = k \cdot BD$.
   b. If $\triangle ABC \sim \triangle XYZ$ and $k \cdot AB = XY$, then $\angle A \cong \angle X$ and $k \cdot AC = XZ$. If D and W are midpoints of $\overline{AC}$ and $\overline{XZ}$, respectively, then $AD = \frac{1}{2}AC$ and $XW = \frac{1}{2}XZ$. If $k \cdot AC = XZ$, $AD = \frac{AC}{2}$, and $XW = \frac{XZ}{2}$, then $2kAD = 2XW$ or $k \cdot AD = XW$. If $k \cdot AB = XY$, $\angle A \cong \angle X$, and $k \cdot AD = XW$, then $\triangle ABD \sim \triangle XYW$ with scale factor k. If $\triangle ABD \sim \triangle XYW$ with scale factor k, then $YW = k \cdot BD$.
   c. If $\overline{BD} \perp \overline{AC}$ and $\overline{YW} \perp \overline{XZ}$, then $\angle BDA \cong \angle YWX$ because both are right angles. If $\triangle ABC \sim \triangle XYZ$, then $\angle A \cong \angle X$. If $\angle A \cong \angle X$ and $\angle BDA \cong \angle YWX$, then $\triangle ABD \sim \triangle XYW$. If $\triangle ABD \sim \triangle XYW$ and $XY = k \cdot AB$, then the scale factor between $\triangle ABD$ and $\triangle XYW$ is k. If $\triangle ABD \sim \triangle XYW$ with scale factor k, then $YW = k \cdot BD$.
5. a. Since $\overleftrightarrow{TO} \parallel \overleftrightarrow{SP}$, we know $\angle TOS \cong \angle PSO$ (alternate interior angles). Since $\overleftrightarrow{TH} \parallel \overleftrightarrow{PA}$, we know $\angle THO \cong \angle PAS$ (alternate interior angles). We were given $\overline{TO} \cong \overline{SP}$. If $\angle TOS \cong \angle PSO$, $\angle THO \cong \angle PAS$, and $\overline{TO} \cong \overline{SP}$, then $\triangle THO \cong \triangle PAS$ by the AAS Congruence Theorem. Therefore, $\overline{TH} \cong \overline{PA}$ (CPCTC).
   b. Since $\overleftrightarrow{TO} \parallel \overleftrightarrow{SP}$, we know $\angle TOS \cong \angle PSO$ (alternate interior angles). We were given that $\overline{TO} \cong \overline{SP}$ and we know that $\overline{SO} \cong \overline{SO}$. So $\triangle TOS \cong \triangle PSO$ by the SAS Congruence Theorem. Therefore, $\angle TSH \cong \angle POA$ (CPCTC). Also, $\angle SHT \cong \angle OAP$ because they are alternate exterior angles for parallel lines $\overleftrightarrow{TH}$ and $\overleftrightarrow{AP}$. From Part a we know that $\overline{TH} \cong \overline{PA}$. Therefore, $\triangle STH \cong \triangle OPA$ by the AAS Congruence Theorem.

Organizing

1. a. Perpendicular Bisector Algorithm for $\overline{AB}$.
   Step 1: With compass point at A and radius greater than $\frac{1}{2}AB$, draw an arc above and below $\overline{AB}$.
   Step 2: With compass point at B and the same radius as used in Step 1, draw arcs above and below $\overline{AB}$ that intersect the two arcs drawn in Step 1. Label the points of intersection X and Y.
   Step 3: Draw $\overleftrightarrow{XY}$. $\overleftrightarrow{XY}$ is the perpendicular bisector of $\overline{AB}$.

See additional Teaching Notes on page T344J.

Unit 4

3. In the diagram at the right, $AE = k \cdot AC$ and $AD = k \cdot AB$.

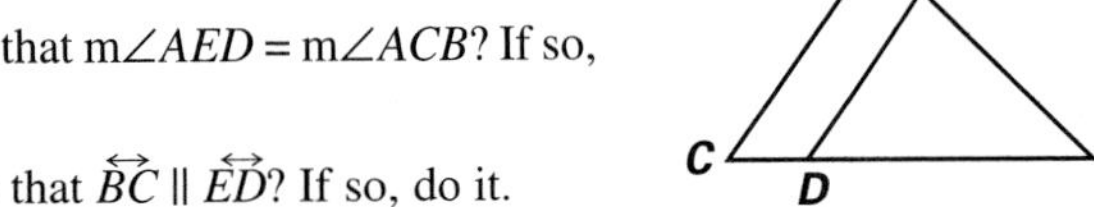

   a. Can you prove that $m\angle AED = m\angle ACB$? If so, do it.

   b. Can you prove that $\overleftrightarrow{BC} \parallel \overleftrightarrow{ED}$? If so, do it.

   c. Can you prove that $\frac{AE}{AC} = \frac{ED}{CB}$? If so, do it.

4. In the diagram below, $\triangle ABC \sim \triangle XYZ$ with scale factor k. So $XY = k \cdot AB$. In each part below, you are given additional information.

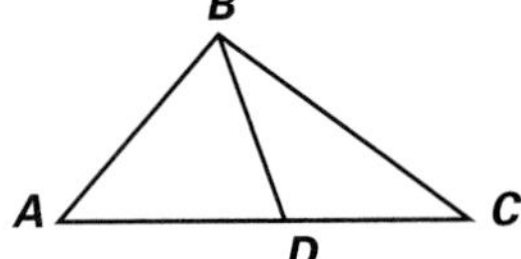

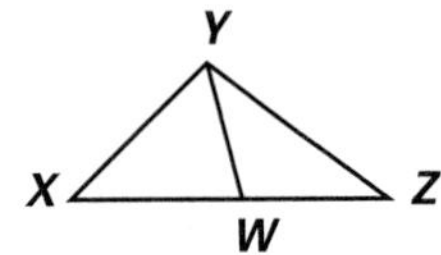

   a. In addition, $\overrightarrow{BD}$ bisects $\angle ABC$, and $\overrightarrow{YW}$ bisects $\angle XYZ$. Prove that $YW = k \cdot BD$.

   b. In addition, point D is the midpoint of $\overline{AC}$, and W is the midpoint of $\overline{XZ}$. Prove that $YW = k \cdot BD$.

   c. In addition, $\overline{BD} \perp \overline{AC}$ and $\overline{YW} \perp \overline{XZ}$. Prove that $YW = k \cdot BD$.

5. In the diagram shown here, $\overline{TO} \cong \overline{SP}$, $\overleftrightarrow{TO} \parallel \overleftrightarrow{SP}$, and $\overleftrightarrow{TH} \parallel \overleftrightarrow{PA}$.

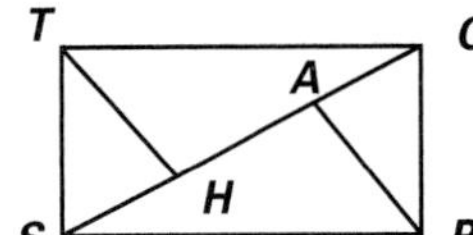

   a. Prove that $\overline{TH} \cong \overline{PA}$.

   b. Prove that $\triangle STH \cong \triangle OPA$.

Organizing

1. A **perpendicular bisector of a segment** is a line (or segment or ray) that is perpendicular to the segment at its midpoint.

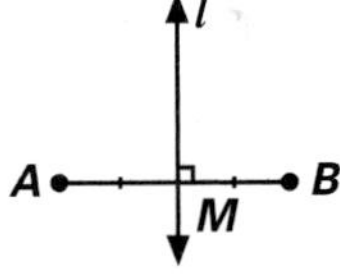

   a. Refer back to the Angle Bisector Algorithm in Modeling Task 1, page 320. How could you modify that algorithm to develop a *Perpendicular Bisector Algorithm* for a segment AB?

   b. Draw a segment AB. Use your algorithm and a compass and straightedge to construct the perpendicular bisector of the segment. Prove that your algorithm produces the perpendicular bisector of $\overline{AB}$.

2. Refer back to your proof of the Angle Construction Algorithm, which you developed in Part b of Modeling Task 2 (page 320).

   a. On which of the congruence theorems (SAS, ASA, AAS, or SSS) did your proof depend?

   b. Develop triangle construction algorithms that are based on two of the other congruence theorems. Test your algorithms and explain why they will always work.

Unit 4

LESSON 2 • REASONING ABOUT SIMILAR AND CONGRUENT TRIANGLES 321

3. Suppose $\Delta ABC \sim \Delta XYZ$ with scale factor k such that $XY = k \cdot AB$.

   a. Is it correct to say $\frac{XY}{AB} = \frac{YZ}{BC} = \frac{XZ}{AC}$? If so, what is the common ratio? Explain your reasoning.

   b. Find the value of $\frac{XY}{AB} + \frac{YZ}{BC}$. Find the value of $\frac{XY + YZ}{AB + BC}$.

   c. If $\frac{XY}{AB} = \frac{YZ}{BC}$, do the equations below necessarily follow? For each, explain why or why not.

   - $\frac{XY + AB}{AB} = \frac{YZ + BC}{BC}$
   - $\frac{XY - AB}{AB} = \frac{YZ - BC}{BC}$

4. Recall that a proportion is a statement that two ratios are equal, such as $\frac{a}{b} = \frac{c}{d}$.

   a. Suppose $\Delta ABC \sim \Delta XYZ$ and the scale factor is k. Why is it correct to say the corresponding sides are proportional?

   b. Restate the SAS and SSS Similarity Theorems using the language of proportions.

   c. Solve this proportion for t: $\frac{t+3}{5} = \frac{t}{4}$.

5. Prove or disprove each of the following statements.

   a. If $\overline{AB}$ and $\overline{CD}$ are congruent chords in a circle with center O, then the central angles, $\angle AOB$ and $\angle COD$, are congruent.

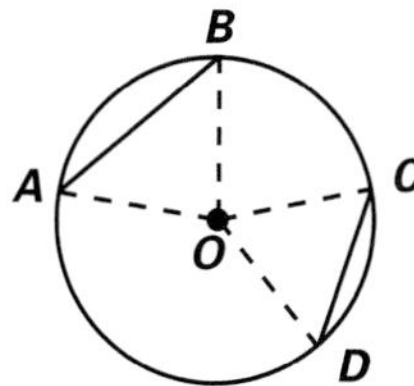

   b. If a line through the center of a circle is perpendicular to a chord AB, then it bisects the chord.

Reflecting

1. In this unit, you have used the term "corresponding angles" in the context of parallel lines cut by a transversal and in the contexts of similarity and congruence of triangles. Draw sketches illustrating the different meanings of "corresponding angles."

2. Is similarity or congruence harder for you to detect visually? Is similarity or congruence of shapes more difficult for you to prove? Explain your thinking.

3. What determines the shape of a polygon, its angles or its sides? Explain your reasoning.

Unit 4

322 UNIT 4 • SHAPES AND GEOMETRIC REASONING

3. **a.** The similarity implies $XY = kAB$, $YZ = kBC$, and $XZ = kAC$. Therefore, it is correct to say $\frac{XY}{AB} = \frac{YZ}{BC} = \frac{XZ}{AC}$. Each ratio is equal to k.

b. $\frac{XY}{AB} + \frac{YZ}{BC} = k + k = 2k$

$\frac{XY + YZ}{AB + BC} = \frac{kAB + kBC}{AB + BC} = k\left(\frac{AB + BC}{AB + BC}\right) = k$

c. ■ This statement is true.

$\frac{XY + AB}{AB} = \frac{XY}{AB} + \frac{AB}{AB} = \frac{YZ}{BC} + \frac{BC}{BC} = \frac{YZ + BC}{BC}$

■ This statement is true.

$\frac{XY - AB}{AB} = \frac{XY}{AB} - \frac{AB}{AB} = \frac{YZ}{BC} - \frac{BC}{BC} = \frac{YZ - BC}{BC}$

4. **a.** Since similarity implies $XY = kAB$ and $YZ = kBC$, then $\frac{XY}{AB} = k = \frac{YZ}{BC}$. Thus, the sides are proportional.

b. SAS: If the lengths of two sides of one triangle are proportional to the lengths of the corresponding sides of another triangle and the included angles are congruent, then the triangles are similar.

SSS: If the lengths of three sides of one triangle are proportional to the lengths of corresponding sides of another triangle, then the triangles are similar.

c. $\frac{t + 3}{5} = \frac{t}{4} \Rightarrow (t + 3)4 = 5t \Rightarrow 4t + 12 = 5t \Rightarrow t = 12$

5. **a.** The statement is true. In a circle, all the radii are equal. Thus, $OB = OD$ and $OA = OC$. We are given that $AB = CD$. Thus, by the SSS Congruence Theorem, $\triangle ABO \cong \triangle CDO$. It follows that $\angle AOB \cong \angle COD$ since they are corresponding angles.

b. Students should draw a diagram before trying to prove that this statement is correct. The proof given here refers to the diagram at the right. Draw radii $\overline{OB}$ and $\overline{OA}$. In $\triangle AOC$ and $\triangle BOC$, $AO = OB$ (radii of the same circle), $CO = CO$, and $\angle ACO \cong \angle BCO$ (both are right angles). Thus, $\triangle BOC \cong \triangle AOC$ by the Hypotenuse Leg Theorem. (See Extending Task 3, page 315). Thus, $AC = CB$ since they are corresponding parts. So $\overleftrightarrow{OC}$ bisects $\overline{AB}$.

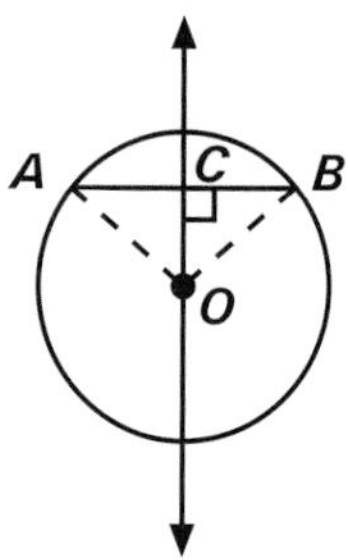

Reflecting

1. In the context of parallel lines cut by a transversal, corresponding angles are angles that are in the same relative position with respect to the parallel lines and the transversal. For example, in the diagram at the right, $\angle 1$ and $\angle 5$ are corresponding angles. The other pairs of corresponding angles are $\angle 2$ and $\angle 6$, $\angle 3$ and $\angle 7$, and $\angle 4$ and $\angle 8$.

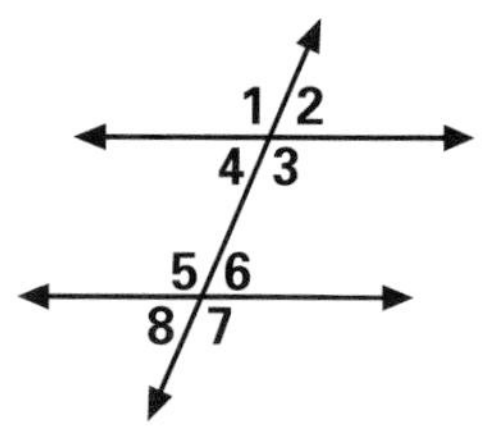

In the context of similarity and congruence of triangles, corresponding angles are those angles that are congruent. If $\triangle ABC \sim \triangle DEF$, then corresponding angles are $\angle A$ and $\angle D$, $\angle B$ and $\angle E$, and $\angle C$ and $\angle F$.

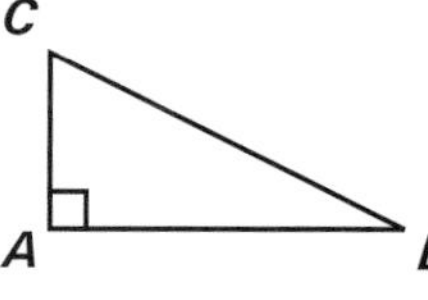

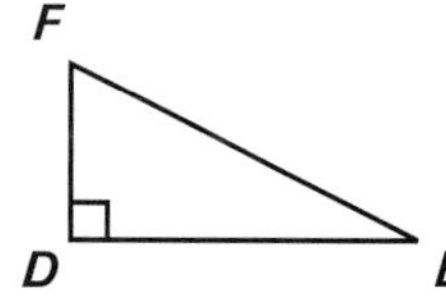

2. Most students will probably say that similarity is harder to detect than congruence. Students should give some explanation for their responses.

3. The angles determine the shape. The side lengths determine only the size of the shape when the angle sizes remain constant.

MORE *continued*

4. This is a valid test. It simply uses a size transformation to check for similarity.

5. **a.** In the diagram at the right, if l is the perpendicular bisector of $\overline{AB}$, then $\overline{AM} \cong \overline{MB}$. Also, if X is any point on l, then $\angle XMB \cong \angle XMA$ and $\overline{XM} \cong \overline{XM}$. Thus, $\triangle XMA \cong \triangle XMB$ by the SAS Congruence Theorem. Thus, $XA = XB$, since $\overline{XA}$ and $\overline{XB}$ are corresponding parts of congruent triangles.

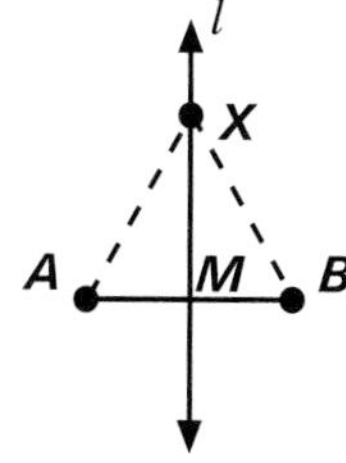

   b. If a point is on the perpendicular bisector of a segment, then it is equidistant from the endpoints of the segment.

   c. If a point is equidistant from the endpoints of a segment, then the point is on the perpendicular bisector of the segment. The converse is a correct statement in this case. Consider the diagram to the right, with X any point that is equidistant from points A and B ($XA = XB$). Draw the line through point X and perpendicular to $\overline{AB}$. Call the point of intersection M. Then $\triangle AXM \cong \triangle BXM$ by the Hypotenuse Leg Theorem. (See Extending Task 3, page 315.) Thus, $AM = BM$ and so X is on the perpendicular bisector of $\overline{AB}$.

Extending

NOTE: Be sure that students include the Triangle Inequality Theorem in their Math Toolkits.

1. By the Law of Cosines, we know that

$$a^2 = b^2 + c^2 - 2bc\cos A.$$

However, $\cos A \geq -1$. If we replace $\cos A$ in the above expression with -1, we are replacing it with the smallest value it could be. Thus, $b^2 + c^2 - 2bc(-1)$ is the *largest* value that $b^2 + c^2 - 2bc\cos A$ could be. (The value of $\cos A$ is -1 only when $m\angle A = (180 + 360k)^\circ$, where k is an integer. This cannot happen in a triangle, so we can remove the equality.)

$$a^2 = b^2 + c^2 - 2bc\cos A$$
$$a^2 < b^2 + c^2 - 2bc(-1)$$
$$a^2 < b^2 + c^2 + 2bc$$
$$a^2 < b^2 + 2bc + c^2$$
$$a^2 < (b + c)^2 \text{ and}$$

$a < b + c$ Since a, b, and c are all lengths, they must be positive. Thus, negative square roots can be ignored.

4. A quick test that engravers and photographers use to determine whether two shapes are similar is illustrated in the diagram below.

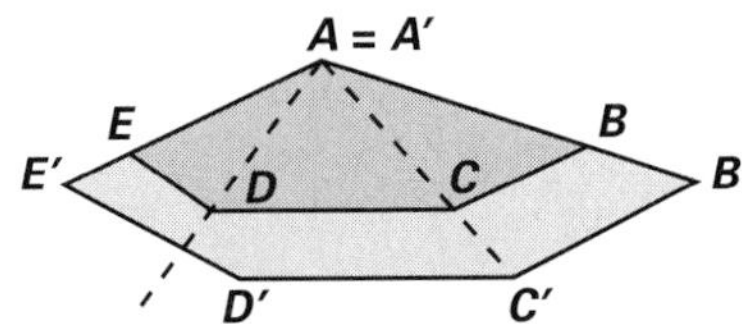

One shape is placed on top of the other so that the vertices of a pair of corresponding angles are at the same point and corresponding sides coincide. If each line from the vertex of an angle of one polygon contains the corresponding vertex of the other, then the shapes are similar. Explain why this is, or is not, a valid test.

5. A very useful geometric fact is that *any* point on the perpendicular bisector of a segment is equidistant from the endpoints of the segment (see Organizing Task 1, page 321).
   - **a.** Explain why this fact is true.
   - **b.** Write this fact in if-then form.
   - **c.** Write the converse of the statement in Part b. Is the converse a correct statement in this case? Why or why not?

Extending

1. After the Pythagorean Theorem, the Triangle Inequality Theorem is perhaps one of the geometry theorems most widely used in mathematics. The theorem captures a very simple idea: The shortest distance between two points is a straight line.

Triangle Inequality Theorem

The sum of the lengths of two sides of a triangle is greater than the length of the third side.

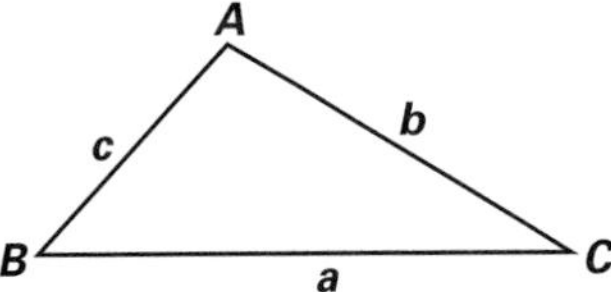

Use the Law of Cosines and the fact that $\cos A \geq -1$ to prove that in $\triangle ABC$, $b + c > a$.

LESSON 2 • REASONING ABOUT SIMILAR AND CONGRUENT TRIANGLES 323

2. Use the following diagram for Parts a and b.

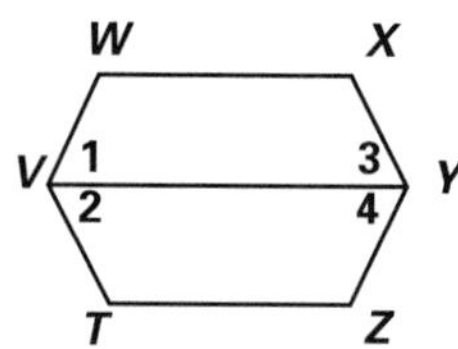

a. Given: $\angle 1 \cong \angle 2$, $\overline{VW} \cong \overline{VT}$, $\overline{WX} \cong \overline{TZ}$, and $\overline{XY} \cong \overline{YZ}$

Prove: $\angle W \cong \angle T$ (*Hint:* You need triangles; draw some segments to form them.)

b. Given: $\overline{WV} \cong \overline{VT}$, $\angle 1 \cong \angle 2$, $\angle 3 \cong \angle 4$, and $\overline{XY} \cong \overline{YZ}$

Prove: $\overline{WX} \cong \overline{TZ}$

3. Recall that an isosceles triangle is a triangle with at least two sides congruent. Suppose triangle *PQR* is an isosceles triangle in which $\overline{QR} \cong \overline{PR}$.

R

P Q

a. Using the idea of line symmetry, what can you conclude about $\angle P$ and $\angle Q$?

b. Prove your conjecture in Part a by first drawing the bisector of $\angle R$ on a copy of the diagram.

c. Prove your conjecture in Part a by first drawing a segment connecting point *R* and the midpoint of $\overline{PQ}$ on a copy of the diagram.

d. Write a coordinate proof of your conjecture in Part a by first placing $\triangle PQR$ on a coordinate system with $P(0, 0)$, $Q(2a, 0)$, and $R(a, b)$.

4. In the diagram at the right, $\overline{BF}$ is the perpendicular bisector of $\overline{AC}$ (see Organizing Task 1, page 321) and $\angle 1 \cong \angle 2$. Prove that $\overline{DB} \cong \overline{BE}$.

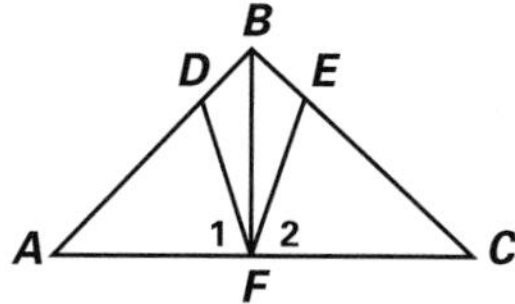

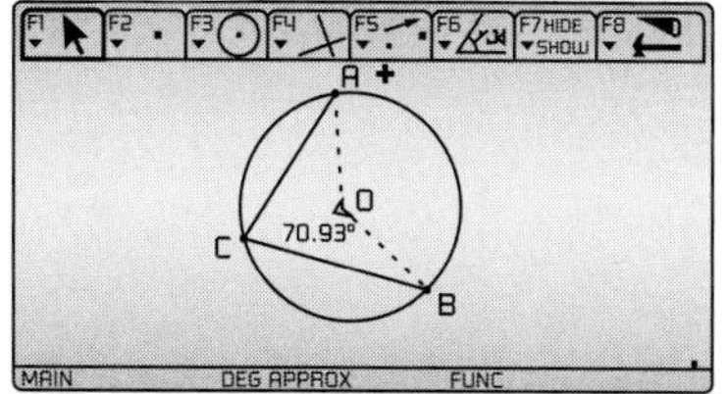

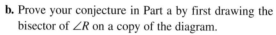

5. Investigate how the measures of an inscribed angle and a central angle which intercept the same arc on a circle are related.

a. Suppose $\angle ACB$ is inscribed in a circle with center *O* and *O* is on $\overline{CB}$. Determine the relation between the measures of $\angle ACB$ and $\angle AOB$.

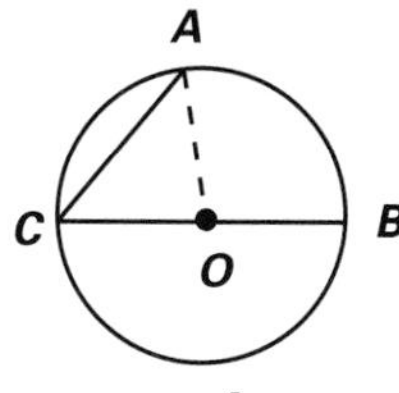

b. Suppose $\angle ACB$ is inscribed in a circle with center *O* and *O* is not on $\overline{CB}$. Determine the relation between the measures of $\angle ACB$ and $\angle AOB$.

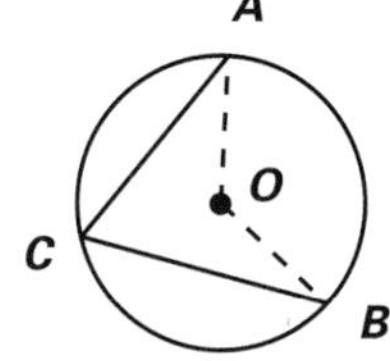

c. The degree measure of *minor arc AB* (written $\overset{\frown}{AB}$) is the measure of its central angle, $\angle AOB$. What is the relation between the measures of an inscribed angle and its intercepted arc?

Unit 4

324 UNIT 4 • SHAPES AND GEOMETRIC REASONING

Assessments 164–166

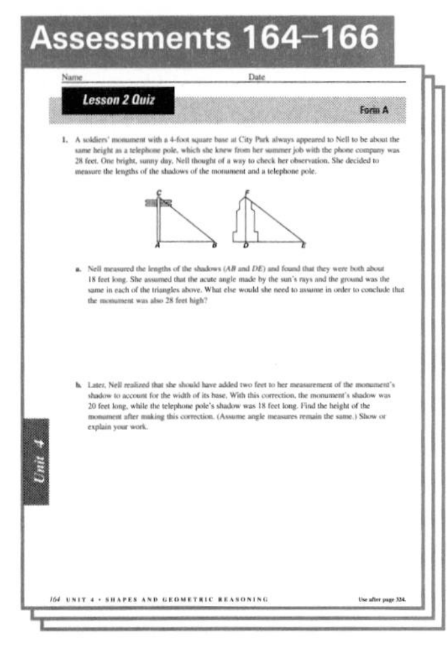

2. a. Draw $\overline{WY}$ and $\overline{TY}$. We are given that $\angle 1 \cong \angle 2$ and $\overline{WV} \cong \overline{VT}$. Also, $\overline{VY} \cong \overline{VY}$. So $\triangle VWY \cong \triangle VTY$ by the SAS Congruence Theorem. Thus, $\overline{WY} \cong \overline{TY}$ and $\angle VWY \cong \angle VTY$ by CPCTC. Since $\overline{WY} \cong \overline{TY}$, $\overline{WX} \cong \overline{TZ}$, and $\overline{XY} \cong \overline{YZ}$, $\triangle WXY \cong \triangle TZY$ by the SSS Congruence Theorem. So $\angle YWX \cong \angle YTZ$ by CPCTC. If $\angle VWY \cong \angle VTY$ and $\angle YWX \cong \angle YTZ$, then $m\angle VWY + m\angle YWX = m\angle VTY + m\angle YTZ$. But $m\angle VWY + m\angle YWX = m\angle VWX$ (that is, $\angle W$) and $m\angle VTY + m\angle YTZ = m\angle VTZ$ (that is, $\angle T$). Thus, $m\angle W = m\angle T$ and $\angle W \cong \angle T$.

   b. Draw $\overline{WY}$ and $\overline{TY}$. We are given that $\overline{WV} \cong \overline{VT}$ and $\angle 1 \cong \angle 2$. Also, $\overline{VY} \cong \overline{VY}$. So $\triangle VTY \cong \triangle VWY$ by the SAS Congruence Theorem. Thus, $\overline{WY} \cong \overline{TY}$ and $\angle WYV \cong \angle TYV$ by CPCTC. We are also given that $\angle 3 \cong \angle 4$, so $m\angle 3 - m\angle WYV = m\angle 4 - m\angle TYV$ or $m\angle WYX = m\angle TYZ$ (by subtracting equals). Thus, since $\overline{XY} \cong \overline{YZ}$, $\overline{WY} \cong \overline{TY}$, and $m\angle WYX = m\angle TYZ$, $\triangle WYX \cong \triangle TYZ$ by the SAS Congruence Theorem. Thus, $\overline{WX} \cong \overline{TZ}$ by CPCTC.

Assessments 167–169

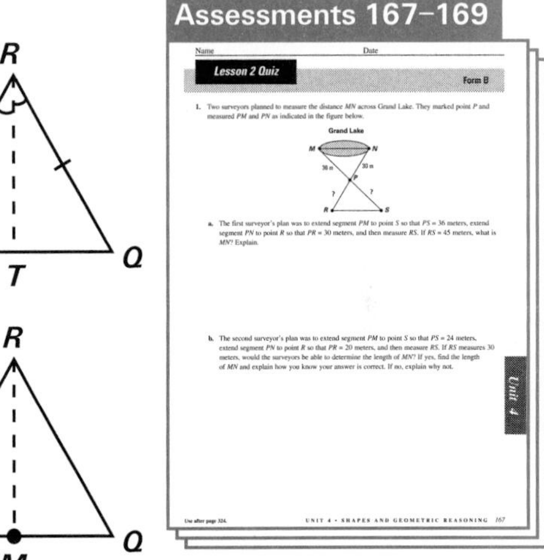

3. a. Since isosceles triangle PQR has a symmetry line that contains point R and is perpendicular to $\overline{PQ}$, we can conclude that $\angle P \cong \angle Q$.

   b. We are given that $\triangle PQR$ is isosceles, with $\overline{PR} \cong \overline{QR}$. If $\overline{RT}$ bisects $\angle PRQ$, then $\angle PRT \cong \angle QRT$. Also, $\overline{RT} \cong \overline{RT}$. Thus, by the SAS Congruence Theorem, $\triangle PRT \cong \triangle QRT$. Since $\angle P$ and $\angle Q$ are corresponding parts of the congruent triangles, $\angle P \cong \angle Q$.

   c. Let point M be the midpoint of $\overline{PQ}$. Then $\overline{PM} \cong \overline{QM}$. We are given that $\overline{PR} \cong \overline{QR}$. Thus, $\triangle PRM \cong \triangle QRM$ by the SSS Congruence Theorem. So by CPCTC, $\angle P \cong \angle Q$.

   d. To show that $\angle P \cong \angle Q$, we can show that they have the same sine, cosine, or tangent. Let M be the point with coordinates $(a, 0)$. We know that $\overline{PR} \cong \overline{QR}$. Let $PR = QR = c$. Further, $\triangle PMR$ and $\triangle QMR$ are right triangles because $\overline{RM}$ is a vertical segment and $\overline{PQ}$ is horizontal. Then $\cos(\angle RPM) = \frac{a}{c}$ and $\cos(\angle RQM) = \frac{a}{c}$. Since both are acute angles, $m\angle RPM = m\angle RQM$ and $\angle RPM \cong \angle RQM$.

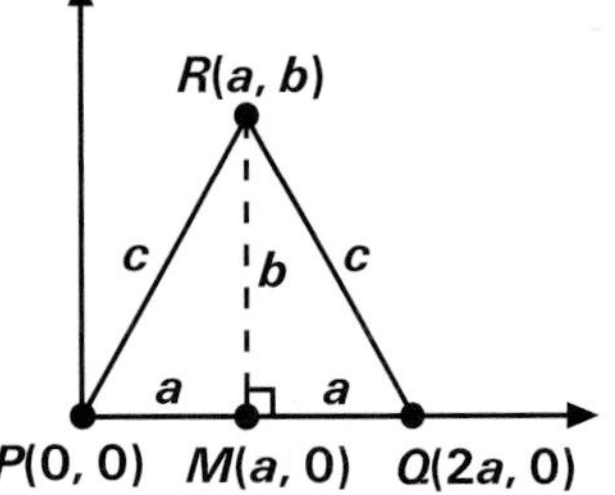

4. Here is one possible proof. There are other correct proofs.
Since $\overline{BF}$ is the perpendicular bisector of $\overline{AC}$, $\overline{AF} \cong \overline{FC}$ and $\angle BFA \cong \angle BFC$. Also, $\overline{BF} \cong \overline{BF}$. So $\triangle BFA \cong \triangle BFC$ by the SAS Congruence Theorem. Thus, $\angle A \cong \angle C$ by CPCTC. Since we also are given that $\angle 1 \cong \angle 2$, we can conclude that $\triangle DFA \cong \triangle EFC$ by the ASA Congruence Theorem. Thus, $\overline{DF} \cong \overline{EF}$ by CPCTC. If $\angle 1 \cong \angle 2$ and $\angle BFA \cong \angle BFC$, then $m\angle BFA - m\angle 1 = m\angle BFC - m\angle 2$, so $\angle BFD \cong \angle BFE$. Thus, $\triangle DBF \cong \triangle EBF$ by the SAS Congruence Theorem. Thus, $\overline{DB} \cong \overline{EB}$ by CPCTC.

5. a. Since $\overline{CO}$ and $\overline{AO}$ are radii, $CO = AO$ and $\triangle COA$ is isosceles. Thus, $m\angle C = m\angle A$. Since $\angle AOB$ is an exterior angle, $m\angle AOB = m\angle C + m\angle A = 2m\angle C$. Thus, $m\angle C = \frac{1}{2}m\angle AOB$. The measure of the inscribed angle is half that of the central angle.

Unit 4

Master 106

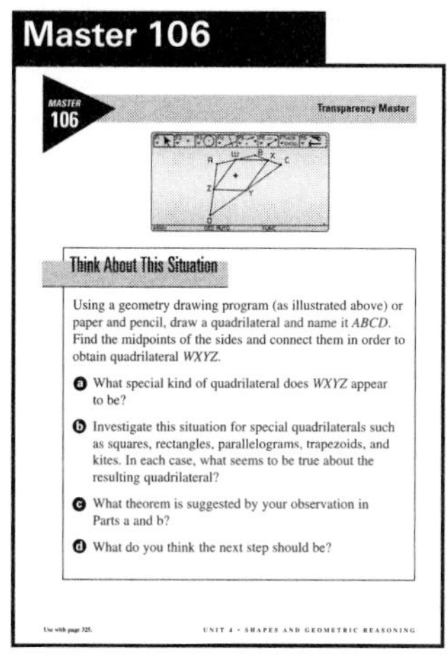
MASTER 106 — Transparency Master

Think About This Situation

Using a geometry drawing program (as illustrated above) or paper and pencil, draw a quadrilateral and name it *ABCD*. Find the midpoints of the sides and connect them in order to obtain quadrilateral *WXYZ*.

a. What special kind of quadrilateral does *WXYZ* appear to be?
b. Investigate this situation for special quadrilaterals such as squares, rectangles, parallelograms, trapezoids, and kites. In each case, what seems to be true about the resulting quadrilateral?
c. What theorem is suggested by your observation in Parts a and b?
d. What do you think the next step should be?

Use with page 325. — UNIT 4 • SHAPES AND GEOMETRIC REASONING

Lesson 3 *Parallelograms: Necessary and Sufficient Conditions*

LESSON OVERVIEW The two investigations in this lesson emphasize the parallelogram as an important shape. First, parallelograms are defined, and students are asked to use deductive reasoning to prove properties of a parallelogram. Conditions that ensure a quadrilateral is a parallelogram are then considered. Finally, special parallelograms and their properties are introduced. All this is done in the deductive mode followed throughout the unit. This lesson gives practice using triangle congruence and similarity as deductive tools.

Lesson Objectives

- To know and be able to use both necessary and sufficient conditions for parallelograms
- To know and be able to use properties unique to special parallelograms
- To know and be able to use the Midpoint Connector Theorems for Triangles and Quadrilaterals

LAUNCH full-class discussion

Think About This Situation

See Teaching Master 106.

a. From the drawing, *WXYZ* looks like a parallelogram.

b. Each of the quadrilaterals *WXYZ* appears to be a parallelogram. In addition, some appear to be squares, rectangles, or rhombuses.

c. We have made a conjecture using inductive reasoning. If the midpoints of the sides of a quadrilateral are connected to form a quadrilateral, then the new quadrilateral is a parallelogram.

d. To ensure the correctness of the observation, we need to try to prove the conjecture through deductive reasoning.

Lesson 3

Parallelograms: Necessary and Sufficient Conditions

At the beginning of this unit, you had a small set of geometric tools to use to prove the correctness of conjectures. These included the Pythagorean Theorem, the Law of Sines, and the Law of Cosines, which were proved in previous units. Now you have a large inventory at your disposal. You have properties of parallel lines and several relations among pairs of angles when two parallel lines are cut by a transversal. You have properties of similar triangles and ways to prove them similar. And you have properties of congruent triangles and methods to conclude when two triangles are congruent. These are some of the most important properties and relations in Euclidean geometry.

Properties and relations involving parallelism of lines, congruence of triangles, and similarity of triangles can help you establish properties of other polygons. In this lesson, you will explore conditions that will ensure that a quadrilateral is a parallelogram.

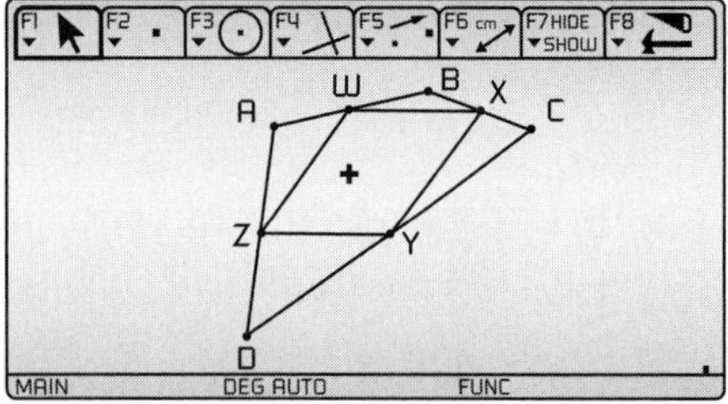

Think About This Situation

Using a geometry drawing program (as illustrated above) or paper and pencil, draw a quadrilateral and name it *ABCD*. Find the midpoints of the sides and connect them in order to obtain quadrilateral *WXYZ*.

a What special kind of quadrilateral does *WXYZ* appear to be?

b Investigate this situation for special quadrilaterals such as squares, rectangles, parallelograms, trapezoids, and kites. In each case, what seems to be true about the resulting quadrilateral?

c What theorem is suggested by your observation in Parts a and b?

d What do you think the next step should be?

Unit 4

LESSON 3 • PARALLELOGRAMS: NECESSARY AND SUFFICIENT CONDITIONS 325

INVESTIGATION 1 Reasoning about Parallelograms

In previous courses, you have investigated applications of parallelograms and their properties. Such applications range from the design of pop-up greeting cards to the design of windshield wipers and outdoor swings. You probably have a good idea of what a parallelogram is, but in order to have a starting point for reasoning about parallelograms, everyone must agree on the same definition.

A quadrilateral is a **parallelogram** *if and only if both pairs of opposite sides are parallel.*

Recall that the "if and only if" in this definition allows you to use either part of the definition as given information to conclude the other part. In the following activities, you will investigate how the definition allows you to place a parallelogram on a coordinate system and specify its vertices.

1. Draw a parallelogram $ABCD$ on a coordinate system with one vertex at the origin and one side on the positive x-axis, as shown at the right.

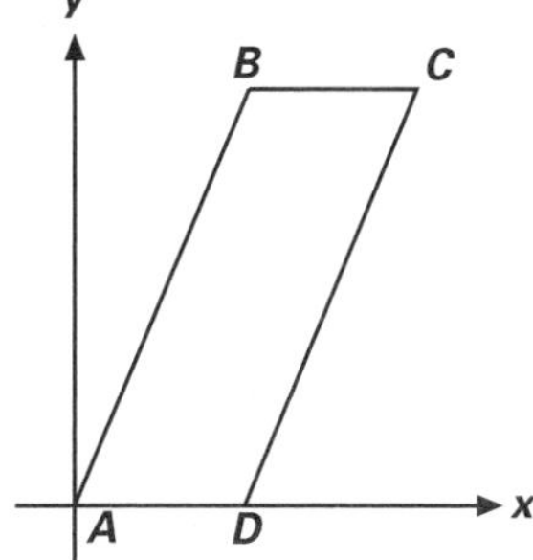

a. What are the coordinates of point A? Record these on your diagram.

b. Consider vertex D. If $AD = c$ units, what is the x-coordinate of point D? What is the y-coordinate of point D? Record these on your diagram.

c. Now consider vertex B. If $AB = p$ units, is p the x-coordinate of point B? Is the y-coordinate p? Explain.

d. Call the coordinates of point B (a, b) and record them on your diagram. How are sides $\overline{BC}$ and $\overline{AD}$ related? What is the y-coordinate of point C? Explain your reasoning.

e. How can you use the fact that side AB and side DC are parallel to help determine the x-coordinate of point C? Record the coordinates of point C on your diagram.

f. Compare your coordinate labeling of parallelogram $ABCD$ to those of other groups. Resolve any differences.

326 UNIT 4 • SHAPES AND GEOMETRIC REASONING

EXPLORE small-group investigation

INVESTIGATION 1 Reasoning about Parallelograms

There are several points about the first activity that may cause your students confusion (and you frustration) if they are not discussed by the full class. First, students have not used coordinate geometry much, if at all, to construct proofs; second, they may find the idea of being able to place the parallelogram on the axes in a convenient way to be "cheating"; third, students will have already made conjectures about the properties of a parallelogram, and so they will have trouble separating the facts on which they are permitted to build (opposite sides are parallel) from the assumptions that they have been carrying along in their minds for a considerable time (about lengths of sides and sizes of angles). Therefore, it is recommended that Activity 1 be a large-group activity, allowing you to point out that we cannot use assumptions about lengths, but only about slopes, and that we can place the parallelogram conveniently on the axes as long as we do not violate the condition about parallel sides. Activities 2 and 3 are then accessible to small-group investigation. See the notes preceding Activity 4 for one suggested approach to that activity.

1. **a.** $A(0, 0)$

   b. $D(c, 0)$

   c. The x-coordinate of B is *not* p. Nor is p the y-coordinate of B. Since B is not on an axis and $AB = p$, the coordinates of B are each less than p. In fact, if B has coordinates (x, y), the Pythagorean Theorem tells us that $x^2 + y^2 = p^2$.

   d. $\overline{BC} \parallel \overline{AD}$

   C and B have the same y-coordinates since B and C lie on a line parallel to the x-axis, so the y-coordinate of C is b.

   e. Since $\overline{AB}$ and $\overline{DC}$ are parallel, the slopes of the lines $\overleftrightarrow{AB}$ and $\overleftrightarrow{DC}$ are equal. The slope of $\overleftrightarrow{AB} = \frac{b-0}{a-0} = \frac{b}{a}$. The slope of $\overleftrightarrow{DC}$ is also $\frac{b}{a}$. But this slope is $\frac{b-0}{x-c}$ where x is the x-coordinate of point C.

   $$\frac{b}{a} = \frac{b}{x-c}$$
   $$x - c = a$$
   $$x = a + c$$

   Therefore, the x-coordinate of C is $a + c$.

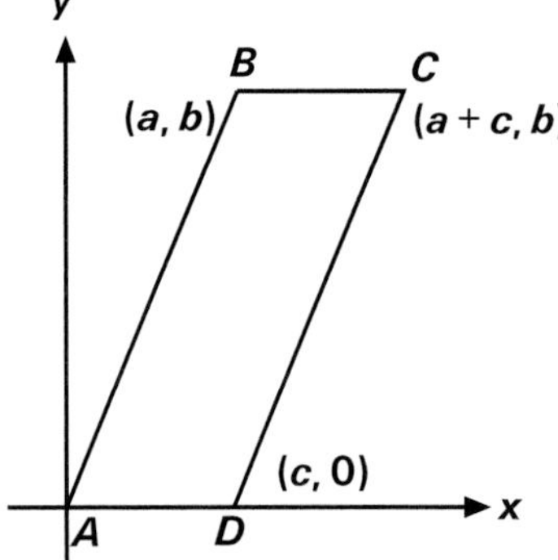

   f. Groups should compare their coordinate diagrams.

Unit 4

EXPLORE ***continued***

2. a. $C(10, 3)$
   b. $C(7, 4)$
   c. $C(4, 9)$
   d. $C(p + r, s)$

Unit 4

2. For each of the parallelograms shown, determine the coordinates of point C.

a.

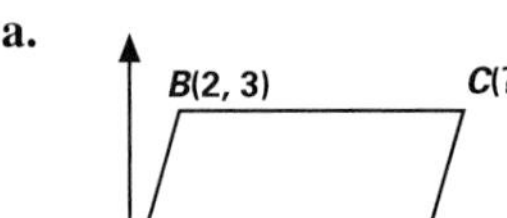

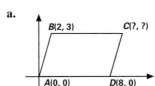

b.

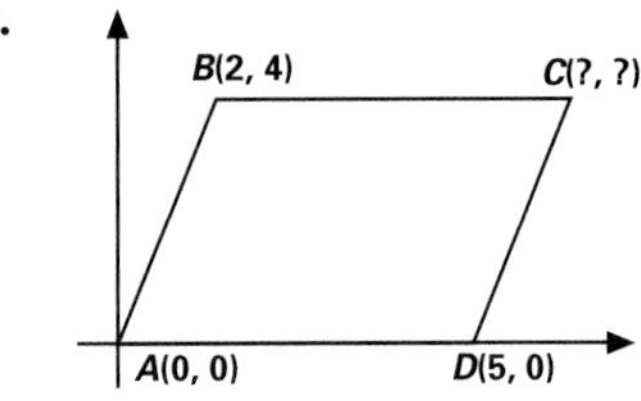

c.

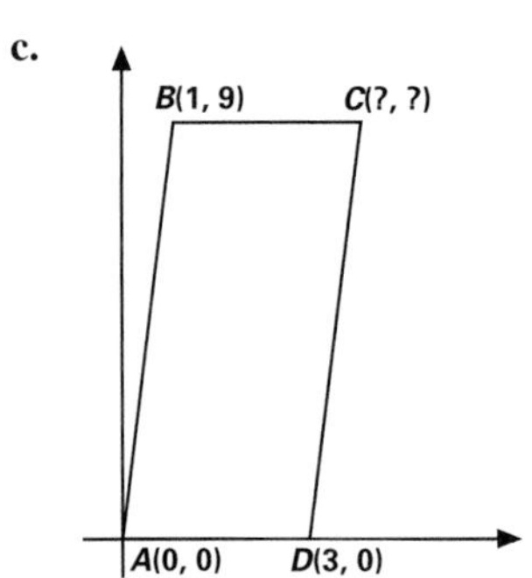

d.

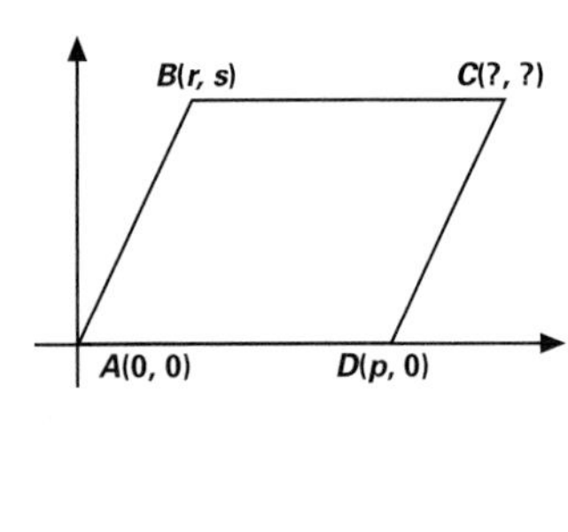

As you saw in Unit 3, "Symbol Sense and Algebraic Reasoning," placing shapes on a coordinate system and assigning general coordinates to their vertices provides an algebraic tool for reasoning about the shapes.

3. Examine the following two arguments that $\overline{AB} \cong \overline{CD}$ in parallelogram $ABCD$.

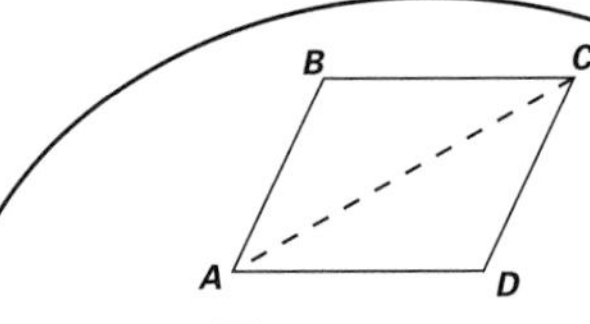

First draw $\overline{AC}$ in parallelogram $ABCD$.
Since $\overline{AB} \parallel \overline{CD}$, $m\angle BAC = m\angle DCA$ because they are alternate interior angles.
Since $\overline{BC} \parallel \overline{AD}$, $m\angle BCA = m\angle DAC$.
$\overline{AC}$ is a corresponding side of $\triangle ABC$ and $\triangle CDA$.
So $\triangle ABC \cong \triangle CDA$ by ASA.
It follows by corresponding parts that $\overline{AB} \cong \overline{CD}$.

Hans

Kara

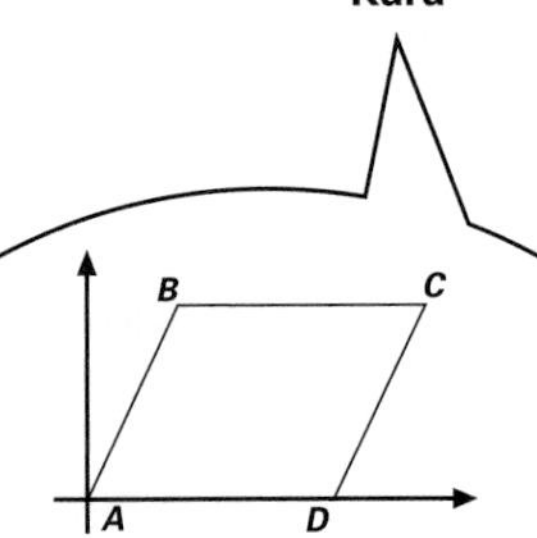

First place $ABCD$ on a coordinate system with point A at the origin and point D on the x-axis.
The vertices have coordinates $A(0, 0)$, $B(a, b)$, $C(a + c, b)$, and $D(c, 0)$.
Using the distance formula:

$$AB = \sqrt{(a-0)^2 + (b-0)^2} = \sqrt{a^2 + b^2}$$

$$CD = \sqrt{(a+c-c)^2 + (b-0)^2} = \sqrt{a^2 + b^2}$$

Thus, $AB = CD$ or $\overline{AB} \cong \overline{CD}$.

Unit 4

LESSON 3 • PARALLELOGRAMS: NECESSARY AND SUFFICIENT CONDITIONS 327

a. Is Hans' argument valid? What previously proved information did he use?

b. Is Kara's argument valid? What information did she use to make her argument?

c. Could Hans conclude other facts about parallelograms once he deduced $\triangle ABC \cong \triangle CDA$? What other facts?

d. Could Kara also conclude other facts about parallelograms once she used the distance formula to get $AB = CD$? What other facts?

e. Whose proof is easiest to follow and why? Which of these methods of proof would you have used and why?

Hans' proof is called a **synthetic proof** because it applies to a figure with no coordinates. Kara's argument is called an **analytic** or **coordinate proof** since it uses coordinates. Sometimes one argument form is easier and sheds more light on other possible deductions than the other.

4. Listed below are conjectures about properties of every parallelogram. Examine each to see if your group thinks it is correct. If you think it is correct, construct a proof. If you think it is incorrect, give a counterexample. Share the work among your group members. Then discuss each other's proofs.

If a quadrilateral is a parallelogram, then the following is true:

a. Opposite angles are congruent.

b. Opposite sides are congruent.

c. Adjacent angles are supplementary.

d. All angles are congruent.

e. Each diagonal divides the shape into two congruent triangles.

f. The diagonals bisect each other.

g. The diagonals are congruent.

h. The diagonals are perpendicular.

Checkpoint

In addition to its recognizable shape, a parallelogram has many geometric properties that can be proved.

a Make a list summarizing the properties about the sides, angles, and diagonals of a parallelogram that you were able to prove.

b How do synthetic and analytic arguments differ?

Be prepared to share your list and explanation with the entire class.

Unit 4

328 UNIT 4 • SHAPES AND GEOMETRIC REASONING

EXPLORE *continued*

Master 107

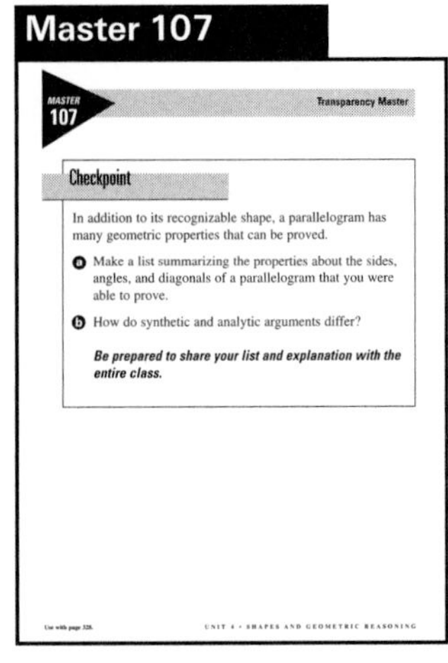
MASTER 107

Transparency Master

Checkpoint

In addition to its recognizable shape, a parallelogram has many geometric properties that can be proved.

a Make a list summarizing the properties about the sides, angles, and diagonals of a parallelogram that you were able to prove.

b How do synthetic and analytic arguments differ?

Be prepared to share your list and explanation with the entire class.

Use with page 328.

UNIT 4 • SHAPES AND GEOMETRIC REASONING

3. **a.** Hans's argument is valid. He used the fact that alternate interior angles formed by parallel lines have equal measure, the ASA Congruence Theorem, and the fact that corresponding parts of congruent triangles are congruent.

b. Kara's argument is valid. She used the coordinates of the vertices and the distance formula, which is based on the Pythagorean Theorem.

c. Hans could also conclude that $BC = AD$ and $\angle B \cong \angle D$.

d. Kara could not conclude anything else based on her proof.

e. Students may choose either proof. Some may argue that Hans's argument is more productive because other facts can be concluded.

One way to handle Activity 4 is to have the members of each group decide amongst themselves which conjectures they agree with and which they think are false and then to reach consensus in a large group about which seem to be true. Assign each group one or two proofs to do, making sure that the proof of each plausible conjecture is attempted by at least two groups. Before students start, emphasize that only the condition about pairs of opposite sides being parallel may be assumed. (You might prepare large sheets of bulletin paper ahead of time, with the statement of the conjecture and a drawing of a parallelogram. If you do not mind the extra effort and waste of paper, it is satisfyingly dramatic to rip up the conjectures for which students produce counterexamples.) When the groups have made their best attempt to create a logical proof, they should check with any other groups assigned the same proof. These proofs can be presented to the full class and then posted on the bulletin board for future reference.

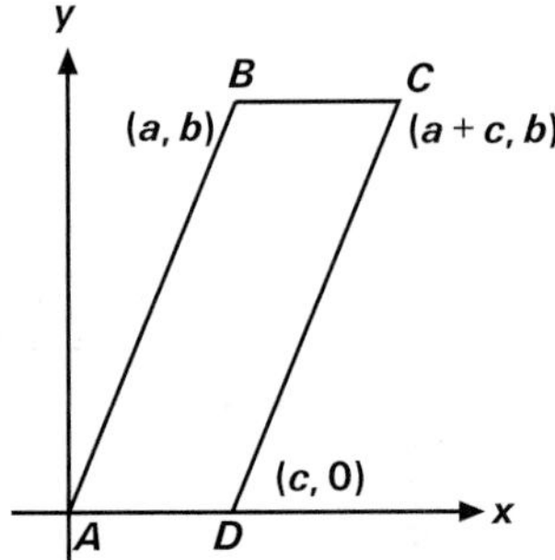

4. Proofs may vary.

a. Correct. See Hans's proof.

b. Correct. See Hans's or Kara's proof.

c. Correct. Since opposite sides are parallel, the adjacent angles are interior angles on the same side of the transversal and so are supplementary.

d. Not correct. Any parallelogram that is not a rectangle will not have all angles congruent.

e. Correct. See Hans's proof.

f. Correct. Use the coordinates as in Activity 1: $A(0, 0)$, $B(a, b)$, $C(a + c, b)$, and $D(c, 0)$. Then the midpoint of $\overline{AC}$ has coordinates $\left(\frac{a+c}{2}, \frac{b}{2}\right)$. The midpoint of $\overline{BD}$ has coordinates $\left(\frac{a+c}{2}, \frac{b}{2}\right)$. Since these are the same point, the midpoints of the two segments are the same point.

g. Not correct. A counterexample is any nonrectangular parallelogram. The lengths can be calculated and shown to be unequal.

h. Not correct. A counterexample is any parallelogram that is not a rhombus.

CONSTRUCTING A MATH TOOLKIT: Students should include the properties of parallelograms in their Math Toolkits, along with appropriate illustrations.

Unit 4

See additional Teaching Notes on page T344J.

MORE

ASSIGNMENT *pp. 333–339*

Students can now begin Reflecting Task 1, 2, or 4 from the MORE assignment following Investigation 2.

APPLY individual task

On Your Own

There are several possible conjectures that students could make, for example:

A rectangle has four right angles.

A rectangle has congruent diagonals.

A rectangle has two lines of symmetry.

The proofs will vary.

EXPLORE small-group investigation

The following activities about sufficient conditions probably should also be started as a large group to ensure that students are all aware of the shift in emphasis. Try to build on the informal language that they develop. For example, "two pairs of opposite sides congruent forces a parallelogram" or "two pairs of opposite angles congruent is not enough to ensure a parallelogram" is not precise but conveys understanding. You might repeat the statement with more precise language: "Two pairs of opposite sides in a quadrilateral being congruent forces the quadrilateral to be a parallelogram."

5. a. Drawings should support the conjecture.

b. One proof follows:

Quadrilateral $ABCD$ has $\overline{AB} \cong \overline{CD}$ and $\overline{BC} \cong \overline{DA}$. Include the diagonal BD and notice that $\overline{BD} \cong \overline{BD}$. Thus, in $\triangle ABD$ and $\triangle CDB$, $\overline{AB} \cong \overline{CD}$, $\overline{BD} \cong \overline{DB}$, and $\overline{AD} \cong \overline{CB}$. Thus, $\triangle ABD \cong \triangle CDB$ by the SSS Congruence Theorem. Thus, $\angle ABD \cong \angle CDB$ by CPCTC and so $\overline{AB} \parallel \overline{CD}$ (alternate interior angles are congruent). Similarly, $\angle ADB \cong \angle CBD$ and so $\overline{BC} \parallel \overline{AD}$. Therefore, $ABCD$ is a parallelogram by the definition of parallelogram.

6. a. Yes.

b. No; see the note following Activity 7.

c. Yes.

d. No, it could be an isosceles trapezoid.

e. No, it could be a kite.

f. Yes.

7. From 6.a. Quadrilateral $ABCD$ has $\angle A \cong \angle C$ and $\angle B \cong \angle D$. Let $m\angle A = m\angle C = x$. Let $m\angle B = m\angle D = y$. Then we know that $2x + 2y = 360°$ or $x + y = 180°$. So $\angle C$ and $\angle D$ are same side interior angles that are supplementary. Thus, $\overleftrightarrow{BC} \parallel \overleftrightarrow{AD}$. Similarly, $\angle A$ and $\angle D$ are same side interior angles that are supplementary, so $\overleftrightarrow{DC} \parallel \overleftrightarrow{AB}$. If $\overleftrightarrow{BC} \parallel \overleftrightarrow{AD}$ and $\overleftrightarrow{DC} \parallel \overleftrightarrow{AB}$, then $ABCD$ is a parallelogram.

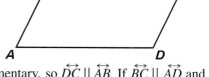

B C A D

See additional Teaching Notes on page T344K.

On Your Own

A **rectangle** may be defined as a parallelogram with a right angle.

Since a rectangle is a parallelogram, everything about parallelograms is also true about rectangles. Using inductive reasoning, make a conjecture about a property of all rectangles that is not also true for all parallelograms. Develop a proof for your conjecture.

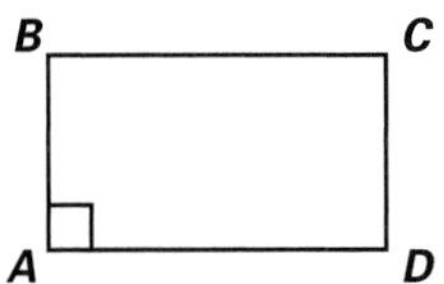

You now have a list of theorems that give properties of parallelograms. These are useful whenever you know that a quadrilateral is a parallelogram. If a quadrilateral is *not* known to be a parallelogram, then you cannot conclude that any of those properties hold. In the remainder of this investigation, you will explore conditions that ensure that a quadrilateral is a parallelogram. You already know one condition from the definition of a parallelogram. Namely, if a quadrilateral has two pairs of opposite sides parallel, then the quadrilateral is a parallelogram.

5. Examine this conjecture that Shiomo made after drawing and analyzing a few quadrilaterals.

If a quadrilateral has two pairs of opposite sides congruent, then the quadrilateral is a parallelogram.

a. Experiment with drawings to see if this conjecture makes sense.

b. Construct a proof or a counterexample of Shiomo's conjecture.

6. Here are additional conditions that may or may not ensure that a quadrilateral is a parallelogram. Investigate each conjecture by drawing shapes satisfying the conditions and checking to see if the quadrilateral is a parallelogram. Share the workload among members of your group. Compile a group list of conditions that seem to guarantee that a quadrilateral is a parallelogram.

a. If a quadrilateral has two pairs of opposite angles congruent, then it is a parallelogram.

b. If a quadrilateral has one pair of opposite angles and a pair of opposite sides congruent, then it is a parallelogram.

c. If a quadrilateral has diagonals that bisect each other, it is a parallelogram.

d. If a quadrilateral has one pair of opposite sides parallel and the other pair of opposite sides congruent, then it is a parallelogram.

e. If a quadrilateral has two distinct pairs of adjacent sides congruent, then it is a parallelogram.

f. If a quadrilateral has one pair of opposite sides congruent and parallel, then it is a parallelogram.

7. For each condition you listed in Activity 6, construct a proof that your conjecture is correct. Share the workload and then discuss the proofs within your group.

Unit 4

LESSON 3 • PARALLELOGRAMS: NECESSARY AND SUFFICIENT CONDITIONS 329

Checkpoint

Make a list of several conditions on a quadrilateral that guarantee it to be a parallelogram.

Be prepared to demonstrate to the class a proof of each condition in your list.

On Your Own

The figure *STOP* is a quadrilateral. For each set of conditions, explain why the conditions do or do not ensure that *STOP* is a parallelogram.

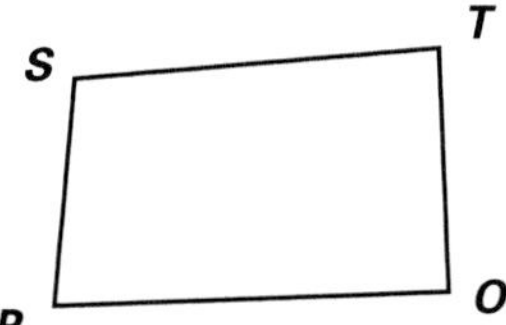

a. $\angle S \cong \angle O$ and $\angle T \cong \angle P$

b. $\overline{ST} \parallel \overline{OP}$ and $\overline{TO} \cong \overline{SP}$

c. $\overline{ST} \cong \overline{OP}$ and $\overline{TO} \cong \overline{SP}$

d. $\angle S \cong \angle O$ and $\overline{ST} \cong \overline{OP}$

e. $\overline{ST} \cong \overline{TO}$ and $\overline{OP} \cong \overline{PS}$

f. M is the midpoint of $\overline{SO}$ and of $\overline{TP}$

INVESTIGATION 2 Special Kinds of Parallelograms

One special parallelogram, with a pair of congruent adjacent sides, is a rhombus. Since every parallelogram has its *opposite* sides congruent, it follows that a rhombus has four congruent sides. (Why?) The rhombus shown at the left below can be used to make a pair of tiles called a *dart* and a *kite*. In the first course of *Contemporary Mathematics in Context*, you may have discovered that a rhombus will form a tiling of the plane that has translation symmetry. What is interesting about these particular figures, discovered by Roger Penrose, a professor at the University of Oxford, is that copies of these two shapes can be used to form a tiling, a portion of which is shown at the right below, which does *not* have translation symmetry.

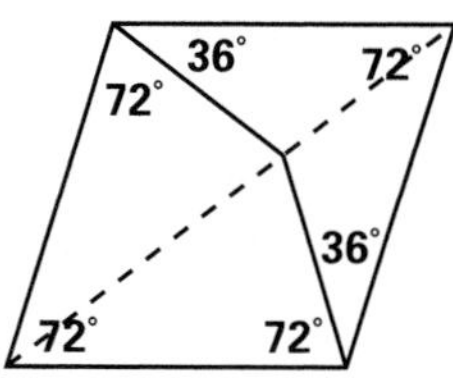

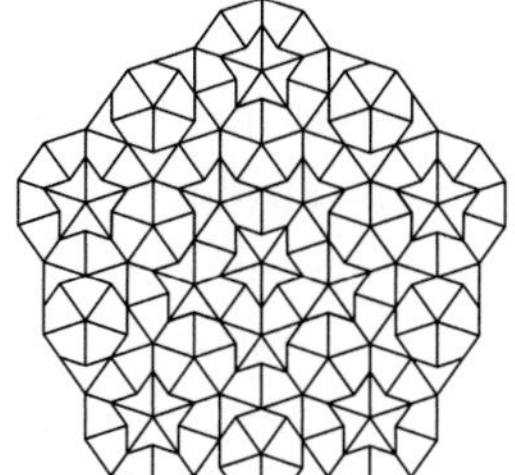

Unit 4

330 UNIT 4 • SHAPES AND GEOMETRIC REASONING

SHARE AND SUMMARIZE full-class discussion

Checkpoint

See Teaching Master 108.

The following conditions guarantee a quadrilateral is a parallelogram:

- Both pairs of opposite sides are parallel.
- Both pairs of opposite angles are congruent.
- Both pairs of opposite sides are congruent.
- The diagonals bisect one another.
- One pair of opposite sides is congruent and parallel.

Master 108

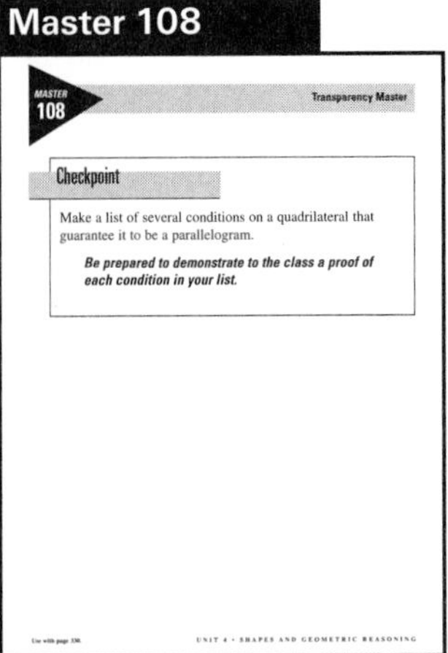
MASTER 108
Transparency Master
Checkpoint
Make a list of several conditions on a quadrilateral that guarantee it to be a parallelogram.
Be prepared to demonstrate to the class a proof of each condition in your list.

CONSTRUCTING A MATH TOOLKIT: Students should record the various conditions needed to show that a quadrilateral is a parallelogram in their Math Toolkits, along with appropriate illustrations.

APPLY individual task

On Your Own

a. Figure *STOP* is a parallelogram because both pairs of opposite angles are congruent.

b. Figure *STOP* is not a parallelogram. An isosceles trapezoid is a counterexample.

c. Figure *STOP* is a parallelogram because both pairs of opposite sides are congruent.

d. Figure *STOP* is not a parallelogram. See the dart portion of the figure at the bottom of page 330 for a counterexample.

e. Figure *STOP* is not a parallelogram. A kite is a counterexample.

f. Figure *STOP* is a parallelogram because the diagonals bisect each other.

MORE

ASSIGNMENT pp.333–339

Students can now begin Modeling Task 1 or Organizing Task 1 from the MORE assignment following Investigation 2.

EXPLORE small-group investigation

INVESTIGATION 2 Special Kinds of Parallelograms

In this investigation, students investigate and then prove the Midpoint Connector Theorem for Triangles and Quadrilaterals. Also, the rectangle, square, and rhombus are seen as specific kinds of parallelograms.

The development of this investigation is similar to Investigation 1. Students are asked to conjecture about properties of a rhombus and to prove their conjectures. They are then asked to speculate about which additional properties a parallelogram would have to possess to ensure that it is a rhombus, and finally they are asked to prove these sufficient conditions. This sequence is repeated for a rectangle and for a square in the Organizing tasks on page 335.

See additional Teaching Notes on page T344L.

EXPLORE *continued*

1. a. Students should note that all of the properties or characteristics of a parallelogram are true:

- Opposite angles are congruent.
- Opposite sides are congruent.
- Adjacent angles are supplementary.
- Each diagonal divides the shape into two congruent triangles.
- The diagonals bisect each other.

b–c. Students may make the following observations:

- If $ABCD$ is a rhombus, then all four sides are congruent.
- If $ABCD$ is a rhombus, then the diagonals are perpendicular.
- If $ABCD$ is a rhombus with diagonals that intersect at X, then $\triangle ABX \cong \triangle CBX \cong \triangle CDX \cong \triangle ADX$.

d. For all properties that the rhombus shares with the parallelogram, it is sufficient to say that a rhombus is a parallelogram and we have already proved that the property holds for parallelograms.

Conjecture: If $ABCD$ is a rhombus, then all four sides are congruent.

Proof: $ABCD$ is a rhombus with $\overline{BC} \cong \overline{AB}$. If $ABCD$ is a rhombus, then $ABCD$ is a parallelogram because all rhombuses are parallelograms. If $ABCD$ is a parallelogram, then $\overline{BC} \cong \overline{AD}$ and $\overline{AB} \cong \overline{CD}$ because opposite sides of a parallelogram are congruent. If $\overline{AB} \cong \overline{CD}$ and $\overline{BC} \cong \overline{AB}$, then $\overline{BC} \cong \overline{CD}$ since they are both congruent to $\overline{AB}$. If for quadrilateral $ABCD$ we know $\overline{BC} \cong \overline{AB}$, $\overline{BC} \cong \overline{AD}$, and $\overline{BC} \cong \overline{CD}$, then $\overline{BC} \cong \overline{AB} \cong \overline{AD} \cong \overline{CD}$ since they are all congruent to $\overline{BC}$. Therefore, if $ABCD$ is a rhombus, then all four sides are congruent.

Conjecture: If $ABCD$ is a rhombus, then the diagonals are perpendicular.

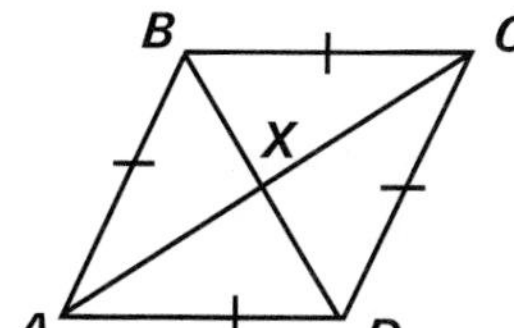

Proof: $ABCD$ is a rhombus. Draw diagonals $\overline{AC}$ and $\overline{BD}$ and mark the intersection X. If $ABCD$ is a rhombus, then $ABCD$ is a parallelogram since all rhombuses are parallelograms. If $ABCD$ is a parallelogram, then $\overline{AX} \cong \overline{XC}$ because the diagonals of a parallelogram bisect each other. If $ABCD$ is a rhombus, then $\overline{AD} \cong \overline{CD}$ because all four sides of a rhombus are congruent. $\overline{XD} \cong \overline{XD}$ because a line segment is congruent to itself. If for $\triangle AXD$ and $\triangle CXD$ we know $\overline{AX} \cong \overline{XC}$, $\overline{AD} \cong \overline{CD}$, and $\overline{XD} \cong \overline{XD}$, then the triangles are congruent by the SSS Congruence Theorem for triangles. If $\triangle AXD \cong \triangle CXD$, then $m\angle AXD = m\angle CXD$ because corresponding parts of congruent triangles are congruent. If $\overline{AC}$ and $\overline{BD}$ intersect to form straight angles, then $m\angle AXD + m\angle CXD = 180°$ because the sum of the measures of two angles that form a straight angle is 180°. If $m\angle AXD + m\angle CXD = 180°$ and $m\angle AXD = m\angle CXD$, then $m\angle AXD = 90° = m\angle CXD$. If $m\angle AXD = 90° = m\angle CXD$, then $\overline{AC}$ and $\overline{BD}$ are perpendicular. Therefore, if $ABCD$ is a rhombus, then the diagonals are perpendicular.

See additional Teaching Notes on page T344M.

Unit 4

Penrose Tiles quilt made by Elaine Krajenke Ellison

Penrose's discovery is based on a particular rhombus. In the next two activities, you will explore additional properties of any rhombus.

1. Sketch several different rhombuses with and without their diagonals.

a. What are some properties of a rhombus that are consequences of the fact that a rhombus is a parallelogram?

b. Now visually inspect your sketches. Make a group list of other characteristics observed in the sketches that might be correct for all rhombuses.

c. Write each of your conjectures in if-then form.

d. Construct proofs for your conjectures. Share the work and then discuss the proofs within your group.

2. Given below are various conditions on a parallelogram. Determine if each condition is sufficient to conclude that the parallelogram is a rhombus. For each condition that seems to ensure that the parallelogram is a rhombus, write the corresponding if-then statement and a proof.

a. The diagonals bisect each other.

b. The diagonals are perpendicular.

c. The diagonals bisect the angles.

d. A pair of adjacent angles are congruent.

Now refer back to the "Think About This Situation" at the beginning of this lesson, page 325. You and your classmates may have conjectured that the shape formed by connecting the midpoints of consecutive sides of a quadrilateral is a parallelogram. In the remainder of this investigation, you will examine this situation further.

3. Consider first the case of connecting midpoints of two sides of a triangle.

a. Draw several triangles and locate the midpoints of two sides for each one. Connect the midpoints in each. What appears to be true about the segment determined by the midpoints?

b. In $\triangle ABC$, M is the midpoint of $\overline{AB}$ and N is the midpoint of $\overline{AC}$. How does $\triangle AMN$ appear to be related to $\triangle ABC$? Prove that your observation is correct.

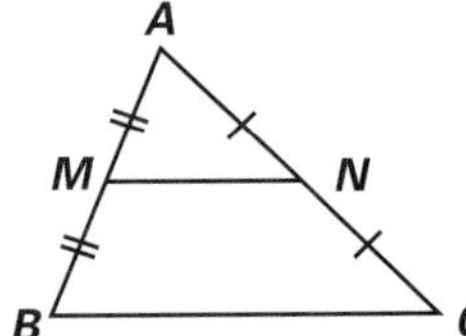

c. Given your deduction in Part b, prove that $\overleftrightarrow{MN} \parallel \overleftrightarrow{BC}$.

d. What can you conclude about the relative lengths of $\overline{MN}$ and $\overline{BC}$? Why?

Unit 4

LESSON 3 • PARALLELOGRAMS: NECESSARY AND SUFFICIENT CONDITIONS 331

The theorem you proved in Activity 3 Parts c and d is often called the **Midpoint Connector Theorem for Triangles**.

4. The midpoint connector theorem which you conjectured for quadrilaterals may be stated as follows:

If the midpoints of consecutive sides of any quadrilateral are connected, the resulting quadrilateral is a parallelogram.

a. Draw a diagram representing the **Midpoint Connector Theorem for Quadrilaterals**.

b. Write a proof of this theorem.

Checkpoint

As quadrilaterals become more specialized, they exhibit properties in addition to the properties for more general cases.

a List two properties of every rhombus that are not properties of every parallelogram.

b How does your work in this lesson with the Midpoint Connector Theorem for Quadrilaterals illustrate how inductive reasoning and deductive reasoning support each other?

c A rectangle is a special kind of quadrilateral. If the midpoints of consecutive sides of any rectangle are connected, is a special kind of parallelogram formed? Write an argument justifying your conclusion.

Be prepared to share your responses and reasoning with the entire class.

On Your Own

Consider the following information about quadrilateral *ABCD*.

- $\overline{AC} \perp \overline{BD}$
- $\overline{AC}$ bisects $\angle A$ and $\angle C$

a. Make several sketches of quadrilaterals satisfying these conditions.

b. Do the sketches suggest *ABCD* is a parallelogram? A rhombus?

c. State one conjecture about *ABCD* that you think is always true.

d. Prove your conjecture.

Unit 4

332 UNIT 4 • SHAPES AND GEOMETRIC REASONING

4. a.

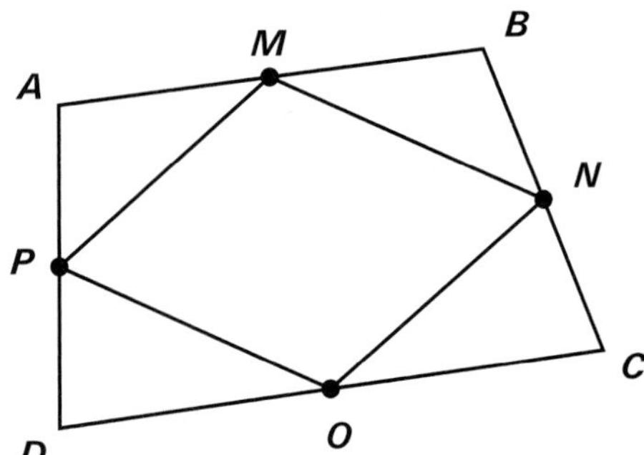

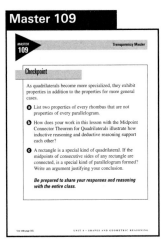

b. Draw $\overline{DB}$. Then by the Midpoint Connector Theorem for Triangles, $\overline{PM} \parallel \overline{DB}$ and $PM = \frac{1}{2}DB$. Also, $\overline{ON} \parallel \overline{DB}$ and $ON = \frac{1}{2}DB$. Thus, $\overline{PM} \parallel \overline{ON}$ and $PM = ON$. This ensures $PMNO$ is a parallelogram.

Master 109

MASTER 109 — Transparency Master

Checkpoint

As quadrilaterals become more specialized, they exhibit properties in addition to the properties for more general cases.

ⓐ List two properties of every rhombus that are not properties of every parallelogram.

ⓑ How does your work in this lesson with the Midpoint Connector Theorem for Quadrilaterals illustrate how inductive reasoning and deductive reasoning support each other?

ⓒ A rectangle is a special kind of quadrilateral. If the midpoints of consecutive sides of any rectangle are connected, is a special kind of parallelogram formed? Write an argument justifying your conclusion.

Be prepared to share your responses and reasoning with the entire class.

Use with page 332. UNIT 4 • SHAPES AND GEOMETRIC REASONING

SHARE AND SUMMARIZE full-class discussion

Checkpoint

See Teaching Master 109.

ⓐ The diagonals are perpendicular. The diagonals bisect the angles. The diagonals form four congruent triangles in the rhombus.

ⓑ Student responses will vary. One tactic may be to say that inductive reasoning was used when examining several quadrilaterals and the quadrilaterals formed by joining consecutive midpoints, which suggested visually that the new quadrilaterals were always parallelograms. Deductive reasoning was needed to prove that the conjecture was true for all quadrilaterals.

ⓒ The parallelogram formed is a rhombus. Draw in diagonals $\overline{AC}$ and $\overline{BD}$ as shown in the diagram below.

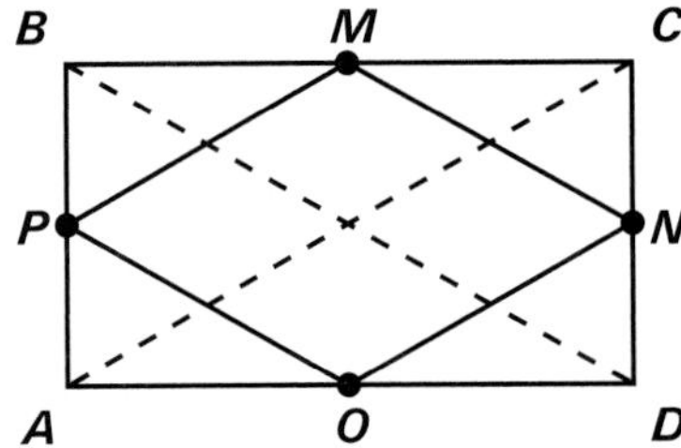

The Midpoint Connector Theorem for Triangles tells us that $PM = \frac{1}{2}AC$ and $MN = \frac{1}{2}BD$. But since $ABCD$ is a rectangle, $AC = BD$. So $PM = \frac{1}{2}AC = \frac{1}{2}BD = MN$. Thus, $MNOP$ is a parallelogram with two consecutive sides congruent, and so $MNOP$ is a rhombus.

NOTE: See additional Checkpoint discussion suggestions on page T344N.

CONSTRUCTING A MATH TOOLKIT: Students should include in their list of theorems the Midpoint Connector Theorem, along with illustrating diagrams and the properties that ensure that a parallelogram is a rhombus.

Unit 4

See additional Teaching Notes on page T344N.

MORE

ASSIGNMENT pp. 333–339

Modeling: 1 and choice of one*
Organizing: 1 or 2, and 3*
Reflecting: Choose one*
Extending: 1

*When choice is indicated, it is important to leave the choice to the student.
NOTE: *It is best if Organizing tasks are discussed as a whole class after they have been assigned as homework.*

MORE independent assignment

Modeling

1. **a.** They can conclude that $ABCD$ is a parallelogram, since both pairs of opposite sides are congruent.

   b. In the "On Your Own" on page 329, students may have conjectured and proved that a property of rectangles is that the diagonals are the same length. However, this situation asks them to consider the converse of that statement. They are asked to prove that if a parallelogram $ABCD$ has diagonals $\overline{AC}$ and $\overline{BD}$ such that $AC = BD$, then $ABCD$ is a rectangle.

   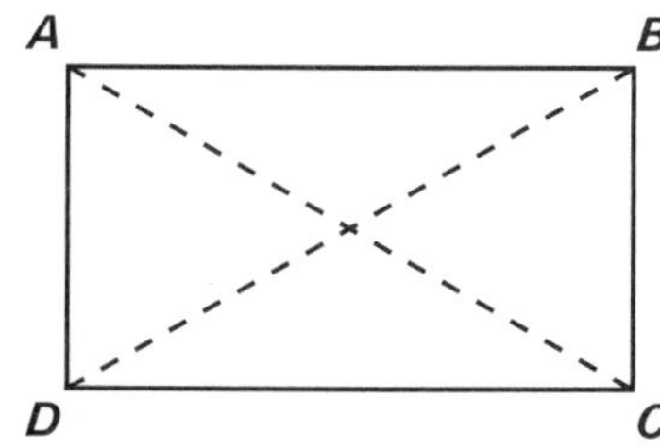

   If $ABCD$ is a parallelogram, then $BC = AD$. We are assuming that $AC = BD$, and we know that $AB = AB$. Thus, by the SSS Congruence Theorem, $\triangle ABC \cong \triangle BAD$. Thus, by CPCTC $m\angle ABC = m\angle BAD$. But since $ABCD$ is a parallelogram, we know that $m\angle ABC + m\angle BAD = 180°$. So $m\angle ABC = 90°$, and $ABCD$ is a rectangle.

   c. This method uses the converse of the Pythagorean Theorem to conclude that $\angle DAB$ is a right angle and thus that $ABCD$ is a rectangle.

   d. Only one angle needs to be tested. This is the case because a rectangle is defined (on page 329) as a parallelogram with one right angle.

   e. Yes. If you tested three of the angles and found that they were right angles, you could be assured that the quadrilateral was a rectangle. Making sure $\angle DAB$ and $\angle ADC$ were right angles would ensure that $\overline{AB} \parallel \overline{DC}$. If in addition you knew that $\angle DCB$ was a right angle, then you could conclude that $\overline{AD} \parallel \overline{BC}$. Now you know both pairs of opposite sides are parallel and there is at least one right angle, so you can be sure that $ABCD$ is a rectangle.

Unit 4

MORE

Modeling • Organizing • Reflecting • Extending

Modeling

1. When a building construction crew lays the foundation for a house or garage, they often need to be certain that the foundation is rectangular.

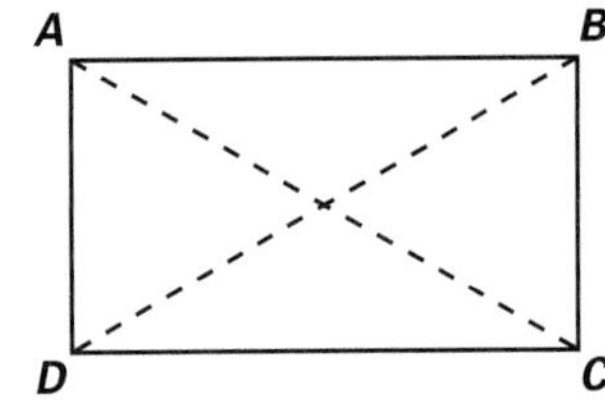

   a. They first measure the sides of quadrilateral *ABCD* and find that $AB = DC$ and $AD = BC$. What can they conclude? Why?

   b. Next, they measure the diagonals and find that $AC = BD$. Prove why they then can conclude that *ABCD* is a rectangle.

   c. Once the test in Part a has been completed, there are other ways to ensure that the foundation is rectangular. One method that does not involve measuring such long distances is as follows:

   - Mark a point *P* on $\overline{AB}$ so that $AP = 3$ feet.
   - Mark a point *Q* on $\overline{AD}$ so that $AQ = 4$ feet.
   - Measure $\overline{PQ}$. If $PQ = 5$ feet, then the foundation is rectangular.

   Explain why this method works.

   d. A carpenter's square is often used to make a quick test for a right angle. Once the test in Part a has been completed, how many corners would need to be tested with a carpenter's square to ensure that the foundation is rectangular?

   e. If you had a carpenter's square, could you avoid the test in Part a? Explain your reasoning.

Unit 4

LESSON 3 • PARALLELOGRAMS: NECESSARY AND SUFFICIENT CONDITIONS 333

2. The diagram at the right illustrates a quadrilateral with $DA = CB$ and $DC = AB$. Points D and C are fixed in place.

   a. Make a similar linkage using plastic or cardboard strips and paper fasteners.

   b. What shape is $ABCD$? Explain.

   c. If $\overline{AD}$ is turned about point D, what path does point A follow? Explain.

   d. If $\overline{AD}$ is turned about point D, what paths do points P, Q, and R follow? Explain.

   e. What happens to $\overline{DB}$ and $\overline{AC}$ as $\overline{DA}$ turns about point D?

3. $ABCD$ is a parallelogram linkage with $\overline{AB}$ fixed and $\overline{DC}$ crossing $\overline{AB}$.

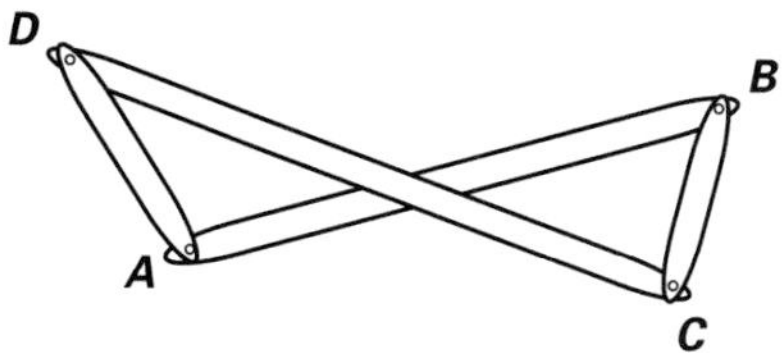

   a. Construct a model of this linkage using plastic or cardboard strips and paper fasteners.

   b. If point D is turned clockwise about point A, what type of path does point C follow?

   c. If $AB = DC = 6$ cm and $AD = 2$ cm, how will varying the length of $\overline{BC}$ affect the motion of point C?

4. For the diagram below, $\triangle ORQ \cong \triangle TSQ$ and O is the midpoint of $\overline{PR}$. Prove each of the following conclusions.

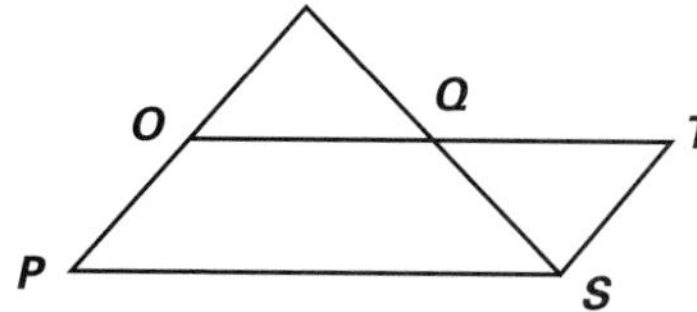

   a. Q is the midpoint of $\overline{RS}$.

   b. $POTS$ is a parallelogram.

   c. $\triangle TSQ \sim \triangle PRS$

   d. $PS = 2 \cdot OQ$

5. In the diagram below, $STAM$ is a rectangle and $SAMP$ is a parallelogram. Prove, if you can, that $\triangle TMP$ is an isosceles triangle. If the triangle is not isosceles, explain how you know.

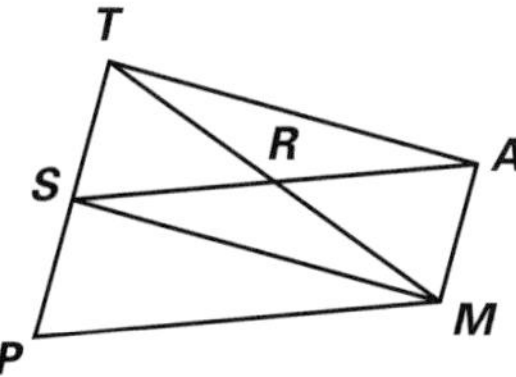

334 UNIT 4 • SHAPES AND GEOMETRIC REASONING

2. **a.** Students should build a similar linkage.
   b. Quadrilateral $ABCD$ is a parallelogram because both pairs of opposite sides are congruent.
   c. Point A follows a circular path since point A remains at a distance DA from point D.
   d. Each follows a circular path, which can be seen by drawing a point X on $\overline{DC}$ such that $\overline{PX} \parallel \overline{DA}$. Then $DAPX$ is always a parallelogram as point A moves. Thus, point P follows a circular path. Paths for Q and R can be shown in a similar manner.
   e. Their lengths change, but they always bisect each other.
3. **a.** Students should construct a model of the linkage.
   b. Point C turns along a circular path.
   c. As the length of $\overline{BC}$ varies, point C continues to move in circular arcs, but it may not revolve all the way around point B.
4. **a.** Since $\triangle ORQ \cong \triangle TSQ$, by CPCTC $\overline{RQ} \cong \overline{SQ}$ and thus Q is the midpoint of $\overline{RS}$.
   b. Since $\triangle ORQ \cong \triangle TSQ$, by CPCTC $\angle ROQ \cong \angle T$. Thus, $\overline{PO} \parallel \overline{TS}$ since $\angle ROQ$ and $\angle T$ are congruent alternate interior angles. Also, $\overline{TS} \cong \overline{OR}$ by CPCTC and $\overline{PO} \cong \overline{OR}$ (given). Thus, $\overline{PO} \cong \overline{TS}$. Since $\overline{PO} \parallel \overline{TS}$ and $\overline{PO} \cong \overline{TS}$, quadrilateral $POTS$ is a parallelogram.
   c. Since Q is the midpoint of $\overline{RS}$, O is the midpoint of $\overline{RP}$, and $\angle R \cong \angle R$, $\triangle ORQ \sim \triangle PRS$ by the SAS Similarity Theorem (scale factor 2). Since $\triangle ORQ \cong \triangle TSQ$ and $\triangle ORQ \sim \triangle PRS$, then $\triangle TSQ \sim \triangle PRS$.
   d. Since O is the midpoint of $\overline{PR}$ and Q is the midpoint of $\overline{RS}$, $PS = 2 \cdot OQ$ by the Midpoint Connector Theorem for Triangles.
5. Since $STAM$ is a rectangle, $\overline{TM} \cong \overline{SA}$ (diagonals are congruent). Since $SAMP$ is a parallelogram, $\overline{SA} \cong \overline{PM}$ (opposite sides are congruent). Thus, $\overline{TM} \cong \overline{PM}$ and $\triangle TMP$ is an isosceles triangle.

Unit 4

Organizing

CONSTRUCTING A MATH TOOLKIT: After you have discussed Organizing Tasks 1 and 2 as a whole class, students should include the properties of rectangles, squares, and rhombuses in their Math Toolkits.

1. **a.** ■ The opposite angles in a parallelogram are congruent, and the measures of all the angles sum to 360°. A rectangle has one right angle, which means the opposite angle must also be right. The two remaining angles must have measures that sum to 180°. Since those angles are congruent, they must each be right angles also.

■ Since the opposite angles in a parallelogram are congruent and in a rectangle one pair of adjacent angles are congruent, there are two pairs of congruent adjacent angles. Since all angles must be congruent to an adjacent angle as well as the opposite angle, all four angles must be congruent. The sum of the four angle measures is 360°, so each angle measures 90°.

b. Since all the angles of rectangle *ABCD* are congruent by Part a and *ABCD* is a parallelogram, then $\triangle ABC \cong \triangle BAD$. Thus, $\overline{AC} \cong \overline{DB}$ by corresponding parts.

c. This is not true for rectangles. Any rectangle that is not a square provides a counterexample.

d. Since a rectangle is a parallelogram and a parallelogram has diagonals that bisect each other, a rectangle's diagonals bisect each other.

e. If $\overline{AC} \cong \overline{BD}$ in parallelogram *ABCD*, then $\triangle ABC \cong \triangle BAD$ by SSS. Thus, $\angle B \cong \angle A$ by corresponding parts. Since $\angle A \cong \angle C$ and $\angle B \cong \angle D$, then all of the angles are congruent and thus are 90° angles. Therefore, *ABCD* has one right angle and so is a rectangle. (Or *ABCD* has at least one pair of congruent adjacent angles and so is a rectangle.)

NOTE: You may wish to remind students that a trapezoid is defined as a quadrilateral that has exactly one pair of parallel sides in this curriculum.

2. **a.** If a quadrilateral is a square, then it is a parallelogram that has one right angle, and thus it satisfies the definition of a rectangle.

b. If a quadrilateral is a square, it has one pair of congruent adjacent sides and is a parallelogram. Thus, it is a rhombus.

c. Since a square is a rhombus, it has diagonals that are perpendicular to and bisect each other.

d. Since a square is a rhombus and the diagonals of a rhombus bisect the angles of the rhombus, then so do the diagonals of the square.

3. **a.** Rhombuses, rectangles, and squares will have the characteristic, because each is also a parallelogram.

b. Rhombuses and squares will have the characteristic, because each is also a kite.

Organizing

1. A rectangle may be defined in several ways. Here are two ways:
   - A quadrilateral is a *rectangle* if and only if it is a parallelogram and it has one right angle.
   - A quadrilateral is a *rectangle* if and only if it is a parallelogram and it has one pair of congruent adjacent angles.

   For each statement below, use one definition or the other to prove that the statement is correct or find a counterexample.

   a. If a quadrilateral is a rectangle, then it has four right angles.

   b. If a quadrilateral is a rectangle, then it has congruent diagonals.

   c. If a quadrilateral is a rectangle, then its diagonals are perpendicular.

   d. If a quadrilateral is a rectangle, then it has diagonals that bisect each other.

   e. If the diagonals of a parallelogram are congruent, then the parallelogram is a rectangle.

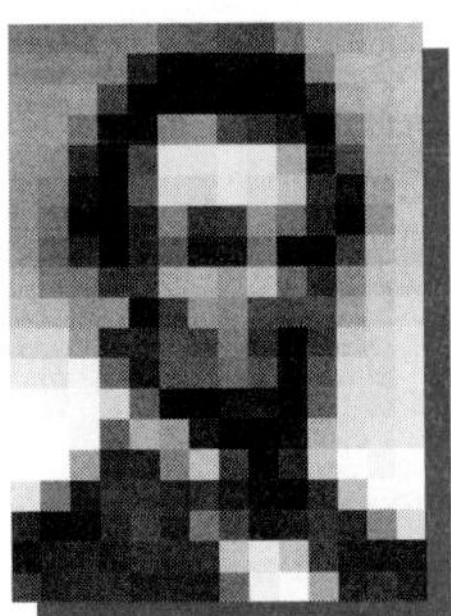

This pattern of squares was created in an experiment to determine the amount of detail needed for a picture to be recognizable.

2. A **square** is a parallelogram with one right angle and one pair of adjacent sides congruent. Use this definition of a square to prove the statements in Parts a through d.

   a. If a quadrilateral is a square, then it is a rectangle.

   b. If a quadrilateral is a square, then it is a rhombus.

   c. If a quadrilateral is a square, then the diagonals are perpendicular to and bisect each other.

   d. If a quadrilateral is a square, then the diagonals bisect the angles of the square.

3. Quadrilaterals come in a variety of specialized shapes. There are trapezoids, kites, parallelograms, rhombuses, rectangles, and squares, as well as everyday quadrilaterals with no special additional characteristics.

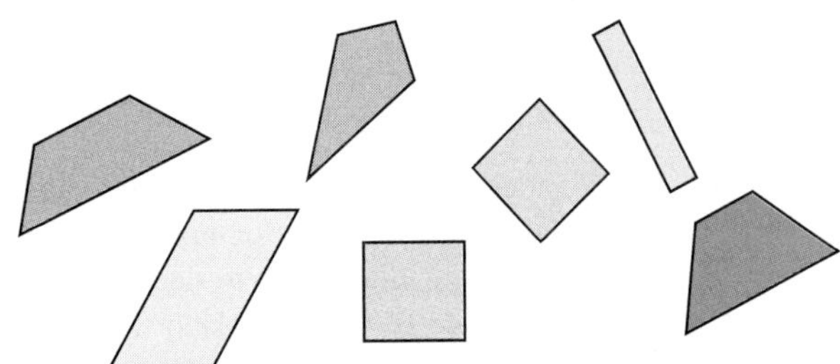

   a. Suppose you know that a characteristic X is true for parallelograms. For which other quadrilaterals must characteristic X also be true? Explain your reasoning.

   b. Suppose a characteristic Y is true for all kites. Which other quadrilaterals must also have characteristic Y? Explain your reasoning.

Unit 4

LESSON 3 • PARALLELOGRAMS: NECESSARY AND SUFFICIENT CONDITIONS 335

c. Complete a copy of the *quadrilateral tree* shown at the right by writing the names of the quadrilaterals in the ovals. If the oval for a shape is connected to one or more ovals *above* it, then that shape must also be an example of the shape or shapes in the ovals to which it is connected.

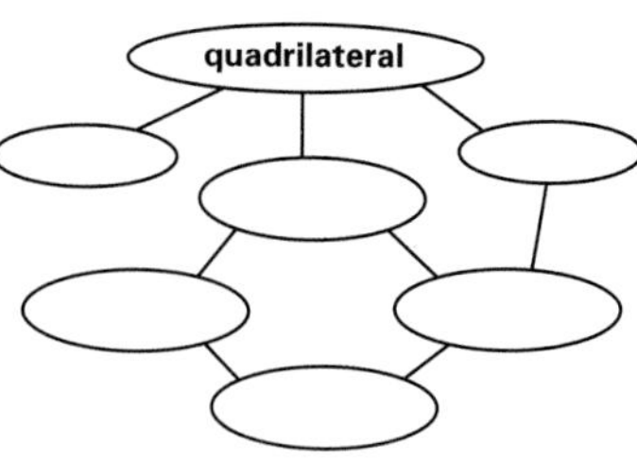

d. How can you use the quadrilateral tree to help decide on responses to questions like those in Parts a and b on the previous page?

4. Definitions are stated in "if and only if" form: *p if and only if q*. This is done because *p if and only if q* means

- p if q ($q \Rightarrow p$) and
- p only if q ($p \Rightarrow q$).

Thus, you can conclude p when you know q, and you can conclude q when you know p.

a. Consider the definition of a parallelogram: *A quadrilateral is a parallelogram if and only if both pairs of opposite sides are parallel.* In which direction is the definition being used when you conclude that the opposite sides of a parallelogram are parallel? In which direction is it being used when you conclude that a quadrilateral is a parallelogram because its opposite sides are parallel?

b. In Investigation 1, page 326, you proved (i) that the opposite sides of a parallelogram are congruent and (ii) that if the opposite sides of a quadrilateral are congruent, then the figure is a parallelogram. Write this information in a single "if and only if" statement.

c. Review the statements of other theorems about parallelograms and rhombuses you proved in Investigations 1 and 2. Combine those that can be combined into single "if and only if" statements.

d. If you were asked to prove "r if and only if s," what two things would you need to do?

5. Parallelograms are related to translations. Each side of a parallelogram is the translation image of its opposite side. What is the magnitude of such translations? How can the direction be represented?

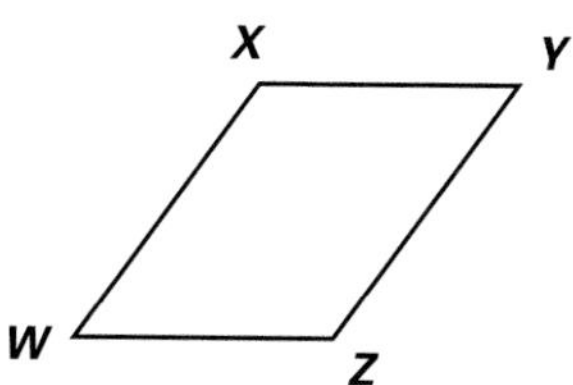

Unit 4

336 UNIT 4 • SHAPES AND GEOMETRIC REASONING

3. c.

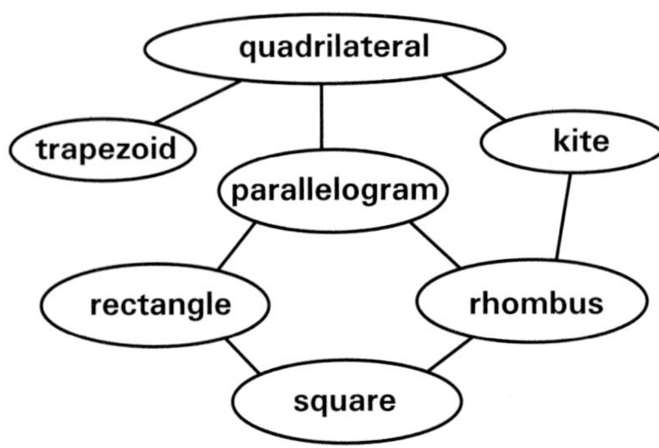

d. Properties of a shape transfer to those shapes below it and to which it is connected.

4. a. When you conclude that the opposite sides of a parallelogram are parallel, you are using the "only if" direction. When you conclude that a quadrilateral is a parallelogram because its opposite sides are parallel, you are using the "if" direction.

b. A quadrilateral is a parallelogram if and only if the opposite sides are congruent.

c. All of the theorems about parallelograms and rhombuses can be stated in if-and-only-if form.

d. You would need to prove (1) if *r* then *s* and (2) if *s* then *r*.

5. The magnitude of the translation of a side is the length of the adjacent side of the parallelogram. Use a vector (students will probably say "arrow") parallel to and the same length as the adjacent side of the parallelogram.

Reflecting

1. **Responses may vary. This is an opportunity for students to take a moment and reflect on what it means to learn mathematics and how it is that they go about doing it. This writing should help them to see that learning mathematics is a process and that it often happens in stages. It also gives them an opportunity to identify the parts of the process that they found enjoyable and interesting.**
2. **a.** Points X and X'' are the same point.
   b. If point X is the midpoint of $\overline{BC}$, then $X = X'$.
3. Both activities are important, so students may defend either choice. Explanations will vary.
4. Responses will vary. Knowing where to begin is not easy. Basically, you need to look at what you know about the situation and see what happens when you try to reason using accepted properties, theorems, and definitions. Sometimes it is helpful to look at the conclusion and ask what you would need to know to be able to state the conclusion (reasoning backwards). Students need to realize that the road to mathematical proof is not always a direct one. People often start in one direction only to get stuck and have to go back and start over. Students also need to realize that there is often more than one way to prove something.

Reflecting

1. Your work in this lesson with the Midpoint Connector Theorem for Quadrilaterals can be thought of as a mathematical journey. It began with experimentation, which led to a conjecture, and ended with a proof.

a. Write a paragraph outlining what you believe to be the main features of this journey.

b. What aspects of this journey were most interesting to you? Why?

c. Give another instance of a similar mathematical journey you made in this unit.

2. The Midpoint Connector Theorem for Quadrilaterals is an amazing result. It was first proved by a French mathematician, Pierre Varignon (1654–1722). A more recent unexpected result was discovered when applying the following "point connector" algorithm.

Step 1: Carefully draw a large $\triangle ABC$. Choose a point X between points B and C.

Step 2: Through point X, draw a segment parallel to $\overline{AB}$. Label the point of intersection with $\overline{AC}$ as point Y.

Step 3: Through point Y, draw a segment parallel to $\overline{BC}$. Label the intersection with $\overline{AB}$ as point Z.

Step 4: Through point Z, draw a segment parallel to $\overline{AC}$. Label the point of intersection with $\overline{BC}$ as point X'.

Step 5: Repeat steps 2 through 4 starting with the point X'. Label the new points Y', Z', and X'' respectively.

a. What appears to be true about X and X''?

b. Is there a point X on $\overline{BC}$ so that after applying this algorithm, $X = X'$?

3. Which mathematical activity do you think is more important: discovering properties of a shape, such as those of a parallelogram, or using certain properties to conclude that a shape must be a particular type of shape, such as a parallelogram? Explain your position.

4. One of the most commonly asked questions by students learning to write mathematical proofs is "How do you know where to begin?" Based on your experiences in this unit and in previous ones, how would you respond to this question?

Unit 4

LESSON 3 • PARALLELOGRAMS: NECESSARY AND SUFFICIENT CONDITIONS 337

Extending

1. Suppose you had two parallelograms *ABCD* and *STOP*. What would be the least amount of information about the two needed for you to prove each statement below?

   a. $STOP \sim ABCD$

   b. $STOP \cong ABCD$

2. Look back at Part b of the "Think About This Situation" on page 325.

   a. What conjecture did (or can you) make about the quadrilateral formed by connecting, in order, the midpoints of the sides of the following special quadrilaterals:

      square
      rectangle
      parallelogram (other than a square or rectangle)
      trapezoid
      kite

   b. Select two of your conjectures and for each, write
      - a synthetic proof,
      - a coordinate proof.

3. An **equilic quadrilateral** is a quadrilateral with a pair of congruent opposite sides that, when extended, meet to form a 60° angle. The other two sides are called *bases*.

   a. Draw an equilic quadrilateral.

   b. Quadrilateral *ABCD* is equilic with bases $\overline{AB}$ and $\overline{CD}$ and $\overline{AD} \cong \overline{BC}$.

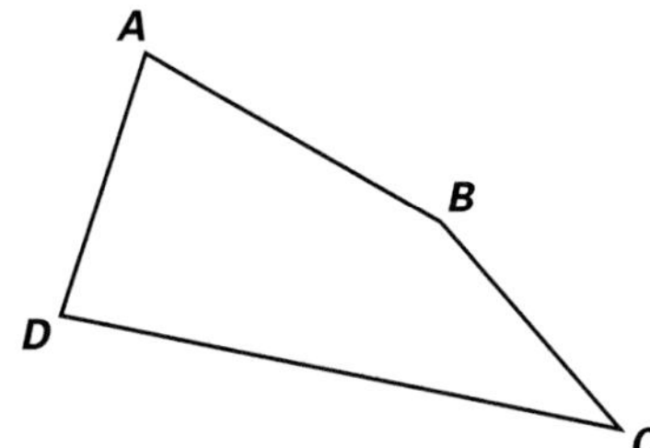

      - Could base $\overline{AB}$ be parallel to base $\overline{CD}$? Explain your reasoning.
      - Could $\overline{AB} \cong \overline{CD}$? Explain.
      - Find $m\angle D + m\angle C$.
      - Find $m\angle A + m\angle B$.

Unit 4

338 UNIT 4 • SHAPES AND GEOMETRIC REASONING

Extending

1. **a.** In a parallelogram, the measure of one angle determines the measures of all the angles, so no more than one pair of corresponding congruent angles is needed. The measures of one pair of corresponding angles and one pair of proportional sides is not sufficient, since the other corresponding sides may not be proportional. Thus, one pair of corresponding congruent angles and two pairs of adjacent proportional sides are needed to ensure similarity. Also, two pairs of adjacent proportional sides are not enough, since the shape is not rigid and angles could vary.

   b. By an analysis similar to the one in Part a, you can conclude that two pairs of corresponding sides and one pair of corresponding angles must be congruent.

2. **a.** The quadrilateral formed by joining the midpoints of:

   a square is a square
   a rectangle is a rhombus
   a parallelogram (not a square or rectangle) is a parallelogram
   a trapezoid is a parallelogram
   a kite is a rectangle

   b. Student proofs will vary.

3. **a.** Two sample drawings are provided below.

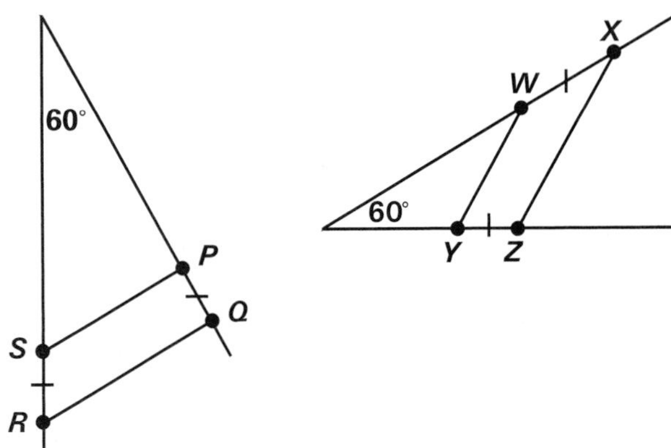

   b.
   - Yes, $\overline{AB}$ and $\overline{CD}$ could be parallel. The shape would be an isosceles trapezoid.
   - No, $\overline{AB}$ and $\overline{CD}$ could not be congruent. If they were, the shape would be a parallelogram, and the congruent opposite sides would not meet to form a 60° angle.
   - Extending $\overline{AD}$ and $\overline{BC}$ would give a triangle with base angles D and C and a third angle of measure 60°. Thus, $m\angle D + m\angle C = 180° - 60° = 120°$.
   - Subtract the sum $m\angle D + m\angle C$ from the sum of all interior angle measures to get $m\angle A + m\angle B = 360° - 120° = 240°$.

Assessments 170–172

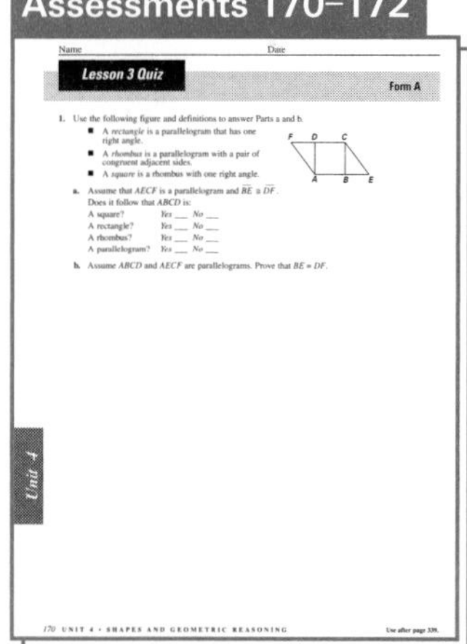
Lesson 3 Quiz
Form A

Assessments 173–175

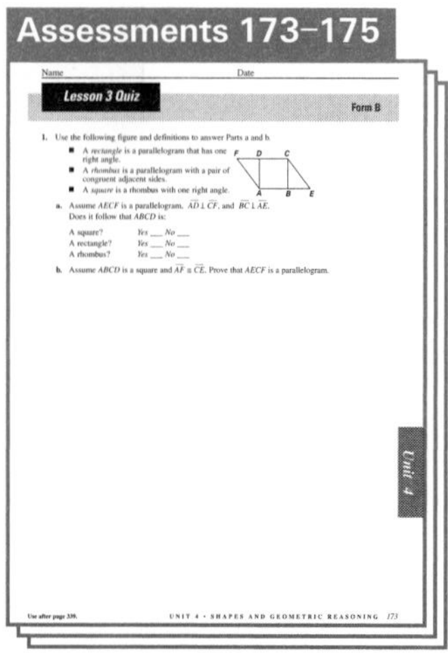
Lesson 3 Quiz
Form B

Unit 4

MORE *continued*

3. c. The four points are the vertices of rhombus $JLKM$.

$$MJ = \frac{1}{2}AD$$

$$LK = \frac{1}{2}AD$$

$$JL = \frac{1}{2}BC$$

$$MK = \frac{1}{2}BC$$

Since $\overline{BC} \cong \overline{AD}$ and $\frac{1}{2}AD = \frac{1}{2}BC$, all the sides of $JLKM$ are equal and $JLKM$ is a rhombus.

d. Points P, C, and D are vertices of an equilateral triangle.

Proof: We are interested in $m\angle PAD$ and $m\angle PBC$, since they are included angles of two pairs of congruent sides ($AD = CB$ and $BP = AP$). If these two angles can be shown to be congruent, $\triangle PAD$ and $\triangle PBC$ are also congruent.

From Part b, we know

$$m\angle DAB + m\angle CBA = 240^\circ$$

$$m\angle DAB = 240^\circ - m\angle CBA.$$

We also know

$$m\angle PBC = m\angle PBA + m\angle ABC$$

$$= 60^\circ + m\angle ABC$$

Now,

$$m\angle PAD = 360^\circ - m\angle DAB - m\angle PAB$$

$$= 360^\circ - m\angle DAB - 60^\circ$$

$$= 300^\circ - m\angle DAB$$

$$= 300^\circ - (240^\circ - m\angle CBA)$$

$$= 60^\circ + m\angle ABC$$

$$= m\angle PBC$$

Thus, $\triangle PAD \cong \triangle PBC$ by SAS. So $\overline{DP} \cong \overline{CP}$ by CPCTC.

Also by CPCTC, $\angle DPA \cong \angle CPB$. $m\angle APC + m\angle CPB = m\angle APB = 60^\circ$, so $m\angle APC + m\angle DPA = 60^\circ$. Thus, $\triangle DPC$ is isosceles with a 60° angle, so $\triangle DPC$ is equilateral.

4. a.

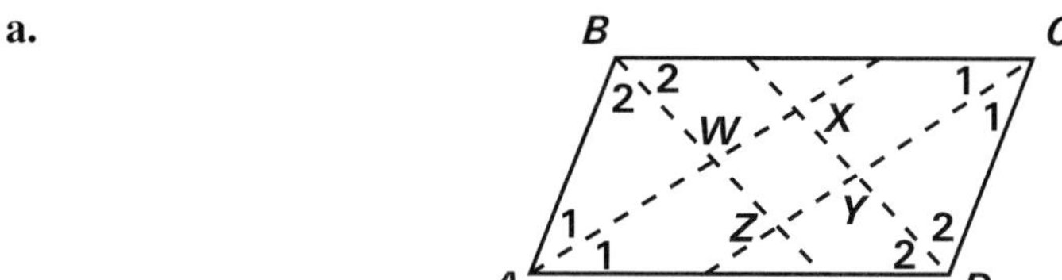

$$2(m\angle 1) + 2(m\angle 2) = 180^\circ$$

$m\angle BWA = 180^\circ - (m\angle 1 + m\angle 2) = 180^\circ - 90^\circ = 90^\circ$

Similarly, $m\angle CYD = 90^\circ$

$m\angle AXD = 180^\circ - (m\angle 1 + m\angle 2) = 90^\circ$ (from $\triangle AXD$)

Thus, $WXYZ$ is a rectangle.

b. For the kite, one diagonal bisects its two angles. Thus, no quadrilateral is formed, but rather the figure reduces to a point.

See additional Teaching Notes on page T344O.

c. Suppose you have an equilic quadrilateral *ABCD* with $\overline{AD} \cong \overline{BC}$ and diagonals $\overline{AC}$ and $\overline{BD}$; points *J*, *K*, *L*, and *M* are midpoints of sides $\overline{AB}$ and $\overline{CD}$ and diagonals $\overline{AC}$ and $\overline{BD}$ respectively. How are the four points *J*, *K*, *L*, and *M* related? Prove you are correct.

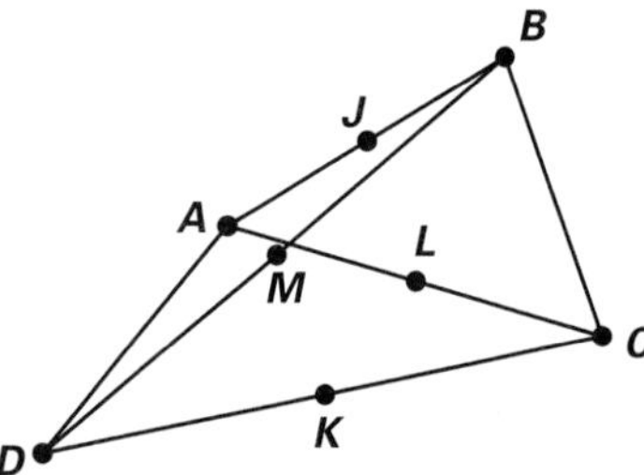

d. Draw an equilic quadrilateral *ABCD* with $\overline{AD} \cong \overline{BC}$ and $AB < CD$. Draw an equilateral triangle on base $\overline{AB}$ that shares no points with the interior of quadrilateral *ABCD*. Label the third vertex *P*. How are points *P*, *C*, and *D* related? Prove your conjecture.

4. Carefully draw an example of each quadrilateral listed below. Then carefully draw or construct the bisectors of each angle and call the four points of intersection of pairs of bisectors *W*, *X*, *Y*, and *Z*. Consider quadrilateral *WXYZ* in each case. If *WXYZ* is identifiable as a special kind of quadrilateral, name it. Prove you are correct.

a. Parallelogram

b. Kite

c. Rectangle

d. Isosceles trapezoid

e. Trapezoid

f. General quadrilateral

Unit 4

LESSON 3 • PARALLELOGRAMS: NECESSARY AND SUFFICIENT CONDITIONS 339

Lesson 4

Looking Back

In this unit, you were involved in an extended journey in geometric thinking. Beginning with some accepted mathematical ideas, you were able to deduce many additional relations. You started by proving relations among angles formed by two intersecting lines or by two parallel lines cut by a transversal. You then used the Law of Cosines and the Law of Sines to deduce the similarity and congruence conditions for triangles. Finally, you used the latter tools to investigate and prove properties of parallelograms and related quadrilaterals.

The journey was long but important. It illustrated well the way new mathematics is developed: A person or group of people thinks there is a possible new relation in a setting, explores it with examples, makes a conjecture, and then tries to confirm the conjecture deductively based on accepted mathematical knowledge. In the activities that follow, you will have the opportunity to review this process and the major theorems and to apply them in new settings.

1. Suppose you are given a theorem in the form "if *s*, then *t*," where *s* and *t* are mathematical statements.

a. Explain the significance of the mathematical information given in statement *s*.

b. Suppose you know the statement "if *s*, then *t*" is correct.

- If you also know the conditions in *s* are satisfied in a particular situation, what can you conclude about the conditions in *t* for that situation? Give an example that illustrates this kind of reasoning in geometry. Give an example that illustrates this kind of reasoning in algebra.
- What can you conclude about the statement *t* if you know nothing about the truth of the statement *s*?

2. You are given $l \parallel m$, $m \parallel n$, and a transversal *t* as shown. Prove each statement below under these conditions.

a. $l \parallel n$

b. $\angle 1 \cong \angle 3$

c. $\angle 2$ and $\angle 3$ are supplementary

d. $\angle 2 \cong \angle 6$

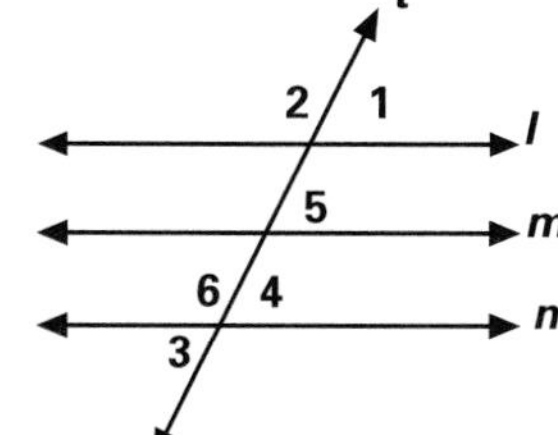

Unit 4

340 UNIT 4 • SHAPES AND GEOMETRIC REASONING

Lesson 4 *Looking Back*

SYNTHESIZE UNIT IDEAS small-group activity

In this section, students are asked to employ their skills in a variety of situations. Remind the groups that when something is proved, it can be used in later proofs. This is especially important in Tasks 2, 6, and 7. Sharing responsibility for some parts, such as Task 4 Part c, will improve the progress through the lesson.

1. **a.** The information given in the hypothesis is accepted as true and is expected to be of use in the deduction of the conclusion. In other words, this is the information you know about a situation.

b. ■ The correctness of "if s then t" always implies the correctness of the conditions in t when the conditions in s are satisfied. Examples will vary.

■ You cannot conclude anything about t when you know nothing about the truth of s.

2. **a.** Since $l \parallel m$, $\angle 1 \cong \angle 5$ by the Parallel Lines Property. Similarly, since $m \parallel n$, $\angle 5 \cong \angle 4$. Since $\angle 1 \cong \angle 5$ and $\angle 5 \cong \angle 4$, it follows that $\angle 1 \cong \angle 4$. Since $\angle 1 \cong \angle 4$ and $\angle 1$ and $\angle 4$ are corresponding angles for transversal t and lines l and n, l is parallel to n.

b. In Part a, we proved $l \parallel n$. We use that fact here. Since $l \parallel n$ and t is a transversal, $\angle 1$ and $\angle 3$ are alternate exterior angles. When parallel lines are cut by a transversal, the alternate exterior angles are congruent. Thus, $\angle 1 \cong \angle 3$.

Alternate proof: In Part a, we proved $\angle 1 \cong \angle 4$. But $\angle 3 \cong \angle 4$ because they are vertical angles. Thus, $\angle 1 \cong \angle 3$.

c. In Part b, we proved $\angle 1 \cong \angle 3$. Thus, since $\angle 1$ and $\angle 2$ are supplementary, $m\angle 1 + m\angle 2 = 180°$. Since $\angle 1 \cong \angle 3$, $m\angle 1 = m\angle 3$. Substituting $m\angle 3$ in the equation $m\angle 1 + m\angle 2 = 180°$, we get $m\angle 3 + m\angle 2 = 180°$. Thus, $\angle 2$ and $\angle 3$ are supplementary since their measures add to 180°.

d. In Part a, we proved that $l \parallel n$. Since $\angle 2$ and $\angle 6$ are corresponding angles for transversal t with parallel lines l and n, $\angle 2 \cong \angle 6$.

Master 110

SYNTHESIZE *continued*

3. **See Teaching Master 110.**
   a. See diagram at the right.
   b. The ball leaves $\overline{AB}$ for the second time at 60°. Using triangles and the fact that the sides of the tables are parallel lets us find the angle measures as given in the diagram in Part a.
   c. $\overline{QR}$ and $\overline{ST}$ are parallel. Angle measures can be determined as shown in the diagram at the right. Since $\angle QRS$ and $\angle RST$ are supplementary and interior angles on the same side of the transversal, $\overleftrightarrow{QR} \parallel \overleftrightarrow{ST}$.

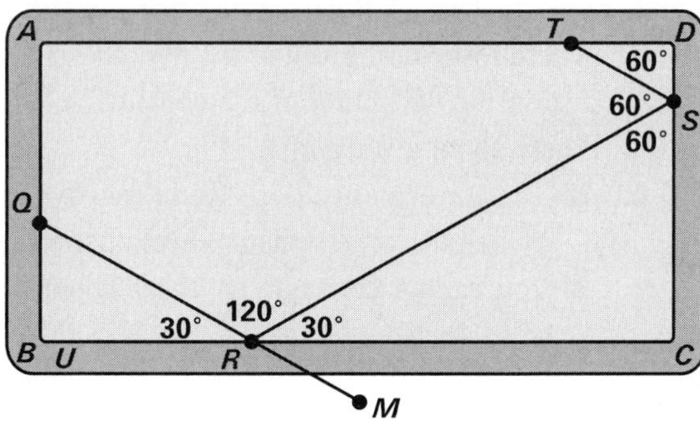

   d. ■ See diagram at the right
      ■ Let S be the reflection of U across $\overleftrightarrow{BC}$. Draw $\overline{ZS}$. Since $RT = RT$, $UT = TS$ (line reflection preserves distance) and $\angle RTU \cong \angle RTS$ ($\overline{US}$ is perpendicular to $\overline{BC}$ and $\overline{RT}$), $\triangle RTU \cong \triangle RTS$. Since $\triangle RTU \cong \triangle RTS$, $\angle URT \cong \angle SRT$ and the ball will hit U, the preimage of S.

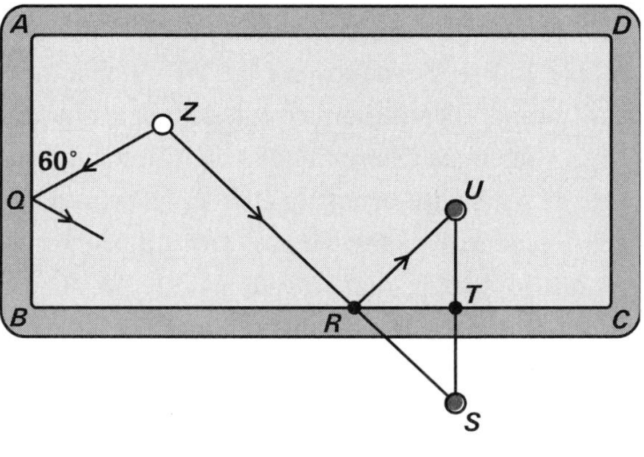

4. a. $\triangle PSR$, $\triangle QSR$, $\triangle PTS$, $\triangle STR$, $\triangle QTR$, $\triangle PTQ$, $\triangle PQR$, $\triangle PQS$
   b. $\triangle PSR$ and $\triangle QRS$; $\triangle PTS$ and $\triangle QTR$; and $\triangle SPQ$ and $\triangle RQP$
   c. Here it is important to choose the appropriate pair to begin with. That pair is $\triangle PTS$ and $\triangle QTR$. $\triangle PTS \cong \triangle QTR$. $\overline{PS} \cong \overline{QR}$, $\overline{PT} \cong \overline{QT}$, and $\overline{ST} \cong \overline{RT}$ are given as initial information. Thus, $\triangle PTS \cong \triangle QTR$ by the SSS Congruence Theorem. $\triangle SPQ \cong \triangle RQP$: From the initial information you know $\overline{PS} \cong \overline{QR}$. Since $\triangle PTS \cong \triangle QTR$, you know $\angle PSQ \cong \angle QRP$ by corresponding parts. But $SQ = ST + TQ$ and $RP = RT + TP$. Since the addends are equal ($RT = ST$ and $TP = TQ$), $SQ = RP$. Thus, $\triangle SPQ \cong \triangle RQP$ by the SAS Congruence Theorem. $\triangle PSR \cong \triangle QRS$: These triangles can be proven congruent using the same tactic that was used in the proof above. Thus, the SAS Congruence Theorem is used with $\angle SPR \cong \angle RQS$, $\overline{PS} \cong \overline{QR}$, and $\overline{SQ} \cong \overline{PR}$.
   d. The remaining pair of triangles is $\triangle STR$ and $\triangle QTP$.
      $\triangle STR \sim \triangle QTP$: $\angle PTQ \cong \angle RTS$ since they are vertical angles. Since it is given that $\overline{PT} \cong \overline{QT}$ and $\overline{ST} \cong \overline{RT}$, $\frac{PT}{RT} = \frac{QT}{ST} = k$ (or $PT = k \cdot RT$ and $QT = k \cdot ST$). Thus, $\triangle STR \sim \triangle QTP$ by the SAS Similarity Theorem.
   e. $\overline{PQ}$ is parallel to $\overline{SR}$: Since $\triangle STR \sim \triangle QTP$, the alternate interior angles, $\angle TSR$ and $\angle TQP$, are congruent. So $\overline{PQ} \parallel \overline{SR}$.

3. When a billiard ball with no spin and medium speed is banked off the cushion of a table, the angles at which it strikes and leaves the cushion are congruent.

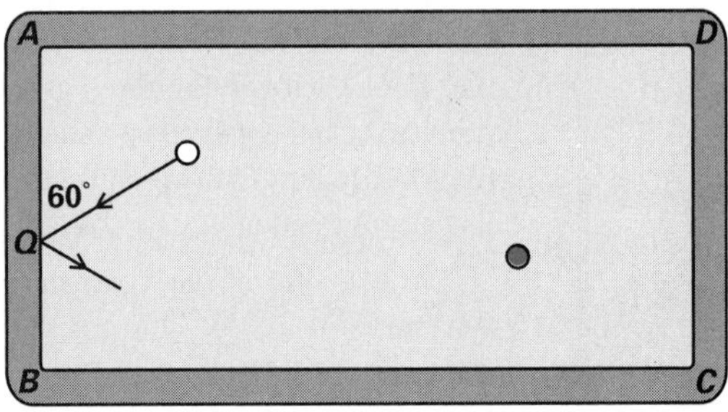

   a. On a copy of the billiards table, sketch the path of the ball as it rebounds from $\overline{AB}$, from $\overline{BC}$, from $\overline{CD}$, from $\overline{AD}$, and from $\overline{AB}$ again. (This assumes that the ball has enough speed to travel the whole path, of course!) Label the points where the ball strikes the cushions *R*, *S*, *T*, and *U* respectively.

   b. At what angle does the ball leave $\overline{AB}$ the second time? Explain your reasoning.

   c. What appears to be true about $\overline{QR}$ and $\overline{ST}$? Write a proof of your conjecture.

   d. At what point on the cushion $\overline{BC}$ would you aim if you wish to bank the white ball off that side and strike the orange ball? (Hint: Consider the reflection image of the orange ball across $\overleftrightarrow{BC}$.)

      - On a copy of the billiards table, draw the path of the white ball.
      - Prove that if the ball has no spin and sufficient speed, it will follow the drawn path and strike the orange ball.

4. For the diagram below, $\overline{PS} \cong \overline{QR}$, $\overline{PT} \cong \overline{QT}$, and $\overline{ST} \cong \overline{RT}$.

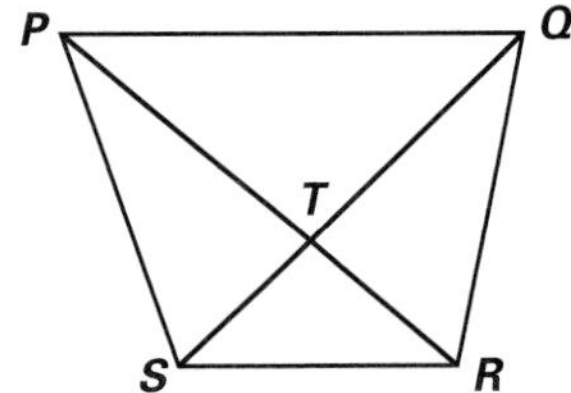

   a. Identify and name eight triangles in the diagram.

   b. Which pairs of the eight triangles seem to be congruent? Name each pair.

   c. Based on the given information, prove or disprove that each identified pair of triangles are congruent.

   d. Are the remaining pairs of triangles similar? If so, provide an argument.

   e. What can you conclude about $\overline{PQ}$ and $\overline{SR}$ when you know the given information? Write a proof for your conjecture.

LESSON 4 • LOOKING BACK 341

5. Civil engineers, urban planners, and design engineers are frequently confronted with "traffic center" problems. In mathematical terms, these problems often involve locating a point that is equidistant from three or more given points or for which the sum of its distances from the given points is as small as possible. In cases involving three given points that are vertices of a triangle, the problems can be solved by using geometric theorems which you are now able to prove. In the first two parts of this task, you are to write and analyze a synthetic proof and an analytic proof of the following theorem:

The midpoint of the hypotenuse of a right triangle is equidistant from its vertices.

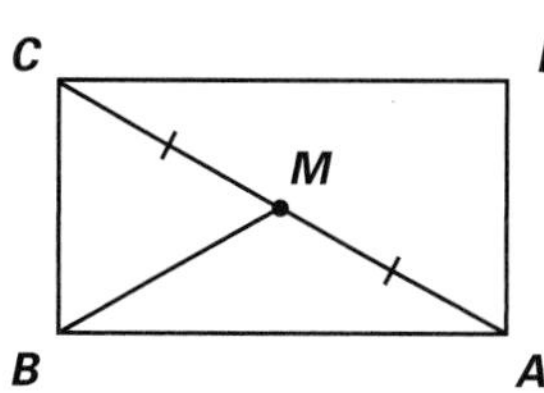

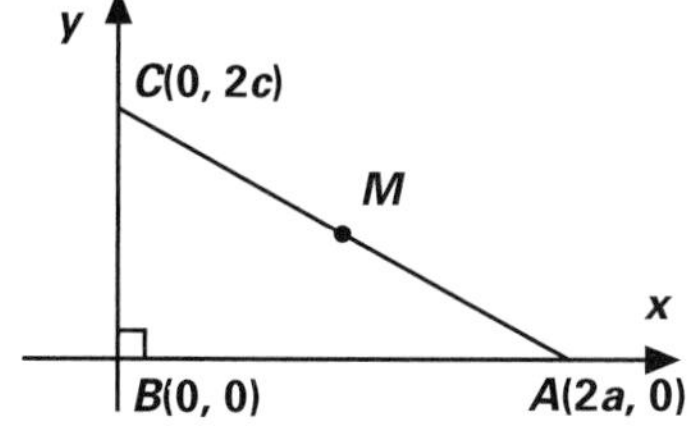

a. In the diagram on the left, $\triangle ABC$ is composed of two adjacent sides and a diagonal of rectangle *ABCD*. Using that diagram, write a synthetic proof that if *M* is the midpoint of $\overline{AC}$, then $MA = MB = MC$.

b. Using the diagram above on the right, write an analytic proof that if *M* is the midpoint of $\overline{AC}$, then $MA = MB = MC$.

c. For the proof in Part b, why do you think the coordinates of points *A* and *C* were assigned $(2a, 0)$ and $(0, 2c)$ rather than simply $(a, 0)$ and $(0, c)$ respectively?

d. While deductive reasoning is always used in proving theorems, this form of reasoning can also be used to discover new theorems. Look back at Reflecting Task 5 on page 323. How can you use the fact given in that task to determine where to locate a point *D* so that it is equidistant from the vertices of a general triangle *ABC*?

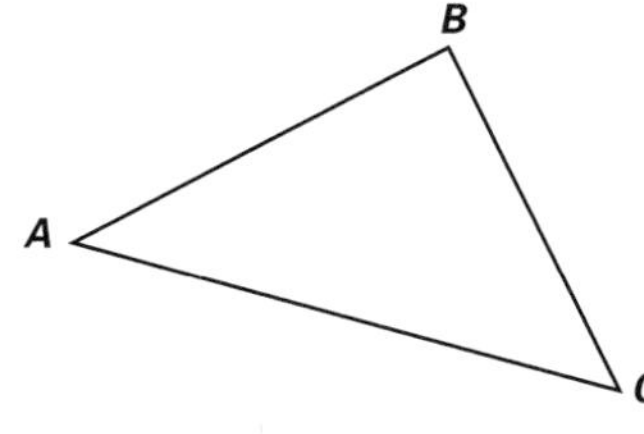

6. In the diagram below, $\overleftrightarrow{DF} \parallel \overleftrightarrow{AB}$, $\overleftrightarrow{ED} \parallel \overleftrightarrow{AC}$, $BD = 6$, $DC = 4$, $FC = 6$, and $AE = 3$.

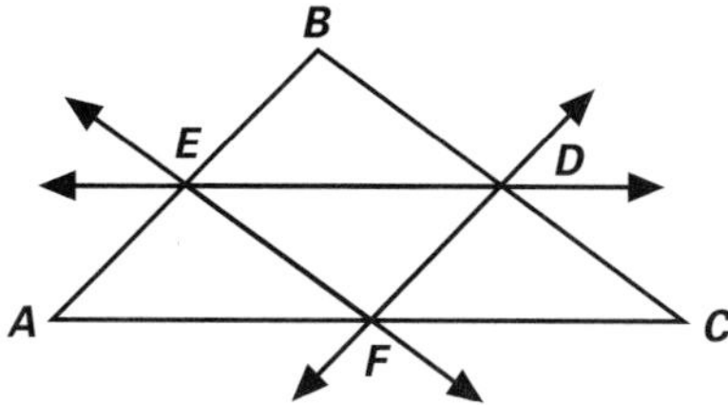

Unit 4

342 UNIT 4 • SHAPES AND GEOMETRIC REASONING

5\. **a.** Draw $\overline{NM}$ where N is the midpoint of $\overline{BC}$. Since N is the midpoint of $\overline{BC}$, $\overline{BN} \cong \overline{NC}$. $\overline{NM}$ is a side common to both $\triangle MNB$ and $\triangle MNC$. $\overline{NM} \parallel \overline{BA}$ by the Midpoint Connector Theorem. This means that since $\angle CBA$ is a right angle ($ABCD$ is a rectangle), $\angle 1$ is also a right angle (corresponding angles). Also, $\angle 1$ and $\angle 2$ form a linear pair, so $\angle 2$ must also be a right angle. Therefore, $\triangle MNB \cong \triangle MNC$ by SAS Congruence Theorem. Thus, $\overline{MC} \cong \overline{MB}$ by CPCTC. Since $\overline{MA} \cong \overline{MC}$, by substitution $\overline{MB} \cong \overline{MA} \cong \overline{MC}$.

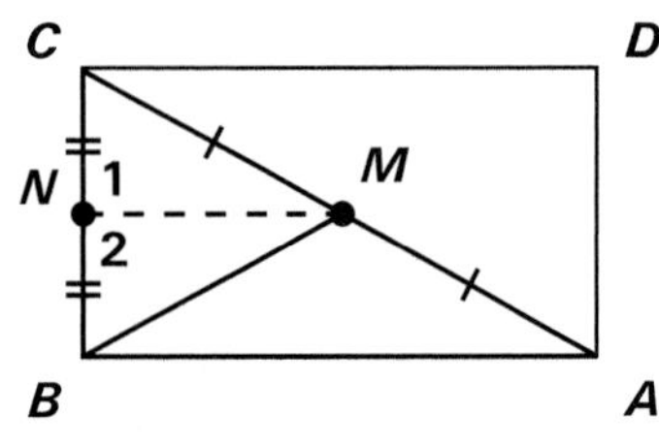

b. If M is the midpoint of $\overline{AC}$, then its coordinates must be $\left(\frac{2a}{2}, \frac{2c}{2}\right) = (a, c)$. By the distance formula,

$MB = \sqrt{a^2 + c^2}$

$MA = \sqrt{(2a - a)^2 + (0 - c)^2} = \sqrt{a^2 + c^2}$

$MC = \sqrt{(0 - a)^2 + (2c - c)^2} = \sqrt{a^2 + c^2}$

Therefore, all three segments have equal length.

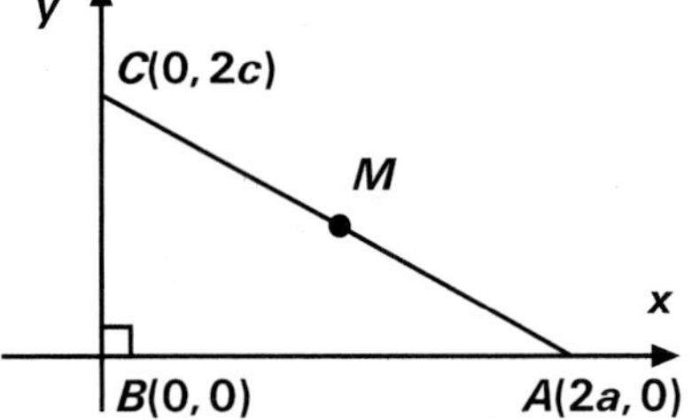

c. Assigning $2a$ and $2c$ as the x- and y-coordinates eliminates fractions when using the midpoint formula.

d. Any point on the perpendicular bisector of $\overline{AB}$ is equidistant from A and B, and any point on the perpendicular bisector of $\overline{BC}$ is equidistant from B and C. The point D where the two perpendicular bisectors intersect is the same distance from all three vertices A, B, and C.

Unit 4

SYNTHESIZE *continued*

6. **a.** Angle C is common to both triangles. $\angle C \cong \angle C$. Since $\overline{DF} \parallel \overline{AB}$, $\overline{BC}$ is a transversal. $\angle B$ and $\angle FDC$ are corresponding angles, so $\angle B \cong \angle FDC$. Thus, $\triangle ABC \sim \triangle FDC$ by the AA Similarity Theorem.

b. Since $\triangle ABC \sim \triangle FDC$: $\frac{BC}{DC} = \frac{AC}{FC}$. Substituting, we get $\frac{10}{4} = \frac{AF + 6}{6}$.

$$60 = 4(AF + 6)$$
$$60 = 4AF + 24$$
$$36 = 4AF$$
$$9 = AF$$

c. $\triangle ABC \sim \triangle EBD$ using a similar proof as in Part a.

$$\frac{EB}{BA} = \frac{BD}{BC}$$
$$\frac{EB}{EB + 3} = \frac{6}{10}$$
$$10EB = 6EB + 18$$
$$4EB = 18$$
$$EB = 4.5$$

d. If $\overline{EF}$ were parallel to $\overline{BC}$, then $\triangle BAC$ would be similar to $\triangle EAF$ and $\frac{BA}{EA}$ would equal $\frac{AC}{AF}$. But $\frac{BA}{EA} = \frac{7.5}{3}$ and $\frac{AC}{AF} = \frac{15}{9}$. Thus, $\frac{BA}{EA} \neq \frac{AC}{AF}$. Thus, $\overline{EF}$ is not parallel to $\overline{BC}$.

e. $\triangle ABC$ is not similar to $\triangle DFE$.

Since $\overline{DF} \parallel \overline{AB}$, then $\angle EDF \cong \angle BED$. Since $\overline{ED} \parallel \overline{AC}$, then $\angle BED \cong \angle A$. Therefore, $\angle EDF \cong \angle A$. Also, since $\overline{DF} \parallel \overline{AB}$, then $\angle EFD \cong \angle AEF$. But since $\overline{EF}$ is not parallel to $\overline{BC}$, $\angle AEF$ is not congruent to $\angle B$. Therefore, $\angle EFD$ is not congruent to $\angle B$. Similarly, $\angle FED$ is not congruent to $\angle C$. Thus, $\triangle ABC$ is not similar to $\triangle DFE$.

f. There is only one parallelogram in the figure, and it is $AEDF$ since $\overline{AE} \parallel \overline{DF}$ and $\overline{ED} \parallel \overline{AF}$.

7. **a.** Since $ABCD$ is a parallelogram, $\overline{AD} \parallel \overline{CN}$. Thus, $\angle MNB \cong \angle ADM$ since they are alternate interior angles formed by parallel lines. Also, $\angle AMD \cong \angle BMN$ since they are vertical angles. Since M is the midpoint of $\overline{AB}$, $\overline{AM} \cong \overline{MB}$. Thus, $\triangle AMD \cong \triangle BMN$ by the AAS Congruence Theorem.

b. The two shapes have identical areas. Since $\triangle AMD \cong \triangle BMN$, Area ($\triangle AMD$) = Area ($\triangle BMN$).

Area ($ABCD$) = Area ($\triangle AMD$) + Area ($DMBC$)
= Area ($\triangle BMN$) + Area ($DMBC$)
= Area ($\triangle DNC$)

Unit 4

a. Prove $\triangle ABC \sim \triangle FDC$.

b. Find AF.

c. Find EB.

d. Is $\overleftrightarrow{EF} \parallel \overleftrightarrow{BC}$? Explain.

e. Is $\triangle ABC \sim \triangle DFE$? Why or why not?

f. Identify each quadrilateral in the diagram that is a parallelogram. Give a justification for each claim.

7. Below, $ABCD$ is a parallelogram and M is the midpoint of $\overline{AB}$. $\overline{DM}$ and $\overline{CB}$ are extended to meet at point N.

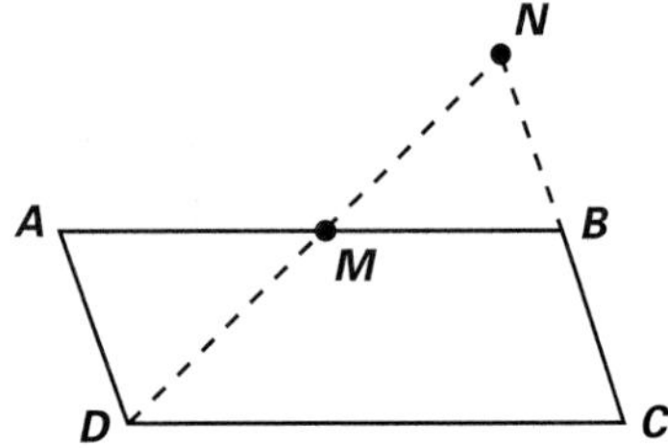

a. Prove $\triangle AMD \cong \triangle BMN$.

b. Compare the areas of $\triangle DNC$ and parallelogram $ABCD$.

8. In this unit, you were able to deduce many new geometric relations. You began with the Pythagorean Theorem, the Law of Cosines, and the Law of Sines, which you proved in previous units, and you assumed the Linear Pairs Property and Parallel Lines Property to be true.

Some of the theorems you proved are represented below as vertices of a concept map.

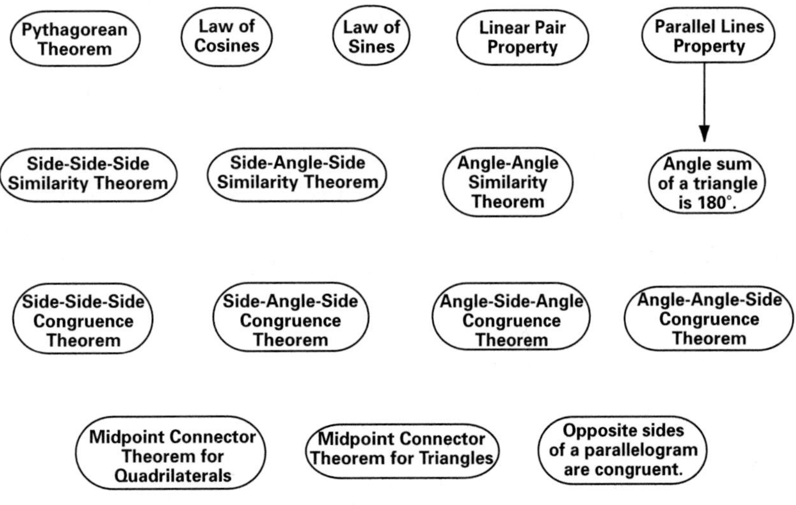

Unit 4

LESSON 4 • LOOKING BACK 343

a. On a copy of the concept map on the previous page, draw a directed edge *from* a vertex labeled A *to* a vertex labeled B if Statement A was used to prove Theorem B.

b. Use your completed concept map to identify which of these properties and theorems contributed to the Midpoint Connector Theorem for Quadrilaterals. Include statements that contributed directly, by being used in the proof, or indirectly, by being used to prove a theorem on which the proof depended.

c. Add a new vertex representing some other theorem you proved in this unit. Draw directed edges from other vertices whose statements were somehow needed in the proof of this theorem. (You may want to use a different color.)

Checkpoint

In this unit, you have extended your understanding of geometric shapes and sharpened your skills in mathematical reasoning.

a When trying to prove an if-then statement, with what facts would you begin? What would you try to deduce?

b Identify at least two relations between angles formed by two lines and a transversal that ensure the lines are parallel. Draw and label a sketch to illustrate the relations.

c What conditions on two triangles ensure that the triangles are congruent? Are similar?

d How are the ideas of congruence and similarity related?

e Identify at least four conditions that permit you to conclude that a pair of angles are congruent.

f Identify at least two conditions on a quadrilateral that guarantee that it is a parallelogram.

g In the first Checkpoint of this unit, page 265, you were asked to identify what you considered to be the most important characteristics of a valid argument. Now that you have completed the unit, answer the question again and compare your thinking then and now.

Be prepared to share your descriptions, conclusions, and reasoning with the entire class.

On Your Own

Write, in outline form, a summary of the important mathematical concepts and methods developed in this unit. Organize your summary so that it can be used as a quick reference in future units and courses.

344 UNIT 4 • SHAPES AND GEOMETRIC REASONING

SYNTHESIZE *continued*

8. **See Teaching Master 111.**

a.

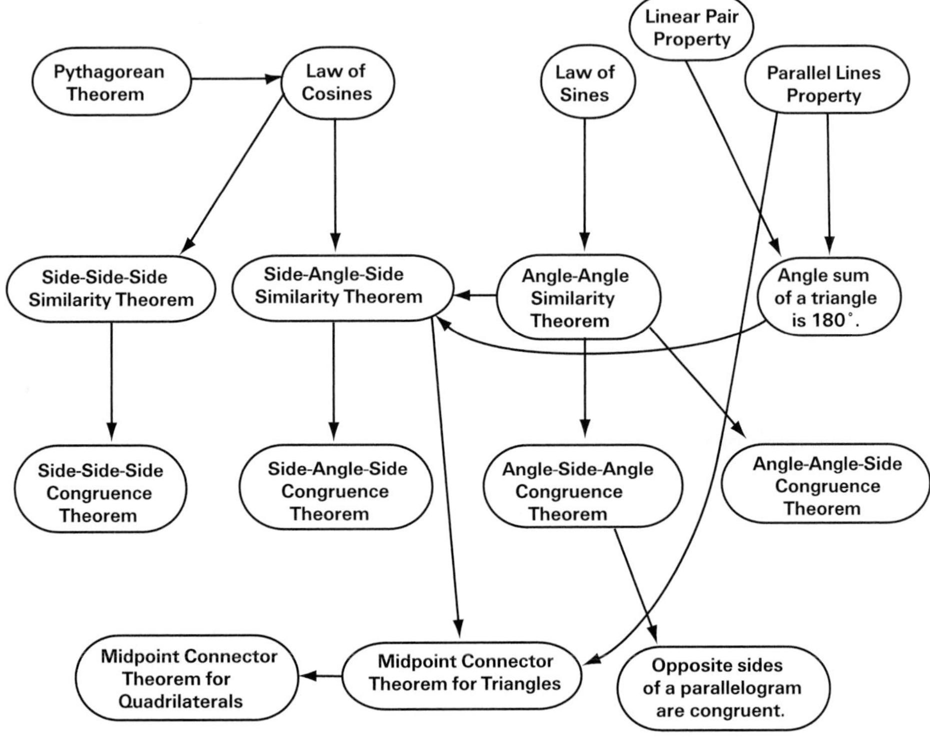

b. The proof of the Midpoint Connector Theorem for Triangles uses:
SAS Similarity, Law of Cosines, Pythagorean Theorem,
SAS Similarity, AA Similarity, Law of Sines,
or SAS Similarity, Angle Sum of a Triangle is 180°, Linear Pairs Property,
Parallel Lines Property

c. New vertices will be student selected based on the theorems they personally proved.

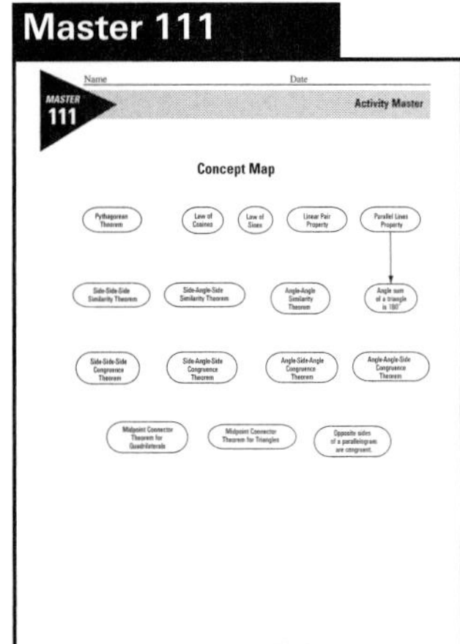

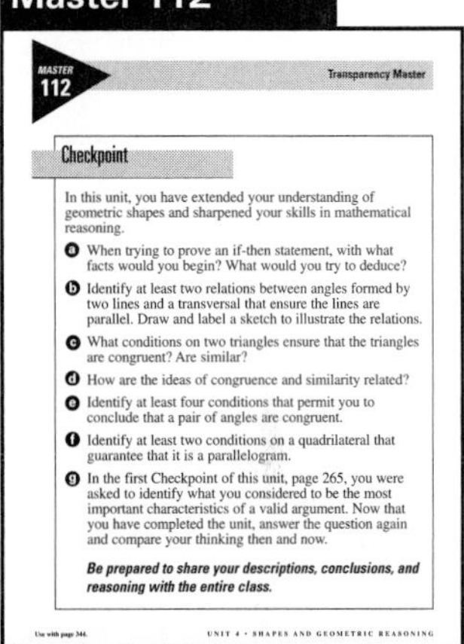

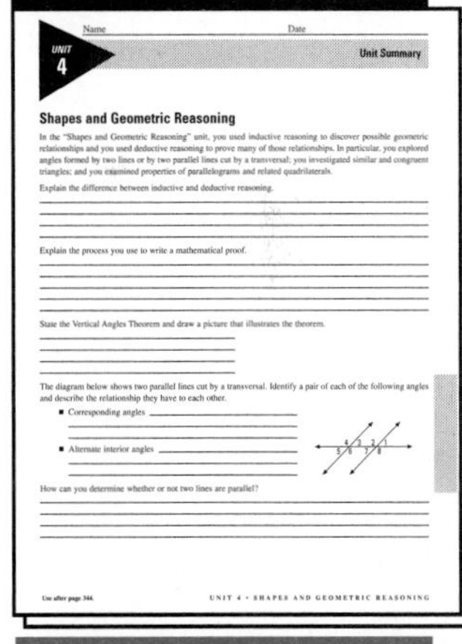

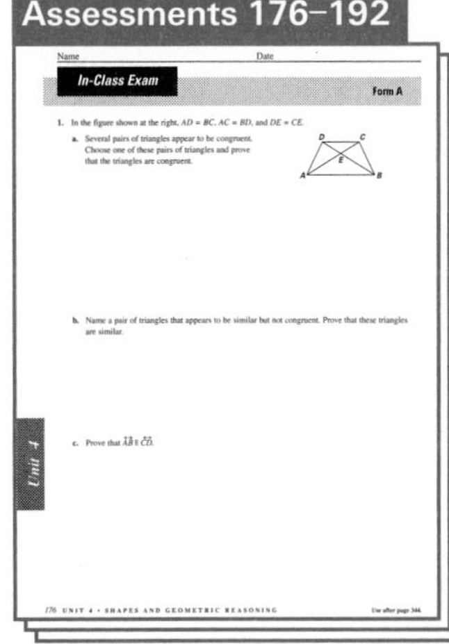

SHARE AND SUMMARIZE full-class discussion

Checkpoint

See Teaching Master 112.

ⓐ You begin with what is given in the hypothesis and try to deduce what is stated in the conclusion.

ⓑ There are many possibilities. Two lines are parallel if any one of the following conditions occurs:

- The measures of a pair of alternate interior angles are equal.
- The measures of a pair of alternate exterior angles are equal.
- The measures of a pair of corresponding angles are equal.
- A pair of interior angles on the same side of the transversal are supplementary.
- A pair of exterior angles on the same side of the transversal are supplementary.
- Two lines are perpendicular to the same line.

See additional Teaching Notes on page T344P.

Unit 4

Looking Back, Looking Ahead

Reflecting on Mathematical Content

If you look back over the geometry introduced in this curriculum, you will see that we began visually and concretely with the introduction of shapes and some of their properties in the first course. In the second course, the coordinate plane was introduced and coordinates were used to find distance and points of intersection or division of segments, and to describe transformations of the plane. The usefulness of plane geometric shapes, especially triangles, quadrilaterals, and circles, was studied next. This experience led to deeper appreciation of shapes and their functions in the real world, and to the introduction of the trigonometric ratios sine, cosine, and tangent. The present unit helps students organize some of these geometric ideas by bringing the content into a more logically organized whole. Assumptions, logical reasoning, algebraic representation, and trigonometry are used to formalize geometric ideas that were developed previously using inductive reasoning and intuition. This is a major step for students to make in developing mathematical power.

Looking ahead, you will see that the geometry strand continues to expand. The next step, in Course 4, is to introduce the notion of vector and its application in the representation of linear and nonlinear motions. Vectors and transformations resurface in the study of complex numbers. Visualization of shapes is prominent again in the study of space geometry, including the algebraic representation of planes and other surfaces in space; even though the initial emphasis of visualization of shapes in space is maintained, students will see that the representation of the shapes can be algebraic as well as graphic. Analysis of cross sections of a double cone leads to an alternate way of thinking about special curves previously studied—the circle, ellipse, parabola, and hyperbola. Certainly the future will be as exciting geometrically as the past!

Unit 4 Assessment

	Assessment Resources
Lesson Quizzes	
Lesson 1 *Reasoned Arguments*	pp. 158–163
Lesson 2 *Reasoning about Similar and Congruent Triangles*	pp. 164–169
Lesson 3 *Parallelograms: Necessary and Sufficient Conditions*	pp. 170–175
In-Class Exams	
Form A	pp. 176–180
Form B	pp. 181–184
Take-Home Assessments	pp. 185–188
Unit 4 Projects	
Reasoning with Coordinates	pp. 189–190
Symmetries and Other Properties	pp. 191–192

Notes continued from page T260

LAUNCH full-class discussion

The launch for this lesson emphasizes the need to identify and make explicit the assumptions used to support a particular argument or point of view. You may wish to discuss the assumptions assumed by the toothpaste and pen ads before tackling the political context, since it will be more difficult for students to understand. Students may not be aware of the difference of opinion about the budget for education expressed by the Republican and Democratic parties. To help students focus on the discrepancy in claims, ask them to suggest how the same information could be used to support the contention that education expenses could be increased by both 4.2% and 11.5%. After some discussion of the need to have acceptable definitions, ask groups to read and discuss the "Think About This Situation" Parts b and c and to share their thinking in each instance. Consider borrowing several popular magazines from the media center for students to look through to help answer Part c.

Think About This Situation

See Teaching Master 87.

a The writer of the toothpaste advertisement assumes that using Dentacleen will make his smile brighter, that boys get dates because they have great smiles, and that the reason he doesn't get dates is that his smile is not bright. All but the first assumption are not reasonable.

The writer of the pen advertisement assumes that pens that run dry somehow affect creativity and that pens with larger capacity affect creativity less often. These assumptions are probably not reasonable.

In the political campaign, the two parties are assuming two different starting points for their discussion of increasing Medicaid funds. The Republicans are starting with the current funding level. The Democrats are starting with the pre-approved 10% increase for the following year.

b The conclusions that the advertisers want us to make are that using Dentacleen will get the boy dates and that using the advertised pen will make your writing better. If students don't agree with the assumptions, then they probably won't agree with these conclusions.

c Responses will vary. You may wish to have students identify advertisements with outrageous assumptions. These advertisements could be posted in the classroom along with a short analysis of the assumptions.

Teaching Notes continued

Notes continued from page T279

As students prove conjectures in the investigations that follow, it will be very helpful for them to maintain a list of these theorems with labeled illustrations. The unit moves very quickly through several different geometric contexts. Consider having the theorems organized around the shape relations as they are presented in this unit. These include two intersecting lines, parallel lines cut by a transversal, triangles, and quadrilaterals (parallelograms, rhombuses, and rectangles). Students' Math Toolkits would be a natural place for them to retain their theorems. These theorem lists should be kept with students' lists of new vocabulary, sample proofs, and techniques for proofs that can be applied to other conjectures. Some of the theorems will be proven while doing MORE assignments. Since this investigation will probably span more than one class period, a class discussion on the new vocabulary and the new theorems proven each day would provide closure to the class period.

1. **a.** $m\angle 2 = 108°$, $m\angle 3 = 72°$, $m\angle 4 = 108°$

b. $m\angle 1 = 50°$, $m\angle 3 = 50°$, $m\angle 4 = 130°$

c. The following pairs of angles are supplementary (have a sum of 180°): $\angle 1$ and $\angle 4$; $\angle 1$ and $\angle 2$; $\angle 2$ and $\angle 3$; and $\angle 3$ and $\angle 4$.
Pairs that are equal in measure are $\angle 2$ and $\angle 4$, as well as $\angle 1$ and $\angle 3$.

d. Yes, they will hold for all pairs of intersecting lines.

e. Other angles that form a linear pair are $\angle 1$ and $\angle 2$; $\angle 2$ and $\angle 3$; and $\angle 3$ and $\angle 4$.

f. The other pair of vertical angles is $\angle 1$ and $\angle 3$.

g. If two lines intersect, then vertical angles will be equal in measure.

h. Comparing conjectures to those of other groups allows students to see other conjectures and to see other wording for their conjectures. You may wish to do this comparison as a full-class discussion.

Notes continued from page T281

c Students probably used some of the properties of equality, the Linear Pair Property, and the Vertical Angles Theorem. Specific responses will depend on the proofs provided.

d $\overleftrightarrow{AC} \perp \overleftrightarrow{DE}$

NOTE: Students will use the new vocabulary awkwardly at first. Typically, students will use "supplementary" when they mean "linear pair" and "adjacent" when they mean "linear pair" or "supplementary." You can help them with this by encouraging students to use their new vocabulary carefully. You can also keep a corner of the board or bulletin board for sketches which illustrate these terms. For example, the top two figures at the right show adjacent angles that are not supplementary. The bottom two figures show supplementary angles that are not linear pairs.

Unit 4

Notes continued from page T282

If some of your students find writing proofs very difficult, they may benefit from seeing and critiquing the proofs of others. You also might provide skeleton proofs for them to critique and complete. Gradually remove this support as students develop formal skills. Adhering to the if-then format is not as important as being logical. Other phrases like "whenever . . ., it follows that . . ." or "We know . . ., so we can conclude that . . ." may be more comfortable for your students. Providing variations in the skeleton proofs may provide a transition to more formal language.

1. Since this investigation builds on the exploration and conjectures students generate in the first activity, it is important that every student have a complete list of conjectures to prove and use in later activities. Encourage groups to look carefully for as many relationships as they can find among the pairs of angles and to be prepared to share their lists with the entire class. Then, as a full-class activity, ask students to share their lists and develop a class list of possible angle relationships that they can use in the remainder of this investigation.
   - **a.** All the following pairs appear equal: ∠1 and ∠3; ∠1 and ∠6; ∠1 and ∠8; ∠2 and ∠4; ∠2 and ∠5; ∠2 and ∠7; ∠3 and ∠6; ∠3 and ∠8; ∠4 and ∠5; ∠4 and ∠7; ∠5 and ∠7; ∠6 and ∠8.
   - **b.** All the following pairs appear to be supplements (the linear pairs around a point are not included): ∠1 and ∠5; ∠1 and ∠7; ∠2 and ∠6; ∠2 and ∠8; ∠3 and ∠5; ∠3 and ∠7; ∠4 and ∠6; ∠4 and ∠8.

Notes continued from page T283

4. **a.** The following proofs refer to the diagram in Activity 3, in the student book.

   Interior angles on the same side of the transversal are supplementary.

   Proof: If lines *m* and *p* intersect, then m∠1 + m∠4 = 180° (Linear Pair Property).
   If parallel lines *m* and *n* are cut by a transversal line *p*, then m∠1 = m∠6 since corresponding angles have equal measure.
   If m∠1 + m∠4 = 180° and m∠1 = m∠6, then m∠6 + m∠4 = 180°.
   A similar argument may be repeated to show that m∠3 + m∠5 = 180°.
   Hence, if two parallel lines are cut by a transversal, then interior angles on the same side of the transversal are supplementary.

   Exterior angles on the same side of the transversal are supplementary.

   Repeat the proof of interior angles, but using the appropriate angles. (Students who are confident that they understand and can do this proof do not need to rewrite it.)

   Alternate interior angles are congruent.

   Proof: If parallel lines *m* and *n* are cut by a transversal line *p*, then m∠1 = m∠6 since corresponding angles have equal measure.
   If lines *m* and *p* intersect, then m∠1 = m∠3 since vertical angles have equal measure.
   If m∠1 = m∠6 and m∠1 = m∠3, then m∠6 = m∠3.
   A similar argument may be repeated to show that m∠4 = m∠5.
   Hence, if two parallel lines are cut by a transversal, then alternate interior angles are equal in measure.

   Alternate exterior angles are congruent.

   Repeat the proof for alternate interior angles, but using the appropriate angles. (Again, students may not need to write the proof.)

   b. You may wish to have some groups display their proofs to analyze them as a class.

Notes continued from page T286

b. Parallel. Corresponding angles are congruent.
c. Parallel. Interior angles on the same side of the transversal are supplementary.
d. Not parallel. The angles are vertical and their congruence does not affect parallelism.
e. Parallel. Alternate interior angles are congruent.
f. Not parallel. All linear pairs are supplementary, so this implies nothing about parallelism.

EXPLORE small-group investigation

7. Yes, it is correct to conclude that $\overleftrightarrow{GU} \parallel \overleftrightarrow{SH}$.

Proof: If $m\angle 1 + m\angle 2 = 90^\circ$ and $m\angle 2 + m\angle 3 = 90^\circ$, then by algebraic reasoning, $m\angle 1 = m\angle 3$.

If $m\angle 1 = m\angle 3$, then $\overleftrightarrow{GU} \parallel \overleftrightarrow{SH}$ because if two lines are cut by a transversal so that a pair of alternate interior angles are equal, then the lines are parallel.

Hence if $m\angle 1 + m\angle 2 = 90^\circ$ and $m\angle 2 + m\angle 3 = 90^\circ$, then $\overleftrightarrow{GU} \parallel \overleftrightarrow{SH}$.

Notes continued from page T287

If two lines are cut by a transversal so that interior angles on the same side of the transversal are supplementary, then the lines are parallel.

If two lines are cut by a transversal so that exterior angles on the same side of the transversal are supplementary, then the lines are parallel.

C To prove the theorem that the sum of the interior angles of a triangle is 180°, we began with a line parallel to one side of the triangle through the opposite vertex (in effect assuming that such a line exists). Then, we used algebraic reasoning with the fact that alternate interior angles formed by parallel lines have equal measure and the fact that if adjacent angles form a straight angle, then the angles are supplementary.

NOTE: If your class has not previously discussed converses and "if and only if" statements, it is important to use this time to bring closure to the concepts. See the discussion in teacher notes prior to Activity 6, page T285.

APPLY individual task

On Your Own

Yes, the lines must be parallel.

The following proof is illustrative only, as there are other ways to proceed.

If $\overleftrightarrow{GC}$ and $\overleftrightarrow{HE}$ intersect, then $m\angle 2 = m\angle BFE$ (Vertical Angles Theorem).

If $m\angle 1 + m\angle 2 = 180^\circ$ (given) and $m\angle 2 = m\angle BFE$, then $m\angle 1 + m\angle BFE = 180^\circ$.

If $m\angle 1 + m\angle BFE = 180^\circ$, then there is a pair of interior angles on the same side of the transversal that are supplementary.

If two lines are cut by a transversal and interior angles on the same side of the transversal are supplementary, then the lines are parallel.

Hence, $\overleftrightarrow{AD} \parallel \overleftrightarrow{HE}$.

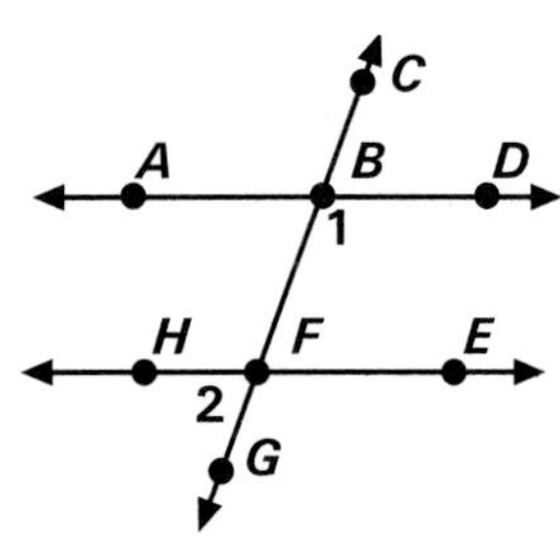

Notes continued from page T297

LAUNCH full-class discussion

The "Think About This Situation" for this lesson helps students move into the context of the first investigation and start thinking about the characteristics that are needed to guarantee triangles will be congruent or similar. Because this is a BIG idea, you may wish to spend a bit of time on it, allowing students to explore these two questions. Be sure that they understand what is meant by *similar* and *congruent*. Many students will already have informal definitions of these terms arising from their previous work; asking for explanations from the class will highlight the difference between similar and congruent for the others.

In addition, you may want to talk for a few moments about what is meant by a "minimum amount of information." You might say, "There are three angles and three sides. Would I have to measure all six to make a similar copy, or would three sides and one angle suffice? Can I do this with fewer than three sides? If I need an angle, can it be any angle or must the angle be in a particular place?" These questions should help students focus on the issues.

One possible approach might be to ask students to pick partners but *individually* develop a conjecture for one of the two questions. (For example, in considering congruence one student may decide, "I think you can give a person only the lengths of two sides from a given triangle, and another person will be able to create a congruent triangle every time.") Next, each student gives his or her partner what he or she believes is the minimal data set from the triangle just drawn. (In this example, the student would give the lengths of two sides of the triangle.) Now the partners attempt to create a triangle using the data they have been given, and they check to see if they were successful. A class discussion following this activity may lead to a tentative list of characteristics needed to create congruent and similar triangles, as well as a list of insufficient conditions. Keep this list for future reference. Remind students that these few examples are not sufficient to *guarantee* we are correct in our conjectures and that we will need to formally prove these statements are true for all triangles.

Think About This Situation

See Teaching Master 96.

a Responses may vary, but the least amount of information is the measures of two of the three angles. There is no need to come to a consensus now.

b Responses will vary. Options include the length of two sides and the measure of the included angle, the lengths of the three sides, and the measures of two angles and the length of any side.

Notes continued from page T301

8. b. $a = \frac{b \sin A}{\sin B}$; $b = \frac{a \sin B}{\sin A}$; $\sin A = \frac{a \sin B}{b}$; and $\sin B = \frac{b \sin A}{a}$.

c. It is possible to find a, c, and $m\angle C$. By subtraction we get $m\angle C = 82°$. Use the Law of Sines to find a and c:

$$\frac{a}{\sin 40°} = \frac{5}{\sin 58°} \Rightarrow a = \frac{5 \sin 40°}{\sin 58°} \approx 3.8$$

$$\frac{c}{\sin 82°} = \frac{5}{\sin 58°} \Rightarrow c = \frac{5 \sin 82°}{\sin 58°} \approx 5.8$$

d. In order to solve for any one of the four variables, a, b, A, or B you need the other three.

e. Once you know $m\angle A$, $m\angle B$, and a, then using the equation from Part b you can find b. By subtracting $m\angle A$ and $m\angle B$ from 180°, you can get $m\angle C$. Then using the Law of Sines you can find a value for c: $c = \frac{a \sin C}{\sin A}$ or $c = \frac{b \sin C}{\sin B}$. All of these values would be unique. Since the three angles are known, the shape of the triangle is determined. Having the length of one side determines the size of the triangle.

Notes continued from page T303

b SAS: (See Activity 4, page 300.)
The Law of Cosines, basic real number properties, and algebraic reasoning
Knowing the lengths of two sides of a triangle and the measure of the included angle uniquely determines a triangle.
The sum of the angles of a triangle is 180°.

SSS: (See Activity 6, page 301.)
The Law of Cosines
Knowing the lengths of all three sides uniquely determines a triangle.

AA: (See Activity 8, page 301.)
The Law of Sines, basic real number properties, algebraic reasoning, and the SAS Similarity Theorem.

c The ratio of any of the pairs of corresponding sides is the scale factor for the triangles.

CONSTRUCTING A MATH TOOLKIT: Students should include the three theorems for proving triangles similar in their list of theorems. These theorems could be included under the heading "Minimal Conditions to Ensure Similarity of Triangles." If students are going to use the abbreviations for a theorem, such as SAS, caution them to make sure they understand what the abbreviations mean. Most students will find it helpful to include a sketch with each of their theorems. You might also have students include sketches of pairs of similar triangles that are not conveniently oriented and sketches of nonexamples. Students should include the theorems from Activities 3 Part e and 8 Part f under the heading "Conditions for Uniquely Determined Triangles."

Notes continued from page T304

In addition to discussing the Checkpoint questions, it may be helpful to ask students to share their work with one another. As they work, groups could record their proofs on the board, large sheets of paper, or acetate sheets for the overhead projector to be reviewed and discussed by the entire class. Students should note that there is more than one correct way to construct a valid argument. Students should also generally consider how to go about constructing a valid argument. Possible questions to use to prompt them include the following: "How can the given information help you? How do you begin a proof? Where do you get other needed characteristics for your proof? What has to be true before you can use one of the new congruence or similarity theorems?"

The third investigation in this lesson will give students lots of practice constructing valid proofs using all of the theorems they have proven in this unit. In this investigation, the important thing is to be sure students understand how a proof should flow from the given information to a final conditional that includes the original conjecture, with all necessary information between these beginning and end points supplied.

Notes continued from page T316

and equal lengths, because I am told that $\overline{BD}$ is perpendicular to $\overline{AE}$ and C is the midpoint of $\overline{BD}$ and $\overline{AE}$. I have enough information to use SAS to prove the triangles congruent. OK. I sketched out the proof, now you (the partner) tell me what to write first." Write down exactly what the partner tells you, and then together refine the proof. Tell students it is important to listen without interruption, initially. Correction and refinement should occur after the proof is first written. Finally, trade roles and have your partner do the initial talking about what is asked, what is known, and what theorems are used.

As students work, your role as a teacher could be to assess the progress that pairs of students are making and to ask particular students to explain a proof to you. Successfully explained proofs could then be written on transparencies and shared with the whole class, particularly if more than one way to construct a proof arises in the classroom. Not every proof needs to be demonstrated to the class by students, but proofs over which some students floundered or for which alternatives exist should be shared. The sharing will take much less time than the initial writing of the proof, and it will help other students see ways to make their proofs more efficient. As students become more confident, you may want these presentations to be done for a grade. In that case, students should have the opportunity to make corrections and possibly post the "best effort" on bulletin-size sheets of paper.

1. Students' arguments should consider the impossibility that stepping higher and stepping lower would allow one to end at the same height level.

Teaching Notes *continued*

Notes continued from page T321

1. b. Students should construct the perpendicular bisector of $\overline{AB}$ using the algorithm described in Part a to get a diagram similar to the one shown below. The construction uses the same radius throughout so $XA = XB = YA = YB$. Also, $XY = XY$. So by the SSS Congruence Theorem, $\triangle AXY \cong \triangle BXY$. Thus, $\angle AXY \cong \angle BXY$. Now $XM = XM$. So by the SAS Congruence Theorem, $\triangle AXM \cong \triangle BXM$. Thus, $AM = MB$ and $m\angle XMA = m\angle XMB$. Furthermore, $m\angle XMA + m\angle XMB = 180°$, so $m\angle XMA = m\angle XMB = 90°$. If $m\angle XMA = 90°$ and $AM = MB$, then $\overleftrightarrow{XY}$ is the perpendicular bisector of $\overline{AB}$.

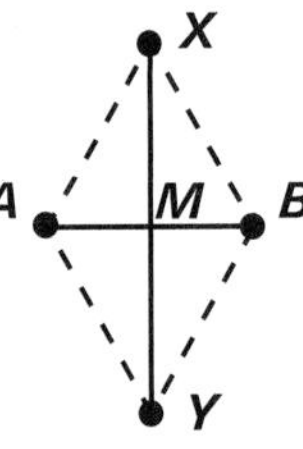

2. a. Responses may vary, depending on student work in Modeling Task 2, page 320.

b. This task helps students clearly define the steps of a process. They must first do the construction and then clearly describe what they have done.

Notes continued from page T324

5. b. Draw a diameter of circle O containing C. Let the other endpoint of the diameter be D. From Part a, we know $m\angle OCB = \frac{1}{2}m\angle DOB$ and $m\angle OCA = \frac{1}{2}m\angle DOA$. Thus, $m\angle ACB = m\angle OCB + m\angle OCA = \frac{1}{2}m\angle DOB + \frac{1}{2}m\angle DOA$. Since $m\angle DOB + m\angle DOA = m\angle AOB$, $m\angle ACB = \frac{1}{2}m\angle AOB$.

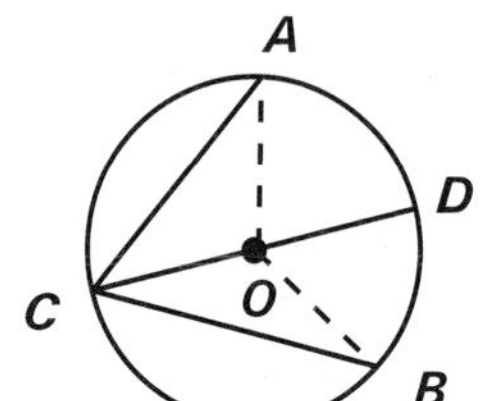

c. From Parts a and b, the measure of an inscribed angle is one-half the measure of its intercepted arc.

See Assessment Resources, pages 164–169.

Notes continued from page T328

SHARE AND SUMMARIZE full-class discussion

Checkpoint

See Teaching Master 107.

a If a quadrilateral is a parallelogram, then the following are true.

- Opposite angles are congruent.
- Opposite sides are congruent.
- Adjacent angles are supplementary.
- Each diagonal divides the shape into two congruent triangles.
- The diagonals bisect each other.

b Analytic arguments use coordinates and algebraic representations. Synthetic arguments represent geometric content using figures and geometric properties and theorems.

JOURNAL ENTRY: Write about how confident you are in making conjectures for new situations and then writing the proofs. Where are you still having difficulties? How confident are you in making conjectures for new situations? Are you comfortable that you are using diagrams correctly? Can you review your own work to decide if it is a complete proof?

Unit 4

Notes continued from page T329

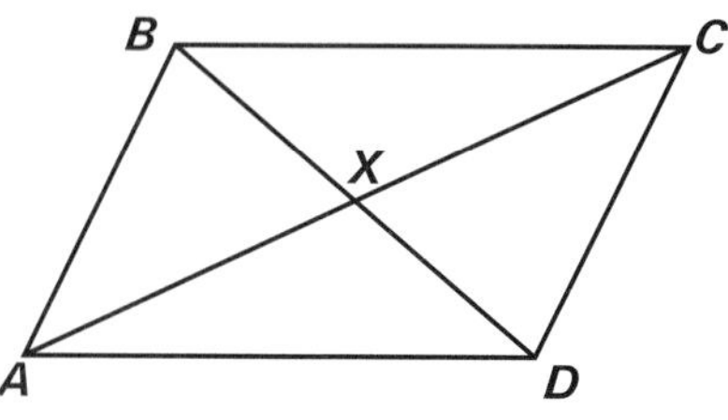

7. **From 6.c.** Quadrilateral *ABCD* has diagonals $\overline{BD}$ and $\overline{AC}$ that bisect each other at *X*. If $\overline{BD}$ and $\overline{AC}$ bisect each other at *X*, then $\overline{BX} \cong \overline{XD}$ and $\overline{AX} \cong \overline{XC}$ because a bisector divides a segment into two congruent segments. If $\overleftrightarrow{BD}$ and $\overleftrightarrow{AC}$ intersect at *X*, then vertical angles, $\angle BXA$ and $\angle DXC$, are congruent. If for $\triangle ABX$ and $\triangle CDX$ we know $\overline{BX} \cong \overline{XD}$, $\angle BXA \cong \angle DXC$, and $\overline{AX} \cong \overline{XC}$, then $\triangle ABX \cong \triangle CDX$ using the SAS Congruence Theorem for triangles. $\angle BAX \cong \angle DCX$ by CPCTC. But these two angles are alternate interior angles and so $\overleftrightarrow{AB} \parallel \overleftrightarrow{CD}$. By a similar argument it can be shown that $\overleftrightarrow{BC} \parallel \overleftrightarrow{AD}$ (using $\triangle BXC$ and $\triangle DXA$). If $\overleftrightarrow{AB} \parallel \overleftrightarrow{CD}$ and $\overleftrightarrow{BC} \parallel \overleftrightarrow{AD}$, then *ABCD* is a parallelogram. Therefore, if a quadrilateral has diagonals that bisect each other, then it is a parallelogram.

   From 6.f. Quadrilateral *ABCD* has $\overline{BC} \cong \overline{AD}$ and $\overline{BC} \parallel \overline{AD}$. Draw diagonal $\overline{AC}$. If $\overleftrightarrow{BC} \parallel \overleftrightarrow{AD}$ with transversal $\overline{AC}$, then alternate interior angles are congruent, so $m\angle BCA \cong m\angle DAC$. $\overline{AC} \cong \overline{AC}$ because a segment is congruent to itself. If for $\triangle ABC$ and $\triangle CDA$ we know $\overline{BC} \cong \overline{AD}$, $\angle BCA \cong \angle DAC$, and $\overline{AC} \cong \overline{AC}$, then $\triangle ABC \cong \triangle CDA$ using the SAS Congruence Theorem for triangles. If $\triangle ABC \cong \triangle CDA$, then $\overline{AB} \cong \overline{CD}$ because corresponding parts of congruent triangles are congruent. If $\overline{BC} \cong \overline{AD}$ and $\overline{AB} \cong \overline{CD}$, then *ABCD* is a parallelogram (by Activity 4). Therefore, if a quadrilateral has one pair of opposite sides congruent and parallel, then it is a parallelogram.

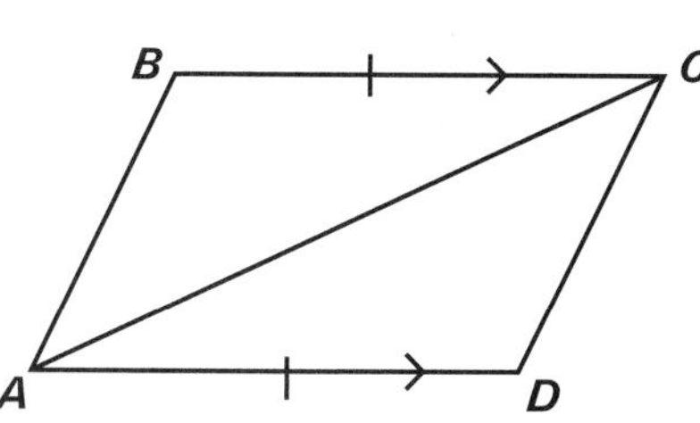

The conjecture that one pair of opposite angles congruent and one pair of opposite sides congruent is sufficient to make a parallelogram seems very plausible. It is difficult for students to create a counterexample. Therefore, if your students decide that this conjecture is true, let them attempt to prove it. They will run into the SSA case, which they have already seen is not a condition for congruent triangles. This experience might lead you into a nice discussion about proof in general. Ask, "If *we* cannot prove something, does that mean it is not true? What about famous theorems that turn out to be true, but for which mathematicians take centuries to find flawless proofs? If *we* cannot find a counterexample, does that mean a conjecture is true? (In this case, we are having trouble drawing a quadrilateral with the given conditions, without it being a parallelogram. Does that mean all quadrilaterals with these conditions are parallelograms?) If we cannot find a proof that some conjecture is false, does that mean the conjecture is true? Could there ever be a case in which we would have to say that something can never be proved or disproved?" (In fact, mathematicians *do* create proofs that some statement cannot be proved or disproved.)

NOTE: You may wish to help students recall the famous four-color problem from Graph Theory that they studied in Course 2.

An example of a counterexample for the given conditions is shown in the margin. Notice that the dart shape is made of two noncongruent triangles $\triangle ABE$ and $\triangle DCB$ on the sides of isosceles triangle *EBC*. $\triangle ABE$ and $\triangle DCB$ satisfy the SSA conditions, but they are not congruent.

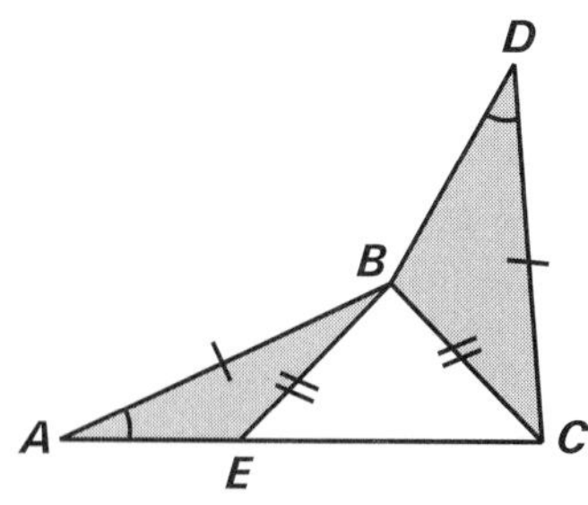

Teaching Notes *continued*

Notes continued from page T330

The Midpoint Connector Theorem provides an interesting result and the answer to the "Think About This Situation" question at the start of this lesson. It is important to have students see the structure of this body of knowledge; they have proceeded from only a few assumptions and definitions to a rich, interconnected set of theorems. The actual results are important and can be encapsulated into Math Toolkit entries, journal entries, or classroom bulletins; however, the mathematical way of proceeding to build a body of knowledge is the bigger message of this unit that students should grasp.

You might introduce this investigation by beginning a quadrilateral family tree. This activity is elaborated in a MORE question. Start with "Quadrilateral" and ask what you would have to know about a quadrilateral to force it to be a parallelogram. Then ask what else you know to be true about a parallelogram. As students respond, organize their answers verbally and pictorially in a network that starts with "Quadrilateral" and connects to parallelogram. Then define a rhombus as a parallelogram with an extra characteristic: adjacent or all sides congruent. Tell your students that they are going to find the properties and the sufficient conditions for a rhombus, and then they can add those to the network.

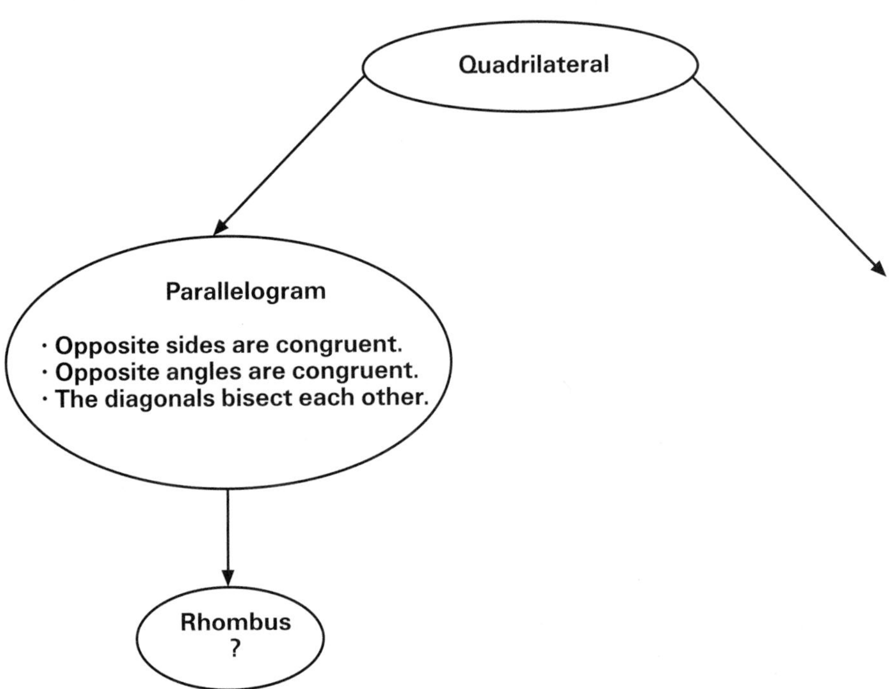

Teaching Notes continued

Notes continued from page T331

1. d. Conjecture: If $ABCD$ is a rhombus with diagonals that intersect at X, then $\triangle ABX \cong \triangle CBX \cong \triangle CDX \cong \triangle ADX$.

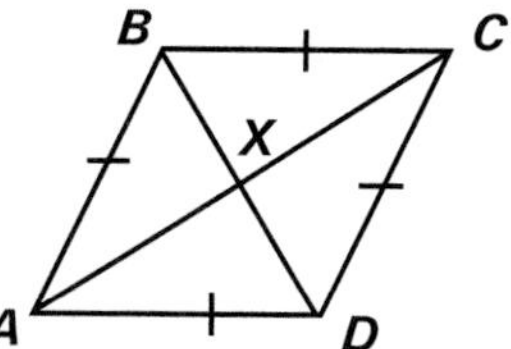

Proof: $ABCD$ is rhombus with diagonals that intersect at X. As in the previous proof, $\triangle AXD \cong \triangle CXD$. By a similar argument it can be shown that $\triangle CXD \cong \triangle AXB$ and $\triangle CXD \cong \triangle CXB$. Since $\triangle AXD$, $\triangle AXB$, and $\triangle CXB$ are all congruent to $\triangle CXD$, they are all congruent to one another. Therefore, if $ABCD$ is a rhombus with diagonals that intersect at X, then $\triangle ABX \cong \triangle CBX \cong \triangle CDX \cong \triangle ADX$.

2. a. Diagonals bisecting each other is a property of all parallelograms. Thus, it does not ensure a rhombus.

b. Diagonals perpendicular does ensure a rhombus.

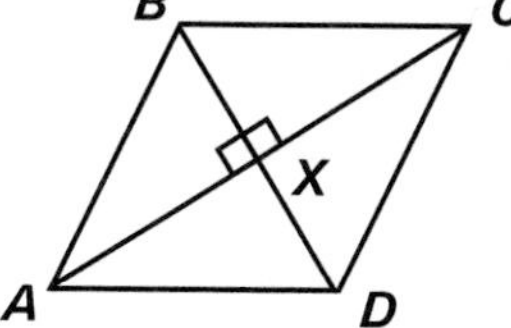

Proof: Let $ABCD$ be a parallelogram with perpendicular diagonals that intersect at point X. Since $ABCD$ is a parallelogram, $\overline{AX} \cong \overline{XC}$. $\overline{BX}$ is congruent to itself. So $\triangle AXB \cong \triangle CXB$ by the SAS Congruence Theorem. Thus by CPCTC, $\overline{AB} \cong \overline{BC}$ and so by the definition of rhombus, $ABCD$ is a rhombus.

c. Diagonals bisecting the angles does ensure a rhombus.

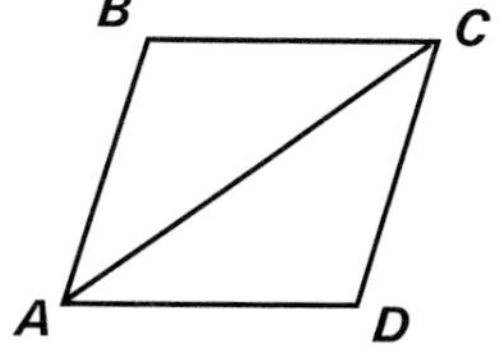

Proof: Let $ABCD$ be a parallelogram with diagonal AC. The condition we are given is that $\overline{AC}$ bisects the angles. Furthermore, since $ABCD$ is a parallelogram, opposite angles are congruent; so $m\angle BAD = m\angle BCD$, which means $\frac{1}{2}m\angle BAD = \frac{1}{2}m\angle BCD$. Since $\overline{AC}$ bisects the angles, $\frac{1}{2}m\angle BAD = m\angle BAC$ and $\frac{1}{2}m\angle BCD = m\angle BCA$. So $\angle BAC \cong \angle BCA$ and $\triangle ABC$ is an isosceles triangle. Thus, $BA = CB$, and so $ABCD$ is a rhombus.

d. A pair of adjacent angles congruent specifies a rectangle, but not a rhombus.

3. a. The segment appears to be parallel to the third side of the triangle. It is also half the length of the third side, but that is usually not observed by students.

b. $\triangle ABC$ appears similar to $\triangle AMN$, but not congruent. Since $m\angle A = m\angle A$, $AM = \frac{1}{2}AB$, and $AN = \frac{1}{2}AC$, the triangles are similar by the SAS Similarity Theorem.

c. Since the triangles are similar, $m\angle AMN = m\angle ABC$. Thus, $\overline{MN} \parallel \overline{BC}$ by the Parallel Lines Property.

d. Since the scale factor between the two triangles is $\frac{1}{2}$ or 2, $MN = \frac{1}{2}BC$ or $2MN = BC$.

Unit 4

Notes continued from page T332

NOTE: You have an opportunity here to assess how comfortable your students are with the idea of building a body of connected knowledge. Refer to the work done in the investigation and ask what other kinds of quadrilaterals students know about. (They should mention rectangle, square, kite, and trapezoid.) Ask students to connect these quadrilaterals to those they already investigated and to frame questions they have about these quadrilaterals. (What are the properties that a rectangle has that a parallelogram does not? What are the properties that a square has that a rectangle does not? What conditions are sufficient for a square? What shape is created by joining the midpoints of a rectangle/square/trapezoid/kite?) You can tell your students that some of these questions will be investigated in the MORE section, but it is important that they begin to frame the questions for themselves.

APPLY individual task

On Your Own

a. Sketches will vary. Samples are given.

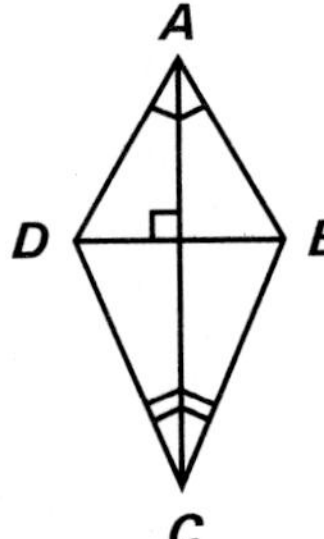

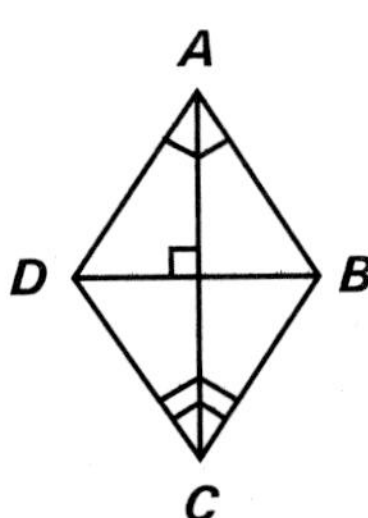

b. The sketches do not support *ABCD* always being a parallelogram or a rhombus.

c. Possible conjectures include the following:

- $\overline{AC}$ bisects $\overline{DB}$.
- $\overline{AD} \cong \overline{AB}$ and $\overline{DC} \cong \overline{BC}$.
- $\overline{AC}$ divides *ABCD* into two congruent triangles.
- $\overline{AC}$ and $\overline{DB}$ together divide *ABCD* into two pairs of congruent triangles.
- $\overline{AC}$ is a line of symmetry for *ABCD*.

d. Proofs will vary.

Unit 4

Teaching Notes *continued*

Notes continued from page T339

4. c. For the rectangle, $WXYZ$ is a square. All bisected angles are 90° angles. Thus, all the triangles formed are isosceles right triangles (and thus similar). In particular, $\triangle BZC \cong \triangle AXD$ and $\triangle ABW$ is isosceles. Thus, $BZ = AX$ and $AW = BW$. $WZ = BZ - BW = AX - AW = WX$. Thus, $WXYZ$ is a rectangle (because the larger figure is a parallelogram) with all sides equal.

   d. An isosceles trapezoid leads to a kite with two right angles.

   Two right angles: Since $\overline{AB} \parallel \overline{CD}$, $\angle 1 \cong \angle 2$ (alternate interior angles). Since $\angle C$ is bisected, $\angle BCX \cong \angle XCD$. Since $\angle B$ is bisected, $\angle EBC \cong \angle 2 \cong \angle 1$. So $\triangle BCX \sim \triangle ECX$ by AA, and $\angle EXC \cong \angle BXC$. Thus, each angle at point X has measure 90°. A similar argument holds for point Z.

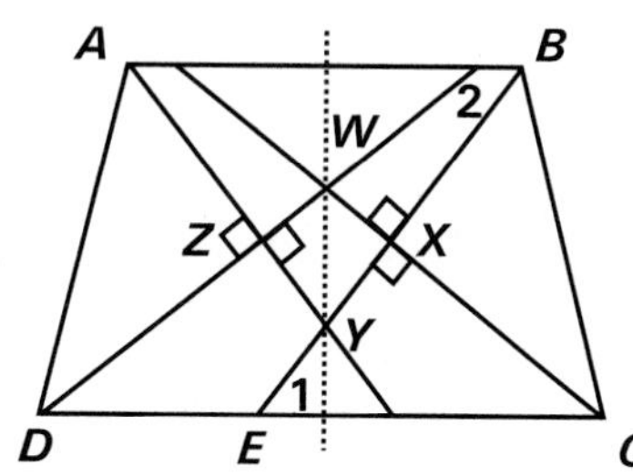

   Kite: Since $ABCD$ is isosceles, there is a line of symmetry, the perpendicular bisector of both $\overline{AB}$ and $\overline{CD}$. The base angles at C and D must be equal, so $\triangle CDW$ is isosceles and $DW = CW$. Point W must therefore be on the perpendicular bisector. A similar argument will show point Y also must be on the perpendicular bisector. Thus, $WZ = WX$ and $YZ = YX$. (Other arguments can be made using congruent triangles.)

   e. A trapezoid leads to a quadrilateral with two right angles. See Part d for the proof.

   f. For the general quadrilateral, the quadrilateral $WXYZ$ only has the property that the two pairs of opposite angles are supplements. Even though there is no reason to expect students to observe it, this means a circle will contain W, X, Y, and Z.

See Assessment Resources, pages 170–175.

Teaching Notes *continued*

Notes continued from page T344

c Two triangles are congruent in the following instances:

- The three sides of one are congruent to the corresponding sides of the other (SSS).
- Two angles and the included side of one are congruent to the corresponding two angles and included side of the other (ASA).
- Two sides and the included angle of one are congruent to the corresponding two sides and included angle of the other (SAS).
- Two angles and a nonincluded side of one are congruent to the corresponding two angles and side of the other (AAS).

Two triangles are similar in the following instances:

- Two angles of one are congruent to the corresponding angles of the other (AA).
- The lengths of three sides of one are a multiple, k, of the lengths of the corresponding sides of the other (SSS).
- The lengths of two sides of one are a multiple, k, of the lengths of corresponding sides of the other and the included angles are congruent (SAS).

d Similarity is the general notion in which angles are congruent and sides are a constant multiple of each other. When the multiple is one, then the shapes are congruent.

e Two angles are congruent if any one of the following conditions occurs:

- They are vertical angles.
- They are alternate interior angles formed by a transversal and two parallel lines.
- They are alternate exterior angles formed by a transversal and two parallel lines.
- They are base angles of an isosceles triangle.
- They are opposite angles of a parallelogram.
- They are corresponding angles of similar or congruent figures.

f A quadrilateral is a parallelogram in the following instances:

- Both pairs of opposite sides are congruent.
- One pair of opposite sides are congruent and parallel.
- Both pairs of opposite sides are parallel.
- The diagonals bisect each other.

g Students' answers may vary, but they should include the following: uses step-by-step logical reasoning; is complete; uses only correct mathematical facts, operations, and relations; is general in nature; and communicates well, using diagrams as needed.

APPLY **individual task**

On Your Own

See Unit 4 Summary Masters.

Responses will vary. Above all, preparation of this unit summary should be something that is useful to the indivdual student. You may wish to have students use the unit summary masters for "Shapes and Geometric Reasoning" to help them organize the information.

See Assessment Resources, pages 176–192.

Unit 4

Index of Mathematical Topics

Symbols

μ, *363*
σ, *364*
Σ, *525*
θ, *555*

A

Absolute value function
  horizontal shifts, *463*
  horizontal stretching and compression, *466–468*
  rules and tables, *442–443, 445, 463*
  vertical stretching and shrinking, *449–452*
  vertical translation, *442–443*
Addition
  associative property of, 194, 274
  commutative property of, 194, 274
Addition Rule for mutually exclusive events, *404–415*
Affirming the hypothesis, 276
Algebra, 25–45, 170–186
Algebraic equations, rewriting in equivalent forms, 15
Algebraic expressions
  common mistakes when writing, 195
  not equivalent, using graph to show, 204
Algebraic operations, 187–224
Algebraic properties, 194
Algebraic reasoning, 240–252
  to find center and radius of a circle, 252
  in geometry, 243–247
  to minimize distance, *559*
  in statistics, 243–247
Amplitude, *429*
Analytic proof, 328
Angle Bisector Algorithm, 320
Angle Construction Algorithm, 320
Angles, 282–287
  adjacent, 281
  alternate exterior, 283
  alternate interior, 283
  bisecting, 308, 320
  central, measure of, 296
  central versus inscribed, 324
  congruent, 305
  corresponding, 283
  exterior, on same side of transversal, 283
  included, 313
  inscribed, measures of, 296
  inscribed versus central, 324
  interior, on same side of transversal, 283
  linear pair of, 279, 281
  Linear Pair Property, 280
  reasoning about, 279–282
  supplementary, 281
  vertical, 279, 281
Area, maximizing, *555–556*
Arguments
  good, 264
  reasoned, 260–296
  synthetic proofs, 312
  valid, 264
Arithmetic growth, *506*
  and linear models, *507*
  recursive formula versus function formula, *506–507*
Arithmetic sequence, *506, 515*
  equations, *507*
  function formula, *507*
  interpreting formulas, *508*
  recursive formula, *506*
  sum of terms, *512*
Arrow's Theorem, 102–105
  fairness conditions, 103–104
Associative property
  of addition, 194, 274
  determining if new operations have, 207
  of multiplication, 194
Assumptions, identifying, 261–265
Asymptotes
  horizontal, *433*
  and inverse functions, *440*
  vertical, *433*
Average, properties of operation, 205
Average run length, *412*

B

Bias in surveys, sources of, 121–124
  information collection, 122–123
  nonresponse, 123
  sample selection, 122
  wording of survey, 122
Binomials, geometric illustration proof for multiplying two, 250
Borda count vote-analysis method, 98

C

Cause-and-effect relationship, *564*
Ceiling function, 185
Census, 117
  when to take, 117
Chaos, *533, 541*
Chord, 296, 322
Circle
  and algebraic reasoning, 252
  average area, 132
  average radius, 132
  equation of, 248
  equation of, center not at origin, 252, *475*
  survey, 125–126
  theorem about, 322
Closed-form formula for a sequence, *525*
Coefficients in standard quadratic form related to factored form, 211
Combinations, 110
Combined recursive formulas, *510*
  function formula, *523, 542*
  and linear function iteration, *546–547*
  and recursive formulas for arithmetic and geometric sequences, *510*
Combined variation, 10, *427*
Common difference, *508*
Commutative property
  of addition, 194, 274
  determining if new operations have, 207
  of multiplication, 194
Compasses, 319
Complete graphs, *516–518*
Compound statement, 278
Conclusion, 267
Condorcet vote-analysis method, 97–98
Confidence intervals, 153–164
  box plot charts to find, 155
  likely populations, 154–159
  margin of error, 156
  90%, 156
  properties of, 157
  and sample size, 159
Congruent triangles, 297–324
  consequences of, 305
  definition, 305
  theorems, 306, 309
Consistent fairness condition, 103
Constraints, 64
  inequalities, 69
Contrapositive, 277
Converse, 277, 285
  and Venn diagram, 274
Coordinate proof, 328
Correction term, 35
Correlation coefficient, *563–564*
  effect of outliers, *564*
  formulas for, *379*
  and standardized scores, *379*
Cosine ratio, 27
Cosines, Law of, 32–36, 298
  coordinate proof of, 314
  to find angle measures, 34
  to find length, 34
  proof of, 245, 251
  versus Pythagorean Theorem, 35
  when to use, 35
Counterexamples, use of, 268
Cubic functions
  patterns in graphs of, *426*
  rules, *446*
  table patterns, *446*
  vertical translation, *446*

D

Dart, 330
Decisive fairness condition, 103
Deductive reasoning, 269, 271
  to establish a relationship, 270
  versus inductive, 275
Detachment, law of, 276
Diagram, marking, 308
Difference equations. *See Recursive formulas.*
Digraph of pairwise-comparison method, 110–111
Direct variation relationships, *426*
  and sequential change, *503–504*
Discrete dynamical systems, *491*
Dissection of shapes, 314
Distance, minimum, *558–561*
  ways to find, *559*
Distributive property
  diagrams illustrating, 206
  multiplication of linear factors using, 210
  of multiplication over addition, 194
  of multiplication over subtraction, 194
Division, 215–218
Divisor, 275
Domain, 177, *438*
  practical, 177
  theoretical, 177

E

Equality, properties of, 15, 37, 62
  to solve equations, 37
  to solve proportions, 39

Page numbers in italic can be found in Course 3, Part B.

Equations
  algebraic, rewriting in equivalent forms, 15
  of circles with center not at origin, 252, *475*
  equivalent, 228
  linked, 46–62
  multiple-variable, solving, 13
  quadratic, 229–234
  reasoning to solve, 225–239
  systems of, 48, 60
Equivalent expressions, 192–197
Equivalent function rules, 189
Euler circuit, 266
Euler's formula, 19
Explicit formula for a sequence, *525*
Exponential functions, 176, *432, 499*
  decay, *425*
  growth, *425*
  half-life, *425*
  interpreting patterns in tables and graphs, 176
  rate of change, *425*
  vertical translation, *445*

F

Factor, 275
Factorial, 110, *415*
  notation, 110
Factoring
  difference of two squares, 212–213
  the quadratic, 209
Fairness conditions, 103–104
  consistent, 103
  decisive, 103
  nondictatorship, 103
  ordered, 103
  relevant, 103
  unanimous, 103
False alarms, *402–405*
  probability of, *403*
Feasible
  combinations, 67
  points, 65, 69
  set, 70, 72
Fermat's problem, *561*
Fibonacci sequence, *527*
Finite differences, *515–518*
  table relation to function formula, *516*
Fixed points, *535*
  attracting, *536*
  of linear function, formula, *539*
  numerical iteration to find, *538*
  repelling, *536*
Floor function, 185
Formulas
  discrete view, *505–529*
  recursive, *492–494, 498*
Formulating definitions, 294
Fractional rules
  finding zeroes of, 221
  undefined, finding input values for, 221
Fractions, 215–218
  combining two by multiplication or addition, 216
  common errors in rewriting algebraic, 217
  and inverse variation rules, 215
  rewriting as a product or sum of terms, 216
Frequency distribution
  standard deviation, *370*
Function, 170–186
  absolute value, *442*
  ceiling, 185
  composition, 186
  decreasing, *439*
  definition, 171
  exponential, 176, *425, 432*
  families, *431–433, 522*
  floor, 185
  graphs and notation, 172
  horizontal transformation, *462–479*
  increasing, *439*
  interpreting graphs, 173, *439*
  inverse power, 179
  iteration, *530–545*
  linear, 175, *424, 432*
  notation, 171–172
  periodic, *429*
  piecewise-defined, 186
  quadratic, 176, *444*
  reflections, *446–449*
  versus relationships, 182
  square root, *433*
  with symbolic rules, 175–179
  trigonometric, 177, 183, *432, 444*
  vertical transformation, *441–446, 449–453*
Function formula, *507*
  combined recursive formulas, *523, 542*
  relation to finite differences table, *516*
  using regression methods to find, *522*
Function iteration, *530–545*
  and long-term behavior, *532*
  and *NOW-NEXT* equations, *531*
  and recursive formulas, *531*
  to solve linear equations, *539*
  to solve quadratic equations, *543*
  using computer or graphing calculator, *544*
Function notation
  advantages and disadvantages of, 185
  using, 171–172, 175
Functions toolkit, *431–433*
  exponential functions, *432*
  linear functions, *432*
  power functions, *432*
  square root function, *433*
  trigonometric functions, *432*

G

Geometric construction
  angle bisector, 320
  congruent angle, 320
  congruent triangle, 320–321
  perpendicular bisector, 321
Geometric growth, *508*
Geometric reasoning, 259–344
  reasoned arguments, 260–296
Geometric sequences, *508, 515*
  interpreting recursive and function formulas, *509*
  sum of the terms formula, *513*
  writing recursive and function formulas, *509*
Geometric series, sum of infinite, *528*
Geometric transformations
  iterating, *544–545*
  method to minimize distance, *559*
Geometry, 25–45
  algebraic reasoning in, 243–247
Golden rectangle, 131
Graphical iteration, *534–535, 544*
Graphing
  connected mode, *500*
  dot mode, *500*
Graphs
  complete, *516–518*
  transformations, *459*
  zeroes, *459*

H

Half-plane regions, 78
Horizontal shifts
  of absolute value functions, *463*
  graphs, *463*
  of periodic functions, *464*
  of quadratic functions, *464*
  relation to quadratic formula, *477–479*
  relation to zeroes of quadratics, *477–479*
  symbolic rules, *463–464*
  tables of values, *463*
Horizontal transformations, *462–479*
  horizontal shifts, *463–466*
  horizontal stretching and compressing, *466–468*
Horizontal translations, *463*
Hypothesis, 267
  affirming the, 276

I

"If and only if" form, 336
If-then statement, 265–266
  symbolic representation of, 267
  and Venn diagrams, 274
Independent events
  Multiplication Rule, *404–405, 410*
  versus mutually exclusive events, *414*
Inductive reasoning, 267, 271
  versus deductive, 275
Inequalities
  constraint, 69
  equivalent, 228
  quadratic, 233
  reasoning to solve, 225–239
  writing and solving, 47–48, 54
Inequality, properties of, 62
Integers, theorems about, 262, 264, 270–271, 273, 275
Interquartile range (IQR) of a distribution, *347*
  effect of adding constant to data values, *351*
  effect of multiplying data values by a constant, *351*
  versus standard deviation, *350*
Intersect option, 70
Inverse, 277
Inverse functions
  and asymptotes, *440*
  reflection across the *x*-axis, *446*
Inverse operations, 37, 62
  to solve equations, 37
  to solve proportions, 39
Inverse power functions, interpreting patterns in tables and graphs, 179
Inverse variation models, 50
Isoperimetric
  Quotient (IQ), *556*
  Theorem, *556*
Iterating functions, *530–545*

K

Kite, 330
Koch snowflake, *521*

L

Lateral surface area, *554*
Lattice point, 65
LCL, *See Lower control limit.*
Least squares regression, 291
Like terms, combining, 205
Likely populations, 154–159
Linear association, *563*
Linear combinations, 11
Linear equalities, graphing, 70
Linear equations, 78–79
  calculator-based methods versus symbolic reasoning to solve, 238
  graphing, 48
  solving system of, by substitution, 83
  solving system of two, 70
  symbolic reasoning to solve, 226–229
  using matrices to solve, *517*
  writing and solving, 47
Linear factors, 209
  multiplication of, using the distributive property, 210
Linear function iteration, *534–537*
  and combined recursive formulas, *546–547*
  to find fixed points, *535*

Linear functions, *432*
graphs, *424*
interpreting patterns in tables and graphs, 175
and long-term behavior of function iteration, *535–536*
rate of change, *424*
reflection across the *x*-axis, *466*
symbolic expressions, *424*
tables of values, *424*
vertical translation, *445*
Linear inequalities, 78–79
calculator-based methods versus symbolic reasoning to solve, 238
graphs of, 78
solving systems of, by graphing, 79
Linear models
and arithmetic growth, *507*
discrete view, *505–529*
interpreting, 53
and patterns in table of values and shape of graph, 50
Linear Pair Property, 280
Linear programming, 63–85
finding best feasible points, 74–77
linear equations and inequalities, 78–79
using an algebraic model, 68–73
Lines, intersecting
reasoning about, 279–282
theorems about, 295
Lines in 3-dimensional space, 293
Linked equations, 46–62
Linked variables, 2–24
patterns in indirect and inverse variation situations, 3–5
patterns in values of direct/inverse combined variation, 14–16
rates and times, combining, 11–14
Logistic equations and long-term behavior, *532, 541*
Long-term behavior
additional amount added/subtracted, *490*
and function iteration, *532*
increase/decrease rate, *490*
influence on, by initial conditions, *489–490*
initial population, *489*
and logistic equations, *532*
Lower control limit (LCL), *389*

M

Majority winner vote-analysis method, 97
Margin of error, 135, 156, 160–161
Matrices
to model sequential change, *499–500*
to solve a system of three linear equations, *517*
Matrix addition, properties of, 205
Maximums and transformations, *458*
Mean
effect of adding constant to data values, *352–353*
effect of multiplying data values by constant, *352*
Mean absolute deviation (MAD), *348*
effect of adding constant to data values, *351*
effect of multiplying data values by constant, *351*
versus standard deviation, *350*
Mean of population symbol (μ), *363*
Mean of sample ($\bar{x}$), *363*
Median-fit procedure, 291
Median-median line, 291
using calculator to find, 293
Midline of the graph, *438*
Midpoint Connector Theorems, 332
Midpoint formula, 19
Midrange, properties of, 249
Minimums and transformations, *458*
Minor arc, 324
Modified box plot, 137
Modified runoff vote-analysis method, 106
Modus ponens, 276
Multiple variable equations, solving, 13
Multiple-variable models, 1–90
algebra, 25–45
geometry, 25–45
linear programming, 63–85
linked equations, 46–62
linked variables, 2–24
trigonometry, 25–45
Multiplication Rule for independent events, *404–405*
Mutually exclusive events
Addition Rule, *404–411*
definition, *409*
versus independent events, *414*

N

Negation of a simple statement, 276
n-gon, formula for sum of measures of exterior angles, 295
90% box plot, 137
for different sample sizes, 144–145
to find confidence intervals, 155–156
finding the width of, 150
interval of likely outcomes, 142
patterns in, 142
and sample size, 146
using simulation and technology to construct, 140
90% confidence interval, 156
interpreting, 157
90% confidence level, formula to estimate margin of error for, 161
Nondictatorship fairness condition, 103
Nonlinear systems of equations, solving, 51, 54
Normal distribution, *362–383*
characteristics, *363–371*
equation of a curve, *381*
overall shape, *367–368*
and percentile rank, *369–375*
relation to distribution of its standardized values, *378*
relation to standard deviation, *363–371*
standardizing scores, *371–375*
using sums to create, *399*
Normally distributed, *363*
NOW-NEXT equations, *438*
function iteration, *531*
for sequential change, *489–491*
subscript notation, *492*
and transformations, *460–461*
Number theory, 275
Numerical iteration to find fixed points, *538*

O

Objective function, 69
Opinion poll, 116
Opposite of a difference, 199
Opposite of a sum, 199
Optimization problems, *552*
Ordered fairness condition, 103
Outcomes, sample
likely versus unlikely, 140–143, 147
as proportions, 146
as totals, 146
Outlier, *347*
effect on mean and standard deviation, *353, 357*
Out-of-control processes, *394–395*
Out-of-control signals, *385–393*
due to mean changing, *385*
due to standard deviation changing, *385*
false alarms, *402–405*
tests, *390–392*
Output, 177

P

Pairwise-comparison vote-analysis method, 97–98, 110–111
Parabola, finding vertex of, 211
Parallel lines, 282–287
theorems, 283, 285, 290
Parallel Lines Property, 285
Parallelograms, 325–339
definition, 326, 336
properties of, 244
reasoning about, 326–330
rhombus, 330
theorems, 317, 327–328
Parameters and patterns in tables and graphs, *431*
Patterns
in direct and inverse variation situations, 3–5
in values of direct, inverse, and combined variation, 15
Percentile rank and normal distribution, *369–375*
interpreting *z*-score to find, *374*
table, *373*
Perimeter, minimizing, *557*
Period, *429*
Periodic change, *428–430*
Periodic functions, 43
changing amplitude, *450*
from function rule, *467*
from graph, *466*
horizontal shifts, *464*
reflection across the *x*-axis, *446*
symbolic rules, *429, 464*
and vertical translation, *444*
Permutations, 110, *415*
Perpendicular Bisector Algorithm, 321
Piecewise-defined function, 186
Plane, tiling the, *553*
Plot over time, *384, 387*
Plurality winner vote-analysis method, 97
compared to sequential-elimination method, 114
Point of inflection, *382*
Point-slope equation of a line, 19
Points-for-preferences vote-analysis method, 98
Polygon
angle measures of regular, *554*
area/perimeter of regular, *553*
formula for sum of measures of angles, 295
rigid, 297
Polynomial
higher-degree, 212
perfect cube, factoring, 220
quadratic, 212
standard form, 196
Polynomial functions
discrete view, *505–529*
writing rules for given zeroes, 210
Population, 117
Power functions, *432*
Preference table, 94
Preferential voting, 93–96
Present value, *502*
Prime number, 268

Probabilities
adding, *410*
multiplying, *410*
using simulation to find, *411–412*
Probability of *A* and *B*, 266
Proof
algebraic, 240–246
analytic, 328
synthetic, 312, 328
using coordinates, 313, 328
Proof presentation
if-then statements, 265–266, 274
paragraph form, 265
pictorally, 265
Properties of equality, 15, 37, 62
to solve equations, 37
to solve proportions, 39
Proportions, 322
Pythagorean Theorem, 26, 28
proof of, 244–245

Q

Quadratic equations
calculator-based methods versus symbolic reasoning to solve, 238
completing the square, 224
factoring the difference of two squares, 212–213
and function iteration, *543*
perfect square, 213, 223
possible roots of, 232
reasoning to solve, 229–234
roots and quadratic formula, 237
solving using factoring, 231
solving using the quadratic formula, 231
Quadratic formula
proof of, 242, *479*
relation to horizontal shifts, *477–479*
Quadratic functions, 208
factored form, *458*
finding maximum/minimum point, 209
finding vertex by symbolic reasoning, 232
graph, relation to formula calculations, 231
horizontal shifts, *464*
interpreting patterns in tables and graphs, 176, *426*
reflection across the *x*-axis, *446*
rules and tables, *444*
standard polynomial form, *458*
using zeroes to write symbolic rules, 232, *464*
vertical stretching and shrinking, *451*
and vertical translation, *444*
Quadratic inequalities
calculator-based methods versus symbolic reasoning to solve, 238
reasoning to solve, 229–234
solving without calculator or graph, 239
Quadratic polynomials, 212
Quadrilateral, 336
equilic, 338
theorems about, 328, 332
tree, 336

R

Random sample, 126
Randomized response technique, 133–134
Range, 177, *438*
practical, 177
versus standard deviation, *350*
theoretical, 177
Rates and times, combining, 11–14
rate-time-amount relations, 12
Reasoned arguments, 260–296
Reasoning, 225–239
algebraic, 240–252
about angles, 279–282
with congruence conditions, 316–319
about congruent triangles, 297–324
deductive, 269–271
inductive, 267, 271
inductive versus deductive, 275
about intersecting lines, 279–282
about linear equations, 226–229
about linear inequalities, 226–229
about quadratic equations, 229–234
about quadratic inequalities, 229–234
about similar triangles, 297–324
with similarity conditions, 316–319
symbolic, 226, 232, 241
Rectangle
definition, 329, 335
golden, 131
properties, 247
theorems about, 316, 328, 333, 335
Recurrence relations. *See Recursive formulas.*
Recursion, *488–504*
mode on calculator/computer, *492*
Recursive formulas, *506*
combined, *510*
and function iteration, *531–533*
and functions, *530*
general form, *494*
interpreting, *493*
long-term trends, *498*
spreadsheets, *501*
using patterns in a table, *503*
versus function formula, *507*
Reflections, *441, 446–449*
across the *x*-axis, *446–449*
symbolic rules and data patterns, *446*
Regression equations, using calculator to get, *459*
Regression line, *564*
effect of outliers, *564*
Relevant fairness condition, 103
Rhombus, 330
Right triangles, theorems about, 290, 312, 315, 342
RMS-plot, *563*
Root mean squared error (RMS), *563*
Roots of a quadratic equation, 232, 237
Run chart. *See Plot over time.*
Runoff vote-analysis method, 97
compared to sequential-elimination method, 114

S

s (standard deviation), *364*
Sample, 115–134
outcomes, 146–147
random, 126
selecting, 124–128
simple random, 126
Sample size
importance of considering, 146
and 90% box plots, 146
relative width of box plot versus, 150
and width of confidence intervals, 159
Sampling distributions, 135–152
definition, 136
intervals of likely sample outcomes, 140–143
likely outcomes versus unlikely outcomes, 136–137
modified box plot, 137
90% box plot, 137, 140, 142, 144–145
simulation using random number generator or table, 136
standard box plot charts, 144–146
Scale factor, 298
Segments
congruent, 305
perpendicular bisectors of, 321
Sequences
arithmetic, *506*
determining type, *509*
Fibonacci, *527*
geometric, *508*
Sequential change
and direct variation, *503–504*
discrete dynamical systems, *491*
mathematical models, *489*
matrices, *499–500*
NOW-NEXT equations, *489–491*
using recursion, *488–504*
using subscript notation, *491–494, 498*
Sequential-elimination vote-analysis method, 114
compared to plurality method, 114
compared to runoff method, 114
Series, *515*
Side, included, 313
Sierpinski
carpet, *509*
triangle, *520*
Sigma (Σ) notation, *525*
Similar figures
properties of, 298–304
theorems, 300–302, 304
Simple random sample, 126
Sine ratios, 27
Sines, Law of, 28–31, 298
ambiguous case for, 306
to find angle measures, 30
to find length, 30
proof of, 245, 251
when to use, 31
Size transformation, 267
Skew lines, 293
Slope and *y*-intercept of a line, formula, 242
Sphere
circumference formula, *426*
surface area formula, *426*
volume formula, *426*
Spreadsheets, *501*
Square root function, *433*
Squares
definition, 335
length of a diagonal of, 248
theorem about, 335
Standard box plot charts, 144
reading and using, 146
using software to construct, 152
Standard deviation
as average distance from the mean, *349–350*
computing and interpreting, *347–350*
effect of adding constant to data values, *352–353*
effect of inserting a new value, *353*
effect of multiplying data values by a constant, *352*
effect of outlier, *353*
of a frequency distribution, *370*
versus interquartile range (IQR), *350*
versus mean absolute deviation (MAD), *348–350*
measuring variation, *346–361*
population (σ), *364*
properties of, *351*
versus range, *350*
relation to normal distribution, *363*
sample (*s*), *364*
using calculator to find, *349*
and variability, *349*

Standardized scores, *360, 371–375*
comparisons, 28
table, *373*
Standardized values (*z*-scores), *372*
formula for computing, *372*
mean of, *378*
standard deviation of, *378*
Statistical process control, *346, 384–415*
out-of-control signals, *385–393*
Statistical regression capability of calculator, *501*
Statistical regression methods, *522*
for distance, *559*
Statistics
algebraic reasoning in, 243–247
Steiner tree problem, *561*
Straightedges, 319
Subscript notation, *491–494*
NOW-NEXT equations, *492–493*
sequential change, *491–494, 498*
Substitution, solving system of linear equations by, 83
Subtraction
multiplication distributing over, 198
and negative numbers, common mistakes in rewriting expressions, 200
neither commutative nor associative, 198
in predicting profit, 197
Sum of squared differences, *563*
Surface area, minimizing, *557*
Surveys, 115–134
bias in, 121–124
to estimate information about a population, 122
factual information versus opinion, 121
judging validity of results, 117
randomized response technique, 133–134
response rate, 117
unbiased, 122
voting methods and, 121
when to take, 117
Symbolic logic, 278
Symbolic reasoning
to find fixed points, *535*
to find vertex of quadratic function, 232
to solve linear equations, 226–227
to solve linear inequalities, 226–227
using for proof, 241
Symbolic rules
and reflection of graphs, *440*
and translation of graphs, *440*
Synthetic proofs, 312, 328
Systems of equations, 48, 60

T

Tangent ratios, 27
Theorems
AA Similarity Theorem, 302, 304
AAS Congruence Theorem, 306, 309
ASA Congruence Theorem, 306, 309
circles, chords and central angles in, 322
integer, product of an even and an odd, 271
integer, sum of an even and an odd, 270
integers, factors of sums of, 275
integers, product of two odd, 273
integers, sum of two even, 264
integers, sum of two odd, 262
about lines perpendicular to a third line, 295
Midpoint Connector
quadrilaterals, 332
triangles, 332
about parallel lines, 290
parallel lines, consequences of, 283
parallel lines and corresponding angles, 283
parallel lines and exterior angles, 283
parallel lines and interior angles, 283
parallelograms, 317
parallelograms, properties of, 327–328
quadrilateral, necessary conditions to be a parallelogram, 328
rectangle, sufficient conditions for, 333, 335
rectangles, 317
rectangles, properties of, 335
relations that guarantee two lines are parallel, 285
rhombus, conditions ensuring that a parallelogram is, 331
rhombus, properties of any, 331
right triangle, sum of measures of acute angles, 290
right triangles, 342
right triangles, proving congruence of, 312, 315
SAS Congruence Theorem, 306, 309
SAS Similarity Theorem, 300–301, 303–304
segment, perpendicular bisector of, 323
square, properties of, 335
SSS Congruence Theorem, 306, 309
SSS Similarity Theorem, 301, 304
trapezoid, angles of, 291
triangle, angle measures of equiangular, 290
triangle, proof that sum of angles is 180°, 287
triangle, sum of measures of exterior angles of, 295
Triangle Inequality Theorem, 323, *559*
triangles, conditions that ensure two are similar (SAS), 300–301
triangles, isosceles, 324
triangles, midpoint connector for, 312–313
triangles, relationship between congruent and similar, 305
vertex-edge graph, degree of a vertex in, 268
Vertical Angle Theorem, 280, 294
Transformations
of graphs, *459*
horizontal, *462–479*
maximums, *458*
minimums, *458*
and *NOW-NEXT* equations, *460*
regression equations, *459*
zeroes, *458*
Transformed data
mean absolute deviation (MAD), 266
mean of, 246, 266
range of, 247
Translation symmetry, *438*
Transversal, 282–287
exterior angles on same side of, 283
interior angles on same side of, 283
Trapezoid
area of, 203, 263–264
theorem about, 291
Trends, detecting over time in data, *401*
Triangle Inequality Theorem, 323, *559*
Triangles
area of, finding, 44
congruent, 297–324
exterior angle of, 295
isosceles, 324
similar, 42, 297–324
theorems, 287, 290, 295, 300–306, 309, 312–313, 315, 323–324, 332, 342
Triangulation, 26–27
Trigonometric functions, 183, *432, 444*
interpreting patterns in tables and graphs, 177
Trigonometric identities, 44, 246
Trigonometry, 25–45
spherical, 45

U

UCL. *See Upper control limit.*
Unanimous fairness condition, 103
Upper control limit (UCL), *389*

V

Variables
linked, 2–24
periodic, *428*
Variance, properties, *361*
Variation, combined, 10, *427*
Venn diagrams, 274
Vertical shrinking, *449–453*
Vertical stretching, *449–453*
Vertical transformation, *441–446, 449–461*
Vertical translation, *442–446*
and absolute value function rules and tables, *442–443*
of exponential functions, *445*
of linear functions, *445*
and trigonometric function rules, *444*
and quadratic function rules and tables, *444*
Volume (*V*), *553*
of a cylinder, *435*
of a sphere, *426*
Vote-analysis methods, 96–102
advantages and disadvantages of, 101
Borda count method, 98
choosing based on situation, 105
Condorcet method, 97–98
majority winner, 97
modified runoff method, 106
pairwise-comparison method, 97–98, 110–111
plurality winner, 97
points-for-preferences method, 98
runoff method, 97
sequential-elimination method, 114
using software to carry out, 99–100
Voting, 116–120
approval, 100–101
fairness conditions, 103–104
insincere, 108
models, 92–114
preferential, 93–96
strategic, 108

W

Waiting-time distribution, *412–413, 524*

X

$\bar{x}$ (mean), *363*

Z

Zero property of multiplication, 209, 222
Zeroes
effect of transformation on, *458*
of a function, 20
of graphs, *459*
and horizontal shift, *477–479*
z-score, *372*
and percentile rank in normal distributions, *374*

Index of Contexts

A

Absenteeism, 140
Accidents
  automobile, 149
  fatal vehicular, 5
ACT scores, *376, 379*
Administration and salaries, 162
Advertisements, 260–261, 265, *566*
Aeneid, The, 555
Affirmative action, college, 273
Age
  and height, 173
  and IQ, 173
Air conditioner, 22
Air pressure, 18
Airline flights, 148
Airplane, 13, 40
  commuter, 31
  jet, 42
Airport, 31
Alexander, Lamar, 107–108
Alumni
  high school, 128
  university, 123
Amusement park
  attendance, 181
  rides, 42
Animal population, *430*
Antibiotic, *491, 494*
Apartment thermostat, *396*
Appliances, electrical, 23
Architects, 87–88, 297, 318
Arrow, Kenneth, 102–103
Astronauts, nutrition of, 66–67, 71–72, 75–76, 78
Athletes, height of, 164
Athletic shoes
  brands preferred, 96–97
  cost, 175, 191–192
  preference table, 97
  purchasers of, 152
Athletic stadium, domed, 235
Atmospheric change, *422–428*
Auto technicians, 277

B

Baby boys, weights of, *369*
Bacterial growth, *508–509*
Balanced federal budget, 272–273
Ballpoint pen, 260
Baseball
  caps, *436*
  in flight, 174
  profit, 234
  strike, 160–161
Basketball, 57, 157
  NCAA men's championships, *380–381*
  NCAA women's championships, *381*
Bees, *553–554*
Bell Laboratories, 335
Bhaskara, 224
Billiards, 341
Births, Bangladesh, *561, 565*
Boeing, *346*
Born Loser cartoon, 276
Boston Logan International Airport, 31
Boston Marathon, *360*
Bowling, *394*
Box. *See Carton.*
BOXCHART feature of the *Sampling* calculator software, 161
Brand name recognition, 159
Breaking point, 3–4
Bridge, high, *515*
Bubble, *557*
Buchanan, Pat, 107–108
Bulbs, flower, 81
Bungee
  experiment, *506–507*
  jumper, 172–173, 184
Bus
  charter, 57, 61
  driver, *395*
  school, 13
  trip, *436*
Bush, George, 101–102
Business costs, 177–178
Butterfly, 274

C

Calculator button production, 416
Calculus, advanced placement, 147, 153
Can, cylindrical, 18, 24
Cancer
  rate of, 147
  rate of deaths, 292
Candy, 150
Carbon dating, *425*
Carbon dioxide (CO_2), *424–425, 428, 461*
Carbon-14, *425, 428*
Car owners, midsize, 141
Car survey, *408*
Cards, playing, 266
Carpenter's square, 308, 333
Carton
  manufacturing facility, 81
  shipping, 23
CD
  earnings, 187
  royalties, 192
Census, U.S., 134, *494*
Cereal box, filling, *398*
Chaos
  Game, *544–545*
  theory, *533, 541–542*
Children, newborn, 142
Chlorine, *496–497*
Chomo-Lungma, 25
Circle survey, 125–126
Class president, 104–105
  preference table, 99, 104, 108
Class ring production, 85
Clinton, Bill, 101–102
Clothing colors, *406–407*
Coding, 275
Coin tossing, 135–137, *400*
College tuition, *519*
Comets, *481–482*
Commuting, 12–13
Comparison shopping, 47–49
Compound interest, *496–497*
Computer
  households with, 140
  sales, 186
Concert
  cost and income, 225, 229
  music, *565–567*
  tickets and income, 14
  tours, 190
Condorcet, Marquis de, 97
Cooling
  graph, *441, 454*
  Newton's Law of, *503–504*
Crafts, 236
Cricket chirps, *519, 521, 526*
Current, electrical, 7–8
Custodial fee, 215
Cylinder
  height, 215
  volume, 215

D

Dance, school, 215–216
Dance studio, 80
  jazz classes, 80
  tap classes, 80
Delivery van, *434*
Democratic Party, 163
Department of Education, 260
Depreciation, *434*
Design perimeters, *356–357*
Diabetes, 181
Diamond cut, 289
Dice
  rolling doubles, *410, 524*
  standard (hexahedral), *465*
  tetrahedral, *413*
Dido, *555*
Dining out, 123
Diploma, high school, 140
Disc jockey, 215
Discipline, school, 156
Dissolution time, *366–367*
Distance, 215
Dole, Bob, 107–108
Dorm room, 262
Draftspeople, 297, 319
Drink carton, 66–67, 71
Drivers
  bus, *395*
  teenaged, 126

E

Eating out, 123
Electricity, 7–8, 22, *449, 468*
  current, 7–8
  Ohm's law, 7
  resistance, 7–8
  voltage, 7–8
Employment
  characteristics preference table, 132
  Federal survey, 129
  of high-school students, 149
  restaurant, 56
  small business, 132
  student, *354*
  summer, 49–51, 58, 61
Encrypting messages, 275
Energy sources, 113–114
  preference table, 114
Engine repair, 277–278
Engineers, 318, 342
Enrollment, high school course, 141
Entertainment events, 14, 52
  costs, 52–54
  income, 52–54
  profit, 52
  ticket price, 61
  ticket sales, 14, 52–55
Environmental protection policies, 106
  preference table, 106
Epidemic, *513*
Escher, M. C., 316
Euler, Leonhard, 19
Everest, George, 25
Extracurricular activities, 142

F

Fast-food
  preference, 92–95
  survey, 121
Female literacy, *562*
Ferris wheel, 177–178, *429, 453, 469*
Fibonacci, Leonardo, *527*
Field trip, 57, 61
Fires, forest, 28
Fishing pond, *488*
Fish population, 179, *488–492, 499, 501, 537*
Food bar, 66–67, 71
Food supply, *525*

Football
game, 201
punter, *436*
Fractal, *509, 520–521, 533, 547*
Freighter, 40, 88
Fundraiser, prom, 85

G

Game preference, 106–107, 109
Gas mileage, *397, 417*
Gauss, Carl Friedrich, *512*
Glaciers, *425, 437*
Global Positioning System (GPS), 45
Global warming, *422–428*
Glottochronology, *521*
Gore, Al, 153–154
Gratuity, 203
Gravitational force, *427–428, 455*
Greenhouse gases, *422–428*
Greeting cards, 326
Gymnastics classes, 84

H

Hairdryer, 23
Hale-Bopp comet, *481–482*
Hand span, *349*
Hardy, G. H., 206
Health insurance, 167
Heart disease, 149–150
Heat flow, 8–9
conductors, 9
insulators, 9
Heat pumps, 22
Heights
American adults, *371, 376*
Chicago Bulls, *349*
female students, *365–366*
hockey team, 266
mothers, *377*
Heroes, opinions about, 116–117
High school graduates, *407*
Hillary, Edmund, 25
Home security systems, *453*
Honeycombs, *553–554*
Hot Wheels®, 171–172
House foundation, 333
Humpty-Dumpty, 294
Hutchins Lake, 311

I

Ice cream
bar, warming, *447*
cartons, filling, *403–404, 411–412, 415*
store, *514*
Industrial design, 319
Infant mortality, *562–564*
Inflation, *434*
Information Age, 133
In-line skates, 81
Insect, 274
Insulin, 181
Integrated Technologies, 63–66, 68–70, 74 –75
Intelligence quotients (IQs), *374–375, 379*
Interest
compound, 16, 58–59, *492–493, 501–502*
simple, 16–17, 58–59
Internet use, 127
Intravenous fluids, 20

J

Jet fuel, 6
Job. *See also Employment.*
approval, 164
John Hancock Building, 282, 304
Joints, expansion, 20
Juice sales, 85
Jump ramp, 171
Jupiter, *426*

K

Karate, 2
Kayaking, 24

L

Lake measurement, 311
Lancaster, California, *402*
Languages, *521*
Left-handed people, 142
Lighthouse, 40, 44
Loan payment, *492–493*
Loss, 188
Lottery, *501–502*
Lou Gehrig's disease, 147

M

M&M's® Chocolate Candies, 157
Makeup, 265
Malthus, Thomas, *525*
Manufacturers, 297
Manufacturing, *346*
Marching band raffle, *454–455*
Mars, *426*
Mascot, 105, 126
Math class enrollment, *357*
Mathematical Association of America (MAA), 100
May, Robert, *541*
Medicinal dosages, 20
adult, 20
child, 20
Mensa, *375*
Mental retardation, *375*
Metal impurity, *384–385, 387*
Micromanage, *399*
Microwave, 23
Milk containers, filling, *385–386, 395*
Minitab, *388*
Miracle-Gro®, 219
Money, paper dollar versus coin, 156
Monopoly®, *410, 524*
Moon, *455, 482*
phases, *482*
Mount Everest, 25
Mountain height, 27
Movie survey, *370*
Music
business, 187–192, 197
festival, 124

N

Nail production, *397*
National Pasta Association, 159
NB 10, *362*
New Hampshire Primary, 107–108
News, spreading, *459*
Newton, Sir Isaac, *503*
Newton's Law of Cooling, *503–504*
Nickels, weight of, *364*
Nighttime activities, preferred, 96
Nike advertisement, 120
Norgay, Tenzing, 25
Number trick, 240, 250–251
Nutrition, astronaut, 66–67, 71–72, 75–76, 78
drink carton, 66–67, 71
food bar, 66–67, 71

O

Ocean
depth, *428–429, 437–438, 449, 451, 469*
surface area, *437*
tides, 180, *428–429, 437, 451, 469*
Ocean water, *426*
Office building, 255
Ohm's law, 7
Oil
engine, 24
fields, *560*
reserves, *461*
tank, *435*
Online services, 163
Opinions about heroes, 116–117
Optical illusions, 316
Oranges, pyramid of, *526*
Orange trees, *355*
Outfitters, 235–236
Ozone, *382–383, 401–402*

P

Package design, 22, 219
Packaging, 18, 22
Paper clip production, *398*
Parallelogram, 274
Park rangers, 28
Pasta bridges, 3–4
Peanut butter, 41
cookie recipe, 41
Peanuts cartoon, 222
Pendulum, *449*
Penrose, Roger, 330–331
Perot, Ross, 101–102
Personality type, *408*
Pets, 148–149
Philosophers, 112
Physical education, 267
Pilot, airplane, 31, 40
Pizza delivery, 219, 226
Pizza oven, *456*
Pizza production
feasibility, 77
meat, 73, 77
vegetarian, 73, 77
Planetary size, *428*
Plumb line, 289
Polar ice caps, *426*
Police poll, 122–123
Political philosophy, *363*
Politics, *541–542*
Polyhedra, 19
Population, *525, 561*
animal, *430*
fish, *488–492, 499, 501, 537*
rabbit, *430*
U.S., 176, 178, *494–495*
wildlife, *493*
world, *436, 480–481*
Portland
Maine, *350*
Oregon, *350*
Preference table
athletic shoe, 97
class president, 99–100, 104
environmental protection, 106
game, 106
New Hampshire Primary, 108
presidential election, 102
restaurant, 94, 98
sanitary landfill, 167
Preferential Voting calculator software, 99, 114
Pregnancy lengths, *375–376*
Presidential election, 101–102, 153–154
Production lines, 10–12, 63
Profit, 52–59, 61, 75, 188–192, 201–202, 215–216, 234–235
Prom fundraiser, 85
Public opinion, modeling, 91–168
Pumping, fuel and water, 6, 42

Q

Quadrilateral, 274
Quality control, *346*
Quality improvement, *346*

R

Rabbit population, *430*
Radio transmission tower, 26
Radioactive waste, 292
Raffle, *454–455*
Rafting, 24
Raisin box, *361*
Random Digit Company, *399–400*
Rate, 215
Record company, 189
Rectangle, perimeter, 17
Refrigerator, 23
Rent, 253–255
Republican party, 107–108
Residents, northeastern states, 146
Resistance, electrical, 7–8

Restaurant
eating out, 123
preference table, 94, 98
Retail rental space, 253–255
Retirement, *496*
Rock tossing, *515–516*
Roller coaster, 170
Roof supports, 297

S

St. Louis Gateway Arch, 238
Sales commission, *520*
Sampling calculator software, 140, 152, 158, 161
Sanitary landfill, 167
SAT scores, *371, 375–376, 379*
Satellite communication systems, 45
Savage River, 24
Savings account, 16–17, 58–59, *497*
interest, 215, *496–497*
School award certificate design, *347*
School board election, 162
Schools, 272
awards, 273
uniforms, 273
Science courses, *407*
Sea levels, *426, 428, 437*
Seat belts, 156–157
Security guard, 250
Selling space, 68
Shadow length, 311
Shewhart, Walter A., *393*
Shipping costs, 185
Shoe, *460*
company, 182
store, *515*
Shoulder width, *376*
SIMBOX option of the *Sampling* calculator software, 140
Site map, 33
Skateboards, 81
Skydiving, *505, 511–512, 522*
Small business help, 132
Small car survey, *408*
personality type, *408*
Sneakers buyers, 138
Soap bubble, *557*
Softball, 218
Soft drinks
bottling, 10
cooling, *441, 454*
Sounds, 86–87, 179
pitch, 86
Spaghetti, 159
Speed limits, 118
Spirals, *527*
Sport, favorite, 166
Sporting goods manufacturer, 81
Spring water, bottling, 11
Square, 274
Stanford-Binet intelligence test, *375*
STDBOX option of the *Sampling* calculator software, 152
Stereo system, 179
Storage containers, *435*
Student survey, 165
Summer
Northern versus Southern Hemisphere, *474*
Sunlight hours, *469*
Havana, Cuba, *471*
Melbourne, Australia, *472*
Oslo, Norway, *472*
Rio de Janeiro, Brazil, *472*
Southern Hemisphere, *472*
Stockholm, Sweden, *472*
Washington, D.C., *471*
Sunrise, *436, 469, 471*
Sunset, *436, 469, 471*
Supply and demand, 49–52
Supreme Court, 272
Surveyor, 27, 33, 36
Surveys, 115–134
Suspension bridge, 181, *470, 475*
Swimming pools, *496–497*
Swings, 326

T

Talent show, 105
Taxes, raising, 123
Teen survey, 130
Telephone
calling cards, *507*
cellular, 49, 160, 186, 229
long distance call, 185
Television, 23
cable, 139, 141
viewing, 115
Temperature
apartment, *396*
Celsius, 202
Des Moines, *467*
Earth, *422–428*
Fahrenheit, 202
Phoenix, *470*
pizza oven, *456*
10-gram weight, *362*
Test scores, *358*
Textbook shortages, 118
Theater seats, *547–548*
Thermal conductivity, 8–9
Thermostat, *396*
Ticket sales, 14, 52–55
basketball game, 57–58
projected income from, 53
and ticket price, 52–55, 61
Tides, 180, *428–429, 437–438, 451, 469*
Time, 215
of a trip, 215
Tipping, 203–204
Tire pump, 18
Toothpaste, 260
Towers of Hanoi, *502–503*
Trampoline, 176, 178, 208–209
Transit, surveyor's, 33, 36
Travel, 12–13, 22, 40, 88
Troubleshooting chart, 277
Trout population, *488–492, 499, 501, 537*
Truck
bed, variable height, 279
speed, 89
T-shirts, 190, *436*
Tuition, college, *519*

U

Unemployment, 129
Used cars, *356*
payments, *492–493*

V

Varignon, Pierre, 337
VCR, 143
Vehicle, renting or leasing, 46, 61, 219, 226
payment plans, 47–48, *492–493*
Video games, 63–66, 68–70, 72
assembly time, 69
production feasibility, 74–75, 78
token production, *398*
Voltage, 7–8, *468*
Volume of a cylinder, 215
Voting
and the Internet, 113
models, 92–114
national and state elections, 113
and social decision-making, 112

W

Wages, hourly, *351–353*
Wallpaper, 262
Water slides, 6
Water sports, 6, 24
Washington, D.C., *382–383, 471*
Wechsler Intelligence Scale for Children, *374*
Weight
of baby boys, *369*
of nickels, *364*
Whales
Alaskan bowhead, *495, 538–539*
Wildlife population, *493*
Windchill, 20
Window design
modern, 87–88
traditional, 87–88
Windshield wipers, 326
Winter
Northern versus Southern Hemisphere, *474*
Women, working, 119, 149, 163
Woodcutting, decorative, 236

Photo Credits

Cover PhotoDisc **T1** Carl Wagner/Chicago Tribune; **T2** AP/Wide World Photos; **T3** Judy Slezak, Prairie High School, Cedar Rapids, IA; **T5** Douglas Pizac/AP Wide World Photos; **T6** Chuck Berman/Chicago Tribune; **T8** Mark Saperstein; **T10** UPI; **T11** Krones, Inc.; **T12** Karen Engstrom/Chicago Tribune; **T13** Frank Hanes/Chicago Tribune; **T14** Phil Schermeister/Tony Stone Images; **T16** David Young-Wolff/PhotoEdit; **T18** Kathy Wright; **T20** MR Medical/West Stock; **T22** National Motorcoach Network, Inc.; **T23** Fran Brown; **T25** Barry C. Bishop/National Geographic Society; **T26** Tom Sheppard/Tony Stone Images; **T28** AP/Wide World Photos; **T33** Patrick Witty/Chicago Tribune; **T36** © T1980 Sidney Harris/American Scientist; **T40** (top) Maine Department of Economic and Community Development, (bottom) George Hall/CORBIS; **T41** Jim Quinn/Chicago Tribune; **T46** Tony Freeman/PhotoEdit; **T47** Michelle Banks; **T50** ETHS Yearbook Staff; **T52** Bonnie Kamin/PhotoEdit; **T56** Michelle Banks; **T57** (top) David Young-Wolff/Tony Stone Images, (bottom) Tony Freeman/PhotoEdit; **T58** David Young-Wolff/PhotoEdit; **T61** Dana White/PhotoEdit; **T62** Texas Instruments Incorporated, Dallas, TX; **T63** Michael Rosenfeld/Tony Stone Images; **T66** NASA; **T69** Matthew Boroski/West Stock; **T70** Texas Instruments Incorporated, Dallas, TX; **T71** NASA; **T73** Home-Run Pizza; **T80** David Young-Wolff/PhotoEdit; **T81** (top) Core-Plus Mathematics Project, (bottom) Breck's; **T84** Karen Engstrom/Chicago Tribune; **T85** (top) Tony Freeman/PhotoEdit, (bottom) Loy Norrix High School Yearbook Staff; **T86** Alan Hicks/Tony Stone Images; **T87** Michael Newman/PhotoEdit; **T91** Billy E. Barnes/Tony Stone Images; **T92** Tom Horan/Sygma; **T93** Core-Plus Mathematics Project; **T94** AFP Photos; **T96** ETHS Yearbook Staff; **T97** (top) Jack Demuth, (bottom) Brown Brothers; **T100** Mathematics Association of America; **T101** Ira Schwartz/Reuters/Archive Photos; **T104** Robert E. Daemmrich/Tony Stone Images; **T105** ETHS Yearbook staff; **T106** (top) Mary Kate Denny/PhotoEdit, (bottom) John Giannini/Chicago Tribune; **T107** Jim Bourg/Reuters/Archive Photos; **T113** (top left) Chuck Berman/Chicago Tribune, (center left) Sally Good/Chicago Tribune, (center right) PEKO, (bottom left) Andras Dancs/Tony Stone Images, (bottom right) UPI; **T115** Copyright T1996, USA TODAY. Reprinted with permission; **T116** (top left) Chicago Tribune, (top right) Robert E. Daemmrich/Tony Stone Images, (middle left) Associated Press, (bottom left) North Wind Picture Archives, (bottom) Scripps Howard News Service; **T117** UPI; **T119** Copyright T1996, USA TODAY. Reprinted with permission; **T120** Copyright T2001, USA TODAY. Reprinted with permission; **T123** Jim Brown; **T124** Jeff Greenberg/PhotoEdit; **T126** Bob Fila/Chicago Tribune; **T129** Tom Horan; **T130** Aaron Haupt; **T131** Sabine Weiss/Rapho/Photo Researchers; **T132** Copyright T1996, USA TODAY. Reprinted with permission; **T133** Jack Demuth; **T134** United States Census Bureau Public Information Office; **T135** Al Francekevich/The Stock Market; **T138** John Riley/Tony Stone Images; **T139** Wayne Eastep/Tony Stone Images; **T141** **T142** ETHS Yearbook Staff; **T143** Billy E. Barnes/PhotoEdit; **T147** AP and Advanced Placement are registered trademarks of the College Board; **T148** Chuck Bruton/AP Wide World Photos; **T149** David Young/Tony Stone Images; **T150** Lillian Vernon; **T153** **T154** Reuters NewMedia, Inc./CORBIS; **T156** Fran Brown; **T157** John Lee/Chicago Tribune; **T159** Michael Budrys/Chicago Tribune; **T162** Milwaukee Journal/Sentinel; **T164** © T1998 The Des Moines Register and Tribune Company. Reprinted with permission; **T166** Copyright T1995, USA TODAY. Reprinted with permission; **T167** Lynette Miller/Chicago Tribune; **T169** Jack Demuth; **T170** Chad Slattery/Tony Stone Images; **T171** © T1998 Mattel, Inc. All Rights Reserved.; **T173** Charles Osgood/Chicago Tribune; **T176** Kathy Wright; **T177** Rich Iwasaki/Tony Stone Images; **T179** Myrleen Cate/PhotoEdit; **T180** Terry Donnelly/West Stock; **T181** Tony Freeman/PhotoEdit; **T182** AP Newsfeatures Photo; **T186** John Kringas/Chicago Tribune; **T187** Matt Meadows; **T188** Michael Newman/PhotoEdit; **T190** Jack Demuth; **T191** Core-Plus Mathematics Project; **T192** Michael

Photo Credits

Newman/Photo Edit; **T199** Texas Instruments Incorporated, Dallas, TX; **T201** ETHS Yearbook Staff; **T202** Tony Freeman/PhotoEdit; **T203** Jim Quinn/Chicago Tribune; **T208** Aaron Haupt; **T215** Jack Demuth; **T216** John Dziekan/Chicago Tribune; **T219** (top) Jose More/Chicago Tribune, (bottom) Miracle-Gro® is a registered trademark of Scotts Company; **T222** PEANUTS reprinted by permission of United Feature Syndicate, Inc.; **T225** Gregg Mancuso/Tony Stone Images; **T229** Jack Demuth; **T234** Brian Stablyk/Tony Stone Images; **T235** Bob Langer/Chicago Tribune; **T236** Bob Langer/Chicago Tribune; **T240** Jim Laser; **T250** Chuck Berman/Chicago Tribune; **T253** Hardy Wetting/Chicago Tribune; **T255** Bill Hedrich; **T259** Helaman Ferguson sculptor/Terry Clough photographer; **T260** Image © BCOP/© Sanford; **T261** Michael Budrys/Chicago Tribune; **T262** Tony Berardi/Chicago Tribune; **T265** PhotoDisc; **T266** Bob Langer/Chicago Tribune; **T267** James Crump/Chicago Tribune; **T269** Switzerland Tourism; **T273** Walter Kale/Chicago Tribune; **T274** (top) Department of Agriculture, (bottom) George Thompson/Chicago Tribune; **T276** THE BORN LOSER reprinted by permission of Newspaper Enterprise Association, Inc.; **T277** (left) Tecumseh Products Company, Grafton WI, (right) Reprinted from NEW FIX IT YOURSELF MANUAL, T1996 The reader's Digest Association, Inc. Used by permission; **T279** *Geometry with Applications and Problem Solving,* Addison-Wesley Publishing Company; **T282** Chicago Tribune; **T288** from SCOTT FORESMAN GEOMETRY by Christian R. Hirsch et al. ©1990 by Scott, Foresman and Company. Reprinted by permissions of Addison Wesley Educational Publishers, Inc.; **T289** (left) L. Clarke/CORBIS; (right) from SCOTT FORESMAN GEOMETRY by Christian R. Hirsch et al. ©1990 by Scott, Foresman and Company. Reprinted by permissions of Addison Wesley Educational Publishers, Inc.; **T291** Texas Instruments Incorporated, Dallas, TX; **T294** *The Annotated Alice* by Lewis Carroll/Illustrator John Tenniel, Clarkson N. Potter, Inc.; **T297** Bob Lalnger/Chicago Tribune; **T298** J. Messerschmidt/Bruce Coleman, Inc.; **T302** David Klobucar/ Chicago Tribune; **T304** John Mulcahy/Chicago Tribune; **T308** Courtesy Megan Klobucar/Chicago Tribune; **T316** "Ascending and Descending" by M.C. Escher. ©1998 Cordon Art-Baarn-Holland. All rights reserved. **T318** George Thompson/Chicago Tribune; **T326** Whisperglide, Hugo MN; **T331** Elaine Krajenke Ellison/Orie Shafer photographer; **T333** (top) Carl Hugare/Chicago Tribune; (bottom) Hickson Bender; **T335** Glencoe file photo; **T341** Carl Hugare/Chicago Tribune.